Georg...... Bill

The Geology and Tectonics
of the Oman Region

Geological Society Special Publications

Series Editor K. COE

GEOLOGICAL SOCIETY SPECIAL PUBLICATION NO 49

The Geology and Tectonics of the Oman Region

EDITED BY

A. H. F. ROBERTSON
Department of Geology and Geophysics
Grant Institute
University of Edinburgh, UK

M. P. SEARLE
Department of Geology
University of Leicester, UK

A. C. RIES
Earth Sciences and Resources Institute
University of Reading, UK

1990

Published by

The Geological Society

London

THE GEOLOGICAL SOCIETY

The Geological Society of London was founded in 1807 for the purposes of 'investigating the mineral structures of the earth'. It received its Royal Charter in 1825. The Society promotes all aspects of geological science by means of meetings, special lectures and courses, discussions, specialist groups, publications and library services.

It is expected that candidates for Fellowship will be graduates in geology or another earth science, or have equivalent qualifications or experience. All Fellows are entitled to receive for their subscription one of the Society's three journals: *The Quarterly Journal of Engineering Geology*, the *Journal of the Geological Society* or *Marine and Petroleum Geology*. On payment of an additional sum on the annual subscription, members may obtain copies of another journal.

Membership of the specialist groups is open to all Fellows without additional charge. Enquiries concerning Fellowship of the Society and membership of the specialist groups should be directed to the Executive Secretary, The Geological Society, Burlington House, Piccadilly, London W1V 0JU.

Published by the Geological Society from:
The Geological Society Publishing House
Unit 7
Brassmill Enterprise Centre
Brassmill Lane
Bath
Avon BA1 3JN
UK
(*Orders:* Tel. 0225 445046)

First published 1990

British Library Cataloguing in Publication Data
Robertson, Alastair, *1949–*
   The geology and tectonics of the Oman region.
   1. Oman. Geological features. Geological
I. Title II. Searle, Michael P. III. Ries, Alison
C. IIII. Series
   555.3'53

ISBN 0–903317–46–X

Printed in Great Britain at the Alden Press, Oxford

Contents

CONTENTS

Acknowledgements

This volume could not have been completed without the help of a number of individuals and institutions. We are indebted to the Ministry of Petroleum and Minerals, Sultanate of Oman and the Governments of the United Arab Emirates for their support. Twenty-six of the papers in this volume derive from work funded by Amoco Oman Petroleum Company, through an operating grant awarded to Professor W. H. Kanes on behalf of the Earth Sciences and Resources Institute based at the University of South Carolina. Those geologists involved sincerely thank AMOCO and ESRI for giving them the opportunity to work in the Oman region; they are also particularly grateful to Dr J. D. Smewing of the Earth Resources Institute, Swansea for his invaluable scientific support and assistance with logistics.

The International Discussion Meeting was held at the Royal Society of Edinburgh from March 29–31st, 1988 and was sponsored by the Geological Society of London and Amoco Production Company (International), with additional financial support from Petroleum Development, Oman; British Petroleum, London; the Earth Sciences and Resources Institute, Reading and the Earth Resources Institute, Swansea.

The conveners of the International Discussion Meeting gratefully acknowledge assistance from the City of Edinburgh's Director of Finance and his staff, and the District of Council's Department of Public Relations and Tourism. We also thank the Royal Bank of Scotland for providing conference materials. The Lord Provost of the City of Edinburgh and the Principal of the University of Edinburgh kindly provided hospitality for the conference participants.

A. H. F. Robertson thanks the Head of the Department of Geology and Geophysics, Professor G. S. Boulton, for facilities to arrange the conference and then edit the volume; and also sincerely thanks Mrs Marcia Wright for her invaluable secretarial assistance with organizing the conference. Dr J. E. Dixon is thanked for producing the design which appears on the front cover of this volume.

Preface

Recent years have seen an extraordinary upsurge of international interest in the Geology and Tectonics of the Oman Region. A notable innovation is extensive collaborative work involving a large number of academic and oil company geologists from different countries. Indeed, a substantial part of the recent work has been sponsored by Amoco Oman Petroleum Company, with the support of the Oman Government's Ministry of Petroleum and Minerals. Publication of this volume demonstrates the effectiveness of collaboration between universities, government institutions and oil companies and shows how this can lead to presentation and publication of much new data on geologically and economically important areas. The Shell-supported Oman Memoir (Glennie *et al.* 1974) laid the foundations for all future studies of the Oman Mountain area. Publication of this sequel will reinforce interest in this now classic area.

Many of the studies reported here focus on the sedimentary and structural evolution of the Late Palaeozoic–Mesozoic–Tertiary continental margin and its relevance to exploiting the area's natural resources, notably the hydrocarbon fields of the central and northern Oman Mountain front and also in South Oman.

The Oman Mountain area is the world's best exposed deformed passive margin and as such is an ideal area to study fundamental geological processes, including rifting, passive margin development, thrusting, foreland basin genesis with the integration of surface geology and subsurface seismic and well data.

The approach adopted here is multidisciplinary and includes aspects of sedimentation, stratigraphy, palaeontology, structural geology, geophysics, geochemistry and marine geology. The area covered is the Oman Mountains, Southern Oman, offshore areas, and the wider tectonic context of Iran and the Indian ocean.

The volume follows an International Discussion Meeting held at the Royal Society of Edinburgh, from March 29–31, 1988, convened by A. H. F. Robertson, M. P. Searle, J. D. Smewing and A. C. Ries.

Introduction

A. H. F. ROBERTSON, M. P. SEARLE & A. C. RIES

The Oman Mountains which occupy the south-eastern corner of the Arabian Peninsula form an arcuate chain, approximately 700 km long and up to 120 km wide, stretching from the Arabian Gulf and Straits of Hormuz in the northwest to the Arabian Sea in the southeast. The Range forms the southeastern margin of the Arabian continental plate, which is bounded by the Red Sea spreading centre in the west, the dominantly transform fault-bounded Arabian Sea margin along the southeast coast and the major Tethyan suture zones along the northern and eastern margins, exposed in Iran, Pakistan and Turkey. The Gulf of Oman is floored by Cretaceous oceanic crust which is currently subducting northwards beneath the Makran active continental margin (White & Ross 1979). Thus the Oman Mountains define a continent-ocean collision boundary of dominantly Late Cretaceous age, but affected by further compression and uplift during the Tertiary.

The Oman Mountains are well known for the world's largest intact and best exposed obducted ophiolite complex, the Semail ophiolite. Underlying the ophiolite is a complicated assemblage of thrust sheets of proximal to distal deep-sea sediments, volcanic and melange units, termed the Hawasina Complex and the Haybi Complex. These thrust units, are in turn structurally underlain by carbonate slope deposits (Sumeini Group), which have been thrust onto the Arabian platform. The shelf carbonate successions are part of the giant Middle Eastern hydrocarbon province and the Oman foreland has been subjected to extensive subsurface seismic exploration and drilling operations. The Oman Mountains are also exceptionally well exposed throughout and form one of the most important field geological laboratories.

History of research

The earliest geological exploration was made during the reconnaissance visits of Blanford (1872), Pilgrim (1908) and Lees (1928). In the late 1950s geologists of the Iraq Petroleum Company were active in the field particularly in the northern mountain area. The first major regional surveys began in the 1960s by geologists of Shell Petroleum Development (Oman) Ltd. (Wilson 1969; Glennie et al. 1973, 1974).

The map (scale 1: 500 000) and memoir produced by the Shell team (Glennie et al. 1974) has become the classic study of the Oman Moun-

tains and formed the basis for all subsequent research. The basic conclusion that the Oman Mountains preserves a tectonically emplaced Late Palaeozoic and Mesozoic continental margin and Tethyan basin sequence, together with a huge slab of Cretaceous oceanic crust and mantle has never since been seriously disputed.

Subsequent research during the 1970s and early 1980s concentrated on more detailed mapping, with emphasis on the Semail ophiolite. The work of a British-funded group, the Open University Oman Ophiolite Project (U.K. 1975–1986) resulted in publication of four maps (scale 1:100 000) of the northern part of the Oman territory, eight PhD theses and a substantial number of journal articles, the results being summarised in a Memoir of the Geological Society (Lippard et al. 1986).

During the earlier part of this period an American-funded group from the United States Geological Survey and the University of California mapped a strip across the southeastern Oman Mountains from Muscat southwards. A detailed map was produced (scale: 1:100 000) and the results, mainly detailing the Semail ophiolite, were published in a special issue of the *Journal of Geophysical Research* (**86**, B4, 1981).

In 1981 Amoco Petroleum Company (International) acquired the concession for much of the Oman Mountain area and during the subsequent six years obtained an improved seismic coverage of the foreland area adjacent to the Oman Mountains. They also funded a major field-based research programme through the Earth Sciences and Resources Institute. Twenty-six papers in this volume are based on the Amoco-funded work.

During 1982–1984 geologists of the French Bureau de Récherches Géologiques et Minières (BRGM) mapped a large area of the central and southern mountains, resulting in publication of 13 maps at 1: 100 000 scale, several theses and related journal articles. French University Groups simultaneously focussed on the Semail ophiolite. The results of the various projects were published in a special volume of *Tectonophysics* **51**, 1988).

Evolution of the Oman passive margin

Key issues addressed in this volume are the rift, drift and emplacement history of the Oman Tethyan continental margin. How and when did

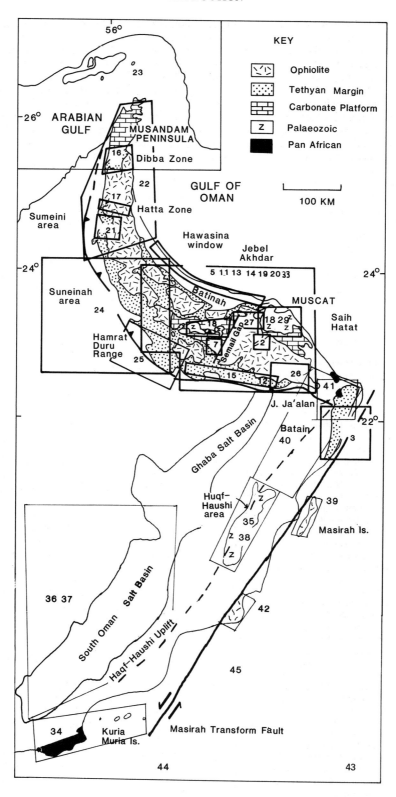

rifting take place? When did ocean floor spreading begin? What was the nature of the continental boundary? How did the platform and slope develop through time, compared with in situ passive margins (e.g. Atlantic). What was the deep-sea basin like? How did the huge mountain-sized volcanic and limestone exotics form? How did Late Cretaceous thrusting affect the margin? How was platform deposition re-established after thrust emplacement? What was the nature of Tertiary deformation — tensional or compressive?

In an introductory paper **Robertson & Searle** review alternative stratigraphic and structural schemes proposed for the Oman Mountains. They propose a compromise stratigraphical nomenclature that as far as possible follows currently accepted international convention. The authors then discuss alternative reconstructions of the Oman passive margin and summarize the structural and emplacement history.

The following papers cover a number of topics, as follows.

(i) Rifting and passive margin evolution

Blendinger *et al.* discuss sub-surface evidence for the timing and mechanism of rifting. Many authors favour Middle to Late Triassic continental break-up (e.g. Lippard *et al.* 1986), but Blendinger *et al.* suggest seafloor spreading was underway by early Late Permian. They favour 'a low-angle normal faulting' model rather than the 'classical (thermal) rift' model. The authors also report new fossil and lithology data for the Permian of the southeastern mountains, and argue it was part of the adjacent Saih Hatat carbonate platform, not a distal Oman Exotic (cf. Bechennec *et al.*).

The Permian of the Oman Mountains is critical to the debate on rift history. **Lee** summarizes the Early and Late Permian platform successions throughout Oman, with emphasis on South Oman. Early Permian lithofacies reflect the Dwyka glaciation of Gondwana, while Late Permian times saw carbonate platform development along the margins of the developing Tethyan basin. Blendinger *et al.* argue for an asymmetrical simple shear rift model in contrast with Glennie *et al.*'s (1974) classical symmetrical rift. Late Permian deep-water sedimentary and volcanic rocks have been confirmed in the Hawasina Complex, as summarized by Bechennec *et al.* and Blendinger *et al.*

Rabu *et al.* synthesize the Permian to Late Cretaceous evolution of the platform successions. They recognize five main depositional cycles. Important controls of platform deposition include Late Permian, and Late Jurassic (Late Tithonian) crustal extension, and Late Cretaceous foreland basin development (Muti Formation). Contrasting stable and unstable shelf areas can be recognized in the Saih Hatat and Jebel Akhdar. **Pratt & Smewing** present new data on the sedimentology and palaeoenvironments of the Mesozoic platform successions. They reconstruct a stepped platform edge and argue that lateral structures, principally the Semail gap, exerted a strong influence on Mesozoic carbonate platform sedimentation.

Accurate chronostratigraphic correlation is clearly essential. **Scott** utilizes a quantitative correlation technique that relates taxa in individual successions to a composite standard and to absolute age. Using this method he determines durations of specific depositional cycles and erosive events in relation to regional tectonics and inferred eustatic sealevel changes.

The evolution of the carbonate platform is also considered by **Haan** *et al.* who discuss the Early Cretaceous Kahmah Group (Rayda, Salil and Habshan Fms.). Information from surface exposures and seismic data provide an integrated picture of facies geometry and distribution. Seismic clinoforms suggest a period of highly diachronous deposition, possibly controlled by salt movement in the basement.

Fig. 1. Outline tectonic map of Oman showing the locations of the areas studied. The numbers are in the order in which they occur in the book, as follows: 1, Robertson & Searle (whole area); 2, Blendiger *et al.* (box); 3, Lee (box); 4, Rabu *et al.* (whole of exposed platform); 5, Pratt & Smewing (mainly in large box); 6, Scott (whole of Cretaceous shelf); 7, Haan *et al.* (box); 8, Wagner (whole shelf); 9, Watts (whole area of platform slope units); 10, Cooper (whole area of basinal units); 11, Bernoulli *et al.* (S part of large box); 12, Tozer & Calon (box); 13, Bechennec *et al.* (large box); 14, De Wever *et al.* (large box); 15, Kickmaier & Peters (box); 16, Robertson *et al.* (a) (box); 17, Robertson *et al.* (b) (box); 18, Mann & Hanna (box); 19, Le Metour *et al.* (large box); 20, Hanna (large box); 21, Searle *et al.* (box); 22, Dunne *et al.* (box); 23, Michaelis & Pauken (Hormuz area); 24, Boote (box); 25, Warburton *et al.* (box); 26, Cawood *et al.* (box); 27, Coffield (box); 28, Shelton (Batinah plain area); 29, El-Shazly & Coleman (large box, mainly E part); 30, Nolan *et al.* (area of Tertiary platform); 31, Skelton *et al.* (circum N mountain area); 32, Mann *et al.* (whole of central mountain flanks); 33, Maizels & McBean (large box); 34, Gass *et al.* (box); 35, Wright *et al.* (box); 36, Mattes & Conway Morris (box); 37, Heward (box); 38, Ries & Shackleton (box); 39, Moseley (box); 40, Shackleton *et al.* (box); 41, Filbrandt *et al.* (box); 42, Shackleton & Ries (box); 43, Mountain & Prell SE continental margin of Oman; 44, Prell (box); 45, Shimmield & Price (box); 46, Glennie *et al.* (whole of Oman-Makran area); 47, Stoneley (S Iran); 48, Sengör (whole of Iran and Oman).

A major goal of industry studies of the platform successions has been to define the nature and extent of reservoir carbonates. Based on a five-well transect, **Wagner** shows that isotope stratigraphy (δ^{13} C, δ^{18} O) and elemental composition (Sr) of carbonates can be used to recognize and correlate diagenetic differences and topographic relationships. Semi-enclosed marine-like conditions with local anoxic events are implied for Early-Middle Cretaceous carbonates from wells in central Oman. Remaining porosity was destroyed below the thrust sheets, but excellent porosity survived beyond the thrust front. Lithofacies is apparently not important in defining porosity distribution.

A priority of recent research has been to determine the depositional environment, and distribution of slope and basinal lithofacies in the Oman Mountains. **Watts** reconstructs the platform edge and slope geometry through time (Sumeini Group). Facies models are important since modern slopes are still imperfectly known. The main controls of slope development were Permian?, Triassic and Jurassic rift events and tectonic oversteepening prior to Late Cretaceous thrust emplacement, modified by eustatic sealevel change and several other factors.

Cooper shows that two contrasting types of succession are present regionally: the shale-rich 'Al Ayn sub-basin' and the more carbonate-rich 'Duru sub-basin'. The shale-rich facies are correlated with base-of-slope carbonate conglomerates in the Hawasina window and are therefore relatively proximal. Palaeocurrent data show that the main source of Jurassic oolitic calciturbidites (Guweyza Limestone Formation) was to the southeast, not the adjacent platform as might be expected. In addition, sediment distribution was apparently influenced by inferred southeasterly trade winds.

Bernoulli et al. recognize four units in the Late Triassic deep-water successions (Zulla Fm.). Detrital components reflect changing margin palaeoenvironments, whereas pelagic sedimentation shows basin-wide oceanographic influences. Chief amongst these are periodic low-oxygen conditions, resulting in laminated dolomite and increased radiolarian abundance, possibly related to changes in circulation and surface-water productivity. The Oman Triassic deep-water sediments have to be seen as part of an elongate South Tethyan seaway stretching as far as the central Mediterranean area.

Also, concerning the deep-water Hawasina Complex, **Tozer & Calon** discuss the detailed biostratigraphy and significance of Triassic ammonoids from detached blocks of condensed pelagic limestones. These are similar to the Ammonitico Rosso and the Hallstatt facies elsewhere in the Tethyan region, where they often signify condensed deposition on seamounts.

Based on the BRGM mapping of the central and southern mountains, **Bechennec et al.** summarize their conception of the Late Permian to Late Cretaceous evolution of the 'Hamrat Duru Basin'. Rifting took place in Late Permian and spreading in Middle to Late Triassic time. The deep-water facies accumulated in a subsided intracontinental basin. A large platform (Baid Platform) was sited northeast of the Arabian platform and then disintegrated into smaller units (Misfah and Baid Horsts) in Middle-Late Triassic time.

In recent years it has become possible routinely to extract well preserved radiolaria from ribbon cherts, and these microfossils have become a powerful stratigraphic tool. A prodigious number of radiolarian chert samples was processed from every major chert horizon in the BRGM mapping area and the main results are reported by **De Wever et al.** Additional radiolarian results obtained by C. Blome (USGS) from the northern mountains (USGS) are reported in **Robertson et al. a, b; Cooper; Watts; Searle et al.** and **Bernoulli et al.** Workers on radiolaria do not yet agree on the age ranges of all taxa, and thus it is important to document species lists in full.

Further insight into pelagic depositional processes come from sedimentary geochemistry. **Kickmaier & Peters** discuss the field relations and structural setting of manganiferous deposits in deep-water distal successions (Wahrah Formation) of Late Jurassic-Early Cretaceous age. Stratiform manganese enrichment is attributed to both sedimentary and tectonic processes. High Mn/Fe ratios and low trace metal abundances favour an origin by settling of widely dispersed hydrothermal precipitates. In contrast to other authors, Kickmaier & Peters apparently envisage ocean floor spreading in the Oman area only in the Late Cretaceous (Semail ophiolite) and suggest the Owen Fracture Zone as a possible source area for the manganese.

(ii) Integrated studies

The development of the Oman continental margin can only be fully understood when the passive margin and the emplacement histories are considered together. Structure has to be properly unravelled if the margin geometry is to be correctly restored and palaeogeography has clearly exerted an important control on thrusting.

Robertson *et al.* **a** discuss the Dibba Zone, northern mountains. They summarize the platform and slope deposition and present new data on deep-water sediments (Hamat Duru Group), major Oman Exotics (Jebel Qamar), melange (Kub Melange) and Late Cretaceous volcanic rocks. The Dibba Zone is interpreted as an oblique rifted (transtensional) margin segment that became largely inactive after continental break-up.

The NW–SE trending Hatta Zone in the northern mountains to the south of the Dibba Zone is interpreted by **Robertson** *et al.* **b** as a right-lateral transform fault, that influenced slope and basinal sedimentation, volcanism and thrust emplacement. The structure is dominated by a major transverse culmination (Jebel Quimah) and a lateral ramp (Jebel Raudha-Masfut ridge). Triassic to Early Cretaceous platform slope and proximal base-of-slope lithofacies predominate. Basement lithologies, not reported elsewhere were transported through northward?-facing channels. Structurally higher, more distal units are dominated by Late Cretaceous basic within-plate, seamount-type volcanic rocks.

(iii) Structure and emplacement history

In the cores of the Jebel Akhdar and Saih Hatat large-scale anticlines, pre-Permian basement rocks reveal a deformation fabric believed to have developed either during regional Late Palaeozoic deformation and metamorphism (Mann & Hanna), or are instead (partly or wholly) related to Late Cretaceous ophiolite obduction (Le Metour. *et al.*). **Mann & Hanna** focus on major basement-cover duplexes in the Saih Hatat and favour an important phase of Late Palaeozoic deformation and low grade metamorphism. In this area the Mesozoic platform succession has clearly been involved in the Late Cretaceous thrusting. **Le Metour** *et al.* report several phases of deformation including NE-directed shearing and blueschist-eclogite facies metamorphism and conclude that these events mainly relate to the Late Cretaceous emplacement.

The Late Cretaceous structural style of the Oman Mountains is discussed by a number of authors, particularly with regard to the sequence of thrusting and the relative age of thrust culminations. **Hanna** argues that in the Jebel Akhdar-Saih Hatat areas all thrust-related structures are Late Cretaceous in age. In contrast, the Tertiary was dominated by extensional tectonics, as discussed in detail by Mann *et al.* for the first time.

In the northern Oman Mountains **Searle** *et al.* show that thrust culmination of slope carbonates in the Jebel Sumeini area was primarily a Late Cretaceous event with Maastrichtian limestones unconformably overlying Cretaceous structures, but that a second phase of shortening involving folding and short-distance thrusting occurred during the Early Tertiary.

Dunne *et al.* present seven structural sections across the foreland west of the mountain front in the northern Oman Mountains based on extensive seismic data. They show that the shelf carbonates are indeed affected by thrusting similar to that observed in the Musandam mountains. The thrusting is a direct consequence of the emplacement of the Semail ophiolite during the Late Cretaceous and subsequent reactivation during the Tertiary.

Michaelis & Pauken show two seismic profiles across the northward extension of the Musandam Peninsula in the Strait of Hormuz. Their data support earlier suggestions of two phases of compression in this area, one during the Late Cretaceous, the other during Oligocene-Miocene time.

Boote *et al.* present an evolutionary history of the Sumeinah foreland basin in the central Oman Mountains southwest of the mountain front and northeast of the Lekhwair peripheral bulge. Through seismic and well data they document the Turonian uplift and erosion of the peripheral bulge and the subsequent formation and infilling of the Suneinah foredeep caused by loading of the crust by the allochthon. A second foredeep was developed during the Tertiary as a result of compression from the north. Boote *et al.* interpret the seismic data in terms of regional transpressional deformation, in contrast to the more orthogonal compression favoured by most other authors.

In several contributions there is discussion of the thrusting in specific areas of the foreland fold and thrust belt, particularly involving the Hawasina basinal rocks. **Warburton** *et al.* describe and interpret the development of the thrust front and associated foreland basin in the Hamrat ad Duru near the front of the central Oman Mountains. They point out that the flexural bulge appears to have remained relative static near the shelf edge, followed by collapse associated with loading during emplacement of the Semail ophiolite.

Cawood *et al.* present data on the Ibra dome and Jebel Ma-jhool culminations in the southeastern Oman Mountains. They relate these structures to an important phase of gravity controlled re-thrusting, in line with earlier suggestions for adjacent areas. **Coffield** describes high-angle normal faults around the eastern

Jebel Akhdar and the western Saih Hatat culminations which are related to gravity-driven culmination collapse. These faults have a similar origin to surge zones described elsewhere. The age of the structures is debatable, with sedimentological evidence of emergence during the Late Cretaceous and reactivation during mid-Tertiary.

Shelton uses potential field data to investigate the location of the Semail ophiolite at depth below the Batinah Plain. He discusses several alternative models and draws comparisons with other passive margins. He concludes that the Semail ophiolite is rootless and that it pinches out to the east near the present coastline. He also discusses possibilities for the configuration of the mountain front. Shelton favours a gravity sliding emplacement mechanism for the Semail ophiolite, similar to that advocated by Glennie *et al.*

(iv) Tertiary margin development

The sedimentary and structural development of the beautifully exposed Tertiary successions are documented here in some detail for the first time.

Nolan et al. present a formally defined stratigraphy for these successions. Whereas in the past the Tertiary platform was assumed to have been relatively tectonically stable, the authors demonstrate a complex and variable pattern of transgression over the emplaced units, of differential subsidence, and the accumulation of slope deposits, including fan deltas, debris flows and turbidites within an unstable shelf.

The history of the initial transgression over the northeastern flank of the Late Cretaceous emplaced thrust sheets is documented in detail by **Skelton et al.** They reconstruct a pattern of rudist-bearing beach deposits that passed laterally and vertically into open shelf facies that are in turn truncated and overlain by Palaeogene slope deposits. The rudist assemblages are similar to other open southern Tethyan shelves in the Mediterranean and Middle East.

Mann et al. show that the Tertiary successions were later deformed, dominantly by extensional tectonics, with evidence of large-scale faults that step down towards the coast, localized block faulting and roll-over folds. In contrast to the Musandam in the north, no definite evidence of mid-Tertiary compressional structures was found in the central and southern Oman Mountains, thus contradicting earlier suggestions of important cross-over folding in this area.

The flanks of the Oman Mountains are mantled by huge volumes of Quaternary alluvium. Their depositional history can best be documented by remote sensing techniques that descriminate on the basis of contrasts in the reflectance and radiance of surface materials. **Maizels & McBean** use Landsat and radar imagery and show that palaeochannels can be recognized within a complete alluvial fan system. At least 20 successive generations of exhumed multistorey palaeodrainage systems are detectable.

One currently enigmatic and controversial aspect is the occurrence of high-pressure/low-temperature blueschist rocks in the Saih Hatat platform unit. How did these rocks come to be metamorphosed at great depths and then largely exhumed all within Cretaceous time? After briefly summarising the occurrence of the metamorphic sole at the base of the Semail ophiolite, **El-Shazly & Coleman** discuss the high-pressure rocks and attribute them to the attempted subduction of the Oman continental margin, or a microcontinent following a change in the plate motion of Africa relative to Eurasia. In contrast to earlier workers, they argue that the deeply buried continental margin rocks followed 'clockwise' $P-T$ paths.

South Oman

For the purposes of this book, South Oman refers to that area of Oman which lies outside the Oman Mountains and consists of basement to Tertiary sediments that form the foreland to the Oman Mountains Thrust Belt. Outcrop is restricted to NE Oman, between the Batain Coast and Wahiba Sands, the Huqf-Haushi area (onshore from Masirah Bay) and the Mirbat area of southern Oman, in addition to Masirah Island and the Kuria Muria group of islands.

The papers on South Oman begin with a comparative account by **Gass et al.** of the structure, metamorphism, geochronology and geochemistry of the Precambrian basement rocks of Oman, which are only exposed at Jebel Ja'alan and Qalhat in NE Oman, the Kuria Muria Islands and the area E of Mirbat in S Oman. These rocks have a similar age, geochemistry and tectonic history to those Precambrian rocks exposed in other parts of the Afro-Arabian Shield and hence the Pan-African domain can now be extended farther to the E.

The oldest non-metamorphic rocks exposed in South Oman are the Infracambrian Huqf Group which is exposed in East Central Oman onshore from Masirah Bay. This area, often known as the Huqf-Haushi area, is a large inlier affording the only exposures of the Palaeozoic sequence in S Oman. The Huqf Group sequence of carbonates and siliciclastics in the Huqf–Haushi area are interpreted from detailed sedimentological studies by **Wright et al.** to be intraplatformal basin deposits, infilling a depression on the Arabian–Nubian shield.

South Oman is becoming increasingly important as a petroleum province, with the main fields occurring on the Eastern flank of the South Oman Salt Basin. **Mattes & Conway Morris** give a detailed account of the sub-surface Infra Cambrian Ara Formation which is an unusual example of a hydrocarbon habitat with trap, seals and source rocks all within a single formation. The authors discuss the facies, palaeoenvironments and palaeontology of five main depositional cycles, including evaporite and red bed accumulation within a major subsiding basin system.

Subsurface data presented by **Heward** indicate that periodic withdrawal and dissolution of the Infracambrian Ara Salt Formation from Infracambrian to the present day has been the main process responsible for the development of the different types of hydrocarbon traps.

The structures seen in the Infracambrian to Cretaceous rocks exposed in the Huqf–Haushi area are documented by **Ries & Shackleton**. The oldest structure is the Huqf–Haushi Uplift, which runs parallel to the SE continental margin of Oman and records a history of intermittent uplift throughout the Phanerozoic, local open folds of probable pre-Ordovician age and two sets of faults trending NNE–SSW and N–S. The latter, of Late Cretaceous age, is related to the Masirah Transform Fault.

The geology and tectonic history of the Masirah ophiolitic complex is reviewed by **Moseley**. This author uses unpublished Tithonian ages from cherts associated with the ophiolite to argue that the Masirah Ophiolite is older and therefore unrelated to the Semail Ophiolite. The origin of the Masirah Melange is attributed to the Masirah Fault and regarded as post mid-Cretaceous. Moseley suggests that the geochemistry of granitic rocks incorporated within the ophiolitic complex indicates derivation from the Arabian continental crust, incorporated during ophiolitic obduction in the Late Cretaceous. The ophiolite is overlain by early Tertiary limestones which are gently folded and faulted.

The previously geologically unknown area of NE Oman, which lies between the Batain coast and the E of Jebel Ja'alan basement high and the Wahiba Sands, has been shown by **Shackleton et al.** to be mostly occupied by a melange, named the Batain Melange, and contains clasts which range in age from Permian to Late Cretaceous. This Melange is argued to be tectonic in origin and is similar to the Hawasina Melange in the Oman Mountains. The dominant structures affecting these rocks are WNW-vergent thrusts and folds, forming the Batain fold and thrust belt, which, from stratigraphic relationships are pre-early Tertiary in age. These structures must be related to compressional motion on the Masirah Fault.

The sedimentology and tectonic history of the Maastrichtian and early Tertiary sequences in the Jebel Ja'alan area are described by **Filbrandt et al.** Maastrichtian fluvial conglomerates, which rest directly on the Precambrian basement, and overlie shallow-water limestones, are overlain by sequences documenting syn-sedimentary deformation associated with the uplift of Jebel Ja'alan. The youngest sediments of middle Eocene age record a sequence of tectonic events associated with the uplift of the Precambrian basement of Jebel Ja'alan. This Tertiary deformation records further transpressional motion on the Masirah Fault.

Shackleton & Ries argue that the main tectonic features of the SE continental margin of Oman, the Masirah Fault, the ophiolitic rocks on Masirah Island, Ras Madrakah and Ras Jibsch, the radiolarites on the Hikman Peninsula, the Huqf–Haushi Uplift and the Batain Melange, all have to be accounted for in any tectonic model developed for the tectonic evolution of this margin. These authors propose Jurassic/Early Cretaceous left-lateral motion along the Masirah Fault and northward displacement of the block once adjacent to the SE Oman margin together with upthrusting of the Masirah Ophiolite, followed by a Late Cretaceous reversal of motion along the Masirah Fault, associated with oblique obduction of the Masirah Ophiolite Zone onto the continental margin and the deformation of the Batain Melange.

Marine geophysical data presented by **Mountain & Prell** indicate that the Owen Basin ocean floor is Late Cretaceous or younger and that the ophiolitic rocks represent fragments of this ocean floor emplaced as a result of transpression along the Masirah Fault. Reorganization of the plate boundaries during the opening of the Gulf of Aden in the Neogene led to further deformation of the SE margin of Oman.

The final two papers in this section deal with the oceanography of the present day passive continental margin of South Oman. **Prell and others** summarize the preliminary results of Ocean Drilling Project Leg 117. The chief objectives of the Leg were to test ideas about the past influence of the Asian summer monsoon on deposition in the northwestern Indian Ocean and to try resolve questions about the tectonic development of the Oman margin and the Owen Ridge. The cores reveal a complex interaction between siliceous biogenic productivity and the tectonic subsidence of slope basins of varied morphology. Up to 1000 m of subsidence has taken place during the late Neogene. Upwelling leading to high organic productivity appears to have begun in early Middle Miocene.

Based on a recent cruise of the R/V Charles Darwin, **Shimmield et al.** report evidence of a pronounced oxygen minimum zone between 200 and 1500 m throughout the northwestern Arabian Sea. The bathymetry of the margin is complex and appears to relate to tectonic movements along the Masirah Line and this also favoured the development of small anoxic basins south of Masirah. Otherwise, upwelling was the main control of calcareous and siliceous deposition on the South Oman margin, as also discussed by Prell et al.

Regional tectonic setting

In this concluding section, Oman geological development is placed in the regional setting of Iran and the Indian Ocean.

Glennie et al. draw on a large body of previously unpublished oil company information on Southern Oman and present a unified tectonic model for the evolution of the Oman margin in relation to Makran. They relate the emplacement of the Semail ophiolite to collision of the Arabian passive margin with a subducting trench, as in some recent models. Crustal relaxation followed collision and this led to uplift and gravity spreading of allochthonous units further onto the Arabian shelf. Continuing convergence was transferred to the Makran margin, giving rise to a long history of subduction and accretion that continues to this day.

Stoneley focusses on apparent differences between the Cretaceous development of the southern Tethyan margin in Iran and Oman. He develops his long-held view that the Iranian ophiolites developed in a setting of Late Cretaceous rifting, followed by gravity gliding over an intra-shelf basin. He suggests that the Iranian and Oman Tethyan margin segments were offset by a major transform fault and thus the genesis

and emplacement of the ophiolites in these two areas took place in different tectonic settings.

Finally, in a wide ranging synthesis, **Şengör** reviews available data for Iran that is relevant to the tectonic setting of Oman. He presents a new tectonic model for the Late Palaeozoic– end Mesozoic evolution of the entire Middle Eastern Tethys area. His main thesis is that the Oman Tethys developed, not as a Red Sea-type small ocean basin as in many conventional models, but instead represents a back-arc (retro-arc) basin generated by spreading behind a major Late Palaeozoic magmatic arc (Podataksasi arc). Şengör compares the Oman Tethys to modern marginal basin settings, including the Tyrrhenian Sea and the Sea of Japan. In his view many aspects of Oman geology are consistent with a similar setting.

References

BLANFORD, W. T. 1872. Notes on Muskat and Musandam on the coast of Arabia. *Records of the Geological Survey of India*, **5**, 75–77.

GLENNIE, K. W., BOEUF, M. G. A., HUGHES CLARKE, M. W., MOODY-STUART, M., PILAAR, W. F. H. & REINHARDT, B. M. 1973. Late Cretaceous nappes in the Oman Mountains and their geologic significance. *American Association of Petroleum Geologists Bulletin*, **57**, 5–27.

GLENNIE, K. W., BOEUF, M. G. A., HUGHES CLARKE, M. W., MOODY-STUART, M., PILAAR, W. F. H. & REINHARDT, B. M. 1974. The Geology of the Oman Mountains. *Verhandelingen van het Koninklijk Nederlands geologisch minjbouwkundig Genootschap*.

LEES, G. M. 1928. The geology and tectonics of Oman and parts of south-eastern Arabia. *Quarterly Journal of the Geological Society of London*, **84**, 585–670.

LIPPARD, S. J., SHELTON, A. W. & GASS, I. G. 1986. *The ophiolite of Northern Oman*. Geological Society, London, Memoir, **11**.

PILGRIM, G. 1908. Geology of the Persian Gulf and adjoining portions of Persia and Arabia. *Memoir of the Indian Geological Survey*, **34**, 1–77.

WHITE, R. S. & Ross, D. A. 1979. Tectonics of the Western Gulf of Oman. *Journal of Geophysical Research*, **84**, 3479–89.

WILSON, H. H. 1969. Late Cretaceous eugeosynclinal sedimentation, gravity tectonics and ophiolite emplacement in the Oman Mountains, southeast Arabia. *American Association of Petroleum Geologists Bulletin*, **53**, 626–71.

Evolution of the Oman Tethyan Continental Margin

The northern Oman Tethyan continental margin: stratigraphy, structure, concepts and controversies

A. H. F. ROBERTSON[1] & M. P. SEARLE[2]

[1] *Department of Geology and Geophysics, University of Edinburgh,*
West Mains Road, Edinburgh EH9 3JW, UK
[2] *Department of Geology, The University, Leicester LE1 7RH, UK*

Abstract: The Oman Mountains constitute one of the best areas in which to study the development and subsequent deformation of a passive continental margin. Pulsed rifting of the Arabian craton in Early and Late Permian time was followed by Middle to Late Triassic sea-floor spreading and opening of the Tethys ocean. Passive margin subsidence continued throughout the Jurassic and Early Cretaceous, interrupted by a pulse of crustal extension in Late Jurassic (Tithonian) time. The Semail ophiolite was generated during the Cenomanian (*c.* 95–98 Ma), probably above a newly initiated intra-oceanic subduction zone. Mesozoic Tethyan oceanic crust was later consumed in an oceanward- (northeastward)-dipping subduction zone. The essential driving force was the attempted subduction of the Tethyan continental margin. Progressive collision led, in turn to the development of a peripheral bulge and foreland basin (*c.* 90 Ma), thrusting and eventual emplacement of the ophiolite onto the margin during late Campanian–Maastrichtian time. Thin-skinned thrust tectonics dominate the entire northern Oman continental margin, with late-stage deeper level thrusting affecting shelf edge and platform carbonates. The basal detachment extends down into deeper levels in the pre-Permian basement in the Musandam Peninsula in the north, and the Jebel Akhdar and Saih Hatat windows further south. During the Early Tertiary, continuing convergence was accommodated along the opposing Makran active margin, while a relatively stable platform was restored in the Oman Mountains area. Renewed compression during the mid-Tertiary, related to continental collision in the Zagros Mountains to the northwest resulted in short distance thrusting further onto the foreland in the northern Oman Mountains. The whole area currently lies within a zone of diachronous continental collision between the African and Eurasian plates.

The purpose of this paper is to review the tectonic and sedimentary development of the Oman Mountains (Fig. 1) in the light of the new data and alternative hypotheses presented in this volume. The Oman Late Palaeozoic–Mesozoic successions can be regarded as the type example of an emplaced Tethyan passive continental margin and the results are widely applicable to other comparable areas. We will begin by critically discussing the relative merits of recent alternative stratigraphical schemes for the continental margin successions and propose a revised classification that we hope will be used by later workers. Below, absolute ages are from the Harland *et al.* (1982) time scale.

Stratigraphical and structural nomenclature

Historical development

Glennie *et al.* (1973, 1974, 1990) produced the first comprehensive stratigraphy of the Oman Mountains (Fig. 2). They defined seven major rock units, which from bottom to top are:

1, *Pre-Permian basement* (exposed in Jebel Akhdar and Saih Hatat culminations); 2, *Hajar Supergroup*, Mid-Permian to Mid-Cretaceous shelf successions; 3, *Aruma Group*, Turonian to Maastrichtian syn-tectonic sediments related to Late Cretaceous deformation and emplacement of the Oman passive margin; 4, *Sumeini Group*, Permian to Late Cretaceous carbonate platform slope sediments; 5, *Hawasina*, tectonically sliced Permian to Late Cretaceous basinal sediments; 6, *Semail ophiolite*, a 600 km long by up to 150 km wide slab of Cretaceous oceanic crust and mantle; 7, Late Maastrichtian and Early Tertiary, neoautochthonous *shallow marine limestones* and basal clastics that overlie all other rock units.

Furthermore, Glennie *et al.* (1973, 1974) subdivided the proximal facies of their Hawasina unit in the central mountains into several formations on the basis of lithology and age (Zulla, Guwayza, Sid'r and Nayid Fms.). Elsewhere formation names were assigned to individual tectonic slices, ranging from proximal (e.g. Dibba Fm.) to more distal (Haliw, Halfa and Wahrah Fms.) (Fig. 3). Successions in each of

From ROBERTSON, A. H. F., SEARLE, M. P. & RIES, A. C. (eds), 1990,
The Geology and Tectonics of the Oman Region.
Geological Society Special Publication No 49, pp 3–25

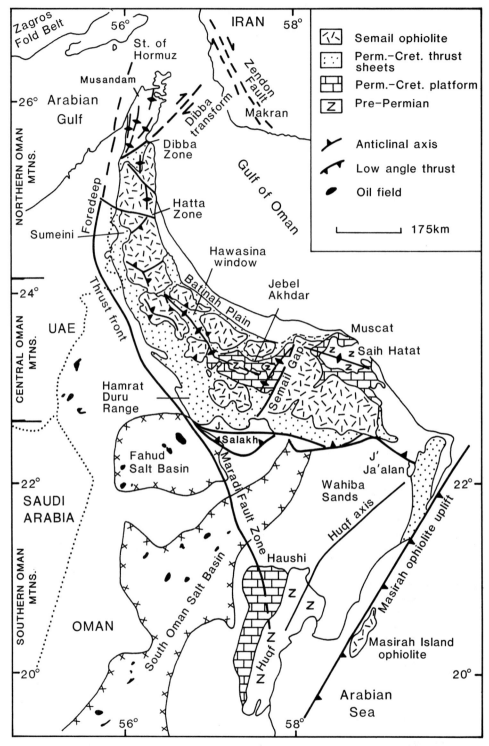

Fig. 1. Structural sketch map of the Oman Mountain area,based on Glennie *et al.* (1974) and Hughes Clarke (1988). Note that areas defined as the Northern, Central and Southern Oman Mountains are shown in the left-hand margin of the figure.

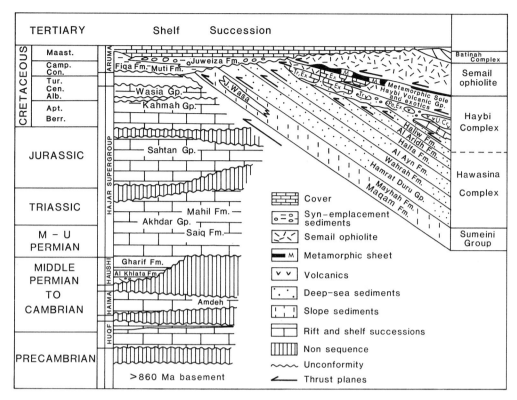

Fig. 2. Generalized tectonostratigraphy of the Oman Mountains, slightly modified and simplified after Glennie *et al.* (1974). The stratigraphy of the Hawasina has since been extensively redefined (see Figs 3 & 4).

these formations potentially span the entire Late Palaeozoic-Late Cretaceous passive margin interval.

During the Open University Oman Ophiolite Project (1975–1986), Glennie *et al.*'s (1973, 1974) stratigraphy was modified as follows (Fig. 3): Searle *et al.* (1980, 1983), Searle & Malpas (1980, 1982) and Lippard *et al.* (1986) defined the highly deformed thrust-bounded upper structural part of the Hawasina unit, beneath the Semail ophiolite, as the *Haybi Complex*, a term that is retained here. This contrasts with the more regularly thrust imbricated mainly deep-sea sedimentary units structurally below. Lippard *et al.* (1986) applied the term Hawasina Assemblage for the Hawasina units, but the name *Hawasina Complex* is preferred here (see below). Woodcock & Robertson (1982a) introduced a new stratigraphy exclusively for the *Batinah Sheets* that structurally overlie the Semail ophiolite along the Batinah coastal plain, but otherwise Glennie *et al.*'s (1974) stratigraphy remained essentially intact.

In the course of the AMOCO-funded project (1981–1987), Cooper (1987) redefined the stra-

tigraphy of the more proximal basinal units of the Hamrat Duru Group and established detailed regional correlations throughout the Oman Mountains for the first time (Fig. 3). In addition, Nolan *et al.* (1990) propose a formalized stratigraphy for the neoautochthonous Maastrichtian and Tertiary successions.

Recently a group from the Bureau de Récherches Géologiques et Minières (BRGM) have introduced a completely new classification for most units in the Oman Mountains, based on 1:100 000 mapping of the central and southern mountains (1982–1986) (Béchennec *et al.* 1988, 1990; Fig. 3).

Stratigraphical principles and problems

The objective of any stratigraphical revision should be to produce a practicable, comprehensive scheme for the Oman Mountains that is based on the internationally accepted rules of stratigraphical nomenclature (Hedberg 1976; Holland *et al.* 1978). Such a stratigraphy would then parallel that of similar deformed Tethyan areas (e.g. Othris, Greece; Smith *et al.* 1975;

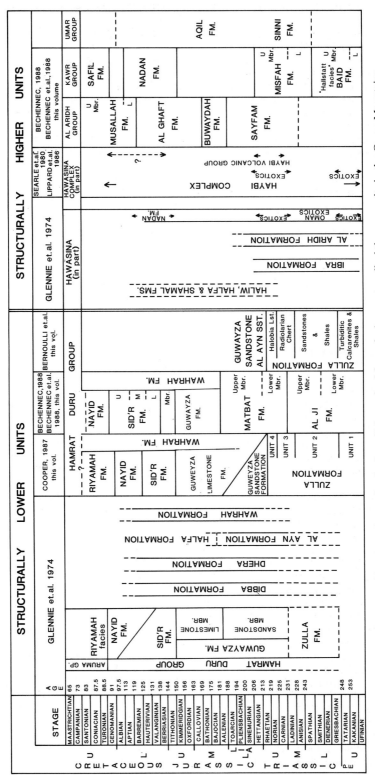

Fig. 3. Summary of alternative stratigraphic nomenclature for the Late Palaeozoic–Mesozoic deep-water allochthonous units in the Oman Mountains.

S. W. Cyprus; Swarbrick & Robertson, 1980). In general, Glennie et al.'s (1974) stratigraphy for the platform, slope and proximal basinal sediments (Hamrat Duru Gp.) remains acceptable. There is, by contrast little to commend the new terms 'Autochthonous units A and B' for the platform (Rabu et al. 1990), particularly as the shelf successions are demonstrably allochthonous, at least in part (see later).

Problems with Glennie et al.'s (1973, 1974) stratigraphy largely result from the existence of important regional facies variations within the deep-sea sediments (e.g. Dibba Fm., northern mountains) and from the uncertain tectonic setting of the more distal units (e.g. Oman exotics). The basis of Glennie et al.'s (1974) stratigraphy was that formation names were given to mapped tectonostratigraphic units (i.e. often individual tectonic slices), which were thus lithologically diverse and long-ranging (e.g. Late Triassic—mid Cretaceous). However, Glennie·et al. (1973, 1974) used a more conventional lithostratigraphic scheme for the more proximal deep-water successions of the Hamrat Duru Group (i.e. the Zulla, Guwayza, Sid'r and Nayid Fms.). Cooper (1987) later slightly modified this scheme for the Hamrat Duru Group and also established correlations with proximal deep-water successions elsewhere in the Oman Mountains (i.e. Dhera, Dibba and Al Ayn Fms.), allowing these units to be assimilated into a simple regionally applicable scheme.

The BRGM's stratigraphic revision, by contrast started from the assumption that it was necessary and appropriate to produce a more or less completely new nomenclature, at least for the central and southern mountain areas mapped by them. As a result, different authors thus now use quite different stratigraphies. Our difficult, but essential task is to propose a workable, compromise stratigraphy that can be used by future workers. In general, we have to say that we feel it is unfortunate that the BRGM scheme has often departed from the established principles of stratigraphical priority (Hedberg 1976; Holland et al. 1978). We are strongly of the opinion that their revision of the proximal deep-sea sediments (Hamrat Duru Gp.) was not warranted, especially as this reassigns Glennie et al.'s (1973, 1974) original formation names to successions of different facies and age (i.e. Sid'r and Nayid Formations), and thus inevitably results in confusion.

Glennie et al. (1973, 1974) defined more distal tectono-stratigraphic equivalents of the Hamrat Duru Group as the regionally extensive Wahrah Formation. Lithofacies similar to the Wahrah Formation are also present in the northern mountains as the siliceous and calcareous Batinah Sheets, structurally overlying the Semail ophiolite (Woodcock & Robertson, 1982b). Jurassic successions, especially calciturbidites were noted to be similar to the Wahrah Formation, but older (Triassic) units presents in the Batinah Melange had not been reported from the Wahrah Formation. For this reason Robertson and Woodcock (1982) choose to define an independent stratigraphy for the Batinah Complex. However, it now appears that the Batinah Sheets can be correlated with Wahrah Formation. Above the Semail ophiolite the Wahrah Formation is truncated by a thrust below Early Jurassic (Liassic) successions (Glennie et al. 1974; Béchennec et al. 1890; De Wever et al. 1990), while the missing Late Triassic successions appear to be present in the Batinah Melange. Accordingly, the time range of the Wahrah Formation is extended from Late Triassic to mid Cretaceous.

Turning to the more distal units, Searle et al. (1980) and Searle & Malpas (1980) defined the Haybi Complex as the structurally complex assemblage of sedimentary, igneous and metamorphic rocks that is sandwiched between the Semail ophiolite above and the Hawasina Complex below. By contrast, the BRGM Group argue that some of Searle et al.'s (1980) Haybi Complex units (e.g. volcanics) are to be included in their other groups (Hamrat Duru, Kawr and Al Aridh Gps.), and thus for them the term is redundant. Instead they recognize the more distal sediments and volcanics as the Umar Group (Sinni and Aqil Fms.). However, Searle et al.'s (1980) Haybi Complex is structurally very complex, locally variable and largely comprises melange and much more work on its internal structure and stratigraphy is still needed. For this reason the definition of the BRGM group's all-embracing Umar Group is premature.

Notwithstanding this, prior to the BRGM group's work only several long-ranging, poorly dated successions (e.g. Ibra, Al Aridh) had been defined in the upper Hawasina units by Glennie et al. (1974) and subsequent workers. Thus the new Al Aridh and Kawr and Groups erected by the BRGM geologists have stratigraphical priority. Detailed definitions of the type localities and successions are given in Béchennec. (1988). When applying this stratigraphy it should nevertheless be borne in mind that the BRGM group's Baid and Misfah Formations (Kawr Group) were previously treated by Glennie et al. (1974) as platform-related facies of the Oman Exotics (including the formally defined Nadan Fm.). These exotic limetones, like the Qamar Exotics in the Dibba Zone (Northern Mountains) are unusual and thus the stratigraphy can only be local.

Glennie *et al.* (1973, 1974) believed that many successions dominated by radiolarian chert were of distal origin (i.e. Halfa, Haliw and Shamal Fms.). However, more recently Bernoulli and Weissert (1987) have established that in the central mountains the Halfa Formation is Late Triassic in age, rather than Late Triassic–Early Cretaceous?, as in Glennie *et al.*'s (1973, 1974) scheme. Cooper (1987, 1988) now correlates the Halfa Formation with proximal facies of the Hamrat Duru Group (Zulla Fm.) in the central mountains. It is thus not now appropriate to apply the term Halfa Formation to the distal radiolarian cherts of the Haybi Complex; for these units Glennie *et al.*'s (1974) term Haliw Formation or the BRGM group's Aqil Formation can be used.

Recommended stratigraphy (Fig. 4)

We believe that Glennie *et al.*'s (1973, 1974) stratigraphy of the carbonate platform should be retained essentially intact. The stratigraphy of the carbonate platform slope (Sumeini Group) also needs only minor modification, as in Watts & Garrison (1986); Watts (1990) and Watts & Blome (1989).

We define the more proximal deep-sea sediments and minor volcanics as the *Hawasina Complex*. We strongly recommend use of Cooper's (1987) redefined *Hamrat Duru Group* for more proximal deep-sea successions. This comprises the *Zulla Formation*, the *Guweyza Sandstone Formation*, the *Guweyza Limestone Formation*, the *Sid'r Formation* and the *Nayid Formation*. This scheme is comprehensive and previous inconsistencies are removed. The relatively structurally high *Wahrah Formation* is retained for the more distal lithofacies and is placed within the Hamrat Duru Group. The *Wahrah Formation* is thus the only (vertical) tectonostratigraphic unit remaining from Glennie *et al.*'s (1974) original stratigraphy. Its time range from the central mountains and the Batinah Sheets (combined) is Late Triassic to mid Cretaceous.

We define the units structurally above the Hawasina Complex as the *Haybi Complex*, composed of structurally complex sedimentary, igneous and metamorphic rocks below the Semail ophiolite. The Haybi Complex is subdivided into the *Al Aridh* and the *Kawr Group*, with the addition of the *Ramaq Group* (Jebel Qamar) restricted to the Dibba Zone. Other units proposed (e.g. Haybi Volcanic Gp., Haliw Fm.,

Sinni Fm., Aqil Fm., Wadi Al Fay Formation) are best regarded as only of local significance at present.

The Late Cretaceous syn-emplacement facies are collectively termed the *Aruma Group*, as in Glennie *et al.*'s (1973, 1974) scheme. Stratigraphically older (Cenomanian–early Campanian) facies (that lack ophiolite-derived sediment) are defined as the Muti Formation, following Glennie *et al.* (1974). Successions unconformably overlying the platform are termed the Sajya Member (upper and lower units) (Robertson 1987b). Lithofacies of the Muti Formation associated with the carbonate platform slope (Sumeini Gp.), the deep-water basin (Hamrat Duru Gp.) and the more distal units of the Haybi Complex are known as the Qumayrah Member, the Riyamah Member and the Buday'ay unit (largely olistostromes), respectively (Robertson 1987a,b; Cooper, 1988, 1990; Watts & Blome 1989). More inboard, generally finer grained syn-emplacement facies comprise the ?Santonian–late Campanian Fiqa Formation. The younger emplacement-related sediments of the Aruma Group make up the late Campanian–Maastrichtian Juweiza Formation and the Simsima Formation (see Nolan *et al.* 1990). The stratigraphy of the Tertiary Neoautochthonous successions is formally defined by Nolan *et al.* (1990) and will not be discussed here.

Having clarified the stratigraphy we now go on to consider alternative interpretations of Oman rift and passive margin development.

Regional rifting setting

Glennie *et al.* (1973, 1974) envisaged symmetrical, thermally controlled (pure shear) rifting. However, Blendiger *et al.* (1990) interpret North Oman as an asymmetrical rift dominated by simple shear. We suspect that the Oman Tethyan continental margin may have been similar to the still poorly known class of 'volcanic margins' (Roberts *et al.* 1985), characterized by thick igneous successions (e.g. Outer Voring Plateau, western Rockall Bank and East Greenland). Such margins exhibit 3–5 km thick volcanic units over 15–20 km thick lower crust of 'intermediate' type. They appear to develop along the flanks of earlier rift basins, producing marginal plateaux. Pure shear models with adiabatic upwelling and elevated thermal anomalies are invoked (Hinz *et al.* 1987). In Oman, a phase of initial rifting in the Late Carboniferous–Early Permian is proposed by Blendiger *et al.* 1990). There is general agreement that major rifting also took place in Late Permian (Glennie *et al.* 1974; Béchennec *et al.* 1990) and

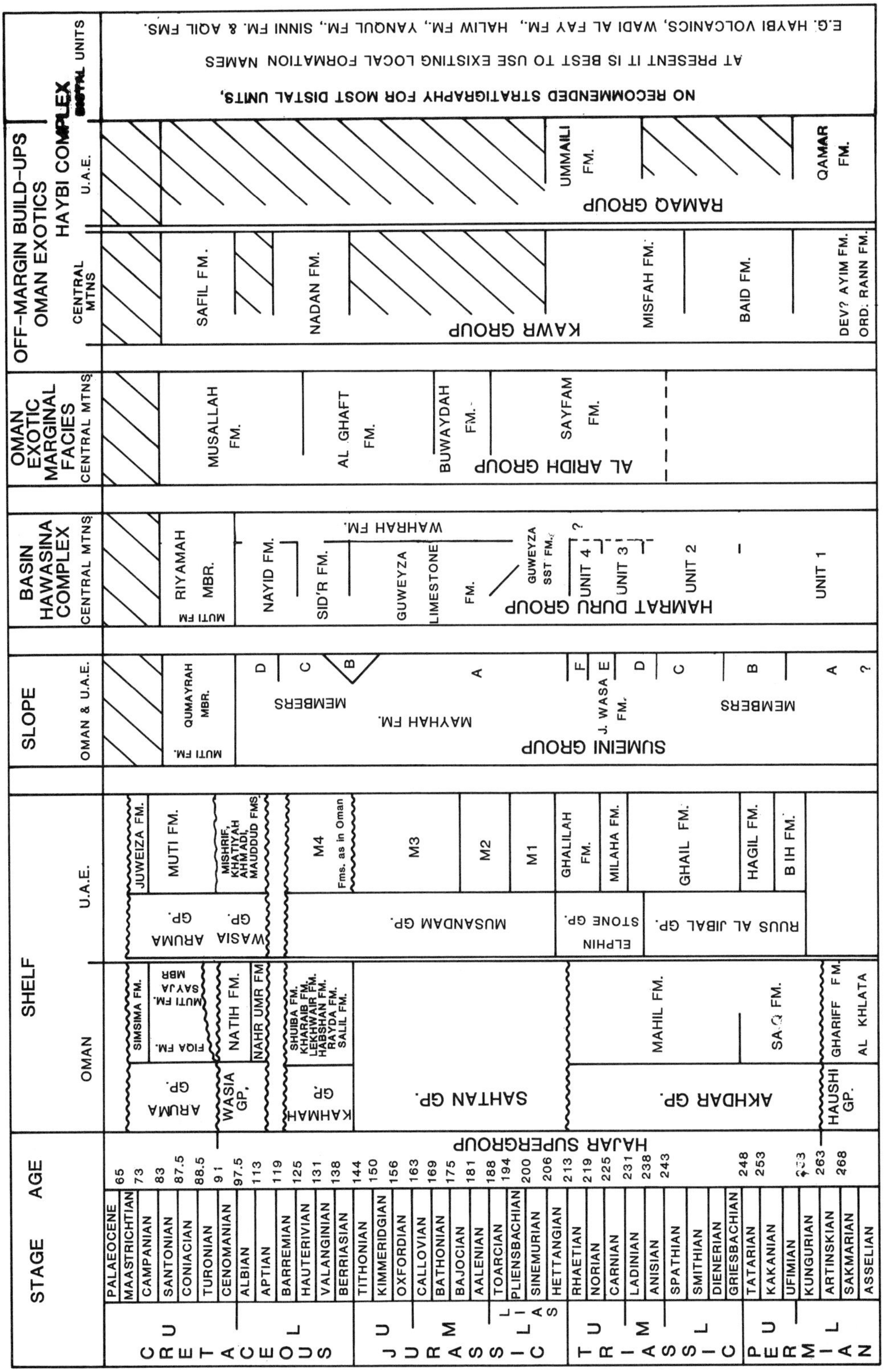

Fig. 4. Unified, proposed stratigraphy of the Late Palaeozoic–Mesozoic platform, slope and basinal units in the Oman Mountains.

in Late Triassic—Early Jurassic time (Glennie *et al.* 1974; Searle *et al.* 1980; Robertson 1986; Béchennec *et al.* 1990). A multistage rift model is thus applicable to Oman, as follows: (i) Early Permian initial 'non-volcanic' rifting dominated by block-faulting; (ii) Late Permian 'intermediate' stage rifting, with volcanism largely restricted to the axial zones; (iii) Middle Triassic—Early Jurassic volcanism recording final continental break-up (i.e. as a 'volcanic margin').

In contrast to the traditional view of North Gondwana as a Late Palaeozoic—Mesozoic Red Sea-type rift and developing passive margin, Sengör (1990) interprets the Oman 'Neo-Tethys' as an extensional retro-arc (back-arc) basin. He infers that the 'Podataksasi arc' was generated in response to subduction of 'Palaeo-Tethys' beneath 'Gondwana-Land'. Sengör (1990) specifically compares Oman with modern backarc basins, including the Sea of Japan and the Tyrrhenian Sea, Central Mediterranean (Kastens *et al.* 1988). In this context, the Haybi Complex would then be a back-arc basin. Some apparent difficulties with Sengör's (1990) model include: (i) the unexpectedly wide separation (i.e. >500 km) between the Oman rift and the inferred Podataksasi arc and the subduction zone; (ii) the absence of a subduction-related geochemical signature of the rift volcanics of the Haybi Complex (Searle *et al.* 1980); (iii) the terrigenous composition of the rift sediments (Graham 1980a,b; Robertson 1986), with no evidence of a volcanic arc provenance; (iv) the apparent absence of any thermal effects related to an active magmatic arc in Pre-Permian rock sequences (e.g. as exposed at Jebel Qamar, Dibba Zone). Alternatively, Bernoulli *et al.* (1990) correlate the Oman rift with a South Tethyan basin ('Pindos—Pichakun Trough' or 'Mesogea'), that possibly extended more or less continuously from Oman to the central Mediterranean area (Dercourt *et al.* 1986). More data on the nature

of rifting of the Neotethys as a whole are needed before chosing between these alternatives, but there is little firm evidence from Oman to support Sengör's (1990) back-arc rifting model.

Palinspastic reconstructions of the Oman passive margin

Three independent criteria have been used for palinspastic reconstruction: first, lithostratigraphic correlation; secondly, restoration of thrust sheets; thirdly, comparison with modern depositional palaeoenvironments. A more or less subjective combination of these considerations has often been used. For Glennie *et al.* (1973, 1974), the basic assumption was that the major thrust sheets contained essentially coeval successions and thus could be most logically reconstructed by restoring them such that the higher thrust sheets were the furthest travelled, most distal palaeogeographic units. Large-scale thickness variations also suggested thinning of the sediment wedge to the northeast, away from the platform edge, with the thinner generally finer-grained successions in the more distal locations (Fig. 5). On this basis, Glennie *et al.* (1973, 1974) suggested a restored half-width of the Hawasina basin of 400—1200 km.

Hawasina as a passive continental margin

Graham (1980a,b) drew a close comparison of Oman with the northeastern Atlantic continental margin. In his model (Fig. 6), Permian continental rifting was followed by active spreading *c.* 50 Ma later, in the Late Triassic, a time when subsidence rates greatly increased. The Permian exotic limestones developed mainly as reefal build-ups within the rift zone. Larger mid—Late Triassic Exotics comprise mainly back-reef lithofacies and developed on subsiding volcanic seamounts that were located close to the site of continental separation. The Hawasina Complex

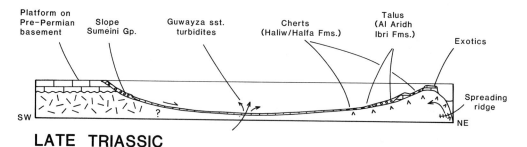

LATE TRIASSIC

Fig. 5. Glennie *et al.*'s (1974) first reconstruction. This assumes Permian to Late Triassic—Early Jurassic rifting and simple in-sequence thrusting.

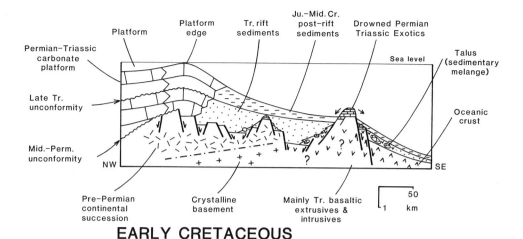

Fig. 6. Graham's (1980a,b) reconstruction. He drew a close comparison with the Mesozoic rift history of the North Atlantic. The Oman exotics were seen as seamounts along the continent–ocean boundary.

was assumed to be underlain by continental and/or transitional crust by Graham (1980a,b).

In agreement with Graham's model, Robertson (1986) suggested that Late Triassic volcanics associated with the structurally highest (i.e. most distal) thrust sheets formed in a very narrow ocean basin, similar to the modern Southern Red Sea. In this context, unmetamorphosed, alkaline-MORB extrusives in the Batinah Melange (northern mountains; Robertson & Woodcock 1983) are depositionally overlain by intact Late Triassic successions of 'basal' Fe/Mn hydrothermal, pelagic, hemipelagic and terrigenous sediments and these could be compared closely with the small ocean basin setting of the modern Gulf of Aden.

Hawasina as an intracontinental basin

The BRGM geologist's reconstruction (Béchennec *et al.* 1990; Fig. 7) is similar to Graham's (1980a,b), except that they infer an entirely continental basement to the Hamrat Duru basin. Glennie *et al*'s. (1973, 1974) suggestion that Permian deep-water sediments and volcanics might lie at the base of some of the Hamrat Duru Group successions has since been neatly confirmed (De Wever *et al.* 1989, 1990; Blendiger 1988). Permian facies have also been discovered from near the base of the carbonate platform slope succession (Sumeini Group, Maqam Formation B Member; Watts & Garrison 1986; Watts 1990). Béchennec *et al.* (1990) favour two

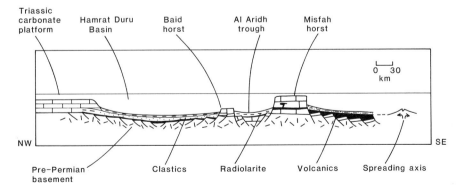

LATE TRIASSIC

Fig. 7. Béchennec *et al.*'s (1988, 1990) reconstruction. This also assumes straightforward in-sequence thrusting, with the Hamrat Duru basin being underlain by stretched continental crust.

phase rifting, as follows. In the Late Permian, a carbonate platform (Baid platform) was split from the Arabian shelf to form a broad, intracontinental deep-water basin (Hamrat Duru Basin); then in the Middle Triassic–Early Jurassic final continental break-up took place, accompanied by voluminous transitional-tholeiitic volcanism and fragmentation of the 'Baid platform' into smaller limestone horsts (Baid and Misfah Horsts). These seamounts were separated by a deep-water basin (Al Aridh Trough). More distal facies accumulated outboard of the limestone horsts along the edge of the Tethys ocean to the northeast (Umar Basin). After Early Jurassic time the margin passively subsided, punctuated by a pulse of inferred crustal extension in Late Jurassic (Tithonian) time.

Several problematic aspects of the BRGM model are as follows. The reconstruction assumes that 'Hamrat Duru Basin' was palaeogeographically simple. However, exotic limestone blocks (Hallstatt facies and Ammonitico Rosso) form a widespread horizon at the top of the Guweyza Limestone Formation of Middle-Late Jurassic age (e.g. in the Hubat and Ba'ad areas: Cooper (1990); Tozer & Calon (1990). This evidence suggests that some limestone exotics were located within the 'Hamrat Duru Basin' and not entirely to the east in a more distal setting. Secondly, the anomalously high structural position of Late Triassic, apparently proximal quartzose clastics (Al Ayn Formation) has been taken by Bernoulli & Weissert (1987) and by Cooper (1987) to indicate out-of-sequence thrusting, therefore calling into question Béchennec et al.'s (1990) assumption of simple (in-sequence) thrusting. Also, there is considerable lateral facies variation, especially of the Oman exotic limestones, which are discontinuous and thus no one two-dimensional reconstruction can be valid for the margin as a whole.

Structurally complex reconstructions

In Glennie et al.'s (1974) alternative reconstruction (Fig. 8), the upper Hawasina units, including the Oman Exotics (e.g. J. Qamar, Dibba Zone) formed on a subsided continental margin rather than in a deep-water oceanic setting. The present structural geometry came about by more complex emplacement than by simple piggyback thrusting. Features that are apparently consistent with this model include the presence of extrusives at the base of the Permian exotics, of Ordovician continental basement below Permian exotics in the Dibba Zone, and the existence of localized granitic clasts in the Hawasina Complex in the Dibba Zone. In this model, continental break-up was delayed until the Late Triassic, when the continental margin was block-faulted, subsiding to become the floor of the deep-sea Hawasina basin. During the Late Cretaceous emplacement, the Hamrat Duru Group, the Oman Exotics and related upper Hawasina units (e.g. Al Aridh Fm.) were detached from the submerged continental borderland along a major thrust plane and emplaced out-of-sequence over the adjacent carbonate platform. The Oman Exotics represent klippes derived from the Arabian platform, rather than from discrete off-margin carbonate build-ups.

In line with Glennie et al.'s alternative reconstruction, Blendiger et al. (1990) interpret Permian limestones in the southern mountains (Ba'id area) as fragments of a north-facing edge of the Arabian platform, rather than as off-margin exotics, as in most other reconstructions.

Complex thrusting of deep-sea units

Bernoulli and Weissert (1987, 1990) proposed a new palaeogeographical reconstruction of the 'Hawasina basin' and argued that the emplacement was achieved by complex, 'out-of-

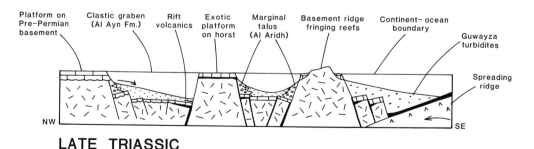

Fig. 8. Glennie et al.'s (1974) alternative reconstruction. In this, rifting is assumed to have taken place in the Late Triassic followed by subsidence and transgression of the continental margin by deep-water sediments. The present stacking geometry was achieved by major out-of-sequence thrusting in the Late Cretaceous.

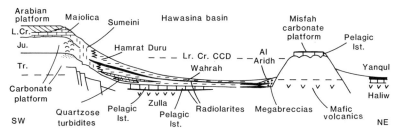

Fig. 9. Bernoulli & Weissert's (1987) reconstruction. This assumes that some of Glennie *et al.*'s poorly dated 'distal units' instead formed the stratigraphically lower, more proximal part of the Hawasina basin. These units were later emplaced to their present high structural position by out-of-sequence thrusting during the Late Cretaceous. The model is based on data from the central Mountains.

sequence' thrusting. Their arguments revolve around detailed stratigraphy, facies, age and structural data from the central mountain area. Their essential point is that ribbon radiolarites in a number of units that Glennie *et al.* (1974) thought to be long-ranging (e.g. Al Ayn, Halfa, Haliw) are instead Late Triassic and thus are potential lateral facies equivalents within the 'Hawasina basin'. Sandstones overlying these radiolarites (Guweyza Sandstone) are correlated with other sandstones, now located in a much higher structural position (Al Ayn Sandstone). As shown in Fig. 9, ribbon radiolarites accumulated throughout the 'Hawasina basin' in Late Triassic time and were then regionally overlain by turbiditic quartzose sandstones and other facies. During the Late Cretaceous thrusting the structurally higher levels of the basin were detached from the lower levels, which were then re-imbricated above, placing proximal units in an anomalously high structural position. One apparent difficulty with his model is that it requires the existence of a low-angle thrust plane near the top of the Triassic succession. This thrust plane must have traversed the considerable width of the Hawasina basin (>200 km?) without cutting up-section, since Jurassic and younger successions are absent from the upper re-thrust units (e.g. Al Ayn). Also, Bernoulli & Weissert's (1987) 'out-of-sequence thrust model' is not necessarily valid for the Northern Oman Mountains (e.g. Dibba Zone). Cooper (1988, 1990) proposes a somewhat different palaeogeographical scheme for the entire area in which the extent of re-thrusting is diminished (see below). However, in general Bernoulli & Weissert's (1987) model represents a breakthrough and is a considerable improvement on Glennie *et al.*'s (1973, 1974) reconstructions.

Out-of-sequence thrusting of contrasting deep-water sub-basins

Cooper (1990) argues that two broadly differing deep-water successions are present in the Hamrat Duru Group based on the presence or absence of shale as a significant component and the existence of contrasting sedimentation patterns (e.g. large sheets versus small discontinuous bodies). Cooper (1988, 1990) (Fig. 10) also argues in favour of shorter distance 'out-of-sequence' thrusting than Bernoulli & Weissert (1987). He concurs that stratigraphic units above the Al Ayn Formation were removed by out-of-sequence thrusting. However, Cooper (1988, 1990) believes the Al Ayn succession did not originally underlie the Guweyza Limestone Formation, as in Bernoulli and Weissert's (1987) model, but instead accumulated in a separate, more proximal 'sub-basin'. Critically, Cooper (1988, 1990) correlates Glennie *et al.*'s structurally high Al Ayn Formation with long intact Triassic 'proximal' successions in the Hawasina window (Zulla and Guweyza Sandstone Formations). Jurassic and Cretaceous proximal sequences there include conglomerates that conformably overlie the Al Ayn Formation and are correlated with the Sumeini Group (Graham 1980). Shaly deep-sea facies also pass laterally into lower slope carbonates (Sumeini Group) in the northern mountains (e.g. Hatta Zone; Robertson *et al.* 1990b). A very proximal rather than a relatively distal setting for the Al Ayn Formation is thus inferred, in contrast to Bernoulli & Weissert's (1987) model.

Cooper (1988, 1990) suggests the presence of two depositional sub-basins within the Hawasina basin. A shale-rich northerly sub-basin was ponded by an ocean floor ridge at its southern end, and relatively small dimension sediment

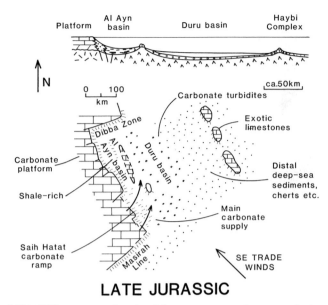

LATE JURASSIC

Fig. 10. Cooper's (1987, 1990) reconstruction, involving two separate deep-water basins separated by a limestone ridge.

bodies were fed into this from numerous point sources along the Oman margin. In the south, and extending northwards outboard (northeast) from this sea-floor ridge, coarse-grained sediment was derived from the Saih Hatat margin and formed a large-scale longitudinal fan (Cooper 1989). The driving force of Cooper's late out-of-sequence thrusting could possibly relate to the thrust wedge maintaining a 'critical taper' as it was overridden by the Haybi Complex and the Semail ophiolite.

Oceanic origin of upper Hawasina units and Haybi Complex

Searle *et al*. (1980) envisaged the Hawasina Complex as accumulating on transitional and/ or oceanic rather than continental crust (Fig. 11). The Late Triassic Oman Exotics, part of the Haybi Complex, were interpreted as ocean island seamounts, based on detailed petrography, geochemistry and K−Ar dating. The Late Triassic Exotics commonly depositionally overlie alkali basalts, ankaramites and tholeiites (Haybi Volcanic Group), typical of modern within-plate ocean islands (Searle *et al*. 1980). Glennie *et al*.'s (1974) earlier concept of the Late Triassic Exotics as atolls or carbonate islands, actually on the spreading ridge (Fig. 5) was discounted, since MORB tholeiites were never found beneath the Exotic limestones. Searle *et al*. (1980) also suggested that Late Cretaceous? depleted, island arc tholeiites near the top of the Haybi Volcanic Group in a few areas might have formed above a subduction zone.

Greenschist facies metamorphic rocks near the base of the Semail ophiolite metamorphic sole mainly comprise quartz-rich sediments, rare pelites, marbles and alkaline-transitional metaigneous rocks, similar to the unmetamorphosed.

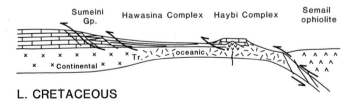

L. CRETACEOUS

Fig. 11. Searle *et al*.'s (1980) reconstruction (during initial Late Cretaceous deformation). In this the Oman exotics are seen as oceanic seamounts, while the Hawasina and Haybi Complexes are interpreted as oceanic units that were incorporated into a subduction−accretion complex.

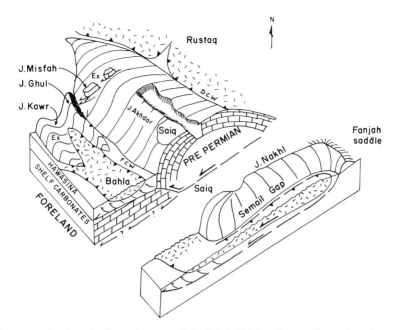

Fig. 12. Summary of styles of deformation around the Jebel Akhdar. See text for explanation.

Haybi Volcanic Group of Searle & Malpas (1980, 1982). The meta-sedimentary protoliths were considered to be both 'distal' deep-sea sediments and more-proximal quartz-rich sandstones which were accreted to the base of the Semail ophiolite during obduction. Structurally overlying amphibolites in the upper part of the metamorphic sole are geochemically similar to tholeiitic MORB, unlike the Haybi Volcanic Group, and were envisaged as remnants of subducted Jurassic or Cretaceous oceanic crust.

Summary of rift and passive margin history

The North Oman continental margin developed as a result of Late Carboniferous−Early Permian, Late Permian and Late Triassic−Early Jurassic-rifting, culminating in continental break-up and sea-floor spreading. We have summarized the key points of data and the interpretations that we favour in Fig. 13. Figure 14 summarises the main factors that controlled the development of the Oman passive continental margin. In summary, the Oman Exotics (e.g. Jebels Misfah, Baid and Qamar) existed as off-margin platforms near the continent-ocean boundary, rather than as klippes derived from the Arabian platform, or atolls formed far out in the Tethyan ocean. The base of the carbonate platform slope and the adjacent deep-sea basin (Hamrat Duru Group) was probably segmented

into several sub-basins, by transform faults and volcanic ridges, resulting in considerable local facies variation. The more distal sedimentary and volcanic units (Haybi Complex) formed along the edge of the Neotethys ocean. Complex and variable thrust scenarios must be invoked to explain the regional facies distribution.

Structural and emplacement history

Permian deformation and metamorphism?

Evidence of Late Palaeozoic? deformation and metamorphism was reported by Glennie et al. (1973, 1974) and Michard (1982) in the form of cleaved, mainly meta-sedimentary rocks from the Jebel Akhdar and Saih Hatat windows and Jebel Ja'alan (Fig. 1). Illite crystallinity studies imply upper greenschist facies metamorphism (Michard 1982). The BRGM geologists emphasise the association with shallow water-derived marble (Rabu et al. 1990) and schistose volcaniclastics, containing Late Permian fossils. They assign these units to the base of the Late Palaeozoic−Mesozoic carbonate platform succession, whereas quartzose metamorphic rocks represent underlying basement (e.g. Ordovician Amdeh Fm.). Rabu et al. (1990) question the reality of any 'Hercynian' metamorphism and deformation. In agreement with this view, the Ordovician-Late Permian succession exposed

System		Stage	Age	SHELF SUCCESSION	CARBONATE PLATFORM SLOPE
C R E T A C E O U S	U	MAASTRICHTIAN	73	Localised erosion, fluviatile deposition, then marine transgression.	Steepening and collapse of slope, lithoclastics, mega-breccias, (Qumayrah Mbr); megabreccias until Coniacian (J. Fayad).
		CAMPANIAN	83	Ophiolite-derived sediment, shale.	
	L	SANTONIAN		Collapse of platform to form foreland basin; siliciclastic turbidites, debris flows.	Radiolarian chert, tectonic flexure of shelf.
		CONIACIAN	88.5		
		TURONIAN	91	Wasia-Aruma break: unstable shelf, slope; subsidence.	
		CENOMANIAN	97.5	Hemipelagic carbonates (J. Salakh). Rudistic carbonate shelf, local basins.	Muddy calcilutite on a carbonate ramp (W. Qumayrah); calcirudites and slumping indicate pre-Cenomanian steepening.
		ALBIAN	113	Regressive mega-sequence, NW prograding carbonate ramp.	
		APTIAN	119	Slope to bathyal in Musandam; also hemipelagic sediments.	Aptian shallow marine progradation (Musandam).
		BARREMIAN	125	Local tectonic instability until Barremian	Radiolarian chert (J. Sumeini) in deep, subsided slope, pelagic calcilutite (S. Hatat), elsewhere relatively shallow; drowning unconformity on Musandam.
		HAUTERIVIAN	131	Maiolica in stable areas (J. Akhdar); calcareous and siliciclastic turbidites in unstable basinal areas (S. Hatat).	
		VALANGINIAN	138		
		BERRIASIAN	144	250km of slope retreat; regional extension and deepening.	
J U R A S S I C	U	TITHONIAN	150	Proximal subtidal massive bioclastic 1st.	Contrasting slope morphologies; J. Sumeini-gullied slope margin and/or erosional escarpment; Hatta Zone-basement exposed on transform rift scarps; Dibba Zone-steep bypass slope marked by fine periplatform ooze; slumping. W. Qumayrah-steep escarpment margin with fault-generated megabreccias (W. thrust sheet has gullied slope). Later became a sloping ramp with periplatform ooze. J. Sham-redeposited facies on slope apron; Saih Hatat-subsided platform and gentle slope.
		KIMMERIDGIAN	156	Lithiotis, oolitic limestones, lagoonal to restricted shelf (J. Akhdar).	
		OXFORDIAN	163		
	M	CALLOVIAN	169	Inner shelf carbonate (Musandam)	
		BATHONIAN	175		
		BAJOCIAN	181	Mixed carbonate-clastic sequence in broad shallow carbonate shelf (J. Akhdar); cf. submerged plateau (S. Hatat), with calciturbidites, pelagic micrite and carbonate debris flows.	
		AALENIAN	188		
	L I A S	TOARCIAN	194	Unconformity on Triassic in J. Akhdar.	
		PLIENSBACHIAN	200		
		SINEMURIAN	206	Unconformity of Rhaetic/Norian; basal siliciclastics; massive and algal limestone with Lithiotis.	Siliciclastic redeposited sediments on slope; extensive by-passing (J. Sumeini).
		HETTANGIAN	213		
T R I A S S I C		RHAETIAN	219	Shallow marine platform in Musandam.	Differential subsidence; normal faulting; escarpment margin suddenly developed; bypass margin with base of slope debris apron. Coeval J. Wasa Fm.-high energy reef margin and debris.
	U	NORIAN	225		
		CARNIAN	231	Very restricted shallow marine to locally continental accumulation on evaporitic (dolomitic) subsiding shelf.	Basement erosion in Hatta Zone
	M	LADINIAN	238		
		ANISIAN	243		
	L	SPATHIAN		Shoaling-upwards cycles similar to modern Abu Dhabi area.	Subsidence (Dienerian), small carbonate fans along faulted margin, growth faults, down-to-N displacements (J. Sumeini)
		SMITHIAN	248	Part of the vast shallow Arabian platform.	
		GRIESBACHIAN	253	Stable shelf (J. Ahhdar), fluvial clastics, restricted; marine transgression with Fe, shelf carbonates and bioherms.	
P E R M I A N	U	TATARIAN			Permian carbonate slope, rift-related subsidence, breccias and intrastratal deformation (extension); distally-steepened ramp.
		KAZANIAN	258	Unstable shelf (S. Hatat); clastics and carbonates; condensed sequences; intraplate volcanism; horsts and grabens; cherty limestones; local evaporites (Late Permian).	
		UFINIAN	263		Relatively deep marine, wide outer shelf, thin-bedded, clayey, spicular limestone, local (J. Sumeini).
		KUNGURIAN		Shelf, hardgrounds, dolomites (Musandam).	
	L	ARTINSKIAN	268		
		SAKMARIAN		Continental clastics prograde against basement high; local unconformity.	
		ASSELIAN	286		

Fig. 13. Summary of the major controls on deposition on the Oman Late Palaeozoic—Mesozoic rift and passive margin.

in the Dibba Zone Exotics (Jebel Qamar, Robertson et al. 1990a) remained undeformed until Late Cretaceous time. On the other hand, based on evidence from the central mountains, Mann & Hanna (1990) favour Glennie et al.'s (1974) recognition of a Late Palaeozoic orogenic event; more work is clearly needed to resolve this controversy.

Transition from a passive margin to a foreland basin

During the Late Cretaceous, intra-oceanic convergence began in the Neotethys northeast of the Oman passive margin. The driving force was possibly related to the opening of the South Atlantic (Lippard et al. 1986). Soon afterwards

DEEP – SEA BASIN	OFF – MARGIN BUILD – UPS	OCEANIC SEDIMENTS AND VOLCANICS
Siliceous sediments; lithoclastic calciturbidites; mass-wasting of platform (Riyamah Fm, Dibba Zone).		
Proximal collapse breccias, distal calciturbidites, tectonic control (Nayid Fm, central Mtns).	Submerged platform; hempelagic clayey calcilutite.	Intraplate-MORB, hyaloclastite, interbedded radiolarian pelagic carbonate; alkaline sills (Dibba Zone), depleted tholeiites (Central Mountains).
Radiolarian sediments, deepening and tectonic subsidence, intra-plate-MORB volcanism (Dibba Zone, Hatta Zone).	Slope: calciturbidites, radiolarites, breccias, platform-derived blocks, intermediate composition volcanics.	
Prograding calciturbidites, lithoclastic grainstones with rare volcanic chips, locally shaly, thinner in N. Mtns. Main controls: sea level fall, shelf progradation, more coccoliths and planktonic foraminifera.	Submerged platform: Maiolica, micritic lst.	Intraplate basalt, hyaloclastite, lava debris flows; sills; minor pelagic calcilutite overlying distal radiolarian cherts; interpreted as shallow water seamount. (Hatta Zone).
Basin deepening, calcirudites, at first near platform, then mainly radiolarian cherts (Sid'r Fm).	Slope: radiolarite, megabreccia, platform lst blocks; supply from local Exotic horsts; fault reactivation.	
Silicified calciturbidites, locally shaly.		Radiolarite, shale, hemipelagic calcilutite (Dibba Zone).
Distal Mn hydrothermal deposits (Wahrah Fm).	Horsts: long hiatus, erosion and/or emergence and karstification, with Fe/Mn crusts on submerged platforms (J. Misfah).	Radiolarian chert (U. Barr; esp. Kimm-Tith-'Halfa Fm').
Local Oman Exotic detritus (Hubat, Ba'ad).	Slope: calciturbidites, radiolarite, intraplate basalts, debris flows calcirudites.	Distal calciturbidites, shale, radiolarite, possibly on MORB oceanic basement.
Thick oolitic calciturbidites (Guwayza lst).	The horsts locally block gravity supply of sediment to ocean.	
3 main cycles of oolitic grainstones, separated by carbonate siltstone and hemipelagics (Hamrat and Duru), more distal to N, local sills (W. Hawasina).	Off-margin platform: alkaline-transitional intraplate volcanics, reef limestone and thick platform carbonate (Baid); back-reef and reef edge facies (Hawasina window); inferred second rift phase; break-up of Baid platform.	Distal radiolarites and calciturbidites, intruded by alkaline dolerite sills and underlain by 'basal' Fe, Mn hydrothermal sediments (Batinah Melange).
Variety of quartzose turbidites, thin to N; absent in Dibba Zone.		
Silicified oolitic calciturbidites and radiolarites; Cooper's division into more proximal 'Al Ayn basin' and more distal 'Duru basin', with Exotic ridge between.	Submerged platform: pelagic calcilutite on drowned shelf, Lr. Triassic is absent (J. Qamar).	Basement is intraplate/transitional/MORB extrusives; reef lst blocks near Exotics (Batinah Melange and Batinah Siliceous Sheets); correlated with greenschists (Haybi Complex).
Inferred source of Duru basin is the Saih Hatat area.	Rift-related sedimentary melange (Kub melange).	
Deep-sea deposition of radiolarite, bivalve-bearing micrite and fine-grained calciturbidites and shale; N-S increase in grain-size (Sumeini area); coarse-grained arenites in central Mtns. (Al Ayn; Hawasina window).	Slope: intraplate basalt, proximal calciturbidites, interbedded radiolarites (Al Aridh).	'Perennial' radiolarites dated as Ladinian-Aptian in most distal deep-sea sediments.
Silicified fine-grained calciturbidites.		
Silicified radiolarian marl and chert turbidites, proximal slope facies locally exposed (Dibba Zone); also local alkaline volcanism (Dibba Zone).		
Rifting and basin subsidence, local low-oxygen conditions.	Intraplate volcanism, then off-margin carbonate platform isolated in 1st rift phase.	
Rifting, deep-water radiolarites, shelf-derived calciturbidites, shales, and minor calcirudites.	Reefal limestones (J. Qamar in Dibba Zone, Hawasina window), also Yanqul and Ibri.	
Input from Arabian platform, possibly also from off-margin platforms.	Mixed siliciclastic shallow marine carbonate sequence on unstable, rifting shelf (J. Qamar).	
Volcanism, mainly intra-plate and transitional (Hawasina window).		

the Semail ophiolite was generated from 98–93 Ma (Tilton *et al.* 1981). Genesis above a young intra-oceanic subduction zone is favoured by some authors (Pearce *et al.* 1981; Lippard *et al.* 1986; Searle & Stevens, 1984; Robertson 1987a), while others prefer a mid-ocean ridge setting (Coleman 1981; Michard *et al.* 1985; see also *Tectonophysics*, Special Issue, **151**, 1988). In the former scenario, it however remains to

be established that the Semail ophiolite was formed above the *same* subduction zone that was associated with the later collision and emplacement onto the Arabian continental margin.

The Turonian Wasia–Aruma break in the platform succession is a regionally significant unconformity that is visible wherever the top of the carbonate platform succession is exposed, for example in the Semail Gap and the

STAGE	AGE	TECTONIC	SEA LEVEL	PHYSIOGRAPHIC	PALEOCEANOGRAPHIC/CLIMATIC
CRETACEOUS U MAASTRICHTIAN	65	ISOSTATIC SUBSIDENCE RELAXATION, UPLIFT		FORELAND BASIN DEVELOPMENT	
CAMPANIAN	73	COLLISION, CONTINENTAL			
CANTONIAN	83	SUBDUCTION & OPHIOLITE			
CONIACIAN	87.5	EMPLACEMENT		RELATIVE COASTAL ONLAP	
TURONIAN	88.5	FLEXURAL COLLAPSE FLEXURAL UPWARP		COLLAPSE OF SLOPE, FOREDEEP DEVELOPMENT	RISE IN CCD
CENOMANIAN	91 / 97.5	EXTENSIONAL VOLCANISM (SEMAIL OPHIOLITE FORMED)	CYCLES OF EUSTATIC SEA LEVEL RISE	INTRASHELF BASINS	ABUNDANT COCCOLITHS AND PLANTONIC FORAMINIFERA
L ALBIAN	113			RELATIVE COASTAL ONLAP	
APTIAN	119				
BARREMIAN	125	STABLE PLATFORM	DROWNING		FALL IN CCD
HAUTERIVIAN	131		SEA LEVEL FALL	SHELF PROGRADATION	? INCREASED RADIOLARIAN PRODUCTIVITY
VALANGINIAN	138	THERMAL SUBSIDENCE			
BERRIASIAN	144	CRUSTAL EXTENSION AND SUBSIDENCE, INFERRED	SUPPLEMENTARY EFFECT OF SEA LEVEL RISE	RELATIVE COASTAL ONLAP	
JURASSIC U TITHONIAN	150	OCEANIC VOLCANISM			SE TRADE WINDS
KIMMERIDGIAN	156	(? SPREADING EVENT)			CONTROL SURFACE CURRENTS
OXFORDIAN	163				
CALLOVIAN	169			LONGITUDINAL FANS IN OUTER DEEP-SEA BASIN	
M BATHONIAN	175	STABLE PLATFORM			OVERALL SEMI-WINDWARD MARGIN INFLUENCE ON FACIES
BAJOCIAN	181	CARBONATE RAMP CYCLES			
AALENIAN	188				
L LIAS TOARCIAN	194			OFF-MARGIN EXOTIC RIDGES	
PLIENSBACHIAN	200				
SINEMURIAN	206			SHALY INNER DEEP-SEA BASIN	
HETTANGIAN	213	THERMAL SUBSIDENCE			
U RHAETIAN	219	CONTINENTAL BREAK-UP	SUPPLEMENTARY EFFECT	PLATFORM-SLOPE	UPWELLING AND ? HIGH
NORIAN	225	THINNING, FAST	OF SEA LEVEL FALL	BASIN MORPHOLOGY;	PRODUCTIVITY IN SMALL
CARNIAN	231	SUBSIDENCE,VOLCANISM	(INCREASED SILICICLASTICS	OFF-MARGIN	OCEAN BASIN
M LADINIAN	238	ORTHOGONAL RIFTING TRANSFORM SEGMENTS	REDUCED CARBONATE INPUT)	PLATFORMS (EXOTICS)	LOCAL LOW-OXYGEN SEA FLOOR
ANISIAN	243				
SPATHIAN					
L SMITHIAN					ARIDITY ON PLATFORM
DIENERIAN					
GRIESBACHIAN	248				
PERMIAN U TATARIAN	253	MAJOR CRUSTAL THINNING SUBSIDENCE, RIFTING,		BROAD, DEEPENING RIFT	
KUNGURIAN?		VOLCANISM		WITH CARBONATE ATOLLS	
UFIMIAN	258			AND PLATFORMS	
KUNGURIAN	263	INITIAL RIFTING, BLOCK-		(EXOTICS)	
L ARTINSKIAN	268	FAULTING, DOMING, LOCAL	MAJOR EUSTATIC		DEGLACIATION
SAKMARIAN		SUBSIDENCE	SEA LEVEL RISE		
ASSELIAN	286				GONDWANA GLACIATION

Fig. 14. Summary of interpretations of depositional, tectonic and volcanic events in the Late Palaeozoic–Mesozoic evolution of the Oman Late Palaeozoic–Mesozoic Tethyan rift and passive margin. Based mainly on papers in this volume.

Musandam Peninsula (Glennie et al. 1974; Murris 1980; Harris & Frost 1984). Robertson (1987a,b, 1988) and Patton & O'Connor (1988) interpret this surface in terms of flexural upwarp to form a peripheral bulge, followed by erosion and gradual subsidence (Late Cenomanian–Santonian?). Watts & Blome (1989) further constrain the time of development to the peripheral bulge to Cenomanian–Coniacian, based on new radiolarian age data from the Qumayrah Member of the Muti Formation. New age data are also provided by Rabu et al. (1990), who suggest that development of the Muti basin was essentially synchronous throughout the Oman Mountains.

Based on data from wells within the northern mountain foreland, Patton & O'Connor (1988) suggest that the flexural upwarp was in the order of 244 m, much less than the up to 600 m uplift of the shelf edge area inferred by Robertson (1987a,b). Theoretical considerations suggest that the flexural bulge will be narrower but greater in amplitude where the crust is thin, while on thicker crust the bulge will be wider but lower (Stockmal et al. 1986). A possible explanation for the differences in estimated uplift may be that flexure was greatest near the Mesozoic shelf edge (i.e. on thin crust), but decreased in amplitude continentwards (i.e. on thicker crust). Warburton et al. (1990) and Rabu et al. (1990) detect no evidence that the peripheral bulge migrated inboard with time (c.f. Boote et al. 1990). It is possible that the peripheral bulge exploited old rift structures near the edge of the carbonate platform. If so the uplift could have been largely 'locked in' once the peripheral bulge started to form, rather than migrating inboard ahead of the advancing thrust load, as in geophysical models (Stockmal *et al.* 1986). As the thrust load converged on the Arabian margin, the carbonate platform edge was downflexed and then collapsed in late Campanian–Maastrichtian time. This facilated emplacement of the ophiolite with little up-slope displacement or large-scale emergence.

The main source of sediment in the siliciclastic foreland basin (Turonian–?Santonian Muti Fm.) was the Arabian continental margin (Glennie *et al.* 1974, 1990). Robertson (1987a,b) suggested that small volumes of coarse-grained clastics (e.g. quartzose conglomerates) were also derived by rapid erosion of uplifted basement fault blocks during thrusting. Rabu *et al.* (1990) invoke a major uplifted basement ridge ('Masqat–Musandam horst') to the northeast as the main sediment source, but provide little supporting evidence for this.

During emplacement onto the continental margin, the ophiolite was dissected into discrete blocks (Graham 1980a; Lippard *et al.* 1986), allowing sub-ophiolite lithologies of the Haybi Complex to protrude upwards, locally spilling onto the ophiolite surface as the Batinah Melange (Robertson & Woodcock 1983). During emplacement, imbricated Hawasina sediments (Wahrah Fm.) were bulldozed ahead of the ophiolite (Glennie *et al.* 1974; Cooper 1988). Some of these units in the central mountains then slid northeastwards onto the surface of the ophiolite (Robertson 1986), giving rise to the Batinah Sheets (Woodcock & Robertson 1982).

After final emplacement of the ophiolite, uplift occurred, possibly in response to flexural relaxation (Robertson 1987a). Large volumes of ophiolite- and Mesozoic deep-sea sediment-derived detritus were then shed into a more inboard foreland basin flanking the mountain front, as the late Campanian-Maastrichtian Juweiza Formation (Glennie *et al.* 1974; Patton & O'Connor 1988; Boote *et al.* 1990; Nolan *et al.* 1990).

Oman Mountains as an imbricate thrust stack

The concept of the Oman Mountains as a series of allochthonous thrust sheets emplaced from northeast to southwest onto the Arabian continental margin dates back to Lees (1928), received support from Allemann & Peters (1972) work in the Dibba Zone, but was not generally accepted until publication of Glennie *et al.*'s (1974) classic memoir and map. Many early workers (e.g. Morton 1959) believed that the Hawasina rocks conformably overlay the shelf carbonates. Wilson (1969) recognized that the

'Oman Exotic' limestones of Permian and Triassic age overlay younger Hawasina sediments and he interpreted them as having slid into a deep-water basin.

The regional mapping and detailed biostratigraphical work of the Shell team confirmed that the allochthonous interpretation was without doubt correct. The deep-sea successions presently crop out *c.* 150 km southwest of the shelf carbonate margin, and thus relatively thin thrust sheets must have been transported astonishingly long distances. Based on restoration of thrust sheets, Cooper (1988) recently estimated a minimum width of 455 km for the Hawasina basin in the central Oman Mountains. What then was the mechanism by which these oceanic rocks were emplaced such long distances onto the Arabian platform margin?

Structural mapping and balanced and restored cross-sections

Recent detailed structural mapping of the thrust sheets beneath the Semail ophiolite has had three main objectives: (i) to determine the sequence of thrusting; (ii) to determine the depth to basal detachment and the extent of thrusting in the shelf succession beneath; (iii) to determine the relative timing of thrusting events. To help achieve these aims, the construction of balanced cross sections and their restoration utilizes a purely geometric approach to analyse the structure of a particular region. Good results are achieved in areas where the thrust structures are relatively simple and the stratigraphical thicknesses well known, for example along the foreland margin of the Hawasina allochthon to the west of the mountain front (Barrette & Calon 1987; Barrette 1988; Cooper 1988) and in tectonic windows beneath the Semail ophiolite (e.g. Searle 1980, 1985, 1988a; Searle *et al.* 1980; Graham 1980a,b; Searle & Cooper 1986; Bernoulli & Weissert 1987). The stratigraphy is, however more difficult or impossible to restore in areas of greatest complexity, for example immediately below the Semail ophiolite (Haybi Complex) and/or where significant strike-slip has taken place (e.g. Dibba Zone; Robertson *et al.* 1990a).

Thrust mechanisms

The initial imbrication of the deep-water successions took place far from the continental margin, probably as a result of accretion during consumption of Tethyan oceanic crust in a northeasterly-dipping subduction zone (Pearce *et al.* 1981; Searle & Stevens 1984). Woodcock &

Robertson (1984) stressed the virtual absence of typical trench-type sediments related to steady-state subduction, probably because the Semail ophiolite formed relatively close to the Arabian continental margin (within *c*. 1000 km). The removal of large areas of basement could only be achieved by subduction if the Hawasina was underlain by oceanic and/or by very thinned (transitional) crust. If the Hawasina Complex restores to several hundred kilometres width and was essentially deposited on continental crust, as in Béchennec *et al*.'s (1988, 1990) model, then what has happened to the basement during Late Cretaceous thrusting?

In common with many orogenic belts the dominant sequence of thrusting was one of foreland-directed piggy-back thrusting where thrusts propagated into the footwall and place older rocks over younger (Boyer & Elliott 1982). In this simplified scenario all the stratigraphic section is preserved and accurate restoration is possible. Detailed mapping of many culminations in the Oman Mountains, however reveals that not all thrusts were 'in sequence' piggy back thrusts. 'Out-of-sequence' thrusting is demonstrated by the truncation of footwall folds and imbricate slices and by the elimination of stratigraphic succession in the footwall (Searle 1985; Bernoulli & Weissert 1987; Cooper 1988). Late-stage rethrusting, both 'in-sequence' breaching thrusts (Butler 1987) and 'out-of-sequence' breakback thrusts (Searle 1988a) are also well documented (Searle 1985, 1988a; Searle & Cooper 1986; Barrette & Calon 1987; Barrette 1988; Cooper 1988; Cawood *et al*. 1990).

Late-stage deeper level thrusting of the Sumeini shelf edge rocks and late-stage breakback thrusting in the hanging wall of the thrust front gave rise to many culminations along the leading edge of the Semail ophiolite (e.g. Searle 1985, 1988a; Searle & Cooper 1986). Also, late-stage NE-facing folds and NE-verging backthrusts which overturned and inverted earlier stacking sequences are important, for example in the structurally complex Hawasina window (Fig. 1; Searle & Cooper 1986; in the Hatta Zone (Robertson 1990b) and in the Ibra dome (Cawood *et al*. 1990).

Hanna (1990) constructs a balanced and restored cross-section across the Saih Hatat region (Fig. 1) and shows that the original thrust geometry was complicated by the occurrence of surge zones, extensional duplexes with normal faulting related to the alignment of frontal, lateral and oblique ramps in the footwall. He explains the apparent missing tectonostratigraphy around the margins of Jebel Akhdar (Fig. 12) by normal faulting that ac-

companied culmination collapse. Glennie *et al*. (1974) earlier envisaged similar normal faulting, although to a lesser extent and without being related to culmination collapse. In Hanna's (1990) model, locally segmented ophiolite blocks and underlying units (i.e. Haybi Complex and Hamrat Duru Group) were downfaulted directly against the platform succession (e.g. along the N margin of Saih Hatat, Fig. 1). Also, as the Jebel Akhdar culmination rose, higher thrust sheets apparently slid towards the foreland (Glennie *et al*. 1974; Graham 1980a,b; Cooper 1988; Cawood 1990; Cawood *et al*. 1990).

Extent of thrusting in the shelf carbonate sequence

Hanna (1990) and Bernoulli & Weissert (1987) suggest that the basal detachment was not above the 'autochthonous' shelf carbonates, as depicted by Glennie *et al*. (1973, 1974), but was located considerably deeper in the pre-Permian basement. The Jebel Akhdar and Saih Hatat domal structures (Fig. 1) were interpreted as culminations above a basal thrust located at depth in the pre-Permian basement, rather than as Tertiary uplift-related structures (Glennie *et al*. 1973, 1974). The inferred sole thrust climbed a ramp along the southern margin of the Jebel Akhdar-Saih Hatat culminations and then followed a shallower level until it emerged at the southern limit of the foreland fold and thrust belt, or is represented by a blind thrust below the foreland folds of Jebel Madamar−Jebel Salakh (Fig. 1).

Further north, thrusting of the shelf carbonates is documented along the western edge of the Musandam Mountains (Searle *et al*. 1983; Searle 1988a,b). Restoration of the Hagab thrust in the Hagil window area (Ras al Khaimah) indicates that the shelf carbonates were thrust from 4 to 15 km over previously thrust-emplaced Hawasina Complex rocks.

Seismic data from the northern mountains also reveal extensive thrusting in the shelf carbonates up to a distance of 30 km west of the mountain front (Dunne *et al*. 1990). Some of these thrusts within the shelf carbonates are of Late Cretaceous age since they appear to be erosionally truncated and overlain by Tertiary sediments in seismic profiles; others are clearly Tertiary, since thrusts penetrate the Early Tertiary Pabdeh and Fars Groups (Dunne *et al*. 1990).

Continental margin subduction

Along the northeastern margin of the Saih Hatat, in the southeastern mountains (Fig. 1) structural complexity is greater when compared with the relatively undisturbed southern flank. Complex folding and thrusting in the shelf carbonates (Hanna, 1990) gives way to high-strain calc-mylonite shear zones and blueschist-eclogite grade metamorphism (Lippard 1983; Michard 1983; Lippard *et al.* 1986; Goffe *et al.* 1988). Peak $P-T$ conditions are approximately 11 kbar at 400°C for the glaucophane-bearing eclogite assemblages, at As Sifah (Goffe *et al.* 1988). These pressures require burial to depths of at least 25 km during the late stages of obduction of the Semail ophiolite (see El-Shazly & Coleman 1990). There is no evidence that Jebel Akhdar to the north was similarly affected and the localized HP metamorphism of Saih Hatat may relate to attempted subduction of a continental margin promontory during collision with a NE-dipping subduction zone. The collision is seen as the main driving force of ophiolite emplacement (Lippard *et al.* 1986; Glennie *et al.* 1990; Le Metour *et al.* 1990). After the collision, continued convergence was possibly taken up further northeast along the Makran active margin (Glennie *et al.* 1990), while resulting flexural relaxation of the Oman margin resulted in uplift, and gravitational spreading and/or gravity sliding of the dissected Semail ophiolite further onto the foreland (Barrette 1988; Cawood 1990; Cawood *et al.* 1990).

Cretaceous versus Tertiary thrusting

Tertiary rocks are not directly exposed in the Jebel Akhdar, Jebel Nakhl or Saih Hatat culminations although relatively undisturbed, gently inclined or open folded Tertiary rocks are present around the margins of these units. Along most of the length of the Oman Mountains Late Maastrichtian and Tertiary neoautochthonous sediments unconformably overlie imbricated Hawasina, Haybi and Semail ophiolite rocks, clearly indicating that thrusting was completed by Late Maastrichtian time (Glennie *et al.* 1974; Nolan *et al.* 1990; Robertson *et al.* 1990b). Sedimentological evidence confirms that the mountain area was emergent in the Late Campanian–Maastrichtian, when laterites and other subaerial ophiolite-derived sediments accumulated in the east (Qahlah Fm.; Glennie *et al.* 1974; Hopson *et al.* 1981; Skelton *et al.* 1990).

For the Sumeini area, northern mountains, Searle *et al.* (1990) demonstrate that thrust culmination was mainly a Cretaceous event, but that a second episode of short-distance thrusting also affected the post-emplacement Maastrichtian limestones. Similar relationships are visible

on seismic sections west of the mountain front (Dunne *et al.* 1990).

The formation of the giant culmination that dominates the Musandam Peninsula was clearly a late-stage event as the earlier Hawasina thrust sheets have been breached by the deeper, younger Hagab thrust and then refolded (Searle 1988b). Earlier reports of Eocene beds in the footwall of the Hagab thrust (Searle *et al.* 1983) are incorrect. Foraminifera have been re-examined and found to be Campanian-Santonian in age (Searle *et al.* 1989).

In summary, the majority of the thrusts exposed in the Northern Oman Mountains are Late Cretaceous and are sealed by Late Maastrichtian–Tertiary limestones. Compression recurred in the northern mountains during the Tertiary with thrusting of the Late Cretaceous Aruma Group and overlying Tertiary rocks in the foreland. This phase of thrust history is shown on seismic profiles west of the northern mountains (Dunne *et al.* 1990; Boote *et al.* 1990). However, at present the exact timing of rethrusting and culmination development can only be constrained as post-Campanian.

The Early Tertiary tectonic history was dominated by extensional tectonics, as summarized by Mann *et al.* (1990) and by Nolan *et al.* (1990). Finally, during later Tertiary time the leading edge of the Arabian margin in the Musandam Peninsula began to collide with the opposing Makran margin (White & Ross 1979; Searle 1988a; Michaelis & Pauken 1990; Glennie *et al.* 1990). Whether this closing is diachronous, or instead occurred in two distinct crustal shortening events in the Late Cretaceous and mid-Late Tertiary remains to be proven.

We gratefully acknowledge our fellow contributors who made their papers available to us during editing the Special Publication, and thank the Open University, Edinburgh University, N.E.R.C. and Amoco Production Company for continuing support of our studies in the Oman Mountains. We are also indebted to the Oman Ministry of Petroleum and Minerals for their continuing encouragement. We benefited considerably from Dr John Smewing's intimate knowledge of Oman Mountain geology and logistics and are particularly grateful to Peter Cawood, David Cooper, Keith Watts and John Smewing for their suggestions for improvements to an earlier draft of this paper.

References

ALLEMANN, F. & PETERS, T. 1972. The Ophiolite-Radiolarite belt of the North Oman Mountains. *Eclogae Geologicae Helvetiae*, **65**, 657–697.

BARRETTE, P. D. 1988. Internal geometry and origin of Hubat structural culmination, Oman Mountains. *Journal of Structural Geology*, **10**, 383–391.

—— & CALON, T. J. 1987. Re-imbrication of the Hawasina allochthons in the Sufrat and Dawd range, Oman Mountains. *Journal of Structural Geology*, **9**, 859–867.

BECHENNEC, F., LE METOUR, J., RABU, D., BOURDILLON-DE-GRISSAC, C. H., DE WEVER, P., BEURRIER, M. & VILLEY, M. 1990. The Hawasina Nappes: stratigraphy and structural evolution of a fragment of the south-Tethyan passive continental margin. *In*: ROBERTSON, A. H. F., SEARLE, M. P. & RIES, A. C. (eds) *The Geology and Tectonics of the Oman Region*. Geological Society, London, Special Publication, **49**, 213–223.

——, ——, ——, VILLEY, M. & BEURRIER, M. 1988. The Hawasina Basin: a fragment of a starved passive continental margin, thrust over the Arabian platform during obduction of the Semail Nappe. *Tectonophysics*, **151**, 323–343.

BERNOULLI, D. & WEISSERT, H. 1987. The Upper Hawasina nappes in the central Oman Mountains: stratigraphy, palinspastics and sequence of nappe emplacement. *Geodynamica Acta*, **1**, 47–58, Paris.

——, —— & BLOME, C. D. 1990. Evolution of the Triassic Hawasina basin. *In*: ROBERTSON, A. H. F., SEARLE, M. P. & RIES, A. C. (eds) *The Geology and Tectonics of the Oman Region*. Geological Society, London, Special Publication, **49**, 189–204.

BLENDINGER, W. 1988. Permian to Jurassic deep water sediments of the Eastern Oman Mountains: the significance for the evolution of the Arabian margin of the South Tethys, *Facies (Erlangen)*, **19**, 1–32.

——, VAN VLIET, A. & HUGHES CLARKE, M. W. 1990. Updoming, rifting and continental margin development during the Late Palaeozoic in northern Oman. *In*: ROBERTSON, A. H. F., SEARLE, M. P. & RIES, A. C. (eds) *The Geology and Tectonics of the Oman Region*. Geological Society, London, Special Publication, **49**, 27–37.

BOOTE, D. R. D., MOU, D. & WAITE, R. I. 1990. Structural evolution of the Suneinah Foreland, Central Oman Mountains. *In*: ROBERTSON, A. H. F., SEARLE, M. P. & RIES, A. C. (eds) *The Geology and Tectonics of the Oman Region*. Geological Society, London, Special Publication, **49**, 397–418.

BOYER, S. E. & ELLIOTT, D. 1982. Thrust systems. *American Association of Petroleum Geologists Bulletin*, **66**, 1196–1230.

BUTLER, R. W. H. 1987. Thrust sequences. *Journal of the Geological Society of London*, **144**, 619–634.

CAWOOD, P. A. 1990. Late stage gravity sliding of ophiolite thrust sheets in Oman and western Newfoundland. *In*: MOORES, E. *et al.* (eds) *Ophiolites and oceanic lithosphere. Proceedings of an international conference, Nicosia, Cyprus, 1987*.

——, GREEN, F. K. & CALON, T. J. 1990. Origin of culminations within the Southeast Oman Mountains at Jebel Majhool and Ibra Dome *In*: ROBERTSON, A. H. F., SEARLE, M. P. & RIES, A.

C. (eds) *The Geology and Tectonics of the Oman Region*. Geological Society, London, Special Publication, **49**, 429–445.

COFFIELD, D. Q. 1990. Structures associated with nappe emplacement and culmination collapse in the Central Oman Mountains *In*: ROBERTSON, A. H. F., SEARLE, M. P. & RIES, A. C. (eds) *The Geology and Tectonics of the Oman Region*. Geological Society, London, Special Publication, **49**, 447–458.

COLEMAN, R. G. 1981. Tectonic setting for ophiolite obduction in Oman. *Journal of Geophysical Research*, **86**, 2497–2508.

COOPER, D. J. W. 1987. Hamrat Duru Group: revised stratigraphy of a Mesozoic deep-water passive margin in the Oman Mountains. *Geological Magazine*, **124**, 157–164.

—— 1988. Structure and sequence of thrusting in deep-water sediments during ophiolite emplacement in south-central Oman Mountains. *Journal of Structural Geology*, **10**, 473–485.

—— 1989. A longitudinal carbonate fan form the Jurassic of the Oman Mountains: the Guweyza Limestone Formation of the Hamrat and Duru. *Sedimentary Geology*, **61**, 253–278.

—— 1990. Sedimentary evolution and palaeogeographical reconstruction of the Mesozoic continental rise in Oman: evidence from the Hamrat Duru Group. *In*: ROBERTSON, A. H. F., SEARLE, M. P. & RIES, A. C. (eds) *The Geology and Tectonics of the Oman Region*. Geological Society, London, Special Publication, **49**, 161–187.

DE WEVER, P., BOURDILLON-DE-GRISSAC, CH. & BECHENNEC, F. 1989. A Permian age from radiolarites of the Hawasina Nappes, Oman Mountains, *Geology*, **16**, 912–914.

——, —— & —— 1990. Radiolarian biostratigraphic data (Permian to Cretaceous) from the Hawasina Complex (Oman Mountains). *In*: ROBERTSON, A. H. F., SEARLE, M. P. & RIES, A. C. (eds) *The Geology and Tectonics of the Oman Region*. Geological Society, London, Special Publication, **49**, 225–238.

DERCOURT, J., ZONENSHAIN, L. P., RICOU, L. E., KAZMIN, V. G., LE PICHON, X., KNIPPER, A. L., GRANDJACQUET, C., SBORTSHIKOV, J. M., GEYSSANT, J., LEPVRIER, C., PECHERSKY, D. H., BOULIN, J., SIBUET, J. C., SAVOSTIN, L. A., SOROKHTIN, O., WESTPHAL, M., BAZHENOV, M. L., LAUER, J. P. & BIJU-DUVAL, B., 1986. Geological evolution of the Tethys from the Atlantic to the Pamirs since the Lias. *Tectonophysics*, **123**, 241–315.

DUNNE, L. A., MANOOGIAN, P. R. & PIERINI, D. F. 1990. Structural style and domains in the Northern Oman Mountains (Oman and United Arab Emirates). *In*: ROBERTSON, A. H. F., SEARLE, M. P. & RIES, A. C. (eds) *The Geology and Tectonics of the Oman Region*. Geological Society, London, Special Publication, **49**, 375–386.

EL-SHAZLY, A. K. & COLEMAN, R. G. 1990. Metamorphism in the Oman Mountains in relation to the Semail ophiolite emplacement. *In*: ROBERTSON,

A. H. F., SEARLE, M. P. & RIES, A. C. (eds) *The Geology and Tectonics of the Oman Region*. Geological Society, London, Special Publication, **49**, 473−493.

GLENNIE, K. W., BOEUF, M. G. A., HUGHES CLARKE, M. W., MOODY-STUART, M., PILAAR, W. F. H. & REINHARDT, B. M. 1973. Late Cretaceous nappes in the Oman Mountains and their geologic significance. *American Association of Petroleum Geologists Bulletin*, **57**, 5−27.

——, ——, ——, ——, —— & —— 1974. Geology of the Oman Mountains. *Verhandelingen van het Koninklijk Nederlands geologisch minjbouwkundig Genootschap*.

——, HUGHES CLARKE, M. W., BOEUF, M. G. A., PILAAR, W. F. H. & REINHARDT, B. W. 1990. Inter-relationship of the Makran−Oman Mountain belts of convergence. *In*: ROBERTSON, A. H. F., SEARLE, M. P. & RIES, A. C. (eds) *The Geology and Tectonics of the Oman Region*. Geological Society, London, Special Publication, **49**, 775−785.

GOFFE, B., MICHARD, A., KIENAST, J-R. & LE MER O. 1988. A case of obduction-related high pressure, low temperature metamorphism in upper crustal nappes, Arabian continental margin, Oman: *P-T* paths and kinematic interpretations. *Tectonophysics*, **151**, 363−386.

GRAHAM, G. M. 1980a. *Structure and sedimentology of the Hawasina Window, Oman Mountains*. PhD thesis, Open University, UK.

—— 1980b. Evolution of a passive margin and nappe emplacement in the Oman Mountains. *In*: PANAYIOTOU, A. (ed.) *Proceedings of the International Ophiolite Symposium*, Cyprus, 1979, 414−423.

HANNA, S. S. 1990. The Alpine deformation of the central Oman Mountains. *In*: ROBERTSON, A. H. F., SEARLE, M. P. & RIES, A. C. (eds) *The Geology and Tectonics of the Oman Region*. Geological Society, London, Special Publication, **49**, 341−359.

HARLAND, W. B., COX, A. V., LLEWELLYN, P. G., PICKTON, C. A. G., SMITH, A. G. & WALTERS, R. 1982. *A geologic time scale*. Cambridge University Press, Cambridge.

HARRIS, P. M. & FROST, S. H. 1984. Middle Cretaceous Carbonate Reservoirs Fahud Field and Northwestern Oman. *American Association of Petroleum Geologists, Bulletin*, **68**, 649−658.

HEDBERG, H. D. 1976. *International Stratigraphic Guide*. Wiley, New York.

HINZ, K., MUTTER, J. C., ZEHNDER, C. M. & NGT Study Group 1987. Symmetric conjugation of continent-ocean boundary structures along the Norwegian and East Greenland margins. *Marine and Petroleum Geology*, **4**, 166−187.

HOLLAND, C. H., AUDLEY-CHARLES, M. G., BASSET, M. G., COWIE, J. W., CURRY, D., FITCH, F. J., HANCOCK, J. M., HOUSE, M. R., INGHAM, J. K., KENT, P. E., MORTON, N., RAMSBOTTOM, W. H. C., RAWSON, P. F., SMITH, D. B., STUBBLEFIELD, C. J., TORRENS, H. S., WALLACE, P. & WOODLAND, A. W. 1978. *A Guide to Strati-*

graphical Procedure. Geological Society of London Special Reprint, **10**.

HOPSON, C. A., COLEMAN, R. G., GREGORY, R. T., PALLISTER, J. S. & BAILEY, E. H. 1981. Geologic section through the Samail ophiolite and associated rocks along a Muscat−Ibra transect, southeastern Oman Mountains, *Journal of Geophysical Research*, **86**, 2527−2545.

HUGHES CLARKE, M. W. 1988. Stratigraphy and rock-unit nomenclature in the oil-producing area of Interior Oman, *Journal of Petroleum Geology*, **11**, 5−60.

KASTENS, K., MASCLE, J. *et al*. 1988. ODP Leg 107 in the Tyrrhenian Sea: insights into passive margin and back-arc basin evolution. *Geological Society of America Bulletin*, **100**, 1140−1156.

LEES, G. M. 1928. The geology and tectonics of Oman and parts of south-eastern Arabia. *Quarterly Journal of the Geological Society of London*, **84**, 585−670.

LE METOUR, J., RABU, D., TEGYEY, M., BECHENNEC, F., BEURRIER, M. & VILLEY, M. 1990. Subduction and obduction: two stages in the Eo−Alpine tectono-metamorphic evolution of the Oman Mountains. *In*: ROBERTSON, A. H. F., SEARLE, M. P. & RIES, A. C. (eds) *The Geology and Tectonics of the Oman Region*. Geological Society, London, Special Publication, **49**, 327−339.

LIPPARD, S. J. 1983. Cretaceous high pressure metamorphism in NE Oman and its relationship to subduction and ophiolite nappe emplacement. *Journal of the Geological Society, London*, **140**, 97−104.

——, SHELTON, A. W. & GASS, I. G. 1986. *The ophiolite of northern Oman*. Geological Society, London, Memoir, **11**.

MANN, A. & HANNA, S. S. 1990. The tectonic evolution of pre-Permian rocks, Central and Southeastern Oman Mountains. *In*: ROBERTSON, A. H. F., SEARLE, M. P. & RIES, A. C. (eds) *The Geology and Tectonics of the Oman Region*. Geological Society, London, Special Publication, **49**, 307−325.

——, —— & NOLAN, S. C. 1990. Post-Campanian tectonic evolution of the central Oman Mountains: tertiary extension of the Eastern Arabian Margin. *In*: ROBERTSON, A. H. F., SEARLE, M. P. & RIES, A. C. (eds) *The Geology and Tectonics of the Oman Region*. Geological Society, London, Special Publication, **49**, 549−563.

MICHAELIS, P. L. & PAUKEN, R. J. 1990. Seismic interpretation of the structure and stratigraphy of the Strait of Hormuz. *In*: ROBERTSON, A. H. F., SEARLE, M. P. & RIES, A. C. (eds) *The Geology and Tectonics of the Oman Region*. Geological Society, London, Special Publication, **49**, 387−395.

MICHARD, A. 1982. Contribution à la connaissance de la marge nord du Gondwana: une chaîne plissée paléozoique, vraisemblablement hercynienne, en Oman. *Comptes Rendu hebdomadaire de l'Academie de Sciences de Paris*, **295**, 1031−1036.

—— 1983. Les Nappes de Mascate (Oman), rampe

épicontinentale d'obduction a faciés schiste bleu, et la dualité apparente des ophiolites Omanaises. *Sciences Géologoqies Bulletin*, **36**(1), 3–16.

——, JUTEAU, T. & WHITECHURCH, H. 1985. L'obduction: revue des modèles et confrontation au cas de l'Oman. *Bulletin de la Societé géologique de la France*, **8**(1), 189–198.

MORTON, D. M. 1959. Geology of Oman. *5th World Petroleum Congress*, New York, **1**, 277–294.

MURRIS, R. J. 1980. Middle East, stratigraphic evolution and oil habitat. *American Association of Petroleum Geologists Bulletin*, **64**, 597–618.

NOLAN, S. C., SKELTON, P. W., CLISSOLD, B. P. & SMEWING, J. D. 1990. Maastrichtian to Tertiary palaeogeography of the Central and Northern Oman Mountains. *In*: ROBERTSON, A. H. F., SEARLE, M. P. & RIES, A. C. (eds) *The Geology and Tectonics of the Oman Region*. Geological Society, London, Special Publication, **49**, 495–519.

PATTON, T. L. & O'CONNOR, S. J. 1988. Cretaceous Flexural History of Northern Oman Mountain Foredeep, United Arab Emirates. *American Association of Petroleum Geologists Bulletin*, **72**, 797–809.

PEARCE, J. A., ALABASTER, T., SHELTON, A. W. & SEARLE, M. P. 1981. The Oman Ophiolite as a Cretaceous arc-basin complex: Evidence and implications. *Royal Society of London Philosophical Transactions*, Ser A, **300**, 299–317.

RABU, D., LE METOUR, J., BECHENNEC, F., BEURRIER, M., VILLEY, M. & DE GRISSAC, CH. 1990. Sedimentary aspects of the Eo-Alpine cycle on the northeast edge of the Arabian platform. *In*: ROBERTSON, A. H. F., SEARLE, M. P. & RIES, A. C. (eds) *The Geology and Tectonics of the Oman Region*. Geological Society, London, Special Publication, **49**, 49–68.

ROBERTS, D. G., BACKMAN, J., MORTON, A. C., MURRAY, J. W. & KEENE, J. B. 1985. Evolution of volcanic rifted margins: synthesis of Leg 81 results on the west margin of the Rockall Plateau. *Initial Reports of the Deep Sea Drilling Project*, **81**, (U.S. Government Printing Office), Washington, DC, 883–911.

ROBERTSON, A. H. F. 1986. Geochemical evidence for the origins of Late Triassic melange units in the Oman Mountains as a small ocean basin formed by continental rifting. *Earth and Planetary Science Letters*, **77**, 318–332.

—— 1987a. The transition from a passive margin to an Upper Cretaceous foreland basin related to ophiolite emplacement in the Oman Mountains. *Bulletin of the Geological Society of America*, **99**, 633–653.

—— 1987b. The Upper Cretaceous Muti Formation: transition of a Mesozoic carbonate platform to a foreland basin in the Oman Mountains. *Sedimentology*, **34**, 1123–1143.

——, BLOME, C.D., COOPER, D. W. J., KEMP, A. E. S., & SEARLE, M. P. Evolution of the Arabian continental margin in the Dibba Zone, Northern Oman Mountains. *In*: ROBERTSON, A. H. F., SEARLE, M. P. & RIES, A. C. (eds) *The Geology*

and Tectonics of the Oman Region. Geological Society, London, Special Publication, **49**, 251–284.

——, KEMP, A. E. S., REX, D. C. & BLOME, C. D. Sedimentary and structural evolution of a transform lineament: the Hatta Zone, Northern Oman Mountains. *In*: ROBERTSON, A. H. F., SEARLE, M. P. & RIES, A. C. (eds) *The Geology and Tectonics of the Oman Region*. Geological Society, London, Special Publication, **49**, 285–305.

—— & WOODCOCK, N. H. 1983. Genesis of the Batinah melange above the Semail ophiolite. Oman. *Journal of Structural Geology*, **5**, 1–17.

SEARLE, M. P. 1985. Sequence of thrusting and origin of culminations in the northern and central Oman Mountains. *Journal of Structural Geology*, **7**, 129–143.

—— 1988a. Thrust tectonics of the Dibba zone and the structural evolution of the Arabian continental margin along the Musandam Mountains (Oman and United Arab Emirates). *Journal of the Geological Society, London*, **145**, 43–53.

—— 1988b. Structure of the Musandam culmination and the Straits of Hormuz syntaxis. *Journal of the Geological Society of London*, **145**, 831–845.

—— & COOPER, D. J. W. 1986. Structure of the Hawasina Window culmination, central Oman Mountains. *Transactions of the Royal Society of Edinburgh: Earth Sciences*, **77**, 143–156.

——, —— & WATTS, K. Structure of the Jebel Sumeini-Jebel Ghawil areas, Northern Oman. *In*: ROBERTSON, A. H. F., SEARLE, M. P. & RIES, A. C. (eds) *The Geology and Tectonics of the Oman Region*. Geological Society, London, Special Publication, **49**, 316–374.

—— & GRAHAM, G. M. 1982. 'Oman Exotics' — Oceanic carbonate build-ups associated with the early stages of continental rifting. *Geology*, **10**, 43–49.

——, JAMES, N. P., CALON, T. J. & SMEWING, J. D. 1983. Sedimentological and structural evolution of the Arabian continental margin in the Musandam Mountains and Dibba zone. United Arab Emirates. *Bulletin of the Geological Society of America*, **94**, 1381–1400.

——, LIPPARD, S. J., SMEWING, J. D. & REX, D. C. 1980. Volcanic rocks beneath the Samail ophiolite nappe in the northern Oman Mountains and their significance in the Mesozoic evolution of Tethys. *Journal of the Geological Society, London*, **137**, 589–604.

—— & MALPAS, J. 1980. The structure and metamorphism of rocks beneath the Semail ophiolite of Oman and their significance in ophiolite obduction. *Transactions of the Royal Society of Edinburgh: Earth Sciences*, **71**, 213–228.

—— & —— 1982. Petrochemistry and origin of subophiolitic metamorphic and related rocks in the Oman Mountains. *Journal of the Geological Society, London*, **139**, 235–248.

——, SMEWING, J. D., NOLAN, S. C., HART, M. & RAMSAY, A. T. S. 1989. Correction to 'Sedimentologic and structural evolution of the

Arabian continental margin in the Musandam Mountains and Dibba zone'. *Geological Society of America Bulletin* **101**, 314−316.

— & STEVENS, R. K. 1984. Obduction processes in ancient, modern and future ophiolites. *In*: GASS, I. G., LIPPARD, S. J. & SHELTON, A. W. (eds) *Ophiolites and Oceanic Lithosphere. Geological Society, London, Special Publication*, **13**, 303−320.

SENGÖR, A. M. C. 1990. A new model for the date Palaeozoic−Mesozoic tectonic evolution of Iran and implications for Oman. *In*: ROBERTSON, A. H. F., SEARLE, M. P. & RIES, A. C. (eds) *The Geology and Tectonics of the Oman Region*. Geological Society, London, Special Publication, **49**, 797−831.

SHELTON, A. W. 1990. The emplacement of the Oman ophiolite-potential field constraints. *In*: ROBERTSON, A. H. F., SEARLE, M. P. & RIES, A. C. (eds) *The Geology and Tectonics of the Oman Region*. Geological Society, London, Special Publication, **49**, 459−471.

SKELTON, P. W., NOLAN, S. C. & SCOTT, R. W. The Maastrichtian transgression onto the Northwestern flank of the Proto-Oman Mountains: sequences of rudist-bearing beach to open shelf facies. *In*: ROBERTSON, A. H. F., SEARLE, M. P. & RIES, A. C. (eds) *The Geology and Tectonics of the Oman Region*. Geological Society, London, Special Publication, **49**, 521−547.

SMITH, A. G., HYNES, A. J., MENZIES, M., NISBET, E. G., PRICE, I., WELLAND, M. J. & FERRIERE, J. 1975. The stratigraphy of the Othris Mountains, eastern central Greece: a deformed Mesozoic continental margin sequence. *Eclogae Geologicae Helvetiae*, **68**, 463−481.

STOCKMAL, G. S., BEUMONT, C. & BOUTILIER, R. 1986. Geodynamics models of convergent margin tectonics. Transition from a rifted margin to overthrust belt and consequences for foreland-basin development. *American Association of Petroleum Geologists Bulletin*, **70**, 181−190.

SWARBRICK, R. E. & ROBERTSON, A. H. F. 1980. Revised stratigraphy of the Mesozoic rocks of southern Cyprus. *Geological Magazine*, **117**, 547−63.

TILTON, G. R., HOPSON, C. A. & WRIGHT, J. E. 1981. Uranium-lead isotopic ages of the Samail ophiolite, Oman, with application to Tethyan ocean ridge tectonics. *Journal of Geophysical Research*, **86**, 2763−2775.

TOZER, E. T. & CALON, T. J. 1990. Triassic ammonoids from Jabal Safra and Wadi Alwa, Oman and their significance. *In*: ROBERTSON, A. H. F., SEARLE, M. P. & RIES, A. C. (eds) *The Geology and Tectonics of the Oman Region*. Geological Society, London, Special Publication, **49**, 203−211.

WARBURTON, J., BURNHILL, T. J., GRAHAM, R. H. & ISAAC, K. P. 1990. The evolution of the Oman Mountains foreland basin. *In*: ROBERTSON, A. H. F., SEARLE, M. P. & RIES, A. C. (eds) *The Geology and Tectonics of the Oman Region*. Geological Society, London, Special Publication, **49**, 419−427.

WATTS, K. F. 1990. Mesozoic carbonate slope facies marking the Arabian platform margin in Oman. *In*: ROBERTSON, A. H. F., SEARLE, M. P. & RIES, A. C. (eds) *The Geology and Tectonics of the Oman Region*. Geological Society, London, Special Publication, **49**, 139−159.

— & BLOME, C. D. 1989. Response of the Arabian carbonate platform margin slope to orogenic closing of a Cretaceous ocean basin, Oman. *International Association of Sedimentologists Special Publication 'Evolution of Carbonate Platforms'*.

— & GARRISON, R. E. 1986. Sumeini Group, Oman-evolution of a Mesozoic carbonate slope on a South Tethyan continental margin. *Sedimentary Geology*, **48**, 107−168.

WHITE, R. S. & ROSS, D. A. 1979. Tectonics of the Western Gulf of Oman. *Journal of Geophysical Research*, **84**, 3479−3489.

WILSON, H. H. 1969. Late Cretaceous eugeosynclinal sedimentation, gravity tectonics and ophiolite emplacement in the Oman Mountains, southeast Arabia. *American Association of Petroleum Geologists Bulletin*, **53**, 626−671.

WOODCOCK, N. H. & ROBERTSON, A. H. F. 1982a. Stratigraphy of the Mesozoic rocks above the Semail ophiolite, Oman. *Geological Magazine*, **119**, 67−76.

— & — 1982b. The upper Batinah Complex, Oman: allochthonous sediment sheets above the Semail ophiolite. *Canadian Journal of Earth Sciences*, **19**, 1635−1656.

— & — 1984. The structural variety in Tethyan ophiolite terrains. *In*: GASS, I. G., LIPPARD, S. J., & SHELTON, A. W. (eds), *Ophiolites and Oceanic Lithosphere. Geological Society London, Special Publication*, **13**, 321−332.

Updoming, rifting and continental margin development during the Late Palaeozoic in northern Oman

W. BLENDINGER[1], A. VAN VLIET[2], & M. W. HUGHES CLARKE[1]

[1] Petroleum Development Oman, Exploration Department, P.O. Box
81, Muscat, Oman
[2] Shell Research KSEPL, Volmerlaan 6, Rijswijk ZH, Netherlands

Abstract: Subsurface data from northern interior Oman and new surface data from the Oman Mountains imply that the north Oman passive continental margin developed in the Permian. Late Carboniferous and Permian updoming of an area roughly overlapping the present Oman Mountains is indicated by the northward thinning of the continental clastics of the Haushi Group (Late Carboniferous and Early Permian) in the sub-surface. Well correlations show the thinning as cutouts at internal unconformities proving contemporary uplift along a roughly E−W strike. Deep water sedimentation off northern Oman commenced already in the early Late Permian. Permian deep water sediments of the Hawasina nappes consist of reef-derived sediment gravity flow deposits, cephalopod limestones and radiolarites that were deposited in a slope and basin floor environment north of a coralgal reef tract. Mafic volcanics underlying these deposits show locally tholeiitic characters suggesting that incipient drifting of the Hawasina ocean occurred as early as the Late Permian. Penecontemporaneous flooding of the Arabian shield occurred on an almost unfaulted substratum even in areas close to the inferred shelf edge.
The interpretation of these data in terms of models for continental rifting suggests that north Oman developed on the little faulted side of an asymmetrical rift produced by Permo-Carboniferous low-angle normal faulting of the lithosphere.

One of the major unresolved problems relating to the history of the passive continental margin of north Oman is the initiation of rifting and deep water sedimentation. In the Oman Mountains, thick Permo-Mesozoic shelf carbonates directly overlie a peneplained, Infracambrian to early Palaeozoic substratum. No thick clastics or evaporites, that could evidence rifting, are developed at the base of the shelf succession. There is no clearly developed break-up unconformity (*sensu* Falvey & Middleton 1981), a widely recognized feature in the Tethys realm elsewhere (e.g., Bernoulli & Jenkyns 1974). From the 'autochthon' of the Oman Mountains it appears, therefore, difficult to define the early history of the continental margin. The allochthonous sediments of the Hawasina nappes also provide little evidence for the initial rifting history. They are all deep water sediments, mainly of Triassic to Early Cretaceous age, with the exception of some of the 'Oman Exotics' (Glennie *et al.* 1974; Béchennec 1987). In this paper, recently described Late Permian deep water sediments from the Ba'id area (Fig. 1; Blendinger 1988) will be considered together with Early Permian sediments from the sub-surface of northern Oman with regard to their combined significance in interpreting the south Tethyan margin.

Previous interpretations

Reconstructions of the early history of the Oman passive margin have, to date, been based on outcrop studies in the Oman Mountains. Due to equivocal evidence from the Hawasina sediments, Glennie *et al.* (1974) offered three possibilities for the timing of passive margin development in northern Oman. Continental separation could have occurred prior to the 'Middle' Permian, during the 'Middle' Permian, or during the Late Triassic (Glennie *et al.* 1974, their table 8.3). This uncertainty is still reflected in the recent summary on the Oman Tethys by Lippard *et al.* (1986), who considered that north Oman rifted in both Permian *and* Triassic time and had developed a passive margin by the Early Jurassic. This interpretation was strongly influenced by data from the study of Late Triassic volcanics of the upper Hawasina nappes (the Haybi volcanics: Searle *et al.* 1980), that were interpreted as rift-related but located palaeogeographically far offshore from the Oman margin proper (Searle & Graham 1982). This study does not consider these poorly understood upper Hawasina nappes, but is restricted to the development of the northern margin of the Arabian shield proper.

From ROBERTSON, A. H. F., SEARLE, M. P. & RIES, A. C. (eds), 1990,
The Geology and Tectonics of the Oman Region.
Geological Society Special Publication No 49, pp 27−37

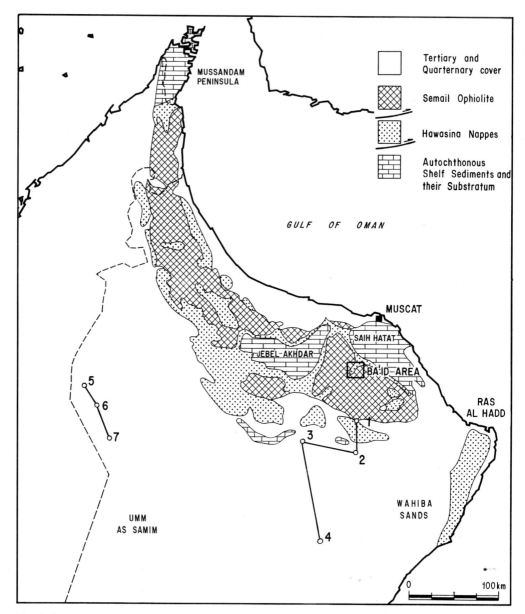

Fig. 1. Location of the studied well sections (1–7), and outcrop area (square) of recently described Permian deep water sediments in northern Oman.

Early Permian siliciclastic sediments of northern interior Oman

Alluvial and, subordinately, shallow marine deposits of Early Permian age are almost ubiquitous in the subsurface of interior Oman and are locally exposed in the Haushi–Huqf area. These sediments have been called Gharif Formation (Hughes Clarke 1988), typically have a consist-

ent thickness of 200 m, and can be subdivided into three units (Fig. 2). The lower Gharif consists of a basal unit of cross-bedded quartz sandstones that locally contain crinoid debris and brachiopods that indicate a shallow marine environment. These sandstones are covered by a carbonate unit, locally called the Haushi Limestone. It consists of bioturbated lime mudstones, cross-bedded oolitic packstones and grain-

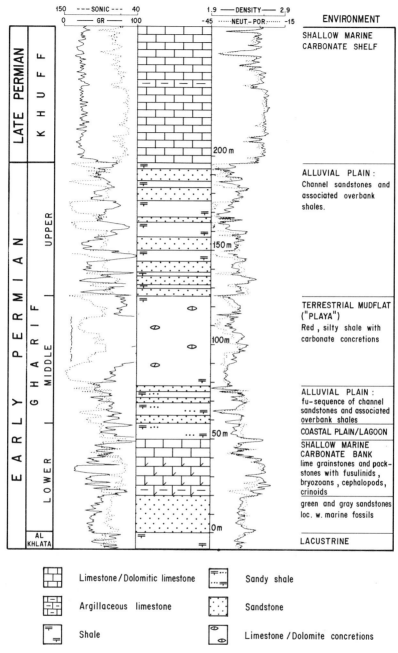

Fig. 2. The Gharif Formation in the subsurface of northern Oman, exemplified by well 4 (for location, see Fig. 1).

stones, and stromatolitic mudstones. The fossil content includes bryozoans, echinoderm debris, pelecypods, brachiopods and fusulinid foraminifers documenting a shallow marine environment. Early Permian cephalopods have been found in outcrops in the Haushi−Huqf area (Miller & Furnish 1957). The middle Gharif consists of trough-cross-bedded quartz sandstones interbedded with red brown shales and siltstones of fluvial origin. The upper part of the middle Gharif usually is a thick interval of red brown shales with well developed calcrete. This shale sequence records the existence of extensive mud flats or playa areas over most of interior Oman. The upper Gharif is similar to the middle Gharif, showing cross-bedded quartz sandstones interbedded with varicoloured shales deposited in an alluvial environment. The boundary with the overlying Khuff Formation is generally gradual.

Underlying the Gharif Formation is the Al Khlata Formation, a glaciogenic sequence (Hughes Clarke 1988). The contact between the two formations is gradual. A readily recognized interval of grey siltstones and shales, the so-called Rahab Shale, is considered as the uppermost horizon of the Al Khlata Formation. It is interpreted as a lacustrine sequence documenting the final phase in the retreat of the Gondwana glaciation (Levell et al. 1988).

The Gharif Formation shows only minor variations of facies and thickness over most parts of interior Oman indicating a very low relief and mature depositional surface. However, both the Gharif- and Al Khlata Formations show significant northward thinning in wells in northern Oman (for location, see Fig. 1). This can be documented by a well correlation transect of the Gharif Formation along the southern edge of the Oman Mountains (Fig. 3) and another further west (Fig. 4). Unconformities within the thinned Gharif succession (Fig. 3) indicate that uplift occurred during deposition of the siliciclastics and that they do not represent onlaps on to a pre-existing high. How much of the Early Permian clastics were derived from the north is still undefined. The Gharif clastics do show some changes in petrographic composition to the north, but the grain sizes do not significantly increase northward suggesting only minor topography of the northern uplift.

The situation documented in well 1 (Fig. 3) is similar to that observed in the Saih Hatat window, where the equivalent of the Khuff Formation, the Saiq Formation, directly overlies the Ordovician quartzites of the Amdeh Formation (Le Métour, 1987). The situation in well 5 (Fig. 4) resembles that of the Jebel Akhdar window, where the Saiq Formation unconformably overlies Infracambrian strata of the Huqf Group (Beurrier et al. 1986).

The Late Permian deep water sediments of the Hawasina nappes

Only recently has clear evidence for the existence of Permian deep water sediments been found in the Oman Mountains (Béchennec 1987;

Blendinger 1988). Such sediments are best exposed in the Ba'id area in the eastern Oman Mountains (Fig. 1), but also occur at the base of the Maqam Formation of the Sumeini Group in the northern Oman Mountains (Watts & Garrison 1986), at the base of the Dhera Formation (Glennie et al. 1974), and in a number of small occurrences elsewhere in the Hawasina nappes (Béchennec 1987). Locally, these Permian sediments have a substratum of mafic pillow basalts and volcaniclastics with an alkaline composition of intraplate character. In places, such as in the Hawasina window, tholeiitic basalts with mid-ocean ridge character occur (Béchennec 1987). This suggests that sea floor spreading in the Hawasina ocean dates back to the early Late Permian.

The Permian of the Ba'id area occurs in three superimposed thrust sheets, where a clear trend from coarse, relatively proximal, to fine, relatively distal sediments can be observed (Fig. 5; see Blendinger (1988) for a detailed sedimentological description). The reef debris limestone consists of corals, calcareous sponges, fenestellid bryozoans, various calcareous algae, the microproblematicum Tubiphytes, and abundant crinoid ossicles. Benthic palaeotextulariid and fusulinid foraminifers and angular particles of mafic volcanics are quite abundant. The clasts range from sand-size to occasionally boulder-size, and the beds in general contain very little lime mud matrix. Graded bedding and flat bases and tops are typical of thinner beds and indicate deposition by turbidity currents. Thicker beds usually show no size grading, irregular tops and bases and are probably debris flows. These sediment gravity flow deposits are up to 200 m thick in the lower imbricate and are cut by numerous, north-dipping neptunian dykes filled with red, bioclastic lime packstones. In the intermediate imbricate, the debris facies is 5−20 m thick and locally overlies decimetre-thick cephalopod limestones. The following ammonoid fauna of early Late Permian age has been identified (determination by B. F. Glenister and W. M. Furnish):

Propinacoceras beyrichi GEMMELLARO
Parapronorites konincki GEMMELLARO
Stacheoceras mediterraneum GEMMELLARO
Neogeoceras marcoui GEMMELLARO
? Aricoceras ensifer GEMMELLARO
Eumedlicottia bifrons GEMMELLARO
Adrianites cf. A. elegans GEMMELLARO
Mongoloceras omanicum GLENISTER & FURNISH
Neocrimites sp., Waagenoceras sp., Pseudogastrioceras sp.
The early Guadalupian age indicated by the

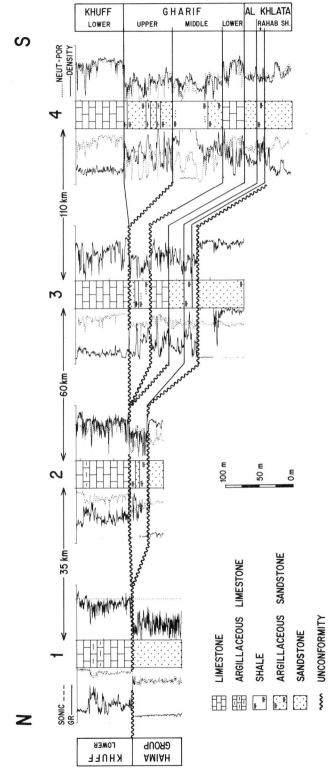

Fig. 3. Correlation of wells 1–4 (for location, see Fig. 1) in northeastern interior Oman. Note the gradual northward cut-out of the Al Khlata- and Gharif Formations, and unconformity within the Gharif Formation in well 3 suggesting uplift of the northern area penecontemporaneous with deposition.

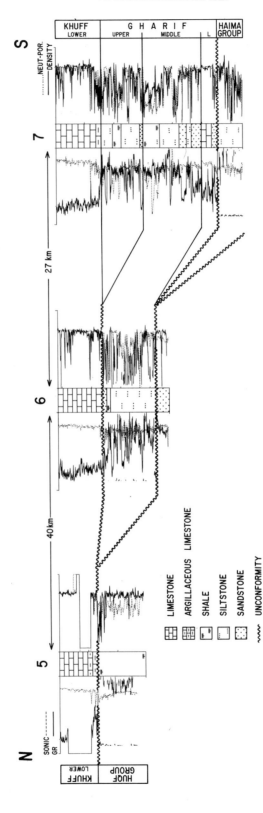

Fig. 4. Correlation of wells 5–7 (for location, see Fig. 1) in northwestern interior Oman. Note stepwise northward cutout of the Ordovician Haima Group and the Early Permian Gharif Formation.

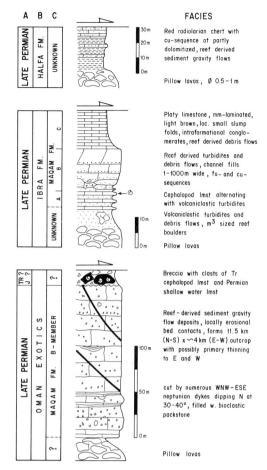

FACIES

Red radiolarian chert with cu-sequence of partly dolomitized, reef derived sediment gravity flows

Pillow lavas, Ø 0.5–1 m

Platy limestone, mm-laminated, light brown, loc. small slump folds, intraformational conglomerates, reef derived debris flows

Reef derived turbidites and debris flows, channel fills 1–1000m wide, fu- and cu-sequences

Cephalopod lmst alternating with volcaniclastic turbidites

Volcaniclastic turbidites and debris flows, m³ sized reef boulders

Pillow lavas

Breccia with clasts of Tr cephalopod lmst and Permian shallow water lmst

Reef–derived sediment gravity flow deposits, locally erosional bed contacts, forms 11.5 km (N–S) x ∼4 km (E–W) outcrop with possibly primary thinning to E and W

cut by numerous WNW–ESE neptunian dykes dipping N at 30–40°, filled w. bioclastic packstone

Pillow lavas

Fig. 5. Stratigraphic columns of the early Late Permian deep water sediments of the Ba'id area (for location, see Fig. 1). These deposits occur in three superimposed thrust sheets and range from coarse, reef-derived gravity flow deposits in the lower sheet to mainly radiolaritic sediments in the upper sheet. A: age; B: lithostratigraphic terms used by Glennie *et al.* (1974); C: probable equivalent deposits of the Sumeini Group (Watts & Garrison 1986).

ammonoid fauna is similar to that obtained from fusulinid foraminifers of the lowest part of the shelf succession, the Saiq Formation (middle to late Murghabien: Le Métour 1987).

In the highest imbricate (Fig. 5), the sediment gravity flow deposits are only locally preserved at the top of a red radiolarite succession. Platy, micritic limestones, termed Al Jil Formation by Béchennec (1987), overlie the reef-derived turbidites in the middle imbricate (Fig. 5). The Permian sediments reflect upper slope (lower imbricate), lower slope debris apron (middle imbricate), and basin floor environments sea-

ward of an extensive reef tract (Fig. 7). The minimum N–S extent of these environments amounted to 80 km, and palaeocurrents indicate a north-facing slope (Blendinger 1988).

The Permian limestones of the Ba'id area have been mapped as typical 'exotic limestones' (Glennie *et al.* 1974). In most interpretations, these 'Oman Exotics' are inferred from a distal position with respect to the Arabian continental margin proper (e.g. Searle & Graham 1982; Bernoulli & Weissert 1987; Lippard *et al.* 1986). This has been suggested by their generally high tectonic position within the nappe pile assuming simple telescoping of the Hawasina sediments. However, the following data suggest that the Ba'id Permian was part of the north-facing Arabian margin.

(i) The facies of the lower imbricate show abundant northward-inclined neptunian dykes that suggest deposition along a northward inclined slope.

(ii) The palaeocurrent pattern suggest exclusively northward transport of carbonate sediment gravity flow deposits.

(iii) There are facies similarities of the middle imbricate with the slope facies of the Sumeini Group of northern Oman.

(iv) The volcanic substrate, which is now known to underlie the Permo-Mesozoic succession in the Saih Hatat area (cf. Fig. 6) can readily be interpreted as a seaward continuation of the Saih Hatat volcanics.

Discussion: Permian rifting and passive margin development in northern Oman

In a rift model for northern Oman, the following constraints have to be considered:

1. The Late Carboniferous and Early Permian uplift of an area that roughly overlaps the Oman Mountains, whose southern margin shows a strike around E–W (Fig. 6).

2. A vast transgression of the Arabian shield that is penecontemporaneous with the earliest record of a deep water area off northern Oman (Fig. 7).

3. A substratum of the Permo-Mesozoic shelf succession that is almost unaffected by horst and graben formation even in parts close to the inferred Late Permian shelf edge. Permian volcanics locally underlie the shelf carbonates (Fig. 6) documenting crustal extension.

According to Wernicke (1985), the development of rift zones can be explained in terms of two 'end member models' that have been called the 'pure shear model' and the 'simple shear model', respectively. The 'pure shear model'

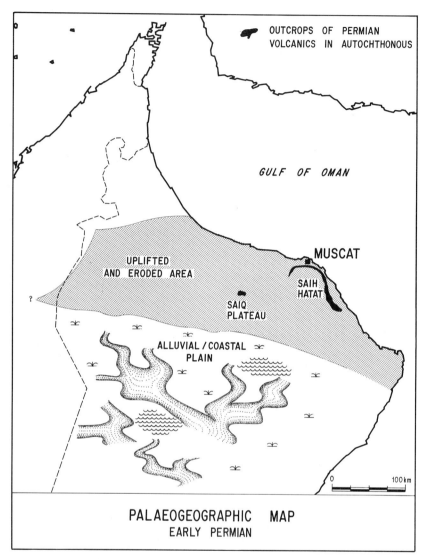

Fig. 6. Palaeogeographic map of the Early Permian of northern Oman. The alluvial plain of the Gharif Formation is confined to the north by a contemporaneously rising area. This stage of uplift was locally associated with the extrusion of volcanic rocks.

produces symmetrical rifts with a consecutive steps of pre-rift thermal updoming, rift collapse associated with horst and graben formation and igneous activity, followed by sea floor spreading (cf. Heezen 1962). The 'simple shear model' invokes extension of the lithosphere by low-angle, normal faulting. It is expected to produce asymmetrical rifts with the stages of (isostatic) uplift and extensional tectonics occurring pene-contemporaneously at different places, followed by sea floor spreading (e.g. Le Pichon & Barbier 1987). These two models are offered as alter-natives in Fig. 8, starting from one coherent landmass in the pre-Late Carboniferous. Which of the two models conforms better with the Permian data of northern Oman?

Stratigraphic data (Figs 3 & 4) suggest that uplift continued in the Early Permian and was followed immediately by subsidence and marine sedimentation on the Arabian shield and deep marine sedimentation off north Oman. This would be difficult to explain in the 'pure shear model' (Fig. 8, left sketch column), because there would be nearly no time left to accomodate

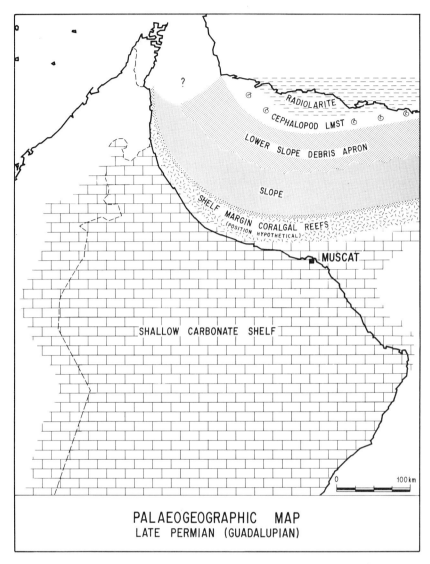

Fig. 7. Palaeogeographic map of the early Late Permian of northern Oman. An extensive carbonate shelf and is confined to the north by a deep water area. Slope and basin (environments after Blendinger (1988) are underlain by volcanic rocks in the eastern part of the newly formed deep water area off north Oman. Inferred location of the shelf edge after Glennie *et al.* (1974; modified).

the important period of rift tectonics and sedimentation. In the 'simple shear model', uplift of north Oman and rift tectonics and sedimentation (hypothetically off north Oman) could have been penecontemporaneous (cf. Wernicke, 1985; this paper: Fig. 8, right sketch column) and have been immediately succeeded by deep water sedimentation north of a newly formed passive margin. Second, the mainly unfaulted substratum of the Permian carbonate shelf, even

in areas close to the inferred shelf edge, is difficult to explain by a symmetrical rifting model. Such areas should be characterized by pronounced, rift-related structures and sediments. According to the 'pure shear model', the Oman margin could have developed on the little deformed side of the rift. A comparable situation has been inferred for the now deformed Galicia margin in the southern Bay of Biscay (Le Pichon & Barbier 1987). Thus it appears that the 'simple

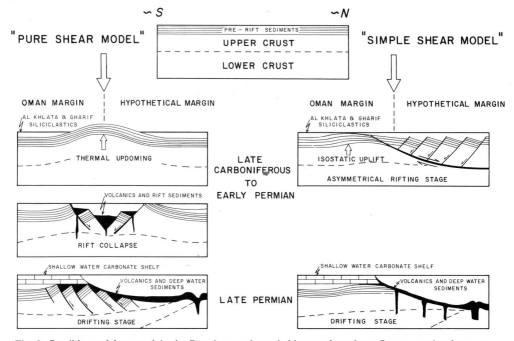

Fig. 8. Possible models to explain the Permian geodynamic history of northern Oman, starting from one coherent land mass in the pre-Late Carboniferous (pre-Al Khlata). The 'pure shear model' is the 'classical' rift model with the consecutive steps of thermal updoming, rift collapse and drifting. The 'simple shear model' implies low-angle normal faulting of the lithosphere and produces asymmetrical rifts with the penecontemporaneous stages of isostatic uplift and rift tectonics followed by drifting. The 'simple shear model' fits better with the Permian data of north Oman.

shear hypothesis' better meets the Permian data of north Oman than the 'classical' rift model, applied by Glennie *et al.* (1974).

Conclusions

Stratigraphic data suggest that continental rifting and ocean development in north Oman occurred during the Permian.

The Early Permian, largely continental, siliciclastics of the Gharif Formation thin northward in north Oman. A number of intraformational unconformities within the thinning succession indicate contemporaneous uplift of an area that overlaps the present Oman Mountains.

The vast Late Permian transgression on the Arabian shield was penecontemporaneous with the deposition of the earliest deep water sediments in the Hawasina basin. Permian deep water sediments include reef-derived sediment gravity flow deposits, cephalopod limestones, and radiolaritic sediments. These were deposited on a substrate of mafic volcanic rocks. Pillow lavas show mid-ocean ridge affinities in places.

These data fit best with the rift model of low-angle, normal faulting of the lithosphere. This model explains why rift-related faults and sediments are absent in the Oman Mountains, and why uplift of the Oman Mountain area was immediately followed by oceanic conditions in the Hawasina basin.

Knowledge of the Permo-Carboniferous siliciclastic units is based on the work of many PDO geologists. In particular, we thank J. Lopez-Lopez for providing a detailed understanding of the Gharif sedimentation. B. F. Glenister and W. M. Furnish identified the Permian cephalopods of the Ba'id area. D. Bernoulli carefully reviewed the manuscript and provided important suggestions for its improvement. This paper appears with the approval of PDO and the Oman Ministry of Petroleum and Minerals.

References

BECHENNEC, F. 1987. *Géologie des nappes Hawasina dans les parties orientale et centrale des montagnes d'Oman*. Thèse de doctorat d'Etat, Université P. et M. Curie, Paris VI.

BERNOULLI, D. & JENKYNS, H. C. 1974. Alpine, Mediterranean, and central Atlantic Mesozoic facies in relation to the early evolution of the

Tethys. *In*: DOTT, R. H. & SHAVER, R. H. (eds) *Modern and ancient geosynclinal sedimentation*. Society of Economic Paleontologists and Mineralogists, Special Publication **19**, 129–160.

BERNOULLI, D. & WEISSERT, H. 1987. The upper Hawasina nappes in the central Oman Mountains: stratigraphy, palinspastics and sequence of nappe emplacement. *Geodinamica Acta*, **1**, 47–58.

BEURRIER, M., BECHENNEC, F., RABU, D. & HUTIN, G. 1986. *Geological map of Rustaq, sheet NF 40 3D*. Explanatory notes. Directorate General of Minerals, Oman Ministry of Petroleum and Minerals.

BLENDINGER, W. 1988. Permian to Jurassic deep water sediments of the eastern Oman Mountains: their significance for the evolution of the Arabian margin of the South Tethys. *Facies*, **19**, 1–31.

FALVEY, D. A. & MIDDLETON, M. F. 1981. Passive continental margins: evidence for a pre-breakup deep crustal metamorphic subsidence mechanism. *In*: BLANCHET, F. & MONTADERT, L. (eds), *Geology of continental margins*. Oceanologica Acta, Proceedings 26. International Geological Congress C3, 103–114.

GLENNIE, K. W., BOEUF, M. G. A., HUGHES CLARKE, M. W., MOODY-STUART, M., PILAAR, W. F. H. & REINHARDT, B. M. 1974. Geology of the Oman Mountains. *Verhandelingen van het Koninklijk Nederlands geologisch mijnbouwkundig Genootschap*, Delft.

HEEZEN, B. C., 1962. The deep-sea floor. *In*: RUNCORN, T. (ed.). *Continental drift*. New York, Academic, 235–288.

HUGHES CLARKE, M. W. 1988. Stratigraphy and rock unit nomenclature in the oil-producing area of interior Oman. *Journal of Petroleum Geology*, **11**, 5–60.

LE METOUR, J. 1987. *Géologie de l'Autochthone des montagnes d'Oman*. Thèse de Doctorat d'Etat, Université P. et M. Curie, Paris VI.

LE PICHON, X. & BARBIER, F. 1987. Passive margin formation by low-angle faulting within the upper crust: the northern Bay of Biscay margin. *Tectonics*, **6**, 133–150.

LEVELL, B., BRAAKMAN, J. H. & RUTTEN, K. W. 1988. Oil bearing sediments of the Gondwana glaciation in Oman. *American Association of Petroleum Geologists Bulletin*, **72**, 775–796.

LIPPARD, S. J., SHELTON, A. W. & GASS, I. G. (eds) 1986. *The ophiolite of northern Oman*. Geological Society, London, Memoir **11**.

MILLER, A. K. & FURNISH, W. M. 1957. Permian ammonoids from southern Arabia. *Journal of Palaeontology*, **31**, 1043–1051.

SEARLE, M. P., LIPPARD, S. J., SMEWING, J. D. & REX, D. C. 1980. Volcanic rocks beneath the Semail ophiolite nappe in the northern Oman Mountains and their significance in the Mesozoic evolution Tethys. *Journal of the Geological Society of London*, **137**, 589–604.

SEARLE, M. P. & GRAHAM, G. M. 1982. 'Oman Exotics': oceanic carbonate build-ups associated with the early stages of continental rifting. *Geology*, **10**, 43–49.

WATTS, K. F. & GARRISON, R. E. 1986. Sumeini Group, Oman. Evolution of a Mesozoic carbonate slope on a south Tethyan continental margin. *Sedimentary Geology*, **48**, 107–168.

WERNICKE, B. 1985. Uniform-sense normal simple shear of the continental lithosphere. *Canadian Journal of Earth Sciences*, **22**, 108–125.

A review of platform sedimentation in the Early and Late Permian of Oman, with particular reference to the Oman Mountains

C. W. LEE

Department of Science, Polytechnic of Wales, Treforest, S. Wales, UK

Abstract: The Permian of Oman consists of two distinct portions. An early Permian sequence of clastics and carbonates, that are conformable with the Carboniferous, and a late Permian sequence of carbonates that may rest with strong unconformity on the underlying sequence. Lower Permian clastic rocks crop out in S and E Central Oman and they also occur extensively in the subcrop of South and Central Oman. They show a glacial affinity and are correlated with the Dwyka glaciogenic deposits of Gondwanaland. Lower Permian marine carbonates are also found in the Haushi region of E Central Oman and from the Batain coast where they are known as the Lusaba Limestone and Qarari Limestone, respectively. The Upper Permian carbonates are found extensively throughout the Oman Mountains where they constitute the Bih, Hagil and Saiq Formations, the Khuff Formation in the subcrop and as blocks in the Batain Melange of NE Oman. Permian carbonates are also found as 'exotics' masses in the higher thrust slices (Haybi Complex) beneath the Semail Ophiolite. These carbonates were deposited on block faulted crust by a major transgression (enhanced by a post-glacial rise in sea level) caused by the onset of continental rifting. The rocks which characterize the autochthonous (parautochthonous) portion of Oman show affinities with Gondwanaland or the southern side of Tethys, while the faunas collected from the Batain coast area of NE Oman have affinities with Timor and possibly the northern side of Tethys in Early Permian times.

Between Permian and early Jurassic times the Tethys Ocean began to open to the north of Oman, and the Mesozoic passive margin was initiated in the Oman Mountains. The onset of this feature was associated with a late Carboniferous–early Permian uplift that had its focus to the east of the present day Oman Mountains. This uplift resulted in differential erosion down to Lower Palaeozoic, Late Precambrian levels in the Oman Mountains and to the Devonian in the interior farther west (Glennie *et al.* 1974). A transgression, over a crust that had already undergone gentle tilting and horst and graben development along older structural trends, occurred earlier in the interior than in the Oman Mountains (Falcon 1967). One long-standing positive axis, the Huqf–Haushi Uplift (Fig. 1), which trends NNE/SSW along the Oman coast from Murbat to Ras al Hadd (Shackleton & Ries 1990), influenced sedimentation from late Palaeozoic times onwards and most rocks including the Upper Permian Khuff Formation (Fig. 2) show a regional thinning towards this axis. The transgression signified the onset of continental rifting (Graham 1980) that later led to the formation of the Hawasina Basin as a southern arm of Tethys and was probably also enhanced by the rise in sea level caused by the deglaciation after the Permo-Carboniferous glacial phase (Hughes Clarke 1988).

Glennie *et al.* (1974) established that much of the Oman Mountains are allochthonous and were emplaced on the Arabian Platform from the NE during the late Cretaceous (Turonian to early Maastrictian). Permian rocks are exposed in the Oman Mountains and constitute the autochthonous carbonate platform beneath the late Cretaceous thrust stack.

Lower Permian rocks crop out in the region of SE Oman (Fig. 1) and are present extensively in the subcrop of interior Oman (Hughes Clarke 1988). Lower Permian clastics and carbonates have also been described from the Haushi region (Hudson & Sudbury 1959) and are present in the Batain Coast area (Shackleton *et al.* 1990). In the Oman Mountains, Upper Permian carbonates crop out in the Jebel Akhdar/Saih Hatat areas. These rocks, known as the Saiq Formation constitute the lower portion of the Akhdar Group (Fig. 2). On the Musandam Peninsula, the Permian is represented by the Bih Dolomite Formation and the Hagil Formation and constitute the lower portions of the Ruus al Jibal Group (Fig. 2). Upper Permian carbonates (the Khuff Formation) are also found throughout the subcrop of interior Oman and also as 'exotic' masses in the highest thrust slices (Haybi Complex) beneath the Semail Ophiolite. The contact between the early and late Permian in south and interior Oman is conformable (Hughes Clarke 1988) while in the Oman Moun-

From ROBERTSON, A. H. F., SEARLE, M. P. & RIES, A. C. (eds), 1990,
The Geology and Tectonics of the Oman Region.
Geological Society Special Publication No 49, pp 39–47

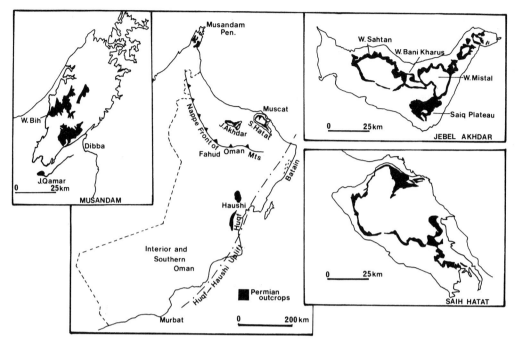

Fig. 1. Location Map.

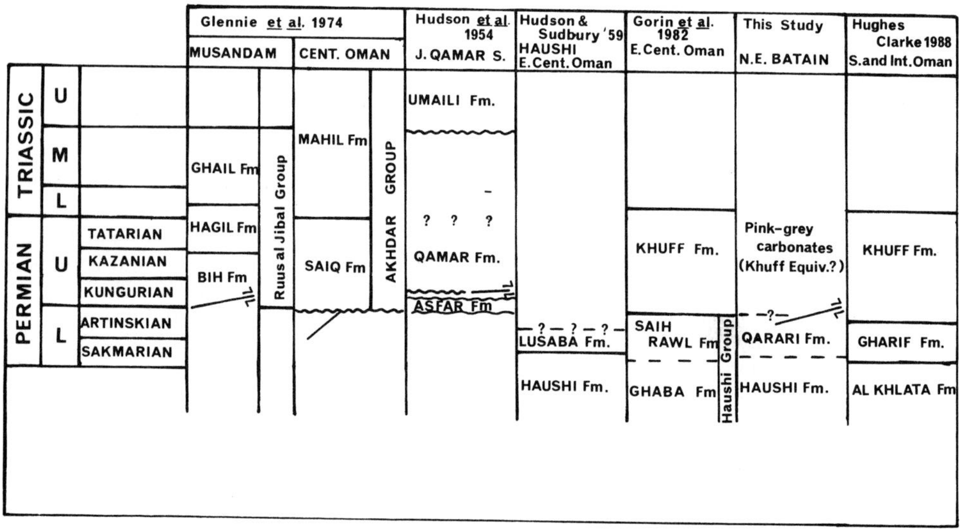

			Glennie et al. 1974		Hudson et al. 1954	Hudson & Sudbury '59	Gorin et al. 1982	This Study	Hughes Clarke 1988
			MUSANDAM	CENT. OMAN	J. QAMAR S.	HAUSHI E. Cent. Oman	E. Cent. Oman	N.E. BATAIN	S. and Int. Oman
TRIASSIC	U				UMAILI Fm.				
	M			GHAIL Fm	MAHIL Fm				
	L		HAGIL Fm		? ? ?		KHUFF Fm.	Pink-grey carbonates (Khuff Equiv.?)	KHUFF Fm.
PERMIAN	U	TATARIAN		SAIQ Fm	QAMAR Fm.				
		KAZANIAN	BIH Fm						
		KUNGURIAN			ASFAR Fm				
	L	ARTINSKIAN				LUSABA Fm.	SAIH RAWL Fm	QARARI Fm.	GHARIF Fm.
		SAKMARIAN				HAUSHI Fm.	GHABA Fm	HAUSHI Fm.	AL KHLATA Fm

(Glennie et al. 1974 CENT. OMAN: Ruus al Jibal Group; Hudson et al. 1954 J. QAMAR S.: AKHDAR GROUP; This Study N.E. BATAIN: Haushi Group)

Fig. 2. Correlation of Permian sequences in Oman.

tain region the late Permian rests with strong unconformity on the rocks below.

Owing to the scattered nature of Permian data, the rocks will be described on a geographical basis.

The Permian of Southern Oman

Rocks of early Permian age crop out in East Central Oman in the Haushi area (Fig. 1) and are known extensively from the subcrop in South and Central Oman. They are described as having a glacial affinity (Braakman *et al.* 1982; de la Grandeville 1982; Hughes Clarke 1988), and have been correlated with the Dwyka glacial deposits of Gondwanaland (Murris 1980). The clastic sequence (Hughes Clarke 1988) which constitutes the lower part of the Haushi Group (Fig. 2) is known as the Al Khlata Formation and unconformably overlies the Misfar, Haima or Huqf Group sediments and conformably underlies the carbonate-dominated Akhdar Group. In this southern area the boundary between the Haushi and the Akhdar Groups is conformable and often transitional, with little evidence of a major break (Hughes Clarke 1988).

The lower Al Khlata Formation consists of a glacially-generated package of sediments with coarse to fine diamictites, conglomerates, gravels, sands and shales which are locally associated with a striated glacial pavement. These sediments are currently interpreted as being derived from the S or SW, (Braakman *et al.* 1982). The Al Khlata Formation is known throughout the subcrop of S Oman and as far north as Fahud (Hughes Clarke 1988). The age of this formation has been established from sporomorphs which range from Carboniferous (Late Westphalian) to early Permian (Sakmarian) (Besems & Schuurman 1989). Glaciogene facies of similar age are also recorded from SW Saudi Arabia and the Yemen Arab Republic (Braakman *et al.* 1982).

The upper portion of the Haushi Group, defined by Hughes Clarke (1988) as the Gharif Formation, consists of a conformable series of sands and shales with a limestone unit. The sediments and fossil content of the Gharif Formation reflect an interplay between marine and coastal-plain processes and, in the SE the sequence is mostly continental (Hughes Clarke 1988). The diverse marine fauna of crinoids, brachiopods, foraminifera and ostracods indicate an early Permian (Sakmarian—Artinskian) age. The Gharif Formation is known throughout SW Oman and as far north as Fahud. In some publications (e.g. Gorin *et al.* 1982) the Haushi Group has been divided into the Saih Rawl and Marmul or Ghaba Formations. These terms have now been replaced by the Al Khlata and Gharif Formations as defined by Hughes Clarke (1988).

Farther south in the Murbat area, the Murbat Sandstone Formation (Lees 1928; Beydoun & Greenwood 1968) has been interpreted by Quidwai *et al.* (1988) as glacial in origin and to unconformably overlie crystalline basement that is intruded by Lower Carboniferous (K/Ar dates) dykes. It may therefore, correlate at least in part with the Al Khlata Formation of the Haushi Group.

The Haushi Formation, as originally defined by Hudson & Sudbury (1959), contains sands, gravels and boulder beds and a very fossiliferous carbonate known as the 'Lusaba Limestone'. This carbonate is dated on various shelly faunas as Artinskian in age. Hughes Clarke (1988) correlates the Lusaba Limestone with the lower portion of the Khuff Formation. However, it is possible that, based on evidence from the Batain Coast farther north, the Lusaba Limestone maybe a lateral equivalent of the upper Gharif Formation, especially as marine influences in the Gharif Formation are known to increase towards the north (Hughes Clarke 1988).

The late Permian in southern Oman comprises the Khuff Formation of the Akhdar Group (Fig. 2). This is dated essentially on microfauna as Kungurian in age but the uppermost part is probably early Triassic in age (Hughes Clarke 1988). The Khuff carbonates thin gently onto the Huqf—Haushi Uplift and change gradually southwards into continental red beds. In central Oman the lower boundary is a sharp change from the clastics of the Gharif to the carbonates of the Khuff Formation. The boundary is transitional in the W but becomes more unconformable towards the Oman Mountains. Its upper boundary is taken at the contact of continuous carbonates with a red/green—grey shale at the base of the Triassic Sudair Formation (Hughes Clarke 1988).

The Permian of the Musandam Peninsula

The Upper Permian succession consists of a few metres of sandstone overlain by 650 m of dolomite (Hudson 1960). The dolomites are bioturbated, grey to dark brown, medium- to thick-bedded with occasional skeletal and oolitic dolomitic grainstones and minor laminated peloidal dolomitic mudstones. The skeletal grainstones consists of mollusc coquinas with some large (mm/sized) intraclasts and coated grains. Hudson (1960) has described foraminifera and the algae *Pseudovermiporella sodatica*. The sequence is extensively dolomitized and lithologies range from dolomudstones to a hypidiomorphic crystalline mass.

The Bih Dolomite Formation passes upwards conformably into the Hagil Formation which is approximately 260 m in thickness (Hudson 1960; Glennie *et al.* 1974). The sequence, characterized by that seen in Wadi Bih, consists of light coloured, thin and well bedded dolomudstones with very fissile dolomudstones and shales and some brown weathering, massive dark grey dolomites. The finely laminated dolomudstones may contain mollusc and echinoid fragments. Occasional oncoliths and intraclasts may be ripple laminated and large laminar fenestral and bioclastic vugs are common. In similar beds, Hudson (1960) recognized foraminifera indicating a Permian and possibly Early Triassic age (Glennie *et al.* 1974). The Hagil Formation passes conformably into the Triassic Ghail Formation.

Owing to the lack of desiccation and evaporitic features, the Bih Dolomite Formation is interpreted as having formed on a subsiding shallow carbonate platform, seaward of the evaporitic area farther to the W (Murris 1980). The original carbonate was deposited in shallow oxygenated waters with a rich burrowing infauna but with a poor epifauna probably due to restricted salinity conditions caused by the shallowness of the platform itself. The fusulinid fauna indicates clear shallow water, while the mollusc coquinas are interpreted as storm deposits. The Hagil Formation, with its abundant desiccation vugs and cryptalgal lamination, suggest peritidal conditions as the sea shallowed during latest Permian times. Evidence for subaerial exposure is more markedly seen in the Triassic Ghail Formation above with abundant solution features and fossil soil development.

Permo−Triassic carbonate sequences are also seen in the Jebel Qamar South exotic block in the Dibba Zone. Here the Ordovician/Silurian Rann Formation (Hudson *et al.* 1954) is overlain by the Ayim Formation of possible Devonian age (Searle *et al.* 1983). The Ayim Formation is overlain with probable unconformity (where rarely not in tectonic contact) by the Asfar Formation (Hudson *et al.* 1954). The Asfar Formation consists of orange calcareous sandstone lenses, and sandy bioclastic and micritic limestones with common productid brachiopods and *Archimedes*-type bryozoans. It passes transitionally into the overlying Qamar Limestone Formation (Fig. 2). This Asfar Formation is interpreted by Robertson *et al.* (1990) as shallow marine in origin, with a nearby source for quartz sand. This quartz sand source waned towards the Artinskian/Kungurian boundary and led to the deposition of pure bioclastic carbonates.

The overlying Qamar Limestone Formation is similar to the Permian exotic blocks seen elsewhere in the Oman Mountains (Hudson 1960; Glennie *et al.* 1974; Searle & Graham 1982; Robertson *et al.* 1990), that marked the growth of a thick pure carbonate, sometimes reefal sequence on a previously shallow marine clastic substatum. The rocks that make up the exotics are generally too recrystallized for facies division but may show recrystallized boundstones and large colonial bivalves (Searle & Graham 1982). Hudson *et al.* (1954) reports corals, brachiopods and the foraminifera *Parafusulina* sp. and *Neoschwagerina* sp. and so are considered to be of a more open marine nature than the more restricted dolomites of the Bih and Hagil Formations of the Musandam Peninsula. They suggest that, during the early Late Permian, exotics similar to Jebel Qamar formed horsts within an marine rift zone. Jebel Qamar South also contains rocks of Triassic age suggesting that these exotics were part of the carbonate platform until at least the Late Triassic time but were rifted away and subsequently drowned (Searle & Graham 1982).

The Permian of the Central Oman Mountains

In the Jebel Akhdar and Saih Hatat areas of the Central Oman Mountains the Upper Permian carbonates, known as the Saiq Formation, constitute the lowest unit of the Akhdar Group (Fig. 2). In these regions the base of the Saiq Formation is unconformable and may rest on steeply dipping pre-Permian beds (Fig. 3).

The Saiq Formation consists essentially of a lower 100 m interval of black, often foetid, limewackestones to packstones/grainstones which are poorly to highly fossiliferous, but may be subject to variable amounts of dolomitization and/or recrystallization. The upper 350 m shows an upward increase in dolomitization with crystalline dolomites developed at the top. Carbonate conglomerates are locally developed at the base of the sequence. In Wadi Bani Kharus, they may be up to 7 m thick (Fig. 4). The clasts are generally supported by a lime mud matrix and consist of angular dolomite fragments and oncoliths. These conglomerates are probably associated with the localized relief on the plane of the unconformity. They generally show a lens-like geometry and tend to be poorly developed or absent where the Saiq carbonates rest on shales beneath the unconformity.

The lower interval of highly fossiliferous black limestones is well seen on the Saiq Plateau where large fasiculate corals heads may be seen in life position (Fig. 5) or slightly tilted to inverted. Here they form true patch reefs interbedded with bioclastic wacke/grainstones with abundant cephalopods, bryozoa, gastropods, brachiopods and fusulinids. Crinoid particles are very common and locally form encrinites. The corals at the base are generally of the fasiculate type, but more cerioid types (indicating higher energy)

Fig. 3. Unconformable contact between Permian carbonates and Lower Palaeozoic rocks, Wadi Bani Kharus.

Fig. 4. Conglomerates developed locally on the basal Permian unconformity, eastern side of Wadi Bani Kharus.

are present in the crinoidal beds. In Wadi Mistal similar cerioid coral heads can be recognized as white recrystallized masses in the otherwise black dolomite.

This shallow marine 'back reef' facies characterizes the lowest part of the Late Permian throughout the Akhdar and Saih Hatat areas. It grades upwards into a more restricted facies with bivalve and gastropod debris although a few horizons in the upper part show coral heads and other normal marine faunas. This upper part of the Saiq Formation in Jebel Akhdar, although often completely dolomitized, does not show any features of sub-aerial exposure and are interpreted as shallow marine deposits.

On the southern side of Jebel Akhdar, the Saiq Formation not only shows a restriction of facies but a shallowing of conditions with planar algal laminites (with fenestral porosity) and cross-bedded dolomitic oograinstones. These lithologies suggest a closer proximity to a shoreline with shallow subtidal/intertidal flats and oolitic tidal deltas prograding from the west. In the Saih Hatat area, however, new evidence from Blendinger *et al.* (1990) suggest that towards the east Upper Permian reef derived gravity flows were being deposited on basaltic crust.

The relief seen on the unconformity may be of a regional nature. It is already known that the late Permian transgression moved in over already segregated, block-faulted crust (Fig. 6) (Falcon 1967). This author suggests that the horsts formed barriers or 'islands' in the late Permian sea. In the Oman Mountains one such positive feature may have run NW−SE through the Jebel Akhdar area and may have separated the 'back-reef' carbonates of the Saiq Plateau from the more open platform carbonates to the

Fig. 5. Large fasiculate coral heads in life position. Saiq Plateau.

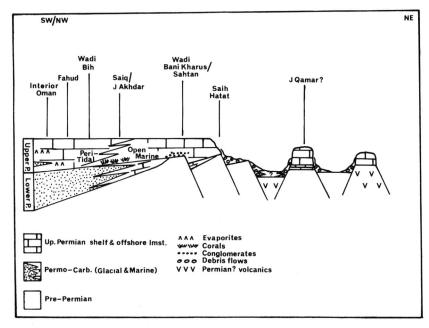

Fig. 6. Idealized diagram to represent the overall configuration of the Permian platform deposits of Oman. The section line trends approximately SW/NE but similar conditions are also appropriate for the NW. The sections marked may not necessarily be in the correct geographical position but are meant only as a guide to the type of sequence they represent (no scale intended).

east. A similar positive area separating 'an organic reefoid shelf' from 'open marine carbonates' is described by Szabo and Kheradpir (1978) in the Zagros Basin of SW Iran. Similar positive areas trending NW–SE (presumably parallel to the Hawasina basin) may have also produced barred basin conditions across the more shoreward (western) areas of Oman where carbonate–evaporite sequences are seen (Sharief 1982; Tschopp 1967).

The Permian of the Batain Coast

Rocks of Lower Permian age have been recently recognized from the Batain Coast area of NE Oman (Shackleton *et al.* 1990). This area is covered mainly by the Batain Melange which contains metre to kilometre-sized blocks of variable age (Palaeozoic to Upper Mesozoic) and composition ranging from continental to deep water sands and gravels, to shelf and reefal carbonates and deep water cherts and shales. Fortunately, many of the Upper Palaeozoic blocks contain recognizable faunas which are believed to be Permian in age. At one locality, marked X on Fig. 7, medium- to fine-grained sands associated with well rounded and sorted pebble beds show a rich shelly fauna with abundant productid brachiopods especially *Reticulatia* cf. *R. americana* (Dunbar & Condra) which indicates an Early Permian (Sakmarian) age (D. V. Ager pers. comm.). These clastics are in apparent normal contact with well bedded nodular dark grey lime mudstones/wackestones and shales that shown an abundant and varied coral and brachiopod assemblage. At Jebel Qarari, the lithofacies is extensively exposed and contains an extensive fauna of silicified productid brachiopods, bryozans, corals, blastoids, crinoids and trilobites that indicate an Early Permian (Artinskian) age (D. V. Ager pers. comm.). Locally, the Qarari Limestone is structurally and probably stratigraphically overlain by massive light grey lime mudstones/wackestones with an abundant shelly fauna dominated by the brachiopods *Dielasma* sp. and *Composita* sp. (D. V. Ager pers. comm.). Other isolated blocks comprise very fossiliferous pink-grey massive carbonates with abundant crinoids, brachiopods, byozons, corals and algae.

The lower clastic deposits with associated pebble beds which are early Permian in age may correlate with and be the marine equivalent of the Haushi Group described by Hughes Clarke 1988. This is not based only on faunal information but also on palaeogeographical trends which indicate that marine influences in the Gharif Formation increase towards the north (Hughes Clarke 1988). The shales and limestones stratigraphically above these clastics, and described as the Qarari Limestone, may be the equivalent of the 'Lusaba Limestone' (Hudson & Sudbury 1959). The light grey–pink limestones that overlie the Qarari Limestone are thought to result from the extensive mid-Permian transgression (Glennie *et al.* 1974) of the region. These limestones are, however, different lithologically from the broadly coeval rock types seen in the Saiq Formation of the Oman Mountains in the Jebel Akhdar/Saih Hatat areas. Owing to the abundance and often intimate growth relationships seen between the brachiopods, corals and algae, the pink–grey carbonates are believed to be either the seaward equivalent of the Saiq Formation or more speculatively may represent carbonate build ups that were present in the Permian depositional basin. They may also, however, be more closely associated with carbonate build ups on basaltic horsts that have been noted by Blendinger *et al.* (1990).

Conclusions

Oman and Iran formed part of Gondwanaland throughout much of the Precambrian and Palaeozoic and presumably continental crust

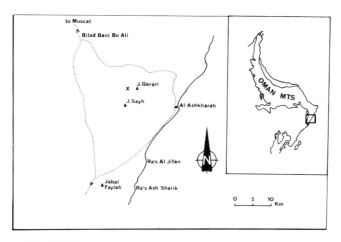

Fig. 7. Location map of the Batain area.

was continuous from Iran, through Oman, Arabia and into North Africa.

The Early Permian is characterized by the glaciogenic Al Khlata Formation that passes upwards into the alluvial plain/shallow marine deposits of the Gharif Formation. Both of these formations were deposited upon block faulted crust that had a regional southerly gradient from a positive area positioned somewhere to the E of the present-day Oman Mountains. This positive area was produced by an uplift event that was latest Carboniferous or earliest Permian in age as the Al Khlata and Gharif Formations onlap this high and show a number of internal unconformities (Blendinger *et al.* 1990). This event produced abundant volcanic rocks in the subsurface of the Oman Mountains and was accompanied by the deposition of siliciclastics (Blendinger *et al.* 1990). With the change in climate from glacial to tropical, an eustatic rise in sea level was enhanced by the collapse of the rift zone when a vast marine transgression gave rise to the thick upper Permian shallow marine carbonates of the subcropping Khuff Formation and the exposed Saiq Formation of the Central Oman Mountains and the Bih and Hagil Formations of the Musandam Peninsula. The overall facies relationships for this body of carbonates is seen in Fig. 3.

The trend from evaporitic/carbonate sequences in the SW and N gives way eastwards to more open marine carbonates and a passive margin to the NE, with deep water deposits of redeposited reef?-derived gravity flows beyond.

Evidence that the earlier pre-Permian block faulting of the crust may have been influencing sedimentation may be inferred from the relationship between the shallow water conglomerates of Wadi Bani Kharus and the 'back reef' coral patch reefs of the Saiq Plateau together with the open marine carbonates farther east. Other exotic carbonates accumulated on volcanic seamounts farther out into the basin.

The position of the Permian rocks of the Batain Coast is more problematical. It is interesting to reflect that the rocks that characterize the Musandam Peninsula, Jebel Qamar South in the Dibba Zone and E Central Oman show strong affinities with Gondwanaland or the southern side of Tethys. The fauna in the Permian rocks of the Batain Melange, however, show strong affinities with Timor and the northern side of Tethys at that time (Shackleton *et al.* 1990).

Figure 8 shows a Late Permian (Kazanian) palaeogeographic map (after Scotese *et al.* 1979). On this, the areas of shallow sea have been indicated. It is unlikely that the relatively

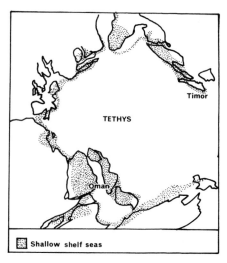

Fig. 8. Palaeogeographical Map for Kazanian (late Permian) times. Redrawn after Scotese *et al.* (1979).

shallow benthos, e.g. brachiopods, blastoids, and trilobites would have crossed such a major ocean barrier that was only somewhat smaller during Artinskian time before the Kazanian transgression. Faunal links must therefore imply fairly major travel around the periferal shallow seas.

As the nature of the Batain Melange and its association with the Oman Melange is still subject to ongoing research it is possible that the correlation of the Permian rocks of the Batain Melange to the Permian rocks of autochthonous (or par-autochthonous) Oman may be correct stratigraphically but may not necessarily be part of the sequence of events that led to the formation of the passive margin in the region of the Oman Mountains from Permian to Late Cretaceous time.

This work was funded by Amoco Oman Petroleum Company through an operating grant awarded to Proj. W. H. Kanes, Earth Sciences and Resources Institute, University of South Carolina. Amoco Production Company is thanked for permission to publish this paper. Special thanks are extended to A. C. Ries, J. D. Smewing and W. Blendinger for helpful criticism of earlier copies of this paper and to D. V. Ager for fossil identification and continuous interest.

References

BESEMS, R. E. & SCHUURMAN, W. M. L. 1989. Palynostratigraphy of Late Palaeozoic glacial deposits of the Arabian Peninsula, with special reference to Oman. *Bulletin of the American Association of stratigraphic Palynologists.*

BEYDOUN, Z. R. & GREENWOOD, J. E. G. W. 1968. *Lexique Stratigraphique International*, **3**, Asie Fasc. 20b2 (Protectorat d'Aden et Dhufar), Paris.

BLENDINGER, W., VAN VLIET, A. & HUGHES CLARKE, M. W. 1990. Updoming, rifting and continental margin development during the Late Palaeozoic in northern Oman. *In*: ROBERTSON, A. H. F., SEARLE, M. P. & RIES, A. C. (eds) *The Geology and Tectonics of the Oman Region*. Geological Society, London, Special Publication, **49**, 27−37.

BRAAKMAN, J. H., LEVELL, B. K., MARTIN, J. H., POTTER, T. L. & VAN VLIET, A. 1982. Late Palaeozoic Gondwana Glaciation in Oman. *Nature*, **299**, 48−50.

FALCON, N. L. 1967. The Geology of the North-East Margin of the Arabian Basement Sheild. *Advancement of Science*, **24**, 31−42.

GLENNIE, K. W., BOEUF, M. G. A., HUGHES CLARKE, M. W., MOODY-STUART, M., PILAAR, W. F. H. & REINHARDT, B. M. 1974. Geology of the Oman Mountains. *Verhandelingen van het Koninklijk Nederlands Geologisch Mijnbouwkundig Genootschaap*, **31**.

GORIN, G. E., RACZ, L. G. & WALTER, M. R. 1982. Late PreCambrian−Cambrian Sediments of Huqf Group Sultanate of Oman. *American Association of Petroleum Geologists Bulletin*, **66**, 2609−27.

GRAHAM, G. M. 1980. Evolution of a Passive Margin and Nappe Emplacement in the Oman Mountains. *Proceedings of the International Ophiolite Symposium* Nicosia, Cyprus. 414−423.

DE LA GRANDVILLE, B. F. 1982. Appraisal and Development of a Structural and Stratigraphic Trap Oil Field with Reservoirs in Glacial and Periglacial clastics. *Memoir of the American Association of Petroleum Geologists*, **32**, 267−286.

HUDSON, R. G. S. 1960. The Permian and Trias of the Oman Peninsula, Arabia. *Geological Magazine*, **92**, 299−309.

——, BROWNE, F. G. S. & CHATTON, M. 1954. The Structure and Stratigraphy of the Jebel Qamar Area, Oman. *Proceedings of the Geological Society of London*, **1513**, XCIX−CIV.

——, McGUGAN, A. & MORTON, D. M. 1964. The Structure of the Jebel Hagab Area, Trucial Oman. *Quarterly Journal of the Geological Society, London*, **110**, 121−152.

—— & SUDBURY, M. 1959. Permian Brachiopoda from South-East Arabia. *Notes Mémoire Moyen-Orient*, **7**, 19−69.

HUGHES CLARKE, M. W. 1988. Stratigraphy and Rock-Unit Nomenclature in the oil-producing area of Interior Oman. *Journal of Petroleum Geology*, **11**, 5−60.

LEES, G. M. 1928. The Geology and Tectonics of Oman and parts of South-Eastern Arabia. *The Quarterly Journal of the Geological Society of London*, **84**, 585−670.

MURRIS, R. J. 1980. Middle East: Stratigraphic Evolution and Oil Habitat. *The American Association of Petroleum Geologists Bulletin*, **64**, 597−618.

QIDWAI, H. A., KHALIFA, M. I. & BA-MKHALIF, K. A. 1988. Evidence of Permo-Carboniferous glaciation in the basal Murbat Sandstone Formation, southern region Sultanate of Oman. *Journal of Petroleum Geology*, **11**, 81−8.

ROBERTSON, A. H. F., BLOME, C. D. COOPER, D. W. J., KEMP, A. E. S., & SEARLE, M. P. 1990a. Evolution of the Arabian continental margin in the Dibba Zone, Northern Oman Mountains. *In*: ROBERTSON, A. H. F., SEARLE, M. P. & RIES, A. C. (eds) *The Geology and Tectonics of the Oman Region*. Geological Society, London, Special Publication, **49**, 251−284.

ROBERTSON, A. H. F., KEMP, A. E. S., REX, D. C. & BLOME, C. D. 1990b. Sedimentary and structural evolution of a transform lineament: the Hatta Zone, Northern Oman Mountains. *In*: ROBERTSON, A. H. F., SEARLE, M. P. & RIES, A. C. (eds) *The Geology and Tectonics of the Oman Region*. Geological Society, London, Special Publication **49**, 285−305.

SCOTESE, C. R., BAMBACH, R. K., BARTON, C., VAN DER VOO R. & ZIEGLER, A. M. 1979. Palaeozoic Base Maps. *Journal of Geology*, **87**, 217−77.

SEARLE, M. P. & GRAHAM, G. M. 1982. The "Oman Exotics" Oceanic carbonate build-ups associated with the early stages of continental rifting. *Geology*, **10**, 43−9.

——, JAMES, N. P., CALON, T. J. & SMEWING, J. D. 1983. Sedimentological and structural evolution of the Arabian continental margin in the Musandam Mountains and Dibba Zone, United Arab Emirates. *Bulletin of the Geological Society of America*, **94**, 1381−400.

SHACKLETON, R. M., RIES, A. C., FILBRANDT, J. B., LEE, C. W. & CUNNINGHAM, G. C. 1990. The Batain Melange of NE Oman. *In*: ROBERTSON, A. H. F., SEARLE, M. P. & RIES, A. C. (eds) *The Geology and Tectonics of the Oman Region*. Geological Society, London, Special Publication, **49**, 673−696.

SHARIEF, F. A. 1982. Lithofacies distribution of the Permian-Triassic rocks in the Middle East. *Journal of Petroleum Geology*, **4**, 299−310.

SZABO, F. & KHERADPIR, A. 1978. Permian and Triassic Stratigraphy, Zagros Basin, South-West Iran. *Journal of Petroleum Geology*, **1**, 57−82.

TSCHOPP, R. H. 1967. Development of Fahud field. *Proceedings of the 7th World Petroleum Congress* (Mexico), **2**, 243−50.

Sedimentary aspects of the Eo−Alpine cycle on the northeast edge of the Arabian Platform (Oman Mountains)

D. RABU[1], J. LE METOUR[1], F. BECHENNEC[1], M. BEURRIER[2], M. VILLEY[2] &
C. BOURDILLON-JEUDY DE GRISSAC[2].

[1] Service Géologqiue National, BRGM, 10 rue Henri Picherit, 44300
Nantes, France

[2] Service Géologique National, BRGM, BP 6009, 45060, Orléans,
France

Abstract: The northeast edge of the Arabian Platform in the Oman Mountains is represented by the autochthonous unit that crops out in the two windows of Jabal Akhdar and Saih Hatat, beneath and in front of the Hawasina and Samail nappes.

The Eo−Alpine orogenic cycle began in the Late Permian with extension on the margin of Gondwana and ended in the Campanian with the formation of a subduction−obduction-type mountain range, the Oman Mountains of the Late Cretaceous. During this cycle, long periods of stable shelf sedimentation were interrupted by tensional tectonic episodes, often accompanied by volcanism and subsidence of the platform, passing into the bathyal domain.

Deposition during the Permian to Campanian occurred during five main sedimentary cycles. In the Late Permian (Murghabian), a widespread marine transgression covered the edge of Gondwana in a tensional setting. The 'Fusulinid Sea' transgression was followed by the deposition, lasting until the Triassic, of a thick regressive sequence, the Akhdar Group, which was terminated by emergence and weathering in a continental environment. The next sedimentary cycle, represented by the Sahtan Group, began in the Pliensbachian, when the Oman Mountains area formed an inner carbonate shelf, and ended in the early Tithonian. The entire margin of the platform was profoundly affected, in the late Tithonian, by extension, listric faulting and foundering into the bathyal domain, with deposition of the Kahmah Group (Maiolica-type deposits: calpionellid-bearing micrite), and rapid retreat of the continental slope by about 250 km. Renewed carbonate shelf deposition then prograded SSW−NNE over the foundered part, though this was still incomplete when the latest Aptian−Albian transgression took place. At the Cenomanian−Turonian boundary, the shelf underwent profound reorganization with the development of the Muti (intrashelf) Basin, in which the Aruma Group was deposited, and the Masqat−Musandam High which provided the detritus filling the Muti Basin on the continentward side and the Hawasina Basin on the oceanic side. Fragments from the advancing nappe were redeposited in the Muti Basin only from the Campanian on, and it was only during this period that a flysch trough became superimposed on part of the Muti Basin. The closure of the Muti Basin was affected with the emplacement of the nappes on the platform and the subsequent deposition of cover formations over both nappes and the autochthon from the late Maastrichtian onward.

The Oman Mountain chain (see Fig. 1), risen out of the Neo-Tethyan sea on its southern margin, was built during two main orogenic cycles. The first cycle, between the Late Permian and Late Cretaceous, took the form of a poly-phase tectonometamorphic event (Le Métour et al. 1986b; Le Métour 1987; Rabu 1987) that culminated in the obduction of the Samail Ophiolite Nappe onto the edge of the Arabian Platform during the Campanian (Glennie et al. 1974). The second cycle (the Alpine cycle s.s.) beginning in the middle Maastrichtian and ending in the Early−Middle Miocene, was a moderate tectogenesis that gave its present shape to the mountain chain and represented the distant reverberation of the continental collisions that occurred farther west, in the Zagros (Ricou 1974) and its continuations in the Alpine chain throughout southern Eurasia during the Tertiary (Aubouin et al. 1980).

In palinspastic reconstructions of the south Tethyan margin, the Oman Mountains auto-chthon is identified with the northeast margin of the Arabian Platform. The Hawasina Nappes (Glennie et al. 1974) represent the sedimentary and volcanic deposits of the starved passive margin (Béchennec 1987), deposited in well-defined tectonic settings. The Samail Ophiolite

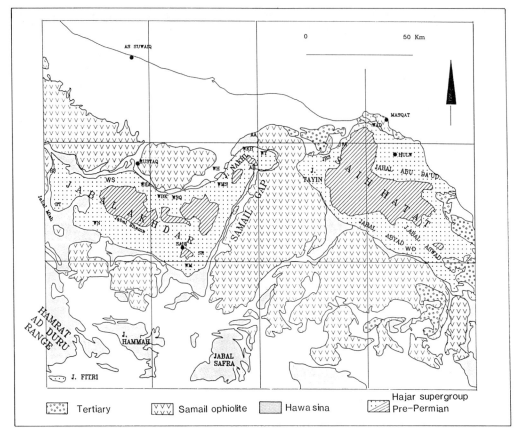

Fig. 1. Geological map of the central Oman Mountains showing location of the main localities mentioned in the text. AA, Al Ajal; AB, Al Bir; BT, Barut; BS, Bani Shahum; JBS, Jabal Bawshar; JM, Jabal Muraydah; SR, Saiq Road; WAD, Wadi Aday; WBA, Wadi Bani Awf; WBK, Wadi Bani Kharus; WD, Wadi Dayqah; WH, Wadi Hedeck; WKH, Wadi Khubrah; WM, Wadi Mu'aydin; WMS, Wadi Misin; WN, Wadi Nakhr; WS, Wadi Sahtan; WSQ, Wadi Saqla; WT, Wadi Taww.

Nappe is a fragment of Neo-Tethyan oceanic lithosphere developed in a back-arc setting (Pearce *et al*. 1981; Lippard *et al*. 1987; Beurrier 1987) and obducted during the Campanian.

In the Oman Mountains the autochthon outcrops beneath the Hawasina and Samail nappes in the Saih Hatat and Jabal Akhdar windows (Tschopp 1967a; Glennie *et al*. 1974; Le Métour 1987; Rabu 1987) and in the Musandam half-window (Ricateau & Riche 1980; Searle *et al*. 1983). It comprises two major units, the Pre-Permian basement (Glennie *et al*. 1974), and the Hajar Supergroup (Glennie *et al*. 1974). The former, which is not known in Musandam, ranges in age from Vendian (Mistal and Hatat Formations, Le Métour 1987; Rabu 1987) to Early Cambrian in Jabal Akhdar (Fara Formation, Rabu 1987) and to Middle to Late Ordovician (Amdeh Formation) in Saih Hatat

(Lovelock *et al*. 1981; Le Métour 1987). Pre-Permian (Hercynian?) deformation has had little effect, creating only open folds, lacking associated cleavage. Nevertheless, block movements have been recorded, and a regional unconformity separates the two autochthonous units.

The overlying Hajar Supergroup (Glennie *et al*. 1974) consists of dominantly carbonate deposits ranging in age from Late Permian to Late Cretaceous. The Hajar Supergroup is divided into five groups. The 1:100 000 scale mapping of Jabal Akhdar and Saih Hatat has led to the subdivision of these groups into formations with, when this seemed necessary, a new terminology (Table 1; Fig. 2). The five groups represent five sedimentary megasequences characterizing the Eo−Alpine cycle on the northeast edge of the Arabian Platform. They are:

(1) The Akhdar Group, representing a transgressive–regressive cycle during the Permo–Triassic.

(2) The Sahtan Group, which corresponds to the establishment of a tilted carbonate shelf in the Tithonian–Berriasian.

(3) The Kahmah Group, which represents the re-covering of the subsided part of the platform, with re-establishment of a shelf beginning in the SSW between the late Tithonian–Berriasian and the early Albian.

(4) The Wasia Group, a transgressive mega-sequence deposited during the middle Albian and the Cenomanian.

(5) The Aruma Group, which represents the establishment of an intra-shelf basin (the Muti Basin) and the development of an active positive zone (the Masqat–Musandam High) separating it from the Hawasina Basin.

The period of deposition of the Hajar Supergroup was marked in this region by three major events: (i) The transgression of the 'Fusulinid Sea' in an extensional setting during the Late Permian. (ii) Extension all along the Arabian continental margin leading to the establishment of a slope-to-bathyal domain during the Late Tithonian–Berriasian on the site of the present Oman Mountains. (iii) Complete reorganization of the palaeogeography of the south Tethyan margin in the Turonian in the context of the first regional deformations of the Eo–Alpine tectogenesis.

The Akhdar Group: a transgressive–regressive cycle during the Permo–Triassic

The Akhdar Group is composed of the Saiq and Mahil Formations (Glennie et al. 1974), which comprise a variety of shelf deposits showing a vertical evolution that corresponds to a transgressive–regressive cycle between the Murghabian (*Neoschwagerina schuberti* zone, Montenat et al. 1976) and Norian to Rhaetic.

Table 1. *Correlation chart between different terms used for groups and formations in autochthonous units of Oman Mountains*

Glennie et al. (1974)	Glennie et al. (1974)	Béchennec et al. (1986) Beurrier et al. (1986) Le Metour et al. (1986) Rabu et al. (1986)	Conally and Scott (1985)	Robertson (1987a,b)
Aruma Gp[1]	Juweyza Fm[1]	not exposed		Juweyza Fm[3].
	Fiqa Fm[1]	not exposed		Fiqa Fm[3].
	Muti Fm[1]	Muti Fm[2]		Muti Fm[3].
	(3 lithofacies)	(8 lithofacies[2])		(6 'units'[3])
		Fitri Fm[2]		
Wasia Gp[1]	Natih Fm[1]	Natih Fm[2]		
		(3 members[3])		
	Nahr Umr Fm[1]	Nahr Umr Fm[1]		
Kahmah Gp[1]	no	Shams Fm[2]	Shuaiba Fm[3]	
			Kharaib Fm[3]	
			Lekhwair Fm[3]	
		Birkat Fm[2]	Habshan Fm[3]	
		(2 members[2] and		
	formations	4 lithofacies[2])	Salil Fm[3]	
		Awabi Fm[2]	Rayda Fm[3]	
		(2 members[3])		
Sahtan Gp[1]	no	Upper Fm[2]		
	formations	Lower Fm[2]		
		(2 lithofacies[2] and		
		3 members[3])		
Akhdar Gp[1]	Mahil Fm[1]	Mahil Fm[2]		
		(2 lithofacies[2])		
	Saiq Fm[1]	Saiq Fm[2]		
		(17 lithofacies[2] and		
		2 members[2])		

[1] mapped at 1/500 000   [2] mapped at 1/100 000   [3] not mapped

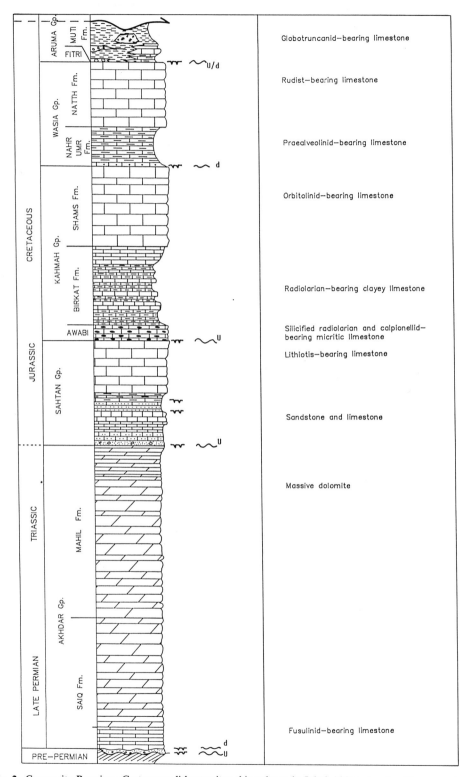

Fig. 2. Composite Permian−Cretaceous lithostratigraphic column in Jabal Akhar showing Groups and Formations mapped at 1/100 000.

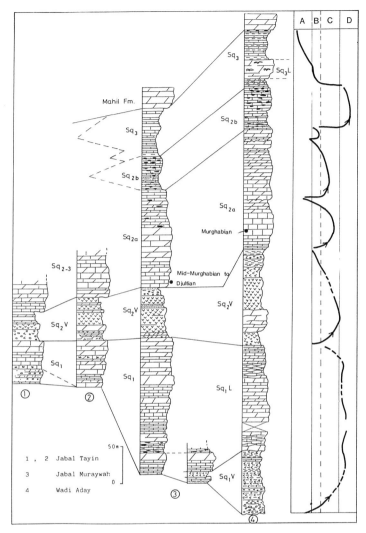

Fig. 3. The transgression of the 'Fusulinid Sea' across the unstable shelf domain: the Saiq Formation in Saih Hatat between Jabal Tayin and Wadi Aday A, supratidal environment; B, upper tidal environment; C, lower tidal environment; D, subtidal environment. Sq1V, tuffite, white tuff, schist and conglomerate; Sq1L, massive crystallized dolomite, nodular limestone at the top; Sq2V, andesite to basaltic pillow-lavas, hyaloclastic rocks at the base; Sq2a, black Fusulinid-bearing limestone and dolomite, oolitic and bioclastic levels; Sq2b, sandstone, and silty yellow limestone at the base, silicified limestone at the top; Sq3, yellowish-grey, thinly bedded mudstone and silty limestone; Sq3L, black stromatolitic limestone.

Permian extension and the transgression of the 'Fusulinid Sea'

The first sediments to be deposited on the exposed and eroded substratum constitute the Saiq Formation, which has been divided into several informal members (Table 1; Le Métour 1987; Rabu 1987). In Jabal Akhdar only two members are recognized (Fig. 4); the basal member is lenticular and consists of terrigenous detritus, up to 20 m thick, the remaining 450 m being an extensive carbonate unit. In Saih Hatat, however, the lithology is much more varied (Fig. 3), including terrigenous detritus, outer and inner shelf carbonates, volcanics and evaporites. Lateral facies variations are common, consistent with an active horst-graben environment of deposition.

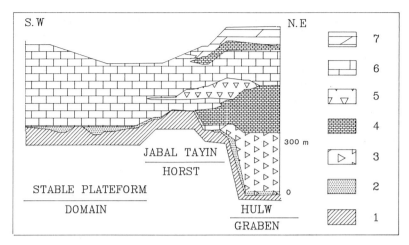

Fig. 4. Palaeogeographical diagram showing the distribution of various lithologic facies on the Permian platform. 1, Pre-Permian series; 2, conglomerate, sandstones and siltstones; 3, rhyodacitic tuffites; 4, external platform (carbonates); 5, trachy-andesitic lavas; 6, internal platform (carbonates); 7, evaporite and carbonate. Total length of the profile, 150 km.

Evidence for extension

A NE–SW profile across these two regions (Fig. 4) shows that two palaeogeographic domains existed during the transgression: (i) in the southwest, a sub-stable shelf (Jabal Akhdar), where the transgression occurred in two main stages, and the extensional tectonism was weak; (ii) in the northeast, an unstable shelf (Saih Hatat), where active extensional tectonism led to the formation of horsts and grabens and was accompanied by within-plate, continental magmatism (Fig. 3).

In the *stable shelf domain* the two states of the transgression are represented by the Lower and Upper members of the Saiq Formation. The first sediments to be deposited on the previously exposed and eroded substratum were immature, basement-derived conglomerates, up to 6 m thick, of diamictite type. They were deposited in a fluviatile to restricted littoral environment and are of local extent only (Wadi Mu'aydin, Saiq Plateau). The establishment of a restricted marine environment is marked by ferruginous deposits, yellowish sandstone and siltstone containing grains that are fractured and have a ferruginous coating indicating deposition in a continental environment. Emergent and lagoonal areas persisted however, as is shown by carbonaceous lenses in Wadi Mu'aydin. In the most open marine areas, carbonate sedimentation commenced with the deposition of bioclastic limestones containing foraminifera

and ostracods (Rabu 1987, Saiq Plateau). The benthic foraminifera indicate a Permian age. The carbonate sedimentation ceased when a tendency to emergence commenced, with the formation of ferruginised surfaces at the tops of the beds.

The main marine transgression was contemporaneous with the establishment of the 'Fusulinid Sea' in the Jabal Akhdar domain and led to the conformable deposition of the carbonate Upper member of the Saiq Formation. Terrigenous detritus is scarce at the base of the transgressive deposits, except in localities that remained emerged during the first stage of the transgression (Wadi Bani Kharus). These deposits were everywhere intercalated with internal shelf carbonate deposits, and very soon small bioherms became established. Benthic foraminifera, mainly fusulinids, are present from the base, and date the regional transgression as late Murghabian (*Neoschwagerina schuberti* zone; Montenat *et al.* 1976). After the transgression, the depositional conditions varied little, and a stable internal shelf became established with a marked tendency to become restricted during the Djulfian.

The *unstable shelf domain* covered principally Saih Hatat and the northeastern part of Jabal Nakhl. The latter was a hinge-area between the stable and the unstable zones, as is shown by the intra-Permian unconformity at the base of the Upper member of the Saiq Formation (Rabu 1987). The first indications of instability of the shelf coincide with the beginning of the trans-gressive phase. In Saih Hatat, the Saiq Forma-tion begins with clastic and carbonate sediments whose deposition was contemporaneous with the establishment of the 'Fusulinid Sea', and small bioherms rapidly became established at the base. The existence of higher and lower areas in the palaeotopography of Saih Hatat is shown by considerable variations in thickness (Fig. 3), the presence of condensed sequences and by rapid lateral variations in lithology (Le Métour 1987). This palaeotopography resulted from tectonic activity contemporaneous with the transgression and with which several mag-matic episodes were associated. Within this palaeogeographic scheme, northeastern Saih Hatat (Jabal Tayin) formed a horst separated from a subsiding graben by a set of near N—S faults (Masqat-Hulw, Jabal Abu Da'ud). E—W dislocations also contributed to the breaking-up of the shelf. Along the N—S faults, sedimen-tation was modified and bears the imprint of active tectonism (megabreccia and conglomer-atic breccia composed of limestones fragments). Whereas in western Saih Hatat (Jabal Abyad) the internal carbonate shelf rapidly became stable and developed similarly to that of Jabal Akhdar, the eastern part remained an area of instability, even though volcanism and terrigen-ous sedimentation had ceased. The instability was reflected in the establishment of reefal zones, followed by rapid subsidence that brought the area near the outer deep shelf environment, with the deposition of cherty limestone. This episode was short, and an abrupt regression of the sea resulted in the deposition of facies of a very restricted environment (evaporite, sulphate-bearing dolomicrite, micrite with algal films) in the upper part of the Saiq Formation (Wadi Aday, Jabal Bawshar). This regressive episode can be recognised regionally. Neverthe-less, evaporites have not been identified in Jabal Akhdar, where the regression is represented by massive, faunally impoverished dolomite attri-buted to the Djulfian on the basis of the presence of *Stafella* cf. *sisonghensis* Sheng. From this time onward the two domains evolved ident-ically and the period of instability is regarded as having come to an end.

In Musandam, the base of the Permian—Cretaceous cover is not known (Glennie *et al.* 1974; Ricateau & Riche 1980; Searle *et al.* 1983) and the probable Permian consists of the clayey dolomite with numerous hardgrounds of the Bih and Hagil Formations, deposited in a shallow environment. By comparison with Saih Hatat and Jabal Akhdar these formations are probably fairly high in the Permian succession, contemporaneous with the regression recorded at the top of the Saiq Formation (Djulfian).

Permian magmatism: characterization of continental within-plate extension.

Two principal volcanic intervals occur in Saih Hatat (Fig. 3). The first is at the base of the Saiq Formation (Hulw graben), where tuffs and tuf-fites occur with subordinate lavas of andesitic to rhyodacitic composition (Le Métour 1987). The second occurs in the same area but also on the Jabal Tayin horst, intercalated in the middle part of the Saiq Formation. This is represented mainly by trachy-andesitic lavas, doleritic sills and laccoliths and microgranite plugs, with minor tuffs and tuffites. Initial geochemical analysis shows that these two horizons represent bimodal, transitional tholeiitic and alkaline magmatism characteristic of a within-plate extensional setting. The bioclastic carbonate sediments within which these intervals occur contain fusulinids; they are thus of middle to late Murghabian age.

The regressive sequence

From the Djulfian onwards, the evolution of the Saih Hatat and Jabal Akhdar areas was identical. From the top of the Saiq Formation, the tendency towards a restricted environment was marked by the deposition of extreme inter-nal shelf carbonate bearing an impoverished microfauna. The Mahil Formation (Glennie *et al.* 1974) includes the essential part of the re-gressive sequence, comprising massive to algal-laminated dolomite containing only a little organogenic debris (Fig. 2). Many horizons show evidence of in situ reworking, with dislocated beds and syndepositional breccias, and of tem-porary subaerial exposure, in the form of mud chips, indicating an intra- to supratidal environ-ment. Rare marine incursions nevertheless al-lowed the deposition of oolitic beds and greater biological activity in the lower part of the sequ-ence (Wadi Bani Kharus). In the Norian—Rhaetic (age given by the presence of *Aulotortus sinuosus*), the return of terrigenous detritus (Jabal Tayin; Le Métour 1987), indicates the recommencement of erosion in the continental areas, under wetter conditions, enabling the transportation of weathering products on the platform (Murris 1980).

At the end of the Triassic, Jabal Akhdar and Saih Hatat were part of a flat, extensive, coastal marine domain, with broad sabkha-type zones, forming part of a stable platform, and finally emerging.

Place of the Oman Mountains autochthon in the Late Permian evolution of the south-Tethys margin

Regionally, the phase of extension contemporaneous with the transgression of the 'Fusulinid Sea' across the Oman Mountains area can be related to major fracturing of the African–Arabian–Iranian crust. At the same time the Hamrat Duru Basin developed upon thinned continental crust in the northeast of the Arabian Platform (Béchennec 1987; Béchennec *et al.* 1988; Béchennec *et al.* 1990). This basin corresponded at that time to a strongly subsiding part of the lithosphere, linking the Arabian and Iranian platforms that finally became separated from each other during the Middle to Late Triassic, giving birth to Neo-Tethys (Dercourt *et al.* 1986). From the Late Permian onward the first stages of disruption of the continent of Gondwana were marked, over large areas of subsiding continental crust (the Tethyan margin), by extensional magmatism that is well characterized in Oman. The magmatism identified at the same time in Iran (Ricou 1974) and in Kashmir and the lower Himalayas (Nakazawa 1985) can probably be attributed to the same cause.

The Sahtan Group: establishment of a tilted carbonate shelf during the late Tithonian–Berriasian

The Jurassic of the Oman Mountains: an internal carbonate shelf.

After emergence of a large part of the northeast border of the Arabian Platform at the end of the Late Triassic, a major, strongly diachronous transgression during the Middle and Late Jurassic initiated a marine, internal shelf environment on the site of the present Oman Mountains.

The Jurassic is represented in Jabal Akhdar and Saih Hatat by the Sahtan Group, which attains its maximum thickness of 400 m in the western part of Jabal Akhdar (Fig. 5A). The group is represented by two main lithological successions (Le Métour 1987; Rabu 1987) comprising a mixed clastic–carbonate lower part of Pliensbachian age (*Orbitopsella primavea prae-cursor*), and an essentially carbonate upper part terminating in the earliest Tithonian (*Protopeneroplis striatus, Kurnubia palestiniensis, Nauticulina oolithica, Alveopsella powersi*).

The base of the Sahtan Group is characterized by alternating clastic terrigenous and carbonate units. The former comprise sandstone, quartz-

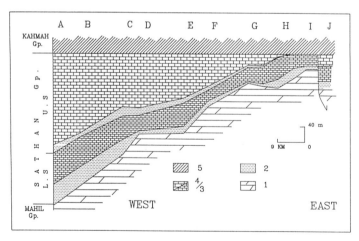

Fig. 5. Palaeogeographical diagram showing the unconformity between the Kahmah and Sahtan Groups in Jabal Akhdar. Total length of the profile, 100 km. 1, Dolomite, Mahil Formation; 2, Sandstone and terrigenous limestone, Sathan Group; 3, Clayey limestone and limestone in small beds, Sahtan Group; 4, Massive oolithic limestone, Sahtan Group; 5, Silicified calpionellid-bearing micrite (maïolica facies), Kahmah Group. L.S, Lower sequence of the Sahtan Group; U.P, Upper sequence of the Sahtan Group. Location of the cross-section (see Fig. 1): A, Wadi Sahtan; B, Wadi Nakhr; C, Wadi Bani Awf; D, Wadi Bani Kharus; E, Wadi Saqla; F, Wadi Mu'aydin; G, Wadi Misin; H, Wadi Hedeck; I, West Wadi Taww; J: Wadi Taww.

ite, oolitic ferruginous sandstone and mass-flow deposits containing large blocks (Wadi Sahtan), while the latter include sandy limestone, dolomicrite and bioclastic limestone including bivalves and benthic foraminifera. This assemblage marks the transgression across an exposed and weathered Triassic substratum in which pockets of weathered rock occur (southeastern Saih Hatat; Le Métour 1987), and that has been eroded and gently tilted, resulting in a slight angular unconformity beneath the Mahil Formation (Glennie *et al.* 1974). The first transgressive sediments were deposited in a marginal coastal environment where temporary emergence was still common.

In Jabal Akhdar (Fig. 5D), the vertical evolution of the Sahtan Group is clearly shown through two well-defined sequences. The lower shows an evolution typical of a transgressive unit, with a progressive decrease of terrigenous input, which is gradually replaced by bioclastic carbonate deposits. Deposition of the upper sequence began, probably during the Bathonian, with the abrupt resumption of sedimentation of terrigenous material, though emergence did not occur, and continued with deposition of proximal subtidal carbonate sediments.

The evolution in two stages is much less clear in Saih Hatat, terrigenous material remaining present in the carbonate deposits and the two sequences not being clearly distinguishable. This palaeogeographic organization was probably influenced by the Huqf axis, which was progressively covered during the transgression, and could have been a source of terrigenous material. It was not submerged until the Bathonian (Morton 1959; Murris 1980), at the time when the deposition of the upper sequence began in Jabal Akhdar. The upper sequence indicates the establishment of a carbonate shelf across the entire Jabal Akhdar–Saih Hatat area, with deposition of massive bioclastic limestone containing accumulations of thick-shelled bivalves (*Lithiotis*) and the development of oolitic shoals separating off areas of restricted, internal lagoon character (Saih Hatat; Le Métour 1987). The oolitic shoals closest to the continental slope acted as sources of sediment supply to the Hamrat Duru Basin, forming the calcareous turbidites of the Guwayza Formation (Glennie *et al.* 1974; Béchennec 1987).

In Musandam, the Jurassic deposits comprise the Ghalilah Formation, at the top of the Elphinstone Group, and the lower part of the Musandam Group (Ricateau & Riche 1980). The Ghalilah Formation (250–300 m thick) rests, apparently conformably, upon the Norian–Rhaetic Milahah Formation, and is composed of littoral deposits of sandstone, shale and carbonate. The general regression in the west during the Late Triassic, whose effects are observed at the top of the Akhdar Group did not lead, in Musandam, to prolonged emergence of the Triassic substratum, and the Jurassic transgression was directly followed by deposition of siliciclastic sediments from the beginning of the Early Lias.

Late Tithonian–Berriasian extension: foundering of the Jurassic platform

The horizontal variations within the Sahtan Group in Jabal Akhdar illustrate well the effects of the late Tithonian–Berriasian extension.

A NE–SW profile (Fig. 5) constructed from sections measured at regular intervals across the massif shows that the total thickness of Jurassic deposits decreases markedly towards the northeast, from 400 m in Wadi Sahtan to 50 m in the 'nose' of Jabal Akhdar (Jabal Nakhl). Thus the bathyal sediments of the Awabi Formation in the Kahmah Group of late Tithonian to Berriasian age overlie progressively older members of the Sahtan Group from west to east, forming a major regional unconformity (Fig. 5). Three explanations are possible for this: (i) Northeastward wedging-out of the Sahtan Group; (ii) Syndepositional erosion of the group; (iii) Post-depositional erosion of the Sahtan Group before its covering by the Awabi Formation (Kahmah Group).

The first hypothesis must be discarded because the reduction in thickness affects only the upper part of the group, i.e., the erosion was from the top downwards. Syn-depositional erosion has certainly played a part, in particular in those regions nearest to the continental slope, as indicated by the sediment supplied to the Hamrat Duru Basin, but on the scale of the entire Jabal Akhdar–Saih Hatat area such erosion was not continuous. Therefore the hypothesis of post-depositional erosion is assumed to be correct. On the northeast side of Jabal Nakhl and in Saih Hatat the Sahtan Group is of greater and more variable thickness than within the Jabal Akhdar block. At the boundary between this domain and the Jabal Akhdar block (in which erosion increases continuously from southwest to northeast), the earliest deposits of the Kahmah Group are atypical, the presence of syndepositional breccia indicating an unstable environment (Rabu 1987). These observations and the disposition of the components of the Sahtan Group beneath the Awabi Formation suggest that the erosion of the Sahtan Group was associated with extensional movements during which the edges of the platform at the margins of a subsiding fault trough were tilted (Boillot 1979).

The effects of this extension were also felt in the Hamrat Duru Basin, where the oolitic turbidites of the Guwayza Formation are capped by post-Kimmeridgian carbonate breccia and overlain by the late Tithonian−Berriasian radiolarite and silicified limestones of the Sid'r formation (Béchennec 1987; Béchennec *et al.* 1988).

On the continental side, the foundering and submergence of the Jurassic platform have been recognized as far as Fahud (Murris 1980), where the new continental slope was situated during the late Tithonian−Berriasian. This sudden retreat of the continental slope, by about 250 km, accompanied by intense erosion between the early and late Tithonian, was an essential element in the new palaeogeography of the Arabian Platform.

The Kahmah Group: a regressive sequence filling a basin opened in the late Tithonian−Berriasian

The Lower Cretaceous is represented in Jabal Akhdar and Saih Hatat by the Kahmah Group (Glennie *et al.* 1974). Three formations have been mapped in this group (Table 1), the Awabi, Birkat and Shams Formations (Le Métour *et al.* 1986c; Beurrier *et al.* 1986; Rabu *et al.* 1986), whose stratotypes are situated in Jabal Akhdar (Rabu 1987). While the mapping was being done, Conally & Scott (1985) proposed subdividing the Kahmah Group into six formations whose stratotypes were situated in oil exploration wells in the United Arab Emirates (Abu Dabi and Sharjah). The boundaries proposed by these authors were the sites of geophysical discontinuities (variations in the gamma or neutron curves) which cannot always be located in the field and which do not necessarily correspond to important lithological boundaries. Surface mapping of these boundaries is in places impossible, as admitted by the authors themselves, who compared their well sections with the Oman Mountains by a section along Wadi Bani Kharus. The three formations that we propose as subdivisions of the Kahmah Group (Rabu 1987) are in contrast readily identifiable lithological units mapped in both the autochthonous inliers in the windows through the Oman Mountains (Table 1).

Arguments for the existence of a basin in the late Tithonian−Berriasian

The Awabi Formation (Fig. 6), at the base of the Kahmah Group, rests unconformably on an indurated surface cut across the Sahtan Group. The lower member, 5−15 m thick, consists of biolithoclastic, locally conglomeratic or micro-breccial limestone, the clasts in which, deposited in a bathyal to slope environment, include fragments of Permo−Triassic internal shelf deposits. Red argillaceous intervals occur in places, associated with thin volcanosedimentary beds (Wadi Mu'aydin). The surface at the base is very locally (Saiq road; Rabu 1987) marked by accumulations of belemnite guards (*Conobelus*) and ray teeth (*Astera canthus*, det. Capetta) or ammonoid casts (Wadi Ruwawah, NE Saiq road). The upper member, 30−40 m thick, is composed of white to pink, highly silicified micrite (Maiolica facies). The fauna and flora are essentially pelagic, and include radiolaria, calpionellids (*Crassicolaria*), silicisponges, pelagic crinoids and belemnites. The calpionellid associations provide a late Tithonian−Berriasian age for the base (*Calpionella alpina*) and a Valanginian age for the top (*Tintinopsella carpathica, Calpionellopsis simplex, C. oblonga*; Conally & Scott, 1985; Le Métour 1987; Rabu 1987). These facies closely resemble the Maiolica facies described from the Alps (Bernouilli & Jenkyns 1974; Bosellini & Winterer 1975) and characteristic of a bathyal

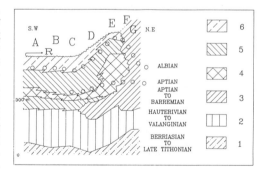

Fig. 6. Palaeogeographical diagram of the Kahmah Group on the stable part of the margin (Jabal Akhdar): a prograding mega-sequence between the late Tithonian−Berriasian and the Albian. Total length of the profile, 100 km. 1, bathyal domain; 2, confined basin; 3, external platform; 4, reef, shoal and external lagoon; 5, internal platform; 6, carbonate ramp. Location of the cross-sections (see Fig. 1): A, Wadi Nakhr, Jabal Shams; B, Saiq road; C, Wadi Bani Kharus; D, Wadi Nakhl; E, Wadi Hedeck; F, Al Bir; G, Wadi Khubrah.

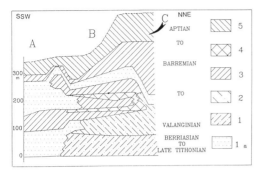

Fig. 7. Palaeogeographical diagram of the Kahmah Group on the unstable part of the margin (Saih Hatat). The prograding mega-sequence was interrupted by several extensional phases underlined by the recurrences of the terrigenous and slope deposits. Total length of the profile, 70 km. la, deep see fan; 1, bathyal domain; 2, slope; 3, external platform; 4, reef, shoal and external lagoon; 5, internal platform. Location of the cross-section (see Fig. 1): A, Jabal Abyad; B, Jabal Aswad, C, Wadi Dayqah.

domain protected from clastic input. The presence of significant silicification indicates that these deposits form close to the Calcite Compensation Depth (CCD). The Awabi Formation is characteristic of a stable deep sea environment, in strong contrast to the proximal subtidal setting described for the top of the underlying Sahtan Group.

The classical lithological association described above occurs virtually throughout Jabal Akhdar and in the eastern part of Saih Hatat (Jabal Aswad). In western Saih Hatat (Fig. 7) and on northeastern Jabal Nakhl the Awabi Formation consists of calcareous siltstone–claystone, quartz-bearing calcarenite and calcareous breccia (Le Métour 1987; Rabu 1987). These are turbidite-type deposits in which intervals of resedimented beds occur, and are composed of lithological assemblages of rocks belonging to the Awabi Formation itself, deposited laterally (a breccia with fragments of calpionellid-bearing micrite occurs on Jabal Nakhl). These particular facies are interpreted as emplaced on a deep-sea fan controlled by 10°N–20°N faults that were still active at the time of deposition, an instability that persisted until the Barremian and can still be recognised in the overlying formations.

The Birkat Formation is some 305 m thick in the stratotype on the Saiq road (Rabu 1987), and consists of a lower and an upper member. The lower member comprises a number of sedimentary sequences and consists of flaky, clayey micritic limestone with disseminated sulphides.

The microfauna are essentially pelagic, comprising radiolaria and planktonic foraminifera with redeposited benthic foraminifera. These deposits are contourites (Heezen et al. 1966), formed in a sediment-covered slope environment, under the influence of weak currents and characterized by calm, restricted conditions, similar to that of the stable domain in which the lower member of the Awabi formation was deposited (mainly in Jabal Akhdar). The upper member is about 70 m thick and consists of bioclastic limestones, bioturbated micrites and horizons of macrofaunal accumulation, representing the establishment of a proximal subtidal shelf during the Hauterivian(?)– Barremian. In Saih Hatat (Fig. 7) and at the northeast end of Jabal Nakhl the instability recognized during the deposition of the upper member of the Awabi Formation persists, and the Birkat Formation consists of biomicrite, calcarenite, conglomeratic breccia and rudist-bearing biostromes, organised in sequences 20–50 m thick and culminating with the temporary development of reefal facies.

In Musandam, Ricateau & Riche (1980) and Searle et al. (1983) described a silicified, calpionellid-bearing micritic limestone of Early Cretaceous (pre-Berriasian) age, overlain by clayey limestone enclosing belemnites, ammonites and pelagic microfauna of Berriasian– Valanginian age, recalling exactly the deposits of the Awabi and Birkat Formations deposited in slope to bathyal environments.

In the Hamrat Duru Basin, the Jurassic succession is capped by a carbonate breccia and overlain by late Tithonian–Berriasian radiolarite and silicified limestone without clastic input from the shelf (Sid'r Formation). In the less deeply subsided parts (Misfah Ridge; Béchennec 1987), Maiolica facies developed (Nadan Formation).

In Interior Oman, calpionellid-bearing micrites have been described above the Jurasic limestone by Glennie et al. (1974), whereas Tschopp (1967b), in the same area, describes anhydritic-bearing maarly limestone above the Jurassic, covered by rudist-bearing limestones (the Thamama Group). These two lithological assemblages represent two palaeogeographic domains (Murris 1980). One, extending far to the south and west, as far as Saudi Arabia, the Arabian Gulf and the southern Zagros, representing a restricted environment with evaporitic tendencies, saw the establishment of a carbonate shelf (top of Thamama Group) with no intermediate bathyal domain. The other, extending northward and northeast, and which includes Jabal Akhdar and Saih Hatat, represents an open marine environment with a slope to bathyal stage before the establishment of an internal carbonate shelf.

Thus throughout the Oman Mountains area, the late Tithonian—Berriasian was a period of profound change in the environment of sedimentation, which, from being proximal subtidal, suddenly deepened to slope-to-bathyal. This was not limited to the Oman Mountains autochthon, for the same phenomenon can be recognized in the Hawasina Basin, in Interior Oman and in part of the Zagros (Ricou 1974). We interpret this deepening as the result of a major phase of extension that affected the whole of the south-Tethyan continental margin, and whose effects can be recognized both in the pre-Tithonian substratum (Kahmah—Sahtan unconformity) and in the new palaeogeographic organization of the margin, with in particular the abrupt retreat of the continental margin which was located until the Oxfordian—Tithonian beyond Saih Hatat, and in the late Tithonian—Berriasian was situated near Fahud, i.e., a retreat of some 250 km. The listric faults associated with the foundering are now difficult to locate. It seems that virtually the whole of Jabal Akhdar formed a uniform tilted block at this time, and the fault that cuts the northeast termination of Jabal Nakhl (between NE of Taww and the mouth of the Samail gap) is interpreted as a listric fault formed at the time of the extension. This type of dislocation was also active in the bathyal environment, and the atypical conglomeratic breccias of the Awabi Formation (near Taww and at the top of Jabal Nakhl) were deposited on the site of the movement, witnessing active tectonism.

The Kahmah Group: a regressive mega-sequence

The new palaeogeographical disposition that resulted from the foundering of the platform and the retreat of the continental slope in the late Tithonian—Berriasian profoundly influenced sedimentation during the Early Cretaceous. This was to be a period of re-covering of the sunken platform, which, starting from the continental slope, would prograde northeastward during deposition of a regressive mega-sequence (Fig. 6).

In the *stable domain* of Jabal Akhdar the mega-sequence begins with calpionellid-bearing micrites (the Awabi Formation), which are followed by the argillaceous micrites enclosing radiolaria and pelagic foraminifera of the Birkat Formation. During the Hauterivian(?)—Barremian a differentiated platform became

established, in which a barrier represented by an oolite and/or rudist shoal separated an internal domain in the west from an external one in the northeast (NNE of Wadi Nakhl). Deposition of the regressive mega-sequence was interrupted during the end-Aptian and early Albian by a transgression (top part of the Shams Formation; Rabu 1987) contemporaneous with the general rise in sea-level (Vail *et al.* 1977). As a result of this rise the rudist barrier reef on Jabal Akhdar disappeared, allowing the development of a carbonate ramp. This transgressive sequence is truncated in Jabal Akhdar by an indurated surface marking the base of the Albian—Cenomanian Wasia Group.

In the *unstable domain* of Saih Hatat and the northeast end of Jabal Nakhl, the evolution of the regressive megasequence was more complex because this domain remained active until the Barremian. At this time, renewed extension, contemporaneous with the opening of the Arabian marine domain in the southwest of the Arabian Peninsula was recorded, with submergence of the Huqf axis and the Gulf of Aden (Murris 1980).

The Wasia Group: a transgressive megasequence

The Wasia Group (Glennie *et al.* 1974), of Albian—Cenomanian age, comprises two formations that together constitute a transgressive mega sequence. The lower of the two is the Nahr Umr Formation, resting on a regional indurated surface, which consists of orbitolinid-bearing (*Orbitolina concava, Simplorbitolina*) marl with a significant clastic terrigenous fraction, deposited on a sedimented internal shelf. Reduction of clastic terrigenous input resulted in the formation of a rudist-bearing shelf represented by the Natih Formation of middle Albian to late Cenomanian age. The biostratigraphy is defined by the successive appearance of various forms of alveolinids and praealveolinids (Glennie *et al.* 1974; Rabu 1987; Simmons & Hart 1987).

Post-Cenomanian erosion cut deeply into the Wasia Group deposits at the northeast end of Jabal Nakhl and over virtually the entire Saih Hatat.

The Aruma Group: beginning of the Alpine tectogenesis in the Turonian

The new palaeogeographic organization

At the end of the Cenomanian, the Oman Mountains area was covered by a rudist-bearing carbonate shelf (Natih Formation, Glennie *et al.* 1974; Rabu 1987; Simmons & Hart 1987) with a complex palaeogeography, and a narrow intrashelf basin existed between Qatar and Musandam (Murris 1980). The Turonian–Senonian was a period of extreme disturbance of the palaeogeography of the border of the Arabian Platform and ended with the closure of Neo-Tethys and the emplacement of the platform of nappes of sedimentary (Hawasina Nappes) and ophiolitic (Samail Nappes) rocks. In the Oman Mountains (Table 1), the Turonian–Senonian is represented by the Aruma Group, comprising the Muti, Juweiza, Fiqa and Simsima formations (Glennie *et al.* 1974), and the newly defined Fitri Formation (Béchennec *et al.* 1986; Rabu 1987).

The Fitri Formation (named after Jabal Fitri, at the foot of the Hamrat Duru Range; Béchennec *et al.* 1986) has been divided into three members (Rabu 1987), consisting of limestone and calcschist enclosing bivalves, echinoderms, calcisponges and cephalopods (*Vascoceras* sp.). The presence of planktonic foraminifera, calcispheres, pelagic crinoids, ammonites and siliceous concretions indicate an external shelf environment of deposition, with some input from an internal platform in the form of benthic microfauna and rudist debris. Although they differ both in lithology and in environment of deposition from the Wasia Group, these deposits, which herald those of the Muti Formation, were formerly included in the Wasia Group (Members a, b and c of the Wasia Limestones, Tschopp 1967b; Murris 1980; the Rumaila and Khatiyah facies, Harris & Frost 1984; Robertson 1987b). The age of early Turonian proposed by Rabu (1987) for this formation agrees with those advanced for facies equivalents elsewhere (see above; Harris & Frost 1984; Robertson 1987a). To the west, the Fitri Formation extends as far as the western end of Jabal Akhdar and at the front of the Hamrat Duru Range (Fig. 9). Lying conformably and without hiatus upon the Cenomanian Natih Formation, the Fitri Formation represents the beginning of subsidence of the shelf, which in this area did not pass through a stage of emergence, although a period of non-deposition marked the passage to the Muti formation.

The Muti Formation (Glennie *et al.* 1974) comprises a number of vertical and lateral facies variants (Rabu 1987; Robertson 1987a,b) whose relationships enable a complex palaeogeography to be reconstructed, an example of which is provided by Jabal Akhdar (Fig. 8). A description of the formation by facies follows:

(1) Biomicrite enclosing planktonic foraminifera and radiolaria is the most common facies, and it occurs fairly uniformly throughout the Oman Mountains, including at the front of the nappes, where it occurs as the Shargi member (Fiqa Formation, Glennie *et al.* 1974). The detrital fraction, both carbonate and terrigenous, is important everywhere, the lithoclasts being derived from the erosion of the pre-Turonian shelf. The planktonic foraminiferal associations yield ages ranging from early to middle Turonian for the base of the formation where *Marginotruncana* gp. *helvetica* Bolli has been identified in samples from the south flank of the Hamrat Duru Range (Janjou *et al.* 1986), equivalent to the Hanya member of Robertson (1987b), and *Marginotruncana praehelvetica* in samples from Wadi Nakhl (Rabu 1987). At the top of the formation the association *Globotruncana fornicata*, *Marginotruncana angusticarinata*, *M.* gr. *coronata linnelana* and *Ulcarinella concavata* identified in samples from Jabal Mish give a late Coniacean–Santonian age (Rabu 1987). These determinations invalidate Robertson's (1987a,b) proposals for division of the Muti Formation into a Sayjah Member, localized on the periphery of Jabal Akhdar and whose base is of late Turonian age, and a Hanya Member localized at the front of the nappes and of post–mid-Santonian age.

(2) Discontinuous units of dispersed-clast, monogenic conglomerate comprise, in varying proportions, pebbles of black limestone in a matrix of biomicrite enclosing planktonic foraminifera. The pebbles contain large benthic foraminifera characteristic of the Natih Formation (Wasia Group), and the conglomerate is distributed over an area that corresponds closely to that of the Natih (Fig. 8).

(3) Radiolarian cherts form widespread sequences on the south flank of Jabal Akhdar (Rabu 1987) and at the nappe front in the Hamrat Duru Range (Béchennec *et al.* 1986; Rabu 1987; Robertson 1987b). In the former area, the association *Zifondiium pauperum*, *Ultranapora spinifera* and *Crucella messinae*(?) (det. P. De Wewer) indicates an early to middle Turonian age, showing that no hiatus exists between the Fitri and Muti formations in the area.

(4) Ferruginous oolite and related facies occur locally both laterally and vertically, but are well identified in Jabal Akhdar along a zone about 10 km wide and in Wadi Mu'aydin (Fig. 8). The ferruginous oolites

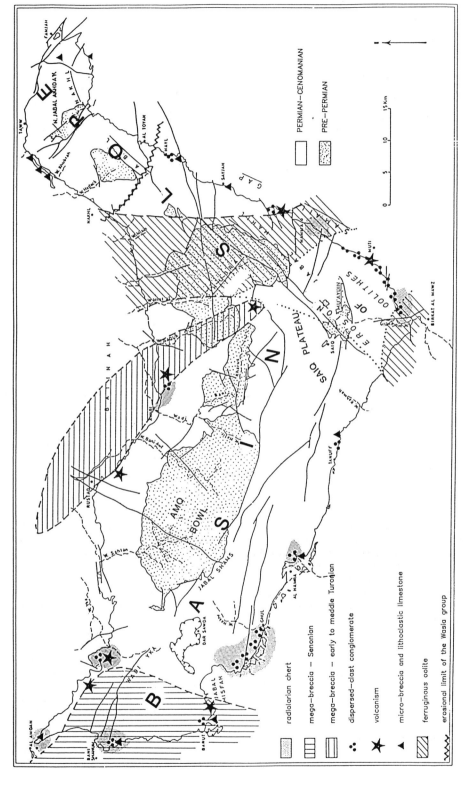

Fig. 8. The Muti lithofacies in the Jabal Akhdar and the new palaeogeographic organization of the Turonian.

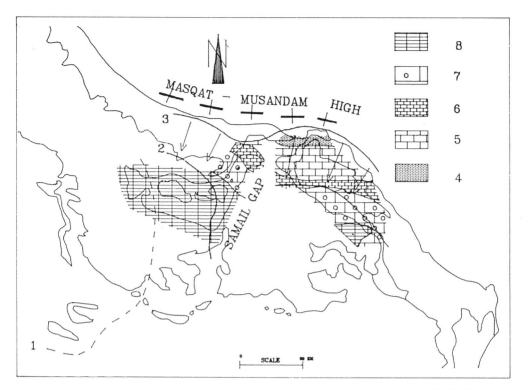

Fig. 9. Evidences for the Masqat−Musandam High: sketch map of the Muti substratum in Jabal Akhdar and Saih Hatat. From the Southwest towards the Northeast, the Muti Formation lies over older deposits (Wasia to Sahtan Group). In the Southern part of the Jabal Akhdar and further towards the Southwest, neither erosion nor lack of sedimentation are recognized between the Muti and Fitri formations. 1, limits of the Fitri Formation; 2, bottom of the slope underlined by cataclysmic mega-breccias; 3, edge (continental side) of the Masqat−Musandam High; 4, lower part (sandstone) of the Sahtan Group; 5, upper part (massive limestone) of the Sahtan Group; 6, Awabi and Birkat Formations (Kahmah Group, lower part); 7, Shams Formation (Kahmah Group, upper part); 8, Nahr Umr and Natih Formations (Wasia Group).

are associated with yellowish biolithoclastic limestones at the base of the Muti Formation. The lowest ferruginous horizon has yielded an association of planktonic foraminifera in Wadi Mu'aydin, including *Pithonella sphaerica* Kaufmann and *P. ovalis* Kaufmann, no older than early Turonian.

(5) *Breccia and microbreccia* form discontinuous units within the radiolaria-bearing biomicrites. They are widespread throughout the Oman Mountains, but are particularly well developed around Jabal Nakhl, where they form thick resistant units at Al Ajal and Taww. They bear witness to the erosion of an indurated carbonate platform known to form the substratum of the Muti Formation and identified through reworked lithoclasts (Mahil,

Sahtan and Kahmah facies). The matrix includes planktonic foraminifera of at least middle Turonian age.

(6) Reefal limestone mega-breccia forms widespread, commonly mappable units (Beurrier *et al.* 1986; Rabu *et al.* 1986). A notable example is the Awabi mega-breccia, several kilometres long, which extends from Rustaq to the Saiq Plateau. It rests upon several metres of radiolaria-bearing biomicrite, and at its base is associated with pillow lavas and tuff beds. The constituent blocks are as much as several tens of metres across and consist in part of Murghabian reefal limestone (Rabu 1987). The matrix has yielded a pelagic microfauna no younger than early to middle Turonian (*Marginotruncana praehelvetica*, *Hedbergella* cf. *delrioensis*). The reworking of the

Permian platform from this time onward implies very active vertical tectonics. The chaotic character of the breccia and the size of the blocks indicate that it is a scarp-foot breccia formed in front of a retreating escarpment, with virtually no transportation.

Other breccias containing reefal fragments are known as Bani Shahum and Barut (Fig. 8), at the west end of Jabal Akhdar and at the front of the Hamrat Duru Range, but they do not have the character of scarp-foot breccia. They have been reworked in a deep-water (radiolarian chert), volcanic environment and date from the Permian and Triassic. Their age of emplacement is much younger than that of the Awabi megabreccias, since on the west flanks of Jabal Akhdar they fill erosion channels in planktonic foraminifera-bearing biomicrites of late Coniacian–early Santonian age (Rabu 1987).

(7) Volcanic rocks, essentially amygdaloidal pillow lavas and crystal tuffs are everywhere poorly exposed, and are known only in Jabal Akhdar and Saih Hatat in association with reefal-block mega-breccia.

The distribution of facies and the relationships between the Muti Formation and its substratum enable the distinction of three domains from northeast to southwest (Figs 8 & 9):

(i) A positive axis formed by the edge of the Permo-Cretaceous Arabian Platform, the erosion of which fed the Muti Basin situated to its southwest. The Permo-Triassic was undoubtedly affected in the area north of Masqat. The same arrangement has been recognised in Musandam (Ricateau & Riche 1980) with emerged Jurassic and Triassic shelf supplying an intrashelf basin open to the southwest. Thus, from Musandam to Masqat, a tectonically active ridge at least temporarily controlled the extension of the Muti Basin on the Arabian continental margin and supplied it with detritus. The name Masqat–Musandam High is proposed for this new structure.

The Masqat–Musandam High occupied a key position in the palaeogeographic organisation of the Arabian continental margin, acting as an axis of symmetry separating two basins of broadly similar characteristics, the Muti Basin to the SSW and the Hamrat Duru Basin to the NNE. The sedimentary gradients in the two basins decrease away from this axis, and the zones of detrital input are located along it. This positive axis, created by the upwarping and

disruption of the pre-Turonian strata, is bounded by steep faults with strong vertical throw above which scarp-foot breccias were deposited. These cataclysmic-type deposits in both the Muti Basin (Awabi-type breccia) and the Hamrat Duru Basin (breccia of Member C of the Mayhah Formation in the Sumeini Group, Watts & Garrison, 1986; Riyamah Member of Muti Formation, Robertson 1987b; proximal facies of the Nayid Formation in the Hawasina Window, Béchennec 1987).

Towards the southwest, a slope domain in Jabal Nakhl and Saih Hatat, with coarse sedimentation, forms a junction zone between the Masqat-Musandam High and the basin domain.

(ii) A restricted foot-of-slope domain where ferruginous oolites were formed very early, in the early Turonian, and scarpfoot megabreccias (Awabi type) were deposited.

(iii) A basin domain of more distal sedimentation characterized by the presence of radiolarian chert.

This organization persisted at least until the late Coniacian–Santonian, a period during which appreciable modifications occurred, with the arrival far into the basin of mega-breccias enclosing reefal blocks of Permian and Triassic age (at the front of the Hamrat Duru Range).

Evolution of the Muti Basin

The Muti Basin, for Robertson (1987a,b), represents a foreland basin migrating across the Arabian Platform in front of the Samail and Hawasina nappes, following the theoretical model of Stockmal *et al.* (1986). While very attractive, this model cannot be applied directly to the Muti Basin since it assumes strong diachronism of the Muti facies from northeast to southwest, which is not in agreement with the chronostratigraphical relationships determined for the facies of this formation in Saih Hatat (Le Métour *et al.* 1986a,b; Le Métour 1987), Jabal Akhdar (Beurier *et al.* 1986; Rabu *et al.* 1986; Rabu 1987) and at the front of the Hawasina Nappes (Béchennec *et al.* 1986; Rabu 1987). We have been able to show that the subsidence of the Muti Basin and the warping of the northeast margin of the Arabian Platform were synchronous, and that the erosion of the uplifted Masqat-Musandam High was contemporaneous with these movements and lasted, at least locally, until the Santonian.

In the early Turonian (possibly at the end of the late Cenomanian), the subsidence of the SSW part of the Jabal Akhdar extended the intrashelf basin of Interior Oman, where the Fitri Formation was deposited (Fig. 9). During the same period, uplift of the platform in the NNE began, the ferruginous oolites marked the flexure zone, rapidly cut into by higher-energy slope deposits (dispersed-clast conglomerate). The uplift was controlled by faults aligned in general NNW–SSE, which also controlled the erosion of the Wasia Group in Jabal Akhdar and the Kahmah Group in Saih Hatat. The emplacement of the megabreccias was controlled by faults of this type. In this scheme, the Saih Hatat area possesses the characteristics of an active high deeply incised by submarine canyons that were rapidly filled by high-energy sediments. Jabal Akhdar was in a more distal situation and the units representing the passage to the Permian–mid-Cretaceous shelf are preserved uneroded. Towards the SSW, in the extensive Muti Basin, fine sediments were deposited, disturbed from time to time by the arrival of mainly carbonate (conglomerate), but sometimes terrigenous (radiolaria-bearing sandstone) detritus. Radiolarian cherts were deposited during quiet periods, the earliest of which was during the middle Turonian. These observations invalidate the hypothesis of a depositional hiatus proposed by Glennie et al. (1974), and subsequently adopted by several authors (Searle et al. 1983; Harris et al. 1985; Robertson 1987a,b). The biostratigraphical results from the Jabal Akhdar and Saih Hatat massifs demonstrate that the erosion of the platform was contemporaneous with the deposition of the Muti Formation and began in the Turonian.

The extension of the radiolarites is limited to the NNE by the slope domain. Towards the SSW, in the Fahud area, the Fitri Formation (Rumaila–Khatiyah facies) is covered by distal facies (= Fiqa Formation, Glennie et al. 1974) derived from active zones that were too distant to provide coarse clastic input. The lack of radiolarian chert suggests that this area was not in the most subsident part of the Muti Basin, which must have been in the region of the Hamrat Duru Range. In the Fahud area, the Muti Basin was filled fairly rapidly and a carbonate shelf established there from the Maastrichtian (Arada member of the Fiqa Formation; Glennie et al. 1974).

In Saih Hatat, the Muti Formation has been strongly affected by the subduction and obduction tectonics of the Eo–Alpine tectogenesis (Le Métour et al. 1990) and although no biostratigraphical data give ages younger than late Turonian, the existence of younger deposits cannot be excluded. In the western part of the Jabal Akhdar and at the front of the Hawasina Nappes (on the southern slope of the Hamrat Duru Range), a further stage in the evolution of the Muti Basin was reached in the Coniacian–Santonian. In this domain, that hitherto had been in a distal position, megabreccias were deposited consisting of blocks of Late Permian and Late Triassic reefal limestone. Deposited in a bathyal environment in association with radiolarian chert, these breccias no longer have the character of collapse breccias, but have undergone considerable transport before their deposition. The reefal nature of the blocks of Triassic limestone (unknown in the Masqat area) makes it possible to locate their source area in the NNW of the Masqat–Musandam High.

The Muti Basin and the Eo–Alpine tectogenesis

The reorganization of the northeast border of the Arabian Platform starting in the Turonian took place in the much wider context of the beginning of the Eo–Alpine tectogenesis. From the Turonian, the relative movement of the African–Arabian and Eurasian plates changed (Patriat et al. 1982; Livermore & Smith 1984) and the positive zones formerly oriented SW–NE (Qatar arc, Huqf axis) became NW–SE, perpendicular to the new movement vector of the plates shown by the orientation of the Masqat–Musandam High. The entire system then came under compression and the upwarping and disruption commenced, initiating the creation of the Masqat–Musandam High, which fed symmetrically with mega-breccia the Hamrat Duru Basin on the oceanic side and the Muti Basin on the continental side. At the same time, partly intra-oceanic subduction was initiated, causing the northeast corner of the peri-Arabian lithosphere to descend northeastward beneath Neo-Tethys (Pearce et al. 1981; Beurrier 1987). The blocking of subduction that was responsible for synmetamorphic, oceanward-verging deformation in the platform (Le Métour et al. 1986b; Le Métour 1987; Rabu 1987; Le Métour et al. 1990) led to the closure of Neo-Tethys by the overthrusting of its southern margin and the obduction of the Samail back-arc basin.

Conclusions

The Eo–Alpine orogenic cycle in Oman can be separated into two periods:
(1) From the Permian to the Early Cretaceous (170 Ma), during which the passive continental margin of Oman developed, opening onto the expanding Neo-Tethys.
(2) The Late Cretaceous (about 25 Ma), when

the Eo-Alpine chain of the Oman Mountains was built in response to a process of closure of the southern margin of Tethys.

During the *first period*, two major events were recorded on the edge of the Arabian Platform:

(i) In the Murghabian, a first phase of extension and rifting affected the Arabo–Iranian craton, resulting in the formation of a broad intracontinental basin (the Hamrat Duru Basin), now thrust onto the platform, but whose southern border, representing the passage to the stable platform, can be recognized among the autochthonous units (Saiq Formation in Saih Hatat). Distinctive sedimentation and magmatism in the basin occurred in a horst-and-graben setting. The Oman edge of the Arabian Platform remained stable from the Djulfian until the Late Jurassic, with a long period of continentalization at the passage from the Triassic to the Jurassic, associated with weak movements, recorded in the unconformity between the Mahil formation and the Sahtan Group (Glennie *et al.* 1974).

(ii) In the late Tithonian–Berriasian a second period of crustal extension provoked the foundering of the Arabian Platform, which passed into the littoral to bathyal domain, with a sudden retreat of the continental slope of about 250 km towards the southwest. The earliest postextension sediments were micrites enclosing calpionellids and radiolaria (Maiolica facies), marking the beginning of a regressive megasequence that was part of the recovering of the subsided part of the platform, with progradation of a carbonate shelf from southwest to northeast.

During the *second period*, the northeast border of the Arabian Platform was reorganized in response to the closure of Neo-Tethys. The new, Turonian palaeogeographic scheme corresponded to a warping of the Permo-Cenomanian shelf (the Masqat–Musandam High) that accompanied marked subsidence in the bordering intrashelf basin (Fitri and Muti formations). These phenomena are underlined by the deformation of the pre-Turonian strata and mark the beginning of the Eo–Alpine tectogenesis. This arrangement extended around the Arabian promontory from Oman all along the south Tethyan continental margin, through the southern Zagros, to Turkey (Ricou 1974; Kazmin *et al.* 1986).

This reorganization of the south Tethyan border was the result of the compressive dynamics brought on by new relative directions of movement of the African–Arabian and Eurasian plates.

This paper has been written in the context of the Bureau de Récherches Géologiques et Minières programme for mapping of Oman. The authors express their gratitude to M. H. Kassim, Director, Directorate of Minerals, Oman Ministry of Petroleum and Minerals for the constant help they had throughout the mapping project. J. Kemp, Service Géologique National, France, translated the text.

References

AUBOUIN, J., DEBELMAS, J. & LATREILLE, M. 1980. Les chaînes alpines issues de la Téthys: introduction générale. Mémoir du BRGM, **115**, 7–12.

BÉCHENNEC, F. 1987. Géologie des Nappes Hawasina dans les parties orientale et centrales des Montagnes d'Oman. Thèse Doct. ès-Sciences, Université P. et M. Curie, Paris 6 — Documents du BRGM, n°127, 412 p.

BÉCHENNEC, F., BEURRIER, M., RABU, D. & HUTIN, G. 1986. Geological map of Bahla. Sheet NF 40–7A, scale 1/100 000. Explanatory notes. Directorate General of Minerals, Oman Ministry of Petroleum and Minerals.

BÉCHENNEC, F., LE METOUR, J., RABU, D., VILLEY, M. & BEURRIER, M. 1988. The Hawasina Basin: a fragment of starved, passive, continental margin thrust over the Arabian platform during obduction of the Samail Nappe. *Tectonophysics*, **151**, 323–343.

BÉCHENNEC, F., LE METOUR, J., RABU, D., BOURDILLON-DE-GRISSAC, C. H. DE WEVER, P., BEURRIER, M. & VILLEY, M. 1990. The Hawasina nappes: stratigraphy and structural evolution of a fragment of the south-Tethyan passive continental margin. *In*: ROBERTSON, A. H. F., SEARLE, M. P. & RIES, A. C. (eds) *The Geology and Tectonics of the Oman Region*. Geological Society, London, Special Publication, **49**, 213–225.

BERNOUILLI, D. & JENKYNS, H. 1974. Alpine, Mediterranean, and Central Atlantic Mesozoic facies in the relation to the early evolution of the Tethys. In: DOTT, R. H. & SHAVER, R. H. (eds) *Modern and ancient geosynclinal sedimentation*, Society of Economic Palaeontologists and Mineralogists, Special Publication, **19**.

BEURRIER, M. 1987. Géologie de la Nappe Ophiolitique de Samail dans les parties orientale et centrale des Montagnes d'Oman. Thèse Doct. ès-Sciences, Université P. et M. Curie, Paris 6 — Documents du BRGM.

BEURRIER, M., BÉCHENNEC, F., RABU, D. & HUTIN, G. 1986. Geological map of Rustaq. Sheet NF 40–3D. Scale 1/100 000. Explanatory Notes. Directorate General of Minerals, Oman Ministry of Petroleum and Minerals.

BOILLOT, G. 1979. Géologie des marges continentales — Masson ed., Paris.

BOSELLINI, A. & WINTERER, E. L. 1975. Pelagic limestone and radiolarite of the Tethyan Mesozoic: a genetic model. *Geology*, **3**, 279–282.

CONALLY, T. C. & SCOTT, R. W. 1985. Carbonates sediment-fill of an oceanic shelf, lower Cretaceous, Arabian Peninsula. Deep-water carbonates: buildups, turbidites, debris-flows and chalks, *In*: CREVELLO & HARRIS (ed.) SEPM core workshop, **6**, 266–302.

DERCOURT, J., ZONENSHAIN, L. P., RICOU, L. E., KAZMIN, V. G., LE PICHON, X., KNIPPER, A. L., GRANDJACQUET, C., SBORTSHIKOV, I. M., GEYSSANT, J., LEPVRIER, C., PECHERSKY, D. H., BOULIN, J., SIBUET, J. C., SAVOSTIN, L. A., SOROKHTIN, O., WESTPHAL, M., BAZHENOV, M. L., LAUER, J. P. & BIJU-DUVAL, B. 1986. Geological evolution of the Tethys belt from the Atlantic to the Pamir since the Lias. *Tectonophysics*, **123**, 241–315.

GLENNIE, K. W., BOEUF, M. G. A., HUGHES-CLARKE, M. W., MOODY-STUART, M., PILAAR, W. F. H. & REINHARDT, B. M. 1974. *Geology of the Oman Mountains*. Verhandelingen Koninlajk Nederlands Geologisch Mijnbouwkundig Genootschap, 31. Part 1 2 3.

HARRIS, P. M. & FROST, S. H. 1984. Middle Cretaceous Carbonate reservoirs, Fahud field and Northwestern Oman. *American Association of Petroleum Geologists Bulletin*, **68**, 649–658.

HARRIS, P. M., FROST, S. H., SEIGLIE, G. A. & SCHNEIDERMANN, N. 1985. Regional unconformities and depositional cycles, Cretaceous of the Arabian Peninsula. *In*: SCHLEE, J. S. (ed.) *Interregional unconformities and hydrocarbon accumulations*, American Association of Petroleum Geologists Memoir, **36**.

HEEZEN, B. C., HOLLISTER, C. D. & RUDDIMAN, W. F. 1966. Shaping of the continental rise by deep geotropic contour-currents. *Science*, 502–508.

JANJOU, D., MINOUX, L., LE METOUR, J., VILLEY, M. & GRAMONT DE X. 1986. Geological map of Ibri. Sheet NF 40–2F. Scale 1/100 000. Explanatory notes. Directorate general of Minerals. Oman Ministry of Petroleum and Minerals.

KAZMIN, V., RICOU, L. E. & SBORTSHIKOV, I. M. 1986. Structure and evolution of the passive margin of the Eastern Tethys. *Tectonophysics*, **123**, 153–170.

LE METOUR, J. 1987. Géologie de l'Autochtone des Montagnes d'Oman: la fenêtre du Saih Hatat. Thèse Doct. ès-Sciences, Université P. et M. Curie, Paris 6 — Documents du BRGM, 129.

LE METOUR, J., VILLEY, M. & GRAMONT DE X. 1986a. Geological map of Quryat. Sheet NF 40–4D. Scale 1/100 000. Explanatory notes. Directorate General of Minerals, Oman Ministry of Petroleum and Minerals.

LE METOUR, J., RABU, D., TEGYEY, M., BECHENNEC, F., BEURRIER, M. & VILLEY, M. 1986b. Le métamorphisme régional crétacé de faciès éclogites — schistes bleus sur la bordure omanaise de la plate-forme arabe: conséquences d'une tectogénèse précoce anté-obduction. Comptes-rendus

Académie Sciences Paris, t. 302, série II, n°4, p. 905–910.

LE METOUR, J., VILLEY, M. & GRAMONT, DE X. 1986c. Geological map of Masqat. Sheet NF 40–4D. Scale 1/100 000. Explanatory notes. Directorate General of Minerals, Oman Ministry of Petroleum and Minerals.

LE METOUR, J., RABU, D., TEGYEY, M., BÉCHENNEC, F., BEURRIER, M. & VILLEY, M. 1990. Subduction and obduction: two stages in the Eo-Alpine tectono-metamorphic evolution of the Oman Mountains *In*: ROBERTSON, A. H. F., SEARLE, M. P. & RIES, A. C. (eds) *The Geology and Tectonics of the Oman Region*. Geological Society, London, Special Publication, **49**, 327–339.

LIPPARD, S. J. SHELTON, A. W. & GASS I. G. 1987. The ophiolite of Northern Oman. *The Geological Society, London, Memoir*, **11**.

LIVERMORE, R. A. & SMITH, A. G. 1984. Some boundary conditions for the evolution of the Mediterranean region in: NATO AEI, Erice, Silicy, vol. on Mediterranean tectonics.

LOVELOCK, P. E. R., POTTER, T. L., WALSWORTH, E. B. & WIEMER, W. M. 1981. Ordovician rocks in the Oman Mountains: the Amdeh formation — Geologie en Mijnbouw, 487–495.

MONTENAT, C., LAPPARENT, DE, LYS, M., TERMIER, G., TERMIER, H. & VACHARD, D. 1976. La transgression permienne et son substratum dans le Jabal Akhdar (Montagnes d'Oman, Péninsule Arabique). *Annales Société Géologique du Nord, France*, XCVI, **3**, 239–258.

MORTON, D. M. 1959. The geology of Oman. Proceedings of the 5th World Petroleum Congress, New York, **14**(1), 227–280.

MURRIS, R. J. 1980, Middle East: stratigraphic evolution and oil habitat. *American Association of Petroleum Geologists Bulletin*, **64**, 597–618.

NAKAZAWA, K. 1985. The Permian and Triassic systems in the Tethys. *In*: NAKAZAWA & DICKINS (eds) *The Tethys, her Paleogeography and Paleobiogeography from Paleozoic to Mesozoic*, Todai University press.

PATRIAT, P., SEGOUFIN, J., SCHLICH, R., GOSLIN, J., AUZENDE, J. M., BEUZART, P., BONNIN, J. & OLIVET, J. L. 1982. Les mouvements relatifs de l'Inde, de l'Afrique et de l'Eurasie. *Bulletin Société Géologique France*, (7) XXIV, **2**, 363–373.

PEARCE, J. A., ALABASTER, J., SHELTON, A. W. & SEARLE, M. P. 1981. The Oman ophiolite as a cretaceous arc-basin complex: evidence and implications. *Royal Society of London Philosophical Transaction*, **A300**, 299–317.

RABU, D., BÉCHENNEC, F., BEURRIER, M. & HUTIN, G. 1986. Geological map of Nakhl. Sheet NF 40–3E. Scale 1/100 000. Explanatory Notes. Directorate General of Minerals, Oman Ministry of Petroleum and Minerals.

RABU, D. 1987. Géologie de l'Autochtone des Montagnes d'Oman: la fenêtre du jabal Akhdar. — La semelle métamorphique de la Nappe ophiolitique de Samail dans les parties centrale et orientale des Montagnes d'Oman: une revue.

Thèse Doct. ès-Sciences, Univ. P. et M. Curie, Paris 6. — Documents du B.R.G.M., Orléans, 130.

RICATEAU, R. & RICHE, Ph. 1980. Geology of the Musandam peninsula (Sultanate of Oman) and its surroundings. *Journal of Petroleum Geology*, **3**(2), 139–152.

RICOU, L. E. 1974. L'étude géologique de la région de Neyriz (Zagros iranien) et l'évolution structurale des Zagrides. Thèse Doct. ès-Sciences. Université de Paris Sud — Orsay. 1269.

ROBERTSON, A. H. F. 1987a. The transition from passive margin to an Upper Cretaceous foreland basin related to ophiolitic emplacement in the Oman Mountains. *Geological Society of America, Bulletin*, **99**, 633–653.

ROBERTSON, A. H. F. 1987b. Upper Cretaceous Muti Formation: transition of a Mesozoic carbonate platform to a foreland basin in the Oman Mountains. *Sedimentology*, **34**, 1123–1142.

SEARLE, M. P., JAMES, N. P., CALON, T. J. & SMEWING, J. D. 1983. Sedimentological and structural evolution of the Arabian continental margin in the Musandam Mountains and Dibba zone, United Arab Emirates. *Geological Society of America, Bulletin*, **94**, 1381–1400.

SIMMONS, M. D., HART, M. B. 1987. The biostrati-graphy and microfacies of the early to mid-Cretaceous carbonates of Wadi Mu'aydin, central Oman Mountains. *Micropalaeontology of carbonate environments*, Ellis Horwood Chichester.

STOCKMAL, G. S., BEAUMONT, C. & ROUTILIER, R. 1986. Geodynamic models of convergent margin tectonics: transition from rifted margin to over-thrust belt and consequences for foreland-basin development. *American Association of Petroleum Geologists Bulletin*, **70**(2), 181–190.

TSCHOPP, R. H. 1967a. The general geology of Oman. Proceedings of the 7th World Petroleum Congress, Mexico. **2**, 231–242.

TSCHOPP, R. H. 1967b. Developments of the Fahud field. *Proceedings of the 7th World Petroleum Congress, Mexico*, **2**, 243–250.

VAIL, P. R., MITCHUM, R. M. & THOMPSON, J. R. 1977. Seismic stratigraphy and global changes of sea level- part 4: Global cycles of relative changes of sea level. *In*: PAYTON C. E. (ed.) *Seismic stratigraphy applications to hydrocarbon exploration*. American Association of Petroleum Geologists Memoir, **26**, 83–97.

WATTS, K. F. & GARRISON, R. E. 1986. Sumeini group, Oman. Evolution of a Mesozoic carbonate slope on a South Tethyan continental margin. *Sedimentary Geology*, **48**, 107–168.

Jurassic and Early Cretaceous platform margin configuration and evolution, central Oman Mountains

BRIAN R. PRATT[1] & JOHN D. SMEWING[2]

[1] Department of Geological Sciences, University of Saskatchewan,
Saskatoon, Saskatchewan S7N 0WD, Canada

[2] Earth Resources Institute, University Innovation Centre, Singleton
Park, Swansea SA2 8PP, UK

Abstract: The Hajar Supergroup is a Middle Permian to middle Cretaceous sequence dominantly composed of shallow-water carbonate rocks which veneer the eastern edge of the Arabian Platform in the Oman Mountains. The Jurassic and Early Cretaceous components of this package were deposited on the passive margin of Neo-Tethys which developed after initial rifting in the Late Permian and Triassic. Strata studied in Jebel Akhdar, Saih Hatat and neighbouring uplifts document low- and high-energy, shallow-water depositional environments punctuated by two drowning events when deeper water, slope conditions migrated onto the shelf margin. The mid-Jurassic event may have been precipitated by synsedimentary down-faulting of the Saih Hatat area as rifting continued. The latest Jurassic, earliest Cretaceous event, depositing the Rayda Formation, is ascribed to a regional decrease in carbonate production because of widespread evaporitic conditions in the Arabian Platform interior.

The configuration of the Mesozoic platform margin in northern Oman conforms to a series of rift and transform segments inherited from the underlying crust when it separated in the Early Jurassic. The transform segments became the focus of major structural lineaments during subsequent thrusting and obduction. This provides an especially clearcut example of the structural control of passive margin geometry, as well as its effect on collision-related deformation. A new Jurassic lithostratigraphic unit, the Saih Hatat Formation, is formally described.

The Jurassic and Early Cretaceous was a time of maximum transgression of marine conditions onto the Arabian Platform (Murris 1980). This period of widespread carbonate deposition resulted in a vertical and lateral facies mosaic including evaporite seals that constitutes the richest single oil habitat in the world, the Arab A to D reservoirs (e.g. Alsharhan & Kendall 1986). Understanding the factors that controlled the development and facies differentiation of the interior of this platform may be aided by an analysis of the stratigraphy and dynamics of its seaward edge. The deposits of the passive margin record the sedimentary response to the shape of the underlying rifted crust, synsedimentary tectonics, fluctuations in sea-level rise and subsidence rate, as well as changes in the regional hydrographic regime. Furthermore, the configuration of the margin and its internal lithologic contrasts profoundly affected the nature and geometry of tectonic features generated during subsequent deformation.

Deposits of the Mesozoic continental margin of the Arabian Platform and the adjacent basin are only preserved in the Oman Mountains (Fig. 1) where the full spectrum of rock types provides the most complete documentation available of the nature of eastern Neo-Tethys (e.g. Kazmin *et al.* 1986).

Platform-to-basin lithofacies belts can be reconstructed from near-autochthonous sequences and by unravelling successively obducted thrust slices (Glennie *et al.* 1974). In this paper, we focus on the Jurassic and Early Cretaceous deposits of the seaward edge of the platform and the adjacent upper slope in the central Oman Mountains. We show that shallow-water facies alternately prograded and retrograded over a margin that exhibited a configuration conforming to an underlying series of rift and transform segments. The Oman situation thus serves as an excellent general illustration of the dynamics of carbonate sedimentation on an ancient passive continental margin.

Stratigraphy

Lithostratigraphic nomenclature of Mesozoic sedimentary rocks of the central Oman Mountains is largely that defined by Glennie *et al.* (1974; see also Hughes Clarke, 1988). Most of these units can be correlated to those of the

From ROBERTSON, A. H. F., SEARLE, M. P. & RIES, A. C. (eds), 1990,
The Geology and Tectonics of the Oman Region.
Geological Society Special Publication No 49, pp 69–88

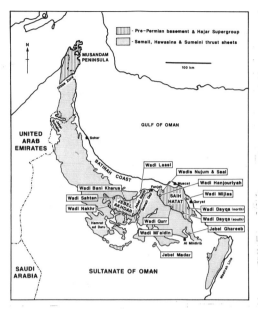

Fig. 1. Map of Oman showing simplified geology of the Oman Mountains and location of place names, wadis and jebels referred to in the text.

adjacent subsurface (Fig. 2). Platform strata of Permian and Mesozoic age, exposed in Jebel Akhdar, Saih Hatat and the foothills to the south, comprise the Hajar Supergroup. They were deposited when the Arabian Platform was flooded during and after rifting and spreading associated with the formation of Neo-Tethys. This event began in the Permian and ceased with the onset of compression in the mid-Cretaceous, with real continental separation starting in the Early Jurassic (e.g. Glennie *et al.* 1974; Dercourt *et al.* 1986; Robertson 1987).

Permian and Triassic sediments in the platform interior are evaporitic (Murris 1980; Koop & Stoneley 1982; Alsharhan & Kendall 1986), but they graded seaward into a relatively narrow belt of cyclic peritidal carbonate rocks which are now exposed in the Oman Mountains.

Deposition of the Jurassic Sahtan Group is thought to have commenced after a hiatus involving platform-wide subaerial erosion due either to a eustatic sea level drop (cf. Haq *et al.* 1988) or to slight flexure of the platform causing block faulting (Hughes Clarke 1988). This erosional period is also reflected by the presence of quartzose sandstone in the basal part of the Sahtan. These strata carry diagnostic Liassic faunal elements, such as the foraminifer *Orbitopsella praecursor* and the bivalve *Lithiotis* (Geyer 1977). The Sahtan is equivalent to the lower six informal members of the Musandam Group of the Musandam Peninsula (Hudson &

Chatton 1959; Ricateau & Riche 1980). The subsurface equivalent in interior Oman (Butabul Group of some authors, e.g Gorin *et al.* 1982) has been subdivided into a series of formations (Hughes Clarke 1988) which, apart from the basal unit, the Mafraq Formation, largely cannot be recognized in sections exposed in Jebel Akhdar. Exact correlation with formations in the subsurface of the United Arab Emirates cannot be made precisely either. The youngest Jurassic deposits there consist of a narrow belt of limestone, the Asab Formation, which grades westward into anhydrite of the Hith Formation.

In Oman, the Sahtan Group was abruptly overlain, after a period of flexure and erosion of the southeastern edge of the Arabian Platform (Murris 1980), by the uppermost Jurassic and Early Cretaceous Kahmah Group. Only the lower part of the sequence is treated here, consisting of the Rayda ('Porcellanite' of Glennie *et al.* 1974), Salil and Habshan Formations. Calpionellids at the base give a biostratigraphic age approximately spanning the Tithonian−Berriasian boundary, and faunas from the Habshan indicate a Valanginian to possibly earliest Hauterivian age (Connally & Scott 1985; Simmons & Hart 1987). A more recent compilation by Scott *et al.* (1988) showed the Rayda−Habshan sequence ranging from upper Berriasian to upper Hauterivian in age. This discrepancy, however, does not alter our view of the relative timing of sedimentary events affecting these units, but it does make it difficult to relate them to current reconstructions of eustatic sea level change. These strata correlate with the informal G to K members of the Musandam Group (Hudson & Chatton 1959; = G member of Ricateau and Riché 1980). The Kahmah is equivalent to the Thamama Group of the subsurface of Saudi Arabia and the United Arab Emirates (e.g. Alsharhan & Nairn 1986), but because the Rayda and Salil Formations represent a regional drowning event that was confined to the platform in Oman, these units do not persist west of easternmost Abu Dhabi and the Habshan rests conformably on the underlying Jurassic Asab and Hith Formations of the platform interior (Hassan *et al.* 1975). Thus, the temporal relationships between the Hith anhydrite and the Rayda are not clear. Alsharhan & Kendall (1986) and Alsharhan & Nairn (1986) considered that these units were deposited contemporaneously, with the anhydrite having accumulated behind a shallow-water oolitic barrier in southeast Abu Dhabi formed by the Asab Formation. On the other hand, Hassan *et al.* (1975), Murris (1980), Connally & Scott (1985) and Hughes Clarke

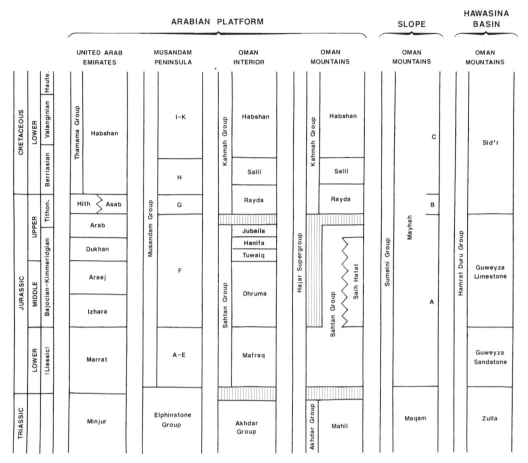

Fig. 2. Table of lithostratigraphic units in the eastern part of the Arabian Platform; not to scale. Sources of nomenclature are as follows. United Arab Emirates: Alsharhan & Kendall (1986), Alsharhan & Nairn (1986). Musandam Peninsula: Hudson & Chatton (1959). Oman interior: Hughes Clarke (1988). Oman Mountains (platform): this paper (Saih Hatat Formation is new). Oman Mountains (slope): Watts & Garrison (1986). Oman Mountains (basin): Cooper (1987).

(1988) indicated that the Rayda is younger than the Hith and is a facies equivalent of the Habshan. We consider that the Rayda and Hith are at least partly coeval (Fig. 3) because this provides a reasonable explanation for widespread drowning. We do not accept, however, the unconformity between the Rayda and Salil shown by Alsharhan & Nairn (1986, fig. 3).

Slope facies coeval with these platform carbonate rocks form the Mayhah Formation of the Sumeini Group which are now exposed as thrust-bounded slices in several areas along the western edge of the Oman Mountains (Glennie et al. 1974; Searle et al. 1983; Watts & Garrison 1986). The succession of deeper water rocks deposited in the Hawasina Basin also occurs only as allochthonous, successively underplated, thrust-bounded packages along the western and

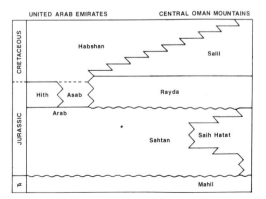

Fig. 3. Schematic cross section of the eastern Arabian Platform showing stratigraphic relationships proposed in this paper; not to scale.

southern Oman Mountains and in the Hawasina Window (Glennie *et al.* 1974; Cooper 1987, 1989; Béchennec *et al.* 1988; Blendinger 1988). These comprise the Hamrat Duru Group, and we follow the revised formational nomenclature of Cooper (1987) here because it is supported by lithologic detail.

Study areas

Relevant sections were measured in this study at twelve places in the central Oman Mountains, in Jebel Akhdar, Saih Hatat, and in the foothills south of Saih Hatat, at Jebel Madar and at Jebel Ghareeb near Al Mintirib (Fig. 1). These

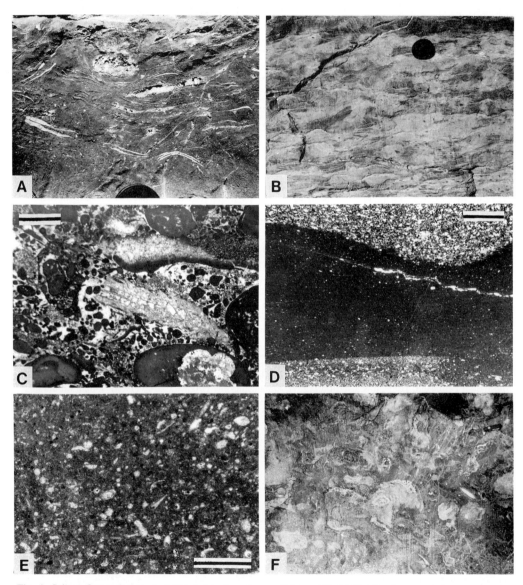

Fig. 4. Sahtan Group facies. A, *Lithiotis* bivalves. Lower Sahtan, Wadi Mi'aidin; lens cap is 6 cm across. B, Outcrop of bioturbated, dolomitic lime mudstone and wackestone. Middle Sahtan, Wadi Bani Kharus; lens cap is 6 cm across. C, Thin section photomicrograph of coarse peloidal and bioclastic grainstone. Top of lower Sahtan, Wadi Qurr; scale bar is 2 mm. D, Thin section photomicrograph of thin argillaceous lime mudstone bed between two peloidal grainstone beds. Saih Hatat, Wadi Qurr; scale bar is 2 mm. E, Thin section photomicrograph of radiolarian packstone. Saih Hatat, Wadi Qurr; scale bar is 0.5 mm. F, Bedding plane of poorly preserved microbial-coral-stromatoporoid boundstone. Uppermost Sahtan, between Wadi Qurr and the south end of Wadi Dayqa; pocket knife (upper right corner) is 9 cm long.

sections are correlated in Fig. 9. Published subsurface data from the interior of Oman and the United Arab Emirates, and outcrop descriptions of the shallow-water sequence on the Musandam Peninsula and allochthonous deep-water strata of the Oman Mountains are briefly summarized.

Jebel Akhdar

The Jurassic and Lower Cretaceous sequence was examined in five places in Jebel Akhdar: Wadis Sahtan, Bani Kharus and Laasi on the northern flank, and wadis Nakhr and Mi'aidin on the southern flank. Wadi Sahtan is the location of the type section of the Sahtan Group (Glennie *et al.* 1974); the type sections for the Rayda and Salil Formations are in Wadi Mi'aidin (Hughes Clarke 1988).

Jurassic. The Sahtan Group varies little in lithologic character around Jebel Akdhar, although its thickness changes because of the amount of erosion that took place prior to deposition of the overlying Rayda. At Wadi Sahtan, it is 415 m thick (Glennie *et al.* 1974), whereas at Wadi Laasi it is only about 123 m thick, and even less at the northern end of Jebel Nakhl. It is about 200 m thick at Wadi Mi'aidin.

The Sahtan overlies abruptly and disconformably buff-weathering peritidal dolostones of the Mahil Formation. The lower portion of the Sahtan at Wadi Sahtan consists of about 200 m of variably bioclastic, oolitic, peloidal, intraclastic and quartz-sandy wackestone, packstone and grainstone, interbedded in the lower part with quartz sandstone. Bioclasts include echinoderms, foraminifera, brachiopods, bivalves and gastropods. *Lithiotis* bivalve accumulations (Fig. 4A) also occur at scattered horizons in the lower 100 m. This unit is overlain by about 50 m of nodular-bedded argillaceous lime mudstone, which is in turn overlain by about 170 m of interbedded, medium- to thick-bedded and massive lime mudstone and bioclastic, peloidal and oolitic wackestone, packstone, grainstone and rudstone; bioclasts include fragments of corals and stromatoporoids. Bioturbation is common throughout (Fig. 4B).

The Sahtan is somewhat different at Wadi Laasi on the western side of Jebel Nakhl where the *Lithiotis* — bearing sequence is again about 100 m thick — but is overlain by 25 m of lime mudstone and packstone containing radiolaria, peloids and other small bioclasts. On the eastern flank of Jebel Nakhl, to the west of the village of Fanjah, a linear contact striking NNE−SSW is visible for 10 km. At this contact, thin- and medium-bedded limestones of the Saih Hatat Formation on the eastern side rest with angular

unconformity on dolostones of the Triassic Mahil Formation on the western side (Fig. 5).

Cretaceous. The Rayda Formation, with its distinctive light-grey colour, overlies the Sahtan abruptly and disconformably at all locations (Fig. 6). It varies in thickness from about 30 m at Wadi Laasi to 83 m at Wadi Sahtan to the west; it is 63 m thick at Wadi Mi'aidin, 74 m thick at Wadi Bani Kharus and 37 m at Wadi Nakhr. The upper boundary with the Salil Formation is gradational. In the wadis along the northern flank of Jebel Akhdar there is also a thin unit of argillaceous limestone resembling the Salil interbedded near the top of the Rayda.

The Rayda consists of thin-bedded cherty lime mudstone to wackestone and rarely packstone containing pelagic microfossils including radiolaria and calpionellids, with echinoderm fragments, foraminifera and belemnites occurring locally. The lime mudstone appears vaguely pelleted in thin section. The amount of argillaceous material is characteristically very low, although thin shaly interbeds are present and exhibit ripple cross lamination and parallel lamination. Fine-grained grainstone interbeds composed of peloids and echinoderm fragments occur in the basal two metres at Wadi Bani Kharus, and a thin, recrystallized conglomerate occurs at the same level in Wadi Mi'aidin. *In situ* benthic fossils are absent, although bioturbation in the form of *Thalassinoides* and *Rhizocorallium* burrow systems is common (Fig. 6E). Networks of these burrows are synsedimentarily stretched in a NNE/SSW direction at Wadi Bani Kharus (Fig. 6D). Large *Arenicolites* burrows occur in the argillaceous unit in the upper Rayda.

Fig. 5. View looking S at the northeastern side of Jebel Nakhl, west of the village of Fanjah, showing E-dipping slope strata of the Saih Hatat Formation (Jurassic) on the left, resting against a NNE−SSW-trending palaeoscarp (shown by lines) on N-dipping Mahil Formation (Triassic) on the right.

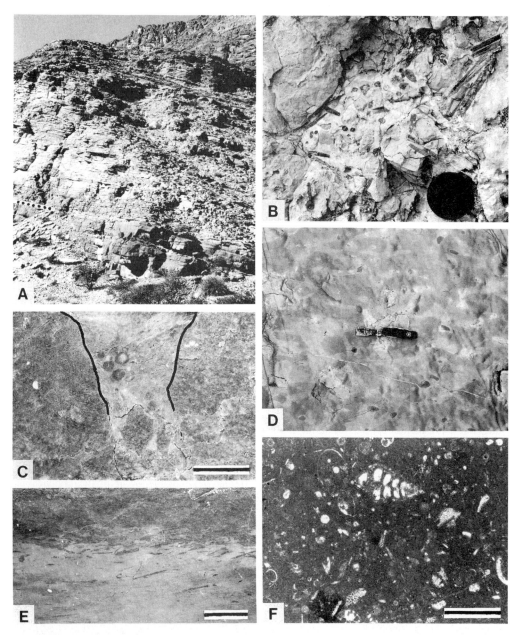

Fig. 6. Rayda Formation facies. A, Section at Wadi Bani Kharus showing dark-coloured, thick-bedded limestones of the Sahtan Group sharply overlain (contact marked by dotted line) by light-coloured, thin-bedded limestones of the Rayda which grade upwards into the Salil Formation. B, Bedding plane showing pits in upper surface of Sahtan containing a lag of bioeroded belemnite rostra. Jebel Madar; lens cap is 6 cm across. C, Sahtan-Rayda contact showing E−W-oriented vertical fissure (partly outlined by black lines) in Sahtan containing belemnite rostra. North end of Wadi Dayqa; scale bar is 5 cm. D, Bedding plane showing *Thalassinoides* burrows synsedimentarily stretched in a NNE−SSW direction. Wadi Bani Kharus; pocket knife is 9 cm long. E, Lime mudstone-grainstone contact exhibiting grainstone-filled *Rhizocorallium* burrows. Wadi Bani Kharus; scale bar is 5 cm. F, Thin section photomicrograph of radiolarian wackestone containing foraminifer, small echinoderm fragments and other microbioclasts. Jebel Madar; scale bar is 0.5 mm.

The overlying Salil Formation also exhibits variation in thickness: 485 m at Wadi Sahtan, 330 m at Wadi Mi'aidin, 295 m at Wadi Bani Kharus and >275 m at Wadi Nakhr. The section at Wadi Laasi is faulted, so while the Salil is >525 m thick there, this includes strata as young as Barremian, on the basis of transported orbitolinids present throughout most of the sequence. Probably about 100 m of the basal Salil is equivalent in age to the Salil and Habshan formations as recognized further west along the north flank of Jebel Akhdar. This is supported by the presence of oolitic grainstones and wackestones over the interval 70−90 m above the base; these grains were probably transported from oolite shoals of the Habshan Formation lying to the southwest.

The Salil is largely composed of thin- to medium-bedded and locally wavy- and nodular-bedded, argillaceous lime mudstones (Fig. 7A),

with interbedded calcareous shale, rare fine-grained peloidal grainstone, and bioclastic wackestones and packstones toward the top. Radiolaria are most abundant in the lower part. Burrowed horizons are common and *Thalassinoides, Chondrites, Taenidium, Arenicolites* and *Diplocraterion* have been recognized (Fig. 7B,C). The upper half of the Salil differs somewhat at Wadi Nakhr where it consists of thick-bedded, sparsely bioclastic lime mudstone containing scattered whole echinoids (Fig. 7D).

The base of the overlying Habshan Formation is gradational and is marked by the first appearance of thick oolitic grainstone and packstone. At Wadi Mi'aidin we therefore place it 18 m higher than the position selected by Simmons & Hart (1987, figs 7 & 10). The upper boundary with the Lekhwair Formation is drawn at the change to lime mudstone and bioclastic, but not oolitic, wackestone and packstone. Thick-

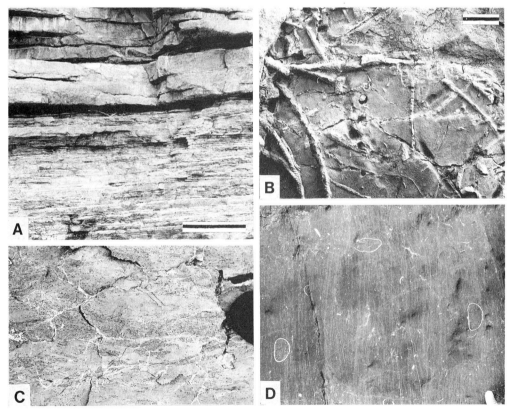

Fig. 7. Salil Formation facies. A, Outcrop of thin- and medium-bedded argillaceous lime mudstone. Lower Salil, Wadi Nakhr; scale bar is 0.5 m. B, Underside of lime mudstone bed showing hyporeliefs of *Taenidium, Planolites* and *Arenicolites* burrows. Lower Salil, Wadi Mi'aidin; scale bar is 5 cm. C, Bioturbated oolitic/pisolitic packstone showing ill-defined *Rhizocorallium* and *Thalassinoides* burrows. Uppermost Salil, Wadi Bani Kharus; lens cap is 6 cm across. D, Lime mudstone containing whole echinoids. Upper Salil, Wadi Nakhr; lens cap is 6 cm across.

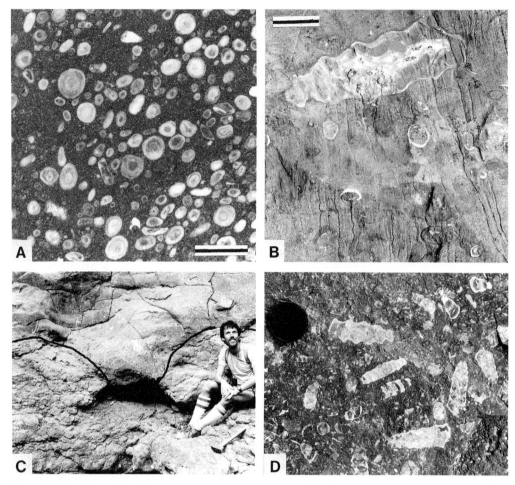

Fig. 8. Habshan Formation facies. A, Polished slab of oolitic/pisolitic grainstone. Wadi Bani Kharus; scale bar is 1 cm. B, Fossiliferous, oncolitic and oolitic grainstone. Wadi Bani Kharus; scale bar is 5 cm. C, Outcrop of patch reefs with chondrodont bivalve-bearing rudstone in hollow between two bioherms (outlined by black line). Wadi Nakhr; scale is JDS. D, Bedding plane view of nerineid gastropod rudstone. Wadi Nakhr; lens cap is 6 cm across.

ness of the Habshan varies from 85 m at Wadi Mi'aidin, 75 m at Wadi Sahtan, and 70 m at Wadis Nakhr and Bani Kharus.

The Habshan consists dominantly of locally cross-stratified, oolitic, oncolitic, peloidal and bioclastic grainstones (Fig. 8B), and packstone where bioturbated. Some ooids, especially at Wadi Bani Kharus where grainstones are best developed, are large enough to be termed pisoids (Fig. 8A). Bioclasts are large and include corals, stromatoporoids, echinoderm debris, gastropods (Fig. 8D), and rudistids and other bivalves. Small sub-metre-sized microbial-coral boundstone knobs occur locally at Wadi Bani Kharus. A 4 m thick microbial-coral-

stromatoporoid patch reef complex formed by bioherms 1–2 m across, separated by grainstones and rudistid and chondrodont bivalve-bearing rudstones, occurs in the upper part of the Habshan at Wadi Nakhr (Fig. 8C).

Sedimentary environments. The Lower Jurassic part of the Sahtan Group in Jebel Akhdar records relatively shallow-water conditions on a mixed carbonate-siliciclastic platform on which a variety of lithologies were deposited. The argillaceous lime mudstone character of the overlying mid-Jurassic portion suggests a tranquil and stable subtidal environment. It is not certain whether this was leeward of a shallow-water barrier to the north, or a deep shelf open to the ocean but somehow protected. The succeeding, commonly oolitic lithologies record a return to a shallow-water regime, but free from siliciclastic input.

Following erosion of the underlying Sahtan, the Rayda was deposited in deep water by pelagic fallout, much of it in the form of faecal pellets (cf. Hattin 1975), without significant periplatform input except as rare grain and debris flows and argillaceous interbeds. Stretched *Thalassinoides* burrow systems suggest slight mass movement before lithification in a northward direction. The Salil, by contrast, is composed of both pelagic and hemipelagic sediment, which is reflected in the proportion of peloidal grainstone and argillaceous material. No slump features were observed in Jebel Akhdar, but a gentle, relatively deep slope environment is likely.

The Habshan Formation records the northward progradation of high-energy ooid shoals which did not reach as far as Wadi Laasi until much later, in the Barremian−Aptian. Associated with these shoals were nearby shallow-water areas that supported a thriving shelly benthos and local patch reefs.

Saih Hatat

The Jurassic and Lower Cretaceous sequence was examined at seven sites on the west, north and south sides of the Saih Hatat massif. Preservation of petrographic detail is generally poor because of tectonically induced recrystallization and, locally, cleavage from ophiolite obduction.

Sections on Saih Hatat show a relatively deep-water, slope sequence of Middle and Late Jurassic age overlying the typical shallow-water, mixed carbonate-siliciclastic deposits of the Lower Jurassic. We formally term this deepwater unit the Saih Hatat Formation. The type section is designated at Wadi Qurr off Wadi Tayin on the south side of Saih Hatat where it is the least disturbed tectonically (see Appendix). *Jurassic.* The Early Jurassic portion of the undivided Sahtan Group was observed at Wadi Hanjouriyah in western Saih Hatat where it is about 200 m thick. It consists of interbedded thin-bedded sandstone, limestones and scattered dolostones in the lower 150 m and medium- to thick-bedded limestones in the upper 50 m. Limestones range from lime mudstone to grainstone. They are locally sandy and argillaceous in the lower part, as well as variably peloidal, bioclastic, oolitic and intraclastic; bioturbation is common and accumulations of *Lithiotis* valves occur throughout. Overlying

strata of the Saih Hatat Formation are in fault contact in Wadi Hanjourijah. At Wadi Qurr, however, the uppermost beds of the undivided Sahtan are medium-bedded oolitic, bioclastic, intraclastic and peloidal grainstones (Fig. 4C). Bioclasts include foraminifera and abraded fragments of sponges, calcareous algae, stromatoporoids and molluscs.

The overlying Saih Hatat Formation at Wadi Qurr consists of 200 m of dominantly dark-coloured, thin- to medium-bedded argillaceous lime mudstone, shale and fine-grained peloidal and bioclastic grainstones (Fig. 4D). Parallel lamination, lenticular bedding and grading are common in the grainstones; shaliness and amount of bioturbation are variable. Bioclasts include radiolaria (Fig. 4E) and miliolid foraminifera, with a bed containing corals, bivalves and gastropods near the top. At Wadis Saal and Nujum in western Saih Hatat, similar strata are about 300 m thick and exhibit local slump folding. Poorly sorted conglomerates near the top contain subangular clasts, up to 20 cm across, of radiolarian lime mudstone, oolitic grainstone, and dolostone from the Mahil Formation. This sequence is overlain by 50 m of graded quartz sandstones with conglomeratic bases, followed by about 50 m of fine-grained intraclastic grainstones and conglomerates. Conglomerates in the upper 100 m contain sandstone clasts in addition to types similar to those in the older conglomerates. The rest of this sequence has been cut out by thrust faulting.

At Wadi Qurr, however, the Saih Hatat Formation is overlain by 30 m of thick-bedded oolitic and intraclastic grainstone of the undivided Sahtan Group. At Wadi Mijlas, at the north end of Wadi Dayqa and at a small unnamed wadi south of Quryat, the uppermost Jurassic unit is a thick-bedded, coarsely recrystallized limestone which lies above thin-bedded more finely crystalline strata. The coarser beds probably had an original grainstone composition. We observed a microbial-coral-stromatoporoid boundstone unit (Fig. 4F) at about the same level between Wadi Qurr and the south end of Wadi Dayqa.

Cretaceous. The Rayda Formation is recrystallized at all Saih Hatat localities, but is still easily recognizable on the basis of its distinctive light-grey colour, the presence of chert nodules, and, in thin section, radiolaria and small ammonites. *Rhizocorallium* and *Chondrites* burrows were observed at scattered horizons. A 3 m thick conglomerate bed composed of rounded tabular and equant clasts up to 3 cm across occurs 10 m above the base of the Rayda at Wadi Mijlas. The formation varies considerably in thickness:

7 m south of Quryat, 17 m at the north end of Wadi Dayqa, 36 m at Wadi Mijlas, and 43 m at Wadi Qurr. Its lower contact is abrupt and the underlying surface of the Sahtan exhibits evidence of erosion, such as at the north end of Wadi Dayqa where there are 10 cm deep, E−W oriented, straight-sided, tapering fissures containing belemnite rostra (Fig. 6C).

The upper contact with the Salil Formation is gradational and is marked by a reduction in the amount of chert and an increase in the argillaceous content giving the rocks a significantly darker colour. At all exposures examined in Saih Hatat, Salil lithologies persist well into the Albian, as indicated by the presence of distinctive orbitolinid foraminifera (M. D. Simmons, pers. comm.) The Berriasian and Valanginian portion is no more than about 75 m thick. The dominant lithology is thin- and medium-bedded, radiolarian-rich, argillaceous lime mudstone with numerous interbeds of fine peloidal grainstone, scattered lenticular beds of matrix-supported, normally graded lithoclastic conglomerates with grainstone matrix, and one intraformational conglomerate.

Sedimentary environments. The Early Jurassic portion of the Mesozoic sequence at Saih Hatat is similar to that of Jebel Akhdar and is thus indicative of a shallow platform regime differentiated into a variety of subenvironments ranging from peritidal to shallow subtidal, both low- and relatively high-energy. Younger strata comprising the Saih Hatat Formation, however, exhibit abundant evidence, such as slumps, grading, conglomerates, thin bedding, argillaceous content, radiolaria, and relatively rare bioturbation, of having been deposited in a tranquil, moderately deep-water slope environment. Sediment source was thus both pelagic and shelf-derived and deposited by grain and debris flows and turbidity currents. Water depth was below storm wave base because of the lack of sedimentary structures generated by bottom-impinging storms. A depth of between about 100−200 m may therefore be estimated, assuming an ocean-facing slope. The uppermost Jurassic strata indicate a return to shallow-water, high-energy conditions, resulting in the formation of reefs and deposition of bioclastic and oolitic grainstones.

The overlying Rayda Formation again records a deep, tranquil environment but dominated by pelagic deposition punctuated rarely by debris flows. The more heterogeneous and argillaceous Salil above reflects a greater influx of sediment derived from shallow water and transported down-slope by turbidity currents and debris flows.

Southern foothills

Two sections relevant to this study were measured in the foothills to the south of Saih Hatat, on the north side of Jebel Madar and on Jebel Ghareeb, 20 km northwest of Al Mintirib. Only part of the Habshan Formation is exposed at the latter locality, whereas the Jurassic-Cretaceous section is complete at Jebel Madar, a collapsed domal feature caused by salt movement.

Jurassic. The Sahtan Group is 69 m thick and consists of medium- to thickly interbedded quartz sandstones, variably silty and sandy bioclastic, oolitic and peloidal grainstones, and local nodular-bedded, argillaceous lime mudstone. The uppermost unit is 3 m of thin bedded lime mudstone interbedded with oolitic, peloidal and oncolitic grainstone. Sedimentary structures in the sandstones include hummocky cross-stratification and common burrows; *Lithiotis* valves and oysters are common in the lower and upper parts, respectively. Smaller bioclasts include foraminifera and calcareous algae, echinoderm, bivalve and gastropod fragments. The upper surface of the topmost Sahtan bed exhibits 5 cm deep pits and is locally pyritized.

Cretaceous. The Rayda Formation is about 40 m thick. Its basal bed contains a lag of abundant macrobored belemnite rostra and glauconitized radiolarian lime mudstone which fill the small depressions in the underlying Sahtan (Fig. 6B). The Rayda consists of clean, light-coloured lime mudstone to rare wackestone and packstone with radiolaria, foraminifera, calpionellids and echinoderm debris (Fig. 6F). It grades upward into argillaceous lime mudstone of the Salil Formation. The Salil at Jebel Madar is 110 m thick and is thin- and locally wavy- and nodular-bedded, with scattered bioturbated horizons and rare bioclastic wackestone and grainstone beds containing peloids, bivalves, gastropods, benthic foraminifera and echinoderm debris.

The Habshan Formation gradationally overlies the Salil and is 67 m thick at Jebel Madar. The upper contact with the Lekhwair Formation is defined by the lithologic change to massive bioturbated peloidal and bioclastic packstone and wackestone containing requienied rudistids. The Habshan is >55 m thick at Al Mintirib but its lower contact is not exposed and the upper boundary is faulted out.

The lower 13 m of the Habshan at Jebel Madar consists of medium-bedded, moderately well sorted bioclastic grainstone with scattered herringbone cross-lamination, *Thalassinoides* burrows and oncolites. This is succeeded by 16 m of thick-bedded, variably bioclastic and oncolitic oolitic grainstones and rudstones with scattered interbeds of bioclastic and peloidal grainstone and rare bioturbated packstone. Small microbial-coral boundstone knobs occur locally within oolitic grainstone. Unidirectional and herringbone cross-lamination give N−S current directions. The succeeding unit is an 11 m thick complex of microbial-stromatoporoid patch reefs with flanking thin- and medium-bedded, cross-laminated bioclastic, oncolitic and oolitic grainstone and rudstone containing boundstone fragments, oysters and chondrodonts. Some of these metre-sized patch reefs are elongated in a N−S direction and also coalesce into wider banks. The reef complex is overlain by 27 m of inter-bedded, medium- to thick-bedded bioclastic and peloidal grainstones and rudstones with scattered *Thalassinoides* burrows. Large fossils include oysters, gastropods, rudistids and stromatoporoids.

The Habshan at Jebel Ghareeb is similar, with a lower part consisting of rudstones containing corals, stromatoporoids and small microbial patch reefs, and an upper part consisting of locally channelized bioclastic and intra-clastic grainstones and rudstones containing corals and caprinid and caprotinid rudists. A chondrodont-bearing wackestone occurs at the top of the Habshan.

Sedimentary environments. The Sahtan and Kahmah Groups are similar to the sequence in Jebel Akhdar although most of the Jurassic has been removed by erosion prior to deposition of the Rayda Formation (Fig. 9). The heterogeneous Early Jurassic facies were deposited in a variety of shallow-water environments. The pelagic Rayda and overlying pelagic and hemipelagic Salil record a major change in water depth, probably in the neighbourhood of 100−200 m based on the absence of large-scale traction structures associated with storm activity. The Habshan represents a high-energy complex of oolitic shoals and patch reefs.

Other areas

Subsurface of Oman and United Arab Emirates. The Jurassic of the United Arab Emirates and the western interior of Oman consists mostly of shallow-water limestones, dolostones and anhydrite which are often cyclically arranged (e.g. Powers *et al.* 1966; Wood & Wolfe 1969; Murris 1980; Ayres *et al.* 1982; Wilson 1985; Alsharhan & Kendall, 1986; Hughes Clarke 1988). These sediments record the evolution of the platform from largely siliciclastic in the

Triassic into a broad, carbonate-depositing epeiric sea by the Bathonian. During the late Oxfordian to early Kimmeridgian, a large intra-shelf basin developed which, by the Tithonian, had shallowed and was the site of widespread evaporite deposition, giving rise to anhydrite of the Hith Formation. The Hith is an important sealing unit for older Jurassic reservoirs (Murris 1980; Alsharhan & Kendall 1986), although it is absent in southeast Abu Dhabi.

The Rayda Formation is only present east of the Asab field in Abu Dhabi, with an approximately N−S-trending facies boundary (Hassan *et al.* 1975), and north of about 22°N (Hughes Clarke 1988). The Rayda is 45 m thick in the Sajaa Field of Sharjah (Connally & Scott 1985), whereas to the southeast, in the Lekhwair Field of Oman, it is 55 m thick (Hughes Clarke 1988).

The younger Salil Formation is present over a similar area as the Rayda. It is about 180 m thick in the Sajaa Field (Connally & Scott 1985) and 255 m thick in the Lekhwair Field (Hughes Clarke 1988). The overlying Habshan Formation, which has a slightly greater distribution but not south of about 21°N (Hughes Clarke 1988), ranges from 150 m in the Sajaa Field to 173 m in the Lekhwair Field, but is reported to be some 300 m thick in the western Emirates (Hassan *et al.* 1975).

Musandam Peninsula. Jurassic and Early Cretaceous shallow platform sequences reach their maximum thickness on the Musandam Peninsula, between 1300 m (Hudson & Chatton 1959; Allemann & Peters 1972) and 1450 m (Ricateau & Riche 1980). These carbonates, comprising the Musandam Group, are underlain by the Hagab thrust and are therefore allochthonous, having moved westward a minimum distance of 5 km (Searle *et al.* 1983).

The Musandam Group rests conformably on fossiliferous, shallow-marine sandstones and sandy limestones of the Elphinstone Group. Because the detailed lithologic character of the Musandam has mostly not been determined, the six informal members recognized in the Jurassic portion cannot be correlated precisely with the Sahtan Group further south. Based on the sections at Jebel Hagab and between Wadi Sidakh and Habhab just north of the northern margin of the Dibba Zone, it consists, in general, of a shallow-water sequence composed mainly of thin- to thick-bedded lime mudstone, wackestone, scattered grainstones, and is locally bioclastic, peloidal and oolitic, and commonly bioturbated. Intervals with shaly interbeds occur at several levels, which suggest phases of slightly deeper, more tranquil conditions.

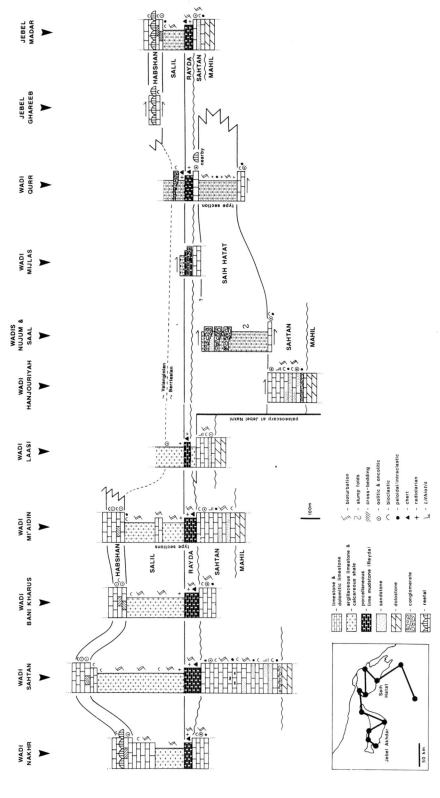

Fig. 9. Stratigraphic cross section showing correlation of principal measured sections. Datum is top of Rayda Formation.

The Jurassic a few kilometres to the south along the northern margin of the Dibba Zone forms a narrow, NE–SW-trending facies belt composed of cross-bedded oolitic and peloidal grainstones and coral-bearing boundstone (Searle *et al*. 1983). These pass southward into a 1 km wide zone of 10°-dipping talus beds consisting of large limestone blocks and conglomerate with finer interbeds; clasts are derived from adjacent Musandam Group strata. This talus grades abruptly into non-bioturbated argillaceous lime mudstone of the Mayhah Formation which exhibits local debris flow conglomerates and synsedimentary truncation surfaces. These sediments can be seen in places to overlie unconformably Upper Triassic reef boundstones. Coeval deeper water strata of the Guweyza Limestone Formation exposed in thrust slices in this area consist of abundant thick beds of oolitic grainstone in reconstructed proximal settings and silicified lime mudstone in distal areas (Cooper 1987).

The disconformably overlying Berriasian–Hauterivian part of the Early Cretaceous reaches some 350 m in thickness on the Musandam Peninsula. According to Hudson & Chatton (1959) and Allemann & Peters (1972) who have provided the more detailed observations, the lower 60 m (Ashhab Limestone) consists of interbedded debris flow conglomerates and locally argillaceous, cherty lime mudstone containing calpionellid tests, radiolaria and foraminifera. This unit is correlative with the Rayda Formation. It is overlain by 240 m of lime mudstone, similar to that of the Salil Formation, which is thin- and medium-bedded in the lower part, becoming thick-bedded and massive in the upper. These rocks are succeeded by thick-bedded bioclastic, oolitic, peloidal and intraclastic limestones probably equivalent to the Habshan Formation.

The Early Cretaceous in the Dibba Zone consists of 'porcellaneous' lime mudstone containing pelagic microfossils and intraformational debris-flow conglomerates, overlain by several hundred metres of bioturbated, argillaceous lime mudstone with slumped horizons. These are succeeded by bioclastic limestones of shallow-water aspect (Searle *et al*. 1983), indicating some basinward progradation of Habshan facies. The corresponding Hawasina Basin deposits of the Sid'r Formation in this area are silicified, turbiditic radiolarian wackestone with interbedded debris-flow conglomerates (Cooper 1987).

Sumeini slope and Hawasina Basin. Jurassic and Early Cretaceous deep-water sediments, deposited on the continental slope and in the adjacent Hawasina Basin, occur as thrust-bounded, imbricate slices and nappes in a number of places in the Oman Mountains south of the Dibba Zone (Glennie *et al*. 1974; Watts & Garrison 1986; Cooper 1987; Blendinger 1988).

Slope sediments of the Sumeini Group have been studied in detail at Jebel Sumeini (Watts & Garrison 1986). In the western part of the jebel, these sediments unconformably overlie Upper Triassic reef boundstones. The Jurassic part at the north end of the jebel, the A member of the Mayhah Formation, consists of about 400 m of lime mudstone and subordinate fine-grained peloidal grainstone and interbedded lenses of oolitic grainstone and debris-flow conglomerates composed of mixed shallow-water and intraformational clasts. At a section nearly 15 km to the southeast, conglomerates and oolitic grainstones are markedly rarer. Coeval basinal sediments of the Hamrat Duru Group in the same area consist of a thin Guweyza Sandstone Formation and overlying limestones similar to the Sumeini Group but lacking conglomerates and containing bioclastic grainstone in the upper part (Cooper 1987). Watts & Garrison (1986) interpreted the Sumeini in the southern section as an upper bypass slope where coarse sediment was transported northward down gullies to accrete as a lower slope prism. We believe, however, that the evidence for a bypass slope model and its implied steep dip is insufficient, and that the coarser nature of the northern section supports a proximal setting for these deposits on a slope of more moderate dip (cf. James & Stevens 1987). An approximately north-to-south, down-slope sediment transport direction agrees better with regional palaeogeographic considerations discussed later in this paper.

The Guweyza Sandstone Formation at its type section on Hamrat ad Duru southwest of Jebel Akhdar is 200 m of quartz-bearing grainstone turbidites (Cooper 1987). This unit thins and becomes shalier to the northwest of Jebel Akhdar, which indicates a generally southern source for detrital siliciclastic sediment. The overlying Guweyza Limestone Formation at its type section on Hamrat ad Duru is 200 m thick and is composed of thick-bedded oolitic grainstone with subordinate turbiditic lime mudstone and wackestone. It too is shalier to the northwest. Lower Cretaceous deep-water deposits of the Sid'r Formation in proximal thrust imbricates consist largely of silicified radiolarian wackestone with shaly partings. More distal lithologies are radiolarian cherts (Cooper 1987).

The Early Cretaceous part of the Sumeini Group at Jebel Sumeini is characterized by a horizon of radiolarian chert erosively overlain by a massive megabreccia about 200 m thick, which has been interpreted as resulting from disintegration of the nearby platform margin (Watts & Garrison 1986). We regard this unit, however, as a mid-Cretaceous synorogenic deposit.

Evolution of the platform margin

The general understanding of the formation of the Mesozoic passive margin in the Oman area is well established. The presence of Permo-Triassic seamounts and basinal strata of the Hamrat Duru Group containing volcanics and Late Permian fossils indicate that rifting was under way by this time (Glennie *et al.* 1974; Searle & Graham 1982; Blendinger 1988). The zig-zag configuration of the Jurassic and Lower Cretaceous shelf margin which we plot in this paper (Fig. 10) refines that shown by Glennie *et al.* (1974, fig. 8.5.5). We also project it southwestward along the Masirah Line since

this lineament separates continental from oceanic crust (Moseley 1969). The morphology imparted by the Musandam and Masirah promontories must have been primarily inherited from the series of rift and transform segments generated by continental separation in the Early Jurassic and locally reactivated in the mid-Jurassic. It subsequently influenced the style of tectonic deformation when the passive margin turned into an active margin.

Sedimentary history

Early Jurassic. The Early Jurassic along the Oman Mountains and adjacent subsurface was a time of shallow-water, mixed siliciclastic-carbonate sedimentation. Corresponding Hawasina basinal deposits consisted of sandy limestone turbidites which grade distally to shales (Cooper 1987). Siliciclastic material was derived from the south, which accounts for the lower proportion of quartz in the lower part of the Musandam Group. The shelf margin pre-

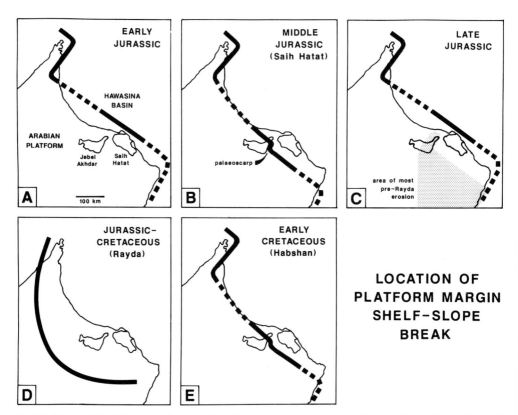

Fig. 10. Maps of the NE corner of the Arabian Platform showing the successive location of the shelf margin during the Jurassic and Early Cretaceous. Because of the lack of outcrop between Jebel Akhdar and the Musandam Peninsula, we show the margin as being straight. In reality it probably also exhibited smaller offsets as postulated by Cooper (1989, Fig. 14).

sumably lay somewhere along the northeast coast of northern Oman, except for a postulated northeastward offset along the Dibba Zone (Fig. 10A). Deep-water limestones overlying Upper Triassic reef limestones in both the Dibba Zone and Jebel Sumeini suggest down-to-basin faulting in these areas during the Early or mid-Jurassic.

Mid-Jurassic. Shallow-water conditions persisted in the Jebel Akhdar and Musandam Peninsula areas, shedding oolitic turbidites into the Hawasina Basin, while peritidal and evaporitic sediments accumulated in the interior of the Arabian Platform. The platform margin appears to have been more or less in a stable location to the northeast of both Jebel Akhdar and the Musandam Peninsula, with the offset along the Dibba Zone. This indicates that the regional palaeogeographic reconstruction presented by Murris (1980, fig. 12) requires revision in the Oman area because it shows the continental slope having advanced over the older platform edge as far as the United Arab Emirates.

On the other hand, deep-water argillaceous limestones, containing debris flow conglomerates and slump structures, overlying shallow-water limestones on Saih Hatat indicate that the mid-Jurassic shelf was drowned in this area, forming an ocean-facing embayment (Fig. 10B). The exact location of the new shelf edge shoals is not certain because the Upper Jurassic sequence has been stripped off at Jebel Madar, but the retreat must have been in the order of 100 km. This drowning event was accompanied by synsedimentary normal faulting along the eastern edge of Jebel Akhdar, such that deep-water slope rocks of the Saih Hatat Formation onlap against a NNE-SSW-trending palaeoscarp and contain lithoclasts eroded from it (Fig. 11). Section correlation (Figs. 9 & 11) suggests the fault had a total syndepositional throw of about 600 m. This episode of faulting probably caused most of the relative sea level rise in the Saih Hatat area, because subsidence rate changes on passive margins are normally accommodated by carbonate deposition (Schlager, 1980). In addition, the palaeogeographic location of the Saih Hatat area on an exposed promontory may have rendered it prone to inhibiting hydrographic factors of the open ocean, such as upwelling of cold water. The lack of Jurassic deposits on the offshore seamounts (Searle & Graham 1982) indicates that these isolated platforms were drowned and therefore exerted negligible control on the regional oceanography affecting the platform margin.

Late Jurassic. During the Late Jurassic the margin prograded rapidly to a position along the southern flank of Saih Hatat (Fig. 10C), as indicated by the occurrence there of shoal-water grainstones and reefs.

Flexure of the Jurassic shelf during subsidence but prior to deposition of the Rayda Formation resulted in a planing off of the Middle and Upper Jurassic mostly along eastern Jebel Akhdar and southeastward towards the Huqf axis (Fig. 10C). For diagrammatic purposes (Fig. 11) we show this by means of a series of vertical faults, but the real geometry of structures associated with this tilting and erosional phase is unknown; it does not appear that the mid-Jurassic palaeoscarp was reactivated. The destination of the eroded limestone is unknown, since concomitant basinal deposits, at least those obducted in the Jebel Akhdar region, do not exhibit unusually conglomeratic intervals. This suggests that erosion was mainly subaerial and involved principally dissolution during karstification. Admittedly, however, Late Jurassic Hamrat Duru rocks have not been described from the eastern Oman Mountains which would have been in the right downslope position seaward of where the maximum erosion had taken place. The cause of the flexure is uncertain, but it may be related to salt movement in salt basins which underlie this area (for location see Gorin *et al.* 1982; Hughes Clarke 1988).

Jurassic–Cretaceous (Rayda Formation). Pelagic lime mudstone of the Rayda Formation sharply overlies eroded Jurassic strata in all areas east of the eastern United Arab Emirates and north of about 22°N latitude. Thus the latest Jurassic–earliest Cretaceous platform margin had again retreated, with a drowned shelf on the oceanward side forming a broad embayment across northern Oman (Fig. 10D). We believe that (1) retreat of the shelf margin, (2) development of regionally evaporitic conditions on the Arabian Platform, and (3) deposition of these pelagic limestones are interrelated phenomena.

Channelized debris flow conglomerates and stretched burrows in the lower Rayda indicate deposition on a gentle slope, NNE-dipping along Jebel Akhdar. Variations, more or less on strike, in thickness of the Rayda suggest that the underlying Jurassic depositional surface was not entirely planar. That it was a surface of protracted non-deposition after erosion, however, is demonstrated by the abruptness of the contact and presence of belemnite lags.

Connally & Scott (1985) argued that the Rayda was deposited during a time when the ocean's oxygen-minimum layer advanced onto the drowned shelf and the sediment surface was anaerobic to dysaerobic, either because of rela-

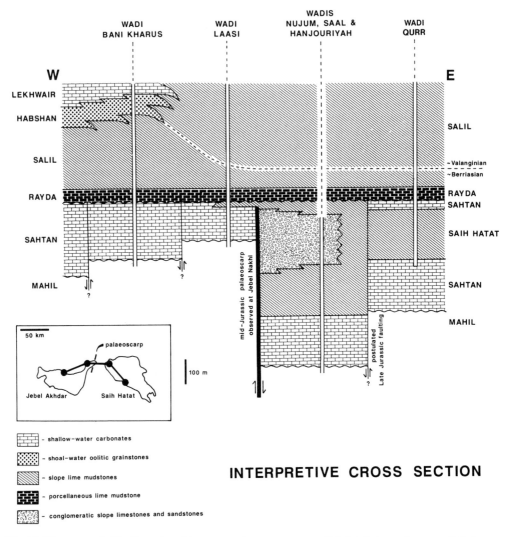

Fig. 11. Diagrammatic W−E stratigraphic cross section across eastern Jebel Akhdar and western Saih Hatat. Datum is Rayda Formation (shown as having constant thickness); dotted line in Salil Formation represents an approximate Berriasian-Valanginian time line. The exact dip of the mid-Jurassic normal fault at Jebel Nakhl is unknown. Faults affecting the pre-Rayda sequence are postulated on the basis of the upwarping that caused differential downcutting.

tive deepening or because of secular climatic variation. Their evidence for this interpretation is the rarity of benthic shelly fossils and bioturbation in the Rayda. A scarcity of skeletonized benthic organisms is a common feature in many other Phanerozoic deeper water sediments, including the overlying Salil Formation, in which there is no firm, independent evidence for dysaerobic or anaerobic conditions. Bottom dwelling communities are governed also by environmental factors such as geotechnical

properties of the sediment, light intensity, nutrient availability and so on. Furthermore, our observations of the Rayda where it is well preserved in wadi exposures of Jebel Akhdar, reveal an abundant, if low-diversity, trace fossil fauna indicative of somewhat cohesive substrates in contact with oxic seawater. The reasons why the Rayda is not totally bioturbated may be related to a low sedimentation rate and continued occupation of pre-existing *Thalassinoides* galleries rather than excavation of new ones by successive filter-feeding burrower generations.

The presence of pelagic fossils and probable faecal pellets making up the bulk of the Rayda indicate that productivity of the overlying water column was high, yet the organic content of these rocks is low. Bottom-oxidizing conditions must be invoked to account for organic decomposition as well as the scarcity of pyrite. These observations negate the possibility of salinity stratification of the drowned Rayda shelf, which might be suspected on the basis of the purported relationship (Fig. 3) with the Hith anhydrite of the platform interior.

Nevertheless, we believe that the Hith and Rayda are contemporaneous deposits because development of extensive evaporitic conditions on the Arabian Platform provides a plausible mechanism for causing a regional drowning event not associated with synsedimentary faulting, by restricting the carbonate sediment generating capacity of the platform on a regional scale. As carbonate production decreased, the shelf edge would have been sucked landward, leaving an extensive drowned platform receiving little shallow-water sediment. Thus, while the Rayda Formation shows a relative sea level rise in Oman, in reality there is no evidence that sea level fluctuated significantly over the rest of the Arabian Platform. Unfortunately, owing to imprecise biostratigraphic data, it is difficult to correlate the Rayda with currently recognized eustatic sea level curves (Haq *et al.* 1988; see also Scott *et al.* 1988, fig. 1), but it illustrates the danger of using such stratigraphic units out of context as evidence for sea level change.

Deeper slope and basinal deposits consist of silicified radiolarian wackestone and grainstone, with radiolarian chert in more distal areas, which led Watts & Garrison (1986) and Cooper (1987) to suggest that deposition of the Rayda and equivalent Sid'r Formations and B member of the Mayhah Formation coincided with a relative rise in the carbonate compensation depth (CCD). Watts & Garrison (1986) proposed that continued subsidence of the continental margin resulted in the slope and basin moving below the CCD. Cooper (1987), by contrast, argued that the decrease in carbonate input caused elevation in the CCD. While this may have affected the deeper basinal deposits, we believe that water depth did not increase dramatically enough over the Rayda interval so that the CCD still did not impinge on the drowned shelf, slope and proximal part of the basin. It appears more reasonable to attribute the pervasive partial silicification of Sumeini and Hamrat Duru limestones to a simple decrease in carbonate

sedimentation rate along with greater proportion of mobile silica from radiolaria.

Early Cretaceous. The transition to the Salil Formation in Oman signalled an increase in the amount of hemipelagic carbonate, clay and organic material supplied to the slope, at the same time as high-energy oolitic shoal deposits of the Habshan Formation started to prograde eastward from the United Arab Emirates and northeastward from central Oman. We interpret this event as recording the evolution of the Arabian Platform from a dominantly evaporitic to a normal-marine, carbonate-generating regime. Progradation is interpreted as having been relatively rapid because of the paucity of oolitic and coarse bioclastic material present in all but the highest Salil sediments. The Habshan shoals reached a position just to the north of Jebel Akhdar during the Valanginian; Wadi Laasi on Jebel Nakhl marks a point just seaward of their limit until the Barremian-Aptian. The Lower Cretaceous platform margin was probably more or less in the same position as its Jurassic predecessor in front of the western and northern Oman Mountains (Fig. 10E). Progradation resulted in a renewed pulse of grainstone turbidites being shed into the Hawasina Basin. By contrast, however, reefal and oolitic shoals like those observed at Jebels Madar and Ghareeb did not prograde as far north as Saih Hatat, so that Salil slope lithologies continued to be deposited there until the Albian. There does not appear to have been synsedimentary faulting to maintain this embayment in its drowned state. Hydrographic factors, such as upwelling, related to its position as a promontory jutting out into Tethys, may have inhibited progradation in this area.

Tectonic effect

The competence contrasts afforded by the zig-zag-shaped platform margin and its major internal lithological differences clearly influenced the pattern of structural deformation during Late Cretaceous and Tertiary compression in Oman. This has already been shown by Searle *et al.* (1983) for the Dibba Zone, where thrust slices of oceanic sediments and ophiolites collided against and were deflected by a solid block of platform carbonate rocks. The Masirah Line must also represent a major lineament formed by the edge of the platform (Moseley 1969). The contrast between platform carbonates of Jebel Akhdar and the largely slope limestones in the upper part of the sedimentary pile in Saih Hatat appears to have presented a weakness exploited by lateral shearing during obduction, resulting in the formation of the Semail Gap, another of the more dramatic structural lineaments in the Oman Mountains.

Conclusions

Jurassic and Early Cretaceous sedimentary sequences at the edge of the Arabian Platform in the central Oman Mountains were deposited in a spectrum of environmental settings ranging from the shallow, low-energy shelf interior, through high energy shelf-margin ooid and reefal shoals, to a deeper, gently dipping slope. On a regional scale, the vertical and lateral distribution of these facies document major migration in the form of shelf margin progradation and retrogradation involving two drowning events. The first of these took place in the mid-Jurassic and may have been provoked by synsedimentary down-faulting of the shelf in the Saih Hatat area. The second drowning event, in the latest Jurassic and earliest Cretaceous, was more regional in extent and is represented by the Rayda Formation. It is interpreted to have been triggered by the development of evaporitic conditions over much of the Arabian Platform interior and resulting in deposition of the Hith Formation, which caused a decrease in the production of carbonate sediment and landward retreat of the shelf margin. Neither event can be ascribed to a eustatic sea level rise.

The Jurassic–Early Cretaceous platform margin in Oman trended in a NW–SE direction, with a series of SW–NE-striking offsets. This zig-zag configuration is interpreted to have been inherited from rift and transform segments gen-erated at the passive margin in the Early Jurassic. Some of these offsets were synsedimentarily reactivated during the mid-Jurassic. The geometry of the Mesozoic continental margin in Oman bears a striking resemblance to that reconstructed for the coast of Palaeozoic North America as a series of promontories and reentrants, generated by rift and transform segments, which left a permanent imprint on the continent even after subsequent tectonic deformation (Thomas 1983).

Field work for this study was funded by Amoco Oman Petroleum Co. through grants to the Earth Sciences and Resources Institute of the University of South Carolina. Permission to publish this manuscript by the Ministry of Petroleum and Minerals of Oman and Amoco Production Co. is gratefully acknowledged. We thank B. P. Clissold, M. Coniglio and K. F. Watts for aiding fieldwork. Various Amoco personnel, especially R. W. Scott and T. C. Connally, provided helpful early discussion of results. BRP thanks S. G. Pemberton and K. J. Hsü for discussion of trace fossil and tectonic aspects, respectively. A. C. Kendall and G. S. Nadon kindly suggested improvements to an earlier version of the manuscript.

Appendix

Type section of Saih Hatat Formation
Location: Wadi Qurr (23°05'N/58°33'E), 2 km north of Qurr, small village at the confluence with Wadi Tayin, south side of Saih Hatat.
Thickness: 207 m
Age: Late Early-Late Jurassic, i.e. mid-Jurassic (estimated; sequence lies above *Lithiotis* — bearing undivided Sahtan Group strata and below Rayda Formation, dated elsewhere as Tithonian–Berriasian.)
Lithologic log:

Unit	Description	Thickness (m) unit	total
	Rayda Formation		
	Lime mudstone and wackestone, thin-to medium-bedded, light-grey colour, common chert nodules, radiolaria	43	
	Sahtan Group (undivided)		
	Grainstone, thick-bedded, oolitic, peloidal, intraclastic	28	
	Saih Hatat Formation		
10	Lime mudstone, argillaceous, and packstone, medium-bedded, peloidal, radiolaria, miliolid foraminifera, mollusc and coral bioclasts at base	35	207
9	Shale, calcareous	5	172
8	Grainstone, medium-bedded, peloidal	6	167
7	Shale, calcareous, lime mudstone, argillaceous, and GRAINSTONE, thin-bedded, locally bioturbated *(Thalassinoides)*, peloidal, radiolaria, miliolid foraminifera	50	161
6	Lime mudstone and grainstone, medium- and lenticular-bedded, parallel-laminated, fine-grained, peloidal, intraclastic, radiolaria, miliolid foraminifera	30	111
5	Lime mudstone, argillaceous, and grainstone, thin- and lenticular-bedded, locally bioturbated *(Thalassinoides)*, peloidal, radiolaria, miliolid foraminifera	40	81

4	Grainstone, medium-bedded, fine-grained, peloidal, partly silicified	3	41
3	Lime mudstone, thin-bedded, locally bioturbated *(Thalassinoides)*, argillaceous, radiolaria, miliolid foraminifera	24	38
2	Grainstone, medium-bedded, fine-grained, peloidal, miliolid foraminifera	3	14
1	Lime mudstone, argillaceous, and packstone, thin- and medium-bedded, locally bioturbated *(Thalassinoides)*, fine-grained, peloidal	11	11

Sahtan Group
(undivided)

| | Grainstone, thick-bedded, locally bioturbated, grading in upper beds, oolitic, bioclastic, peloidal, intraclastic | >25 | |

References

ALLEMAN, F. & PETERS, T. 1972. The ophiolite-radiolarite belt of the north-Oman Mountains: *Eclogae Geologicae Helvetiae*, **65**, 657−697.

ALSHARHAN, A. S. & KENDALL, C. ST. C. 1986. Precambrian to Jurassic rocks of Arabian Gulf and adjacent areas: their facies, depositional setting, and hydrocarbon habitat: *American Association of Petroleum Geologists Bulletin*, **70**, 977−1002.

—— & NAIRN, A. E. M. 1986. A review of the Cretaceous Formations in the Arabian Peninsula and Gulf: Part I. Lower Cretaceous (Thamama Group) stratigraphy and paleogeography: *Journal of Petroleum Geology*, **9**, 365−392.

AYRES, M. G. *et al.* 1982. Hydrocarbon habitat in main producing areas, Saudi Arabia: *American Association of Petroleum Geologists Bulletin*, **66**, 1−9.

BÉCHENNEC, F. *et al.* 1988. The Hawasina Basin: a fragment of a starved passive continental margin, thrust over the Arabian Platform during obduction of the Sumail Nappe: *Tectonophysics*, **151**, 323−343.

BLENDINGER, W. 1988. Permian to Jurassic deep water sediments of the eastern Oman Mountains: their significance for the evolution of the Arabian margin of the South Tethys: *Facies*, **19**, 1−32.

CONNALLY, T. C. & SCOTT, R. W. 1985. Carbonate sediment-fill of an oceanic shelf, Lower Cretaceous, Arabian Peninsula: *In*: CREVELLO, P. D. & HARRIS, P. M. (eds) *Deep-water carbonates: buildups, turbidites, debris flows and chalk − a core workshop*, pp. 266−302, Society of Economic Paleontologists and Mineralogists, Core Workshops No. 6.

COOPER, D. J. W. 1987. Hamrat Duru Group: revised stratigraphy of a Mesozoic deep-water passive margin in the Oman Mountains: *Geological Magazine*, **124**, 157−164.

—— 1989. A longitudinal carbonate fan from the Jurassic of the Oman Mountains: the Guweyza Limestone Formation of the Hamrat ad Duru: *Sedimentary Geology*, **61**, 253−275.

DERCOURT, J. *et al.* 1986. Geological evolution of the Tethys belt from the Atlantic to the Pamirs since the Lias: *Tectonophysics*, **123**, 241−315.

GEYER, O. F. 1977. Die 'Lithiotis − Kalke' im Bereich der unterjurassischen Tethys: *Neues Jahrbuch für Geologie und Paläontologie Abhandlungen*, **153**, 304−340.

GLENNIE, K. W. *et al.* 1974. Geology of the Oman Mountains: *Verhandelingen van het Koninkliik Nederlands geologisch miinbouwkundig Genootschap*, **31**, 1−423.

'GORIN, G. E., RACZ, L. G. & WALTER, M. R. 1982. Late Precambrian-Cambrian sediments of Huqf Group, Sultanate of Oman: *American Association of Petroleum Geologists Bulletin*, **66**, 2609−2627.

HAQ, B. U., HARDENBOL, J. & VAIL, P. R. 1988. Mesozoic and Cenozoic chronostratigraphy and cycles of sea-level change: *In*: *Sea-level changes − an integrated approach*. Society of Economic Paleontologists and Mineralogists, Special Publication **42**, 71−108.

HASSAN, T. H., MUDD, G. C. & TWOMBLEY, B. N. 1975. The stratigraphy and sedimentation of the Thamama Group (Lower Cretaceous) of Abu Dhabi: *Ninth Arab Petroleum Congress (Dubai)*, article 107(B-3).

HATTIN, D. H. 1975. Petrology and origin of fecal pellets in Upper Cretaceous strata of Kansas and Saskatchewan: *Journal of Sedimentary Petrology*, **45**, 686−696.

HUDSON, R. G. S. & CHATTON, M. 1959. The Musandam Limestone (Jurassic to Lower Cretaceous) of Oman, Arabia: *Notes et Mémoires sur le Moyen-Orient*, **7**, 69−93.

HUGHES CLARKE, M. W. 1988. Stratigraphy and rock unit nomenclature in the oil-producing area of interior Oman: *Journal of Petroleum Geology*, **11**, 5−60.

JAMES, N. P. & STEVENS, R. K. 1986. Stratigraphy and correlation of the Cambro-Ordovician Cow head Group, western Newfoundland: *Geological Survey of Canada, Bulletin*, **366**.

KAZMIN, V., RICOU, L.-E. & SBORTSHIKOV, I. M. 1986. Structure and evolution of the passive margin of the eastern Tethys: *Tectonophysics*, **123**, 153−179.

KOOP, W. J. & STONELEY, R. 1982. Subsidence history of the Middle East Zagros Basin, Permian to Recent: *Philosophical Transactions of the Royal Society of London*, **A305**, 149−168.

MOSELEY, F. 1969. The Upper Cretaceous ophiolite complex of Masirah Island, Oman: *Geological Journal*, **6**, 293−306.

MURRIS, R. J. 1980. Middle East: stratigraphic evolution and oil habitat: *American Association of Petroleum Geologists Bulletin*, **64**, 597−618.

POWERS, R. W., RAMIREZ, L. F., REDMOND, C. D. &

ELBERG, E. L. 1966. Geology of the Arabian Peninsula. Sedimentary geology of Saudi Arabia: *U.S. Geological Survey, Professional Paper* 560–D.

RICATEAU, R. & RICHE, P. H. 1980. Geology of the Musandam Peninsula (Sultanate of Oman) and its surroundings: *Journal of Petroleum Geology*, **3**, 139–152.

ROBERTSON, A. H. F. 1987. The transition from a passive margin to an Upper Cretaceous foreland basin related to ophiolite emplacement in the Oman Mountains: *Geological Society of America Bulletin*, **99**, 633–653.

SCOTT, R. W., FROST, S. H. & SHAFFER, B. L. 1988. Early Cretaceous sea-level curves, Gulf Coast and southeastern Arabia: *In: Sea-level changes — an integrated approach*. Society of Economic Paleontologists and Mineralogists, Special Publication **42**, 275–284.

SEARLE, M. P. & GRAHAM, G. M. 1982. 'Oman Exotics' — oceanic carbonate build-ups associated with the early stages of continental rifting: *Geology*, **10**, 43–49.

——, JAMES, N. P., CALON, T. J. & SMEWING, J. D. 1983. Sedimentological and structural evolution of the Arabian continental margin in the Musandam Mountains and Dibba zone, United Arab Emirates: *Geological Society of America Bulletin*, **94**, 1381–1400.

SIMMONS, M. D. & HART, M. B. 1987. The biostratigraphy and microfacies of the Early to mid-Cretaceous carbonates of Wadi Mi'aidin, central Oman Mountains: *In*: HART, M. B. (ed.) *Micropalaeontology of carbonate environments*, 176–207, Ellis Horwood, Chichester.

THOMAS, W. A. 1983. Continental margins, orogenic belts, and intracratonic structures: *Geology*, **11**, 270–272.

WATTS, K. F. & GARRISON, R. E. 1986. Sumeini Group, Oman — evolution of a Mesozoic carbonate slope on a South Tethyan continental margin: *Sedimentary Geology*, **48**, 107–168.

WILSON, A. O. 1985. Depositional and diagenetic facies in the Jurassic Arab-C and -D reservoirs, Qatif Field, Saudi Arabia. *In*: ROEHL, P. O. & CHOQUETTE, P. W. (eds) *Carbonate petroleum reservoirs*. Springer, New York 319–340.

WOOD, G. V. & WOLFE, M. J. 1969. Sabkha cycles in the Arab/Darb Formation off the Trucial Coast of Arabia. *Sedimentology*, **12**, 165–191.

Chronostratigraphy of the Cretaceous carbonate shelf, southeastern Arabia

R. W. SCOTT

Amoco Production Company, P.O. Box 3385, Tulsa, OK 74102, USA

Abstract: Carbonate deposits dominated the southeastern part of the Arabian Shelf from Berriasian to Santonian time, approximately 60 Ma. Deposition was terminated by the development of the Oman Foredeep in Coniacian−Santonian following the initial emplacement of the Hawasina and Semail nappes in the Turonian. The Lower and middle Cretaceous units in Arabia correlate with European reference sections and the current ages of the stage boundaries can be used to form a quantitative scale.

The Thamama−Kahmah Group to the Ilam−Halul Limestone consists of four major unconformity-bounded, shoaling-up depositional sequences that range in duration from 3 to 22 Ma. These sequences represent significant transgressive events on the shelf. The Rayda−Salil−Habshan sequence represents drowning and extensive incursion of the deep shelf landward; it lasted about 13 Ma. Small-scale, possibly climatic cycles comprise the Salil and Rayda formations. The contact with the overlying Lekhwair−Kharaib−Shuaiba sequence is normally sharp with no evidence of erosion. This sequence lasted about 18 Ma and consists of numerous shoaling-up cycles and local disconformities. The unconformity between the Shuaiba and Nahr Umr is a regional disconformity with evidence of local exposure. The hiatus spans most of the Late Aptian in the Oman Mountains, and in Abu Dhabi it spans the youngest part of the Late Aptian.

The Nahr Umr−Natih sequence in Oman spanned about 22 Ma and consists of four shoaling-up cycles. An important drowning event in the Oman Mountains occurred during the earliest Middle Cenomanian and is represented by the submarine hardground at the top of the 'E' member. The youngest sequence consists of the Laffan−Ilam formations in the Khatiyah Basin and lasted about 3 Ma. These depositional sequences correspond to transgressive events on other plates and represent eustatic sea level changes. The onlapping unconformities in the Oman Mountains represent times when the peripheral swell was active.

Restricted, intraplatform basins, in which organic-rich muds were deposited, developed four times. These units are best developed in the Bab-Khatiyah Basin and locally extended eastward into Oman. The Bab Member of the Shuaiba Formation is mainly Late Aptian. The Khatiyah Formation is coeval with the Early Cenomanian, lower 'E' member of the Natih in Oman. The 'B' member of the Natih is Late Cenomanian in age. The Laffan Formation is mainly Coniacian in age and represents the final restricted basin upon the southeastern Arabian Shelf.

An accurate and precise chronostratigraphic correlation of the Cretaceous strata in the Oman Mountains is needed in order to provide rates and durations of deposition, erosion and tectonic events and to correlate stages. Previous biostratigraphic studies provided ranges of well known fossils and zones as the basis for identifying stadial correlations (Glennie *et al.* 1974; Tippit *et al.* 1981; Harris *et al.* 1984; Simmons & Hart 1987). Such correlations are only as accurate as the ranges of these key taxa both in Oman and in the areas intervening between Oman and Europe. Consequently, precision is lacking in determining the absolute time of deposition of the units.

Graphic correlation is a technique of quantitative stratigraphy that determines the maximum ranges of diverse taxa in many sections.

The quantitative scale of ranges is proportional to the first sections graphed to this composite standard (C.S.). Mature data bases can be converted to absolute time so that rates can be measured in years. In addition, the correlation of European stadial boundaries can be determined precisely in Oman by this technique.

The southeastern corner of the Arabian Platform was a relatively stable platform from Middle Permian until the earliest Turonian, a span of approximately 170 Ma. During this time, some 3500 m of mainly carbonate strata accumulated (Searle *et al.* 1983). Numerous regional unconformities formed in response to changes in relative sea level (Harris *et al.* 1984). During the Late Cretaceous, the tectonic regime of this area became unstable as oceanic crust was thrust onto the continental margin. Five

From ROBERTSON, A. H. F., SEARLE, M. P. & RIES, A. C. (eds), 1990,
The Geology and Tectonics of the Oman Region.
Geological Society Special Publication No 49, pp 89−108

Cretaceous genetic depositional sequences were deposited upon the shelf prior to and during this tectonic activity. Slope and rise deposits also reflect this changing tectonic regime (Robertson 1987; Watts 1987). The tectonic events and eustatic sea level changes are both recorded in the shoaling-up sequences separated by drowning unconformities.

A chronostratigraphic scale

A quantitative chronostratigraphic scale based on arbitrary units was constructed for the Berriasian–Turonian part of the Cretaceous System by means of graphic correlation. This technique was pioneered by A. B. Shaw (1964) and applied by Miller (1977). A composite standard (C.S.) data base of tops and bases of fossil ranges was built by graphing 76 sections from the Gulf of Mexico, Europe, the Atlantic Ocean deep-sea cores, North Africa, and the Middle East (Table 1). About 1200 taxa of foraminifers, nannofossils, calpionellids, calcareous algae, palynomorphs, ammonites, bivalves, and corals were identified in these sections by numerous specialists at the Amoco

Table 1. *List of 21 selected localities that control the composite standard ranges which are used in graphing the Oman and U.A.E. sections and in calculating the CSU correlations of Figs 5 & 7. S-outcrop; D-drill cuttings; X-cuttings and core samples.*

LOCALITY	NAME
X	SHELL NO. 1 CHAPMAN, WALLER CO., TEXAS
S	GARGAS, FRANCE (TYPE UPPER APTIAN)
S	LA BEDOULE, FRANCE (TYPE LOWER APTIAN)
S	ANGLES, FRANCE (TYPE HAUTERIVIAN-BARREM.)
X	SHELL No 1 TOMASEK, LIVE OAK CO., TX-ALBIAN
X	SAJAA-1 (10470–13199 FT), THAMAMA GP.
X	SAJAA-2, (14776–15200 FT), SAHTAN GP.
X	SAJAA-2, (11956–14775 FT), THAMAMA GP.
X	SAJAA-3 (11142–13863 FT), THAMAMA GP.
S	WADI MIADIN, OMAN, SAHTAN GP.
S	WADI MIADIN, OMAN, THAMAMA GP.
A	WADI MIADIN, OMAN, LOWER PART WASIA GP.
S	WADI MIADIN, OMAN, UPPER PART WASIA GP.
S	WADI BANI KHARUS, OMAN, SAHTAN GP.
S	WADI BANI KHARUS, OMAN, THAMAMA GP.
S	WADI BANI KHARUS, OMAN, WASIA GP.
S	JEBEL SALAKH, OMAN, WASIA GP.
S	J. MADMAR SOUTH, OMAN, WASIA GP.
S	J. MADAR, OMAN, WASIA GP.
X	MA'MURAH, THAMAMA GP.
X	MA'MURAH, WASIA GP.
S	WADI RUBKHAH, THAMAMA GP.
S	WADI RUBKHAH, LOWER PART OF WASIA GP.
S	WADI RUBKHAH, UPPER PART OF WASIA GP.
S	WADI TANUF, J. AKHDAR, OMAN, LOWER WASIA GP.
S	WADI TANUF, J. AKHDAR, OMAN, UPPER WASIA GP.
S	JABAL MADMAR NORTH FLANK, OMAN, WASIA GP.
S	DLEBTA-CHENAN AAIR, LEBANON, CENOMANIAN
S	NAHR IBRAHIM, JBAIL TORZAYA, LEBANON, CENOMANIAN.
S	SARTHE REGION, NE OF LEMANS, FRANCE, CENOMANIAN.
S	CAPE BOULLONAISE, FRANCE, MIDDLE ALBIAN-CON.

Research Center or by reputable palaeontologists who have published accurate range data.

The technique graphic correlation is fully described by Miller (1977), however, a brief explanation here will clarify the diagrams and conclusions in this report. The basic data of each stratigraphic section are the measurements of the tops and bases of an interdisciplinary set of taxa (Tables 2 & 3). The tops and bases of fossils in common between a section and the composited ranges are plotted on an $x-y$ graph and a line-of-correlation (LOC) is positioned by the palaeontologic–stratigraphic interpreter. The LOC is defined by a regression equation so that the tops and bases can be converted to the C.S. scale. The data base, then, consists of lists of species and their top-base occurrences in sections where they were reported, given in composite standard values. The maximum range of each is used when plotting the C.S. ranges

with ranges in new measured sections or wells. The position of the LOC is an interpretation of how the section correlates with the composite standard.

The first step in constructing the C.S. scale in composite standard units (CSU) was a cross plot on an $x-y$ graph of the ranges of fossils in cored intervals of Aptian to Albian carbonates in two south Texas wells (publication of these data is in preparation). Additional outcrop sections from coeval beds in Texas were added to the C.S. by $x-y$ graphs of foraminiferal and megafossil range data. This C.S. was expanded by graphing sections containing the various microfossil groups from the Tithonian to the Turonian (Table 1). The numerous sections were graphed two or three times after the ranges from additional sections were graphed into the C.S., so that a stable data base emerged.

The stage boundaries were set by graphing

Table 2. *Ranges of taxa recorded in the Cretaceous at Cape Boullonaise section in metres for Fig. 3.*

LOCALITY 21695, CAPE BOULLONAISE, FRANCE

Taxon no.	Taxon name	No. of samples	Lowest sample	Highest Sample
01	GLOBIGERINA WASHITENSIS	1		5.2
02	GAUDRYINA LAEVIGATA	9	80.	121.
03	PLECTINA RUTHENICA	24	12.	76.5
04	GAUDRYINA AUSTINANA	6	78.	122.
05	AMMODISCUS CRETACEUS	16	20.6	109.
06	GLOBOTRUNCANA CORONATA	8	118.	146.
07	ARENOBULIMINA PRESLII	14	88.	117.
08	EPISTOMINA SPINULIFERA	2	.6	10.
09	GLOBIGERINA DELRIOENSIS	49	11.5	171.
10	GLOBOTRUNCANA LINNEIANA	8	95.	141.
11	GLOBOTRUNCANA MARGINATA	9	93.	122.
12	GLOBOTRUNCANA HELVETICA	9	81.	110.
13	GLOBOTRUNCANA SIGALI	7	96.	111.
14	GLOBIGERINA PARADUBIA	10	79.	107.
15	GLOBIGERINA PLANISPIRA	2	.6	10.
16	PRAEGLOBOTRUNCANA DELRIOENSIS	9	13.	56.
17	GLOBOTRUNCANA IMBRICATA	14	77.6	122.
18	ROTALIPORA APPENNINICA	8	12.	33.2
19	DIPOLOCERAS CF BOUCHARDIANUM	1		11.
20	SCHLOENBACHIA SUBVARIANS	2	38.	41.5
21	KANABICERAS SEPTEMSERIATUM	2	76.8	78.
22	INOCERAMUS LABIATUS	2	81.	95.
23	HYSTEROCERAS ORBIGNYI	3	4.4	6.8

Table 2 *(cont)*

LOCALITY 21695, CAPE BOULLONAISE, FRANCE

Taxon no.	Taxon name	No. of samples	Lowest sample	Highest Sample
24	CHIASTOZYGUS LITTERARIUS	4	.2	177.
25	COROLLITHION EXIGUUM	4	38.	145.
26	DEFLANDRIUS CRETACEOUS	3	10.	177.
27	DEFLANDRIUS SPINOSUS	4	10.	177.
28	DISCOLITHUS EMBERGERI	2	11.5	81.
29	LITHRAPHIDITES CARNIOLENSIS	4	10.	177.
30	MICRORHABDULUS DECORATUS	4	38.	177.
31	ZYGOLITHUS DIPLOGRAMMUS	5	.2	177.
32	EIFFELLITHUS TURRISEIFFELI	4	10.	177.
33	CRETARHABDUS CRENULATUS	4	.2	81.
34	KAMPTNERIUS MAGNIFICUS	2	121.	177.
35	LITHASTRINUS FLORALIS	5	.2	177.
36	MICRORHABDULINUS AMBIGUUS	2	80.	177.
37	TRANOLITHUS PHACELOSUS	2	2.5	10.
38	ZYGOLITHUS BIRAMICULATUS	2	76.	78.
39	LUCIANORHABDUS MALEFORMIS	2	80.	177.
40	MARTHASTERITES FURCATUS	2	171.	177.
41	MICRORHABDULUS BELGICUS	2	33.2	81.
42	MICROSTAURUS CHIATUS	2	11.5	41.5
43	COROLLITHION SIGNUM	2	6.8	10.
44	EIFFELLITHUS EXIMIUS	2	121.	145.
45	EIFFELLITHUS TRABECULATUS	2	.2	10.
46	LITHRAPHIDITES ACUTUM	4	26.2	87.
47	COROLLITHION ACHYLOSUM	2	.6	6.8
48	GLOBOROTALITES SUBCONICUS	10	107.	141.
49	QUINQUELOCULINA ANTIQUA	12	5.2	40.
50	GLOBOROTALITES MICHELINIANUS	7	133.	171.
51	ROTALIPORA CUSHMANI	17	33.2	76.8
52	GYROIDINOIDES NITIDUS	32	12.	146.
53	PLATYCYTHEREIS GAULTLINA	4	4.4	8.5
54	SCHULERIDEA JONESIANA	16	.6	37.
55	BAIRDIA PSEUDOSEPTENTRIONALIS	2	10.	54.
56	PROTOCYTHERE LINEATA	3	10.	37.
57	NEOCYTHERE VANVEENI	4	2.1	8.5
58	REHACYTHEREIS LURMANNAE	8	3.3	10.
59	MANDOCYTHERE HARRISIANA	15	.6	11.5
60	CYTHERELLOIDEA STRICTA	8	3.9	42.
61	CENTROCYTHERE DENTICULATA	12	2.1	17.7
62	REHACYTHEREIS RETICULATA	1	1.9	
63	CYTHERELLOIDEA CHAPMANI	2	3.6	3.9

Table 2 *(cont)*

LOCALITY 21695, CAPE BOULLONAISE, FRANCE

Taxon no.	Taxon name	No. of samples	Lowest sample	Highest Sample
64	PROTOCYTHERE ALBAE	6	2.1	3.9
65	ARENOBULIMINA BREVICONA	8	15.	79.2
66	TICINELLA PRIMULA	2	7.5	8.5
67	ROTALIPORA DEECKEI	2	35.	37.
68	PRAEGLOBOTRUNCANA STEPHANI	20	26.2	83.
69	GLOBULINA PRISCA	14	13.	79.2
70	TRITAXIA PLUMMERAE	3	15.	56.
71	DOROTHIA GRADATA	27	3.6	74.
72	GAVELINELLA BALTICA	27	3.9	76.5
73	SPIROPLECTAMMINA PRAELONGA	12	13.	54.
74	NANNOCONUS ELONGATUS	2	84.	177.
75	ROTALIPORA GREENHORNENSIS	4	63.	76.8
76	GLOBOTRUNCANA TURONICA	7	78.	105.
77	LEWESICERAS MANTELLI	2	141.	142.
78	COLLIGNONICERAS WOOLGARI	1		99.
79	SCIPONOCERAS GRACILE	3	76.8	80.
80	ISOCYTHEREIS FORTINODIS	5	2.5	8.5
81	EUCYTHERE TRIGONALIS	1		6.8
82	MATRONELLA MATRONAE	9	1.9	10.
83	REHACYTHEREIS FOLKESTONENSIS	2	6.8	8.5
84	METOICOCERAS GESLINIANUM	2	77.	78.
85	INOCERAMUS MYTILOIDES FIEGEI	2	131.	134.
86	NEOHIBOLITES MINIMUS	1		11.
87	MOJSISOVICSIA SUBDELARUEI	1		2.3
88	ANAHOPLITES INTERMEDIUS	2	.6	1.7
89	DIMORPHOLITES NIOBE	3	1.9	2.3
90	DIPOLOCERAS CRISTATUM	1		3.9
91	HOPLITES DENTATUS	1		.2
92	INOCERAMUS CRIPPSI	2	12.5	42.
93	INOCERAMUS CONCENTRICUS	3	.2	6.8
94	INOCERAMUS SULCATUS	2	4.4	6.1
95	BEUDANTICERAS BEUDANTI	3	3.9	6.8
96	MANTELLICERAS MANTELLI	2	12.5	20.6
97	MANTELLICERAS SAXBII	2	26.2	29.
98	INOCERAMUS PICTUS	2	79.	80.
99	MYTILOIDES MYTILOIDES	2	81.	95.
100	ACANTHOCERAS RHOTOMAGENSE	5	37.	54.
101	SCIPONOCERAS BACULOIDE	1		41.5
102	HYPOTURRILITES TUBERCULATUS	2	12.5	26.2
103	TURRILITES COSTATUS	3	38.	42.

Table 2 *(cont)*

LOCALITY 21695, CAPE BOULLONAISE, FRANCE

Taxon no.	Taxon name	No. of samples	Lowest sample	Highest Sample
104	TURRILITES SCHEUCHZERIANUS	1		41.5
105	CITHARINELLA KARRERI	2	2.3	3.9
106	EPISTOMINA CRETOSA	2	2.5	3.9
107	ARENOBULIMINA CHAPMANI	2	3.9	6.6
108	CITHARINELLA PINNAEFORMIS	2	4.4	6.6
109	HAGENOWIA ADVENA	15	12.	54.
110	ARENOBULIMINA MACFADYENI	2	.2	4.4
111	HOEGLUNDINA CHAPANI	7	.6	6.1
112	HOEGLUNDINA CARPENTERI	4	1.9	4.4
113	PSEUDOTEXTULARIELLA CRETOSA	20	12.	63.
114	EGGERELLINA MARIAE	29	12.	147.
115	PLECTINA MARIAE	25	12.5	77.
116	RAMULINA ACULEATA	20	12.5	74.
117	GAVELINELLA CENOMANICA	31	11.	77.
118	TRITAXIA PYRAMIDATA	31	11.5	77.8
119	GLOBOTRUNCANA HAGNI	7	74.	81.
120	MAMMITES NODOSOIDES	2	81.	94.
121	TRITAXIA TRICARINATA	24	77.8	141.
122	COSCINOPHRAGMA IRREGULARIS	6	110.	123.
123	LINGULOGAVELINELLA GLOBOSA	15	72.	96.
124	TRITAXIA MACFADYENI	22	31.	118.
125	VALVULINERIA LENTICULA	17	81.	142.
126	VERNEUILINA MUENSTERI	3	138.	147.

Table 3. *Range data of taxa in the Thamama and Wasia Groups, Wadi Mi'aidin in feet in Figs 6 & 8.*

Locality 12523, Wadi Mi'aidin Section

Taxon no.	Taxon name	No. of samples	Lowest sample	Highest sample
01	HETEROHELIX GLOBULOSA	2	4650.	4750.
07	ORBITOLINA TEXANA	1	3247.	
45	LENTICULINA SP.	9	205.	2940.
11	SOLENOPORA SP.	2	131.2	459.2
40	PERMOCALCULUS SP.	22	1848.	4750.
39	PSEUDOCYCLAMMINA SP.	2	3362.	4470.

37	QUINQUELOCULINID	10	3213.	4590.
98	CUNEOLINA	8	4110.	4590.
03	NUMMOLOCULINA HEIMI	3	4197.	4337.
17	POLYSTRATA ALBA	2	4322.	4335.
55	DISCORBIS TURONICUS	1	4330.	
38	PSEUDOCYCLAMMINA LITUUS	1	1858.	
60	GLOBIGERINA HOTERIVICA	6	782.	1320.
74	LITHOCODIUM SP.	5	1883.	2750.
28	PSEUDOCYCLAMMINA HEDBERGI	1	2940.	
36	CADOSINA FUSCA	1	1520.	
73	PITHONELLA SPHAERICA	2	3368.	4382.
87	NANNOCONUS STEINMANNI	1	970.	
92	CALPIONELLA ELLIPTICA	1	601.	
95	CALPIONELLITES DARDERI	1	678.	
96	CALPIONELLOPSIS OBLONGA	2	622.	635.
97	CALPIONELLOPSIS SIMPLEX	2	622.	678.
57	CRASSICOLARIA PARVULA	2	601.	622.
25	TINTINNOPSELLA CARPATHICA	2	622.	635.
24	MICRITOSPHAERA OVALIS	9	2444.	3235.
19	HENSONELLA CYLINDRICA	8	2561.	3176.
14	CHONDRODONTA SP.	1	3235.	
12	SALPINGOPORELLA	2	2444.	2805.
18	NEZZEZATA SIMPLEX	15	3247.	4370.
69	CHOFFATELLA DECIPIENS	3	1858.	2881.
20	BACINELLA IRREGULARIS	3	3158.	3228.
23	SPIROSIGMOILINA CRETACEOUS	1	2128.	
31	ORBITOLINA LENTICULARIS	12	2703.	3219.
04	PRAERADIOLITES	7	3784.	4337.
26	CHONDRODONTA JOANNAE	1	4770.	
63	CHRYSALIDINA GRADATA	5	4150.	4408.
64	ORBITOLINA SUBCONCAVA	5	3368.	4049.
65	ORBITOLINA APERTA	3	3617.	3910.
66	ORBITOLINA CONCAVA	1	4130.	
67	OVALVEOLINA OVUM	5	4189.	4357.
68	PRAEALVEOLINA CRETACEA	15	4312.	4750.
41	DICYCLINA SCHLUMBERGERI	1	4280.	
42	VALVULINA	3	2988.	3219.
43	CHRYSALIDINA	2	3219.	4370.
44	ORBITOLINA CONICA	2	4117.	4312.
53	TROCHOLINA ELONGATA	1	3944.	
61	MERLINGINA CRETACEA	5	4150.	4337.
62	BIPLANATA PENEROPLIFORMIS	6	4150.	4337.
93	ORBITOLINELLA DEPRESSA	3	4408.	4495.
54	PSEUDOLITUONELLA REICHELI	1	4782.	
35	TABERINA BINGISTANI	10	4150.	4408.
59	PSEUDEDOMIA DRORIMENSIS	1	4590.	
75	HEMICYCLAMMINA WHITEI	2	3303.	3592.

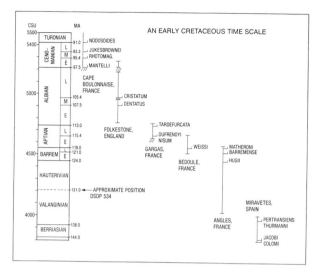

Fig. 1. An Early Cretaceous time scale of composite standard units (CSU) in Cretaceous Carbonate Standard data base and of millions of years (Ma). Reference sections have been graphed to construct the C.S., and the bases of traditional ammonite zones in the C.S. define stadial and substadial boundaries.

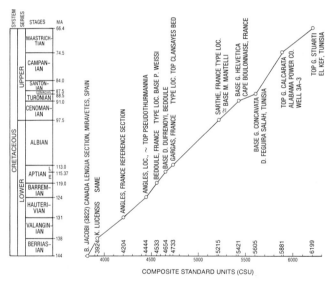

COMPOSITE STANDARD UNITS (CSU)

Fig. 2. Crossplot that converts the CSU scale to the absolute timescale (Palmer 1983) shows reference sections that define the boundaries.

key European reference sections (Fig. 1). The CSU value was determined for each stage boundary by converting the footage of the contact from the reference section. This CSU scale was converted to a radiometric scale by plotting the CSU value of the stage boundary to its absolute time. The Geological Society of America scale (Palmer 1983) was used because it is based on recent, high-temperature radiometric dates and because it provides numbers for all stages. This crossplot (Fig. 2) is not a straight line either because the graphs do not account for changes in rate of rock accumulation, or because the ages of the boundaries are incorrect, or both. Many of the Early Cretaceous ages are not well constrained by

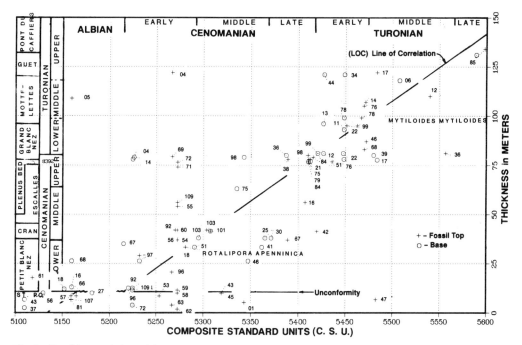

Fig. 3. Graphic correlation of Cape Boulonnais section, France to define Cenomanian–Turonian stages. Plus marks signify range tops (LAD) and circles are bases (FAD). See Table 2 for species names that match the serial numbers. LOC defined by top of *M. mytiloides* and base of *R. apenninica*.

numerous, reliable dates nor by precise stratigraphic control of those dates. The post-Turonian part of this C.S. is not well developed and certain sections may need regraphing. This younger part of the C.S. was not employed in the Middle East; instead a different C.S. was used to interpret the drilled section; however, it has not been converted to absolute time, so that ages and rates cannot be measured.

The Gulf Coast C.S. was extended to the Middle East by incorporating geographically intermediate, carbonate sections in France (Fig. 3) (Amedro *et al.* 1978) and in Lebanon that contain both planktic and benthic, Albian-Cenomanian foraminifers (Saint-Marc 1974). The first Oman sections graphed were on the flanks of Jebel Akhdar. The Kahmah and Wasia Groups are well exposed in Wadi Mi'aidin, a local reference section (Fig. 4). Other excellent exposures that we measured are Wadi Bani Kharus and Wadi Tanuf. Several other less complete sections were graphed to the C.S. to form a reliable data base. The next step was to graph numerous drilled sections from Oman and Sharjah, where the ranges had been determined by personal observations. Finally, this C.S. could be used to graph range data provided

by consultants. The important requirement was that enough fossils had been recovered from the well samples and identified to control the line of correlation.

Results of graphic correlation

Thamama–Kahmah Groups

The biostratigraphy of the Thamama Group in Sharjah has been studied in five wells and in Oman, this interval was sampled in two outcrops and two wells (Fig. 4). These data have been graphed with the Composite Standard to produce chronostratigraphic correlations (Fig. 5). We follow the stratigraphic nomenclature of Alsharhan & Nairn (1986). In Oman, these formations were placed in the Kahmah Group (Glennie *et al.* 1974; Hughes Clarke 1988) because the Hith Anhydrite which underlies and defines the base of the Thamama in its type locality in Saudi Arabia, is absent. In Sharjah and Oman, shallow-water limestones of the Sahtan Group underlie the deep-water limestones of the Thamama and the contact is readily mapped. The name is synonymous with *Thamama*.

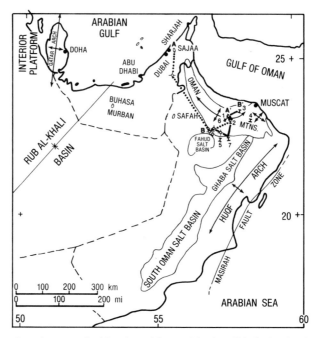

Fig. 4. Tectonic map of southeastern Arabia adapted from Alsharhan (1985) showing locations of wells, measured sections and cross sections A–A' and B–B'. 1, Wadi Bani Kharus; 2, Wadi Mi'aidin; 3, Wadi Rubkhah; 4, Wadi Tayin; 5, Jebel Salakh; 6, Wadi Tanuf; 7, Jebel Madmar.

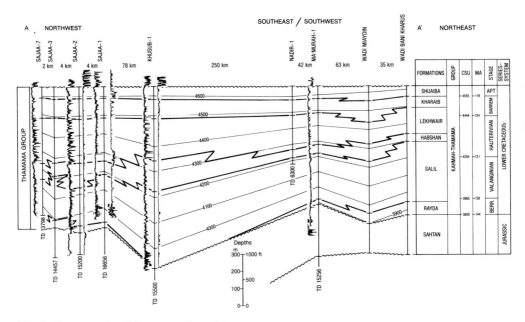

Fig. 5. Chronostratigraphic cross section of Thamama–Kahmah Group from Sajaa Field to the Oman Mountains (see Fig. 4 for location).

The Thamama Group is an unconformity-bounded, depositional mega-sequence, up to 1075 m thick, that consists of two major shoaling-up depositional sequences separated at the Habshan–Lekhwair contact. This mega-sequence spans a 27 Ma period when the maximum rate of sediment accumulation was 4.0 cm/1000 yrs. The base of the Thamama Group is a regional disconformity and a sequence boundary that represents a widespread drowning event during the Berriasian. In Wadi Tayin, Oman, the top of the Jurassic limestone is an iron-coated, bored hardground. The Rayda Formation onlaps and transgressed the Sahtan Group from southeast to northwest in Oman (Fig. 5). In Sharjah, the Rayda pinches out between the Sajaa Field and the Khusub-1 well suggesting local paleotopography. The Rayda ranges from Berriasian to Lower Valanginian based on graphic correlation of diagnostic calpionellids (Connally & Scott 1985; Simmons & Hart 1987). The Salil Formation consists of middle to outer shelf facies that filled the drowned shelf by progradation (Connally & Scott 1985). It is mainly Valanginian in age in Sharjah and its upper part becomes Early Hauterivian where it prograded offshore into Oman (Fig. 5). The Valanginian age is based on calpionellids (Connally & Scott 1985) and calcareous algae (Simmons & Hart 1987). The

Hauterivian age is based on graphs with the composite standard (Fig. 6).

The Habshan Formation is a shoal-water depositional system that prograded from northwest to southeast across the shelf. It consists of coral-stromatoporoid reefs and high-energy rudist sand banks. Its age ranges from Valanginian to Hauterivian by graphic correlation, which is supported by the ranges of foraminifers, calcareous algae, and rudists (Connally & Scott 1985; Simmons & Hart 1987). The contact of the Habshan with the overlying Lekhwair Formation is a comformable sequence boundary in Oman and Sharjah (Connally & Scott 1985) and is disconformable in Abu Dhabi (Hassan et al. 1975). In outcrops in Jebel Akhdar, this contact is sharp and it separates dark blue-grey, medium-bedded, rudist limestones of the Lekhwair from moderate-grey, thick-bedded, bioclastic-ooid-oncoid limestones of the Habshan. In the subsurface of Sharjah, the contact is less distinct and possibly interbedded because more radioactive beds are interlayered with less radioactive units. By graphic correlation, the base and top of the Habshan prograde from northwest to southeast (Fig. 5).

The Lekhwair Formation represents a slight sea-level rise forming a quiet-water, shelf lagoon behind the shelf rim formed by the Habshan. It ranges in age from Hauterivian to Barremian

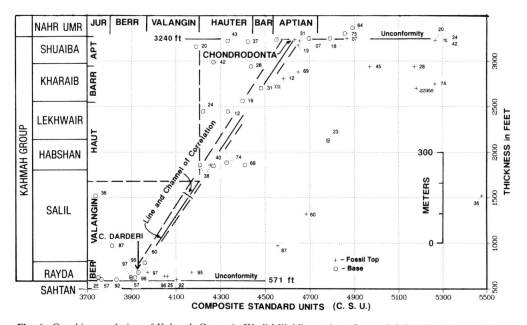

Fig. 6. Graphic correlation of Kahmah Group in Wadi Mi'aidin section, Oman. LOC defined by top of *Chondrodonta* sp. and base of *C. darderi*. See Table 3 for species names that match the serial numbers.

based on graphic correlation and on the occurrence of calcareous algae and foraminifers (Simmons & Hart 1987). At Wadi Bani Kharus *Palorbitolina lenticularis* (Blumenbach) Barremian—Lower Aptian in Oman) occurs in the uppermost beds of the Lekhwair.

The Kharaib Formation consists of shallow shelf limestone that ranges from Barremian to basal Aptian in age. The base and the top of the Kharaib are virtually isochronous in Sharjah (Fig. 5). The variation of 11 to 12 CSUs is probably a result of the imprecision in the correlation. The base at Wadi Mi'aidin in Oman, however, is significantly older and represents an authentic difference based on a thicker Kharaib section. Evidently, the environmental changes resulting in the Kharaib deposition occurred virtually at the same time behind the shelf margin from Sharjah to central Oman, over 300 km distant, but occurred somewhat earlier towards the shelf margin in Jebel Akhdar. The Kharaib consists of oncoid packstones suggestive of quiet, restricted conditions that may have originated directly behind the shelf edge and spread westward across the shelf. The clearing up to less restricted conditions represented by the foram wackestones and patch reefs of the Shuaiba may have originated by an oceanic water mass that first encroached at the margin, and then spread quickly across the shelf.

The Shuaiba Formation is Lower Aptian based on graphic correlation with the French Bedoule and Gargas sections in the C.S. The top of the Shuaiba is a regional disconformity in Arabia (Alsharhan & Nairn 1986; Murris 1980) and is a sequence boundary. In parts of Oman and Sharjah, geochemical and petrographic data of the uppermost Shuaiba indicate that it was not subaerially exposed (Moshier *et al.* 1988; Wagner 1990), but elsewhere the surface may have been subaerially exposed (Harris & Frost 1984). This surface is virtually isochronous in the Sajaa Field and in the Khusub-1 and Nadir-1 wells, but eastward towards the shelf edge it becomes older. This, in addition with the easterly onlapping of the basal Nahr Umr Formation (Fig. 7), supports the concept of a peripheral bulge proposed by O'Conner & Patton (1986) and elaborated upon by Robertson (1987). This bulge was first active during the early part of the Late Aptian. The timing of events westward in Abu Dhabi are not so precisely defined. The Shuaiba contains similar fossils as to the east and is overlain by the Bab Member, a dark gray argillic limestone containing Late Aptian ammonites (Hassan *et al.* 1975). Log correlations by Alsharhan & Nairn (1986) and Alsharhan (1985) suggest that

the Bab is a lateral facies of the Shuaiba. However, at least part of the Bab is younger than the Shuaiba and was deposited in a restricted intra-platform basin. It represents the Late Aptian sea level rise, which is indicated in Oman by the Shuaiba—Nahr Umr disconformity.

The Shuaiba—Nahr Umr disconformity represents a eustatic sea-level rise because it is the same age as other intra-Aptian drowning disconformities in the Gulf of Mexico and elsewhere (Scott 1987; Scott *et al.* 1989). The top of the Shuaiba is locally a submarine, bored, iron-coated hardground indicating drowning and non-deposition prior to the Nahr Umr Formation. The Nahr Umr ranges in age from uppermost Aptian to Late Albian. The base yields Late Aptian nannoplankton (Shaffer, pers. comm. 1986).

Wasia Group

The Wasia Group in Oman is an unconformity-bounded depositional sequence, up to 538 m thick, that consists of four shoaling-up cycles deposited during latest Albian to Cenomanian time (Glennie *et al.* 1974, pp. 219—220; Entsminger 1981; Hughes Clarke 1988; Alsharhan & Nairn 1988). We measured and sampled nine outcrop sections, studied samples from three wells, and graphed consultant's biostratigraphic data from 14 other wells. The four cycles consist in ascending order: (1) the Nahr Umr Formation and 'G' and 'F' members, (2) the 'E' member, (3) the 'D' and 'C' members, and (4) the 'B' and 'A' members of the Natih Formation.

The Nahr Umr Formation at the base of the Wasia Group is up to 200 m thick. It consists of marine shale and thin-to-medium-bedded limestone that onlaps the Shuaiba Formation from southwest to northeast (Fig. 7). This suggests that the shelf margin was a palaeotopographic feature, perhaps a precursor of the younger peripheral bulge in Sharjah. The Nahr Umr may contain numerous diastems within the section because it accumulated at a much slower rate than the overlying Natih Formation: 1.43 cm/1000 yrs for the Nahr Umr and 4.84 cm/1000 yrs for the Natih (Fig. 8). The basal Nahr Umr contains *Orbitolina* (*Mesorbitolina*) *texana* Roemer, which ranges from uppermost Aptian to upper Early Albian in the C.S. Although Moullade, *et al.* (1985) show *O. texana* ranging into the Late Albian, Schroeder & Neumann (1985) show it ranging into Middle Albian; but in our sections, it has not been found that young. The succession of orbitolinid species throughout the Nahr Umr indicates that it is as

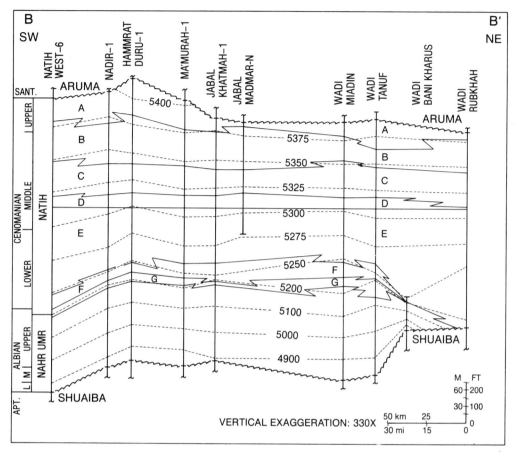

Fig. 7. Chronostratigraphic correlation of Wasia Group from wells in the Fahud Salt Basin to the Oman Mountains.

young as Late Albian (Simmons & Hart 1987). The Nahr Umr grades up into the Natih by decrease in thickness of shale beds and increase in limestone thickness.

The Natih Formation was divided into seven informal members designated by letters a–g from top to base (Tschopp, 1967a, b; Hughes Clarke, 1988). The members are mappable lithologic units that can be correlated readily in the subsurface by log characteristics, particularly by the gamma-ray log (Fig. 9). These units are well exposed in Wadi Mi'aidin and Wadi Tanuf on the south flank of Jebel Akhdar.

Member 'A' consists of 45–60 m of wackestone and packstone with planktic (globigerinids and heterohelicids) and benthic (textulariids) foraminifers, calcispheres, and rudist fragments. It is thin to medium-bedded, and its gamma curve is consistently non-shaly. The top and base are marked by distinct gamma peaks cor-

responding to the basal Aruma shales above and the 'B' member below.

The 'B' member is thin interbedded argillic lime mudstone, organic-rich lime mudstone and marl 55–67 m thick. In outcrop this unit weathers as a recessive interval of repetitive thin beds; and in the subsurface the top and base are picked on the highest and lowest gamma-ray peaks.

Member 'C' is a 60–90 m unit of packstone and wackestone with rudists and benthic forams. It forms medium- to thick-bedded cliffs in outcrop and in the subsurface is an interval of low gamma activity.

Member 'D' is a 15–30 m thick interval of repetitive shale and bioclastic packstone–wackestone. In most sections, five or six shale-limestone couplets can be identified. This member forms a distinctive recessive outcrop unit of thin beds with sharp basal and upper

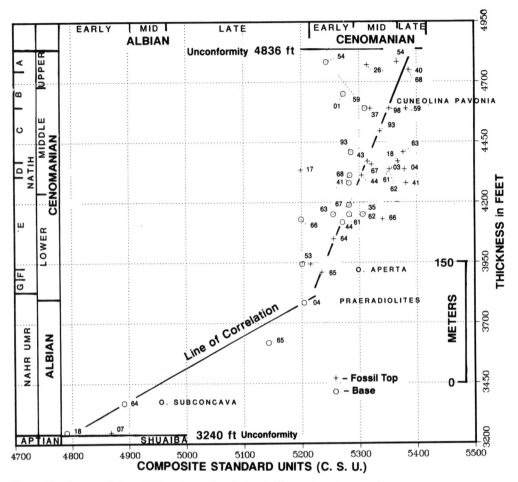

Fig. 8. Graphic correlation of Wasia Group in Wadi Mi'aidin section, Oman. The LOC for the Nahr Umr is defined by the bases of *Praeradiolites* and *O. subconcava*; the LOC for the Natih is defined by *C. pavonia* and *Praeradiolites*. The Wasia is bounded by unconformities. Table 3 gives species names for the serial numbers.

contacts. At Wadi Mi'aidin the basal marl overlies a hardground surface on the top bed of member 'E'. Bored hardgrounds are also developed on the top of the two lower limestone beds. In the subsurface, this unit is demarcated by an interval of very high gamma readings and forms a widespread marker unit (Fig. 9).

Member 'E' is a heterogenous interval 90–150 m thick consisting of rudist-peloid grainstone-packstone, foram wackestone, and planktic foram mudstone with chert nodules. The outcrop interval consists of cliff-forming, thick to massive beds in the upper part. The lower part consists of medium beds of burrow-mottled wackestone. West of Wadi Tanuf in both outcrop and subsurface an interval of thin-bedded, organic-rich, planktic foram mudstone develops in the basal part of the 'E' member.

This unit is traceable in the subsurface by its high gamma peak and represents a low-oxygen, restricted, intraplatform basin (Connally & Scott 1987).

The top of the 'E' member is virtually synchronous within this part of Oman (Fig. 7). This contact is a bored, iron-stained, phosphatic, hard-ground surface in the outcrops of Jebel Akhdar. In the core of the Jebel Khatmah well, it is a sharp lithological change. The 'D' member thins northeastward and is scarcely recognizable at Wadi Rubkhah near the shelf margin. Apparently, the peripheral bulge was still present and the 'D' member pinches out on it. The contacts of the 'A', 'B', and 'C' members are regionally diachronous, but no directional trend is apparent (Fig. 7).

The 'F' member is less than 30 m thick and

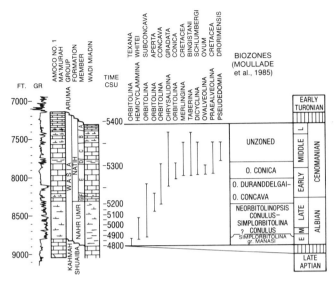

Fig. 9. Stratigraphy and ranges of key fossils in the Wasia Group, Oman. Composite Standard units (CSU) have been graphed in the Wadi Mi'aidin section and the ranges of the fossils in the C.S. are shown; not all of the fossils occur in the Wadi Mi'aidin section.

consists of medium-bedded, burrow-mottled wackestone. In the outcrop, its top is at the base of the cliff-forming 'E' member or the base of the bituminous, thin-bedded interval. The base is the top of the highest shale bed, which is marked by a gamma peak on logs.

Member 'G' is a thin interval, 15–40 m thick, of thin- to medium-bedded wackestone above the highest thick shale unit of the Nahr Umr. In outcrop the base is placed below the persistent, cliff-forming limestone beds. In wells, the base is marked by the significant gamma-ray reduction.

Correlation of the stage and substage boundaries in the Wasia Group is based on graphing the Cape Boulonnaise section, France (Amedro et al. 1978) and the Isle of Wight, England, reference sections to the composite standard (Fig. 3). The stage and substage boundaries are those defined traditionally by the ammonite succession in the European reference sections (Birkelund et al. 1984; Kennedy 1984; Robaszynski 1984). The stage boundaries are assigned CSU values by this graph. They are correlated to the Oman sections by means of graphs of these sections. The maximum ranges of the key taxa in the Wasia Group are derived by graphing the Oman and Sharjah sections. These ranges expressed in composite standard units (CSU) are plotted relative to the lithostratigraphic units at Wadi Mi'aidin (Fig. 8).

The Albian–Cenomanian boundary corre-

lates approximately with the uppermost Nahr Umr and basal Natih (Fig. 9). This boundary is within the overlap interval of *Orbitolina aperta* Erman and *Orbitolina concava* Lamarck. The boundary between the Early and Middle Cenomanian correlates with the Upper 'E' member and does not correspond with any of the foraminiferal tops or bases. The Middle-Late Cenomanian boundary, as defined by the base of *Calycoceras naviculare* (Mantell) at Cape Boulonnaise correlates within the 'B' member of the Natih Formation and is just above the local tops of *Merlingina cretacea* Hamaoui & Saint-Marc and *Pseudedomia drorimensis* Reiss, Hamaoui & Ecker. The top of the Natih is an eroded surface, and only one of our sections spans the Cenomanian–Turonian boundary. At Jebel Salakh, the top of the Natih is basal Turonian by graphic correlation and by planktic forminifers. An $x-y$ graph of the section at Jebel Salakh with the C.S. indicates that 5.6 CSUs at the top fall within the Turonian, about 76000 years. Also, two Turonian forams have bases about 4 m below the Natih top: *Helvetoglobotruncana praehelvetica* (Bolli) and *Dicarinella algeriana* (Caron) (M. Simmons, pers. comm. 1987). Furthermore, two ammonites from near the top of the Natih at Jebel Salakh collected by T. C. Connally and identified by Dr. Keith Young (written comm. 1983) straddle the Cenomanian–Turonian boundary: genus aff.

Choffaticeras and genus aff. *Kamerunoceras*. The Natih is younger here in the Fahud Salt Basin than elsewhere in Oman (Fig. 7).

Aruma Group

The youngest depositional sequence of the stable Arabian carbonate platform consists of the Laffan and Halul-Ilam formations at the base of the Aruma Group. This unconformity-bounded, shoaling up, depositional sequence of approximately Coniacian–Santonian age is about 100 m thick. Fossils present are *Dicyclina schlumbergeri* Munier-Chalmas and rotaliid forams in the Halul and the nannofossil, *Biscutum castrorum* Black (identified by L. F. Lichty, Amoco) in the Laffan which is cored in the Mubarek J-1 well, offshore Sharjah. The Laffan represents a drowning of the platform and a restricted, intraplatform basin, in which terrestrial organic matter was concentrated. Depositional conditions eventually became open marine and foram wackestone and foram-peloid packstone were deposited. Rudist pack-stone suggests local growth of radiolitid bioherms within the zone of wave action.

The Fiqa Shale and Simsima Limestone, with local, near-shore facies mapped as Muti Formation, Juweiza Formation, and Qahlah Formation (comprise the Aruma Group onshore Sharjah (Glennie *et al.* 1974; Hughes Clarke 1988). These units are the youngest Cretaceous, unconformity-bounded, depositional sequence. In the Sajaa Field, the base of the Aruma is graphed as uppermost Santonian–Campanian and the top is approximately Middle Maastrichtian. In Omani wells, the base is graphed as Coniacian–Santonian (B.A. Masters, pers. comm. 1986). The Fiqa is Santonian–Campanian based on planktic forams (Glennie *et al.* 1974) and represents a major subsidence event forming the Aruma Foreland Basin (Murris 1980). The Simsima is Lower to Middle Maastrichtian based on the rudists and the large foraminifers (Skelton *et al.* 1990).

The Muti, Fiqa, Juweiza, and Simsima units were deposited in a rapidly subsiding, foreland basin that developed upon the outboard area of the preceding Cretaceous carbonate shelf. Subsidence began in west-central Oman where the oldest basinal deposits are Coniacian–Santonian. At the same time in the western Emirates, the stable shelf was the site of the Laffan-Halul sequence. These depositional sites were apparently separated by a positive feature in western Oman and the eastern Emirates (P. Manoogian, pers. comm. 1987), which may have been a peripheral bulge. However, by the beginning of the Campanian, the extent of the foreland basin spread westward, drowning this last vestige of the carbonate shelf. At the margins of this basin, tectonic features controlled deposition of conglomerates and carbonate debris units, the Muti and Juweiza (Robertson 1987). During the Early–Middle Maastrichtian, a narrow carbonate shelf was formed along the eastern margin of the Aruma Basin where the Simsima was deposited. Southwards into south–central Oman, the basin shallowed and widespread shallow shelf sands and carbonates were deposited. Deep-water conditions prevailed in the central part of the basin represented by exposures in Jebel Hafit in southeastern Abu Dhabi.

Timing of Tectono-Eustatic Events

Tectonic events are clearly recorded in the Cretaceous sequences in Oman and the Emirates (Glennie *et al.* 1974; Ricateau & Riché 1980; Entsminger 1981; Coleman 1981; Tippit *et al.* 1981; Lippard 1983; Searle *et al.* 1983; Robertson 1987; Searle 1988). The record of these events consists of unconformities, facies successions and near-source conglomerates (Fig. 10).

During the Berriasian and probably beginning in the Late Jurassic, the Oman shelf subsided and was drowned by a concomittant eustatic sea level rise (Scott *et al.* 1989). An early Berriasian eustatic rise is documented elsewhere (Haq *et al.* 1987). Subsidence is indicated by the development of the Early Cretaceous ramp upon which the Habshan, Salil and Rayda formations accumulated (Glennie *et al.* 1974; Hassan *et al.* 1975; Ricateau & Riché 1980). Facies of the underlying Sahtan Group indicate that a Jurassic shallow water, carbonate shelf and shelf margin were developed in eastern Oman. This area was submerged to 100–200 m depth during the Berriasian (Connally & Scott 1985) and the substrate sloped upwards to the west. The rate of relative sea level rise was 4 cm/1000 yrs, if all the change occurred during the Berriasian and 200 m of drowning occurred.

The shelf remained relatively stable for about 12.5 Ma as the Habshan prograded eastward across the sediment wedge that filled the drowned Jurassic shelf. Beginning about 130–127 Ma ago, the Lekhwair Formation was deposited in deeper lagoonal environments upon the shelf behind the Habshan shelf-edge shoal. The 11.7 Ma long Lekhwair to Shuaiba sequence indicates slow shoaling across much of the shelf, so early during Lekhwair deposition, slight subsidence occurred. Possibly sea level

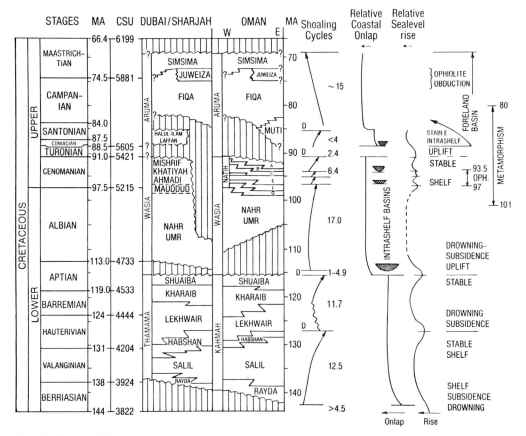

Fig. 10. Timing of Cretaceous stratigraphic and tectonic events is southeastern Arabia.

rose as well, because an intra-Hauterivian deepening is documented elsewhere in the Tethys (Haq *et al*. 1987; Scott *et al*. 1989). Local intrashelf subsidence formed the Aptian Bab Basin in the Emirates, but generally the shelf was stable. Local salt movement in Abu Dhabi may have occurred during deposition of the Habshan and Lekhwair (Hassan *et al*. 1975).

The top Shuaiba Formation is a regional unconformity that records both a eustatic sea level change and Arabian tectonics. A world-wide sea level rise is documented on other carbonate platforms and in terrigenous sequences (Haq *et al*. 1987; Scott *et al*. 1989). The rate of sea level change in Oman was 7−10 cm/1000 yrs, if sea level rose 70 to 100 m during the 1 Ma between Shuaiba and Nahr Umr deposition.

Uplift of the Ha'il−Rutbah Arch in northern Saudi Arabia provided terrigenous sediments for the alluvial and littoral facies of the Wasia Group (Entsminger 1981). The affects of this arch were diminished by earliest

Cenomanian when the Ahmadi Shale was deposited (Entsminger 1981). Also, local uplift of the Shuaiba surface within the Emirates is suggested by leached porosity (Harris & Frost 1984). The presence of a marginal uplift, perhaps an early expression of the peripheral bulge, is suggested by southeastward truncation of the Shuaiba across Jebel Akhdar outcrops (Fig. 5).

The latest Aptian−Early Albian sea level rise drowned the shelf and the Nahr Umr Formation onlapped across the Oman shelf towards the east and northeast (Fig. 7). Here, a relatively stable shelf persisted for 23.4 Ma during deposition of the Nahr Umr and Natih formations. The four shoaling cycles in the Wasia Group probably represent eustatic sea-level changes. The mid-Cenomanian drowning between the Natih 'E' and 'D' members correlates with a major sea-level change recorded on other plates (Scott *et al*. 1989). The other cycles have not yet been correlated precisely with other shelf sections, but numerous eustatic changes during the Albian-Cenomanian are proposed by Haq *et al*.

(1987). Towards the western strand line, five cycles of regression-transgression are recorded in the Wasia Group that may represent eustatic cycles (Entsminger 1981). It is desirable to correlate this section precisely with the Oman section to determine the synchroneity of these cycles. Similarly, in the Rub'Al Kahli Basin, three sea level rises are recognized in the Wasia Group (Newell & Hennington 1983).

Four deposits of organic-rich beds accumulated in intrashelf, restricted basins (Wilson 1975; Newell & Hennington, 1983; Jordan et al. 1985; Alsharhan & Nairn 1986). Each of these units in Oman and the Emirates, the Bab, lower 'E', 'B', and Laffan shale, formed during the drowning of the shelf and a relative sea level rise. In the Rub'Al Kahli Basin, the two source rock units are the upper Safaniya Member and the lower part of the Mishrif Formation (Newell & Hennington 1983), which may correlate with the lower 'E' and 'B' members of the Natih in Oman. Probably, the older of these two events is also recorded offshore of the Emirates as the Khatiyah or Shilaif formations (Jordan et al. 1985), because it yields the Albian-Early Cenomanian foraminifer, Favusella [Globigerina] washitensis (Carsey). A detailed biostratigraphy of these sections is needed to demonstrate these correlations.

The first major tectonic movement began during the Wasia—Aruma hiatus (Glennie et al. 1974; Ricateau & Riche 1980; Robertson 1987; Searle 1988). The duration of this hiatus was less than 2.5 Ma in Oman (Fig. 10). Following Wasia deposition, the shelf edge was uplifted to form a peripheral bulge (Glennie et al. 1974; Ricateau & Riché 1980; O'Conner & Patton 1986; Robertson 1987). Extensive erosion across this positive feature removed much of the Wasia beds in Sharjah and northern Oman. This debris was not deposited upon the shelf, therefore it must have been shed into the oceanic realm. By the Coniacian to early Campanian, some of this debris was retained on the shelf as the Muti Formation, but after the structural setting of this area changed from a positive feature to the foreland basin. Also, during this Turonian hiatus local salt movement formed early structures in the Emirates, some of which became petroleum reservoirs (Tschopp 1967b; Ricateau & Riche 1980; Jordan et al. 1985).

The mainly Turonian uplift was preceded by formation of the oceanic crust within a 4.4 Ma span from 97.9 to 93.5 Ma (Tippit et al. 1981; Searle 1988). This crust became the ophiolite that eventually was thrust upon the shelf. A regional metamorphic event was associated with formation of the ophiolite and is dated from 101 to 80 Ma by the K—Ar method (Lippard 1983). This crust is overlain by Cenomanian—early Turonian pelagic oceanic sediments (Tippit et al. 1981).

The first record of the foreland Aruma Basin is Conacian—Santonian by planktic forams (Glennie et al. 1974) and by graphic correlation (B.A. Masters, pers. comm. 1986). This interval occurs in a small area of west—central Oman in the subsurface (P. Manoogian, pers. comm. 1988). During the same time, the stable shelf persisted in the offshore Emirates area where the Laffan and Ilam—Halul formations were deposited. The areal extent of the Aruma Basin expanded during a 4 to 5 Ma span and uppermost Santonian to lowermost Campanian strata of the Fiqa Formation were deposited over the entire region. The Fiqa onlaps westward over the Halul sequence. This foreland basin existed throughout the remaining Late Cretaceous and a 15 Ma record is preserved.

During the late Campanian and earliest Maastrichtian obduction of the ophiolite allochthon occurred and contributed debris to the Juweiza Formation. Carbonate deposition became more widespread following the obduction event and the Simsima Formation accumulated during the Early—Middle Maastrichtian. This was accompanied by transgression, probably associated with a eustatic sea level rise (Haq et al. 1987) and development of a narrow shallow shelf rimming the emplaced nappes (Skelton et al. 1990). Subsidence resumed producing deep water Simsima facies in some areas; deposition was terminated during the Late Maastrichtian and/or early Palaeocene and a regional unconformity developed between Cretaceous and Tertiary strata. The timing of these events cannot be measured precisely at this time.

Amoco Oman Petroleum Company is most sincerely thanked for its help with this work. The paper is published with the permission of Amoco Production Company.

References

ALSHARHAN, A. S. 1985. Depositional environment, reservoir units evolution, and hydrocarbon habitat of Shuaiba Formation, Lower Cretaceous, Abu Dhabi, United Arab Emirates. American Association of Petroleum Geologists Bulletin, 69, 899—912.

—— & NAIRN, A. E. M. 1986. A review of the Cretaceous formations in the Arabian Peninsula and Gulf: Part I. Lower Cretaceous (Thamama Group) stratigraphy and paleogeography. Journal of Petroleum Geology, 9, 365—392.

—— & —— 1988. A review of the Cretaceous formations in the Arabian Peninsula and Gulf: Part II. Mid-Cretaceous (Wasia Group) stratigraphy and paleogeography. *Journal of Petroleum Geology*, **11**, 89–116.

AMEDRO, F., DAMOTTE, R., MANIVIT, H., ROBASZYNSKI, F. & SORNAY, J. 1978. Echelles biostratigraphiques dans le Cénomanien du Boulonnais. *Géologie Méditerranéenne*, **5**, 5–18.

BIRKELUND, T., HANCOCK, J. M., HART, M. B., RAWSON, P. F., REMANE, J., ROBASZYNSKI, F., SCHMID, F. & SURLYK, F. 1984. Cretaceous stage boundaries – proposals. *Geological Society of Denmark Bulletin*, **33**, 3–20.

CONNALLY, T. C. & SCOTT, R. W. 1985. Carbonate sediment-fill of an oceanic shelf, Lower Cretaceous, Arabian Peninsula. *Society of Economic Palaeontologists and Mineralogists Core Workshop*, No. 6, Deep-Water Carbonates, 266–302.

—— & —— 1987. Shelf and intrashelf basin facies of the middle Cretaceous, Rub-Al-Khali Basin, southern Arabian Peninsula (abst.). *Society of Economic Palaeontologists Mineralogists Midyear Meeting*, **4**, 17.

COLEMAN, R. G. 1981. Tectonic Setting of ophiolite obduction in Oman. *Journal of Geophysical Research*, **86**, No. B4, 2497–2508.

ENTSMINGER, L. D. 1981. Sedimentary response to tectonic and eustatic changes: an example from the mid-Cretaceous Wasia Formation, Saudi Arabia. *Society of Petroleum Engineers*. Bahrain Middle East Technical Conference, 159–170.

GLENNIE, K. W., BOEUF, M. G. A., HUGHES CLARKE, M. W., MOODY-STUART, M., PILAAR, W. F. H. & REINHARDT, B. M. 1974. Geology of the Oman Mountains (Parts one, two and three). *Verhandelingen van het Koninklijk Nederlands Geologisch Mijnbouwkundig Genootschap*, 31, The Hague, Martinus Nijhoff.

HAQ, B. U., HARDENBOL, J. & VAIL, P. R. 1987. Chronology of fluctuating sea levels since the Triassic. *Science*, **235**, 1156–1167.

HARRIS, P. M. & FROST, S. H. 1984. Middle Cretaceous carbonate reservoirs, Fahud Field and northwestern Oman. *American Association of Petroleum Geologists Bulletin*, **68**, 649–658.

——, ——, SEIGLIE, G. A. & SCHNEIDERMANN, N. 1984. Regional unconformities and depositional cycles, Cretaceous of the Arabian Peninsula. *American Association of Petroleum Geologists Memoir*, **36**, 67–80.

HASSAN, T. H., MUDD, G. C., & TWOMBLEY, B. N. 1975. The stratigraphy and sedimentation of the Thamama Group (Lower Cretaceous) of Abu Dhabi. *Ninth Arab Petroleum Congress*. Dubai, article 107 (B-3).

HUGHES CLARKE, M. W. 1988. Stratigraphy and rock unit nomenclature in the oil-producing area of interior Oman. *Journal of Petroleum Geology*, **11**, 5–60.

JORDAN, C. F., Jr., CONNALLY, T. C., Jr. & VEST, H. A. 1985. Middle Cretaceous carbonates of the Mishrif Formation, Fateh Field, offshore Dubai, U.A.E. *In*: ROEHL, P. O. & CHOQUETTE, P. W., (eds) *Carbonate Petroleum Reservoirs*. Springer,

New York, 425–442.

KENNEDY, W. J. 1984. Ammonite faunas and the 'standard zones' of the Cenomanian to Maastrichtian stages in their type areas, with some proposals for the definition of the stage boundaries by ammonites. *Geological Society of Denmark Bulletin*, **33**, 147–162.

LIPPARD, S. J. 1983. Cretaceous high pressure metamorphism in NE Oman and its relationship to subduction and ophiolite nappe emplacement. *Journal of the Geological Society of London*, **140**, 97–104.

MILLER, F. X. 1977. The graphic correlation method in biostratigraphy. *In*: KAUFFMAN, E. G. & HAZEL, J. E. (eds) *Concepts and Methods of Biostratigraphy*. Dowden, Hutchinson and Ross, Inc., Stroudsburg, Pennsylvania, 165–186.

MOSHIER, S. O., HANDFORD, C. R., SCOTT, R. W. & BOUTELL, R. D. 1988. Giant gas accumulation in a 'chalky'-textured micritic limestone, Lower Cretaceous Shuaiba Fm., Eastern United Arab Emirates. *Society of Economic Palaeontologists and Mineralogists Core Workshop*, No. 12, Giant Oil and Gas Fields, 229–272.

MOULLADE, MICHEL, PEYBERNES, B., REY, J. & SAINT-MARC, P. 1985. Biostratigraphic interest and paleobiogeographic distribution of Early and mid-Cretaceous Mesogean Orbitolinids (Foraminiferida). *Journal of Foraminiferal Research*, **15**, 149–158.

MURRIS, R. J. 1980. Middle East: stratigraphic evolution and oil habitat. *American Association of Petroleum Geologists Bulletin*, **64**, 593–618.

NEWELL, K. D. & HENNINGTON, R. D. 1983. Potential petroleum source rock deposition in the Middle Cretaceous Wasia Formation, Rub' al Khali, Saudi Arabia. *Society of Petroleum Engineers*. Middle East Technical Conference, Bahrain, 151–160.

O'CONNOR, S. J. & PATTON, T. L., 1986. Middle Cretaceous carbonate reservoirs Fahud Field and northwestern Oman: Discussion. *American Association of Petroleum Geologists Bulletin*, **70**, 1799–1801.

PALMER, A. R. 1983. The decade of North American geology: 1983 geologic time scale. *Geology*, **11**, 503–504.

RICATEAU, R. & RICHÉ, P. H. 1980. Geology of the Musandam Peninsula (Sultanate of Oman) and its surroundings. *Journal of Petroleum Geology*, **3**, 139–152.

ROBASZYNSKI, F. 1984. The Albian, Cenomanian and Turonian Stages in their type-regions. *Geological Society of Denmark Bulletin*, **33**, 191–198.

ROBERTSON, A. H. F. 1987. The transition from a passive margin to an Upper Cretaceous foreland basin related to ophiolite emplacement in the Oman Mountains. *Geological Society of America Bulletin*, **99**, 633–653.

SAINT-MARC, P. 1974. Etude Stratigraphique et micropaléontologique de l'Albien, du Cénomanien et du Turonian du Liban. *Notes et Mémoires Moyen-Orient*, **13**, 7–298.

SCHROEDER, R. & NEUMANN, M. 1985. Les grandes

Foraminiferes de Cretace moyen de la region Mediterranenne. *Geobios*, Memoire special 7.

SCOTT, R. W. 1987. Stratigraphic architecture of two Cretaceous carbonate platforms Gulf Coast and Arabia (abst.). *American Association of Petroleum Geologists Bulletin*, **71**, 612.

——, FROST, S. H. & SHAFFER, B. L. 1989. Early Cretaceous sea level curves, Gulf Coast and southeastern Arabia. *Society of Economic Palaeontologists and Mineralogists*, Special Publication, **42**, 275–284.

SEARLE, M. P. 1988. Thrust tectonics of the Dibba zone and the structural evolution of the Arabian continental margin along the Musandam mountains (Oman and United Arab Emirates). *Journal of the Geological Society, London*, **145**, 43–53.

——, JAMES, N. P., CALON, T. J. & SMEWING, J. D. 1983. Sedimentological and structural evolution of the Arabian continental margin in the Musandam Mountains and Dibba zone, United Arab Emirates. *Geological Society of America Bulletin*, **94**, 1381–1400.

SHAW, A. B. 1964. *Time in stratigraphy*. McGraw-Hill, New York.

SIMMONS, M. D. & HART, M. B. 1987. The biostratigraphy and microfacies of the Early to mid-Cretaceous carbonates of Wadi Mi'aidin, Central Oman Mountains. *In*: M. D. HART, (ed.) *Micropalaeontology of Carbonate Environments*. Ellis Horwood, Chichester, 176–207.

SKELTON, P. W., NOLAN, S. C. & SCOTT, R. W. 1990. The Maastrichtian transgression onto the north-western flank of the proto-Oman Mountains: sequences of rudist-bearing beach to open shelf facies. *In*: ROBERTSON, A. H. F., SEARLE, M. P. & RIES, A. C. *The Geology and Tectonics of the Oman Region*. Geological Society, London, Special Publication, **49**, 521–547.

TIPPIT, P. R., PESSAGNO, E. A., Jr. & SMEWING, J. D. 1981. The biostratigraphy of sediments in the volcanic unit of the Samail Ophiolite. *Journal of Geophysical Research*, **86**, No. B4, 2756–2762.

TSCHOPP, R. H. 1967a. The general geology of Oman. *7th World Petroleum Congress*. Mexico, Proceedings, **2**, 231–242.

—— 1967b. Development of the Fahud Field. *7th World Petroleum Congress*. Mexico, Proceedings, **2**, 243–250.

WAGNER, P. D. 1990. Geochemical stratigraphy and porosity controls in Cretaceous carbonates near the Oman mountains. *In*: ROBERTSON, A. H. F., SEARLE, M. P. & RIES, A. C. (eds) *The Geology and Tectonics of the Oman Region*. Geological Society, London, Special Publication, **49**, 127–137.

WATTS, K. F. 1987. Response of a passive continental margin carbonate slope to closing of a Mesozoic ocean basin — Mayhah Formation and Qumayrah Facies of Muti Formation, Oman. *American Association of Petroleum Geologists Bulletin*, **71**, 625–626.

WILSON, J. L. 1975. *Carbonate facies in geologic history*. Springer, New York.

The Lower Kahmah Group of Oman: the carbonate fill of a marginal shelf basin

E. A. HAAN[1], S. G. CORBIN[2], M. W. HUGHES CLARKE[1] & J. E. MABILLARD[3]

[1] *Petroleum Development Oman LLC, XXG/3, P.O. Box 81, Muscat, Sultanate of Oman*

[2] *I LASMO Cy. Ltd., Bastion House, 140 London Wall, London EC2Y 5DN, UK*

[3] *Koninklijke Shell Exploratie en Productie Laboratorium, EPX/36, Volmerlaan 6, 2288 GD Rijswijk, The Netherlands*

Abstract: Following the rifting and spreading related to the opening of the Tethys Ocean during the Triassic and Early Jurassic, relaxation and subsidence affected its passive margins. In Iran and Oman, such subsidence of the continental margins gave rise to deeper marine, marginal shelf basins, that initially were filled with pelagic sediments, but were progressively infilled by prograding shallow shelf-derived sediments. In Oman the fill sequence is well displayed for study in surface outcrops in the Oman Mountains as well as in subsurface geological and geophysical data. This paper provides an integrated picture of the geometry and facies distribution of the sediments, which filled this marginal shelf basin. The pelagic facies comprises the Rayda Formation and the basin, therefore, is named the Rayda Basin. The prograding, shelf-derived, fill facies comprises the Salil Formation. Surface-type sections of these two formations are described from outcrops in the Oman Mountains. The last stage of the basin fill is represented by a diversified shallow marine facies, referred to as the Habshan Formation, which is defined in Abu Dhabi. This unit prograded over the entire sag basin and almost levelled the pre-existing basin topography in such a way that overlying deposits hardly reflect the original Rayda Basin outline. The Habshan shoal facies is therefore in part coeval with the Rayda and Salil and exhibits a complex interdigitation with those two formations towards the basin margin. The seismostratigraphic expression of the Habshan, Salil and Rayda Formations provides a valuable tool for defining basin outline and mode of infill. A number of seismic lines are presented in relation to well log correlation panels to highlight the complexity of the sedimentary processes affecting these units. The fill of the basin was completed by the Valanginian and the ovelying Lekhwair Formation of Hauterivian to Barremian age represents a renewed marine transgression.

The Lower Cretaceous strata of the Kahmah Group in Oman (Fig. 1) consist of the Rayda, Salil and Habshan Formations, which are Berriasian to Valanginian/Hauterivian in age (Glennie *et al.* 1974; Hughes Clarke 1988). These units are capped by the Lekhwair, Kharaib and Shuaiba Formations, which are Late Hauterivian to Aptian in age. The lower Kahmah is at the surface in the Oman Mountains and is present in the subsurface of North Oman, extending up to the northern part of the Ghaba Salt Basin (Fig. 2).

The geological history of the Kahmah Group was controlled by an interaction of eustatic sea level variations and local subsidence, resulting in a number of shallowing upward cycles of varying duration. Following a period of general uplift, leading to the truncation of Late Jurassic strata in North Oman; rapid subsidence in combination with a sea level rise, led to the gener-

ation of a deep marine shelf basin on the margin of the Tethys Ocean, which extends into Iran (Koop & Stoneley 1982). Pelagic carbonates and marls of the Rayda and Salil Formations accumulated in this basin, which has a distinct southern limit, close to the 21°N latitude line (Fig. 3). Along the southern rims of the basin, shallow marine, high-energy deposits of the Habshan Formation, prograded northwards and the influx of substantial amounts of carbonate detritus, resulted in a complex interdigitation with the deeper marine facies of the Salil and Rayda Formations towards the north, thus creating an overall shallowing upward cycle. This relationship was not only controlled by sea-level fluctuation and subsidence, as in the case for the Rayda and Salil Formations, but also by the rate and amount of sediment input from the south. The basin fill was more or less completed by the Valanginian and by that time

From ROBERTSON, A. H. F., SEARLE, M. P. & RIES, A. C. (eds), 1990,
The Geology and Tectonics of the Oman Region.
Geological Society Special Publication No 49, pp 109–125

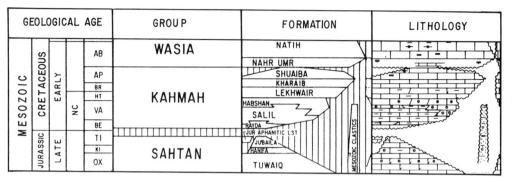

Fig. 1. Oman subsurface stratigraphy.

the Habshan Formation had almost levelled the pre-existing basin topography. The overlying Lekhwair Formation marks a renewed period of transgression and subsequently almost the entire area of Oman was covered with argillaceous limestone shelf sedimentation.

The complexity of the interdigitation of Habshan, Salil and Rayda Formations can be seen on reflection seismic data and various geometries of the Habshan carbonate shelf can be distinguished. By contrast, the relationship of the three formations is far less complex towards the north and in the outcrop area of the Jebel Akhdar. To illustrate this, surface outcrop sections of the three formations are presented and compared with detailed well log correlations, which are callibrated with seismic data.

Stratigraphy

Outcrop Sections

The chosen study area for the outcrop sections is the southeast corner of the Jebel Akhdar, which is located *c.* 100 km southwest of Muscat. Jebel Akhdar is an eroded antiform, with a core of Precambrian sediments overlain by Permian to Cretaceous carbonates, which, in the main study area, vary in dip from horizontal to 20° to the south and east. Aerial photographs (Scale 1:20 000) were used to provide a base map (Fig. 4) and to establish the local fault pattern. Possible measurable sections were then selected between the faults. In the field the most accesible and complete sections proved to be close to the graded road, where a composite section (Fig. 5) in excess of 500 m was measured and sampled from the top Mahil Formation to the Habshan Formation. This sequence includes the stratotypes of the Rayda and Salil Formations at coordinates E:57°41′30″, N: 23°02′00″. In addition to the mapped area, wadi

sections were examined on both the northern and southern flanks of the Jebel Akhdar. In these exposures the Sahtan and lower Kahmah proved easily recognisable due to the recessive weathering character of the Rayda and Salil Formations (Fig. 5).

Rayda Formation. The stratotype of the Rayda Formation (Witt 1971 unpublished; Hassan *et al.* 1975; Hughes Clarke 1988; Connally & Scott 1985; Simmons & Hart 1987) was measured in sections 1 and 2 (Figs 4–7) and is about 150 m thick. The base of the Rayda Formation is marked by an abrupt change in lithology, bedding character and weathering colour from the underlying Dhruma Formation. The top of the Rayda Formation is marked by a change in bedding and weathering profile, but lithologically the boundary is gradational and a transitional relationship with the overlying Salil Formation is observed.

The Lower member of the Rayda Formation comprises *c.* 65 m of light grey-weathering, thin-bedded, lime mudstones with nodular and laminar cherts (Fig. 7). A condensed horizon is locally developed at the base of the formation. This bed comprises undated corroded limestone pebbles, numerous vertebrate teeth and bones, casts of ammonites and belemnites, set in a reddened lime wackestone matrix. The overlying beds (*c.* 10 m) are recrystallized, locally silicified, dolomitic limestones and calcareous dolomites with chert. This suggests slow deposition below or close to the calcite compensation depth. These beds pass upwards into mud/wackestones containing abundant radiolaria, crinoid bioclasts, ostracods, sponge spicules, rare textularid foraminifera and micropelletoids. The cherts, which, in this outcrop area, do not contain radiolaria or bioclasts, become progressively less common towards the top of this lower sequence, where they are typically nodular.

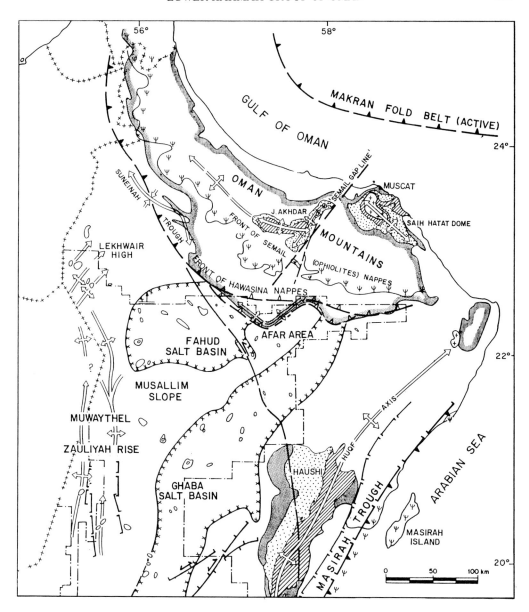

LEGEND:

▦ MESOZOIC	⊞ BASEMENT	⊓ NORMAL FAULTS	
⬚ PALAEOZOIC	✕✕✕ SALT BASIN MARGIN	⊿ REVERSE FAULTS AND THRUSTS	
▨ PRE-CAMBRIAN	⇕ MEGAFOLDS OR PERSISTENT HIGHS	⊙ OIL / GAS FIELD	
Ψ Ψ OPHIOLITES			

Fig. 2. Mega-tectonic framework of North Oman.

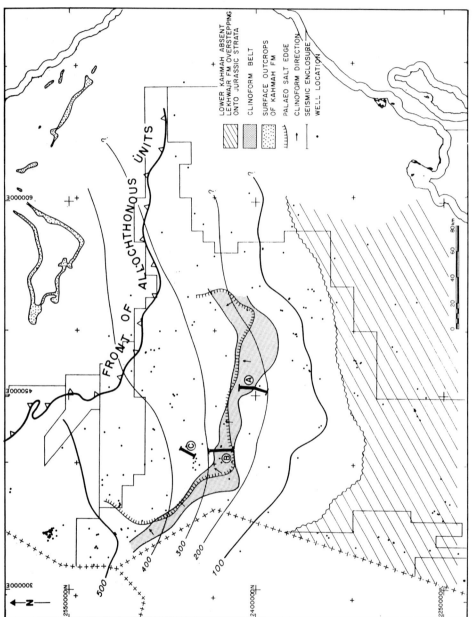

Fig. 3. Generalized isopach map of the Lower Kahmah Group in Oman.

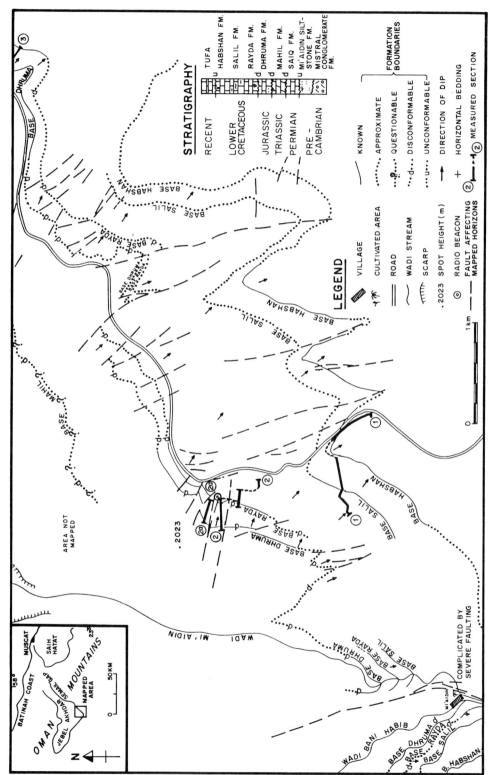

Fig. 4. Surface geological map of the Kahmah outcrop area.

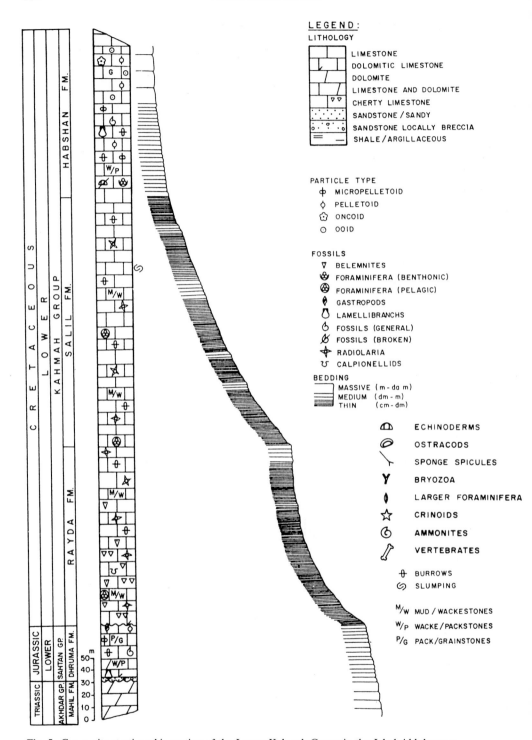

Fig. 5. Composite stratigraphic section of the Lower Kahmah Group in the Jebel Akhdar area.

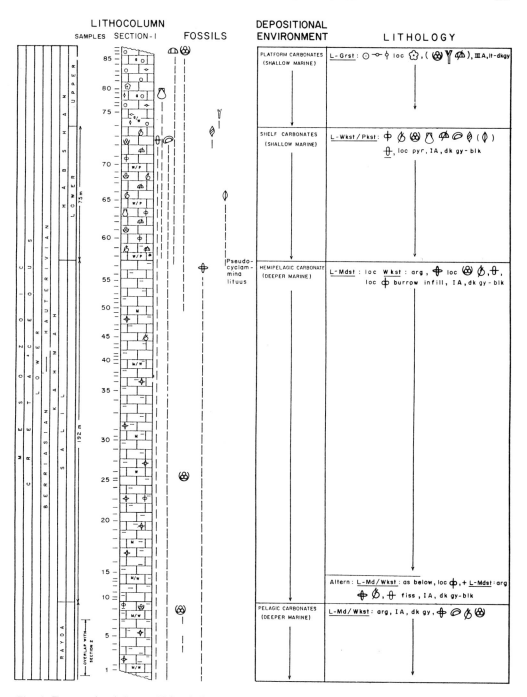

Fig. 6. Type section 1, Lower Kahmah Group, see text for explanation.

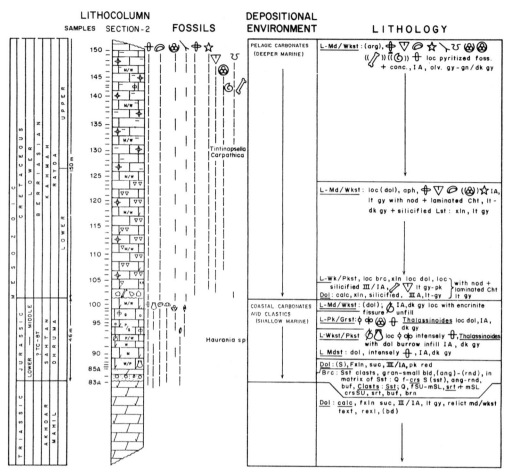

Fig. 7. Type section 2, Lower Kahmah Group, see text for explanation.

The Upper member of the Rayda Formation consists of *c*. 70 m of medium- to thin-bedded, olive to dark grey-weathering mud/wacke-stones, in gradational contact with the lower member. In outcrop belemnites are common in these beds, but ammonites occur only rarely and are found as pyritized moulds. Radiolaria are abundant throughout the sequence but tintinnids, principally *Tintinnopsella carpathica* (Murgeanu & Fillipescu), occur rarely. Planktonic and benthonic foraminifera, sponge spicules, ostracods and crinoid debris occur in varying proportions. Bioturbation is common at most horizons, particularly fine branching burrows. The uppermost beds of the Rayda Formation are medium- to thick-bedded, dark grey to black-weathering mudstones.

Based on fauna and sedimentology, a deep

marine environment of deposition is interpreted for the Rayda Formation. The facies change between the lower and the upper members probably reflects the start of the regressive phase following an initial drowning.

Age-diagnostic fossils are rare in the Rayda Formation in outcrop. The presence of *Tintinnopsella carpathica* indicates an Early Cretaceous age for at least the middle part of the formation.

Salil Formation. The stratotype of the Salil Formation (Scherer 1969 unpublished; Hassan *et al.* 1975; Hughes Clarke 1988, Connally & Scott 1985; Simmons & Hart 1987) as measured in section 1 (Figs 4–7) is about 192 m thick and has a distinctive weathering profile, comprising a series of thin-bedded, recessive units separated by thicker-bedded scarps. The sequence is lithologically monotonous, consisting of black argillaceous lime mudstones, which characteristically weather olive-green or brown-grey. Macrofossils are less common than in the Rayda Formation and bioturbation is more intense. Radiolaria are found throughout the formation, whilst ostracods and benthonic foraminifera occur in small numbers. Patches of micropelletoids represent burrow infill of faecal pellets. The uppermost beds contain an increasing proportion of bioclastic material and are transitional to the overlying Habshan Formation.

A deep marine environment above the calcite compensation depth is interpreted for the Salil Formation. Continued shallowing of the basin is indicated particularly at the top of the sequence where facies grade into those of the Habshan Formation. Although no age-diagnostic fossils were recorded in our samples from the Salil Formation, *Calpionella darderi* (Colom) and *Tintinnopsella carpathica* are present in collections made from the formation in other parts of the Jebel Akhdar, which indicate a Valanginian age.

Habshan Formation. The Habshan Formation (Hassan *et al.* 1975; Hughes Clarke 1988; Connally & Scott, 1985; Simmons & Hart 1987) is incomplete in section 1 (Figs 4–7), where the top part has been eroded. The base of the formation is gradational with the upper part of the Salil Formation. The formation can be subdivided into a lower wacke/packestone member (*c.* 70 m) and an upper grainstone member (45 m measured). Within the lower part of the sequence there is a general increase in bed thickness. Bedding eventually becomes massive and cliff-forming. The dark grey- to buffweathering limestones of the lower member contain proportions of bioclastic material. Echinoid and mollusc debris is common. Foraminifera are locally abundant and micropelletoids occur in bioturbated intervals. Above a transitional sequence the upper member consists of oolitic and pelletoidal grainstones, with varying amounts of coated grains, oncoids and bioclasts.

The lower member is interpreted to represent a shallowing upward succession from deep marine (ramp, slope?) to shallow marine. The regression culminates in the development of very shallow deposition of carbonate shoals in the upper member.

The occurrence of *Pseudocyclammina lituus* (Yokoyama) throughout the lower member suggests an age in the range of Late Jurassic to Early Cretaceous. However, from regional considerations, a Valanginian to Hauterivian age is suggested for these beds.

Reflection seismic data

Screening of seismic data for seismostratigraphic features in the Early Cretaceous sequence of North and Central Oman has revealed the presence of extensive clinoforms in the unit. At the southern margin of the basin a subparallel to low-angle reflection configuration is present, culminating in a band of high-angle clinoforms, which locally are arranged in a chaotic manner. The distribution of these high-angle clinoforms has been mapped and shows an elongate occurence curving NE to NW, oblique to the general isopach trend of the basin (Fig. 3). In general the internal reflection configuration of the clinoform belt is parallel to tangential (Mitchum *et al.* 1977) and toplaps are only locally present in an overall sigmoidal configuration (Fig. 8a). Variations of this generalised geometry may result from changes in (a) eustatic sea level, (b) sedimentation rates on the platform or in the basin, (c) relative subsidence (Bosellini 1984) or (d) relative position to prevailing wind or current direction (Eberli & Ginsburg 1987).

The clinoform belt coincides over large parts with the inferred depositional edge of the Infra-Cambrian Ara salt, suggesting that the distribution of the clinoform belt might have been be controlled by localized salt movement and/or deep seated faulting, which generated minor differentiation in the pre-existing platform bathymetry. The salt movement itself could have been triggered by the overall subsidence following the collapse of the Tethyan margin.

The Habshan clinoforms may exhibit discrete pulses of progradation as can be shown on seismic data (Fig. 8b), where a relative drop in base level in combination with high rates of sediment input were the controlling factors. Towards the north, the dip of the clinoforms decreases and a very low-angle configuration of high-amplitude seismic events is observed (Fig. 8c).

The presence of angular events in the Lower Kahmah throughout the major part of the basin is taken as evidence of strong diachronaity of the units involved. The actual physical meaning of the clinoforms is still under investigation and presently a core is being analysed, which covers one full seismic cycle over a clinoform. Preliminary investigation of this core shows that locally, the hard impedance 'kicks' on seismic data result from hardgrounds or dolomitic horizons, but whether this applies to all the clinoform interfaces is currently unknown.

(a)

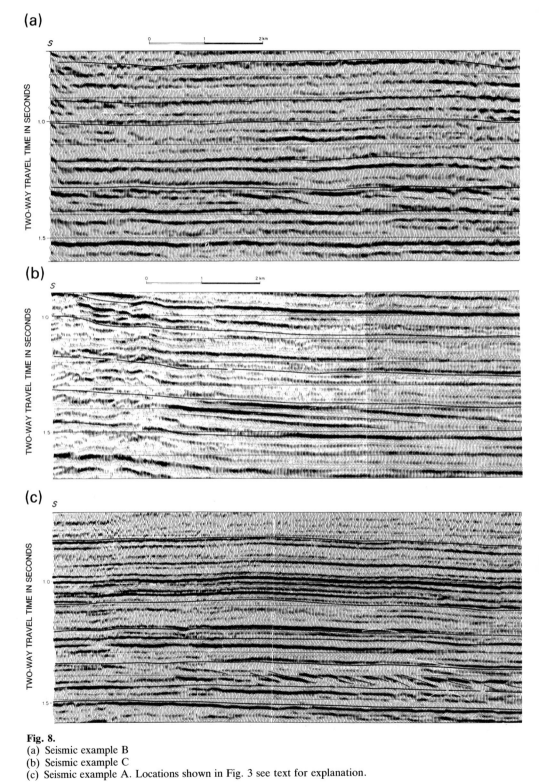

Fig. 8.
(a) Seismic example B
(b) Seismic example C
(c) Seismic example A. Locations shown in Fig. 3 see text for explanation.

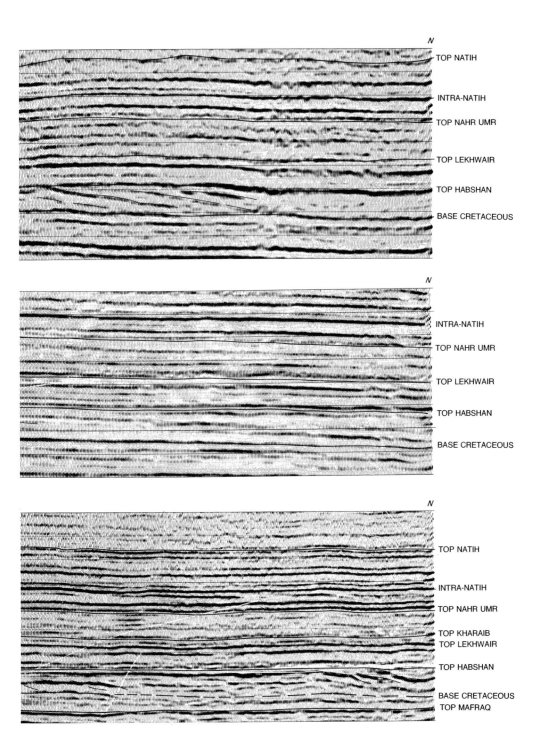

Subsurface geological data

The subsurface data from some 70 relevant exploration wells (Fig. 3), that penetrated the Lower Kahmah Group were evaluated and detailed log correlation panels were prepared in order to calibrate sequence boundaries and pick consistent formation tops.

The distribution of the lower Kahmah has a well defined southern limit at around the 21° latitude line (Fig. 3). South of this line, the Lekwair Formation oversteps the lower Kahmah and lies directly on Jurassic or older strata. Towards the north the lower Kahmah thickens rapidly to *c.* 100 m at a distance 20–30 km north of the depositional limit and then further to the north the gradient to thickening decreases slightly, but still shows an overall thickening up to well over 500 m in the Lekhwair area.

One of the main problems, which became apparent after the log correlation exercise, was the fact that although the overall basin geometry is understood, detailed correlations in areas with close well control may deviate substantially from the large-scale model, especially along the clinoform belt. Log-based subdivisions into Habshan, Salil and Rayda Formation become less apparent towards the southern part of the basin, and sometimes it can be questioned whether clear differences in log response truly reflect the subdivision as it is proposed in the surface outcrop sections.

Two examples are given from separate fields (Yibal and Al Huwaisah), with dense well control, where a subdivision could be made into Habshan and Rayda/Salil Formation. In the first example (Fig. 9) the Habshan Formation is represented by a unit with low gamma-ray response and a small LDL/CNL separation. The log shape is blocky, and an alternation of tight and porous streaks is present. The tight streaks most probably represent more cemented or dolomitic zones.

The underlying Salil/Rayda Formations show a higher gamma-ray response in combination with a marked increase in LDL/CNL separation, which is characteristic of more argillaceous, tightly cemented lime/mudstones. The log character is serrate and results from a high-frequency alternation of tight and slightly more porous beds. Locally the unit can contain well expressed zones with less argillaceous and more porous streaks. At the base of the Salil/Rayda Formation, a unit can be distinguished with a discrete lowering in gamma-ray response in combination with a reduction in separation of the LDL/CNL logs. The log character is highly serrate. This unit could be considered as the basinal porcellanite of the Rayda Formation, but in relation with more northerly wells it contains too much argillaceous material, which in general is taken as being diagnostic of the Salil Formation.

The Habshan Formation has an almost constant thickness throughout the field. Individual log markers in the Salil/Rayda Formation show a good correlation with an apparently constant sedimentary dip towards the north. If the basal unit represents the Rayda Formation it would imply that it thins towards the basin (in a northerly direction), which taking the overall geometry into consideration, seems unlikely. This implies that the log-based units do not necessarily coincide with specific sedimentary facies boundaries.

This example is taken from an area on the basinward side of the clinoform belt and is situated in the domain of low-angle reflection configurations. If the seismic expression is taken into account it can be understood that internal markers of the Habshan and Salil/Rayda Formations can be correlated and also would show a low-angle configuration towards the basin and most probably are timelines.

In the second example (Fig. 10) the Habshan Formation is represented by a low gamma-ray log response in combination with a small LDL/CNL separation. The log character locally is highly serrate and results from intercalation of very tight carbonate and dolomites. An overall thickening of the unit towards the north can be observed.

The top of the Salil/Rayda Formation is picked on a high gamma-ray peak although this does not coincide with a marked increase in separation on the LDL/CNL logs (this only occurs in the northernmost well). The character is serrate throughout the section and no further subdivision of a basal unit is possible. Within the Habshan and Salil/Rayda no apparent correlation of individual markers seems possible, which is attributed to the fact that this example is situated in the high-angle clinoform belt and high primary sedimentary dips (6–10°) only allow correlation over short distances.

Cutting descriptions of wells in both examples show an abundance of shallow marine grainstones in the Habshan Formation, grading into pack/wackestones and eventually mudstones towards the base of the Salil/Rayda Formation. The overall contrast of the sequences in both examples compared to the surface geological sections implies that the subdivision between Salil and Rayda becomes less clear or nonexistent towards the south and that the overall

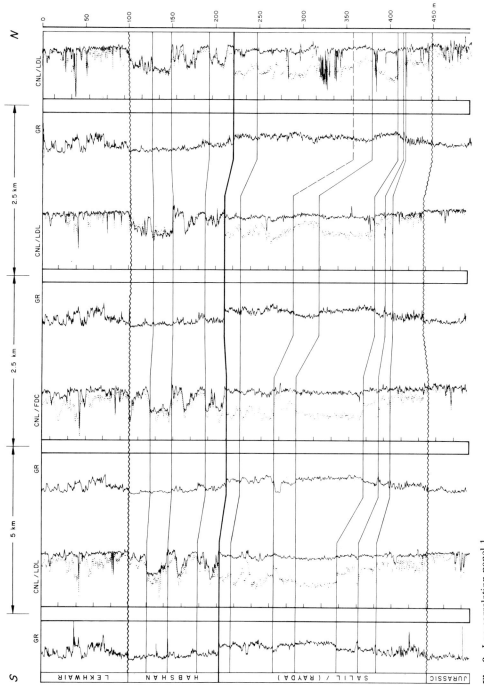

Fig. 9. Log correlation panel 1.

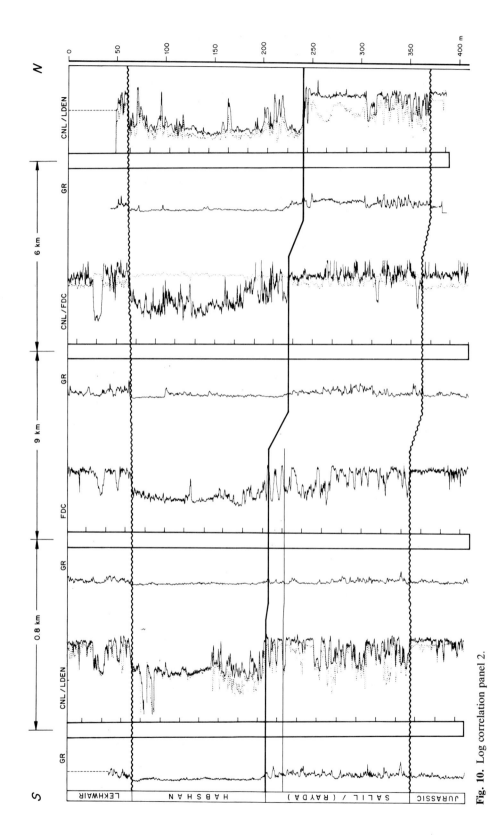

Fig. 10. Log correlation panel 2.

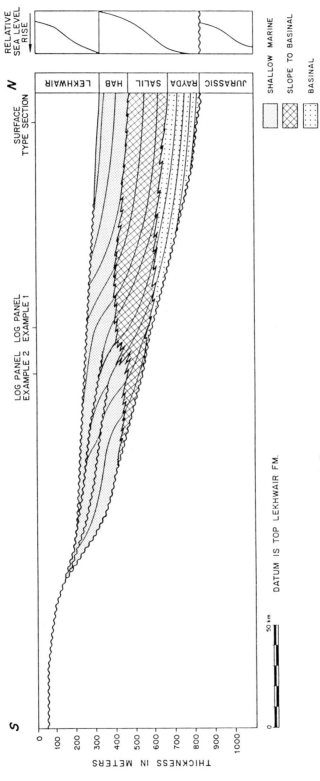

Fig. 11. Regional geological cross section of the Lower Kahmah Group.

environment of deposition seems to become shallower in the same direction.

Conclusions

The sedimentary fill of the northern part of the Rayda Basin can be described as a shallowing-upwards sequence and as such is clearly subdivided into the basinal Rayda Formation, the deep marine slope deposits of the Salil Formation and the shallow marine high-energy deposits of the Habshan Formation (Fig. 11). Units are readily recognizable in surface outcrops and stratotypes are assigned.

Towards the southern part of the basin only subsurface data are available, either as reflection seismic data, well log data, cuttings descriptions or locally core data. Detailed analysis of the subsurface data reveal that the threefold subdivision as defined in the mountain sections cannot be applied consistently over the entire basin and a complex interdigitation of the three formations is present towards the south, with the overall sedimentary facies of the Habshan/Salil and Rayda Formations also becoming shallower in that direction. Seismic data indicate the presence of a clinoform belt, which is interpreted to result from a minor step in the substrate. This step is considered to be controlled primarily by salt movement, because it skirts the inferred palaeo-salt edge, although locally, deep seated faulting may have influenced the system as well. Local variation in clinoform geometry may also result from changes in eustatic sea-level and/or fluctuating sediment input rates on the platform or in the basin.

The presence of clinoforms throughout the sequence is taken as evidence that the entire unit is highly diachronous, although no direct age-indicative evidence can be given at this moment to support this. The latter being due primarily to poor bio stratigraphic resolution within the lower Kahmah Group. In cases where detailed stratigraphy is known and can be tied to seismic data, seismostratigraphic analysis can be applied to produce predictive geological models (Langdon & Malececk 1987; Mitchum & Uliana 1985).

Primarily due to the problems involved in defining sensible units in the lower Kahmah and taking the strong diachronaity and facies variation into account, it could be argued that a subdivision into three formations should not have been made. However, the three units can be traced widely in the northern part of the basin, at surface and in the subsurface and the complexities towards the southern part of the

basin merely demonstrate the realities of diachronous correlation.

The authors wish to acknowledge the work of many colleagues in Petroleum Development Oman and express their gratitude to the Ministry of Petroleum and Minerals of the Sultanate of Oman and Shell Internationale Petroleum Maatschappij for granting permission to publish the data.

References

BOSELINI, A. 1984. Progradation geometries of carbonate platforms: examples from the Triassic of the Dolomites, northern Italy. *Sedimentology*, **31**, 1–24.

CONNALLY, T. C. & SCOTT, R. W. 1985. Carbonate Sediment-Fill of an Oceanic Shelf, Lower Cretaceous, Arabian Peninsula. *SEPM Core Workshop No. 6, New Orleans, March 23–24.* 266–302.

EBERLI, G. P. & GINSBURG, R. N. 1987. Segmentation and coalescence of Cenozoic carbonate platforms, Northwestern Greater Bahama Bank. *Geology*, **15**, 75–79.

GLENNIE, K. W., BOEUF, M. G., HUGHES CLARKE, M. W., MOODY-STUART, M., PILAAR, W. F. H. & REINHARDT, B. M. 1974. Geology of the Oman Mountains: *Koninklijk, Nederlands Geologisch Mijnbouwkundig Genootschap, Verhandelingen*, **31**.

HASSAN, T. H., MUDD, G. C. & TWOMBLEY, B. N. 1975. The Stratigraphy and Sedimentation of the Thamama Group (Lower Cretaceous) of Abu Dhabi. *Proceedings of the 9th Arab Petroleum Congress Dubai. UAE.*

HUGHES CLARKE, M. W. 1988. Stratigraphy and Rock Unit Nomenclature in the Oil-Producing Area of Interior Oman. *Journal of Petroleum Geology*, **11**, 5–60.

KOOP, W. J. & STONELEY, R. 1982. Subsidence history of the Middle East Zagros Basin, Permian to Recent. *Philosophycal Transactions Royal Society of London*, **A305**, 149–168.

LANGDON, G. S., & MALECECK, S. J. 1987. Seismic Stratigraphic Study of Two Oxfordian Carbonate Sequences, Eastern Saudi Arabia. *Bulletin of the American Association of Petroleum Geologists*, **71**, 403–418.

MITCHUM, Jr. R. M. & ULIANA, M. A. 1985. Seismic Stratigraphy of Carbonate Depositional Sequences, Upper Jurassic-Lower Cretaceous, Neuquén Basin, Argentina. *In*: BERG, O. R. & WOOLVERTON. D. G. (ed.), *AAPG Memoir 39: Seismic Stratigraphy II. An Integrated Approach*, 255–274.

——, VAIL P. R. & SANGREE, J. B. 1977. Seismic Stratigraphy and Global Changes of Sea Level, Part 6: Stratigraphic Interpretation of Seismic Reflection Patterns in Depositional Sequences. In: PAYTON, C. E. (ed.), *AAPG Memoir 26: Seismic Stratigraphy-applications to hydrocarbon exploration*, 117–133.

Simmons, M. D. & Hart, M. B. 1987. The Bio-stratigraphy and Microfacies of the Early to Mid-Cretaceous Carbonates of Wadi Mi'aidin, Central Oman Mountains. *In*: Hart, M. B. *Micropalaeontology of Carbonate Environments*. 176–207.

Geochemical stratigraphy and porosity controls in Cretaceous carbonates near the Oman Mountains

P. D. WAGNER

Amoco Production Company, P.O. Box 3385, Tulsa, OK, 74102, USA

Abstract: Geochemical stratigraphy is an investigative tool useful (a) for discerning the mode and spatial extent of diagenetic processes in carbonates, (b) for making diagenetic correlations between localities, and (c) for inferring palaeotopography. $\delta^{13}C$ and $\delta^{18}O$ stratigraphies of a five-well transect across central Oman indicate that most of the Cretaceous U. Kahmah−Natih interval stabilized under semiclosed, shallow burial, marine-water-like conditions. A 'depositional' $\delta^{13}C$ isotopic signal is preserved. Local anoxic−suboxic events are also recognized, as well as depth-limited effects of early meteoric diagenesis. Isotopic stratigraphic relationships clearly indicate the presence of a local palaeotopographic high in central Oman during deposition of the Natih E member. Good diagenetic−stratigraphic correlations are shown between locations in central Oman and Sharjah, a distance of about 300 miles.

Porosity type and distribution within Cretaceous carbonates is related both to early diagenesis and to later structural events. Early cementation associated with marine hardgrounds and subaerial exposure surfaces occluded primary porosity in a limited depth−thickness sense. Later, all existing porosity types were regionally destroyed below the Hawasina thrust sheet in central Oman by thrusting-induced burial stylolitization and associated cementation. Foreland basin carbonates not involved in nappe emplacement retained excellent reservoir properties. Porosity in foreland basin wells consists of primary macro- and micro-porosity, and secondary selective-leach microporosity; selective leaching fluids moved along the subsurface 'plumbing system' of the primary porosity−permeability network. Small volumes of pore space were formed in low porosity subthrust carbonates by late aggressive (meteoric?) leaching along fractures and stylolites. Rock texture (facies) did not play a major role in defining the distribution of porosity in the immediate study area.

The aim of this study was to define the nature and extent of reservoir carbonates in area. This goal was pursued through the integrated use of petrographic and geochemical data in a stratigraphic context. Use of stable isotopic and cationic data to construct the geochemical stratigraphy of the area greatly aided petrographic interpretations.

This paper deals mostly with diagenesis of Lower and Middle Cretaceous U. Kahmah (U. Thamama)−Natih shelf limestones (Fig. 1), although a limited amount of geochemical data will be presented from older rocks. The main focus of this paper is central Oman. Fig. 2 shows the general area of well and outcrop sampling. Omani well locations are shown by letters. Outcrop samples are from Wadi Maiadin, Wadi Bani Kharus and Wadi Rubkhah. One well from Sharjah was included to test the geographic range of isotopic signals observed in central Oman wells.

Working definitions

'Subthrust' and similar terms are meant to describe the geographic area directly overridden by the ophiolite-containing (Hawasina) thrust nappe. It is not meant to include associated thrust-faulted areas in the foreland basin.

'Stabilization' is used to indicate the general process whereby metastable carbonate phases chemically alter to stable low-Mg calcite (LMC). The general term 'stabilization' includes processes of early 'recrystallization' of high-Mg calcite (HMC) to LMC (a reaction involving a single mineral type), and of 'wet transformation' of aragonite to LMC (a reaction involving two different mineral types). It is not meant to include the less common case where LMC 'recrystallizes' to LMC (e.g. the formation of some caliches or of marble in the deep subsurface).

The terms 'open' and 'closed' are used to describe how much the geochemistry of stabilized mineral phases were dominated by the geochemistry of the original sediment. 'Open' geochemical systems most closely reflect the geochemistry of the pristine stabil-

From ROBERTSON, A. H. F., SEARLE, M. P. & RIES, A. C. (eds), 1990,
The Geology and Tectonics of the Oman Region.
Geological Society Special Publication No 49, pp 127−137

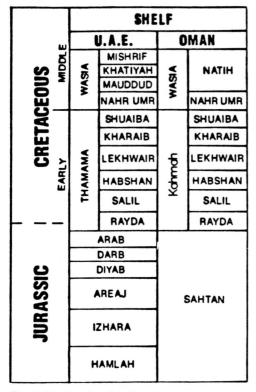

Fig. 1. Stratigraphy of shelf carbonates in Oman and the northern UAE.

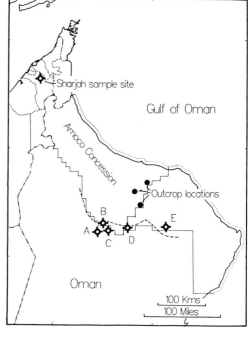

Fig. 2. Location map for the central Oman study area and the Sharjah location. The leading edge of the Hawasina thrust front is indicated by a dotted line. Sampling locations from wells are designated with letters. Surface samples came from outcrops at Wadi Maiadin (southernmost dot), Wadi Bani Kharus, and Wadi Rhubkah (northernmost dot).

izing fluid. 'Closed' geochemical systems reflect the geochemistry of a stabilizing fluid that has come into full chemical equilibrium with the dissolving sediment through extensive water−rock interaction. The concept of open and closed diagenetic systems is not necessarily synonymous with the concept of open and closed hydrologic systems.

Methods

Stable isotopes

Analyses of samples from wells 'A', 'B', 'C', 'D' and 'E' were performed at Amoco's Research Center, Tulsa, on a Finnigan MAT 251 mass spectrometer. Samples were first vacuum roasted for one hour at 375°C. Several samples from organic rich intervals were both roasted and allowed to stand 24 hours in a 5% solution of sodium hypochlorite; the additional oxidation step produced no significant change in isotopic values compared with powder that was roasted only (Charef & Sheppard 1984). Samples were then reacted with '100%' o-phosphoric acid at 50°C for one hour. Samples from well 'C' had been analyzed previously by Everest Geotech as part of a project done for Amoco. Samples from the Sharjah location were analyzed by Global Geochemistry Corporation, and by Amoco for a PhD thesis project by S. O. Moshier. All results are reported relative to the PDB scale.

Elemental analyses

A limited number of samples were prepared for elemental analysis by dissolution in a buffered acetic acid solution to minimize leaching of cations from associated clastic minerals. Data were generated with a Bausch and Lomb 3510 ICP Spectrometer at Amoco's Research Center in Tulsa.

Petrography

Petrography was done by microscope and SEM. Thin sections were prepared from core and cuttings samples impregnated with blue epoxy. Impregnation included both evacuation and pressurizing steps to maximize penetration of epoxy into microporous networks. SEM work was carried out on an ISI 100 unit. Samples were coated with a mixture of gold and palladium. Best results were obtained in the magnification range of 500× to 5000×.

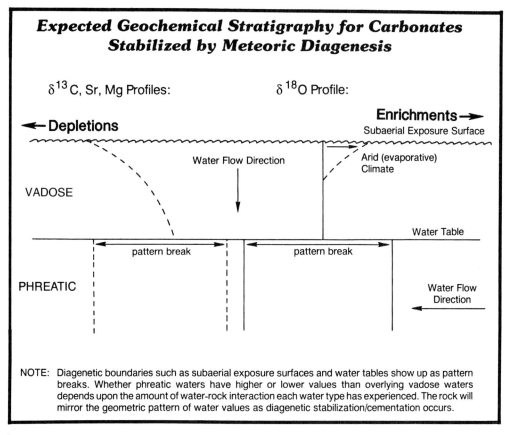

Fig. 3. Expected stratigraphic patterns in geochemical data from meteoric diagenesis, modified from Wagner (1983). Patterns are related to subsurface water flow directions, degrees of water-rock interaction, and positions of diagenetic boundaries such as subaerial exposure surfaces and water tables.

Geochemical results and discussion

Geochemical data were collected in stratigraphic context to determine the diagenetic environments of stabilization of central Oman carbonates. Geochemical data (e.g. $\delta^{13}C$, $\delta^{18}O$, Sr) are a source of information independent from petrography that can be combined with petrography to yield better-founded diagenetic models. Collection of geochemical data in stratigraphic context is the best way to recognize spatial signatures of many diagenetic processes that affect the reservoir quality of carbonates (Allan & Matthews 1977, 1982; Wagner 1983; Wagner & Matthews 1982). For example, Fig. 3 shows the stratigraphic profiles in geochemical data expected from meteoric stabilization. Patterns are related to subsurface waterflow directions, degrees of water−rock interaction, and positions of diagenetic boundaries such as

subaerial exposure surfaces and water tables. Collection of geochemical data in stratigraphic context is also the only way to recognize 'depositional' signals related to time-dependent changes in global seawater chemistry (e.g. Renard 1986).

$\delta^{13}C$ and $\delta^{18}O$ stratigraphies will be presented and discussed in the next two sections. Sr profiles through the Natih interval in two wells will also be presented. Samples from the U. Kahmah−Natih interval were taken about every 30 feet, and almost all samples are well cuttings.

$\delta^{13}C$ data

$\delta^{13}C$ profiles from five central Oman wells are shown in Fig. 4. A well developed waveform stratigraphy of $\delta^{13}C$ values is evident that correlates from one location to another. Some signals remain nearly constant in thickness across the transect length, whereas others appear to thin

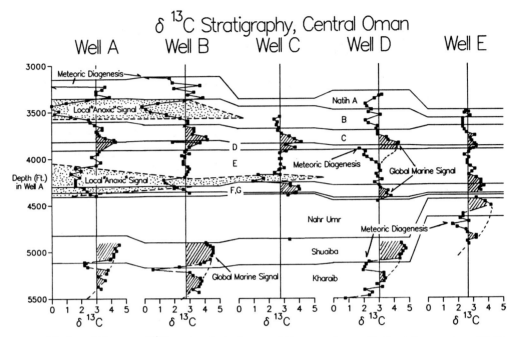

Fig. 4. Whole-rock limestone $\delta^{13}C$ stratigraphy in the central Oman study area. Section is hung on top of Natih E member. Positive excursions are interpreted to represent 'global' depositional patterns related to time-dependent changes in the seawater $\delta^{13}C$ values. Carbonate in these intervals probably stabilized under semi-closed, shallow-burial, marine-water-like conditions. They are generally porous. Negative excursions are interpreted to represent either effects of early meteoric diagenesis or closed-system burial diagenesis in organic-rich intervals. Carbonates in these intervals are generally non-porous. The presence of a local palaeotopographic high near the 'D' well is indicated by stratigraphic thinning of organic-rich intervals exhibiting an 'anoxic−suboxic' signal, and by an inferred intraformational palaeo-exposure at the top of the E member. Note that little or no evidence exists for palaeo-exposure of the top of the Shuaiba Formation, but that a likely intraformational palaeo-exposure exists in the lowermost Shuaiba−upper Kharaib interval. Data are reported relative to the PDB scale.

in an easterly or westerly direction. This $\delta^{13}C$ stratigraphy is present in other wells with a lower sampling density.

Positive excursions in $\delta^{13}C$ values are interpreted to be 'depositional' signals that were retained when the carbonate stabilized under semiclosed, shallow burial, marine-water-like conditions. Negative excursions in $\delta^{13}C$ values are interpreted to be diagenetic overprint signals sourced from degrading organic matter associated with stabilizing carbonates (either at palaeo-exposures or in buried, organic-rich beds). A discussion of each process follows.

A $\delta^{13}C$ stratigraphy of positive excursions is present in the Omani transect of wells that extends over 100 miles in length. Excursions match similar stratigraphies in $\delta^{13}C$ values from other data sets around the world. Such 'global' $\delta^{13}C$ excursions have been related to time-dependent changes in the $\delta^{13}C$ of seawater (Scholle Arthur 1980; Jenkyns 1985; Hilbrecht Hoefs 1986). Preservation of depositional pat-

terns through most intervals indicate the lack of wholesale diagenetic overprinting. $\delta^{13}C$ patterns in these intervals are interpreted to be true depositional signals that were never overprinted by effects of meteoric diagenesis. In support of this inference, no petrographic evidence of meteoric diagenesis was observed in these 'marine' intervals. And significant from a reservoir exploration standpoint, porosity is best developed there (discussed later).

Negative $\delta^{13}C$ excursions in the lowermost Shuaiba−upper Kharaib interval, and locally present at the tops of the Natih A and E members, are interpreted to be due to diagenetic overprinting by early meteoric diagenesis (Fig. 4). These intervals are generally associated with negative excursions in $\delta^{18}O$ (Fig. 5) and with a coarsely aggraded microspar texture that is generally non porous (discussed later). More detailed isotopic−cationic profiles through one of these sections (Natih Formation in the 'D' well, Fig. 6) clearly indicate the presence of a

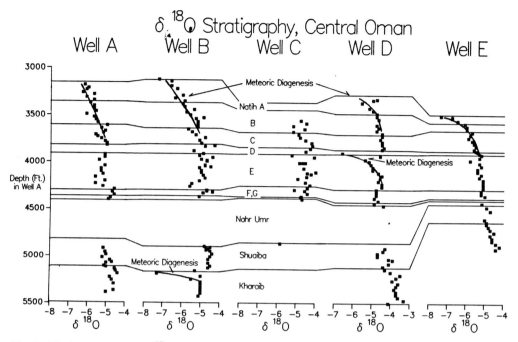

Fig. 5. Whole-rock limestone $\delta^{18}O$ stratigraphy in the central Oman study area. Section is hung on top of Natih E member. Negative pattern excursions are generally associated with inferred palaeo-exposures. Constant-value patterns in $\delta^{18}O$ are generally associated with intervals that retained 'depositional' $\delta^{13}C$ values (Fig. 4). Data re reported relative to the PDB scale.

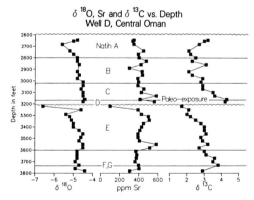

Fig. 6. Geochemical stratigraphies through the Natih interval of Omani well 'D'. A major pattern break in all data sets occurs at the top of the E member, indicating a diagenetic boundary. Palaeo-exposure is inferred from geochemical patterns below the boundary, and from petrographic observations.

major diagenetic boundary; subjacent geochemical profiles match closely with expected patterns produced by meteoric diagenesis.

A combined depositional–diagenetic $\delta^{13}C$ signal is interpreted to exist in portions of

the Natih B and E–F–G intervals in Fig. 4. Negative excursions in downhole $\delta^{13}C$ values in these Natih member units closely correlates with the presence of non-porous, organic-rich wackestones and packstones. The combination of high organic content in the sediment with abundant planktonic fossils indicates the presence of a stratified oxic–suboxic water column during deposition. Negative-valued excursions in $\delta^{13}C$ data through these organic-rich intervals probably developed as the carbonate stabilized in the subsurface. Stabilized carbonate apparently inherited minor amounts of highly negative carbon from associated organic matter that was degrading through biologic and/or thermogenic processes (e.g. Irwin *et al.* 1977), as well as comparatively large amounts of strontium from precursor aragonite (Fig. 7). Available geochemical data suggest the organic-rich beds stabilized under the most closed-system diagenetic conditions.

The ability to correlate $\delta^{13}C$ patterns from well to well gives insights into central Omani palaeotopography. The presence of a local subaerial exposure surface at the top of the Natih E in the 'D' well suggest that the nearby structural high had some topographic expression during

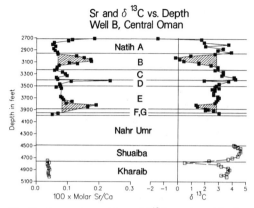

Fig. 7. Comparison of Sr and $\delta^{13}C$ stratigraphies in Omani well 'B'. Note that organic-rich beds within the Natih A and E−F−G members are characterized by carbonates with comparatively light $\delta^{13}C$ and enriched strontium values. Rocks in these intervals are interpreted to have undergone the most closed-system stabilization of any in the section; a burial diagenetic environment is inferred.

Natih time. This palaeotopographic inference is in good agreement with electric log and $\delta^{13}C$ data that indicate thinning of anoxic−suboxic beds toward the high.

Interestingly, the top of the Shuaiba Formation shows little or no evidence of subaerial exposure in the central Oman area, although most stratigraphic columns for Oman show a regional unconformity capping the Kahmah group. If subaerial exposure did occur, it had little discernible physical or chemical effect on the rock. Similar results were described by Moshier (1987) from cores at the Sharjah location. Also interesting is the presence of an inferred intraformational palaeo-exposure in the lowermost Shuaiba Formation, near the top of the Kharaib Formation. No previous work has identified such a feature at this stratigraphic position. A palaeo-exposure interpretation is made here based on limited geochemical and petrographic work, and despite the fact that the 'global' $\delta^{13}C$ curve shows a negative excursion during this time interval (Renard 1986).

Correlation of $\delta^{13}C$ data over a wider geographic range is evident in a comparison of Omani well 'E' with the Sharjah location (Fig. 8). Note in Fig. 8 that the entire Lower Cretaceous interval is compared; the interval equivalent to the Middle Cretaceous Natih Formation is erosionally missing at the Sharjah location. Distinct isotopic breaks occur in both profiles at the tops of the Habshan Formation and Jurassic section; both levels generally con-

sidered to represent times of subaerial exposure in the general area (Harris *et al.* 1984; Hassan *et al.* 1975). Isotopic breaks also occur in the lowermost Shuaiba Formation near the top of the Kharaib Formation.

$\delta^{18}O$ data

$\delta^{18}O$ data from the five-well transect in Oman are shown in Fig. 5. These data present a much simpler stratigraphy than is evident in the $\delta^{13}C$ data. Stratigraphic trends in $\delta^{18}O$ are limited to constant downhole 'plateaus' and pronounced negative-valued excursions. Correlation of $\delta^{18}O$ data over a wider geographic range is evident in a comparison of Omani well 'E' with the Sharjah location (Fig. 9).

Intervals with 'plateau' patterns in $\delta^{18}O$ data are interpreted to have stabilized under uniform, shallow-burial, marine-water-like conditions. These intervals also exhibit 'depositional' $\delta^{13}C$ signals. The best observed porosity values are generally found within these intervals of 'plateau' $\delta^{18}O$ and 'depositional' $\delta^{13}C$ patterns.

Intervals with pronounced negative-valued excursions in $\delta^{18}O$ data are interpreted to have been geochemically overprinted by effects of early meteoric diagenesis. These intervals also exhibit pronounced negative-valued excursions in $\delta^{13}C$ data. Petrographically, the amount of cement is generally much higher in these intervals, and the porosity is correspondingly lower. The stratigraphic trend towards lighter $\delta^{18}O$ values near presumed subaerial exposure surfaces is consistent with a meteoric diagenetic model. $\delta^{18}O$ values of meteoric water will be

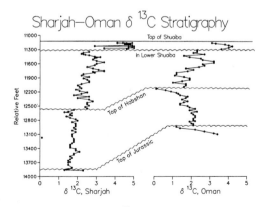

Fig. 8. Correlation of $\delta^{13}C$ patterns between Omani well 'E' and the Sharjah location. A 'global' waveform pattern is evident that is locally overprinted by effects of meteoric diagenesis at presumed palaeo-exposures.

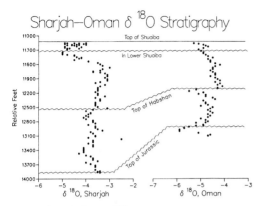

Fig. 9. Correlation of $\delta^{18}O$ patterns between Omani well 'E' and the Sharjah location. Pattern breaks occur at stratigraphic levels presumed to represent palaeo-exposures.

lighter than those from associated marine water (e.g. Gat & Gonfiantini 1981). Meteorically-produced values as light as those observed in Oman (-7 to -8 permil PDB) have been recorded under similar low-relief, low-latitude conditions (Saller 1984). The lack of negative $\delta^{18}O$ excursions at every location below presumed palaeo-exposures (e.g. lowermost Shuaiba Formation) is problematic without more detailed sampling, but may have been related to local meteorological conditions.

Petrographic results and discussion

This section describes the types and distributions of porosity in Cretaceous-aged U. Khamah—Natih carbonates near and in the Oman Mountains. It also discusses controls on porosity trends in the area. A geometric dividing plane was found to exist near the leading edge of the Hawasina thrust front in central Oman. The plane divides volumes of rocks in the foreland basin that have high porosities from those having little or no porosity beneath the Hawasina thrust sheet. The two major carbonate porosity types in foreland basin wells are primary macro-porosity and secondary microporosity. The major porosity type in subthrust carbonates of the Oman Mountain highlands is vuggy porosity that formed from late aggressive leaching along fractures, stylolites and relict primary porosity pathways. Facies (rock texture) was found to have only a minor influence on porosity amount and distribution. Thrust-induced burial stylolit-ization and associated cementation was found to be one of the dominant porosity controls.

Porosity types, distributions, and timings of formation

Primary porosity is one of the two dominant porosity types in the Cretaceous section of fore-land basin wells that were not overridden by the thrust sheet. Primary porosity is present as intergranular and intragranular macro-porosity and as intercrystalline microporosity. As suggested by Moshier (1987), 'primary' inter-crystalline microporosity probably formed as cement crystals precipitated between dissolving metastable crystals. The cement crystals aggraded until all metastables had dissolved. The matrix remained porous unless additional cement was introduced.

Petrographic and geochemical data indicate that abundant primary macro- and micro-porosity was preserved during initial chemical stabilization of the sediments under semi-closed, shallow-burial, marine-water-like conditions. This earliest-formed network of primary porosity and permeability acted as the 'plumbing system' for later subsurface leaching fluids.

Selective leach microporosity is the second major porosity type in the Cretaceous section of foreland basin wells, and becomes dominant in lower-porosity sections near the Hawasina thrust front. This porosity type is secondary in nature, and results from selective dissolution of submicron-size calcite crystals from the finest textured component present in the rock (commonly benthic foram tests and micritized grains). Where selective leaching was most active, microporosity may grade into 'pseudo'-moldic porosity. Selective leaching also enhanced primary intercrystalline microporosity by attacking more soluble crystal edges and corners. An increase in effective permeability could also have been attained by selective leaching through enlargement of porethroat sizes. Selective leach microporosity occurs abundantly in all carbonate rock textures. No facies control exists on selective leaching as such, but indirect facies control may be exhibited where an interval contains abundant fine-crystalline components.

Petrographic examination of many thin sections indicates that the timing of selective leaching occurred after complete chemical stabilization of the section. Similar microporous textures have been reported from the Edwards Group of Texas (Longman & Mench 1978) and from the Lisburne Group of Alaska (Harris & Kendall 1986). In both cited cases, selective leaching occurred when slightly undersaturated pore fluids invaded the host rock long after chemical stabilization of the original sediment.

Selective leach microporosity in foreland basin wells probably formed episodically. This is suggested by the variety of fluids capable of producing the texture, and the length of time the section has remained porous. Possible fluid types for leaching include: undersaturated marine-water-like water (Saller 1986; Berner 1980), carbon-dioxide−organic acid-charged water (Surdam et al. 1982), deep-moving meteoric water (Longman & Mench 1978) and de-watering fluid−brine mixtures (Harris & Kendall 1986). The section may have been invaded by one or all of these fluid types in the ±100 million years since stabilization and preservation of the primary porosity−permeability network.

Aggressive leach porosity (vugs, and solution-enhanced forms of fracture, stylolite and primary porosity) is the major porosity type in the subthrust portion of the study area, but it is not abundant in absolute terms. Primary porosity and secondary microporosity are uncommon to absent in subthrust carbonates. Aggressive, non-selective leaching produced porosity in all formations studied (Kharaib, Shuaiba, Nahr Umr and Natih) from Jebel Akhdar outcrop locations. No rock textural (facies) control in leaching is evident. This porosity type is rarely observed in foreland basin wells.

Aggressive leach porosity probably formed from penetrating meteoric waters during and after uplift of the Jebel Akhdar area. Leaching was largely restricted to fracture and stylolitic pathways because whole-rock porosities and permeabilities had been dramatically lowered or obliterated by thrust-induced burial stylolitization and associated cementation (discussed later). Most aggressive leaching probably occured comparatively recently, although occlusion of aggressive leach porosity by calcite spar suggests some history of leaching and cementation. No clear evidence of bitumen staining was seen in any of the outcrop samples; such staining is common in well cuttings and cores from locations to the south. Aggressive leach porosity probably formed after hydrocarbon migration in the area.

Controlling factors for porosity loss

This second petrographic section addresses processes that affected porosity in a negative way. It is a general counterpoint to the preceding discussions of porosity retention and enhancement in the subsurface.

Early cementation. Early cementation destroyed porosity in a limited depth−thickness sense at marine hardgrounds and in some meteorically-altered intervals associated with subaerial exposure surfaces. Marine hardgrounds are particularly abundant in the E Member of the Natih Formation at Wadi Maiadin. Thick rim cements have occluded all porosity. The rim cements have relict fibrous texture. They were probably precipitated as aragonite near the sediment-water interface, and stabilized to low-Mg calcite after burial. Similar marine cementation was observed scattered throughout the study area, and was probably responsible for local porosity occlusion in all formations.

Early meteoric diagenesis also destroyed porosity in a limited depth−thickness sense. The inferred intraformational subaerial exposure present at the top of the Natih E in the 'D' well is associated with one of the few non-porous intervals in the section. Intense cementation helped seal the meteorically-affected interval from later selective leaching. A good example of porosity loss at inferred subaerial exposures is in the lowermost Shuaiba−upper Kharaib interval. Low porosity values are observed at this stratigraphic level across the study area and beyond.

Facies controlled porosity? Previous workers have indicated that a strong facies control on porosity may exist in the area (e.g. Harris & Frost 1984). This very common correspondence in carbonates is a reflection of the tendency for finer-grained rocks (mudstones and wackestones) to rapidly lose their reservoiring capacity to burial-induced chemical compaction. Since facies relationships with porosity can be proposed over a wide range of scales, the question was addressed at several comparison levels. The following paragraphs describe results of those comparisons.

The most general level of comparison between facies and porosity was pursued on a regional scale by considering all available petrographic and electric log data. This survey showed a consistent trend from highly porous Cretaceous carbonate rock in the foreland basin to virtually non-porous rock beneath the Hawasina thrust. These trends were noted at all stratigraphic levels examined. The relevant point is that the surveyed foreland basin wells come from a very broad geographic area that contain many different facies; it does not seem to matter which facies are present at a certain location, as they are all generally porous. A parallel argument can be made for the general lack of porosity in any rock textures or facies types in subthrust carbonates.

A finer scaled comparison of rock textures against porosity was pursued by looking at the same stratigraphic unit over a small area.

Sections in the 'A' and 'B' wells are selected for comparison because they are only about 10 miles apart and have essentially identical geochemical stratigraphies, indicating similar diagenetic histories up to a point in time. A comparison of facies within the Natih Formation in the two wells revealed similar downhole rock textures, although the depositionally updip 'B' well is somewhat more grainy. Despite the marked similarities in diagenetic stratigraphies, and the trend towards slightly grainier rocks in the direction of the 'B' well, substantially lower porosity values typify the 'B' well (Fig. 10). A similar facies comparison between the two wells in the U. Kahmah Group yielded the same lack of correlation between porosity and facies.

An even finer-scaled relationship between porosity and facies were investigated in adjacent facies within single wells. Analysis of downhole textures versus porosity values for both the 'A' and 'B' wells indicated the presence of a weak, inconsistent facies control. For example, the Natih Formation in the two wells shows a weak relationship of higher porosity in the grainstones (a condition partially caused by later 'channelized' leaching through thin grainstone in-

tervals). But the U. Kahmah group facies comparisons from the 'A' and 'B' wells showed either no facies effect or an actual inverse relationship of more porosity in the muddier facies.

The smallest scale comparisons between porosity and facies were done on a sample-by-sample basis for 300+ thin sections. No relationship between porosity and rock texture was recognized. Samples of mudstones, wackestones, packstones and grainstones were found to range from highly porous to non-porous. Virtually identical rocks from similar footages in the same well were often seen to have fundamentally different porosity values. It is clear from these and preceding comparisons that neither rock texture nor early diagenetic history controlled porosity amounts or distributions in any general way around the Hawasina thrust front in central Oman.

Thrusting-induced burial stylolitization. An excellent positive correlation exists between the geographic limit of the Hawasina thrust sheet and the geographic distribution of non-porous carbonates. Virtually identical carbonate facies may exist on either side of the imaginary dividing

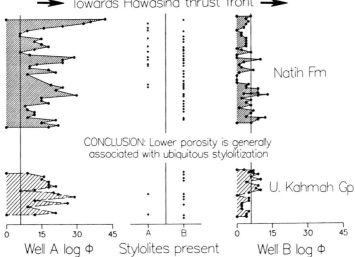

Fig. 10. Comparison of interval porosities and degrees of stylolitization between Omani wells 'A' and 'B'. Higher porosity and much less severe stylolitization is typical of carbonate intervals in foreland basin wells such as 'A'. Porosity values drop dramatically in sections close to the leading edge of the Hawasina thrust front, and stylolitization becomes pervasive and severe. Subthrust carbonates have little or no porosity, and are severely stylolitized. Vertical lines indicate six percent porosity values, one measure of the economic breakpoint between porous and non-porous carbonates.

line between high and low porosity values (i.e. close to the leading edge of the thrust sheet). The only first-order petrographic or geochemical difference the author has recognized between high and low porosity intervals is the degree of stylolitization (Fig. 10). A semi-quantitative petrographic study of samples from the 'A' and 'B' wells reveals that the low-porosity 'B' well has suffered much more pervasive and intensive stylolitization than the 'A' well. More generally, cuttings and cored intervals in all subthrust locations show profound effects of stylolitization. Cuttings samples from foreland basin wells located well away from the thrust front show significantly fewer effects of stylolitization and are generally porous. A fundamental association of thrusting-induced stylolitization and massive porosity loss is inferred.

Interestingly, porosity loss in the 'E' well from thrusting-induced burial stylolitization did not obliterate the earlier-formed isotopic stratigraphy. Preservation of the original geochemical stratigraphy indicates that porosity destruction occurred without the aid of massive injections of 'foreign' carbonate material. A process of in situ burial stylolitization and associated cementation seems to have been sufficient to obliterate most primary and early secondary porosity. Before thrusting, 'subthrust' carbonates probably had porosity values similar to those then present in the foreland basin.

Conclusions

(1) Geochemical stratigraphy is useful for discerning the mode and spatial extent of diagenetic processes, for making diagenetic correlations between wells, and for inferring palaeotopographic relationships. Isotope stratigraphy of a five-well transect across central Oman indicates that most of the U. Kahman−Natih section stabilized under semi-closed, shallow burial, marine-water-like conditions that preserved the depositional isotopic signal. Local anoxic −suboxic events are also recognized, as well as depth-limited effects of meteoric diagenesis. Isotope stratigraphy clearly indicates that a local structural high was present during deposition of the Natih E member in central Oman.

(2) Porosity type and distribution is closely related to the area's structural history. Abundant primary inter−intragranular and secondary selective leach porosity exists in U. Kahmah−Natih samples from foreland basin wells that were little-affected

by Cretaceous-aged Hawasina thrusting. However, total porosity values drop sharply toward the Hawasina thrust front, and selective leach porosity becomes dominant in relative terms. Little or no primary or selective leach porosity is present in well or outcrop samples from the subthrust area. Minor aggressive leach porosity is present in outcrop samples from Jebel Akhdar; leaching occurred along stylolites and fractures.

(3) Porosity-modifying events in the U. Kahmah-Natih interval of the Oman Mountain area are ranked by importance as follows:

First order

(a) Primary inter−intragranular porosity and some primary intercrystalline microporosity was retained during stabilization in a semi-closed, shallow burial, marine-water-like environment.

(b) Most porosity below the Hawasina thrust sheet was destroyed by thrusting-induced burial stylolitization and associated cementation.

Second order

(a) Secondary intercrystalline microporosity was formed, and other porosity types were enhanced by selective leaching in the subsurface.

(b) Primary porosity was locally destroyed by early cementation associated with marine hardgrounds and subaerial exposure surfaces.

Third order

(a) Microvuggy porosity formed by aggressive meteoric leaching along stylolites and fractures in uplifted carbonates of Jebel Akhdar.

(b) Primary porosity and selective leach microporosity were sometimes better retained/developed in grainstones.

(4) Intercrystalline microporosity formed both by early chemical stabilization of muddy carbonates in a semi-closed, shallow burial, marine-water-like environment (Moshier 1987) and by later selective leaching of fine-crystalline carbonate components in the subsurface. Late selective leaching occurred after complete chemical stabilization. Selective leaching by slightly undersaturated pore fluids occurred along the existing 'plumbing system' of the primary porosity−permeability network. Extensive thicknesses of microporous carbonates formed episodically or continuously in the subsurface.

(5) Facies play only a minor role in describing the distribution of U. Kahmah (U.

Thamama)—Natih porosity in the vicinity of the central Oman Hawasina thrust front. This conclusion is offered for this particular study area only. Facies-porosity relationships must be reestablished for each new study area. Facies porosity correlations are known to become much stronger in less structurally disturbed areas to the west and northwest.

(6) Limited meteoric diagenesis occurred in the study area at least two different times, and had opposite effects on porosity development. Early meteoric diagenesis associated with subaerial exposures (of sediments?) destroyed porosity in a limited depth—thickness sense. Much later exposure of uplifted carbonate rocks to meteoric waters caused localized porosity development by aggressive leaching along stylolites and fractures.

Helpful discussions with Amoco colleagues R. W. Scott, R. D. Boutell, P. R. Manoogian, L. A. Dunne and E. J. Biller are gratefully acknowledged. J. B. Fisher developed the buffered acetic acid technique and analyzed the samples for their cation compositions. R. B. Mace did the isotopic analyses. Thanks are due to E. Haan and A. Fleet for reviewing the manuscript. Thanks are also due to Amoco Production Company and the Sultanate of Oman for permission to publish this work.

References

ALLAN, J. R. & MATTHEWS, R. K. 1977. Carbon and oxygen isotopes as diagenetic and stratigraphic tools — data from surface and subsurface of Barbados, West Indies. *Geology*, 5, 16–20.

—— & —— 1982. Isotope signatures associated with early meteoric diagenesis. *Sedimentology*, 29, 797–817.

BERNER, R. A. 1980. *Early Diagenesis, A Theoretic Approach*. Princeton University Press.

CHAREF, A. & SHEPPARD, M. F. 1984. Carbon and oxygen isotope analysis of calcite or dolomite associated with organic matter. *Isotope Geoscience*, 2, 325–333.

GAT, J. R. & GONFIANTINI, R. 1981. *Stable Isotope Hydrology: Deuterium and Oxygen-18 in the Water Cycle*. International Atomic Energy Agency, Vienna.

HARRIS, D. C. & KENDALL, A. C. 1986. Secondary porosity in upper Lisburne Group carbonates (Wahoo Limestone: lower Pennsylvanian); North Slope, Alaska (abstract). *Society of Economic Paleontologists and Mineralogists Mid-Year Meeting Issue*, 50.

HARRIS, P. M. & FROST, S. H. 1984. Middle Cre-

taceous carbonate reservoirs, Fahud Field and northwestern Oman. *American Association of Petroleum Geologists Bulletin*, 68, 649–658.

——, FROST, S. H., SEIGLIE, G. A. & SCHNEIDERMANN, N. 1984. Regional unconformities and depositional cycles, Cretaceous of the Arabian peninsula. *American Association of Petroleum Geologists Memoir*, 36, 67–80.

HASSAN, T. H., MUDD, G. C. & TWOMBLEY, B. N. 1975. The stratigraphy and sedimentation of the Thamama group (Lower Cretaceous) of Abu Dhabi. *Ninth Arab Petroleum Congress, Dubai, article*, 107 (B-3).

HILBRECHT, H. & HOEFS, J. 1986. Geochemical and paleontologic studies of the $\delta^{13}C$ anomaly in boreal and north Tethyan Cenomanian–Turonian sediments in Germany and adjacent areas. *Palaeogeography, Palaeoclimatology, Palaeoecology*, 53, 169–189.

IRWIN, H., CURTIS, C. & COLEMAN, M. 1977. Isotopic evidence for source of diagenetic carbonates formed during burial of organic-rich sediments. *Nature*, 269, 209–213.

JENKYNS, H. C. 1985. The early Toarcian and Cenomanian-Turonian anoxic/suboxic events in Europe: comparisons and contrasts. *Geologische Rundschau*, 74, 505–518.

LONGMAN, M. W. & MENCH, P. A. 1978. Diagenesis of Cretaceous limestones in the Edwards aquifer system of south — central Texas: a scanning electron microscope study. *Sedimentary Geology*, 21, 221–276.

MOSHIER, S. O. 1987. *On the nature and origin of microporosity in micritic limestone*. PhD Thesis, Louisiana State University.

RENARD, M. 1986. Pelagic carbonate stratigraphy (Sr, Mg, ^{18}O, ^{13}C). *Marine Micropaleontology*, 10, 117–164.

SALLER, A. H. 1984. *Diagenesis of Cenozoic limestones on Enewetak Atoll*. PhD Thesis, Louisiana State University.

SCHOLLE, P. A. & ARTHUR, M. A. 1980. Carbon isotope fluctuations in Cretaceous pelagic limestones: potential stratigraphic and petroleum exploration tool. *American Association of Petroleum Geologists Bulletin*, 64, 67–87.

SURDAM, R. C., BOESE, S. & CROSSEY, L. J. 1982. Role of organic and inorganic reactions in development of secondary porosity in sandstones. *American Association of Petroleum Geologists Annual Meeting Abstract Book, Calgary*, 116.

WAGNER, P. D. 1983. *Geochemical characterization of meteoric diagenesis in limestone: development and applications*. PhD Thesis, Brown University.

—— & MATTHEWS, R. K. 1982. Porosity preservation in the Upper Smackover (Jurassic) carbonate grainstone, Walker Creek Field, Arkansas: response of palaeophreatic lenses to burial processes. *Journal of Sedimentary Petrology*, 52, 3–18.

Mesozoic carbonate slope facies marking the Arabian platform margin in Oman: depositional history, morphology and palaeogeography

K. F. WATTS

Department of Geology and Geophysics, Geophysical Institute,
University of Alaska, Fairbanks, Alaska, USA 99775

Abstract: Carbonate slope sediments of the Sumeini Group mark the northeastern margin of the Arabian carbonate platform. Most slope sediments exposed in the Oman Mountains are of Jurassic or Cretaceous age. Older slope deposits at Jebel Sumeini indicate establishment of the Oman continental margin and subsidence accompanied by faulting in the Early Triassic (Dienerian), Middle Triassic (Ladinian) and possibly earlier (Permian).

Widespread Jurassic slope deposits indicate significant variations in declivity and facing direction of the continental margin slope in Oman. At Jebel Sumeini, a gullied bypass slope formed an apron along the NNW-trending slope, previously established as a Triassic block-faulted escarpment. In the Dibba Zone, a steep bypass slope formed along an inactive, NE-trending, transform lineament. Farther south near Wadi Qumayrah, a Middle to Late Jurassic base-of-slope apron containing megabreccias formed along a possible NNW-trending fault scarp. East of Wadi Qumayrah, an open-end embayment in the margin separated this area from coarse-grained slope apron deposits at Jebel Sham. Carbonate slope deposits at Saih Hatat indicate a complex history of subsidence culminating in Jurassic platform drowning and development of a long-lived submerged plateau bounded by gently inclined ramp slopes. This general geometry of the Oman passive continental margin was maintained through Jurassic and Early Cretaceous time.

Major changes in platform margin sedimentation occurred in the Late Cretaceous (Cenomanian to Coniacian), as recorded by the upper Mayhah Formation and overlying siliceous Qumayrah Formation. Thick Cenomanian(?) to Coniacian syn-orogenic megabreccias associated with pelagic sediments formed due to collapse of oversteepened slopes, possibly resulting from tectonic downbowing of the Oman margin toward a northward-dipping oceanic subduction zone. Later, the geometry of the passive continental margin may have had a significant effect on the emplacement of nappes and formation of the Sumeini culminations during the structural development of the Oman mountain belt.

The geometry and nature of the continental margin bounding the Arabian carbonate platform in the area of the Oman Mountains was disrupted during the Late Cretaceous Oman orogeny. Extensive thrust sheets (nappes) of the Semail Ophiolite and Hawasina Complex cover most of the Arabian carbonate platform margin except at the major tectonic windows at the Musandam Peninsula, Jebel Akhdar, and Saih Hatat (Glennie *et al.*, 1973, 1974; Fig. 1). However, carbonate slope deposits of the Sumeini Group which form structural highs (culminations) in the western Oman Mountains provide valuable clues for understanding the nature of the continental margin in Oman (Fig. 2, Watts & Garrison 1986; Watts & Blome 1989).

Numerous lines of evidence suggest that a passive continental margin developed be-tween the Arabian carbonate platform and Hawasina basin (South Tethys Sea) in Permian and Triassic times (Glennie *et al.* 1973, 1974; Béchennec *et al.* 1988; Rabu *et al.* 1990). Subsidence and development of deep-marine limestone and radiolarian chert in the Permian Oman Exotics, Al Aridh Formation, and lower part of the Sumeini Group may be related to early phases of rifting (Watts & Garrison 1986; Bernoulli *et al.* 1990; Blendinger *et al.* 1990; Cooper 1990). A major phase of rifting in Triassic time was accompanied by normal and transform faulting, development of escarpment slopes, volcanism, and rapid subsidence (Searle & Graham 1982; Searle *et al.* 1980, 1983; Watts 1988). Jurassic carbonate slope deposits suggest continued rifting accompanied by faulting and subsidence (see below; Watts & Blome 1989). Tectonic subsidence of the margin and sea-

From ROBERTSON, A. H. F., SEARLE, M. P. & RIES, A. C. (eds), 1990,
The Geology and Tectonics of the Oman Region.
Geological Society Special Publication No 49, pp 139–159

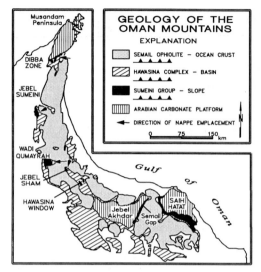

Fig. 1. Geological map of Oman Mountains, showing the location of the Sumeini Group exposures and the inferred direction of structural emplacement. The Qarn Nazwa locality is too small to show at this scale; it is located approximately at the "L" in Jebel Sumeini.

level rise outpaced carbonate sedimentation in latest Jurassic to Early Cretaceous (Tithonian to Valanginian) time, resulting in deep-water limestone in the platform sequence and widespread chert in the slope and basinal sequences (Murris 1980; Harris et al. 1984; Connally & Scott 1985). Later in the Early Cretaceous, carbonate sediments prograded to once again cover the platform, slope and basin.

In mid-Cretaceous (Cenomanian to Coniacian) time, changing plate motions dramatically influenced patterns of sedimentation along the Oman margin (Allemann & Peters 1972; Glennie et al. 1973, 1974; Robertson 1988; Patton & O'Connor 1988; Watts & Blome 1989). The carbonate platform sequence is marked by a major unconformity, the Cenomanian to Coniacian 'Wasia-Aruma break' (Murris 1980). However, the carbonate slope sequence has preserved a record of this tectonically important segment of time, showing a major transition from upper Mayhah Formation carbonate sediments to Cenomanian siliceous sediments of the Qumayrah Formation. The upper part of the Qumayrah Formation includes Coniacian synorogenic megabreccias that signify slope instabilities resulting from tectonic steepening and deformation (Watts & Blome 1989).

Although the original paleogeography of the Oman margin has been disrupted by the Late

Cretaceous Oman orogeny, the slope deposits of the Sumeini Group provide insights on the origin, morphology and tectonic history of the Oman continental margin slope (Watts & Garrison 1986; Watts & Blome 1989). Slope facies at several critical localities, Jebel Sumeini, the Dibba Zone, Qarn Nazwa, Wadi Qumayrah, Jebel Sham, and Saih Hatat (Figs 1 & 3), can be interpreted in terms of basin geometry, declivity of the slope, facing direction, nature of slope sedimentation, and evolution of the platform margin and slope. The slope deposits are particularly sensitive indicators of tectonically induced steepening of the continental margin slope.

Structural geology and regional tectonic setting

In the Late Cretaceous, as the Oman passive continental margin approached an inferred northward-dipping oceanic subduction zone, the Semail ophiolite and deep-water units of the Hawasina Complex were progressively emplaced over the autochthonous Arabian carbonate platform (Glennie et al. 1973, 1974; Gealey 1977; Bernoulli & Weissert 1987; Robertson 1987; Patton & O'Connor 1988). In the latest stages of deformation, the parautochthonous Sumeini Group slope carbonates were detached and thrust-faulted westward over the Arabian platform margin. The amount of displacement of the Sumeini Group culminations is unknown but is certainly less than the structurally higher allochthonous rocks (Watts & Garrison, 1986). Although displacement may have been considerably larger, the paleogeographic reconstruction assumes minimal amounts of tectonic transport (Fig. 4).

Estimates of structural displacement, direction of emplacement and trend of platform margins

Because each Sumeini Group occurrence formed as separate thrust sheets, each area is considered individually, focusing on important structural and sedimentologic interrelationships. This allows determination of the minimum tectonic displacements and the inferred trends of the platform margin slope, In general, folds, thrust faults and facies patterns in the Sumeini Group imply emplacement vectors perpendicular to the platform margin. The minimum displacement of individual thrust sheets is slightly greater than the width of each Sumeini Group culmination, accounting for internal shortening due to folding and assuming mini-

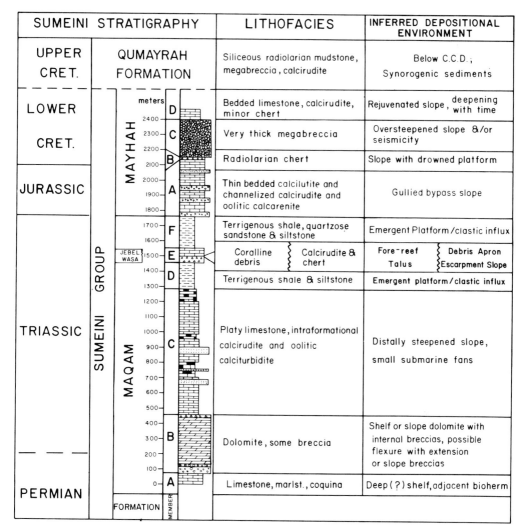

SUMEINI STRATIGRAPHY			LITHOFACIES	INFERRED DEPOSITIONAL ENVIRONMENT
UPPER CRET.	QUMAYRAH FORMATION		Siliceous radiolarian mudstone, megabreccia, calcirudite	Below C.C.D.; Synorogenic sediments
LOWER CRET.	MAYHAH	D	Bedded limestone, calcirudite, minor chert	Rejuvenated slope, deepening with time
		C	Very thick megabreccia	Oversteepened slope &/or seismicity
		B	Radiolarian chert	Slope with drowned platform
JURASSIC		A	Thin bedded calcilutite and channelized calcirudite and oolitic calcarenite	Gullied bypass slope
		F	Terrigenous shale, quartzose sandstone & siltstone	Emergent Platform /clastic influx
	JEBEL WASA	E	Coralline debris { Calcirudite & chert	Fore-reef { Debris Apron / Talus {Escarpment Slope
		D	Terrigenous shale & siltstone	Emergent platform/clastic influx
TRIASSIC	MAQAM	C	Platy limestone, intraformational calcirudite and oolitic calciturbidite	Distally steepened slope, small submarine fans
		B	Dolomite, some breccia	Shelf or slope dolomite with internal breccias, possible flexure with extension or slope breccias
		A	Limestone, marlst., coquina	Deep(?) shelf, adjacent bioherm
PERMIAN	FORMATION			

Fig. 2. Stratigraphy and inferred evolution of depositional environments of the Sumeini Group at Jebel Sumeini (modified after Watts & Garrison 1986).

mum displacements along thrust faults (tens of km, and possibly more). The amount of displacement along range-front faults cannot be determined because the location of footwall cutoffs from which the Sumeini thrust sheets were detached is unknown.

The actual amount of displacement suffered by the Sumeini thrust sheets may be greater than these minimum estimates. The original location of the Mesozoic Arabian platform margin may be farther to the north, possibly closer to the present-day Oman continental margin.

Seismic data from across the Oman Mountains is of poor quality but has been interpreted to reflect a more northerly position of the shelf margin (Dunne *et al.* 1990), requiring considerable tectonic displacement of the Sumeini thrust sheets. Nonetheless, the palaeogeographic reconstruction (Fig. 4) provides a general picture of the variations in slope deposits and their relationships to underlying structure along the Oman margin if not their precise location and geometry.

Jebel Sumeini. The Jebel Sumeini area consists

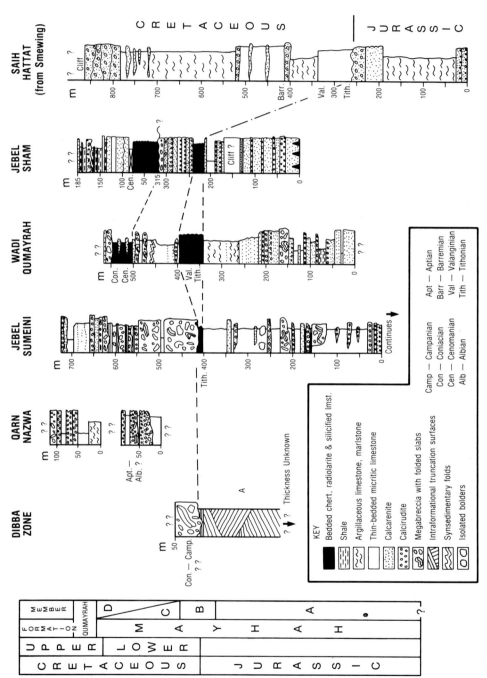

Fig. 3. Stratigraphic correlation diagram for Jurassic and Cretaceous slope deposits of Oman.

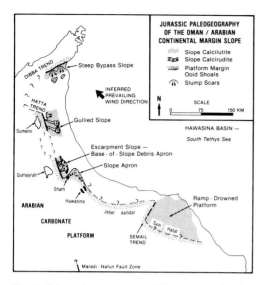

Fig. 4. Schematic palaeogeographic reconstruction for Jurassic carbonate slope deposits along the Oman passive continent margin. Position of the Arabian platform margin slope assumes minimum tectonic displacement of the Sumeini culminations (actual displacement may be more). Note NE−SW trending transform margins and NNW−SSE trending block faulted margins.

of three major thrust sheets with fault-related folds indicating a WSW-directed displacement (Watts 1985; Watts & Garrison, 1986; Searle et al. 1990). In the western thrust sheet, the Jurassic Mayhah Formation unconformably overlies platform-margin forereef talus of the Late Triassic Jebel Wasa Formation. The Mayhah Formation of the eastern thrust sheet overlies Late Triassic base-of-slope debris apron deposits of the E Member of the Maqam Formation (and intervening siltstone and sandstone of the F Member). Because the shelf-edge reefs formed at the top of an escarpment slope and the coeval E-Member debris apron formed at the base of this escarpment (separated by a few tens of km at most), displacement on the intervening thrust fault was probably small (Watts & Garrison 1986). The palaeogeographic reconstruction (Fig. 4) assumes minimum displacement with the slope facies pulled back to the trailing edge of the thrust sheet (Wadi Mayhah), with additional shortening due to internal folds and thrust-faults in the Jebel Sumeini culmination. Restored deformation and facies relationships of genetically-related slope facies indicate that the Mesozoic platform margin trended NNW−SSE, perpendicular to the WSW-directed emplacement direction (Watts 1985; Watts & Garrison 1986; Watts 1988).

Dibba Zone. Three major exposures of thin-bedded Jurassic slope limestones of the lower Mayhah Formation occur as large fault-bounded blocks along the length of the Dibba Zone (Glennie et al. 1974; Searle et al. 1983). Allemann & Peters (1972) interpreted these mountain-sized blocks to be large olistoliths in marginal facies of the Hawasina Complex (cf. Abbate et al. 1970). Folds and thrust faults in these rocks and associated deformation in the Hawasina Complex show a generally westward vergence oblique to the SW−NE trending platform margin of the Dibba Zone (Searle 1988a,b). However, debris flows generated by slope disintegration in the Late Cretaceous and later normal faulting interpreted as culmination collapse features also served as mechanisms of post-depositional movement of the slope deposits (Robertson et al. 1990a,b). Thus, although tectonic displacement is evident in the area, slumping, sliding and debris flows moving off the steep Musandam platform margin in the Dibba Zone were also important in establishing the present distribution of slope facies.

Qarn Nazwa. At Qarn Nazwa, isolated outcrops of Cretaceous slope deposits are surrounded by Recent sands of the Rub al Khali (Glennie et al. 1974). The exposures, located 30 km NW of Jebel Sumeini, are too small (2 km × 0.5 km) to illustrate on the map (Fig. 1). These rocks form a NNW-trending anticline, possibly a WSW-directed, fault-related fold. Given the limited extent of these exposures and the lack of available subsurface information, the amount of tectonic displacement is unknown.

Wadi Qumayrah. The culmination at Wadi Qumayrah is comprised of two major thrust sheets, each having significant internal deformation (Watts 1985; Watts & Blome 1989). Vergence directions in fault-related folds denote emplacement toward the west, perpendicular to the Jurassic platform margin. Jurassic channelized calcirudites and intraformational truncation surfaces in the western thrust sheet formed in an upper slope setting. In the eastern thrust sheet, extensive coalesced beds of redeposited limestones developed as a base-of-slope debris apron. Again, this suggests that the amount of displacement along the intervening thrust fault was relatively small (the width of the steep slope). The displacement along the range-front thrust fault is unknown but the minimum offset of the thrust sheets is slightly greater than the width of the Qumayrah culmination to account for internal deformation. The actual displacement and original palaeogeographic position cannot be precisely determined, therefore the palaeogeographic relationship of the Qumayrah rocks to the adjacent Sumeini and Sham areas is poorly understood.

Jebel Sham. The Jebel Sham area forms a structural high at the northwestern end of the Hawasina Window (Haybi Corridor of Searle 1985). Being a window through nappes of the Semail Ophiolite and Hawasina Complex, this culmination has very complex structure. An upper thrust sheet comprised of an intact stratigraphic sequence including the Mayhah Formation and superjacent Qumayrah Formation was apparently thrust SSW over a structurally repeated sequence of the Qumayrah Formation rocks. The leading edge of the exposed thrust sheet is truncated by later down-to-south normal faulting. Again, displacement is at least the width of the Jebel Sham exposures and probably greater.

Hawasina Window. The Mayhah Formation exposed in the Hawasina Window is highly deformed and recrystallized to the point that little information can be extracted on the nature of the platform margin in this region. Searle (1985) interpreted these rocks as large pop-up structures, with significant vertical displacement and an unknown amount of horizontal shortening. Presumably, the platform margin was originally situated farther to the north.

Jebel Akhdar. Jebel Akhdar is a very large anticlinal structure of parautochthonous platform carbonates that formed due to late-stage compressional tectonics along the Oman continental margin (Glennie *et al.* 1973, 1974; Bernoulli & Weissert 1987). It is probably detached along a thrust fault at depth to allow for shortening due to folding (Searle 1985; Bernoulli & Weissert 1987; several km to a few tens of km). The competent platform limestones forming this major culmination show little internal or small-scale deformation. The location of the platform margin is unknown but certainly was north of Jebel Akhdar where shelf-edge facies are only locally developed (e.g. in the Cretaceous of Wadi Laasi).

Saih Hatat. The Saih Hatat structure is a broad anticlinorium similar to the Jebel Akhdar structure in that it is cored by pre-Permian continental rocks and flanked by Permian to Triassic platform carbonates (Glennie *et al.* 1974). In Permian to Jurassic time, the Saih Hatat region was tectonically unstable, being affected by block-faulting and differential subsidence (Rabu *et al.* 1990). In Jurassic time, this unstable carbonate platform was drowned, contrasting with the Tithonian−Early Cretaceous drowning event affecting Jebel Akhdar and the rest of the outer Arabian platform. The Saih Hatat culmination is northeast of the Jebel Akhdar culmination, separated by the major NE-trending structures forming the Semail Gap and the Jebel Nakhl (NE kink or extension of Jebel Akhdar anticline). Internal deformation of the Mesozoic platform sequence at Saih Hatat is relatively severe, reflecting significant southward displacement (Mann & Hanna 1990). However, deformation and displacement is considerably less than that affecting the structurally higher Semail and Hawasina nappes. Smewing (pers. comm. 1988) suggests that Semail Gap follows a NNE-trending platform margin shelf-slope break that developed due to rifting and transform faulting in Early Jurassic time (see below) and the presence of this feature is reflected by the Semail Gap structural trend.

Evidence for faulting along platform-margin slopes

The Sumeini Group apparently developed along the Oman passive continental margin which was bounded by a series of normal and transform faults. This structural grain was established during the early rifting of the margin, providing the foundation upon which a thick succession of platform margin carbonates developed. This underlying structure controlled the geometry of the basin margin, the morphology of the slope and the evolution of carbonate slope facies through time.

Patterns of sedimentation in the Sumeini Group at Jebel Sumeini and Wadi Qumayrah suggest that NNW−SSE trending, down-to-east, normal faults formed in the Triassic and Jurassic (see below). These structures may be related to preexisting deep-seated basement structures, possibly a continuation of the Maradi-Nafun fault belt or comparable structures which trend NNW across the interior of Oman toward the Wadi Qumayrah and Jebel Sumeini areas (Fig. 4; Hughes Clarke 1988; Watts & Blome 1989). Thrust faults in the Sumeini Group of both areas might follow preexisting structures, possibly reactivating (inverting) normal faults which developed during the earlier passive margin phase (cf. Jackson 1980).

NE−SW trending platform margins such as the Dibba Zone and possibly the Semail Gap trend may have developed along transform faults (see below; Robertson *et al.* 1990a,b). Transform-faulting favours the establishment of steep continental margin slopes, as inferred for the Dibba Zone which was maintained even after fault activity ceased (see below).

Factors controlling slope sedimentation: basic concepts

A number of factors control the nature of carbonate slope deposits, many relating to the palaeogeograhy of the platform margin.

(i) Steepness of the slope (declivity). Relatively gentle accretionary slopes versus progressively steeper bypass (gullied and escarpment) and erosional escarpment slopes (Schlager & Camber 1986).

(ii) Facing direction (windward vs. leeward). This determines the flux of sediment off the carbonate platform (Mullins & Neumann 1979).

(iii) Nature of the carbonate platform sedimentation. Shelf margin facies are the major source of carbonate sediment deposited on the slope as exemplified by widespread redeposited Jurassic ooids (Watts & Garrison 1986).

(iv) Fluctuations in sea level (resulting from eustasy and subsidence). Rapid relative rise in sea level can lead to platform drowning and reduced carbonate sedimentation rates such as that characterizing the Tithonian to Valanginian of Oman (Kendall & Schlager 1981).

(v) Structural control (faulting along platform margin). The world's best developed carbonate platforms are established on passive continental margins where carbonate sedimentation patterns are primarily controlled by subsidence history and the structural geometry of the margin (cf. Mullins & Lynts 1977; Mullins 1983).

(vi) Pre-existing topography and depositional history. Optimum rates of carbonate production occur in shallow water within the euphotic zone, closely tied to topography inherited from the previous evolution of the platform (Schlager 1981).

Stratigraphy and facies analysis

By comparing and interpreting all the known slope deposits of the Sumeini Group, a model for the depositional settings, evolution and paleogeography of Mesozoic carbonate slope facies along the Oman/Arabian continental margin slope can be developed (Fig. 4). In most of the Oman Mountains, the slope sediments are of Jurassic and Cretaceous age. However, the more complete sequence at Jebel Sumeini provides the only exposed record of the Permian and Triassic evolution of the Arabian platform margin slope in Oman, which reflect the tectonic history of the Oman continental margin (Fig. 2).

Jurassic slope sediments across the Oman Mountains have significant facies changes which are interpreted in terms of variations in slope declivity, facing direction, structural and sedimentologic evolution and patterns of slope sedimentation (Figs 3 & 4). The Jurassic slope facies reveal a complex paleogeography along the structurally controlled Oman passive continental margin. This model for the Jurassic paleogeography is relatively simplistic when compared to the great variability of modern carbonate platform margins which are typified by embayments and extremely varied slope deposits (Schlager & Ginsberg 1981).

Passive margin sedimentation continued until Late Cretaceous (Cenomanian) time when a dramatic reorganization of patterns of sedimentation preceded the Oman Orogeny. The final section considers the response of this margin to impending collision and nappe emplacement of the Oman orogeny.

Permian and Triassic sequence at Jebel Sumeini

Permian. Permian (and Triassic) exposures of the Sumeini Group are limited to the Jebel Sumeini area (Figs 1 & 2; Watts & Garrison 1986). Here, the lowest part of the Sumeini Group (A member of the Maqam Formation) consists of thin-bedded, argillaceous, spicular limestones which formed in a relatively deep-marine (outer shelf) setting. A lenticular fossiliferous limestone includes a varied and well preserved Permian assemblage of brachiopods, corals, bryozoans, and crinoids, possibly denoting nearby bioherms (Fig. 2; Watts & Garrison 1986). Breccias and intrastratal deformation in the upper part of the unit and in the lower B member of the Maqam Formation denote establishment of a Permian carbonate slope. Thus, a relatively deep-water setting existed in the area, suggesting either early stages of rift-related tectonic subsidence or proximity to the Palaeotethys sea in Permian time. Distended sedimentary breccias in the dolomites of the Permian to Triassic (?) B Member may have formed as slope sediments in an extensional rift setting (Watts & Garrison 1986).

The Permian Oman Exotics and Al Aridh Formation are associated with carbonate slope deposits and radiolarian chert, implying tectonic subsidence at this time (Bernoulli & Weissert 1987; Bernoulli *et al.* 1990; Blendinger *et al.* 1990). The Permian Saiq Formation at the base of the Arabian platform sequence may also have developed due to syn-rift (?) tectonic subsidence of the Arabian platform margin (Hughes

Clarke 1988). At Saih Hatat, tectonic instability is displayed by slope breccias, volcanic rocks, and facies changes that suggest a complicated block-faulted paleogeography (Rabu *et al.* 1990; Blendinger 1990; Bernoulli *et al.* 1990).

Triassic. A major phase of rifting in Triassic time played a primary role in the development of the Oman continental margin. At Jebel Sumeini, tectonic subsidence in Early Triassic (Dienerian; S. Carey, pers. comm. 1988) time led to the development of small (1–4 km across) carbonate submarine fans along a NNW–SSE trending margin as expressed by facies patterns and paleocurrents (Watts 1988). Growth faults occur in these submarine fan deposits in northern Jebel Sumeini, where ENE-trending faults show left-lateral or down-to-north displacements, possibly related to the Hatta Zone transform lineament (Robertson *et al.* 1990a,b). These syn-sedimentary faults show a decrease in displacement upsection and seem to have influenced patterns of submarine fan sedimentation (Watts 1988).

Later in the Triassic (Ladinian to Norian) following an influx of terrigenous sediment, the carbonate slope succession was suddenly marked by thick megabreccias, calcirudites, and turbiditic calcarenite. The debris includes large clasts derived from slope and shallow-marine limestones which denote establishment of a steep bypass margin and base-of-slope debris apron. The sudden development of an escarpment slope suggests structural control with down-to-east normal faulting and differential subsidence, possibly along preexisting basement structures. Higher in the section, boulders of coralgal lime-stone and other material were eroded from the coeval Jebel Wasa reefal assemblage that formed along a high-energy shelf-margin at the top of the escarpment (Watts & Garrison 1986).

This major phase of divergent tectonism is also evident in the Triassic Haybi volcanics (Searle *et al.* 1980). Rapid rates of sedimentation in the Triassic Oman Exotics accompanied rapid tectonic subsidence (Glennie *et al.* 1974). The stratigraphy of the Hawasina Complex (Zulla Formation) is similar to that in the Triassic part of the Sumeini Group (D to E Members, Watts & Garrison 1986; Cooper 1987, 1990; Bernoulli *et al.* 1990), but the Zulla Formation generally lacks coarse redeposited calcirudite (particularly megabreccia), being somewhat removed from the platform margin.

A major pre-Jurassic unconformity, the pre-Murrat unconformity, punctuates the top of the Triassic platform sequence in Oman (Glennie *et al.* 1973, 1974; Watts & Garrison, 1986). Silici-

clastic sediments of Late Triassic and/or Liassic age (the Ghalilah Formation and basal Sahtan Group) occur in the Arabian platform sequence of the Oman Mountains (Hudson 1960; Allemann & Peters 1972; Glennie *et al.* 1974; Searle *et al.* 1983; Rabu *et al.* 1990). Terrigenous quartzose sediments of this age also occur in the slope sequence (F Member, Maqam Formation; Watts & Garrison 1986) and basinal deposits (Guwayza Sandstone; Cooper 1987, 1990). This is an excellent example of reciprocal sedimentation where platform emergence during a sea-level low-stands allowed most of the terrigenous sediment to bypass the platform and be deposited in the deep basin (Watts & Garrison 1986).

Jurassic slope facies

Jurassic slope deposits of the Mayhah Formation (A member) are more widespread than younger and older parts of the Sumeini Group, providing the most complete picture of basin geometry and variations in slope morphology. Notably, redeposited oolitic calcarenite is common in the slope and basinal deposits of the Oman Mountains (Glennie *et al.* 1973, 1974; Watts & Garrison 1986; Cooper 1986; 1990; Watts & Blome 1989). The nature of slope deposits varies among Sumeini Group exposures, indicating differences in slope declivity, facing direction and patterns of sedimentation that are, in part, related to rift-tectonism along the Oman passive continental margin (Fig. 3; Table 1).

Jebel Sumeini. At Jebel Sumeini, thin-bedded limestones are cut by lenticular beds of channelized calcirudite (limestone conglomerate and breccia) which represent gullies filled with debris transported from platform-margin and slope sources (Figs 4 & 5). Isolated rock-fall boulders and intraformational truncation surfaces (slump scars) also imply carbonate slope deposition (Watts & Garrison 1986). Calcirudites including blocks of coralline limestone originating from the Late Triassic Jebel Wasa reefal assemblage reveal that the upper slope was erosional with gullies cutting into older reefal deposits. Alternatively, the upper slope may have been an erosional escarpment passing basinward into a gullied slope and base-of-slope apron similar to the northern Little Bahama Bank (Mullins *et al.* 1984). The gullied slope formed on a moderately sloping (6–20°C) apron which aggraded over the underlying base-of-escarpment apron deposits of the E Member and intervening terrigenous sediments of the F Member of the Maqam Formation (Watts & Garrison 1986). The periodic channelized beds of calcirudite

Table 1. *Descriptions and paleoenvironmental interpretations of Jurassic slope deposits at different localities*

Location	Lithologies	Interpretation
Dibba Zone	Thin-bedded calcilutite with intraformational truncation surfaces, minor calcirudite	Peri-platform Ooze, Steep Bypass Slope
Jebel Sumeini	Thin-bedded calcilutite with channelized beds of calcirudite and oolitic calcarenite. Clasts include Upper Triassic reefal material.	Erosional Upper Slope — Gullied Lower Slope Conglomerate-filled Channels on Lower Slope
Wadi Qumayrah	Sequence of coalesced lenticular beds of calcarenite calcirudite and megabreccia	Escarpment, Base-of-slope Debris Apron
Jebel Sham	Thick sequences of generally unchannelized bioclastic calcarenite and calcirudite	Slope Apron on Leeward Margin of skeletal-rich Carbonate Platform.
Saih Hatat	Thin-bedded argillaceous calcilutite with minor calcirudite and calcarenite	Carbonate Ramp over Continental Basement, Relatively Shallow Drowned Platform

Fig. 5. Jurassic gullied slope deposits at Jebel Sumeini. The thick channelized calcirudite (R) is incised into thin-bedded calcilutite (L — periplatform ooze). Clasts include Triassic coralgal limestone and slabs of thin-bedded slope limestone and the matrix contains abundant ooids (modified after Watts & Garrison 1986).

might have been triggered by oversteepening and seismicity along the faulted margin. Alternatively, the preexisting faulted margin may have become inactive and the channelized calcirudites could represent randomly occurring gullied-slope deposits on an aggradational slope (Watts & Garrison 1986).

Slightly to the north in the Hatta Zone, previously unrecognized slope facies include slumped calcilutite, channelized calcirudite, and calcarenite (Robertson *et al.* 1990). Clasts in the calcirudites include platform and slope limestones and significant terrigenous material (metamorphic and granitic rock fragments and Permian sandstone) which are interpreted to have been eroded from basement rocks exposed along transform fault scarps (Robertson *et al.* 1990).

Dibba Zone. Along the Dibba zone, thin-bedded calcilutite of the Mayhah Formation formed as periplatform ooze exported from the adjacent carbonate platform of the Musandam Peninsula (cf. Schlanger & James 1978). The finely laminated, unburrowed, fossiliferous nature of these dark-colored, organic-rich calcilutites suggests deposition within a euxinic, oxygen-minimum zone that impinged on the slope (Searle *et al.* 1983). The rarity of coarse redeposited limestones (intraformational calcirudite) suggest that this was a very steep bypass slope mantled by fine-grained periplatform ooze (Fig. 4). Abundant intraformational truncation surfaces are interpreted as slump scars, most common in upper slope settings (Figs 3, 6; cf. Davies 1977). The steep margin along the Dibba Zone may have formed over an inactive

Fig. 6. At the Dibba Zone, thin-bedded Jurassic calcilutites (peri-platform ooze) are cut by numerous intraformational truncation surfaces (slump scars), indicating a steep upper slope environment.

transform faulted margin that became established in this area in Triassic time (Falcon 1967; Robertson *et al.* 1990a,b). Jurassic shelf-edge facies exposed in the Musandam of the northern Dibba Zone contain cross-stratified oolitic and peloidal calcarenite and local coral boundstone which formed as a narrow belt of ooid shoals and patch reefs. Searle *et al.* (1983) also describe a thick but localized (1 km wide belt) calcirudite/megabreccia containing abundant clasts of neritic limestone interpreted as periplatform talus. The rarity of platform-derived material in the thin-bedded calcilutites of the Mayhah Formation suggests that the area was along a windward margin similar to the present-day east-facing Bahama escarpment (Fig. 4; cf. Heath & Mullins 1984). However, the Hawasina Complex contains abundant redeposited oolitic calciturbidite which must have bypassed the slope. Calcirudites in the unit which contains clasts of Jurassic and Triassic platform limestones indicating that the slope was at least locally erosional (Cooper 1990a,b).

Wadi Qumayrah. In the Wadi Qumayrah area, a thick interval of calcirudite and megabreccia in the lower part of the Mayhah Formation formed along a steep escarpment slope, possibly bounded by a down-to-east normal fault (see above; Figs 3, 4 & 7; Watts & Blome 1989). The megabreccias may have been generated by

Jurassic seismicity and oversteepening of the block-faulted margin (cf. Mutti *et al.* 1984).

In the western nappe, localized beds of channelized calcirudite represent large gullies or canyons. Associated calcilutites have abundant intraformational truncation surfaces, interpreted as slump scars that formed on the upper slope. In the eastern nappe, a series of coalesced lenticular beds of polymictic calcirudite (containing clasts of neritic and slope limestones) and oolitic calcarenite formed as a base-of-slope debris apron (Figs 3 & 4; Watts & Blome 1989). Later in the Jurassic, thin-bedded limestones, interpreted as periplatform ooze, comprise the upper part of the Jurassic A Member (Fig. 3). The lack of coarse calciclastic limestones suggest that the faulted margin became inactive. With tectonic quiescence, the basin margins evolved into a gently sloping ramp configuration (approximately 1 degree of slope) along which mass-movements and sediment-gravity-flows were unlikely.

The calcareous nature of the overlying B Member chert and the implications of the ramp slope margin which developed in the Wadi Qumayrah area suggest the slope bounded a relatively shallow marginal basin or embayment opening northward to the Hawasina basin. Perhaps this marginal basin formed a reentrant into the Arabian platform, which was bounded

Fig. 7. At Wadi Qumayrah, a thick Jurassic megabreccia (M) is widespread and contains clasts of neritic limestone and huge blocks of thin-bedded slope limestone (up to 1 km across). Together with associated calciclastic sediments shown in this overturned sequence, the unit formed as an extensive base-of-slope debris apron (modified after Watts & Blome 1989).

on the west by the Wadi Qumayrah slope deposits and bounded on the east by slope apron deposits of Jebel Sham (see below). Modern analogs of reentrants, such as the Tongue of the Ocean and Exuma Sound, are common in the Bahamas (Schlager & Ginsberg 1981) and ancient embayments have been recognized in the Tethyan Seaway (e.g. Bosellini *et al.* 1981).
Jebel Sham. At Jebel Sham in the northwestern Hawasina Window, the Jurassic part of the Mayhah Formation consists of thick intervals of coarse oolitic and bioclastic calcarenite and calcirudite (Fig. 3). This sequence differs from other exposures of the Mayhah Formation in that thin-bedded calcilutite (periplatform ooze) is rare. These coarse calciclastic deposits are indistinctly bedded with numerous amalgamation surfaces and appear to form a laterally continuous sediment body, suggesting that they formed an extensive slope apron deposit (Fig. 4; Mullins & Cook 1986). This apron could

represent the eastern boundary of the Wadi Qumayrah marginal basin and may have developed along a west- or northwest-facing leeward margin of a promontory bounding the Arabian platform margin at the Hawasina Window (Searle *et al.* 1990; Cooper 1990). This contrasts with the southeast-facing windward margin of the Dibba Zone and may be analogous to sediment drifts of coarse sediment (aprons with slopes of < 2 degrees) along the northwestern promontories of the Great Bahama and Little Bahama Banks (Mullins & Neumann 1979; Mullins *et al.* 1980).

The Hawasina Complex (Guwayza Limestone) of the Hawasina Window is also much coarser-grained than that near the Wadi Qumayrah area (Cooper 1990). It includes abundant coarse calciclastic sediments which form a coarsening upward progradational sequence interpreted as a base-of-slope apron on a leeward platform margin with paleocurrents directed to the northeast (Cooper 1990).
Saih Hatat. In the Saih Hatat region, Jurassic slope and basinal deposits are dominated by thin-bedded calcilutite (periplatform ooze) but also include rare localized beds of calcirudite and slump-folded beds (Fig. 3). Although the transitional facies are not exposed, these deep-marine carbonates overlie shallow-marine carbonates of the Triassic Mahil Formation. This Jurassic drowning of the Saih Hatat platform led to the formation a submerged plateau similar to the Blake Plateau north of the Bahama Banks (Sheridan & Enos 1979). The submerged plateau formed a marginal basin which was relatively shallow in comparison to the oceanic Hawasina Basin proper. Because redeposited calciclastic sediments and other evidence of steep slopes are rare, the Saih Hatat plateau seems to have had ramp-like margins with gentle slopes (Fig. 4).

The Saih Hatat region had a long history of tectonic subsidence culminating in Jurassic subsidence and drowning (Rabu *et al.* 1990). The shallow-marine platform margin bounding Jebel Akhdar on the western side of Saih Hatat plateau may have trended along the Semail Gap. This basin was shallow relative to the Hawasina Basin, having developed over continental or transitional basement such as that exposed in the core of Saih Hatat. During the Early Cretaceous platform drowning event, deep-water limestones similar to those in the carbonate platform sequence formed at Saih Hatat rather than the radiolarian chert characterizing the Hawasina Basin, supporting the notion that this was a relatively shallow basin/submerged plateau above the CCD.
Interpretive summary — the Jurassic slope. A

variety of Jurassic slope deposits developed along the Oman continental margin (Fig. 3). The different trends of the margin appear to be structurally controlled along the Oman passive continental margin (Fig. 4). NNW–SSE-trending platform margins appear to have developed along block-faulted rifted magins at Jebel Sumeini and Wadi Qumayrah. Local inactive transform lineaments form NE–SW-trending platform at the Dibba Zone and the Semail Gap (Saih Hatat). This inherited geometry and structure played a major role in controlling the nature of slope sedimentation by pre-determining slope declivity, slope facing direction, subsidence, sea-level history, and resultant mechanisms of slope sedimentation.

The continental margin slope at Jebel Sumeini continued to develop along a preexisting block-faulted margin with a thick apron of redeposited carbonate sediment cut by gullies (Fig. 4). This NNW-trending margin may have been truncated by a transform offset along the Hatta trend. The inferred embayment may account for younger Cretaceous slope deposits at Qarn Nazwa and would be bounded on the north by another oblique transform margin along the Dibba trend. The slope along the Dibba Zone was a very steep bypass slope characterized by large slumps and slides. South of Jebel Sumeini at Wadi Qumayrah, a steep escarpment slope and debris apron developed with possible associated faulting. Reduction in coarse redeposited limestones suggests tectonic quiescence and development of a relatively shallow marginal basin or embayment east of Wadi Qumayrah. On the eastern margin of the inferred embayment, a thick apron of coarse calciclastic sediment developed along the leeward margin of an inferred promontory in the Hawasina Window region (Cooper, 1990). The region between the Hawasina Window and Jebel Akhdar is *terra incognita* with respect to the Sumeini Group slope deposits but the Hawasina Complex here may contain coarse-grained base-of-slope apron deposits (Cooper 1990). Farther east in the Saih Hatat region, Jurassic platform drowning led to the formation of a long-lived submerged plateau with ramp margins (J. Smewing, pers. comm. 1988).

Late Jurassic (Tithonian) to Early Cretaceous (Valanginian) drowning of the outer Arabian platform

In Late Jurassic (Tithonian) to Early Cretaceous (Valanginian) time, the outer part of the Arabian carbonate platform was drowned (cf. Kendall & Schlager 1981), resulting in deep-marine calcilutites of Rayda and Salil For-

mations (Glennie *et al.* 1973, 1974; Murris 1980; Searle *et al.* 1983; Harris *et al.* 1984; Connally & Scott 1985; Watts & Garrison 1986). This drowning event was apparently due to inability of the carbonate platform to keep pace with rapid sea level rise resulting from tectonic subsidence of the Oman continental margin (Harris *et al.* 1984) in addition to the end-Jurassic high stand of eustatic sea level (Vail *et al.* 1977; Hallum 1987; Haq *et al.* 1987; Watts & Blome 1990; Cooper 1990). The drowning event may have been preceded by an interval or rift-related thermal uplift of the Oman margin at the end of the Jurassic (Rabu *et al.* 1990). A unconformity of short duration (Hughes Clark 1988; Watts & Blome 1989) may be responsible for significant pre-Rayda erosion of the Jurassic of Jebel Akhdar (Rabu *et al.* 1990). If rift-related uplift occurred at the end of the Jurassic, the rapid subsidence of the outer Arabian platform could represent post-rift, passive margin subsidence due to crustal cooling (Bechennec *et al.* 1988).

At Jebel Sumeini, red radiolarian chert denotes deposition below the carbonate compensation depth (CCD) in a relatively deep basin as do many of the equivalent bedded cherts in the Hawasina Complex. The marginal basin in the Wadi Qumayrah and Jebel Sham areas was apparently shallower than the Hawasina Basin so that the B Member cherts consist of calcareous chert or silicified radiolarian calcilutite (Watts & Blome 1989). Alternatively, greater amounts of periplatform carbonate may have been supplied to this area, resulting in a deeper CCD. An interval of chert does not occur in the Mayhah Formation at the Dibba Zone due to non-deposition or erosion. At Saih Hatat, Tithonian to Valanginian calcilutite resembles the Rayda and Salil Formations of Jebel Akhdar supporting the notion that this was a relatively shallow submerged plateau above the CCD (J. D. Smewing, pers. comm. 1988).

Early Cretaceous restoration of carbonate slope facies

By Valanginian time, a carbonate ramp containing shallow-marine fossiliferous limestones (Habshan Formation) prograded over most of the drowned Arabian platform (Salil Formation; Glennie *et al.* 1973, 1974; Hassan *et al.* 1975; Murris 1980; Harris *et al.* 1984; Connally & Scott 1985). Concomitantly, carbonate sedimentation resumed in the upper Mayhah Formation and Hawasina Complex (Watts & Garrison 1986; Cooper 1987, 1990; Watts and Blome 1990). In the Mayhah Formation, the recorded restoration of carbonate slope sedimentation is most complete in the Wadi

Qumayrah succession, but is missing from the other exposures.

At Wadi Qumayrah, Valanginian bedded chert (silicified radiolarian calcilutite) of the B Member is sharply overlain by thin-bedded calcareous calcilutite of the D Member of the Mayhah Formation (Fig. 3). In the lower part of the unit, widespread chert-clast breccia beds were apparently eroded from the underlying chert interval higher on the slope. These breccias may be equivalent to the two intervals of calcirudite in the Musandam platform succession (see below) and/or could have formed due to gravitational instabilities affecting the relatively incompetent cherts. The bulk of the D Member consists of thin-bedded argillaceous calcilutite lacking redeposited calciclastic sediment, indicating return to carbonate deposition on the ramp bounding the Qumayrah embayment (similar to that of the Late Jurassic; Watts & Blome 1989). However, slump folded beds and beds of intraformational calcirudite containing folded slabs of calcilutite denote steepening of the slope in pre-Cenomanian time (?, overlain by Cenomanian radiolarian chert of the Qumayrah Formation (Watts & Blome 1989). Steepening of the slope was apparently due to tectonic flexure (downbowing) of the Arabian platform margin as it approached an inferred northward-dipping subduction zone and was downloaded by the Hawasina nappes (Robertson 1987; Patton & O'Connor 1988; Watts & Blome 1989).

The platform succession of the Musandam Peninsula is marked by a drowning unconformity (cf. Schlager & Camber 1986) bounded by Jurassic (upper Tithonian) shallow marine limestones below and Valanginian to Barremian deep-marine limestones above (Allemann & Peters 1972). Thus, the platform in this region remained drowned until the Aptian (?) progradation of shallow-marine bioclastic calcirudite (Allemann & Peters 1972; Ricateau & Riche 1980; Searle et al. 1983). In the lower part of the drowned platform succession (within the Valanginian Ashhab Limestone and equivalent rocks), two rather thick beds of calcirudite (up to 13 m thick) may be related to the drowning unconformity.

At Saih Hatat where platform drowning occurred earlier in the Jurassic, the area remained as a long-lived submerged plateau until at least Aptian time when bioclastic calcirudite and calcarenite advanced over southern Saih Hatat (J. D. Smewing, pers. comm. 1988).

Late Cretaceous megabreccias

In Cenomanian time, major changes in patterns of sedimentation occurred along the Oman continental margin in response to changing plate motions and convergent tectonics (Glennie et al. 1973, 1974; Gealy 1977; Robertson 1987; Patton & O'Connor 1988; Watts & Blome 1989). Apparently, the Arabian carbonate platform slope became steeper and subsided below the CCD as it approached a northward-dipping subduction zone (Gealey 1977; Coleman 1981; Robertson 1987; Patton & O'Connor 1988; Watts & Blome 1989).

Megabreccias and associated calciclastic sediments record the early response of the continental margin slope to attempted subduction of a passive continental margin (Watts & Blome 1989). Because of gravitational instabilities associated with steep carbonate slopes, thick megabreccias were generated due to collapse or disintegration of the carbonate platform margin and may have been triggered by seismicity or faulting (cf. Mutti et al. 1984). Such catastrophic megabreccias and other sediment gravity flows are common in Late Cretaceous slope deposits (Qumayrah Formation and other units) at numerous localities in the western Oman Mountains including Jebel Sumeini, Dibba Zone, Qarn Nazwa and Wadi Qumayrah (Table 2).

Jebel Sumeini megabreccias. At Jebel Sumeini, the C Member of the Mayhah Formation is a thick sequence of megabreccia (>240 m) which unconformably overlies the Early Cretaceous B Member chert and gradationally underlies the Cenomanian or younger D Member of the Mayhah Formation (Fig. 3). In the lower part two very thick (the first is >70 m thick), laterally extensive megabreccias have clast-supported fabrics and lack any matrix (Fig. 8). Debris flows require some matrix so these megabreccias represent huge debris avalanche deposits which formed due to collapse of the carbonate platform margin (Watts & Garrison 1986; cf. Mullins et al. 1986).

Overlying the megabreccias, the D Member of the Mayhah Formation includes redeposited calcarenite which contain Cenomanian foraminifera (*Nummoloculina ? heimi Bonet*; M. Hart, pers. comm. 1982) providing a minimum age (it could be reworked). The megabreccia has an erosional contact with the underlying radiolarian chert of the B Member which is Tithonian to Early Cretaceous in age, having formed during the platform drowning event. Unfortunately, the age of the megabreccia itself has not been determined and imprecise dating provided by bounding units does not allow for a full understand of the significance of the platform margin collapse and its relationship to convergent tectonics. Clearly, something caused

Table 2. *Stratigraphy, description and ages of Upper Cretaceous megabreccias of the western Oman Mountains*

Location	Lithologic Units	Lithologies	Age
Dibba Zone*			
Bathi Mahani	Ausaq Conglomerate	Thick (up to 50 m) localized calcirudite with clasts of slope(?) and neritic limestones, associated with marlstone and thin calcirudite.	Campanian–Coniacian
Jebel Agah	unnamed	Thick megabreccia overlies eroded Jurassic slope limestone and includes clasts of slope limestone and neritic limestone containing Barremian-Aptian *Orbitulina* sp.; associated with radiolarite, chert, marl, and shale.	Coniacian–Santonian
J. Hagab	Lakhshaifa Beds Fukhaira Beds	Polymictic calcirudite overlies Shammal Chert. Contains clasts of igneous and metamorphic rocks in addition to limestone boulders.	post Aptian–Albian, Campanian
Jebel Sumeini	C Member Mayhah Formation	Two very thick megabreccias pass upward into thinner beds of calcirudite. Erosional base cuts into both the B and A Members (Mayhah Formation). Contains a variety of clasts including Triassic reefal debris and bedded slope limestones.	pre-Cenomanian?
Qarn Nazwa	upper Mayhah Fm and Qumayrah Fm?	Thick conglomerates contain a variety of clasts, interbedded with limestone in lower part. At top overlying shale and marlstone, thick beds of calcirudite contain rudistid boulders.	Post Aptian–Albian
Wadi Qumayrah	Qumayrah Formation	Thick megabreccia locally has an erosional base cut into deformed slope carbonates. Elsewhere, a widely occurring megabreccia overlies Cenomanian-Coniacian radiolarite.	Coniacian or younger

* Dibba zone data from Alleman & Peters (1972).

the slope to become unstable in order for it to collapse. Tectonically, as the Oman continental margin approached a northward-dipping subduction zone and was downloaded by the Hawasina nappes, the slope would have become steeper as it was flexed downward (Glennie *et al.* 1973, 1974; Robertson 1987; Patton & O'Connor 1988). If the pre-existing faults inherited from earlier rifting were reactivated, fault movements and associated seismicity may have triggered the collapse of the platform margin.

Dibba Zone megabreccias. At the Dibba Zone, a similar megabreccia, the Ausaq Conglomerate, is at least 50 m thick, lies unconformably over a number of platform carbonate units along Wadi Batha Mahani and contains clasts of neritic and slope limestone (Allemann & Peters 1972; localities mentioned below are documented in this useful paper; see also Robertson *et al.* 1990a,b). At Jebel Agah, an unnamed thick megabreccia unconformably overlies thin-bedded limestone of the Jurassic A Member and contains abundant clasts of limestone containing *Orbitulina sp.* limestone. The megabreccia locally abuts against possible fault scarps and nearby associated calciclastic sediments and interbedded pelagic sediments lap onto the underlying Mayhah Formation (Fig. 9). Allemann & Peters (1972) provide ages of Campanian to Coniacian and Coniacian to Santonian for the respective units. Being composed of limestone clasts eroded from the platform margin and slope, these megabreccias apparently

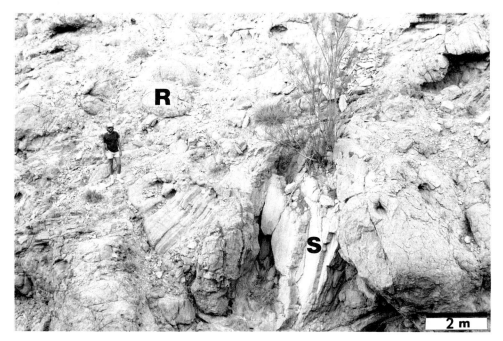

Fig. 8. Thick, widespread Upper Cretaceous megabreccias at Jebel Sumeini contain rounded blocks of Triassic reefal debris (R) and folded slabs of thin-bedded slope limestones (S).

Fig. 9. At the Dibba Zone, a megabreccia (M) and associated calciclastic and pelagic sediments unconformably overlie slope limestones (L, peri-platform ooze) at Jebel Agah.

154   K. F. WATTS

formed due to gravitational collapse of the platform margin slope, similar to that envisioned
for the Jebel Sumeini.

At Jebel Hagab, the Lakshaifa and Fukhairi
beds (50 m thick) overlie the Shamal Chert and
contain an assortment of clasts including limestone, igneous and metamorphic rock fragments
(Hudson *et al.* 1954). The age is uncertain but is
younger than the Aptian to Albian *Orbitulina
sp.* contained in platform-derived clasts (Searle
et al. 1983) and is probably Campanian (Allemann & Peters 1972). This material was probably eroded from the advancing Hawasina
nappes (Allemann & Peters 1972).

Qarn Nazwa megabreccias. Megabreccias and
associated calciclastic sediments are common in
the isolated exposures of Qarn Nazwa. In the
lower part, individual megabreccias (up to 8 m
thick) having erosional bases are interbedded
with thin-bedded calcilutite and contain clasts
of neritic limestones and tabular slabs of slope
limestone. Graded calcarenites contain Aptian
to Albian *Orbitulina sp.* (J. Jenner, pers. comm.
1984). The association with thin-bedded calcilutite suggests a correlation with upper Mayhah
Formation (C and/or D Members).

Overlying green and light-grey marlstone
in the upper part of the exposed sequence
(? contact is covered and may be faulted), thick
megabreccias (up to 18 m) contain abundant
rudist-bearing, neritic limestones and lesser
slope limestone. Interbedded green to red mudstones are poorly exposed. Although age data is
lacking for the unit, it is similar to the Qumayrah
Formation of Wadi Qumayrah.

The Qarn Nazwa area is 30 km NW of Jebel
Sumeini area, slightly west of the projection of
the Qumayrah-Sumeini platform margin trend
(Fig. 4). The locality lies on a projection of the
Hatta trend (Robertson *et al.* 1990) suggesting
that it formed along an embayment in the platform margin bounded by the Hatta and Dibba
trends. Slope instabilities along this structurally
controlled margin may be related to steepening
of the slope prior to the Oman orogeny, similar
to that inferred for the better understood sequence at Wadi Qumayrah.

Wadi Qumayrah megabreccias. Overlying the
Mayhah Formation at Wadi Qumayrah, the
Late Cretaceous (Cenomanian to Coniacian)
Qumayrah Formation was originally defined
as a siliceous equivalent of the Muti Formation, which is actually younger (Coniacian
to Maastrichtian; Glennie *et al.* 1973a,b;
Robertson, 1987; Watts & Blome 1989). A
laterally variable megabreccia and associated
beds of calciclastic sediment form the upper
part of the unit (Watts & Blome 1989).

As noted above, debris sheets in the uppermost Mayhah Formation contain slabs of folded
slope limestone formed by slumping of thin-
bedded calcilutite down a steep slope into extensive debris flows (cf. Cook & Mullins 1983).
The sudden onset of such slumping and sediment gravity flows suggest abrupt tectonic steepening of the slope. The Mayhah Formation
is overlain by siliceous mudstone and radiolarian chert of the Cenomanian to Coniacian
Qumayrah Formation. These siliceous sediments formed in relatively deep water beneath
the carbonate compensation depth (CCD), indicating tectonically induced deepening of the
slope and1)or reduced supply of carbonate sediment from the Arabian platform (Watts &
Blome 1989).

The uppermost Qumayrah Formation chert
is Coniacian in age and is overlain by laterally variable megabreccias and associated redeposited limestones (Fig. 10). At one critical
locality (Jebel Fayad; Watts & Blome 1989),
the megabreccia unconformably overlies deformed Mayhah Formation from which numerous folded slabs of thin-bedded calcilutite were
eroded. The Mayhah Formation was previously
deformed (folded) and eroded along anticlinal
highs suggesting that the megabreccia represents
synorogenic sediments (Watts & Blome 1989).
This structural deformation either resulted from
early thrust faulting and folding propagating
through the slope sequence or, alternatively,
formed by down-slope sliding and deformation
of mountain-sized olistoliths (Watts & Blome
1989). Radiolaria extracted from intercalated
chert yield a Coniacian age. Associated calcirudite and turbiditic calcarenite contain clasts
eroded from rudist banks in addition to reworked slope deposits denoting wholesale collapse of the margin.

*Summary of Late Cretaceous platform margin
collapse.* The Qumayrah Formation formed
during the final phases of sedimentation and
deformation which immediately preceded emplacement of the nappes over the Arabian platform (Watts & Blome 1989). By Coniacian
time, the oversteepened margin collapsed as a
series of sediment gravity flows forming megabreccias at several localities. The present-day
Oman continental margin may represent an
excellent analog to the Late Cretaceous situation with tectonic steepening and slumping
occurring along the slope as it approaches the
Makran subduction zone and accretionary prism
(R. S. White, pers. comm. 1988). Interestingly,
deformation along the present Oman margin is
locally progressing upslope and may be analogous to the synorogenic deformation and

Fig. 10. At Wadi Qumayrah, radiolarian chert and siliceous mudstone (R, mostly covered) of the Qumayrah Formation unconformably overlie thin-bedded calcilutite of the Mayhah Formation (L). A thick megabreccia (M) overlies the radiolarite which is as young as Coniacian in age (modified after Watts & Blome 1989).

megabreccias of the Qumayrah Formation. The Australian shelf margin approaching the Timor trench is another good modern analog for re-organization of the Oman margin as it approached a northward-dipping subduction zone (Veevers *et al.* 1978).

Influence of Oman continental margin geometry on Late Cretaceous nappe emplacement

The structural grain and trend of the Arabian platform margin were inherited from Permo-Triassic rifting of the Oman passive continental margin. Although mantled by younger platform margin deposits, this pre-existing structural grain also controlled the position and geometry of Late Cretaceous structures related to the Oman orogeny. In general, thrust sheets were emplaced perpendicular to the Oman continental margin as suggested by facies relationships and vergence direction of folds (Figs 1 & 4).

Radiolarian chert and megabreccias of the Qumayrah Formation indicate that the Hawasina Complex was not emplaced over the slope deposits until at least Coniacian time.

Later, after emplacement of the Hawasina nappes, the Sumeini Group was involved in out-of-sequence, leapfrog thrust-faulting causing the Sumeini Group to be thrust over the Hawasina Complex (and locally over the Semail Ophiolite; Watts & Blome 1989). Each of the Sumeini Group exposures represent major culminations (structural highs) which formed during the latest stages of deformation. The culminations are isolated thrust sheets with doubly plunging flanks marking lateral ramp cut-offs (Watts 1985; Watts & Garrison 1986; Watts & Blome 1989). Major thrust faults separating different facies of the Sumeini Group (upper escarpment slope versus base-of-slope apron deposits, see above) at Jebel Sumeini and at Wadi Qumayrah could represent pre-existing listric normal faults that were reactivated (inverted) as thrust faults in response to convergent tectonism in the Late Cretaceous (cf. Jackson 1980).

The platform margin is hidden beneath the Late Cretaceous nappes across most of the Oman Mountains but it may control the overall structural geometry of the Oman mountain belt/ thrust sheet. A major question is why does the Sumeini Group only occur at isolated exposures rather than as a continuous belt. Searle *et al.* (1990) suggest that the Sumeini Group culminations formed due to localized detachment of the Sumeini Group along promontories marking the Oman margin and their emplacement over the Arabian platform. The regional geology and slope facies relationships at Jebel Sumeini suggest that it formed a two-sided promontory bounded on the east by a normal-faulted passive margin intersecting with an inferred extension of the Hatta transform to lineament the north (Robertson *et al.* 1990). The Jebel Sham area also seems to represent a promontory bounded to the west by the Qumayrah marginal basin and forming a slope apron along northwest-facing leeward margin. Cooper (1990) suggests that the Hawasina Complex of the Hawasina Window might have also formed adjacent to a promontory. The geometry of the Wadi Qumayrah slope deposits is unclear although it apparently formed a west-facing normal-faulted margin. Depending on palinspastic reconstructions, the Wadi Qumayrah slope deposits are generally aligned with those at Jebel Sumeini, suggesting that they formed along the same platform margin trend. The promontory model would require an embayment between the Jebel Sumeini and Wadi Qumayrah areas, but we lack the data required to test this hypothesis (Searle *et al.* 1990). The Dibba Zone forms the southwest margin of a major promontory (the ancestral Musandam Peninsula; Robertson *et al.* 1990) and the mechanism of emplacement of the Sumeini Group is more complicated, being a mixture of thrust-faulting oblique to the margin and sliding of olistoliths of Jurassic slope limestones down a steep slope.

Conclusions

Slope facies of the Sumeini Group and Qumayrah Formation provide insights into the history of the Oman continental margin. The Oman passive continental margin developed in response to rifting events in the Permian (?), Triassic and Jurassic. The location and nature of carbonate slope deposits along the Arabian platform margin were controlled by normal and transform faults which developed during these rifting events. Thick sequences of slope limestones mantled this passive continental margin. Later, with changing plate motions and convergence along the Oman continental margin, tectonic steepening of the slope and possible seismicity led to the formation of extensive megabreccias. Finally, the orthogonal emplacement of the thrust sheets comprising the Sumeini culminations over the Arabian platform

margin was also controlled by the preexisting structural geometry of the platform margin and slope.

I sincerely thank his majesty Sultan Qaboos and the people of Oman for their great hospitality and especially the Ministry of Petroleum and Minerals. Greatest thanks is owed to Dr. Robert Garrison who supervised my PhD thesis work and provided much inspiration. Field studies in Oman were funded by Amoco Oman Petroleum Company, through the Earth Science and Resource Institute (ESRI). John Smewing, leader of the ESRI Oman project, provided excellent support and valuable advice. Many insights were gained through discussions with ESRI and Amoco geologists working in Oman, particularly Alastair Robertson and Daniel Bernoulli. Mary Anne McKittrick and Jim Sample were outstanding field assistants, contributing directly to geological mapping studies. The University of California, Santa Cruz provided educational opportunities and financial support through teaching assistantships, two Amoco research fellowships, and a patent fund grant. Fossil age dates were determined by C. Blome (radiolarians), D. Ager (brachiopods), N. Silberling (pelagic bivalves), C. Stevens (corals), M. Hart and R. Scott (foraminifera). D. Coccia, J. Filut and J. Smith are thanked for practical assistance. The paper benefitted from reviews by D. Cooper, A. Krumhardt and J. Clough and is published with the permission of Amoco Production Company.

References

ABBATE, E., BORTOLOTTI, V. & PASSERINI, P. 1970. Olistostromes and olistoliths. *Sedimentary Geology*, **4**, 521–557.

ALLEMANN, F. & PETERS, T. 1972. The ophiolite-radiolarite belt of the northern Oman Mountains. *Eclogae Helvetiae*, **65**, 657–697.

BECHENNEC, F., LE METOUR, J., RABU, D., VILLEY, M. & BEURRIER, M. 1988. The Hawasina Basin: a fragment of starved, passive continental margin thrust over the Arabian platform during obduction of the Semail Nappe. *Tectonophysics*, **151**, 323–344.

BERNOULLI, D. & WEISSERT, H. 1987. The upper Hawasina nappes in the central Oman Mountains: stratigraphy, palinspastics and sequence of nappe emplacement. *Geodinamica Acta (Paris)*, **1**, 47–58.

BERNOULLI, D., WEISSERT, H. & BLOME, C. D. 1990. Evolution of the Triassic Hawasina Basin. *In:* ROBERTSON, A. H. F., SEARLE, M. P. & RIES, A. C. (eds) *The Geology and Tectonics of the Oman Region*. Geological Society, London, Special Publication, **49**, 189–204.

BLENDINGER, W., VAN VLIET, A. & HUGHES CLARKE, M. W. 1990. Updoming, rifting and continental margin development during the Late Palaeozoic in northern Oman. *In:* ROBERTSON, A. H. F., SEARLE, M. P. & RIES, A. C. (eds) *The Geology and Tectonics of the Oman Region*. Geological

Society, London, Special Publication, **49**, 27−37.

BOSELLINI, A., MASETTI, D. & SARTI, M. 1981. A Jurassic "Tongue of the Ocean" infilled with oolitic sands: The Belluno Trough, Venetian Alps, Italy. *Marine Geology*, **44**, 59−95.

COLEMAN, R. G. 1981. Tectonic setting for ophiolite obduction in Oman. *Journal of Geophysical Research*, **86**, 2497−2508.

CONNALLY, T. C. & SCOTT, R. W. 1985. Carbonate sediment-fill of an oceanic shelf, Lower Cretaceous Arabian Peninsula. *In*: CREVELLO, P. D. & HARRIS, P. M. (eds), *Deep-water carbonates: Buildups, Turbidites, Debris Flows, and Chalks*. Society of Economic Paleontologists and Mineralogists Core Workshop, **6**, 266−302.

COOK, H. E. & MULLINS, H. T. 1983. Basin margin environment. *In*: SCHOLLE, P. A., BEBOUT, D. G. & MOORE, C. H. (eds) *Carbonate depositional environments*. American Association of Petroleum Geologist Memoir, **33**, 540−617.

COOPER, D. J. W. 1987. Hamrat Duru Group: revised stratigraphy of a Mesozoic deep-water passive margin in the Oman Mountains. *Geological Magazine*, **124**, 157−164.

―― 1990. Sedimentary evolution and Paleogeographical reconstruction of the Mesozoic continental rise in Oman: evidence from the Hamrat Duru Group. *In*: ROBERTSON, A. H. F., SEARLE, M. P. & RIES, A. C. (eds) *The Geological Tectonics of the Oman Region*. Geological Society, Special Publication, **49**, 161−187.

DAVIES, G. R. 1977. Turbidites, debris sheets, and truncation surfaces in Upper Paleozoic deepwater carbonates of the Sverdrup Basin, Arctic Archipelago. *In*: COOK, H. E. & ENOS P. (eds) *Deep-water carbonate environments*. Society of Economic Paleontologists and Mineralogists Special Publication, **25**, 221−247.

DUNNE, L. A. & MANOOGIAN, P. R. & PIERINI, D. F. 1990. Structural style and domains in the northern Oman Mountains (Oman and United Arab Emirates). *In*: ROBERTSON, A. H. F., SEARLE, M. P. & RIES, A. C. (eds) *The Geology and Tectonics of the Oman Region*. Geological Society, London, Special Publication, **49**, 375−386.

FALCON, N. L. 1967. The geology of the north-east margin of the Arabian basement shield. *Advancement of Science*, **24**, 31−42.

GEALEY, W. K. 1977. Ophiolite obduction and geologic evolution of the Oman Mountains and adjacent areas. *Geological Society of America*, **88**, 1183−1191.

GLENNIE, K. W., BOEUF, M. G. A., HUGHES CLARKE, M. W., MOODY-STUART, M., PILAAR, W. F. H. & REINHARDT, B. M. 1973. Late Cretaceous nappes in the Oman Mountains and their geologic evolution. *Bulletin of the American Association of Petroleum Geologists*, **57**, 5−27.

――, ――, ――, ――, ―― & ―― 1974. *Geology of the Oman Mountains*. Verhandelingen van Ket Koninklijk Nederlands geologisch Mijnbouwkundig Gcnootschap Verhandelingen, **31**.

HAQ, B. U., HARDENBOL, J. & VAIL, P. R. 1987. Chronology of fluctuating sea levels since the Triassic. *Science*, **235**, 1156−1167.

HALLUM, A. 1984. Pre-Quarternary sea-level changes. *Annual Review: Earth and Planetary Sciences*, **12**, 204−243.

HARRIS, P. M., FROST, S. H., SEIGLIE, G. A. & SCHNEIDERMANN, N. 1984. Regional unconformities and depositional cycles, Cretaceous of the Arabian Peninsula. *In*: SCHLEE, J. S. (ed.), *Interregional unconformities and hydrocarbon accumulation*. American Association of Petroleum Geologists Memoir, **36**, 67−80.

HEATH, K. & MULLINS, H. T. 1984. Open-ocean offbank transport of fine-grained carbonate sediments in northern Bahamas. *In*: STOW, D. A. V. and PIPER, D. J. W. (eds), *Fine-grained sediments: Deep-water processes and environments*. Geological Society of London, Special Publication, **11**, 199−208.

HUDSON, R. G. S. 1960. The Permian and Trias of the Oman Peninsula, Arabia. *Geological Magazine*, **47**, 299−308.

―― & CHATTON, M. 1959. The Musandam Limestone (Jurassic to Cretaceous) of Oman, Arabia. *Notes Memoir Moyen-Orient* VII, 69−93.

――, McGUGAN, A. & MORTON, D. M. 1954. The structure of Jebel Hagab area, Trucial Oman. *Quarterly Journal of the Geological Society of London*, **110**, 121−152.

HUGHES CLARKE, M. W. 1988. Stratigraphy and rock-unit nomenclature in the oil-producing area of interior Oman. *Journal of Petroleum Geology*, **11**, 5−61.

JACKSON, J. A. 1980. Reactivation of basement faults and crustal shortening in orogenic belts. *Nature*, **283**, 343−346.

KENDALL, C. G. St. C. & SCHLAGER, W. 1981. Carbonates and relative changes in sea level. *In*: CITA, M. B. & RYAN, W. B. F. (eds) Carbonate platforms of the passive continental margins, present and past. *Marine Geology*, **44**, 181−212.

MANN, A. & HANNA, S. S. 1990. The tectonic evolution of pre-Permian rocks, central Oman Mountains. *In*: ROBERTSON, A. H. F., SEARLE, M. P. & RIES, A. C. (eds) *The Geology and Tectonics of the Oman Region*. Geological Society, Special Publication **49**, 307−325.

MULLINS, H. T. 1983. Structural controls of contemporary carbonate continental margins, Bahamas, Belize, Australia. *In*: COOK, H. E. & MULLINS, H. T. (eds) *Platform margin and deep water carbonates*. Society of Economic Paleontologists and Mineralogists Short Course Notes, **12**, 2−1 to 2−57.

―― & COOK, H. E. 1986. Carbonate apron models: Alternatives to the submarine fan model for palaeonenvironmental analysis and hydrocarbon exploration. *Sedimentary Geology*, **48**, 37−79.

――, GARDULSKI, A. F. & HINE, A. C. 1986. Catastrophic collapse of the west Florida carbonate platform margin. *Geology*, **14**, 167−170.

――, HEATH, K. C., VAN BUREN, H. M. & NEWTON, C. R. 1984. Anatomy of modern open-ocean carbonate slope: Northern Little Bahama Banks. *Sedimentology*, **31**, 141–168.

—— & LYNTS, G. W. 1977. Origin of the northwestern Bahama platform: review and reinterpretation. *Geological Society of America Bulletin*, **88**, 1447–1461.

—— & NEUMANN, A. C. 1979. Deep carbonate bank margin structure and sedimentation in the northern Bahamas. *In*: DOYLE, L. J. & PILKEY, O. H. (eds) *Geology of continental slopes*. Society of Economic Paleontologists and Mineralogists, Special Publication, **27**, 165–192.

——, ——, WILBER, R. J., HINE, A. C. & CHINBURG, S. J. 1980. Carbonate sediment drifts in the northern Straits of Florida. *Bulletin American Association of Petroleum Geologists*, **64**, 1701–1717.

MURRIS, R. J. 1980. Middle East: stratigraphic evolution and oil habitat. *Bulletin of the American Association of Petroleum Geologists*, **64**, 597–618.

MUTTI, E., RICCI-LUCCHI, F., SEQURET, M. & ZANZUCCHI, G. 1984. Seismoturbidites: a new group of resedimented deposits. *Marine Geology*, **55**, 103–116.

PATTON, T. L. & O'CONNOR, S. J. O. 1988. Cretaceous flexural history of northern Oman Mountain foredeep, United Arab Emirates. *American Association of Petroleum Geologists Bulletin*, **72**, 797–809.

RABU, D., LE METOUR, J. BECHENNEC, F., BEURRIER, M., VILLEY, M. & BOURDILLON-JEUDY, DE GRISSAC, C. 1990. Sedimentary aspects of the Eo–Alpine cycle on the northeast edge of the Arabian Platform (Oman Mountains). *In*: ROBERTSON, A. H. F., SEARLE, M. P. & RIES, A. C. (eds) *The Geology and Tectonics of the Oman Region*. Geological Society, London, Special Publication, **49**, 49–68.

RICATEAU, R. & RICHIE, P. H. 1980. The geology of the Musandam Peninsula (Sultanate of Oman) and its surroundings. *Journal of Petroleum Geology*, **3**, 139–152.

ROBERTSON, A. H. F. 1986. Geochemical evidence for the origin of Late Triassic melange units in the Oman Mountains as a small basin formed by continental rifting. *Earth and Planetary Science Letters*, **77**, 318–332.

—— 1987. The transition from a passive margin to an Upper Cretaceous foreland basin related to ophiolite emplacement in the Oman Mountains. *Geological Society of America Bulletin*, **99**, 633–653.

——, BLOME, C., COOPER, D. J. W., KEMP, A. E. S., & SEARLE, M. P. 1990. Evolution of the Arabian continental margin in the Dibba Zone, northern Oman Mountains. *In*: ROBERTSON, A. H. F., SEARLE, M. P. & RIES, A. C. (eds) *The Geology and Tectonics of the Oman Region*, Geological Society, London, Special Publication, **49**, 251–284.

——, KEMP, A. E. S., REX, D. C. & BLOME, C. D. 1990b. Sedimentary and structural evolution of a transform lineament, the Hatta zone northern

Oman Mountains. *In*: ROBERTSON, A. H. F., SEARLE, M. P. & RIES, A. C. (eds) *The Geology and Tectonics of the Oman Region*, Geological Society, London, Special Publication, **49**, 285–305.

SCHLAGER, W. 1981. The paradox of drowned reefs and carbonate platforms. *Geological Society of America Bulletin*, **92**, 197–211.

—— & CAMBER, O. 1986. Submarine slope angles, drowning unconformities, and self-erosion of limestone escarpments. *Geology*, **14**, 762–765.

—— & GINSBURG, R. N. 1981. Bahama carbonate platforms — The deep and the past. *Marine Geology*, **44**, 1–24.

—— & JAMES, N. P. 1978. Low magnesian calcite limestone forming at the deep-sea floor, Tongue of the Ocean, Bahamas. *Sedimentology*, **25**, 675–702.

SEARLE, M. P. 1985. Sequence of thrusting and origin of culminations in the northern and central Oman Mountains. *Journal of Structural Geology*, **7**, 129–143.

—— 1988a. Thrust tectonics of the Dibba zone and the structural evolution of the Arabian continental margin along the Musandam mountains (Oman and United Arab Emirates). *Journal of the Geological Society, London*, **145**, 43–53.

—— 1988b. Structure of the Musandam culmination (Sultanate of Oman and United Arab Emirates) and the Straits of Hormuz syntaxis. *Journal of the Geological Society, London*, **145**, 831–845.

—— & COOPER, D. J. W. 1986. Structure of the Hawasina Window culmination, central Oman Mountains. *Transactions of the Royal Society of Edinburgh*, **77**, 143–56.

——, —— & WATTS, K. F. 1990. Structure of the Jebel Sumeini–Jebel Ghawil area, northern Oman. *In*: ROBERTSON, A. H. F., SEARLE, M. P. & RIES, A. C. (eds) *The Geology and Tectonics of the Oman Region*. Geological Society, Special Publication, **49**, 361–364.

—— & GRAHAM, G. M. 1982. The "Oman Exotics" — Oceanic carbonate build-ups associated with early stages of continental rifting. *Geology*, **10**, 43–49.

——, JAMES, N. P., CALON, T. J. & SMEWING, J. D. 1983. Sedimentological and structural evolution of the Arabian continental margin in the Musandam Mountains and Dibba Zone, United Arab Emirates. *Geological Society of America Bulletin*, **94**, 1381–1400.

——, LIPPARD, S. J., SMEWING, J. D. & REX, D. C. 1980. Volcanic rocks beneath the Semail ophiolite nappe in the northern Oman Mountains and their significance in the Mesozoic evolution of Tethys. *Journal of the Geological Society of London*, **137**, 589–604.

SHERIDAN, R. E. & ENOS, P. 1979. Stratigraphic evolution of the Blake Plateau after a decade of scientific drilling. *In*: TALWANI, M. *et al.* (eds) *Deep drilling results in the Atlantic Ocean, continental margins and paleoenvironments*. American Geophysical Union, Maurice Ewing Symposium Series, **3**, 109–122.

VAIL, P. R., MITCHUM, R. M. Jr. & THOMPSON III, S. 1977. Global cycles of relative changes of sea level. *In*: PAYTON, C. E. (ed.), *Seismic Stratigraphy — Applications to hydrocarbon exploration*. American Association of Petroleum Geologists Memoir, **26**, 129–144.

VEEVERS, J. J., FALVEY, D. A. & ROBINS, S. 1978. Timor trough and Australia: Facies show topographic wave migrated 80 km during last 3 m.y. *Tectonophysics*, **26**, 217–227.

WATTS, K. F. 1985. Evolution of carbonate slope facies along a south Tethyan continental margin, the Mesozoic Sumeini Group and the Qumayrah Facies of the Muti Formation, Oman. *Ph.D. Dissertation*, University of California, Santa Cruz.

—— 1988. Triassic carbonate submarine fans bounding the Arabian carbonate platform margin, Sumeini Group, Oman. *Sedimentology*, **34**, 43–71.

—— & BLOME, C. D. 1989. Response of the Arabian carbonate platform margin to collisional orogeny. *In*: TUCKER, M. E., WILSON, J. L., CREVELLO, P. D., SARG, J. R. & READ, J. F. (eds) *Carbonate Platforms: Facies, sequences and Evolution*. International Association of Sedimentologists Special Publication **9**.

—— & GARRISON, R. E. 1986. Sumeini Group, Oman — Evolution of a Mesozoic carbonate slope on a south Tethyan continental margin. *Sedimentary Geology*, **48**, 107–168.

Sedimentary evolution and palaeogeographical reconstruction of the Mesozoic continental rise in Oman: evidence from the Hamrat Duru Group

D. J. W. COOPER

Department of Geology, Leicester University, Leicester LE1 7RH, UK

Abstract: The mainly Mesozoic Hamrat Duru Group represents deep-water, primarily continental rise Neo-Tethyan sediments derived from the Oman continental margin and later emplaced onto the Arabian carbonate platform during the Late Cretaceous obduction of the Semail ophiolite.

Sediment patterns reflect fluctuations in sea level relative to the platform, with carbonate input dominant during periods of platform stability. High and low sea-level stands, controlled by eustacy or tectonism, were accompanied by significant reductions of carbonate production and input into the basins. Raised calcite compensation depths associated with high sea levels resulted in the deposition of cherts whereas, during low stands, terrigenous clastics prograded across or by-passed the platform into the Hawasina basin.

The Hawasina basin was divided into two sedimentary basins separated by a submarine high. The shale-rich 'Al Ayn sub-basin' contained coarse-grained sediments that formed either small fans, or laterally coalescing sediment bodies that were fed by multi-source input of carbonate and terrigenous clastics. This is preserved as the Hamrat Duru Group of the northern and central Oman Mountains. The carbonate-rich 'Duru sub-basin' was fed exclusively from the south and large sediment bodies with sheet-like morphologies extended northwards parallel to the margin, outboard from the Al Ayn sub-basin, with thinning and fining trends to the NW and NE. Duru basin units are found in the central and southern Oman Mountains. Contrasting sedimentation patterns in the Al Ayn sub-basin and the Duru sub-basin may reflect the influence of prevailing SE trade winds on the margin.

During the Mesozoic, the area of the Oman Mountains, SW Arabia (Fig. 1), formed a segment of the southern Neo-Tethyan passive continental margin. Continentally-derived terrigenous clastics and sediment produced on a carbonate platform (Hajar Supergroup) were transported into deeper water environments to accumulate on the continental slope (Sumeini Group) and continental rise (Glennie *et al.* 1973, 1974; Béchennec *et al.* 1986; Cooper 1986, 1987; Watts & Garrison 1986; Pratt and Smewing, 1990). The continental rise sediments of the Hawasina basin, that part of Oman Neo-Tethys adjacent to the Oman margin, are preserved in the Hamrat Duru Group. The tectonostratigraphy of this group, erected by Glennie *et al.* (1974), has been modified by Cooper (1987) to link identifiable lithostratigraphical units between structural duplexes, and the group has been expanded to include the previously-defined Dibba, Dhera and Al Ayn Formations. The Wahrah Formation, representing finer-grained sedimentation related to the Hamrat Duru Group, is retained as a separate entity.

The Hamrat Duru Group is divided into five formations spanning the Late Permain to Late Cretaceous (Fig. 2). The Zulla Formation is further divided into four informal units (Cooper 1987; Bernoulli *et al.* 1990). A mixed calcarenite and shale unit (Unit I) is overlain by sandstone (Unit II), then radiolarian chert and silicified limestones (Unit III) then limestone containing *Halobia* (Unit IV). The Guweyza Sandstone Formation is characterized by quartz sandstones and quartz-bearing calcarenites, although it is geographically restricted to the central and southern parts of the Oman Mountains. The Guweyza Limestone Formation is an interval of oolitic calcarenites which is overlain by silicified limestones and radiolarian cherts of the Sid'r Formation. A return to carbonate deposition marks the onset of the Nayid Formation. Locally, sediments related to the onset of ophiolite obduction lie conformably above the Nayid Formation. These cherts, shales and limestones have been assigned to the Riyamah unit of the Muti Formation (Aruma Group) by Robertson (1987a) although, in the southern Oman Mountains, their temporal equivalents are indistinguishable from the Nayid Formation,

From Robertson, A. H. F., Searle, M. P. & Ries, A. C. (eds), 1990,
The Geology and Tectonics of the Oman Region.
Geological Society Special Publication No 49, pp 161–187

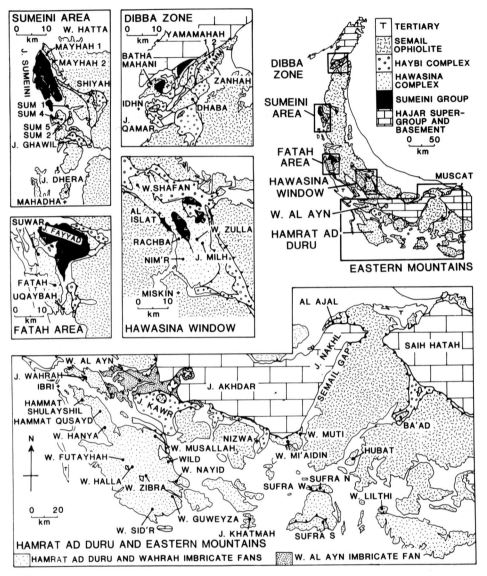

Fig. 1. Geological and location maps of the Oman Mountains from Glennie *et al.* (1974), Open University Oman Ophiolite Project Maps, Searle *et al.* (1983), Searle & Cooper (1986) and author's observations.

in which they have been included by Béchennec *et al.* (1986). The sedimentological facies developed in the Hamrat Duru Group show close affinities with those described from deep-water terrigenous systems (e.g. Mutti & Ricci-Lucchi 1972; Walker & Mutti 1973; Pickering *et al.* 1986), with sediment input from high- and low-density turbidity currents and hemipelagic and pelagic fall-out.

Two distinct stratigraphical successions can be identified within the Hamrat Duru Group.

In the southern mountains (J. Sufra, Hubat, Hamrat ad Duru and J. Wahrah, Fig. 1) the group is characterized by the virtual absence of shale, and sections are almost exclusively composed of redeposited limestone. In the central and northern Oman Mountains (W. Al Ayn, Hawasina window, Fatah area, Sumeini area and Dibba zone, Fig. 1) the group is significantly richer in terrigenous components with carbonate-free sandstones and shales in addition to redeposited limestones. Although close correla-

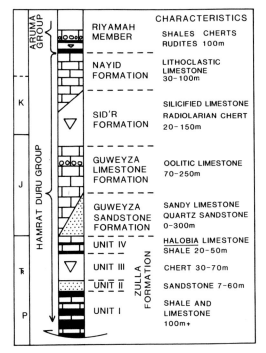

		CHARACTERISTICS
ARUMA GROUP	RIYAMAH MEMBER	SHALES CHERTS RUDITES 100m
	NAYID FORMATION	LITHOCLASTIC LIMESTONE 30-100m
	SID'R FORMATION	SILICIFIED LIMESTONE RADIOLARIAN CHERT 20-150m
	GUWEYZA LIMESTONE FORMATION	OOLITIC LIMESTONE 70-250m
	GUWEYZA SANDSTONE FORMATION	SANDY LIMESTONE QUARTZ SANDSTONE 0-300m
	UNIT IV	HALOBIA LIMESTONE SHALE 20-50m
	UNIT III	CHERT 30-70m
	UNIT II	SANDSTONE 7-60m
	UNIT I	SHALE AND LIMESTONE 100m+

Fig. 2. Summary of the stratigraphy of the Hamrat Duru Group.

tions can be made between sections in these two domains, the differences have important palaeogeographical cannotations and the interpretation of these stratigraphical distinctions suggests the development of two separate sedimentary sub-basins in the Hawasina basin.

The deposition of the Hamrat Duru Group close to the Oman margin is reflected in its structurally low position within the allochthonous Neo-Tethyan sediments of the Hawasina Complex. Duplexes and imbricate fans of the Hamrat Duru Group are exposed along the south and western edge of the Semail ophiolite and in tectonic windows through structurally higher thrust sheets (Figs 1 & 3). The Hamrat

Duru sole thrust usually separates the deep-water lithologies from the essentially autochthonous Mesozoic Oman carbonate platform and foredeep sediments of the Aruma Group. Imbricates within duplexes and imbricate fans dip towards the Arabian continental margin and structural trends follow the arcuate morphology of the present-day coastline. Imbricates strike N−S in northern areas, swinging to WNW−ESE in the south. Imbrication patterns are consistant with piggy-back thrust propagation, although later-stage modifications of the thrust stacking sequence within the Hamrat Duru Group have been documented (Searle & Cooper 1986; Barrette & Calon 1987; Barrette 1988; Cooper 1988; Cawood et al. 1990).

This paper provides an overview of the continental rise sedimentation patterns recorded in the Hamrat Duru Group, from which time-sequential reconstructions the Hawasina basin are developed. The more distal sediments of Oman Neo-Tethys, preserved in the upper parts of the Hawasina Complex and the Haybi Complex have been considered by Glennie et al. (1974), Searle & Graham (1982), Béchennec et al. (1986), Béchennec (1987) and Bernoulli & Weissert (1987) and are not discussed here.

Sedimentary evolution of the Hamrat Duru group

Zulla Formation

The Zulla Formation (Fig. 4) is primarily confined to the central and northern mountains area, although it can be correlated with parts of the Halfa and Haliw Formations in the upper Hawasina nappes of the southern mountains (Bernoulli & Weisser 1987). Béchennec (1987) has also identified a Triassic sequence in the J. Sufra area that is correlated with the Zulla Formation.

Unit I is composed of incompetent shales with thin-bedded wackestone and grainstone turbidites that are largely concentrated in the

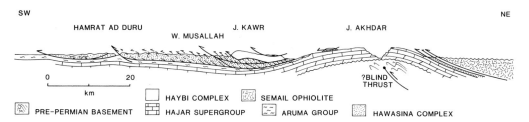

Fig. 3. Structural cross section across the central Oman Mountains modified after Glennie et al. (1974) and Searle (1985).

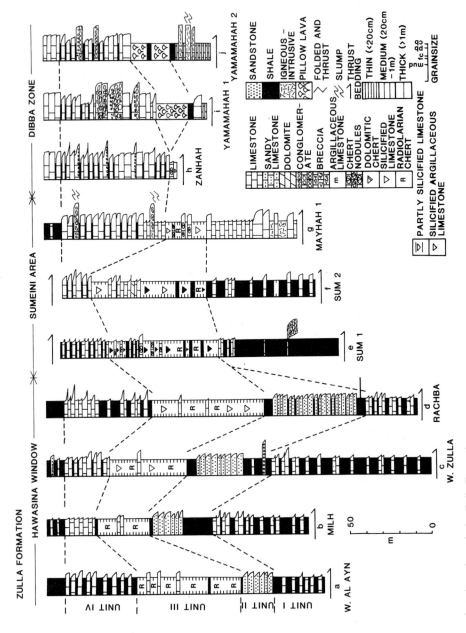

Fig. 4. Measured sections through the Zulla Formation.

upper stratigraphical levels. Radiolarian cherts overlying alkaline volcanics at the base of this unit have yielded Late Permian ages (Béchennec *et al.* 1986).

In the Sumeini area (Fig. 4e−g), a shale-rich sequence contains channelized conglomeratic bodies up to 100 m across and 12 m thick, with neritic and slope-derived carbonate clasts. Associated lenticular oolitic grainstones can be correlated with channelised carbonate submarine fans on the adjacent continental slope (C-member, Maqam Formation, Sumeini Group; Watts & Garrison 1986; Watts 1987). Similarly, oolitic limestones, interbedded with shale crop out at equivalent stratigraphical levels in the Dibba Zone (Fig. 4h−j). Degraded basaltic lavas occur at both the base (Late Permian-aged) and within (Ladinian-aged) this unit in the Hawasina window (Bechennec 1987), and in Unit I in the Sumeini area and Dibba zone.

Unit II is characterized by green-weathering, fine-grained sub-litharenites with interbedded green shale. Rare conglomeratic horizons contain both platform-derived dolomite clasts and abundant metamorphozed sandstone and siltstone clasts, indicating derivation from the continental basement. Unit II is restricted to the Hawasina window, where it thins to the south, and W. Al Ayn areas (Fig. 4a−d), and is absent from the more northerly areas, although the Sumeini Group of J. Sumeini contains an equivalent interval of terrigenous siltstones and shales (D-member of the Maqam Formation; Glennie *et al.* 1974; Watts & Garrison 1986). Similar sands have also been noted from the Halfa Formation (Bernoulli & Weissert 1987) and from J. Sufra in the southern Oman Mountains (Béchennec 1987).

Unit III is a widespread chert interval of Ladinian-Norian age (C. Blome, pers. comm.). Silicified fine-grained carbonate turbidite sequences, that are laterally discontinuous se-quences, are common in the Hawasina window where they pass into silicified radio-larian marls and cherts. Cherts typically contain relict sedimentary structures suggesting depo-sition by dilute turbidity currents. In both the W. Al Ayn and Sumeini areas, radiolarian cherts and redeposited silicified radiolarian marls pre-dominate, although silicified shales with inter-bedded cherty limestones become increasingly important up-section. A lateral transition is seen locally in the Dibba Zone where, in coarser-grained, more proximal deposits tran-sitional to the slope facies of the Sumeini group, platey limestones with intraformational con-glomerates pass southwards into silicified lime-stones, representing the passage of a slope through the CCD. The degree of replacement must, however, represent the interplay between the introduction of carbonate *via* turbidity cur-rents into the sub-CCD environment and the length of time that the carbonate was exposed to carbonate-undersaturated sea and pore waters. The elongation of extruded pillow lavas at the top of the unit suggests a south-facing palaeoslope.

Unit IV marks a return to limestone depo-sition, characterized by coquina, primarily of the bivalve *Halobia*, with interbedded shale. In the Hawasina window, grainstone and wacke-stone turbidites show considerable lateral vari-ation in both grain size and sedimentary facies. Thick successions that contain abundant medium-grained turbidites coexist with thinner, finer-grained sections where wackestones grade into hemipelagic calcareous mudstones. Similar fea-tures are seen in the W. Al Ayn area, where both hemipelagic and graded turbiditic *Halobia* wackestones are developed.

Lateral variations are also prominent in the Sumeini area. Fine-grained wackestones with interbedded shales in the south and central Sumeini area pass into coarser-grained turbidite successions (Fig. 4e−g), composed of deci-metre-bedded grainstones that contain abun-dant lithoclastic, echindoderm and bivalve debris.

Interpretation: Late Permian−Triassic

Prior to Ladinian times, Unit I carbonate sedi-mentation was low in volume and reflects the distally-steepened ramp morphology of the Sumeini Group in the northern Oman Moun-tains postulated by Watts & Garrison (1986), with a wide outer shelf acting as a sediment trap. Thus, in the absence of significant pelagic carbonate-producing organisms before the Late Jurassic (Garrison & Fischer 1969), relatively small volumes of carbonate reached the basin. The channelling of oolitic sediment across the shelf must have occurred to transport ooids into the basin to form small, laterally discontinuous fan lobes in the Sumeini area.

Sedimentation was, however, interrupted by a phase of rifting and basin subsidence, recorded in Units II to IV (Fig. 5). Initially, uplift of the carbonate platform hinterland, may have been driven by the thermal response to widespread alkaline volcanism both in the Triassic Haybi Complex (233−200 Ma, Searle *et al.* 1980; Lippard & Rex 1982) and within the Hamrat Duru Group itself. This may account for the increased carbonate input observed at the top

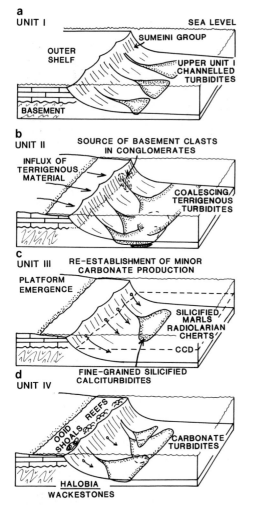

a
UNIT I   SEA LEVEL
                        SUMEINI GROUP
    OUTER
    SHELF   UPPER UNIT I
                                   CHANNELLED
                                   TURBIDITES
    BASEMENT

b
UNIT II   SOURCE OF BASEMENT CLASTS
                IN CONGLOMERATES
INFLUX OF
TERRIGENOUS
MATERIAL   COALESCING/
                               TERRIGENOUS
                               TURBIDITES

c
UNIT III   RE-ESTABLISHMENT OF MINOR
               CARBONATE PRODUCTION
PLATFORM
EMERGENCE
                               SILICIFIED
                               MARLS
                               RADIOLARIAN
                               CHERTS
                                    CCD

d   FINE-GRAINED SILICIFIED
UNIT IV   CALCITURBIDITES
    REEFS
  OOID SHOALS   CARBONATE
                          TURBIDITES

            HALOBIA
         WACKESTONES

Fig. 5. Model of the sediment deposition patterns of the Zulla Formation in the central Oman Mountains. See text for discussion.

of Unit I. Erosion of the platform hinterland resulted in progradation of terrigenous sands over the platform. The locus of this transgression, as suggested by the distribution of deep-water clastics, was in the Hawasina window/W. Al Ayn area, where quartz sands were able to reach the basin to form a small base-of-slope sediment wedge (Unit II, Fig. 5b). Sands prograded no further than the slope in the Sumeini area (Glennie *et al.* 1974; Watts & Garrison 1986) and, in the Dibba Zone, the exposed shelf succession shows a marked wedging of the sandy platform Galilhah Formation into reefs that persisted along the shelf edge (J. Smewing 1982, pers. comm.), thus

accounting for the absence of Unit II sands from the northernmost areas.

Gross changes in ocean water productivity (Berger 1976), a deepening of Neo-Tethys as a response to a major rifting phase and a reduction in off-margin carbonate transport are all factors that may have driven the subsequent fluctuation in the CCD. At the cessation of terrigenous sand input, radiolarian marls accumulating on the slope were emplaced by turbidity currents into a basin with a shallow CCD where they were silicified, producing the cherts of Unit III (Fig. 5c). As carbonate input increased with the re-establishment of a wide carbonate platform, the CCD was depressed and limestone deposition returned to the Hawasina basin (Unit IV, Fig. 5d). The reef complexes in the Dibba Zone and Sumeini area, that provided the reef-talus comprising the Jebel Wasa Formation in the Sumeini area (Watts & Garrison 1986), also supplied the coarse-grained sediment for the fans of the Sumeini area and the base-of-slope sediment wedge of the Dibba Zone. Here, continued tectonic instability associated with submarine volcanism and basin extension resulted in a local collapse of the shelf edge and the formation of base-of-slope conglomerates. Elsewhere, pelagic and resedimented *Halobia* limestones can be correlated with similar lithologies that are widely scattered throughout the Mediterranean and Asian Tethyan belt (e.g. Bernoulli & Jenkyns 1974; Ladakh Himalaya, Fuchs, 1979; SW Turkey, Robertson & Woodcock 1981; Syria, Delaune-Mayere, 1984).

Guweyza Sandstone Formation

The Guweyza Sandstone Formation crops out in all areas with the exception of the Dibba Zone (Fig. 6) and reaches a maximum thickness of 250 m. It spans the Late Triassic to early Middle Jurassic (Glennie *et al.* 1974; Béchennec *et al.* 1986), although it thins to the north and is absent in the Dibba Zone where Hettangian radiolarian cherts assigned to the Zulla Formation are overlain by oolitic limestones and argillaceous lime-mudstones of the Guweyza Limestone Formation.

In the Hamrat ad Duru, it is characterized by quartz-bearing grainstone turbidites, with the lowest stratigraphical levels (Later Triassic–Liassic, Glennie *et al.* 1974) augmented by limestone conglomerates (Fig. 6c,d) that pass up into a widespread interval of partially silicified lime-mudstones. The rest of the formation consists of decimetre-bedded sandy limestones with interbedded slightly argillaceous lime-mudstones. Notable lateral variation exists

GUWEYZA SANDSTONE FORMATION

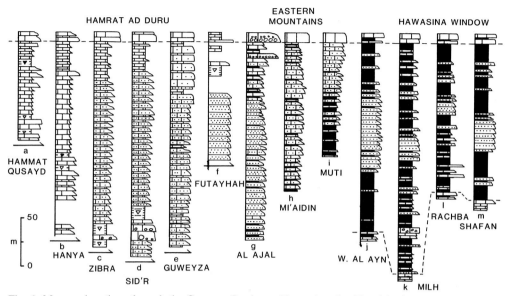

Fig. 6. Measured sections through the Guweyza Sandstone Formation. See Fig. 4 for key.

within the Hamrat ad Duru (Fig. 6a−f). The coarsest grained quartz sandstones, with abundant carbonate allochems and subordinate limestone conglomerates, occur in windows through the main imbricate fan of the Hamrat ad Duru into a more localized duplex (Cooper 1988). Medium-grained quartz-bearing grainstones in the southern and central parts of the range fine towards the north with a concomitant reduction in quartz, and successions in the northern Hamrat ad Duru contain no quartz in lime-mudstone-rich turbidites.

Scattered exposures in the eastern mountains (Fig. 5g−i) are medium- to coarse-grained with quartz contents varying from >5% to <70%. In general, significant lateral variations in coarse-grained sequences are seen and sections may take the form of single coarsening-upwards sequences or be more random with packets of sandstone separated by shale-rich intervals. At J. Sufra, dating by Béchennec et al. (1986) has shown that the formation is represented by hemipelagic, sometimes argillaceous, lime-mudstones.

In the Hawasina window and W. Al Ayn area, the Guweyza Sandstone Formation is markedly different (Fig. 6j−m), and characterized by the presence of coarse-grained quartz-arenites that contain little carbonate. The formation can be divided into three parts: (a) a lower shale-rich interval containing subordinate

thin-bedded sandstones, limestones and thin matrix-supported debris flow deposits; (b) a middle zone of medium- to thick-bedded quartz-arenites, and (c) an upper shale-rich zone. Within the central sandstone unit, beds typically occur in fining-upwards sequences up to 20 m thick, and although lateral correlation is difficult, these sequences appear to have lenticular morphologies on a kilometre scale. Two major groupings are developed, the lower having a locus of deposition towards the north of the Hawasina window and thinning southwards, whilst the upper shows northwards thinning in the Hawasina window.

Sections in the Sumeini area (Fig. 7v,y) are shale-rich, with subordinate quartz-sandstones or thin-bedded lime-mudstones. In this area, the formation is no more than 20 m thick.

Interpretation: Late Triassic−Early Jurassic

Regional Liassic extension, including rifting in the central Mediterranean, resulted in the transgression of the Oman platform and the development of the middle Liassic basal clastics of the Sahtan Group that unconformably overlie the Triassic Mahil Formation (Glennie et al. 1974). The Triassic Saih Hatat platform foundered to become a broad slope (Pratt & Smewing 1990), possibly generating the conglomerates of the

Fig. 7. Measured sections through the Guweyza Limestone Formation. See Fig. 4 for key.

lower Guweyza Sandstone Formation in the Hamrat ad Duru. In the south and central Oman Mountains, coarse-grained sands were carried onto the carbonate platform. Two distinct patterns evolved.

In the south, on the platform hinterland to the Hamrat ad Duru and eastern exposures of the Hamrat Duru Group, quartz sands were admixed with shelf-edge carbonate sands prior to their deposition by turbidity currents into deep-water environments. Such mixing may have been responsible for the size-fractionation of quartz grains — fine silts and muds are conspicuously absent and largely restricted the proximal localities of W. Mi'aidin and Al Ajal.

On the platform hinterland to the Hawasina window and W. Al Ayn depocentres, coeval sedimentation was of predominantly fine-grained sands and quartz-bearing lagoonal carbonates (Glennie et al. 1974; Béchennec et al. 1986) whereas, in the Hawasina basin, coarse-grained quartz sands and shales were deposited. Coarse-grained quartz sand was transported across the shelf to the shelf edge, where accumulations were redeposited by turbidity currents to produce a coalescing base-of-slope sediment wedge. The concentration of sandstone in the middle of the formation suggests a tectonic control on their deposition.

A thin shale and quartzarenite interval in the Sumeini area and coeval sands in the Sumeini Group (Watts & Garrison 1986) imply that the Early Jurassic terrigenous wedge just reached the basin. However, the Musandam Peninsular remained a stable, largely terrigenous-free carbonate platform and the shelf edge reefs inherited from the Triassic were augmented by ooid shoals (J. Smewing et al. pers. comm.)

Guweyza Limestone Formation

The characteristic oolitic limestones of the Guweyza Limestone Formation span the Middle and Late Jurassic (Tithonian), although the radiolarian cherts that typify the overlying Sid'r Formation occur in the equivalent, but finer-grained Wahrah Formation (and possibly in the structurally highest, most distal parts of the Hamrat Duru Group) during the Callovian.

Throughout the southern mountains (Fig. 7a–m), three sequences of light grey-weathering, metre-bedded oolitic grainstones are separated by intervals of redeposited carbonate siltstone and mudstone. Interbedded bioturbated hemipelagic lime-mudstone is recognized by being more argillaceous. The three coarse-grained units are best developed in the Hamrat ad Duru (Fig. 7a–f) where individ-

ual sheet-like beds can be traced across distances in excess of 25 km. A lateral progression of sedimentary facies occurs, with the most proximal, matrix-supported pebbly grainstones concentrated in the southern parts of the range, thick-bedded massive sandstones in the central parts, and thinner calciturbidites with complete Bouma sequences, concentrated in the north and northeast of the range. Such a progression of proximal to more distal facies is consistant with palaeocurrent measurements (see later) and the northwards thinning of beds.

Whilst the tripartite input patterns of coarse-grained redeposited limestones is maintained in the eastern mountains (Fig. 7g–m), their definition is less precise with greater lateral and vertical variation. The clearest example of this variability is at J. Sufra (Fig. 7i–k), where massive grainstones thin to the east and mildly silicified hemipelagic lime-mudstones are developed. Fine-grained carbonate input is also progressively reduced towards the east and, at W. Lilthi, oolitic grainstones are separated by intervals of siliceous argillaceous lime-mudstones and shale.

A widely correlated horizon at the top of the Guweyza Limestone Formation contains cobbles, boulders and, most spectacularly developed at Hubat and Ba'ad, rafts of limestone similar to the Oman Exotics and Hallstatt facies ammonite limestone (T Calon, pers. comm. 1988). The largest of these rafts are over 100 m long and 30 m thick, clearly indicating a local source of recrystallized reef-talus limestone (an Oman Exotic) within the depocentre of the Hamrat Duru Group in this part of the Hawasina basin.

Extremely coarse-grained deposits at W. Mi'aidin, where the tripartite system is seen, and at Al Ajal, where two large-scale fining-upwards sequences are developed, contain numerous conglomeratic horizons, interbedded with massive grainstones and turbiditic lime-mudstones and represent proximal deposits. Furthermore, abundant large-scale (30 cm) cross-laminations indicate a rapid decelleration of turbidity currents (Allen 1982), suggesting a base of slope environment.

Thin oolitic grainstone sequences along the Semail gap (Béchennec 1987) may correlate with slope sediments related to a SE-facing slope between a platform area at J. Nakhl and the newly created slope of Sail Hatat (Pratt and Smewing 1990).

Similarities between the Guweyza Limestone Formation of the southern and northern mountains are largely restricted to the characteristic oolitic petrography of grainstones and, in the northern areas, shale continues to be important. The formation is preserved in all areas, although the greater part has been tectonically eliminated in the W. Al Ayn area.

Sections in the Hawasina window (Fig. 7n–q) start at an interval of grainstones, 5–30 m thick, followed by a single coarsening-upwards mega-sequence, shale-rich at its base, with a prominant interval of chert and silicified marl. Carbonate input occurs firstly as lime-silt and mudstone turbidites, followed by coarser-grained classic turbidites and ultimately massive grainstones. These are dark grey and organic-rich, containing traces of petroleum residues. Matrix-supported debris flows, containing a diverse platform-derived clast assemblage, occur in coarse-grained sections but pinch out laterally into thinner and finer-grained sections that were by-passed by most coarse-grained input. The uppermost 25–50 m of the formation mark a return to finer-grained carbonate silt and mud input with shale partings prior to the rapid transition, over 2–5 m, into the silicified limestones of the Sid'r Formation. Sections in the Fatah area (Fig. 7r–t) show close affinities with those in the Hawasina window, although the sediments are consistantly finer grained and more distal in character.

In the Sumeini area (Fig. 7u–y), shale-rich successions in the south and central parts of the area contrast with northern localities which represent a depositional locus of massive and classic turbiditic oolitic grainstones. Destabiliza-tion of the margin is indicated by an interval of thick (up to 11 m) conglomerate beds. Along the 30 km of N–S exposure of this interval, significant lateral variation in the proportions of recrystallized reef-derived limestone, similar to the J. Wasa Formation of the Sumeini Group, Ladinian-Norian radiolarian cherts and pen-econtemporaneous, laminated slope-derived lime-mudstones are consistant with a line source. The deposition of this interval was associated with a major reorganization of sediment input patterns. Subsequent sediment distribution was *via* more numerous channels that varied from a few tens of metres to a few hundreds of metres. Channel axis sequences of conglomeratic and turbidite deposits pass laterally into thin-bedded 'overbank' lime-mudstone turbidites with locally coarser grained channelized bases. All sequences show fining-upwards trends that probably reflect the gradual cut-off of sediment supply prior to the deposition of the Sid'r Formation.

Sedimentation patterns in the Dibba Zone (Fig. 7z–cc) continue the depositional trends developed during the Triassic. In the most proxi-mal areas, metre-bedded oolitic grain-stones pass laterally southwards into thinner-bedded classic turbidites with interbedded shale. In Batha Mahani, marly lime-mudstone turbidite input was silicified and interbedded with non-calcareous shale indicating that sedimentation occured below the CCD. Oolitic turbidites are seen towards the top of the formation, repre-senting the progradation of the locus of coarse-grained deposition into the more distal parts of the northern Hawasina basin. In common with most localities of Guweyza Limestone outcrop, the top of the formation is characterized by the development of thick (up to 10 m) conglome-rates that, here, contain a diverse clast assem-blage derived from both platform and basement (meta-sandstones and shales and rarer granitic/dioritic cobbles).

Interpretation: Middle and Late Jurassic

In common with many Neo-Tethyan passive margins (Bernoulli & Jenkyns 1974), the Middle and Late Jurassic of Oman was characterized by the development of widespread ooid shoals along the shelf edge that fed sediment into the Hawasina basin. The gross sedimentation patterns were inherited from Guweyza Sand-stone times and thus, in the southern mountain areas, the Guweyza Limestone Formation is characterized by highly calcareous sediments, whilst in the north, a greater terrigenous component is observed.

In the southern mountains, large volumes of oolitic sediment accumulated at the shelf edge. These were emplaced into deeper water en-vironments during three distinct episodes to form large, unconfined sheet deposits that fined away from the margin into the Wahrah Forma-tion. They were superimposed on fine-grained dilute turbidity current and hemipelagic input. In the Hamrat ad Duru, the trends of sediment deposition, as indicated by sedimentary facies, the thinning and fining of beds and palaeo-currents, lay parallel to the margin, extending towards the north. Such sedimentation patterns characterize the development of a longitudinal fan in this area (Cooper 1989).

Broadly lenticular sediment bodies at J. Sufra reflect the continuation of the trends developed during the Early Jurassic. Hemipelagic carbon-ate accumulated on topographical highs whilst intervening areas were the locus of coarser-grained sedimentation. The presence of large Oman Exotic limestone blocks suggests either the development of an adjacent limestone-capped seamount within the Hawasina basin (Cooper 1986) or faulting within the Hawasina basin exposing a carbonate platform substrate to the Hamrat Duru Group (Cawood *et al.* 1990).

In the northern Oman Mountains, the input of carbonate, both by turbidity currents and as hemipelagic deposits was greatly reduced when compared with the southern Oman Mountains. In all places shale is an important fine-grained sedimentary component. The only exception was in the Dibba Zone, where in the most shelf-proximal units, the Early Jurassic base-of-slope sediment wedge persisted into the Late Jurassic. Elsewhere, small lenticular sediment bodies formed in the northern Hawasina basin which, in the Hawasina window, coalesced to form a coarsening-upwards, prograding base-of-slope sediment apron.

Widely-developed conglomerates at the top of the Guweyza Limestone Formation indicate regional destabilization of the shelf edge at the top of the Jurassic. This can be related to the processes that initiated the deposition of the cherts of the Sid'r Formation (next section).

Sid'r Formation

The Tithonian to Early Cretaceous deep-water sediments of the Oman Mountains are characterized by silicified limestones and radiolarian cherts that, in the Hamrat Duru Group, form the Sid'r Formation (Glennie *et al.* 1974; Fig. 8). The base of the formation is sharp, with the appearance of chert over 2−5 m. This has been dated as Tithonian (Glennie *et al.* 1974; Béchennec *et al.* 1986; C. Blome, pers. comm.) although Béchennec *et al.* (1986) have dated the base of the equivalent unit in the Wahrah Formation, where radiolarian cherts are interbedded with oolitic grainstones, as Callovian.

In the southern mountains (Fig. 8a−i), the Sid'r Formation is mainly composed of thin-bedded, partly silicified (30−70%) radiolarian wackestones, that contain sedimentary structures consistant with deposition from dilute turbidity currents. They are interbedded with partings of non-calcareous shale. Coarser-grained lithoclastic grainstone turbidites are partially replaced by nodular and ribbon chert. In the Hamrat ad Duru, such beds reach 50 cm in thickness and are concentrated at the bases of sections in the south of the range. Radiolarian chert becomes the main lithology in the structurally highest imbricates of the Hamrat ad Duru and in the Wahrah Formation, reflecting deposition in a more distal environment. The transition from sections dominated by partially

silicified radiolarian wackestones to those dominated by radiolarian cherts occurs across a minimum distance of 8 km after restoration of the imbricate fan (Cooper 1988).

In the eastern mountain areas, greater diversity is seen (Fig. 8h,i) and the thinner sections of the Sid'r Formation show reduced silicification in successions dominated by structureless hemipelagic lime-mudstone that contain horizons of nodular chert. These are interbedded with thinning- and fining-upwards sequences of decimetre-bedded lithoclastic limestone turbidites with replacement chert ribbons. Only in the structurally highest imbricates of the J. Khatmah area is the transition to radiolarian cherts seen.

The Sid'r Formation in the Hawasina window (Fig. 8j,k) contains abundant shale although there is a comparative increase in limestone, primarily as moderately to almost completely silicified turbiditic radiolarian wackestones. Subordinate components are coarser-grained lithoclastic limestones and radiolarian cherts. Coarser- and finer-grained sections indicate laterally variable input on a kilometre scale. A prominent marker interval of red shale and silicified ferruginous granule conglomerates can be traced across the Hawasina window and may also correlate with a radiolarian chert interval seen in the Fatah area. It is underlain by a 12 m zone of unsilicified limestones attesting to local fluctuations in the level of the CCD during this period. The Fatah area sections (Fig. 8l,m) are similar, but consistently fine-grained and silicified (<90%), and sequences are dominated by radiolarian marls and cherts.

In the Sumeini area (Fig. 8n−p) and the Dibba Zone (Fig. 8q,r), the Sid'r Formation shows two stages of development. The lower parts of sections show the continued input of grainstones following channels established during Guweyza Limestone times. These sequences are placed within the Sid'r Formation on account of the high incidence of replacement chert. Laterally-equivalent finer-grained sediments also show increased silicification. All sections fine upwards, and silicified marls, radiolarian cherts and shales become more abundant. An episode of shelf edge instability is recorded in both areas by laterally extensive conglomeratic horizons that again show evidence of a line source and contain rare rounded cobbled granite. Above this interval, sections are shalier, with abundant radiolarian cherts and silicified marls. The most distal sections in the Dibba Zone have a relatively thinned upper interval (12 m), composed exclusively of radiolarian cherts with shale partings.

SID'R FORMATION

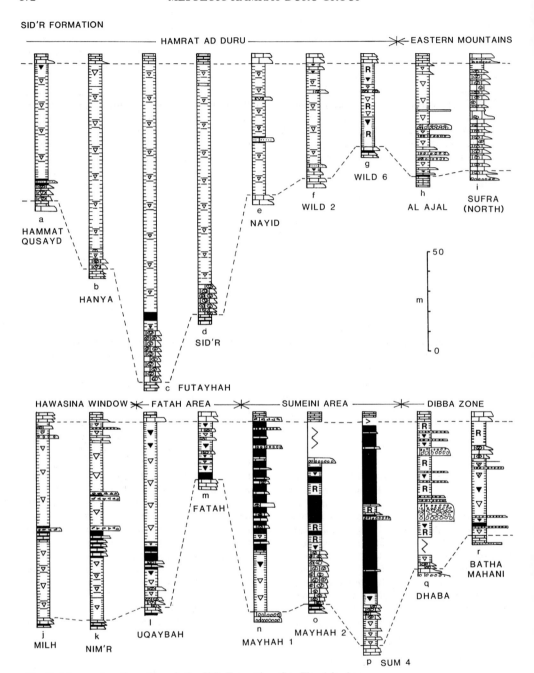

Fig. 8. Measured sections through the Sid'r Formation. See Fig. 4 for key.

Interpretation: Tithonian–Early Cretaceous

The development of radiolarian cherts and silicified limestones during the Tithonian–Early Cretaceous represents an important rise in the CCD. This is a widespread Neo-Tethyan feature seen throughout the Mediterranean realm (Bernoulli & Jenkyns 1974). The base of the Mediterranean chert interval is, however,

Oxfordian in age, and the later onset of silicification in the Oman Mountains must reflect the local modification of regional controls. Contributing factors may have been the more open-ocean conditions away from the narrow, wedge-shaped western Neo-Tethys affecting the productivity of carbonate and silica-producing pelagic organisms and the local suppression of the CCD related to higher off-margin carbonate transport. The precise control on the later initiation of chert deposition in the Oman sector of Neo-Tethys remains unclear. Indeed, the development of Callovian cherts in more distal parts of the Hawasina basin (Béchennec *et al.* 1986) suggests an earlier subsidence of the Wahrah Formation (and possibly distal Hamrat Duru Group) ocean floor beneath the CCD.

Coeval platform sediments of the Rayda and Sahil Formations (Glennie *et al.* 1974; Connally & Scott 1985) are argillaceous radiolarian wackestones and porcellanites which indicate a deepening of the platform resulting from the tilting of the platform to the west, with the deposition of evaporites in inland areas (Murris 1980). This reduced the effective width of main carbonate producing areas from about 700 km to about 100 km (Murris 1980), thus reducing the volume of carbonate available for transport into the basin. At the same time, sediments had to cross a wide, drowned platform area on which much carbonate material would be trapped.

The initial drowning of the platform resulted from tectonic subsidence, recorded by widespread conglomerates at the top of the Guweyza Limestone Formation. This event was augmented by a rise in sea level, although whilst the Late Jurassic represents the culmination of the Jurassic supercycle of Vail *et al.* (1977), Ager (1981) and Hallam (1981) both show this sea level maximum occuring in the Oxfordian, in line with the onset of Mediterranean chert deposition, and significantly pre-dating the onset of the Sid'r Formation. Indeed, Schlager (1981) has demonstrated that sea level rises alone are not rapid enough to outpace vertical reef accretion and permit the drowning of carbonate platforms. In this case, clear evidence of a tectonic control exists, to supplement the high stand of sea level in the Late Jurassic.

Interbedded non-calcareous shales and rare red cherts of the Sid'r Formation of the southern Oman mountains suggest a sub-CCD environment of deposition. Residual carbonate in silicified wackestones indicates that the input of lime mud by turbidity currents exceeded the rate of carbonate dissolution, such that beds were removed from the zone of active dissolution by burial. In the more distal localities and in the Wahrah Formation, the dissolution of carbonate exceeded deposition rates, resulting in red cherts, shales and subordinate fully-silicified limestones.

In the northern Oman mountains, shale deposition was still important. Initially, coarse-grained carbonate input, associated with shelf edge destabilization at the top of the Guweyza Limestone Formation, was followed by shale and chert deposition, augmented by radiolarian marls introduced by dilute turbidity currents from the outer platform or slope. Coarse-grained carbonate material was almost wholly retained on the drowned platform.

Nayid Formation

The base of the Nayid Formation, following Glennie *et al.* (1974), is marked by a reduction in the degree of silicification and the reintroduction of coarse-grained carbonate material into the Hawasina basin. In many places, these occur at the same stratigraphical level, although an interval of lime-mudstones may precede the coarser-grained limestones. Cherts at the top of the Sid'r Formation have yielded Valanginian/Hauterivian ages (C. Blome, pers. comm.). However, Béchennec *et al.* (1986) have redefined the Sid'r and Nayid Formations on the basis that interbedded fine-grained sediments continue to be silicified, and they place the top of their Sid'r Formation after a second interval of silicified limestones.

In the Hamrat ad Duru (Fig. 9a–e), coarse-grained limestones are restricted to the structurally higher imbricates. Decimetre-bedded lithoclastic grainstones with rare volcanic fragments are grouped in a fining-upwards sequence that passes into an interval of poorly-exposed limestone turbidites with abundant replacement chert. These cherts have been dated as Late Albian–Early Cenomanian, and overlying limestone turbidites are of Late Cenomanian to Early Santonian age (Béchennec *et al.* 1986). This latter interval forms the Nayid Formation of Béchennec *et al.* (1986). In the SW, lime-mudstone turbidites are dominant, with coarser-grained components largely absent. The structurally lowest imbricates along the leading edge of the Hamrat ad Duru, around the W. Futayhah area contain an anomalous succession that lacks significant carbonate. Red shales are abundant, interbedded with lime-mudstones and fine-grained grainstones. However, local horizons near the base of the formation are conglomeratic and are composed of cobbles of recrystallized limestone.

NAYID FORMATION, RIYAMAH UNIT

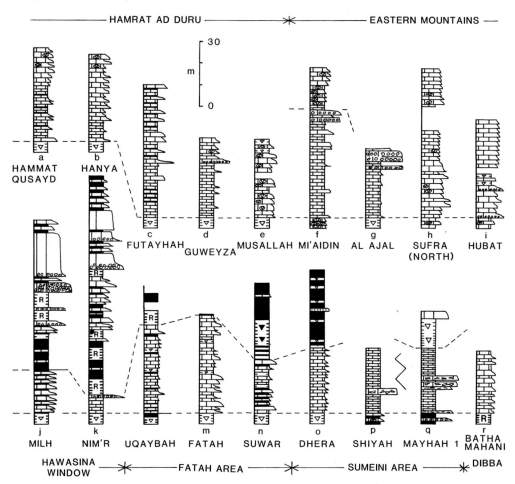

Fig. 9. Measured sections through the Nayid Formation and the Riyamah unit of the Muti Formation. See Fig. 4 for key.

Sections at Al Ajal and W. Mi'aidin (Fig. 9f–g) contain abundant graded lime-mudstones with laterally discontinuous coarse-grained bases and show similarities to by-pass slope deposits recorded from the C-member, Mayhah Formation, Sumeini Group (Watts & Garrison 1986). At the latter locality, lenticular pebble-based grainstones and channelized turbidites increase in abundance up-section. Both areas thus continue to display evidence of a shelf-proximal location.

In the northern mountain areas, the Nayid Formation is relatively thin and, in all areas, the transition from the Sid'r Formation is sharp and occurs over 1–3 m. When compared with the preceding Triassic and Jurassic sedimentation patterns, the Nayid Formation shows a conspicuous reduction in shale and is characterized by lime-mudstone-rich successions. In the Hawasina window (Fig. 9j, k), it is represented by 20 m of turbiditic lime-mudstones. However, the distinction between the Nayid Formation and the overlying Riyamah unit is, in this area, blurred and a sequence of shale, radiolarian chert, limestone turbidites and conglomerates has been placed, on temporal or lithological grounds, in the Nayid Formation (Béchennec et al. 1986) or the Riyamah unit (Cooper 1987; Robertson 1987b).

In the Fatah area (Fig. 9l–n), up to 50 m of 10 cm bedded redeposited lime-mudstones with shale partings contain four thin sequences of grainstone turbidites. Two distinctive cherty intervals can be correlated across the area. Sections in the central part of the area contain a greater grainstone component when compared with more peripheral areas.

In the Sumeini area (Fig. 9o−q), the Nayid Formation is represented by at least 30 m of platey limestones and intraformational breccias, although structural complexities prevent detailed correlation between localities. Shale is almost completely absent and restricted to thin partings.

The Nayid Formation of the Dibba Zone (Fig. 9r) contains two distinct sedimentary facies. In the more proximal areas, platey limestones contain lenticular beds of limestone conglomerate and channelized grainstones. Degraded ?extrusive volcanics are also seen. The generally finer-grained sections, however, contain mostly decimetre-bedded grainstone turbidites which grade up into thick limemudstones.

Aruma Group − Riyamah unit, Muti Formation

The Riyamah unit of the Muti Formation (Robertson 1987a,b) forms a distinctive interval of radiolarian chert and shale above the limestones of the Nayid Formation in the northern Oman Mountains. Radiolaria from cherts close to the sharp contact with the Nayid Formation have yielded Cenomanian ages (C. Blome, pers. comm.). The age of the top of the unit is unknown but this unit is probably laterally equivalent to the Late Cretaceous limestones of the Nayid Formation in the southern Oman Mountains.

In the northern mountains, the Riyamah unit lies in stratigraphical continuity above the Hamrat Duru Group. All sections are shale-rich with radiolarian cherts at the base of the unit. Coarser-grained limestones are restricted to the Hawasina window (Fig. 9j, k), where lenticular sequences of lithoclastic grainstone turbidites are interbedded cherts and shales, then overlain by a regional, cliff-forming conglomeratic/massive grainstone interval, followed by a return to finer-grained limestone and shale deposition.

In the Fatah area (Fig. 9l−n), 20 m of Cenomanian radiolarian cherts pass up into a thick (>50 m), tectonically disturbed shale interval that contains rare oolitic grainstone turbidites, probably derived from coeval ooid shoals on the shelf edge, such as those identified by Robertson (1987a) at J. Akhdar. A thin section in the southern Sumeini area (Fig. 9o) is mostly shale, but also contains rare, fine-grained quartz-arenites.

In the southern mountains, sediments of the Aruma Group are restricted the SW edge of Hamrat ad Duru. Warburton et al. (1989) have reported the occurrence of thick limestone conglomerates that lie with an angular unconformity over the Hamrat Duru Group. These have been interpreted as products of the cannabalisation of the Hamrat Duru Group by erosion of imbricates during their emplacement and assigned to the Fiqa Formation of the Aruma Group.

Interpretation: Cretaceous

The resumption of calcareous sedimentation in the Hawasina Ocean reflects the interaction of three main controls. A global sea level fall around the Valanginian (Vail et al. 1977) lowered the position of the CCD relative to the continental margins and brought parts of the Hawasina ocean floor above the CCD. Furthermore, the progradation of the Early Cretaceous shelf edge across the drowned outer platform simultaneously increased the width of the carbonate-producing area and decreased the width of the outer shelf that had to be crossed by sediment before it could reach the basin, thereby increasing carbonate input into the basin areas. This increase in carbonate input was not confined to the Oman sector of Neo-Tethys and could thus contribute to a regional lowering of the CCD. Finally, the evolutionary diversification of the coccolithoporids in the Late Jurassic increased pelagic carbonate input exerted a control on the CCD (Bosellini & Winterer 1975) and, as a factor for the cessation of chert deposition, has been applied to the Oman margin by Graham (1980). However, this event predated the onset of the Nayid Formation, and its role as a mechanism to account for the end of the Sid'r Formation remains unclear.

The rapid transition to the Nayid Formation in the southern mountains also reflects the introduction of coarse-grained carbonate. Thicker (>20 cm) beds show reduced susceptibility to dissolution, whilst fine-grained units in distal areas were still affected. With carbonate almost completely absent from the hemipelagic and pelagic components, it is probable that the Nayid Formation was deposited close to the CCD and that the preservation of coarse-grained carbonate reflects the reduced silicification potential of these allochems, rather than a significant rise in the CCD. Indeed, Béchennec (1987) has interpreted the input of coarse-grained limestones, followed by a return to the deposition of silicified limestone (upper part of the Sid'r Formation of Béchennec *et al.* 1986) as the product of progradation of the platform in the Barremian followed by renewed basin extension and subsidence in the late Albian–early Cenomanian, possibly related to opening of the Semail basin.

The relative increase of carbonate input into the northern Oman Mountains areas represents a major change in sedimentation, implying a radical reorganization of the off-margin sediment transport systems. Most carbonate occurs as lime-mudstone introduced into the basin by dilute turbidity currents, and the absence of coarse-grained material may reflect the development of a distally-steepened ramp margin on which coarse-grained carbonate was retained. J. Smewing (1982, pers. comm.) has shown that, in the Dibba Zone, the Early Cretaceous succession of the Hajar Supergroup represents a shallowing- upwards, regressive regime with the development of a clear north to south facies change from shelf to shelf edge to outer platform.

The development of the Riyamah unit of the northern Oman Mountains reflects the initial phase of margin destabilization related to the earliest stages of ophiolite obduction. Robertson (1987b) has identified two phases in early active margin development.

The first stage (Cenomanian–Turonian) consisted of the uplift and erosion of the shelf edge with mass wasting along an over-steepened margin producing widespread debris flows and glide blocks around J. Nakhl and megabreccias in the Sumeini Group in the Sumeini area (Watts & Garrison 1986). Similar megabreccias from the Sumeini Group in the Hawasina window may correlate with a massive conglomerate/ grainstone interval in the Riyamah unit (Graham 1980).

The widespread subaerial erosion of the shelf edge (Glennie *et al.* 1974; Robertson 1987a) reduced carbonate input. The emergent shelf edge acted as a barrier to off-margin carbonate transport and sedimentation in the northern parts of the Hawasina basin was dominated by shales and cherts. The rise in the CCD possibly reflects the deepening of the basin with the onset of subduction. Subordinate debris flows and turbiditic limestones were derived from continued mass-wasting along the margin.

The second phase of active margin development was the flexural down-warping of the shelf edge ahead of the advancing ophiolite nappe pile in the late Turonian–Coniacian (Robertson 1987b; Patton & O'Connor 1988). This was associated with the development of a siliciclastic

foredeep (Robertson 1987b), although limestone turbidites continued to be deposited in the southern Oman Mountains (Béchennec *et al.* 1986).

Palaeogeographical reconstruction of the Oman Margin

The palaeogeographical reconstructions developed for the Hamrat Duru Group are dependent on the position and shape of the shelf edge and the relationship between the southern carbonate-rich successions and the northern shale-rich successions. Because the Hamrat Duru Group is allochthonous, the relative positions of the different tectonic units can be constrained only by the integration of sedimentological, stratigraphical and structural data to produce an internally consistant model. The structural implications have been discussed elsewhere (Cooper 1988).

The position of the shelf-slope break in the following palaeogeographical reconstructions is constrained by exposures in the Musandam Peninsula (J. Smewing pers. comm. 1982; Searle *et al.* 1983) and in the post-Triassic of Saih Hatat (Pratt & Smewing 1990). Elsewhere, an irregular margin is indicated, following arguments that the development of culminations within the slope sediments of the Sumeini Group was dependent on their positions at promontories along the shelf edge (Cooper 1986; Searle & Cooper 1986; Searle *et al.* 1990).

Palaeocurrents

The use of palaeocurrent directions, measured from the orientation of turbidite sole structures and ripples, to aid the development of palaeogeographical reconstructions is deemed to be valid despite the lateral translation of the Hamrat Duru Group. It is suggested that there has been no significant rotation of thrust sheets from their original basin orientations during their emplacement onto the Oman margin. This is justified by the absence of structures within thrust sheets indicating differential rotation. Furthermore, the constancy of the strikes of thrust sheets parallel to the margin edge suggests that individual duplexes and imbricate fans of the Hamrat Duru Group have not rotated relative to each other.

Palaeocurrent orientations from the Hamrat Duru Group are shown in Fig. 10. The clearest characteristic is that most are directed away from the continental margin, to the NE, although significant margin-parallel components exist.

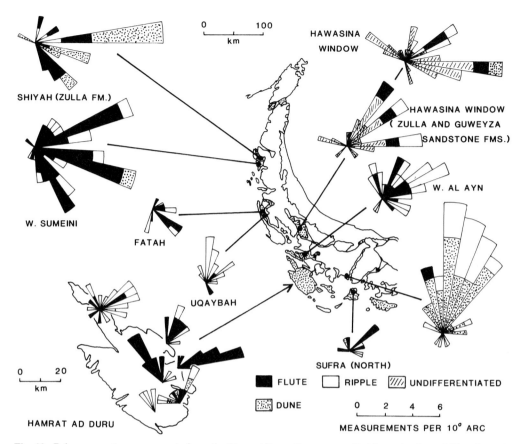

Fig. 10. Palaeocurrent measurements from the Hamrat Duru Group, compiled from the data of Glennie *et al.* (1974), Graham (1980) and Cooper (1986).

In the southeastern mountains, palaeocurrent trends are dominantly to the N to NE, although at J. Sufra, a wider spread, from NW to ENE is seen.

In the Hamrat ad Duru, palaeocurrents measurements are primarily from the Guweyza Limestone Formation, although a subordinate data set from the Nayid Formation shows similar trends. Along the SW side, palaeocurrent orientations are margin-parallel and NW-directed, whereas those from localities to the NE contain more variable NW to NE components and the structurally highest localities have consistently NE-directed palaeocurrents. Measurements from the northern Hamrat ad Duru have a consistently greater variability and a wide spectrum of directions are recorded, ranging from NW to S, as well as E. Current splitting, however, plays an important role and individual graded beds may yield a variety of directions within individual Bouma sequences. All beds

show a similar trend, with variable palaeocurrents measured from flutes and lower rippled intervals to more consistently east-directed palaeocurrents from upper ripples. These are taken to represent waning flow deposition on the regional palaeoslope, whilst the more variable lower palaeocurrents reflect either the interaction of a margin-parallel current component with this slope, and also possibly with sea floor irregularities, or the development of helical vortices within individual turbidity currents (Cooper 1989).

Palaeocurrents in the southern part of the northern mountains area (W. Al Ayn, Hawasina window) not only show NE-directed flows, but also significant margin-parallel components to both the NW and SE, implying longitudinal deposition. Indeed, within the Guweyza Sandstone Formation of a single measured section in W. Al Ayn, diametrically opposed NW- and SE-directed currents are seen. When combined with the sediment distribution patterns, this suggests a multi-source input. Rare SW-directed palaeocurrent (i.e. towards the margin) may be due to the deflection of currents by a submarine topographical feature (e.g. Pickering & Hiscott 1985).

The more northerly areas of Fatah and Sumeini show moderate to considerable variations. Directions are dominantly away from the margin (ENE), although they range from north to south. Such variation is greatest in the Sumeini area and reflects the smaller-scale, localized input of sediment into discrete, laterally discontinuous sediment bodies.

Central Oman palaeogeography

The crux of the palaeogeographical interpretation of the Hamrat Duru Group is the relationship between the southern carbonate-rich and the northern shale-rich successions. The critical relationships are displayed in the central Oman Mountains (Fig. 11a), between the northern Hamrat ad Duru and the Hawasina window in the three structural components of the Hamrat ad Duru (Hamrat Duru Group) and J. Wahrah (Wahrah Formation) imbricate fans and Al Ayn (Hamrat Duru Group) duplex, termed the HDIF, WIF and AAD respectively (Cooper 1988). These lie structurally on top of each other, with the AAD at the highest structural level. This apparent overlap of differing sedimentary successions becomes even more marked when the thrust sheets are restored to their original positions in the Hawasina basin, on account of the concave morphology of the Oman margin.

A simple palinspastic reconstruction of this structural succession would suggest that the AAD was more distal than the WIF which was, in turn, distal to the HDIF (e.g. Glennie et al. 1974). However, although the sedimentologically and stratigraphically similar HDIF and WIF clearly belong to the same depositional system, with the uniformly finer-grained WIF lying in a more distal position, the AAD cannot be considered part of this system. It shows a shale-rich succession similar to that of the Hawasina window, that bears little relationship to the HDIF stratigraphy.

Whereas Bernoulli & Weissert (1987) have considered that the undated sandstones at the top of the AAD formed the substrate to the HDIF, to be later decoupled during emplacement, this model is not favoured. Stratigraphical sections from W. Al Ayn are identical to those for the Zulla and Guweyza Sandstone Formations of the Hawasina window, yet detailed stratigraphical correlations in the younger components of the Hamrat Duru Group between the these areas and the Hamrat ad Duru cannot be made. The stratigraphical and sedimentological differences between the Guweyza Limestone Formation in the Hawasina window (major coarsening-upwards sequence with interbedded shale and considerable small-scale lateral variation) and the Hamrat ad Duru (three intervals of oolitic grainstones separated by lime-mudstone turbidites and hemipelagites, with negligible shale) are irreconcilable and show no evidence of interdigitation. They must, therefore, represent deposition in separate areas.

Matrix-supported conglomerates in the Guweyza Sandstone and Limestone Formations of the Hawasina window indicate a margin-proximal location, since such flows would be expected to evolve into clast-supported types (Naylor 1978) and basement clasts require a continental source. Similarly, the high volumes of quartz sand deposited into the Hawasina basin during the Triassic and Early Jurassic (Unit II, Zulla Formation and Guweyza Sandstone Formation) require an emergent continental hinterland. A continental mass could not have existed in the Hawasina basin without exerting a profound influence on later thrusting and ophiolite obduction, by its accretion to the Oman margin or its incorporation into the Haybi Complex. As such features are not seen and there is no realistic scenario in which it could be removed by, for example, strike-slip processes, the Oman margin itself must have been the source of the quartz sands.

Fig. 11. Palaeogeographical reconstruction of the Hawasina basin showing the relationships between the present-day distribution of the Hamrat Duru Group and their pre-obduction configuration. (a) Present-day cross section through the central Oman Mountains. (b) Pre-thrusting cross section of the Hawasina basin showing the restored positions of the Hamrat ad Duru (H) and J. Wahrah (W) imbricate fans and the W. Al Ayn (A) duplex. Ha: Halfa Formation cherts. (c) Pre-ophiolite obduction configuration of the Oman margin showing the Al Ayn and Duru sub-basins, the approximate restored positions of the main areas of Hamrat Duru Group outcrop and representative stratigraphical sections from the central Oman Mountains, and the shape of the margin edge. All distances on the restored section and map are minima and calculated from restored cross sections (Cooper 1986).

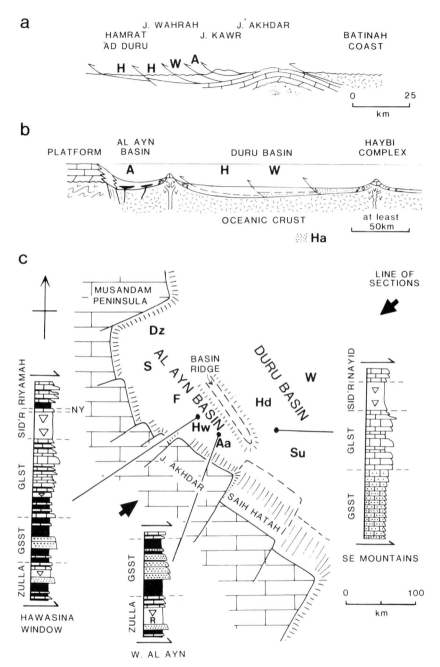

Palaeocurrents further indicate that the Hawasina window and AAD depocentres lay adjacent to this margin. Bi-directional, margin-parallel components in single stratigraphical sections are accounted for by the input of sediment into the Hawasina window and AAD from a variety of sources producing sedimentary bodies that overlapped. The margin-parallel palaeo-current component in the Hawasina window and AAD and rare SW-directed palaeocurrents suggest that turbidity currents were ponded in a margin-parallel trough, with a raised distal edge deflecting flows, and preventing any interaction between the sediments of the AAD and HDIF. The absence of any continental material in the Hawasina basin suggests that this topographical feature was oceanic in nature, possibly a volcanic ridge on which exotic limestones accumulated. Isolated cobbles of exotic limestone in the Guweyza Sandstone Formation and conglomeratic horizons in the Nayid Formation of the SW Hamrat ad Duru may have originated from this ridge although its precise form is ill-defined.

Conversely, palaeocurrent and facies distribution patterns in the Hamrat ad Duru indicate a primary sediment source to the south of the restored position of the HDIF, with sediment spreading to the NW, parallel to the margin, and NE, away from the margin (Cooper 1989). No input from the north may indicate that no source was available.

The development of organic-rich, fetid limestones in the Late Jurassic of the Hawasina window may reflect deposition close to the oxygen minimum zone. Similar limestones are restricted to the coarsest-grained, most proximal deposits in the southern Oman Mountains (W. Mi'aidin), further suggesting that the Hawasina window area represents deposition in a relatively shallow base-of-slope environment. The Hamrat ad Duru deposits, lying distal to the W. Mi'aidin area, must have accumulated at a greater water depth, and thus must have been distal to the Hawasina window.

It is suggested that two separate sedimentary sub-basins existed in the Hawasina basin. The AAD and Hawasina window units were deposited in the 'Al Ayn sub-basin', that lay adjacent to, and parallel to the margin and was characterized by shale-rich successions. The Dibba Zone, Sumeini area and Fatah area all lay in its northwards extension. The HDIF and WIF were deposited in a second basin, the 'Duru sub-basin'. This lay to the south of the Al Ayn sub-basin, but extended northwards and oceanwards from the Al Ayn sub-basin. This extension formed the depositional area of the Hamrat ad Duru, and carbonate-rich sediment input was from the south. These relationships are shown in Fig. 11b,c.

Whilst a piggy-back thrust sequence can account for the internal arrangement of imbricates within individual duplexes and imbricate fans, the present-day configuration of these tectonic slices does not conform to a simple distal over proximal sequence of thrusting. Instead, more proximal lithologies lie structurally above more distal ones. A multi-stage sequence of thrusting must, therefore, be invoked to account for this feature (Cooper 1988).

Palaeo-wind controls on sedimentation

The input of coarse- and fine-grained carbonate sediment into the Hawasina basin was primarily by the transport of material from the Oman platform and upper slope by turbidity currents. Purely pelagic components are volumetrically subordinate and the distribution of the deep-water sediments of the Hamrat Duru Group in the Duru and Al Ayn sub-basins reflects both the availability of sediment on the shelf edge and the dominant sediment transport mechanisms operating on the platform. Studies on modern carbonate platforms, most notably the Bahamas, (e.g. Mullins & Neumann 1979; Hine et al. 1981; Heath & Mullins 1984) have shown that wind-driven currents transport sediment and that the orientation of the platform with respect to the prevailing wind systems determines whether sediment will be carried onto or off the platform. It is reasonable to infer that such wind controls also operated on the Jurassic Oman margin.

Palaeogeographical reconstructions place the Africa/Arabia segment of Gondwanaland at a latitude approximately 15° south of the equator (Irving 1977; Smith et al. 1981), rotated about 10–15° clockwise relative to the present-day orientation (Fig. 12). In this position, the margin would have lain in the SE trade wind belt. These winds could have driven surface currents across the southern margin of the Oman platform which, along the Mashirah transform would have faced towards the SSE. Sediment could be transported nearly parallel to the top of the sub-leeward Saih Hatat slope until it intersected with the Semail gap fault and the J. Nakhl platform. It was then periodically emplaced into the basin. Lime-mud would similarly by transported by these wind-driven currents to the slope, from where they would be emplaced into the Duru sub-basin by turbidity currents, or as hemipelagic deposits. Only in the easternmost locality of W. Lilthi did shale

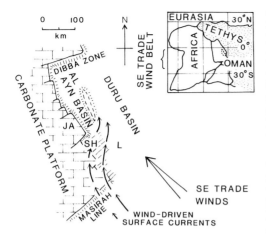

Fig. 12. Oman as a Jurassic semi-windward margin. See text for discussion.

Dominant wind-driven surface currents would have been parallel with, and onto the margin, thereby reducing off-margin sediment transport. Indeed, the gullied by-pass slope developed on J. Sumeini (Watts & Garrison 1986) suggests a semi-windward margin and evidence of a steep slope in the Dibba Zone, largely devoid of coarse-grained sediment input (Watts 1990; Robertson et al. 1990) further support the contention that this area was a windward margin.

The reorganization of sedimentation patterns during deposition of the Nayid Formation, marked by an increase in carbonate input into the Al Ayn sub-basin may have been influenced by the northwards drift of the Oman margin to latitudes close to the equator (Irving 1977; Smith et al. 1981) out of the influence of the SE trade wind belt that dominated sedimentation in the Triassic and Jurassic. However, increased pelagic carbonate productivity in the Cretaceous (Bosellini & Winterer 1975) can also account for this change.

deposition dominate, by virtue of its palaeo-geographical position near the eastern extremity of the margin.

To the north, the Al Ayn sub-basin did not benefit from cross-shelf currents, being sheltered by the SE-facing slope along the SE margin of J. Nakhl that marked the northern edge of the zone of Jurassic Saih Hatat subsidence.

Summary: Evolution of the Mesozoic continental rise of Oman

The Hawasina basin was created as a response to the rifting of the Central Iranian and

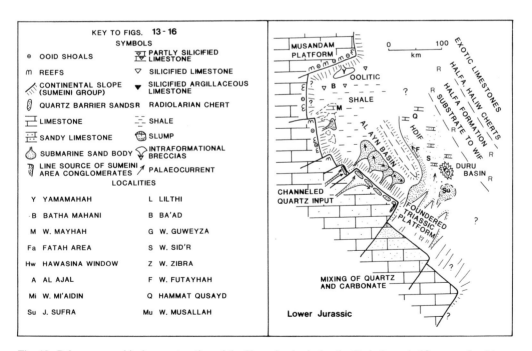

Fig. 13. Palaeogeographical reconstruction of the Hawasina basin for the Early Jurassic (Guweyza Sandstone Formation).

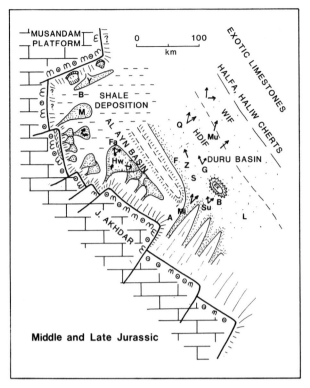

Fig. 14. Palaeogeographical reconstruction of the Hawasina basin for the Middle Jurassic-pre-Tithonian Late Jurassic (Guweyza Limestone Formation).

Afghanistan microcontinental blocks from the northern margin of Gondwanaland during the formation of Neo-Tethys (e.g. Boulin 1981; Sengör 1984). The formation of this segment of Oman Neo-Tethys is constrained by Late Permian (Murghabian) radiolarian cherts over alkaline rift volcanics (Béchennec 1987); De Wever & Bourdillon de Grissac 1990). Fossils of Permian age also have been found in the Zulla Formation of the Sumeini area (Glennie et al. 1974) and some deep-water components of the Al Aridh and Ibra Formations date from the Late Permian (Glennie et al. 1974); Blendinger et al. 1990).

Initially, Late Permian and Triassic sedimentation (Fig. 5) reflected relatively stable carbonate platform development and relatively low volumes of carbonate sediment were transported into the Al Ayn sub-basin, although insufficient volumes of the Zulla Formation are preserved from proximal areas of the Duru sub-basin to determine detailed sedimentation patterns. Triassic uplift, recorded by the introduction of quartz sands, preceded a second rift

event, marked by basin subsidence and the deposition of Ladinian to Norian cherts. A return to carbonate sedimentation, characterized by the bivalve *Halobia* indicates a deepening of the CCD.

During the Early Jurassic (Fig. 13), quartz sands prograded onto the Oman carbonate margin. They did not reach the north of the Al Ayn sub-basin, where sediments from ooid shoals on the shelf edge were transported to the base of the continental slope to form laterally discontinuous bodies. In the southern part of the Al Ayn sub-basin, coarse-grained quartz sands by-passed the platform and were deposited, *via* a number of input points, as a series of coalescing sediment bodies.

Subsidence of the carbonate platform of the Saih Hatat area, to form a slope at the western side of the Duru sub-basin may have promoted the higher input of carbonate into this area. Quartz sand mixed with carbonate sand on the platform, then were transported by turbidity currents into the Duru sub-basin, where they were carried northwards, to the east of the Al

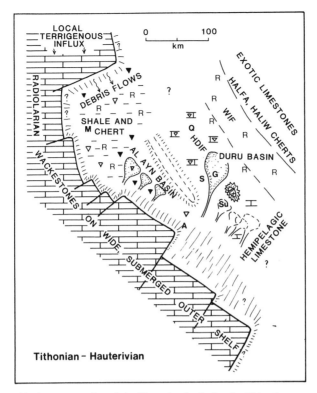

Fig. 15. Palaeogeographical reconstruction of the Hawasina basin for the Tithonian to Early Cretaceous (Sid'r Formation).

Ayn sub-basin. The denser quartz grains were preferentially removed from suspension, and more distal sedimentation was quartz-free. In the SE part of the Duru sub-basin, quartz input was reduced, and an irregular sea-floor topography promoted the deposition of hemipelagic lime-muds on ridges and coarse-grained carbonate material in broad gullies.

Sedimentation patterns during the Middle and Late Jurassic (Fig. 14) were influenced by the development of ooid shoals along the length of the Oman shelf edge. In the Al Ayn sub-basin, the deposition of shale continued. Low-volume, off-margin sediment transport resulted in the development of laterally discontinuous, channel-fed carbonate fans. Local instability of the shelf edge produced conglomerates that were derived from line sources. Increased off-margin transport in the southern Al Ayn sub-basin produced a prograding sediment wedge.

Deposition in the Duru sub-basin was characterized by three intervals of high volume oolite input. Oolitic sediments formed laterally continuous sediment sheets that extended north-wards to form a longitudinal fan. In the southern part of the Duru sub-basin, sea-floor depressions were gradually filled and sediment bodies became more sheet-like.

Destabilisation of the platform edge at the top of the Jurassic generated widespread conglomerates that marked the onset of tectonic subsidence of the Oman platform, the reduction of carbonate input into the Hawasina basin and an interval of a shallow CCD. Cherts thus characterize sediments of the Tithonian to the Hauterivian (Fig. 15), augmented by shale and silicified limestones in the Al Ayn sub-basin. In the Duru sub-basin, the volume of carbonate lime-mud input exceeded the rate of carbonate dissolution and limestones with replacement chert nodules predominate. Indeed, the proximal areas of the southern Duru sub-basin were either sufficiently shallow or had a high enough input carbonate for hemipelagic limestones to be preserved. Radiolarian cherts were restricted to the most distal areas of Hamrat Duru Group deposition in the Duru sub-basin.

With the progradation of shallow-water car-

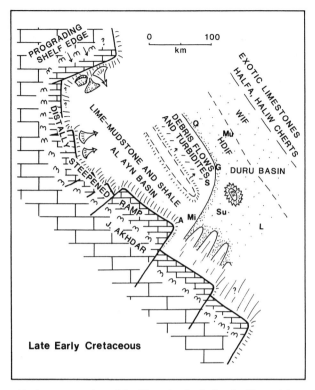

Fig. 16. Palaeogeographical reconstruction of the Hawasina basin for the Hauterivian to Cenomanian (Nayid Formation).

bonates across the platform, associated with a fall in sea level during the Hauterivian, coarse-grained carbonate deposition returned to the Duru sub-basin (Fig. 16), although the area remained close to the CCD and fine-grained sediments were replaced by chert. A renewed deepening, possibly representing a phase of basin subsidence, prompted a return to the deposition of limestones which were replaced by silica in a sub-CCD environment. During the late Cenomanian, a deepening of the CCD allowed a return to carbonate deposition, which persisted up to the Santonian (Béchennec 1987).

In the Al Ayn sub-basin, fine-grained carbonate material was deposited, marking a significant departure from preceeding sedimentation patterns, and the input of shale was minimal. In the Cenomanian, however, there was a return to shale deposition, associated with radiolarian cherts and, in the southern Al Ayn basin, limestone conglomerates and turbidites.

Conclusions

1. The evolution of the Hawasina basin continental rise sedimentary succession can be linked to broader platform events, most notably to variations in sea level. Periods of maximum carbonate production and transport into the basins coincide with periods of stable platform evolution, when a wide (700 km, Murris 1980) carbonate-producing area abutted the margin edge. Relative sea level rises promoted the retreat and narrowing of the carbonate-producing platform environments into the interior of the Arabian platform, with the development of a wide outer shelf area on which sediment could be trapped prior to its entry into the Hawasina basin. Eustatic rises in sea level and basin subsidence, augmented by fluctuations in ocean water productivity resulted in decreased carbonate input and

raised the CCD, promoting the deposition of cherts. Unit III of the Zulla Formation and the Sid'r Formation can be accounted for by this mechanism. Conversely, negative movements of sea level were accompanied by the stifling of carbonate production by terrigenous material, resulting in a reduction of off-margin carbonate transport. Unit II of the Zulla Formation and the Guweyza Sandstone Formation represent sedimentation influenced by this process. The shape of the margin did, however, also influence the volumes of sediment transported into the basin, which varied along the length of the margin.

2. The Hawasina basin was divided into two distinct components, the shale-rich Al Ayn sub-basin in the north, and the carbonate-rich Duru sub-basin in the south and extending northwards outboard from the Al Ayn sub-basin. These sub-basins show fundamentally different depositional patterns throughout the evolution of the Hawasina Ocean, whilst deriving sediment from adjacent parts of the same carbonate platform.

3. Deep-water sedimentation patterns reflect the processes responsible for the accumulation and transport of sediment off the margin edge. By comparison with modern-day carbonate environments, it is suggested that prevailing wind patterns exercised a strong influence in determining the patterns of deep-water sedimentation and that the Mesozoic Oman margin had a semi-windward orientation.

This work forms part of a PhD thesis undertaken at the Grant Institute of Geology, Edinburgh, funded by the Natural Environment Research Council. Constructive discussions with A. Robertson, J. Smewing, M. Searle, S. Hanna, K. Watts and B. Pratt greatly augmented my understanding of Oman geology. C. Blome (U.S.G.S.) kindly dated radiolaria extracted from cherts. Comments by F. Béchennec, P. Cawood, K. Pickering, K. Watts and H. Weissert improved earlier drafts of the manuscript. Amoco Oman Petroleum Company is most sincerely thanked for its help with funding the fieldwork. The paper is published with the permission of Amoco Production Company.

References

AGER, D. V. 1981. Major marine cycles in the Mesozoic. *Journal of the Geological Society of London*, **138**, 159–166.

ALLEN, J. R. L. 1982. Sedimentary structures – their character and physical basis. *Developments in Sedimentology: 30B*. Elsevier, Amsterdam, New York.

BARRETTE, P. D. 1988. Internal geometry and origin of the Hubat structural culmination, Oman Mountains. *Journal of Structural Geology*, **10**, 383–391.

—— & CALON, T. J. 1987. Re-imbrication of the Hawasina allochthons in the Sufrat ad Dawd range, Oman Mountains. *Journal of Structural Geology*, **9**, 859–867.

BÉCHENNEC, F. 1987. Géologie des nappes Hawasina dans les parties orientale et centrale des montagnes d'Oman. *PhD thesis*, University Pierre et Marie Curie, Paris.

——, BEURRIER, M., RABU, D. & HUTIN, G. 1986. *Geological map of Oman, Barka. Explanatory notes*. Oman Ministry of Petroleum and Minerals.

BERGER, W. H. 1976. Biogenous deep-sea sediments: Production, preservation, interpretation. *Chemical Oceanography*, **5**, 265–387.

BERNOULLI, D. & JENKYNS, H. C. 1974. Alpine, Mediterranean and central Atlantic Mesozoic facies in relation to the early evolution of Tethys. *In*: DOTT R. H. & SHAVER, R. H. (eds), *Modern and ancient geosynclinal sedimentation*. Special Publication, Society of Economic Palaeontologists and Mineralogists, Tulsa, **19**, 129–160.

—— & WEISSERT, H. 1987. The upper Hawasina nappes in the central Oman Mountains: stratigraphy, palinspastics and sequence of nappe emplacement. *Geodinamica Acta*, **1**, 47–58.

——, —— & BLOME C. D. 1990. Evolution of the Triassic Hawasina basin. *In*: ROBERTSON, A. H. F. SEARLE, M. P. & RIES, A. C. (eds) *The Geology and Tectonics of the Oman Region*. Geological Society, London, Special Publication, **49**, 189–204.

BOSELLINI, A. & WINTERER, E. L. 1975. Pelagic limestone and radiolarite of the Tethyan Mesozoic: a genetic model. *Geology*, **3**, 279–282.

BOULIN, J. 1981. Afghanistan structure, Greater India concept and eastern Tethys evolution. *Tectonophysics*, **72**, 261–281.

CAWOOD, P. A., GREEN, F. K. & CALON, T. J. 1990. Origin of administration within the southeast Oman Mountains at Jebel MaJhool and Ibra Dome. *In*: ROBERTSON, A. H. F, SEARLE, M. P. & RIES, A. C. (eds) *The Geology and Tectonics of the Oman Region*. Geological Society Special Publication, **49**, 429–445.

CONNALLY, T. C. & SCOTT, R. W. 1985. Carbonate sediment-fill of an oceanic shelf, Lower Cretaceous, Arabian Peninsular. *In*: CREVELLO P. D. & HARRIS, P. M. (eds). *Deep-water carbonates: Buildups, tubidites, debris flows and chalks – a core worskshop*. Society of Economic Palaeontologists and Mineralogists, Tulsa, Core Workshop, **6**, 266–302.

COOPER, D. J. W. 1986. The Hamrat Duru Group: Evolution of a Mesozoic passive carbonate margin in the Oman Mountains. *PhD thesis*, University of Edinburgh.

—— 1987. Hamrat Duru Group: Revised stratigraphy of a Mesozoic deep-water passive margin in the Oman Mountains. *Geological Magazine*, **124**, 157–164.

—— 1988. Structure and sequence of thrusting in deep-water sediments during ophiolite emplacement in the south-central Oman Mountains. *Journal of Structural Geology*, **10**, 473–485.

—— 1989. A longitudinal carbonate fan from the Jurassic of the Oman Mountains: The Guweyza Limestone Formation of the Hamrat ad Duru. *Sedimentary Geology*.

DELAUNE-MAYERE, M. 1984. Evolution of a Mesozoic passive continental margin: Baer-Bassit (NW Syria). *In*: DIXON, J. E. & ROBERTSON, A. H. F. *The Geological Evolution of the Eastern Mediterranean*: Geological Society, London, Special Publication, **17**, 151–159.

FUCHS, G. 1979. On the geology of western Ladakh. *Jahrbuch Geologie*, B.-A **122**, 513–540.

GARRISON, R. E. & FISCHER, A. G. 1969. Deep-water limestones and radiolarites in the Alpine Jurassic. *In*: FRIEDMAN G. M. (Ed.) *Depositional environments in carbonate rocks*. Special Publication, Society Economic Palaeontologists and Mineralogists, Tulsa, **14**, 20–56.

GLENNIE, K. W., BOEUF, M. G. A., HUGHES CLARKE, M. W., MOODY-STUART, M., PILAAR, W. H. F. & REINHARDT, B. M. 1973. Late Cretaceous Nappes in the Oman Mountains and their geologic evolution. *American Association of Petroleum Geologists Bulletin*, **57**, 5–27.

——, ——, ——, ——, —— & —— 1974. Geology of the Oman Mountains (parts 1 and 2). Verhandeling van het Koninklijk Nederlands Geologisch Mijnbouwkundig Genootschap, **13**.

GRAHAM, G. M. 1980. Structure and stratigraphy of the Hawasina window, Oman Mountains. *PhD thesis*, Open University.

HALLAM, A. 1981. A revised sea-level curve for the early Jurassic. *Journal of the Geological Society of London*, **138**, 735–743.

HEATH, K. C. & MULLINS, H. T. 1984. Open-ocean, off-bank transport of fine-grained carbonate sediment in the northern Bahamas. *In*: STOW, D. A. V. & Piper, D. J. W. (eds) *Fine-grained sediments: Deep-water processes and facies*. Geological Society, London, Special Publication, **4**, 199–208.

HINE, A. C., WILBER, R. J., BANE, J. M., NEUMANN, A. C. & LORENSEN, K. R. 1981. Off-bank transport of carbonate sands along open leeward bank margins, northern Bahamas. *Marine Geology*, **42**, 327–348.

IRVING, E. 1977. Drift of the major continental blocks since Devonian. *Nature*, **270**, 304–309.

LIPPARD, S. J. & REX, D. C. 1982. K–Ar ages of alkaline igneous rocks in the Oman Mountains, NW Arabia and their relation to rifting, passive margin development and destruction of the Oman Tethys. *Geological Magazine*, **119**, 497–503.

MULLINS, H. T. & NEUMANN, A. C. 1979. Deep carbonate bank margin structure and sedimentation in the northern Bahama. *In*: DOYLE, L. J. & PILKEY, O. H. (eds) *Geology of continental slopes*. Special Publication, Society Economic Palaeontologists and Mineralogists, Tulsa, **27**, 165–192.

MURRIS, R. J. 1980. Middle East, stratigraphic evolution and oil habitat. *American Association of Petroleum Geologists Bulletin*, **64**, 597–618.

MUTTI, E. & RICCI-LUCCHI, F. 1972. Turbidites of the northern Apennines, introduction to facies analysis. *International Geological Revue*, **20**, 125–166.

NAYLOR, M. A. 1978. A geological study of some olistostromes and melanges. *PhD thesis*, University of Cambridge.

PATTON, T. L. & O'CONNOR, S. J. 1988. Cre-taceous flexural history of northern Oman Mountain foredeep, United Arab Emirates. *American Association of Petroleum Geologists Bulletin*, **72**, 797–809.

PICKERING, K. T. & HISCOTT, R. N. 1985. Contained (reflected) turbidity currents from the Middle Ordovician Cloridorme Formation, Quebec, Canada: An alternative to the antidune hypothesis. *Sedimentology*, **32**, 373–394.

——, STOW, D. A. V., WATSON, M. P. & HISCOTT, R. N. 1986. Deep-water facies; processes and models: A review and classification scheme for modern and ancient sediments. *Earth-Science Review*, **23**, 75–174.

PRATT, B. R. & SMEWING, J. D. 1990. Jurassic and Lower Cretaceous platform margin evolution, central Oman Mountains. *In*: ROBERTSON, A. H. F., SEARLE, M. P. & RIES, A. C. (eds) *The Geology and Tectonics of the Oman Region*. Geological Society, London, Special Publication, **49**, 69–88.

ROBERTSON, A. H. F. 1987a. Upper Cretaceous Muti Formation: Transition of a Mesozoic carbonate platform edge to a foreland basin in the Oman Mountains. *Sedimentology*, **34**, 1123–1143.

—— 1987b. The transition from a passive margin to an Upper Cretaceous foreland basin related to ophiolite emplacement in the Oman Mountains. *Geological Society of American Bulletin*, **99**, 633–653.

—— & WOODCOCK, N. H. 1981. Alakir Cay Group, Antalya Complex, SW Turkey: A deformed Mesozoic carbonate margin. *Sedimentary Geology*, **30**, 95–131.

SCHLAGER, W. 1981. The paradox of drowned reefs and carbonate platforms. *Geological Society of American Bulletin*, **92**, 197–211.

SEARLE, M. P. 1983. Stratigraphy, structure and evolution of the Tibetan-Tethys zone in Zanskar and the Indus suture zone in the Ladakh Himalaya. Transactions of the Royal Society of Edinburgh: Earth-Science. **73**, 205–219.

—— 1985. Sequence of thrusting and origin of culminations in the northern and central Oman Mountains. *Journal of Structural Geology*, 7, 129–143.

—— & COOPER, D. J. W. 1986. Structure of the Hawasina window culmination, central Oman

Mountains. Transactions of the Royal Society of Edinburgh: Earth-Science, 77, 143−156.

——, —— & WATTS, K. Structure of the Jebel Sumeini-Jebel Ghawil areas, Northern Oman. In: ROBERTSON, A. H. F., SEARLE, M. P. & RIES, A. C. (eds) The Geology and Tectonics of the Oman Region. Geological Society, London, Special Publication, 49, 361−374.

—— & GRAHAM, G. M. 1982. 'Oman Exotics': oceanic carbonate buildups associated with the early stages of continental rifting. Geology, 10, 43−49.

——, JAMES, N. P., CALON, T. J. & SMEWING, J. D. 1983. Sedimentological and structural evolution of the Arabian continental margin in the Musandam Mountains and Dibba zone, United Arab Emirates. Geological Society of America Bulletin, 94, 1381−1400.

——, LIPPARD, S. J., SMEWING, J. D. & REX, D. C. 1980. Volcanic rocks beneath the Semail ophiolite nappe in the northern Oman Mountains and their significance in the Mesozoic evolution of Tethys. Journal of the Geological Society of London, 137, 589−604.

SENGÖR, A. M. C. 1984. The Cimmeride orogenic system and the tectonics of Eurasia. Special Publication, Geological Society of America, 195.

SMITH, A. G., HURLEY, A. M. & BRINDON, J. C. 1981. Phanerozoic palaeocontinental world maps. Cambridge University Press.

VAIL, P. R., MITCHUM, J. M. & THOMPSON, S. 1977. Global cycles of relative changes of sea level. In: PATTON, C. E. (ed) Seismic stratigraphy − applications to hydrocarbon exploration. American Association of Petroleum Geologists Memoir, 26, 83−99.

WALKER, R. G. & MUTTI, E. 1973. Turbidite facies and facies associations. In: MIDDLETON, G. V. & BOUMA, A. H. (eds) Turbidites and deep-water sedimentation. Society of Economic Palaeontologists and Mineralogists, Tulsa, Pacific Section Short Course, Anaheim, 119−157.

WATTS, K. F. 1987. Triassic carbonate submarine fans along the Arabian platform margin, Sumeini Group, Oman. Sedimentology, 34, 43−71.

—— 1990. Mesozoic carbonate slope facies marking the Arabian platform margin. In: ROBERTSON, A. H. F., SEARLE, M. P. & RIES, A. C. (eds) The Geology and Tectonics of the Oman Region. Geological Society, London, Special Publication, 49, 139−159.

—— & GARRISON, R. E. 1986. Sumeini Group, Oman − Evolution of a Mesozoic carbonate slope on a south Tethyan continental margin. Sedimentary Geology, 48, 107−168.

WARBURTON, J., GRAHAM, R. H. & ISSAC, K. P. 1989. The sedimentology and structural geology of the Hamrat ad Duru Range, Sultanate of Oman. In: Symposium on hydrocarbon geology in intense thrust zones, U.A.E.

Evolution of the Triassic Hawasina Basin, Central Oman Mountains

D. BERNOULLI[1], H. WEISSERT[1] & C. D. BLOME[2]

[1] *Geology Institute, ETH-Zentrum, CH-8092 Zurich, Switzerland*
[2] *United States Geological Survey, Denver, Colorado 80225, USA*

Abstract: Sediments of Late Triassic age preserved in the upper Hawasina nappes of the Central Oman Mountains document the early sedimentary and oceanographic evolution of a segment of the Triassic seaway bordering the northern Gondwanian continental margin. Within the Zulla Formation of Glennie *et al.* four members can be distinguished.
4. Halobia limestones (Lower to ?Upper Norian)
3. Radiolarian cherts (Ladinian to Lower Norian)
2. Sandstone-shale member
1. Calcarenite-shale member
  Changes in composition and abundance of turbiditic sediments in the Zulla Formation reflect environmental changes in the source areas, probably linked to sea-level fluctuations, whereas changes in the pelagic facies reflect basin-wide oceanographic fluctuations. Episodic low-oxygen conditions are indicated by laminated dolomites in the calcarenite-shale member. An increase in radiolarian abundance may record an increase in surface-water productivity possibly related to a sea-level rise and corresponding changes in the circulation pattern. A deepening of the CCD during the Early Norian is documented by the Halobia limestones. Similar facies types are encountered along the South-Tethyan seaway (Lagonegro−Pindos−Antalya−Pichakun). However, diachroneity of facies changes from radiolarite to limestone point to differences in the bathymetric and/or oceanographic evolution of the basins.

In the Oman Mountains, a series of essentially sedimentary decollement nappes and imbricates is sandwiched between the Semail nappe, a thick slab of oceanic crust and lithosphere, and the sediments and basement rocks of the proximal Arabian margin that are exposed in a number of large post-nappe culminations. The nappes are known as the Sumeini nappe, the Hawasina nappes and the Haybi complex. Their sediments are interpreted as continental slope (Sumeini) to distal continental margin deposits of the Arabian margin and/or as oceanic sediments of the adjacent Tethys (Hawasina nappes s.l., Béchennec *et al*, 1990). The structurally higher Haybi complex is in part a tectonic melange of Permian to mid-Cretaceous sediments, of Permian and Mesozoic volcanics and of subophiolite metamorphic rocks (Glennie *et al.* 1974; Searle *et al.* 1980; Béchennec 1988).

During the Late Cretaceous orogeny, the sediments of the Hawasina Basin were detached from their still unknown basement and accumulated in a stack of nappes below and in front of the Semail nappe. Classically, palinspastic reconstructions postulate simple telescoping of these nappes with the lower nappes derived from the more proximal, the higher ones from the more distal parts of the continental margin/ocean basin complex (Glennie

et al. 1974; Gealey, 1977; Searle *et al.* 1980, 1983; Béchennec *et al.* 1990). However, it turns out that many Hawasina sequences in a high structural position (Al Ayn, Halfa p.p., Glennie *et al.* 1974) contain mainly Triassic to Early Jurassic sediments that can be correlated with the original substratum of lower nappes (Hamrut Duru, Wahrah) (Bernoulli & Weissert 1987). The observed configuration suggests that downward propagation of thrusting in front of the Semail is responsible for cutting the original stratigraphic sequence along detachment horizons into a number of thrust-sheets, involving successively older and more external formations. This kind of thrust propagation eventually led to the emplacement of the Triassic units onto their original Jurassic-Cretaceous cover. The palinspastic section resulting from a tentative kinematic inversion is given in Fig. 1. The stratigraphy observed by us in the Al Ayn and Halfa tectono-stratigraphic terranes of Glennie *et al.* (1974) matches well with lower Hamrat Duru Group stratigraphy established by Béchennec (1988), Beurrier *et al.* (1986) and Cooper (1987) for the Hawasina Basin. In this paper, we shall present new stratigraphical and sedimentological data bearing on the Triassic evolution of the Hawasina Basin.

From ROBERTSON, A. H. F., SEARLE, M. P. & RIES, A. C. (eds), 1990,
The Geology and Tectonics of the Oman Region.
Geological Society Special Publication No 49, pp 189−202

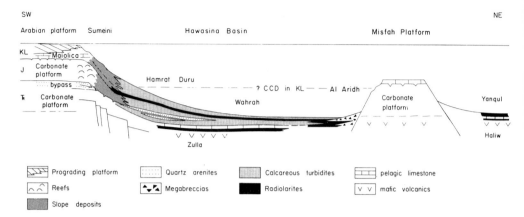

Fig. 1. Palinspastic reconstruction of the Hawasina Basin of the central Oman Mountains for the Early Cretaceous. After Bernoulli & Weissert (1987), modified.

Stratigraphy of the Zulla Formation

We have surveyed the basinal Triassic sequences of the Hawasina nappes (Fig. 2) in the type-area of the Al Ayn Formation of Glennie *et al.* (1974) (locs 2 & 3), N of Rustaq (loc. 4), in the Ibra Dome (loc. 5) and in the Halfa type area (loc. 6). We also remeasured the type-section of the Haliw Formation of Glennie *et al.* (1974), which, however, we now consider to have a more distal origin beyond the Misfah platform of the Oman Exotics (Umar Basin of Béchennec *et al.* 1990; cf. Hutin *et al.* 1986). Within the Zulla (= Al Ayn) Formation of Glennie *et al.* (1974) and Cooper (1987), we could distinguish four lithological members. From top to bottom (see Fig. 3):
(4) Halobia limestones
(3) Radiolarian cherts
(2) Sandstones and shales
(1) Turbiditic calcarenites and shales.

A correlation with the stratigraphic terminology of other authors is given in Table 1.

In the sections investigated by us, the substratum of the Zulla Formation is not exposed. However, at other localities Béchennec (1988) and Blendinger *et al.* (1990) observed below the Triassic sediments Late Permian debris flow deposits, calcarenite turbidites, calcilutites and radiolarites overlying basaltic pillow lavas. The Zulla Formation is overlain by the Guwayza Sandstone Formation. There is now general agreement that the Al Ayn Sandstone and the Guwayza Sandstone of Glennie *et al.* (1974) are identical (Beurrier *et al.* 1986; Bernoulli &

Weissert 1987; Cooper 1987; Béchennec 1988). Béchennec (1988) includes the Guwayza Sandstone and the Al Ayn Sandstone into the upper member of his Matbat Formation.

Turbiditic calcarenites and shales

N of Tawi Shannah (Wadi Al Ayn) the lowermost strata of the Zulla Formation observed are decimetre- to centimetre-bedded, redeposited calcarenites to calcisiltites inter-bedded with calcareous shales and marls. The limestone turbidites have incomplete, base-cut-out Bouma sequences (T_b-T_e), thinner beds are rippled (T_c). Occasional flute-casts at the base of thicker beds indicate a general SE−NW-sediment transport. The turbiditic grainstones contain redeposited shallow-water carbonate material, such as pellets, ooids and intraclasts (Fig. 6a), but no diagnostic fauna were found. Bechennec (1988) reports redeposited faunas of Late Permian age. The age of the unit could therefore span part of the Late Permian and/or of the Early to Middle Triassic. Up-section the hemipelagic and turbiditic deposits pass into siliceous shales alternating with thin-bedded, laminated, fine-grained dolomites (Fig. 4).

N of Rustaq, a sequence of thin-bedded calcarenites to calcisiltites is interbedded with marls and some red shale. The calcarenites to calcisiltites are mainly T_c, sometimes T_b-T_c or T_c-T_d-turbidites in the sense of Bouma (1962). The limestone turbidites are highly recrystallized and intruded by three teschenite sills which have been dated as Early Jurassic by Béchennec (1988).

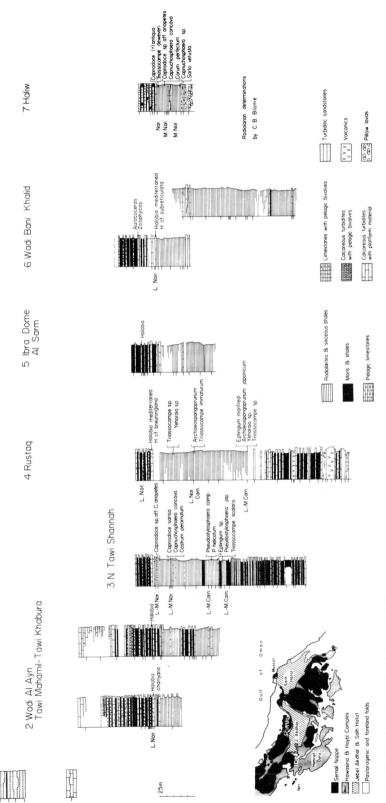

Fig. 2. Stratigraphy of the Zulla and Haliw Formations in the central Oman Mountains. Faunal occurrences are listed to the right of each section. Except for *Zoophycos* (trace fossil), *Aulacoceras* (cephalopod) and *Halobia* species, all other fossils listed are Radiolarians.

Table 1 *Correlation of the members of the Zulla Formation as defined by different authors.*

Glennie et al. (1974)			Bernoulli&Weissert (1987)	Cooper (1987)	Béchennec (1988)		This paper	
HAMRAT DURU	AL AYN	HALFA						
GUWAYZA SANDSTONE	AL AYN FORMATION	?	GUWAYZA SANDSTONE = AL AYN SANDSTONE	GUWAYZA SANDSTONE FORMATION	MATBAT FORMATION	upper member	ZULLA FORMATION	GUWAYZA SANDSTONE
ZULLA FORMATION		HALFA FORMATION	HALFA/ AL AYN LIMESTONES	Unit IV		lower member		Halobia Limestone
			HALFA RADIOLARITES	Unit III	AL JIL FORMATION	upper member		Radiolarian Chert
			Tawi Shannah member / Rustaq	Unit II				Sandstones and Shales
				Unit I		lower member		Turbiditic Calcarenites and Shales

Fig. 3. The Zulla Formation N of Tawi Shannah in Wadi Al Ayn. 1. Turbiditic calcarenites and shales. 2. Sandstones and shales. 3. Radiolarian cherts. 4. Halobia limestones.

Fig. 4. Laminated, slightly bituminous dolomites alternating with grey, yellowish weathering, non-calcareous mudstones. Unit of turbiditic calcarenites and shales, Zulla Formation, N of Tawi Shannah, Wadi Al Ayn.

Sandstones and shales

Up-section unit 1 gradually passes into green shales with intercalated greenish quartzose sandstone turbidites and subordinate calcarenites and calcisiltites. The sandstones are mainly T_b-T_c-turbidites grading upwards into turbiditic mudstones. Compositionally, they are quartzarenites to subfeldspathic arenites with only minor lithoclasts. The rare lithoclasts are mainly volcanic with only a few grains of metamorphics; stable heavy minerals (zircon, garnet, TiO_2 minerals and tourmaline) are common to abundant. In Wadi Al Ayn the turbiditic interval is about 25 m thick, whereas near Rustaq and in Wadi Bani Khalid only a few sandstone intercalations within the shales are observed.

Radiolarian chert

The sandstone-unit grades upward into a monotonous sequence of bedded, carbonate-free ribbon chert with interbedded siliceous shales and radiolarian mudstones. Cherts and shales are typically cm-bedded with a shale/chert ratio varying from 1:1 to 1:10. Size grading (Fig. 5a,c) and ripples (cf. Fig. 5b) indicate redeposition of the radiolarian-rich layers by bottom or dilute turbidity currents. Fine redeposited calcarenites to calcisiltites and rare lithic sandstone turbidites with abundant chloritized volcanic fragments are also intercalated in the upper part of the unit.

The radiolarians identified in our samples (see Fig. 2) indicate an age span of Early/Middle Carnian to Early/Middle Norian for the formation. However, as the overlying Halobia Limestones yield Early Norian *Halobia*-assemblages, the change from radiolarite to pelagic limestone sedimentation must have taken place during the Early Norian. In the Hawasina window, Béchennec (1988) found a Late Anisian to Ladinian radiolarian fauna at the base of the radiolarian cherts.

Halobia limestones

The radiolarian cherts are overlain by alternating marls and limestones (Fig. 6c). In the lower part of the sequence, there are argillaceous pelagic lime wackestones with calcite-filled radiolarian moulds and well preserved shells of *Halobia* (Fig. 6b,e). Other limestones are thin-bedded turbidites, mainly T_c, with layers of lithoclasts, pellets and fine quartz sand (Fig. 6d) and layers packed with pelagic bivalves. Pelagic bivalves are also the major constituents of graded skeletal lime grainstones. Up-section, dm-bedded calcarenite turbidites (T_a-T_c) with redeposited lithoclasts, ooids, bivalves, echinoderms and fine quartz sand dominate the sequence. The combined ranges of different species of the thin-shelled bivalve *Halobia* (det. B. Gruber, see Fig. 2) place the lower part of the unit into the younger part of the Early Norian; from the upper part of the unit Glennie *et al.* (1974) and Béchennec (1988) mention displaced benthic foraminifera of Late Triassic age.

Stratigraphy of the Haliw Formation

The Haliw Formation of Glennie *et al.* (1974) is at its type locality coeval with the upper part of the Zulla Formation, however, it is lithologically distinct. It consists of a lower unit of white to pink pelagic limestones with bands and nodules of diagenetic replacement chert. The limestones are lime wackestones rich in calcite-filled radiolarian moulds. Layers rich in pelagic bivalves ('*Halobia*') were deposited by bottom or dilute turbidity currents (Fig. 7a). The limestones are overlain by red ribbon cherts (Fig. 5b) with thin siliceous shale interbeds and occasional calcarenite turbidites. Up-section, there is an abrupt change to a unit of centimetre- to decimetre-bedded, white, skeletal grainstones, packed with shells of pelagic bivalves (Fig. 7b) and occasional volcanic and pelagic limestone lithoclasts and echinoderm debris. Some of these beds show faint grading, many contain diagenetic replacement chert nodules. The Haliw Formation rests on basaltic pillow lavas.

Glennie *et al.* (1974) did not find any age-diagnostic fossils and thought the Haliw

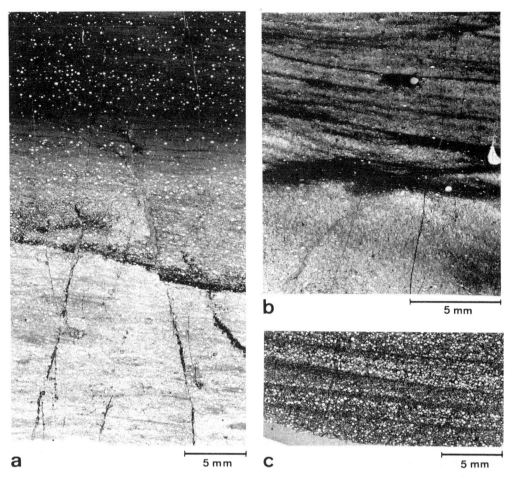

Fig. 5. Microfacies of radiolarites, Zulla and Haliw Formations. (a) Radiolarian chert with closely packed radiolarian moulds in a clay-rich siliceous matrix grading upward into siliceous mudstone with sparse chalcedony-filled radiolarian moulds. Zulla Formation. Sample DB 6264, Wadi Al Ayn, N of Tawi Shannah. Thin-section. (b) Faintly coarse-tail graded radiolarian chert to mudstone, overlain by rippled finer-grained, recrystallized layers rich in partly compacted moulds of tiny radiolarians. Sample DB 6904, Haliw Formation (type-locality). Thin-section. (c) Alternation of layers rich in chalcedony-filled moulds of size-sorted larger radiolarians, alternating with laminae with tiny radiolarians, sponge spicules, and mica. Zulla Formation. Sample DB 6648, Wadi Bani Khalid (near locality 287 of Glennie *et al.* 1974). Thin-section.

Fig. 6. (a) Lime mudstone overlain by graded calcarenite with clasts of fine-grained limestone, ooids, onkoids and skeletal fragments of shallow-water biota (molluscs, echinoderms). Unit of turbiditic calcarenites and shales. Zulla Formation. Sample DB 6250, Wadi Al Ayn, N of Tawi Shannah. Thin-section. (b) Lime wackestone with shells of *Halobia* and calcite-filled radiolarian moulds. Halobia limestone unit of Zulla Formation. Sample DB 6274, Wadi Al Ayn, between Tawi Mahamil and Tawi Khabura. Thin-section. (c) Halobia limestones and interbedded marls overlying radiolarites and siliceous shales. Zulla Formation, Wadi Al Ayn, N of Tawi Shannah. (d) Graded calcarenite with compacted marl clasts, clasts of fine grained limestones, shallow-water biota (molluscs, echinoderms), pelagic bivalves and fine quartz sand. Halobia limestone unit of Zulla Formation. Sample DB 6279, Wadi Al Ayn, between Tawi Mahamil and Tawi Khabura. Thin-section. (e) Well-preserved shells of *Halobia* on a bedding surface. Halobia limestone unit of Zulla Formation. Sample DB 6655, Wadi Bani Khalid (near locality 287 of Glennie *et al.*, 1974). Coin is 2 cm in diameter.

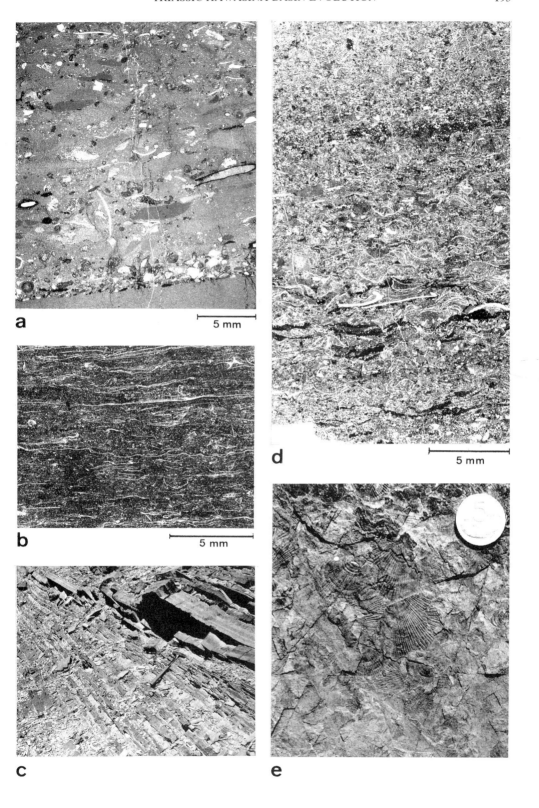

a   5 mm

b   5 mm

c

d   5 mm

e

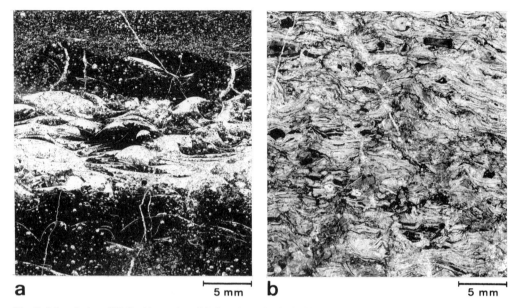

a |⎯⎯⎯⎯⎯| 5 mm **b** |⎯⎯⎯⎯⎯| 5 mm

Fig. 7. Microfacies of Haliw Formation. (a) Couplets of pelagic bivalve coquina and of calcilutite with sparse bivalve shells and calcite-filled radiolarian moulds. The coquina layers are grain-supported and display sheltered cavities below the shells, filled by syntaxial overgrowth cement. The upper boundaries of the coquina layers are modified by burrowing. Deposition was probably by bottom or intrabasinal dilute turbidity currents. Sample DB 6282, Haliw. Thin-section. (b) Calcarenite with closely packed pelagic bivalves, rare echinodermal fragments and pelagic limestones lithoclasts. Pelagic bivalves were broken by compaction and cemented by syntaxial calcite overgrowth. Sample DB 6285, Haliw. Thin-section.

Formation to be a slowly deposited oceanic sediment covering most of the Triassic to mid-Cretaceous timespan. However, at the type-locality, the radiolarites contain a fauna of Middle to Late Norian age (see Fig. 2) and the microfacies of the limestones correspond well to that of other pelagic sediments of the South-Tethyan Triassic. Hutin et al. (1986) place the Haliw Formation into the Aqil Formation of the Umar Group (Béchennec 1988) According to Béchennec, the Umar Group is derived from a more distal realm than the Zulla Formation. Indeed, the episode of terrigenous sedimentation documented in the Guwayza Sandstone Formation of the Hamrat Duru Basin is not recorded in the younger sediments of the Umar Basin which was probably sheltered from terrigenous influx by the seamounts of the Misfah platform(s) (Fig. 1).

Palaeotectonic evolution

The external Hawasina basin (Hamrat Duru Basin of Béchennec, (1988) and Cooper (1987), was already in existence in Late Permian times as documented by the occurrence of Late Permian radiolarites and deep-water limestones (Béchennec 1988; Blendinger et al. 1990). Where exposed, the substratum of these sediments consists of mafic volcanics that are generally of within-plate alkalic type, but locally, MORB-tholeiites occur (Béchennec, 1988). At present, it is not possible to determine whether the Hawasina Basin was underlain by a thinned, foundered continental, a transitional or a marginal oceanic crust. However, there seems to exist a general agreement that the distal Hawasina Basin originated from Permian to Mid/Late Triassic rifting followed by Late Triassic sea floor spreading in this sector of the Tethys and the development of the Arabian margin.

Internally, the basin of the Zulla Formation was separated from the distal (Umar) basin by a number of volcanic edifices capped by shallow-water carbonates (Oman Exotics: Searle & Graham 1982; Baid and Misfah platforms: Béchennec 1988; for an alternative palinspastic reconstruction, see Blendinger et al. 1990). During their later evolution, these carbonate platforms were eventually submerged and evolved into seamounts and submarine plateaus covered by thin pelagic limestones sequences. In the Baid platform (Bechennec 1988), drowning occurred in Early Triassic (T. Calon 1988 pers. comm.), in the Misfah platform in latest Liassic to Middle Jurassic times (pers. observation). Coeval slope sediments of the Maqam Formation (Sumeini Group: Glennie *et al.* 1974; Watts & Garrison 1986) form the platform margin slope which separates the Hawasina Basin from the Arabian carbonate shelf.

The evolution of the basin closely reflects that of its margins and of the adjacent Arabian shelf. The limestone turbidites of unit 1 can be correlated with the C Member of the Maqam Formation which consists of calcirudites to calcarenites deposited in small submarine fans and of perennial platy calcilutites (Watts & Garrison 1986). Our scarce current measurements as well as those of Glennie *et al.* (1974) indicate a SW to NE sediment transport from the Sumeini slope into the Hawasina Basin. The terrigenous turbidites of unit 2 can be correlated with the shales and sandstones of the D Member/Maqam Formation. This increasing influx of terrigenous sediment may record a relative sea level drop, possibly in the Anisian, that allowed the terrigenous detritus to cross the shelf and to be deposited offshore in deeper-water environments. The (?Ladinian) Carnian−Norian radiolarites could reflect a relative deepening of the basin, possibly related to further crustal extension. They also could reflect changes in palaeoceanography as dicussed in the next paragraph or both. The radiolarites and Halobia limestones are best compared with the E Member/Maqam Formation. The E member consists of radiolarites, pelagic limestones and thin-bedded calcarenites which grade laterally into redeposited calcirudites and calcarenites with interbedded radiolarites (Watts & Garrison 1986). In the pelagic facies, radiolarites are overlain by thin-bedded, peloidal, pelagic bivalve calcarenites which can be compared to those of unit 4 of the Zulla or those of the Haliw Formation (compare Fig. 18A and B in Watts & Garrison 1986 with our Fig. 7a). In the uppermost part of the E Member/Maqam Formation, turbiditic calcarenites include small amounts of quartz sand that correlate with those in the upper part of the Halobia limestone (see Fig. 6d).

The Guwayza Sandstone Formation is correlated with the F Member/Maqam Formation. The F Member consists mostly of terrigenous shale with minor graded beds of quartzose sandstone (Glennie *et al.* 1974, Watts & Garrison 1986). Both the slope deposits and the coarse quartzarenite turbidites of the Guwayza Sandstone record a relative drop of sea level at the Triassic−Jurassic boundary

leading to a widespread progradation of fluvial and coastal clastics across the Arabian shelf (Murris 1980). Much of the sand by-passed the margin and slope and was dumped in the submarine fans of the Guwayza Sandstone (Searle *et al.* 1983). On the Misfah platform, this sea-level drop may have interrupted the deposition of shallow-water carbonates before drowning occurred in connection with a subsequent sea level rise.

The Haliw Formation and its volcanic substrate are most probably derived from internally (oceanward) of the Baid/Misfah platforms (Umar Basin of Béchennec (1988)). According to Béchennec (1988), this basin developed not later than in Middle to Late Triassic times and was the site of essentially radiolaritic sedimentation throughout its Mesozoic history (Yanqul Formation of Bernoulli & Weissert 1987).

Palaeoceanography

Siliceous shales of member 1 and 2, radiolarian cherts and Halobia limestones provide a record of the oceanographic evolution of the Hawasina Basin (Fig. 8). Siliceous shales and radiolarites are poor in pelagic carbonate and are interpreted as deposits which accumulated below an elevated Triassic calcite compensation depth. Major element composition of the siliceous sediments is comparable to that of siliceous sediments of Late Triassic age accumulated in the Antalya Basin of SW Turkey (Robertson 1981). If plotted in a Al−Fe−Mn diagram or in a Si−Fe−Mn diagram (Karpoff *et al.* 1989), most of the analysed sediments are chemically comparable to siliceous deposits of hemipelagic environments (Steinberg & Mpodozis Marin, 1978) or to deposits of productive marginal basins such as the Gulf of California (Calvert 1966). Geological arguments confirm that the Hawasina Basin can be considered as a marginal basin of a newly forming Tethys ocean.

Siliceous sediments deposited below a shallow CCD vary in their radiolarian content and in their content of early diagenetic dolomite. While radiolarians in siliceous shales are rare or absent, they are present as rock-forming elements in the radiolarites of member 3 of the Zulla Formation. Conditions favourable for the formation of early diagenetic dolomite in originally laminated sediments existed during the deposition of siliceous shales of member 2. These dolomites could be compared with dolomites formed in anoxic diatomaceous and carbonate-poor sediments of the Gulf of California, where low sulphate concentrations, high alkalinity and Mg/Ca-ratios of at least 5:1

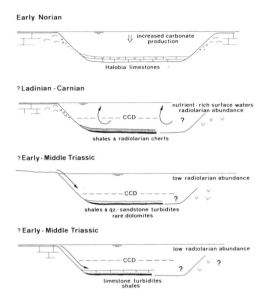

Fig. 8. Schematic diagram illustrating the oceanographic evolution of the Triassic Hawasina Basin.

seem to favour diagenetic dolomitisation (Kelts & McKenzie 1982). Lamination may indicate absence of a benthic fauna in episodically oxygen depleted bottom waters in the small Hawasina Basin.

Fluctuations in radiolarian content and in occurrence of dolomite may indicate changing conditions in Hawasina palaeoceanography. Radiolarites are commonly associated with upwelling conditions in marginal basins and high nutrient levels in surface waters (e.g. Jenkyns & Winterer 1982; Hein & Parrish 1987). The Carnian to Norian radiolarites could, therefore, be interpreted as deposits formed under elevated nutrient concentrations in upwelling waters of the Hawasina Ocean. Siliceous shales with dolomites indicating periodic low oxygen or anoxic bottom water conditions could have formed at times of restricted vertical circulation and lower nutrient levels in surface water. The widespread occurrence of Carnian–Norian radiolarites is remarkable; they occur not only in the Tethys realm (e.g. Robertson 1981), but also in marginal basins of the Pacific Ocean as preserved in the accreted terranes along Baja California (Rangin *et al.* 1981) and in Alaska (Murchey *et al.* 1983). Other chert occurrences of Middle to Late Triassic age are reported from Japan (Sugisaki *et al.* 1982) and from various localities in southeast Asia (Tan 1983). Whether the widespread occurrence of siliceous

deposits during the Middle to Late Triassic reflects specific oceanographic conditions with elevated nutrient levels, remains to be determined by further investigations (see Hein & Parrish 1987; Jones & Murchey 1986).

The Hawasina Basin, with its postulated high productivity during the time of radiolarian ooze formation (comparable to present-day Gulf of California or Sea of Ochotsk (Calvert 1966; Jenkyns & Winterer 1982) and with periods of poorly oxygenated bottom waters as indicated by the laminated dolomites, experienced further oceanographic changes during the Early Norian. Siliceous pelagic sediments were replaced by carbonates signalling a deepening of the CCD. A change in marine phyto- and zooplankton and the associated change in the CCD may reflect a change in surface-water productivity and/or in deep water oxygenation. Decreased nutrient levels could have led to a diminution of the siliceous zooplankton ultimately allowing the growth of carbonate secreting phyto- and zooplankton. Alternatively increased introduction of periplatform ooze could have affected the position of the CCD. However, such changes in pelagic facies seem not restricted to marginal basins of the Tethyan seaway. A similar replacement of Carnian–Norian chert by Norian limestones has been reported from the Baja California sequence mentioned above (Rangin *et al.* 1981). Whether this change in pelagic facies reflects a change in basin-shelf carbonate fractionation or regional or global changes in oceanic nutrient levels, remains open for debate.

Comparisons with other areas

Triassic deep water deposits, pelagic limestones, radiolarian cherts, carbonate turbidites and submarine volcanics, are known from many places along the Alpine–Himalayan chain (Bernoulli & Jenkyns 1974). They document the existence of deeper basins between the extensive carbonate platforms bordering the Gondwanian margin of Palaeotethys. Some of these basins were quite small and short-lived, but others were more extensive and permanent and persisted throughout the Mesozoic. Discontinuously preserved remnants of such basins can be traced from the Hawasina Basin of Oman through the Pichakun Zone of Iran (Ricou 1976), Cyprus (Mamonia Complex: Lapierre 1975), southern Turkey (Antalaya nappes: Dumont *et al.* 1972), and Greece (Pindos: Fleury 1980), to southern Italy (Lagonegro Zone: Scandone 1967; Wood 1981) and Sicily (Sclafani Zone: Broquet *et al.* 1966; Monti Sicani: Mascle

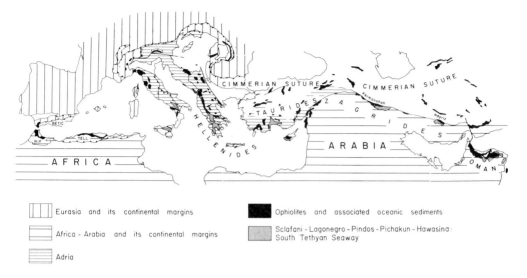

Fig. 9. Occurrences of remnants of the South Tethyan seaway.

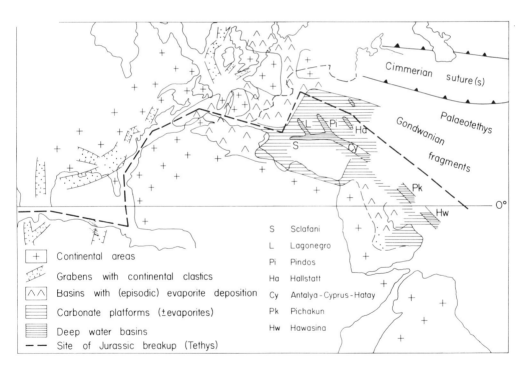

Fig. 10. Tentative palinspastic restoration of the Late Triassic palaeogeography of the Atlantic-Tethyan system showing the deep water basins of the South Tethyan seaway.

1967) (Fig. 9). Together they record the existence of a Triassic seaway along the northern margin of Gondwana (Fig. 10; cf. Scandone 1975).

The sediments of these Permian and Triassic basins invariably have been sheared off their substratum and their basement is unknown. However, a strong similarity between the different basins exists not only in terms of facies, but also of time—space relationships. Permian radiolarites in Sicily (Catalano *et al.* 1988a,b) and in the Hawasina sequence (Béchennec 1988; Blendinger *et al.* 1990) show that the basins existed already in Permian times. Deep water clastics with intercalated megabreccias and olistoliths of Permian shallow-water limestones are described from the Middle Triassic to Lower Carnian sequences of the Sicani Mountains of Sicily (Mascle 1967), the Lagonegro Zone of Southern Italy (Donzelli & Crescenti 1970) and the Hawasina Basin (Béchennec 1988). The Late Triassic sequences typically are composed of pelagic limestones characterized by the thin-shelled bivalve *Halobia* and, in some cases, by radiolarites.

The onset of Mesozoic radiolarite deposition is highly diachronous along the South Tethyan seaway (De Wever & Dercourt 1985): Early Jurassic in Sicily and in the Pindos, possibly Late Norian in parts of the Lagonegro Zone and Ladinian to Early Carnian in the Hawasina Basin. This diachroneity of facies might be due to differences in the bathymetric (subsidence) and/or oceanographic evolution of the basins.

The volcanics associated with the S-Tethyan seaway are typically alkalic to MORB-type basalts (Robertson 1986; Béchennec 1988). The narrow seaway has therefore been interpreted as the result of early rifting of the North Gondwanian margin. How much oceanic crust and lithosphere were already generated in the Triassic remains uncertain.

We sincerely thank his majesty Sultan Qaboos and the people of Oman for their great hospitality and especially the Ministry of Petroleum and minerals. We are grateful for the financial support, given by Amoco Oman Petroleum Company through the Earth Sciences and Resource Institute of South Carolina (ESRI) for field studies in the Oman project, headed by John D. Smewing. We thank B. Gruber for the determination of the Halobias and R. E. Garrison, A. H. F. Robertson, J. D. Smewing, T. Tozer and K. F. Watts for cooperation in the field and stimulating discussions. The paper was reviewed by F. Béchennec, R. E. Garrison, H. C. Jenkyns, J. D. Smewing, and K. F. Watts. The paper is published with the permission of Amoco Production Company.

References

BECHENNEC, F. 1988. *Géologie des nappes Hawasina dans les parties orientale et centrale des montagnes d'Oman*. Editions Bureau de Recherches Géologiques et Minières, document 127.

——, LE METOUR, J., RABU, D., BOURDILLON-DE-GRISSAL, Ch., DE WEVER, P., BEURRIER, M. &

VILLEY, M. 1990. The Hawasina Nappes: stratigraphy, palaeogeography and structural evolution of a fragment of the southern Tethyan passive continental margin. *In*: ROBERTSON, A. H. F., SEARLE, M. P. & RIES, A. C. (eds) *The Geology and Tectonics of the Oman Region*. Geological Society, London, Special Publication, **49**, 213–223.

BERNOULLI, D. & JENKYNS, H. C. 1974. Alpine, Mediterranean and central Atlantic Mesozoic facies in relation to the early evolution of the Tethys, *In*: DOTT, R. H. & SHAVER, R. H. (eds) *Modern and ancient geosynclinal evolution*. Society of economic Paleontologists and Mineralogists, Special Publication, **19**, 129–160.

—— & WEISSERT, H. 1987. The upper Hawasina nappes in the central Oman Mountains: stratigraphy, palinspastics and sequence of nappe emplacement. *Geodinamica Acta*, **1**, 47–58.

BEURRIER, M., BECHENNEC, F., RABU, D. & HUTIN, G. 1986. Rustaq sheet NF 40–3D. Geological map of Oman 1:100′000. Explanatory Notes. Directorate General of Minerals, Masqat, Oman.

BLENDINGER, W., VAN VLIET, A. & HUGHES CLARKE, M. W. 1990. Updoming, rifting and continental margin development during the Late Palaeozoic in northern Oman. *In*: ROBERTSON, A. H. F, SEARLE, M. P. & RIES, A. C. (eds) *The Geology and Tectonics of the Oman Region*. Geological Society, London, Special Publication **49**, 27–37.

BOUMA, A. H. 1962. Sedimentology of some flysch deposits: A graphic approach to facies interpretation. Elsevier, Amsterdam.

BROQUET, P., CAIRE, A. & MASCLE, G. 1966. Structure et évolution de la Sicile occidentale (Madonies et Sicani). *Bulletin de la Société Géologique de France* **(7)8**, 994–1013.

CALVERT, S. 1966. Accumulation of diatomaceous silica in the sediments of the Gulf of California. *Bulletin of the Geological Society of America*, **77**, 569–596.

CATALANO, R., DI STEFANO, P. & KOZUR, H. 1988a. First evidence of Lower Permian Albaillellacea (Radiolaria) in the Tethyan Eurasia. *Società Geologica Italiana, Atti 74° Congresso Nazionale*, **A**, 119–123.

——, ——, & —— 1988b. New results in the Permian and Triassic stratigraphy of Sicily with special reference to the section at Torrente San Calogero SW of the Pietra di Salomone (Sosio Valley). *Società Geologica Italiana, Atti 74° Congresso Nazionale* **A**, 126–135.

COOPER, D. J. W. 1987. Hamrat Duru Group: revised stratigraphy of a Mesozoic deep-water passive margin in the Oman Mountains. *Geological Magazine*, **124**, 157–164.

DE WEVER, P. & DERCOURT, J. 1985. Les Radiolaires triasico-jurassiques: marqueurs stratigraphiques et paléogéographiques dans les chaînes alpines périméditerranéennes: une revue. *Bulletin de la Société Géologique de France*, **(8)1**, 653–662.

DONZELLI, G. & CRESCENTI, U. 1970. Segnalazione di una microbiofacies permiana, probabilmente rimaneggiata, nella formazione di M. Facito

(Lucania occidentale). *Bollettino della Società dei Naturalisti in Napoli*, **79**, 3−19.

DUMONT, J. F., GUTNIC, M., MARCOUX, J., MONOD, O. & POISSON, A. 1972. Le Trias des Taurides occidentales (Turquie). Définition du bassin pamphylien: Un nouveau domaine à ophiolithes à la marge externe de la chaîne taurique. *Zeitschrift der Deutschen Geologischen Gesellschaft*, **123**, 385−409.

FLEURY, J.-J. 1980. *Les zones de Gavrovo-Tripolitza et du Pinde-Olonos (Grèce continentale et Péloponnèse du Nord). Evolution d'une plateforme et d'un bassin dans leur cadre alpin.* Société Géologique du Nord. Villeneuve d'Ascq, Publication 4.

GEALEY, W. K. 1977. Ophiolite obduction and geologic evolution of the Oman Mountains and adjacent areas. *Bulletin of the Geological Society of America*, **88**, 1183−1191.

GLENNIE, K. W., BOEUF, M. G. A., HUGHES CLARKE, M. W., MOODY-STUART, M., PILAAR, W. F. & REINHARDT, B. M. 1974. Geology of the Oman Mountains. *Verhandelingen van het Koninklijk Nederlands geologisch mijnbouwkundig Genootschap*, **31**, 1−423.

HEIN, J. R. & PARRISH, J. T. 1987. Distribution of siliceous deposits in space and time. In: HEIN J. R. (ed.), Siliceous sedimentary rock-hosted ores and petroleum. Evolution of ore fields series. Van Nostrand Reinhold Company, New York, 10−57.

HUTIN, G., BÉCHENNEC, F., BEURRIER, M. & RABU, D. 1986. *Birkat al Mawz. Sheet NF40-7B. Geological Map of Oman 1:100 000*. Directorate General of Minerals, Masqat, Oman.

JENKYNS, H. C. & WINTERER, E. L. 1982. Palaeooceanography of Mesozoic ribbon radiolarites. *Earth and Planetary Science Letters*, **60**, 351−375.

JONES, D. L. & MURCHEY, B. 1986. Geologic significance of Paleozoic and Mesozoic chert. *Annual Review of Earth and Planetary Sciences*, **14**, 455−492.

KELTS, K. & McKENZIE, J. 1982. Diagenetic dolomite formation in Quaternary anoxic diatomaceous muds of Deep Sea Drilling Project Leg 64, Gulf of California. In: CURRAY, J. R., MOORE, D. G. et al. Initial Reports of the Deep Sea Drilling Project 64/2, U.S. Government Printing Office, Washington 553−569.

LAPIERRE, H. 1975. Les formations sédimentaires et éruptives des nappes de Mamonia et leurs relations avec le massif du Troodos (Chypre occidentale). *Mémoires de la Société Géologique de France* **(54)123**, 1−132.

MASCLE, G. 1967. Remarques stratigraphiques et structurales sur la région de Palazzo-Adriano, monts Sicani (Sicile). *Bulletin de la Société géologique de France*, **(7)9**, 104−110.

MURCHEY, B., JONES, D. L. & HOLDSWORTH, B. K. 1983. Distribution, age, and depositional environments of radiolarian chert in western North America. In: IIJIMA, A., HEIN, J. R. & SIEVER, R. (eds.), Siliceous deposits in the Pacific Ocean. *Developments in Sedimentology*, **36**, 109−126.

Elsevier, Amsterdam.

MURRIS, R. J. 1980. Middle East: Stratigraphic evolution and oil habitat. *Bulletin of the American Association of Petroleum Geologists*, **64**, 597−618.

RANGIN, C., STEINBERG, M. & BONNOT-COURTOIS, C. 1981. Geochemistry of the Mesozoic bedded cherts of Central Baja California (Vizcaino-Cedros-San Benito): implications for paleogeographic reconstruction of an old oceanic basin. *Earth and Planetary Science Letters*, **54**, 313−322.

RICOU, L.-E. 1976. Evolution structurale des Zagrides. La région clef de Neyriz (Zagros Iranien). *Mémoires de la Société Géologique de France*, **125**, 1−140.

ROBERTSON, A. H. F. 1981. Metallogenesis on a Mesozoic passive continental margin, Antalya Complex, southwest Turkey. *Earth and Planetary Science Letters*, **54**, 323−345.

—— 1986. Geochemical evidence for the origin of Late Triassic melange units in the Oman Mountains as a small basin formed by continental rifting. *Earth and Planetary Science Letters*, **77**, 318−332.

SCANDONE, P. 1967. Studi di geologia lucana: la serie calcareo-silico-marnosa e i suoi rapporti con l'Appennino calcareo. *Bollettino della Società dei Naturalisti in Napoli*, **76**, 3−175.

—— 1975. Triassic seaways and the Jurassic Tethys Ocean in the central Mediterranean area. *Nature* **256/5513**, 117−119.

SEARLE, M. P. & GRAHAM, G. M. 1982. 'Oman Exotics'−Oceanic carbonate build-ups associated with the early stages of continental rifting. *Geology*, **10**, 43−49.

——, JAMES, N. P., CALON, T. J. & SMEWING, J. D. 1983. Sedimentological and structural evolution of the Arabian continental margin in the Musandam Mountains and Dibba zone, United Arab Emirates. *Geological Society of America Bulletin*, **94**, 1381−1440.

——, LIPPARD, S. J., SMEWING, J. D. & REX, D. C. 1980. Volcanic rocks beneath the Semail ophiolite nappe in the northern Oman Mountains and their significance in the Mesozoic evolution of Tethys. *Journal of the Geological Society of London*, **137**, 589−604.

STEINBERG, M. & MPODOZIS MARIN, C. 1978. Classification géochimique des radiolarites et des sédiments siliceux océaniques, signification paléo-océanographique. *Oceanologica Acta*, **1**, 359−367.

SUGISAKI, R., YAMAMOTO, K. & ADACHI, M. 1982. Triassic bedded cherts in central Japan are not pelagic. *Nature*, **298**, 644−647.

TAN, D. N. K. 1983. Cherts of southeast Asia. In: IIJIMA, A., HEIN, J. R. & SIEVER, R. (eds.), Siliceous deposits in the Pacific Ocean. *Developments in Sedimentology* **36**, 79−92. Elsevier, Amsterdam.

WATTS, K. F. & GARRISON, R. E. 1986. Sumeini Group, Oman — Evolution of a Mesozoic carbonate slope on a South Tethyan continental margin. *Sedimentary Geology*, **48**, 107–168.

WOOD, A. W. 1981. Extensional tectonics and the birth of the Lagonegro Basin (Southern Italian Appennines). *Neues Jahrbuch für Geologie und Paläontologie, Abhandlungen*, **161**, 93–131.

Triassic ammonoids from Jabal Safra and Wadi Alwa, Oman, and their significance

E. T. TOZER[1] & T. J. CALON[2]

[1] *Geological Survey of Canada, Department of Energy Mines and Resources, 601 Booth Street, Ottawa, Ontario, K1A OE8, Canada*
[2] *Department of Earth Sciences, Memorial University of Newfoundland, St. John's, Newfoundland, A1B 3X5, Canada*

Abstract: Triassic ammonoids are recorded from Jabal Safra and Wadi Alwa, Oman. Most or all are from olistoliths. The ammonoids from Jabal Safra are of Early Triassic (Smithian and Spathian) age and are from metre-sized blocks in the Jurassic Guwayza Formation. Those from Wadi Alwa are from blocks ranging from metre- to more than decimetre-size and are Early Triassic (Smithian and Spathian), Middle Triassic (Anisian) and Late Triassic (Norian).

The Early and Middle Triassic ammonoids from both localities are in dense, highly fossiliferous, commonly red limestone where they occur to the exclusion of all other macrofossils. The facies is that of the Hallstatt Limestone which is known from many localities, all in the Tethys. The Late Triassic ammonoids are in a red argillaceous limestone like the Ammonitico Rosso, another characteristic facies in Tethys.

The occurrences at Jabal Safra are in the Hawasina allochthon. The olistoliths evidently came from the east, not from the platform to the west. Seamounts east of the main Hawasina depocentre seem the most likely source for all the Triassic blocks.

Thanks mainly to the work of Glennie *et al.* (1974), it is now known that the Oman Mountains preserve an unusually significant record for the Late Palaeozoic and Mesozoic history of the south margin of Tethys. In general, to the northeast of the Arabian Platform, belts of sedimentation indicate progressively more oceanward sedimentation (Robertson 1987). Today the sequences are tectonically stacked in a series of nappes that were thrust to the southwest. These thrust sheets are overlain by the Semail ophiolite (Fig. 1).

Triassic carbonate rocks occur in the autochthonous and parautochthonous platform sequence (Glennie *et al.* 1974). Triassic rocks have also been recognized in the nappes that lie between the platform sequence and the ophiolite. The lowest nappe is composed of the Sumeini Group of Permian to Cretaceous age. The Triassic part is interpreted as a carbonate slope deposit (Watts & Garrison 1986). Tectonically higher are the Hawasina nappes. The principal rock unit of these nappes is the Hamrat Duru Group. As currently interpreted this is a Triassic to Cretaceous deep-water passive margin sequence (Cooper 1987; Bernoulli & Weissert 1987). Still higher in the tectonic stack is the melange (Haybi Complex) in which the Oman exotics occur. Some of the exotic blocks are Triassic in a carbonate reef facies (Glennie

et al. 1974). These are interpreted as oceanic carbonate build-ups (Searle & Graham 1982). In the interpretation of Béchennec *et al.* (1988) the topmost nappes below the Semail ophiolite include Triassic radiolarites, indicating a basin offshore from the site of the carbonate build-ups.

Macrofossils recorded from the platfom sequence include Late Triassic corals and brachiopods, also megalodonts and other benthonic bivalves (Blanford 1872; Diener 1908; Lees 1928; Hudson 1960; Hudson & Jefferies 1961). The faunas of the Sumeini Group and the Hamrat Duru Group include pelagic bivalves. Ladinian *Daonella* has been recorded from the Sumeini (N. J. Silberling in Watts & Garrison 1986); Norian *Halobia* from the Hamrat Duru (B. Gruber in Bernoulli & Weissert 1987). Corals and megalodonts occur in the Oman exotics (Searle & Graham 1982).

It seems that macrofossils are rare in the slope and deep-water deposits but Radiolaria are known (e.g. C. D. Blome in Watts & Garrison 1986; Béchennec 1988; Béchennec 1990).

The Triassic faunas recorded in this paper from Jabal Safra and Wadi Alwa are entirely different from all those mentioned above. They comprise ammonoids of Early, Middle and Late Triassic age. All from Jabal Safra are Early

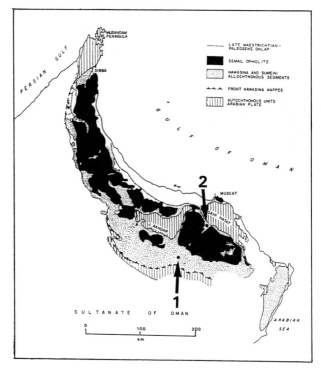

Fig. 1. Sketch map of Oman Mountains showing main geological elements, position of Jabal Safra (1) and Wadi Alwa (2). Modified from Glennie *et al.* (1974) and Gealey (1977).

Triassic (Smithian and Spathian). Early, Middle and Late Triassic faunas have been recognized at Wadi Alwa.

The Early and Middle Triassic ammonoids occur in great abundance in very fine-grained limestone, mostly red, but in part grey or green. No other macrofossils are present. The colour, nature of the matrix, and abundance of ammonoids is the facies of the Hallstatt limestone. This distinctive facies is known only in the Tethys, with occurrences in a belt extending from Austria to Timor, through Yugoslavia, Rumania, Greece, Albania, Chios, Cyprus, Turkey and southern Tibet. At many of these places the rock is manganiferous, the individual ammonoids having a thin coating of a black manganese mineral. The presence of this coating produces natural fractures making it relatively easy to extract the fossils in good, often perfect condition. At the Oman localities the ammonoids lack this manganese coating. This is unfortunate because it has so far proved impossible to extract well preserved specimens from the unweathered rock. Virtually all the determinable ammonoids have been obtained from naturally weathered surfaces.

Most or all of the Oman occurrences are in olistoliths. Many of the Hallstatt limestones of other localities in the Tethys are now known to be olistoliths. This is so in Tibet (Heim & Gansser 1939), Timor (Audley-Charles 1965) and Greece (Krystyn & Mariolakos 1975; Baumgartner 1985). Some of the occurrences of Hallstatt rock at Hallein, near the type area in Austria, are now interpreted as detached blocks, with the detachment and movement related to salt diapirism (Plöchinger 1984). Hallstatt rocks are seldom if ever found in well ordered stratigraphic sequences.

The Hallstatt facies is generally interpreted as a pelagic deposit laid down far from any source of terrigenous sediment. Close juxtaposition of ammonoid zones is the general rule and indicates very low rates of sedimentation. The depth at which Hallstatt rocks formed has long been debated. A summary of views up to about 1970 is given in Tozer (1971). In that account a deep water environment was suggested but the arguments favouring deposition at about 200 m, as on seamounts, seem to be strongest (e.g. Jenkyns 1970).

The Late Triassic rocks of Wadi Alwa are also

Fig. 2. Southwesterly view of north side of Jabal Safra showing exposure of Guwayza Formation. There are several olistoliths on the upper slope, between the two cliffs. The white blocks to the left are probably of Permian age (cf. Béchennec 1988). The Triassic olistoliths (Blocks 2 & 3), below the point of the arrow, are less conspicuous. Geological Survey of Canada photo. 204144–A.

red, but are different from the Hallstatt-type limestones, being nodular and of a marly nature. From a lithofacies standpoint these rocks are more comparable with the 'Ammonitico Rosso'. The Ammonitico Rosso facies, like the Hallstatt, is restricted to the Tethys but the typical occurrences are Jurassic, not Triassic. The environment indicated by this facies was probably not exactly like that of the Halltstatt limestones, but was perhaps influenced by the presence of fine-grained terrigenous sediment.

Description of localities

Localities at Wadi Alwa were found in the winter of 1980–1981 by members of an expedition organized by Imperial College, London. The party included G. Loftus and G. Nichols. No report has been published but in an unpublished account, available at Imperial College, it is recorded that they collected ammonoids which were recognized as Triassic by D. T. Donovan. They made the apt comparison between the beds they had discovered and the Ammonitico Rosso. The Jabal Safra locality was discovered by T. J. Calon and C. Lee in 1983. In 1984 the writers spent three days studying Jabal Safra and three at Wadi Alwa.

Jabal Safra

Jabal Safra (Figs 1 & 2) is about 150 km southwest of Muscat (Sheet NF-40–072, Birkat Al Mawz, 1:100 000). The ammonoid-bearing oli-

stoliths occur in the Hamrat Duru Group (Glennie *et al.* 1974; Copper 1987). The most recent account of this locality is by Béchennec (1988) who assigns the beds in which the olistoliths occur to the Guwayza Formation, dated as Bathonian–Kimmeridgian. Béchennec described and illustrated olistoliths of Permian age, but not Triassic. The discovery of olistoliths with Early Triassic ammonoids was made by Calon and Lee.

The olistoliths studied in detail occur in a belt extending along the strike for about 3 km. They appear to be restricted to a stratigraphic thickness of less than 50 m. The olistoliths studied are of Hallstatt facies. Others, of light coloured limestone (Fig. 2), similar to the one illustrated by Béchennec (1988), were not investigated.

Ammonoids were observed in seven blocks. All are Early Triassic. Numbers given below in parentheses refer to field numbers for ammonoid and conodont collections that will be described in the future.

Block 1. This is the westernmost, at UTM EA 807127. Width about 2 m, stratigraphic thickness, 1 m. Undetermined ammonoids (104A) 30 cm above lower surface.

Block 2. UTM EA 839125. 80 cm red limestone with *Pseudaspenites layeriformis* (Welter) (106A); 33 cm grey limestone with *Paranannites* sp.. (106B); 26 cm grey limestone, no fossils observed.

Block 3. Near Block 2, also UTM EA 839125. This was the block discovered by Calon and Lee in 1983 and studied again in 1984. Stratigraphic thickness is 3.5 m, with stratification parallel to that of surrounding Guwayza beds. Width, 2–5 m. Limestone is well stratified, mottled a red and grey with very numerous ammonoids throughout. *Procarnites kokeni* Arthaber (103A), was collected 35 cm from upper surface. No determinable fossils were extracted from the lower levels.

Blocks 4A–4D. About 300 m east of blocks 2 and 3, UTM EA 842125. Ammonoids were seen in four blocks of red, orange and grey limestone, designated 'A' to 'D'. Each block is about 1 × 1 × 1 m. They lie close together and may be the broken pieces of one larger block.

(a) The weathered surface of block 'A' (109A) shows moderately well preserved ammonoids. It proved impossible to extract them in good condition. Genera probably present: *Pseudosageceras, Paranannites* and *Aspenites.*

(b) Block 'B' (109B): *Gyronites?* sp., *Wyomingites* sp., *Pseudaspidites* cf. *wheeleri* Kummel and Steele, *Aspenites* sp., *Paranannites* sp.

Fig. 3. Easterly view across Wadi Alwa. The bed of the Wadi is below the cliffs which are about 2 km distant. The goat is on the near side of the Wadi. Position of Wadi Alwa I is indicated. Wadi Alwa II is on the lower slope, to the right of the illustration. Wadi Alwa III and IV are not visible, being on the far side of the ridge. Drawing by Carrie Bolton from illustration in Blendinger (1988, Fig. 3).

(c) Block 'C' (112C): *Meekoceras* cf. *indoau-stralicum* Wanner.
(d) Block 'D' (113D): *Paranannites* sp.

Ridge north of Wadi Alwa

This locality (Figs 1 & 3) is about 50 km south of Muscat (sheet NF-40−039 Wadi Tayin, 1: 100 000). Ammonoids were first discovered here by the Imperial College party in 1980−1981. It is a complex area which has not yet been adequately described and mapped. Blendinger (1988, Fig. 3) has published a photograph of the ridge which serves to indicate the position of our localities (see Fig. 3). Our own general observations at this locality were cursory, most of the time being spent searching for ammonoids. The outcrops in the bed of the wadi and on parts of the ridge are of breccia in which there are blocks from grapefruit to house-size. Blocks of several different lithologies are present. Some are of red Hallstatt-type limestone but there are also blocks of grey Permian limestone with verbeekinid Foraminifera, dark chert and amygdaloidal lava. In the time available it was not possible to determine the nature of the matrix. Where this breccia lies in relation to other Hawasina units is uncertain but it is probably fairly high in the tectonic sequence.

Triassic ammonoids were collected from four different places (Wadi Alwa I−IV).
Wadi Alwa I. This, the largest mass of Triassic rock, is near the summit of the ridge (Fig. 3). The maximum dimension is at least 100 m. It is tabular preserving about 25 m of strata, mostly red limestone. The strata dip easterly at a low angle. At the north end of the outcrop bedding planes are covered with ammonoids, with most of the phragmocone preserved as white calcite,

the remainder as red limestone. Most of the ammonoids are too poorly preserved for identification. A few determinable specimens had weathered free (117A). They include *Flemingites* cf. *griesbachi* Krafft and *Hedenstroemia* cf. *himalayica* (Spath).

Near the south extremity of this occurrence the beds form a small bluff where a sequence of three ammonoid beds (118A,B,C) was determined in a stratigraphic thickness of about 25 m.
(1) 118C: *Japonites subacutus* Welter (Lower Anisian). (Stratigraphic separation, about 15 m).
(2) 118B: *Procarnites kokeni* Arthaber (Spathian) (Stratigraphic separation about 10 m).
(3) 118A: *Hedenstroemia* sp., *Aspenites* sp. (Smithian).
The ammonoid sequence shows that the beds range in age from Smithian to Anisian and that they are not inverted.
Wadi Alwa II. This is a small block with dimensions measurable in metres rather than tens of metres, found low on the ridge (Fig. 3). The following rather poorly preserved ammonoids (114B) of Middle Triassic age were collected from the surface of this block: *Ptychites* cf. *rectangularis* Kraus, *Proarcestes* sp. indet., *Monophyllites sphaerophyllus* (Hauer).
Wadi Alwa III. This block is on the southeast face of the ridge, about halfway to the summit, about 1 km above the Wadi (Fig. 3). About 5 metres of red and orange highly fossiliferous limestone is exposed. Bedding is inclined SE at a steep angle. Smithian ammonoids were collected from three levels, as follows:
(1) 120A: *Ussuria* sp. indet. (Stratigraphic separation about 2 m).

(2) 120B: *Kashmirites*? cf. *oyensi* Welter, *Submeekoceras* sp., *Owenites* cf. *koeneni* Hyatt and Smith, *Owenites* cf. *egrediens* Welter, *Pseudosageceras* sp. (Stratigraphic separation about 3 m).
(3) 120C: *Hedenstroemia* sp. indet.

120C appears to be in the stratigraphically highest position but the fauna is the oldest, indicating that the beds are overturned.

Wadi Alwa IV. This locality provided the only Late Triassic fossils. It is also on the southeast side of the ridge, at a higher elevation than III. Strata are inclined southeast at a steep angle. About 4 m of red limestone with *Heterastridium* and *Rhacophyllites* sp. (121A), to the southeast, are adjacent to a covered interval of 10 m. Northwest of the covered interval are about 5 m of reddish strata adjacent to an undetermined thickness of grey limestone. At the southwest side of the 5 m of strata is a bed with abundant *Catenohalorites malayicus* (Welter) (121B). A talus collection from this bed yielded *Pinacoceras* sp. and *Leislingites welteri* (Diener) in addition to *Catenohalorites malayicus* (121T). As already mentioned, the rocks at this locality are more argillaceous than at the other localities, and more like the Ammonitico Rosso than the Hallstatt limestone.

Age and correlation of the ammonoid faunas

Table 1 gives a Triassic Time Scale and shows the age of the Oman ammonoid faunas. Faunas of Early, Middle and Late Triassic age have been recognized. Some faunas can be dated very precisely, others less so. All the Oman faunas have been recognized previously in the Hallstatt facies of Tethys at one or more localities.

At present it is impossible to express precisely the ages of the Smithian faunas in terms of a Tethyan zonal scheme. All dated as Smithian fall within the *Hedenstroemia himalayica* Zone of Table 1. Two or three zones will probably be recognized within this interval and the Oman data may contribute to their recognition. In this paper they are designated Smithian 1, 2 and 3. Smithian 1, the oldest, is characterized by *Hedenstroemia* and *Flemingites*. It is represented at Wadi Alwa I (117A, 118A) and Wadi Alwa III (120C). Smithian 3, the youngest, characterized by *Owenites* also occurs at Wadi Alwa III (120B). Those designated Smithian 2 are of an intermediate age and have affinity with the *Meekoceras gracilitatis* Zone of the western United States. The ammonoids from the eastern blocks at Jabal Safra (109A, 109B,

112C, 113D) probably indicate this age. A well preserved specimen of *Euflemingites* cf. *guyerdetiformis* (Welter) from Jebel Rahbah, in the Wadi Alwa area (Blendinger 1988) is probably Smithian 2. There remains some uncertainty regarding the exact relationship between Smithian 1 and Smithian 2. The Oman occurrences seem to indicate that they represent two early Smithian faunas of different ages. Faunas correlative with Smithian 1, 2 and 3 occur in the Hallstatt facies blocks of Timor, but no single block has all three. Timor and Oman are the only localities that have Smithian in Hallstatt facies.

The occurrences of *Procarnites kokeni* at Jabal Safra (103A) and Wadi Alwa I (118B) are Spathian, indicating a correlation with the *Tirolites cassianus* Zone of Tethys. Correlative beds in Hallstatt facies are known from Albania, Chios and Timor.

Two Middle Triassic faunas have been recognized. The bed with *Japonites subacutus* at Wadi Alwa I (118C) is Anisian, almost certainly Lower Anisian correlative with Lower Anisian beds in Hallstatt facies in Chios, the Kiogars (Tibet) and Timor. The small block, Wadi Aiwa II, is younger, probably upper Anisian or early Ladinian, probably correlative with some part of the Bulogkalk of Yugoslavia.

The fauna at Wadi Alwa IV with *Leislingites welteri* and *Catenohalorites malayicus* is correlated with the middle Norian Macer Zone (Tatzreiter 1981) but it is just possible that it is a trifle younger, of earliest upper Norian age. Previously known occurrences of the Macer Zone in Hallstatt facies are at Hallstatt, Timor and possibly also Cyprus.

Discussion

The Hallstatt-like rocks of Oman, as in other parts of Tethys, indicate a very slow rate of sedimentation, at sites far removed from any source of terrigenous sediment, at a depth inimical to the development of a benthonic fauna. This is best documented at Wadi Alwa I, where Smithian to Anisian time (about 15 Ma) is represented by about 25 m of red limestone in which the only macrofossils are cephalopods. The indicated rate of sedimentation is about 150 cm per Ma. Data from Greece given by Krystyn & Mariolakos (1975) for the Anisian through Carnian (about 17 Ma) deposit of Epidauros, Greece, about 20 m thick, indicates a rate of sedimentation, 118 cm per Ma, of the same order.

Wadi Alwa I represents a time span in Hallstatt facies (Smithian, Spathian, Lower

Table 1. Triassic Time Scale (Tozer 1984) showing the age of the Oman ammonoid faunas. The Middle Triassic fossils from Wadi Alwa II are not precisely dated. A long time span has not been established (see text).

Oman localities (with shaded time-span bars, left to right): Jabal Safra 2, 4 — Jabal Safra 3 — Wadi Alwa I — Wadi Alwa II — Wadi Alwa III — Wadi Alwa IV

SERIES	STAGE	SUBSTAGE	ZONES (*STRATOTYPE IN TETHYS, OTHERS IN NORTH AMERICA)	
UPPER TRIASSIC	NORIAN	Upper Norian	Choristoceras crickmayi / Cochloceras amoenum / Gnomohalorites cordilleranus	Choristoceras marshi*
		Middle Norian (Alaunian)	Himavatites columbianus / Drepanites rutherfordi	Halorites macer* / Himavatites hogarti* / Cyrtopleurites bicrenatus*
		Lower Norian	Juvavites magnus / Malayites dawsoni / Stikinoceras kerri	Malayites paulckei* / Guembelites jandianus*
	CARNIAN	Upper Carnian (Tuvalian)	Klamathites macrolobatus / Tropites welleri / Tropites dilleri	Anatropites beds* / Tropites subbullatus*
		Lower Carnian (Julian)	Austrotrachyceras obesum / Trachyceras desatoyense	Austrotrachyceras austriacum* / Trachyceras aonoides*
MIDDLE TRIASSIC	LADINIAN		Frankites sutherlandi / Maclearnoceras maclearni / Meginoceras meginae / Progonoceratites poseidon / Eoprotrachyceras subasperum	Protrachyceras archelaus* / Eoprotrachyceras curionii*
	ANISIAN	Upper Anisian (Illyrian)	Frechites chischa / Frechites deleeni / Frechites occidentalis / Parafrechites meeki / Gymnotoceras rotelliformis	Ticinites polymorphus* / Paraceratites trinodosus*
		Middle Anisian (Pelsonian)	Anagymnotoceras varium / Balatonites shoshonensis / Acrochordiceras hyatti	"Paraceratites" binodosus* / Anagymnotoceras ismidicum* / Nicomedites osmani*
		Lower Anisian (Aegean)	Lenotropites caurus	
LOWER TRIASSIC	SPATHIAN		Keyserlingites subrobustus / "Olenekites" pilaticus / Neopopanoceras haugi / Subcolumbites beds / Columbites parisianus	Tirolites cassianus*
	NAMMALIAN	Smithian	Wasatchites tardas / Euflemingites romunderi	Anasibirites pluriformis* / Hedenstroemia hinalayica*
		Dienerian	Vavilovites sverdrupi / Proptychites candidus	Gyronites frequens*
	GRIESBACHIAN	Upper Griesbachian (Ellesmerian)	Proptychites strigatus / Ophiceras commune	Ophiceras connectens*
		Lower Griesbachian (Gangetian)	Otoceras boreale / Otoceras concavum	Otoceras woodwardi*

Anisian) unknown elsewhere at a single Tethys locality, although the individual faunas are known in Albania, Chios, Timor and Tibet. A sequence from Smithian to Anisian is known in Afghanistan (Kummel & Erben 1968; Ishii *et al*. 1971) but it is probably not in Hallstatt facies. The faunal record at Wadi Alwa I is not complete for the Smithian—Middle Triassic interval. As presently known there is no indication of late Smithian and latest Spathian. Whether these intervals are represented by diastems or by beds without fossils, is not known. The time span is nevertheless clear. Discovery of a new time span preserved in the Hallstatt facies is of some interest. It would seem that throughout the Tethys three stages is about the limit in any one block of uniform Hallstatt facies. Wadi Alwa I and Epidauros (Anisian through Carnian) seem to hold the record. These occurrences fit a model according to which the Hallstatt sediments were deposited on transient topographic highs at different places in the Tethys seaway. This is the model developed by Jenkyns & Torrens (1971) to account for the condensed beds in the Jurassic of Sicily which are of different inclusive ages at different localities. The evidence from Oman and Epidauros suggests that in the Triassic these highs may have persisted for 15—20 Ma.

The middle Norian rocks of Wadi Alwa IV, being so much younger and of a somewhat different facies compared with the Lower and Middle Triassic rocks of the other localities, were probably deposited in a somewhat different situation but probably also on a seamount.

The position of these Hallstatt-type rocks in the Oman stratigraphic and tectonic sequence poses some interesting questions. There is no doubt that Early Triassic limestones at Jabal Safra are small olistoliths in the Guwayza Formation of Jurassic age. This formation is on a nappe low in the Hawasina nappe complex. The tectonic and stratigraphic situation of the rocks at Wadi Alwa is uncertain. The smaller blocks (e.g. Wadi Alwa II) are presumably olistoliths but the large mass of Wadi Alwa I might be part of an ordered, although tectonized, stratigraphic sequence. However it is significant that the Smithian and Spathian rocks of Wadi Alwa are identical with those forming olistoliths at Jabal Safra. Rocks of this age, in this facies, are unknown elsewhere in Oman. The limestones of Wadi Alwa are much larger masses than those at Jabal Safra. The identical age and facies of the Early Triassic rocks at the two localities and the fact that rocks of this age and facies are unknown elsewhere in Oman suggests to Tozer that they were originally part of a contiguous formation. In this interpretation the small Jabal Safra blocks would be distal olistolithic derivatives, which tumbled to the southeast from the same formation that makes the large masses at Wadi Alwa. Calon questions this interpretation in view of the fact that the localities are now 80 km apart, and that palinspastically they would have been even farther separated.

No Triassic rocks of Hallstatt facies are known in the Platform sequence or in the slope deposits (Sumeini Group). For this reason, coupled with the fact that the largest masses of Early Triassic limestone occur northeast of the smaller ones, it is virtually certain that the source of the Jabal Safra olistoliths was not the platform edge or slope.

Until now the best known occurrences of Triassic olistoliths in Oman have been in the Oman Exotics. Triassic rocks recorded include limestone with corals and megalodont bivalves (Searle & Graham 1982) indicating shallower water conditions compared with that of the Hallstatt-type sediment. Searle & Graham interpret the Triassic Oman Exotics as deposits of oceanic build-ups. These Exotics occur mostly in belts surrounding the Semail ophiolite nappe. This has been taken to indicate that they lie high in the tectonic pile, close to the Semail nappe. This places them higher in the tectonic sequence than the rocks with the best positioned Hallstatt-type limestones, those of Jebel Safra. The Lower Triassic limestones of Wadi Alwa, although identical with those of Jabal Safra, are not necessarily at the same level in the tectonic pile. Possibly the Oman Exotics and the pelagic Triassic limestones of Wadi Alwa are in a comparable tectonic situation.

The occurrences of Triassic pelagic limestone described in this paper contribute to understanding the Triassic palaeogeography of Oman and the south side of Tethys in general. As mentioned at the beginning of this paper, the occurrence in Oman of part of the Arabian Shield, with its platform cover, flanked to the northeast first by slope then by deepwater deposits, has already been documented. The pelagic limestones described in this paper where deposited farther out in the Tethys Sea, presumably on seamounts. The Triassic rocks in the Oman Exotics probably formed in a somewhat similar and possibly nearby situation, but on shallow water banks compared with the deeper seamounts where the Hallstatt sediment formed.

In this interpretation the Triassic rocks of Oman record sedimentation in at least five belts facing northeast, presumably progressively offshore in the Tethys seaway. Going oceanward they are: (1) the deposits of the platform; (2) the Sumeini deposits on the slope; which were bordered by (3) the sediments of the Hawasina basin. Farther offshore were (4) the seamounts. On the deeper seamounts red pelagic limestones formed; on the more shallow, the carbonate with megalodonts, now in the Oman Exotics. Outboard from the seamounts, in the interpretation of Béchennec *et al.* (1988) was (5) the deep Umar Basin, with Triassic radiolarites.

This interpretation of the rocks of Hallstatt facies seems compatible with the model proposed by Béchennec *et al.* and also by Robertson (1987) who refers to the marginal oceanic crust being 'littered with seamounts composed of Permian and Triassic carbonate build-ups and volcanic edifices'. Both Robertson and Béchennec *et al.* visualize the seamounts shedding olistoliths into the adjacent basins. This seems to provide a satisfactory explanation for the situation of the Oman pelagic limestones with Triassic ammonoids.

References

AUDLEY-CHARLES, M. G. 1965. A Miocene gravity slide deposit from eastern Timor. *Geological Magazine*, 102, 267–276.

BAUMGARTNER, P. O. 1985. Jurassic Sedimentary Evolution and Nappe Emplacement in the Argolis Peninsula (Peloponnesus, Greece). *Denkschriften der Schweizerischen Naturforschenden Gesellschaft*, 99.

BÉCHENNEC, F. 1988. Géologie des nappes Hawasina dans les parties orientales et centrale des montagnes d'Oman. *Documents du BRGM*, 127.

BÉCHENNEC, F., LE MÉTOUR, J., RABU, D., BOURDILLON-DE-GRISSAC, CH., DE WEVER, P., BEURRIER, M. & VILLEY M. 1990. The Hawasina nappes: stratigraphy and structural evolution of a fragment the South-Tethyan passive continental margin. *In*: ROBERTSON, A. H. F., SEARLE, M. P. & RIES, A. C. (eds) *The Geology and Tectonics of the Oman Region*. Geological Society, London, Special Publication, 49, 213–223.

——, LE MÉTOUR, J., RABU, D., VILLEY, M. & BEURRIER, M. 1988. The Hawasina Basin: A fragment of a starved passive continental margin, thrust over the Arabian Platform during obduction of the Sumail Nappe. *Tectonophysics*, 151, 323–343.

BERNOULLI, D. & WEISSERT, H. 1987. The upper Hawasina nappes in the central Oman Mountains: stratigraphy, palinspastics and sequence of nappe emplacement. *Geodinamica Acta* (Paris), 1(1), 47–58.

BLANFORD, W. T. 1872. Note on Maskat and Massandim on the East coast of Arabia. *Records of the Geological Survey of India*, 5(3), 75–77.

BLENDINGER, W. 1988. Permian to Jurassic Deep Water Sediments of the Eastern Oman Mountains: Their Significance for the Evolution of the Arabian Margin of the South Tethys. *Facies*, 19, 1–32.

COOPER, D. J. W. 1987. Hamrat Duru Group: revised stratigraphy of a Mesozoic deep-water passive margin in the Oman Mountains. *Geological Magazine*, 124(2), 157–164.

DIENER, C. 1908. Note on some fossils from the Sedimentary rocks of Oman (Arabia). *Records of the Geological Survey of India*, 36, 156–163.

GEALEY, W. K. 1977. Ophiolite obduction and geologic evolution of the Oman Mountains and adjacent areas. *Geological Society of America Bulletin*, 88, 1183–1191.

GLENNIE, K. W., BOEUF, M. G. A., HUGHES CLARKE, M. W., MOODY-STUART, M., PILAAR, W. F. H. & REINHARDT, B. M. 1974. Geology of the Oman Mountains. *Verhandelingen van het Koninklijk Nederlands geologisch mijnbouwkundig Genootschap*, 31.

HEIM, A. & GANSSER, A. 1939. Central Himalaya, geological observations of the Swiss expedition 1936. *Denkschriften der Schweizwerischen Naturforschenden Gesellschaft*, 73(1).

HUDSON, R. G. S. 1960. The Permian and Trias of the Oman Peninsula, Arabia. *Geological Magazine*, 97(4), 299–308.

—— & JEFFERIES, R. 1961. Upper Triassic brachiopods and lamellibranchs from Oman. *Palaeontology* 7(1), 1–41.

ISHII, K., FISCHER, J., BANDO, Y. 1971. Notes on the Permian–Triassic boundary in eastern Afghanistan. *Journal of Geosciences*, Osaka City University, 14(1), 1–18.

JENKYNS, H. C. 1970. The genesis of condensed sequences in the Tethyan Jurassic. *Lethaia*, 4, 327–352.

—— & TORRENS, H. S. 1971. Palaeogeographic Evolution of Jurassic Seamounts in Western Sicily. *Annales Instituti geologici publici Hungarici*, 54 (2), 91–104.

KRYSTYN, L. & MARIOLAKOS, I. 1975. Stratigraphie und Tektonik der Hallstatterkalk Scholle von Epidauros (Griechenland). *Sitzungberichte Oesterreichischen Akademie der Wissenschaften* I, 184, 181–195.

KUMMEL, B. & ERBEN, H. K. 1968. Lower and Middle Triassic Cephalopods from Afghanistan. *Palaeontographica A*, 129(4–6), 95–148.

LEES, G. M. 1928. The geology and tectonics of Oman and of parts of South-eastern Arabia. *Quarterly Journal of the Geological Society, London*, 84(4), 585–670.

PLÖCHINGER, B. 1984. Zum Nachweis jurassisch-kretazischer Eingleitungen von Hallstaetter Gesteinsmassen beiderseits des Salzach-Quertales (Salzburg). *Geologische Rundschau*, 73(1), 293–306.

ROBERTSON, A. H. F. 1987. The transition from a passive margin to an Upper Cretaceous foreland basin related to ophiolite emplacement in the Oman Mountains. *Geological Society of America Bulletin*, 99, 633–653.

SEARLE, M. P. & GRAHAM, G. M. 1982. 'Oman Exotics' — Oceanic carbonate build-ups associated with the early stages of continental rifting. *Geology*, **10**, 43−49.

TATZREITER, F. 1981. Ammonitenfauna und Stratigraphie im hoeheren Nor (Alaun, Trias) der Tethys aufgrund neuer Untersuchungen in Timor. *Denkschriften Oesterreichischen Akademie der Wissenschaften 1*, **121**.

TOZER, E. T. 1971. Triassic Time and Ammonoids: Problems and Proposals. *Canadian Journal of Earth Sciences*, **8**(8), 989−1031.

—— 1984. The Trias and its Ammonoids: the Evolution of a Time Scale. *Geological Survey of Canada Miscellaneous Report* **35**.

WATTS, K. F. 1987. Triassic carbonate submarine fans along the Arabian platform margin, Sumeini Group, Oman. *Sedimentology*, **34**, 43−71.

—— & GARRISON, R. E. 1986. Sumeini Group, Oman — Evolution of a Mesozoic carbonate slope on a south Tethyan continental margin. *Sedimentary Geology*, **48**, 107−168.

The Hawasina Nappes: stratigraphy, palaeogeography and structural evolution of a fragment of the south-Tethyan passive continental margin

F. BECHENNEC[1], J. LE METOUR[1], D. RABU[1], CH. BOURDILLON-DE-GRISSAC[1], P. DE WEVER[2], M. BEURRIER[1] & M. VILLEY[1]

[1] Service Géologique National, BRGM, BP 6009, 45060 Orléans Cédex, France)

[2] CNRS UA 319, Université Pierre et Marie Curie, T 15–16, 75252 Paris Cedex 05, France

Abstract: Lithostratigraphic and biostratigraphic revision of the Hawasina Nappes in the eastern and central Oman Mountains, including the redefinition of the Hamrat Duru Group and the definition of the three new groups, the Al Aridh, Kawr and Umar Groups, has led to a new interpretation of the palaeogeographic and structural evolution of the south-Tethyan continental margin. Margin history began in the Late Permian with a phase of extension and rifting, accompanied by considerable magmatic activity, and led to the development of the Hamrat Duru Basin separating the Arabian Platform to the south from the Baid Platform to the north. In the Middle to Late Triassic renewed extension led to rifting, again accompanied by important magmatic activity, with the break-up of the Baid Platform, and the development of the Al Aridh Trough, the Misfah Horst and the Umar Basin. These Permian and Triassic tectonic units together constituted the Hawasina Basin. A third phase of extension during the Late Tithonian–Berriasian caused a general foundering of the continental margin. The development of the Hawasina Basin terminated in the Santonian, when compression initiated the first stage of obduction that closed the basin. Ongoing obduction, during the Campanian, led to thrusting of the Hawasina and the Samail ophiolite nappes onto the Arabian Platform by gravitational mechanisms.

Mapping of the eastern and central parts of the Oman Mountains at the scale of 1:100 000 has led to a revision of the stratigraphy of the Hawasina Nappes including important changes with respect to the stratigraphy established by Glennie et al. (1974), and to a lesser degree that of Searle et al. (1980). Four lithostratigraphic groups (Table 1) have been either redefined (the Hamrat Duru Group) or newly defined (the Al Aridh, Kawr and Umar Groups; Béchennec 1987; De Wever et al. 1988, 1990), with the definition of various formations and members within the sedimentary and volcanic sequences constituting the groups (Béchennec 1987; Béchennec et al. 1988). These deposits were laid down between the Late Permian and the Early Senonian in the various morphostructural zones of the Hawasina Basin, which are, from the Arabian platform towards the internal zones, the Hamrat Duru Basin, the Baid (relict) Horst, the Al Aridh Trough, the Misfah Horst and the Umar Basin (Figs 1 & 2).

Palaeogeographic and structural evolution of the Hawasina Basin

Development of the Hamrat Duru Basin in the Late Permian

A phase of rifting and extension that commenced during the Murghabian (Late Permian) along the northern part of Gondwana resulted in the development of a broad intracontinental basin, the Hamrat Duru Basin, bounded to the southwest by the Arabian Platform and to the northeast by the Baid Platform.

Magmatic activity occurred during this phase along the margins of the two platforms (Saiq Formation, Le Métour 1987; Baid Formation, Béchennec 1987, Béchennec et al. 1988) and, in particular, in the developing basin, (the Lower Member of the Al Jil Fm, Béchennec et al. 1986a; Béchennec 1987). Volcanism was essentially alkaline, with minor transitional components, and characterizes an intraconti-

From ROBERTSON, A. H. F., SEARLE, M. P. & RIES, A. C. (eds), 1990,
The Geology and Tectonics of the Oman Region.
Geological Society Special Publication No 49, pp 213–223

213

Table 1. *Lithostratigraphy of the Hawasina Nappes. After Béchennec et al. (1988) modified.*

AGE	HAMRAT DURU GROUP	AL ARIDH GROUP	KAWR GROUP	UMAR GROUP
Late Turon.-early Sen.	Nayid Fm. Na (carbonate turbidite)		?	?
Late Cenomanian	Si_2C (silicified limestone) Si_2 (carbonate turbidite)	Musallah Fm. ArR (olistolith of platform carbonate) Ar_4V (andesite-granophyre) Ar_4C (radiolarite-breccia) Ar_4L (carbonate turbidite)	Safil Fm. Sf (micritic clayey limestone)	
Barremian	Sid* Fm. Si_1 (silicified limestone) Si_1L - Si_1LC (silicified limestone-micrite)	Al Ghafat Fm. Ar_3 (radiolarite-megabreccia) ArR (olistolith of platform carbonate)	Nadan Fm. Nd (micritic limestone, majolica)	Aqil Fm. UmL (micritic, sparry limestone) UmLC (micritic limestone-radiolarite) UmC (radiolarite-shale)
Tithonian-Berr. Dogger-Malm	Guwayza Fm. (Gw) (oolitic turbidite) GWR (olistolith of platform carbonate)	Buwaydah Fm. Ar_2 (radiolarite-megabreccia) Ar_2V (hyaloclastite-andesite)		UmR (olistolith of platform carbonate)
Lias	Mb_2C-Mb_2LC (radiolarite-carbonate turbidite) Mb_2St (siltstone-shale-sandstone turbidite) Mb_2 (sandstone turbidite) Mb_2L (calcareous sandstone turbidite)	Sayfam Fm.	Mf (platform carbonate) MfR (reef limestone) Misfah Fm.	Sinni Fm.
Late-mid. Triassic	Matbat Fm. MbR (olistolith of platform carbonate) Mb_1 (carbonate turbidite) Mb_1V (basalt-hyaloclastite) Aj_2C (radiolarite-shale) Aj_2S (sandstone)	Ar_1 (breccia-carbonate turbidite-radiolarite) Ar_1V (basalt)	MfV (andesite-basalt)	UmV_{1-2} (basalt-andesite) UmV_3 (trachyte-granophyre)
Early Triassic	Al Jil Fm. Aj_1 (carbonate turbidite) Aj_1Sh (megabreccia-radiolarite)	?	? Hallstat facies	
Late Permian	Aj_1V (basalt-andesite-keratophyre)		Baid Fm. Bd (platform carbonate) BdV (basalt)	?

WAHRAH Fm. (Wa1-Wac) (carb., turb., radiol.)

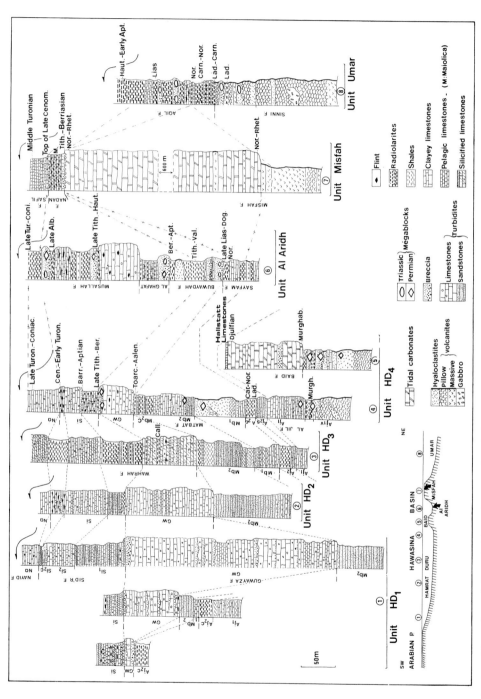

Fig. 1. Stratigraphic sections of the major Hawasina tectonic units in the central and eastern Oman Mountains and their pre-obduction position in the Hawasina basin.

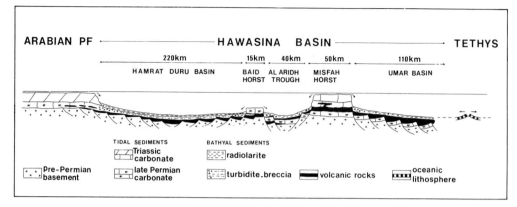

Fig. 2. Palinspatic reconstruction of the Hawasina basin for the Middle to Late Triassic.

nental basin. However, locally, particularly in the Hawasina Window, it also had MORB tholeiite character (Béchennec 1987), a feature that most probably reflects important crustal thinning in the northwestern Hamrat Duru Basin.

The development of the Hamrat Duru Basin was also characterised by, from the Murghabian onwards, bathyal sedimentation with the deposition of pelagic facies and turbiditic carbonates with minor breccias and megabreccias containing fragments of reworked shelf deposits from the two bordering platforms (Murghabian radiolarites and turbidites of the Lower Member of the Al Jil Fm.; Béchennec 1987; De Wever *et al.* 1988, 1989, 1990).

Development of the A1 Aridh Trough, the Misfah Horst and the Umar Basin in the Middle of Late Triassic

A second phase of rifting and extension during the Middle to Late Triassic primarily affected the Baid Platform, which was broken up and turned into a seamount or submarine plateau (Hallstatt facies of T. Calon, 1988, pers. comm.). This platform relict nevertheless played an important role in the subsequent sedimentary history, as it prevented the influx of terrigenous detritus from the Arabian Platform into the internal zones of the Hawasina Basin. The A1 Aridh Trough, the Misfah Horst and the Umar Basin that were also developed at this time, thus remained free of terrigenous material, which was restricted to the Hamrat Duru Basin (Fig. 2).

An important magmatic episode was associated with this phase of extension, in particular in the Umar Basin (Sinni Fm.), on the Misfah

Horst (Lower Member of the Misfah Fm.), in the Al Aridh Trough (Sayfam Fm.) and in the most distal parts of the Hamrat Duru Basin (Lower Member of the Matbat Fm.). The volcanism was in general of within-plate alkaline type, although the sequences in the Sinni Formation show an evolution towards transitional and locally to MORB tholeiitic types (Béchennec 1987). This suggests a marked crustal thinning in the internal parts of the Umar Basin, which probably was continuous with the Neo-Tethyan sea-floor, whose formation by sea-floor spreading began at this time (Whitechurch *et al.* 1984).

Thus, the Hawasina Basin possessed its principal morphological and structural features from the Middle to Late Triassic onward, and was to retain them until the Early Senonian.

Sedimentation in the Hawasina Basin from the Middle Triassic to the Late Jurassic

During this period the Hamrat Duru Basin was characterized by the deposition of a coarsening-upward megasequence indicating a phase of sediment progradation into the basin. This megasequence begins with a series of radiolarites to siliceous micrites of Carnian–Norian age (Upper Member of the Al Jil Fm.; Béchennec 1987) documenting both deepening of the basin related to crustal extension and a decrease in the influx of terrigenous detritus from the Arabian Platform, which was experiencing evaporitic conditions at this time (Murris 1980; Le Métour 1987; Rabu 1987).

This siliceous sequence was followed in Late Triassic time (Bernoulli & Weissert 1987; Bernoulli *et al.* 1990) by a seqence of radiolaria- and bivalve-bearing micrites associated with fine-grained calcareous turbidites (Lower

Member of the Matbat Fm.). In the Jurassic, two major turbidite sequences were deposited; the first one, Liassic, in age, is characterized in particular by a quartzose facies (Upper Member of the Matbat Fm.), and the second one, Middle to Late Jurassic, by limestones containing reworked oolites (Guwayza limestones, Glennie et al. 1974; Cooper 1987; Guwayza Fm. Béchennec 1987). The parallelism between the sequences on the Arabian Platform and those in the Hamrat Duru Basin is remarkable and underlines the fact that the platform was the principal source for the sediments of the Hamrat Duru Basin (Béchennec 1987; Béchennec et al. 1988; Le Métour 1987; Rabu 1987). From the end of the Liassic the sediments of the east-central part of the Hamrat Duru Basin became enriched in silica: the oolitic turbidites equivalent of the Guwayza Formation, are silicified to varying degrees, and there are intercalation of radiolarites (Wahrah Fm., Glennie et al. Béchennec 1987). This local differentiation continued into the Cretaceous.

The relict horst of the Permian Baid Platform bounded the Hamrat Duru Basin to its northeast and protected the internal zones (Al Aridh Trough, and Umar Basin) of the Hawasina Basin from the influx of clastic material from the Arabian Platform. In the Middle to Late Triassic, after the peak of magmatic activity, on the Misfah Platform a sequence of shallow-water carbonates was deposited (Upper Member of the Misfah Fm.) whose thickness (>800 m) reflects rapid subsidence during the Late Triassic. However, during the Jurassic, carbonate sedimentation was extremely reduced on the horst, which was even emerged at some times, as witnessed by the microkarsts and ferromanganiferous encrustations at the top of the Misfah Formation. In contrast, in the Al Aridh Trough and the Umar Basin, pelagic sediments were deposited, with intercalations of breccias and megabreccias (Sayfam Fm. of the Al Aridh Group, Aqil Fm. of the Umar Group). These fragmental deposits yield almost exclusively blocks and megablocks of shallow-water carbonates from the bordering horsts, Late Permian and Late Triassic in age in the Al Aridh Trough, and Late Triassic in age in the Umar Basin.

Subsidence of the continental margin during the Late Tithonian−Berriasian

A new phase of regional extension occurred during the Late Tithonian−Berriasian. On the continental margin this was reflected by subsidence of the edge of the Arabian Platform, with a consequent 250 km southwestward retreat of the continental slope (Le Métour 1987; Rabu 1987; Rabu et al. 1990), and by a general deepening of the Hawasina Basin, whose main morphological and structural features were, however, preserved (Béchennec 1987; Béchennec et al. 1988).

In the Hamrat Duru Basin, the foundering of the Arabian Platform resulted in the deposition of very coarse-grained breccias in the most proximal facies near the top of the Guwayza Formation. Subsequently, the retreat of the continental slope caused by a reduction in clastic influx, and pelagic sedimentation became predominant (Lower Member of the Sid'r Fm.) with a tendency to silicification of the clastic facies due to the concomitant deepening of the basin.

This extensional phase also reactivated the horsts in the internal zones of the Hawasina Basin. Thus the most distal facies near the top of the Guwayza Formation are characterized by large blocks of reworked shallow-water carbonates Late Permian in age from the relict Baid Horst. Similarly breccias and megabreccias with reworked blocks and megablocks of Permian and Triassic shallow-water carbonates became particularly common in the Al Aridh Trough during this period (Buwaydah and Al Ghafat Fms.). This trough, was situated between the Permian and Triassic platforms and was also the site of magmatic activity (Buwaydah Fm.; Béchennec et al. 1986b; Béchennec 1987) whose within-plate alkaline character reflects the continental nature of the basement to the Hawasina Basin.

The Misfah Horst, until this time barely submerged, also subsided during the Late Tithonian−Berriasian, and the carbonate shelf facies was succeeded by the bathyal Maiolica facies of the Nadan Formation (Glennie et al. 1974). Pelagic sedimentaion continued in the Umar Basin.

Cretaceous sedimentation in the Hawasina Basin

Shallow-water carbonate sedimentation prograded during the Valanginian over the foundered part of the Arabian Platform, completely covering it again by Barremian times (Le Métour 1987; Rabu 1987, 1990). In the Hamrat Duru Basin this progradation is reflected by renewed to carbonate turbidite deposition during the Barremian−Aptian (Middle Member of the Sid'r Fm.) (Béchennec 1987).

A new episode of siliceous sedimentation developed during the Albian−Cenomanian (Upper Member of the Sid'r Fm.), perhaps connected with another period of extension, that most probably was responsible for sea-floor spreading in the Samail Basin. However carbonate turbidite sedimentation set in again during the Late Cenomanian−Early Turonian (Nayid Fm.; Béchennec 1987), and continued until at least the Late Turonian−Early Senonian. These turbidites are fairly fine-grained and contain clasts of reworked shelf deposits from the Arabian Platform. At the same time, active faulting along the edge of the platform led to the deposition of channelized breccias and megabreccias, both on the continental slope (Member D of the Mayhah Fm.; Watts & Garrison 1986) and in the most proximal parts of the Hamrat Duru Basin (Nayid Fm. in the Hawasina Window, Béchennec 1987 and Riyamah Fm. Cooper 1987; Robertson 1987).

The Al Aridh Trough was characterised, at least until the late Turonian-early Senonian, by essentially pelagic sedimentation (Al Ghafat and Musallah Fms.) with the intercalation of breccias and megabreccias with reworked, Late Permian and Triassic shallow-water carbonates derived from the two bordering horsts. Magmatic activity, although limited, continued in this zone and is represented by intercalations of basalt, andesite and trachyte, with microgabbro and granophyre (Musallah Fm.; Béchennec 1987).

The Misfah Horst remained in a bathyal environment throughout the Cretaceous. After the deposition of the Maiolica facies sediments during the Tithonian-Valanginian, sedimentation ceased from the Valanginian to the beginning of the Middle Cenomanian, when pelagic sediments resumed for at least until the Middle Turonian.

Sedimentation in the Umar Basin remained essentially radiolarian through most of the Cretaceous.

From the closure of the Hawasina Basin to the formation of an Eo-Alpine chain

Lithological, sedimentological, biostratigraphical and structural data suggest that the main tectonic units that constitute the Hawasina Nappes correspond approximately to the principal palaeogeographical domains of the Hawasina Basin. It also appears to the authors (contrary to Bernoulli & Weissert 1987) that the units from more internal situations override those of more external origin (in regard to the Arabian platform). The Hawasina Nappes can be grouped into lower and upper tectonic megaunits that consist respectively of rocks derived from the Hamrat Duru Basin and Baid Horst,

and from the Al Aridh Trough, the Misfah Horst and the Umar Basin. Each mega-tectonic unit is itself divided into several main units, the structural edifice comprising, from base to top, seven principal units (Béchennec 1987; Béchennec et al. 1988) (Figs 3−5):

1. The Hamrat Duru tectonic unit 1 (HD_1) consists of the most proximal facies of the Hamrat Duru Group. It is thrust over the 'Autochthonous' Unit B (Le Métour 1987, 1990), and mainly crops out at Birkat al Mawz, south of Al Ajal and in the Hawasina Window.

2. The Hamrat Duru tectonic unit 2 (HD_2) comprises the proximal to subproximal facies of the Hamrat Duru Group, and is thrust over either unit HD_1 or the 'Autochthonous' Unit B, cropping out especially in the Hamrat Duru Range, in Jabals Ghubar and Khatma, in southern Jabal Safra, and in the Zukayt area.

3. The Hamrat Duru tectonic unit 3 (HD_3) comprises the subdistal facies of the Hamrat Duru Group. It is locally continuous with unit HD_2 but more commonly it is thrust over it or over the 'Autochthonous' Unit B. This unit (HD_3) crops out essentially in Jabals Wahrah and Hammah, central Jabal Safra and in the Al Ayn and Jabal Misth-Jabal Misfah areas.

4. The Hamrat Duru tectonic unit 4 (HD_4) includes the facies of the Hamrat Duru Group that were the most distal relative to the Arabian Platform, but the most proximal relative to the Baid Horst, a few relics of which are incorporated into it. It is thrust over either the preceding tectonic units or over the 'Autochthonous' Unit B, and mainly crops out in the Doqal area and northeast of the Hawasina Window, in the Nakhl, Taww, Bid-Bid, Hayl, Baid, Mudaybi and Wadi Andam areas, and in northern Jabal Safra.

5. The Al Aridh tectonic unit comprises the rocks of the Al Aridh Group. It is thrust over all the above-mentioned units or rests directly on the 'Autochthonous' Unit B and only occurs along the southern flank of the Oman Mountains, where it forms a narrow but fairly continuous band.

6. The Misfah tectonic unit consists essentially of the Triassic of the Misfah Formation with certain facies of the Umar Group. It is thrust over the preceding units.

7. The Umar tectonic unit comprises the Umar Group. It is thrust over all the preceding units and locally onto the 'Autochthonous' Unit B. It is itself overthrust by the ophio-

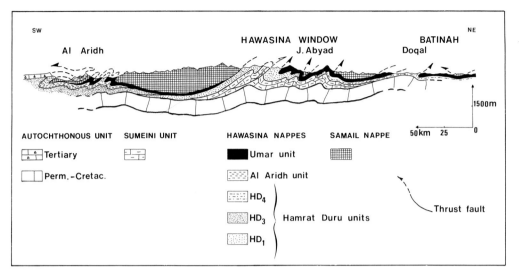

Fig. 3. Tectonic cross section across the western part of the central Oman Mountains showing the stacking sequence of the main allochthonous units and the late-obduction, NNE-facing, back-folding and back thrusting (location on Fig. 5).

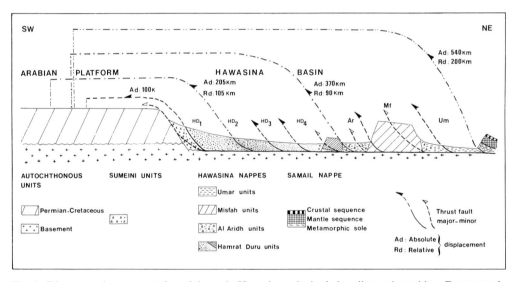

Fig. 4. Diagrammatic representation of the main Hawasina units in their palinspastic position. For some of them the position of the overthrust front, on the Arabian platform, is indicated, and the approximate displacement with respect to their original position (Ad) or to the underlying unit (Rd).

lites of the Samail Nappe or its meta-morphic sole and has for this reason been particularly sliced up.

In the west–central part of the Oman Mountains this order of superposition has locally been reversed by back-folding. The order also varies locally as a result of inter-unit imbrication, in particular on the north flank of Jabal Akhdar.

It is possible, by kinematic reconstruction (Dahlstrom 1969; Hossack 1979), to estimate the original extent of the main tectonic units, and from there to obtain an idea of the order of the original width of the various palaeogeo-graphical units of the Hawasina Basin. The width of the Hamrat Duru Basin, together with the relict Baid Horst, is estimated at 240 km

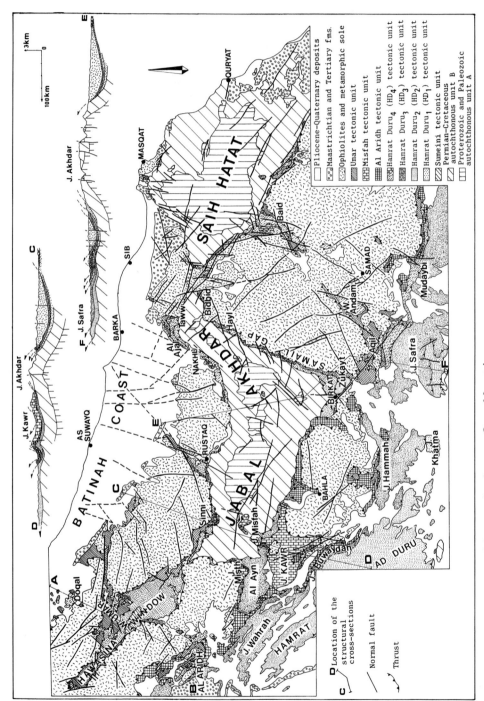

Fig. 5. Structural sketch map of the central and eastern Oman Mountains.

(Béchennec 1987), that of the Al Aridh Trough at 40 km, the Misfah Horst at 55 km and the Umar Basin at a minimum of 110 km, giving a minimum width for the Hawasina Basin as a whole of about 450 km.

Taking into consideration the present position of their southern front on the Oman platform (Fig. 5), it is clear that the various tectonic units have undergone considerable displacement (Fig. 4). This is all the more remarkable in view of their thin-skinned nature and the fact that they have suffered relatively little internal deformation. These features could prompt the suggestion that, instead of compressive stress applied from the rear (Murrel 1981; Merle 1984), gravitational forces were responsible for emplacement of the tectonic units. This would be mechanically compatible with the large displacement and the style of deformation. However, the geometry of thrust planes at the base of the various units is, in general, not compatible with simple gravitational sliding. This would involve basal truncations cutting across the stratigraphy towards the rear of the units, sliced-off folds forming tectonic remnants, and increased deformation towards the front of the units. Structural analysis of the Hawasina Nappes instead shows that development of the main tectonic units and their emplacement onto the Arabian Platform took place in three stages that involved different mechanisms.

The first, 'pre-early obduction' stage, developed in a compressive setting within the broader framework of the Neo-Tethys and its margin. Following Albian−Cenomanian accretion of the Samail Basin along a spreading axis (Beurrier 1987), northeast-directed intraoceanic subduction developed during the Cenomanian−Turonian, between the young oceanic crust of the Samail Basin and older, Early Cretaceous Neo-Tethyan oceanic crust attached to the Arabian margin. The evolution of this setting led to the beginning of continental subduction, for which the main evidence is the continental biotite granites and the oceanward-verging structures with associated high-pressure metamorphism in the Saih Hatat and Jabal Akhdar (Le Métour et al. 1986, 1990; Le Métour 1987; Rabu 1987). This continental subduction led, in the Turonian−Coniacian, to blocking of the subduction system and the formation of intraoceanic detachments. It was from this zone of detachment, behind the subduction zone, that the Samail Nappe was derived; it then reached the internal zones, of the Hawasina Basin during the Santonian-Campanian, with resultant metamorphism of the Umar Group rocks. During this period, in the Hawasina Basin, the major thrusts separating the principal tectonic units

were initiated. Their geometry is consistent with compressive tectonism, and they began in the most internal zones (piggy-back thrusts); thus, although at this stage the displacements remained relatively small, the Hawasina succession was already decoupled from its basement.

The second stage, of 'true' obduction, gave rise to the major displacement of the principal tectonic units and their emplacement onto the Arabian platform. This took place during the Early Campanian−Maastrichtian. The first unit to be emplaced on the platform was the Hamrat Duru tectonic mega-unit, in whcih features of gravity stretching can be seen. Thus, the southern front of the most proximal unit, HD_1, was overridden by the southern front of the sub-proximal unit, HD_2, itself overridden by sub-distal unit HD_3 (Figs 3−5). These various units were then truncated by the Al Aridh tectonic unit, whose southern front is orientated transverse to the fronts of the preceding units. The same is true for the Misfah, Umar and Samail units, so that it appears that the main tectonic units were emplaced individually onto the platform, the latest to be transported being the most internal ones (out-of-sequence thrusts, Searle 1985; Béchennec 1987). However, at a late stage, due to isostatic uplift following continental subduction, the metamorphose autochton formed ascending frontal and lateral ramps (Béchennec 1987; Le Métour 1987). The main consequences of this were the formation of south-verging folds, with an associated cleavage, in the last-emplaced units, the development of 'subtractive' slices in the 'autochthon', intraunit imbrication and, finally, halting of obduction.

The third, 'late obduction' stage, is represented by northeast-verging backfolds, that are particularly well developed in the west−central part of the Oman Mountains (Glennie et al. 1974, Graham 1979, Searle & Cooper 1986), with associated schistosity, greenschist facies metamorphism, fracture cleavage (Béchennec 1987).

After the emplacement of the various tectonic units on the Arabian Platform followed by the early Maastrichtian transgression, a final phase of folding, on axes trending N30°−60° terminated deformation of the Eo-Alpine (Le Métour 1987; Rabu 1987) belt.

Conclusions

The Hawasina Basin developed in two main stages. A first phase of rifting and extension during the Late Permian initiated the formation of the Hamrat Duru Basin, which presents the general morphological, sedimentological and magmatic characteristics of an intracontinental basin. The presence of thick sequences of MORB tholeiites, which locally contain mineralisation comparable with that of the mineralised muds of the Red Sea (Lescuyer *et al.* 1986) seems to indicate that extension locally reached the stage of ocean spreading, but this must then have aborted. A second stage of rifting and extension in the Middle to Late Triassic led to the development of three new morphological units: the Al Aridh Trough, the Misfah Horst and the Umar Basin, internally to the Hamrat Duru Basin, the whole constituting the Hawasina Basin. The main structural features of the Hawasina Basin had thus developed by this time and resembled those of present-day passive continental margins. Furthermore, the magmatism associated with this phase points to a continental nature for the basement of the Hawasina Basin, and is evidence of crustal thinning in the most internal zones, which were adjacent to the Neo-Tethyan ocean crust.

Two other extensional stages subsequently affected the Hawasina Basin, in the Tithonian–Berriasian and in the Albian–Cenomanian. However, during this time the basin acted as a single unit, retaining the structural organization dating from the Permian and Triassic. The reduction in sedimentation from the Late Permian to the Coniacian (Late Cretaceous) reflects the starved character of the margin. The evolution of the Hawasina Basin came to an end in the Coniacian, when the arrival of continental crust in a subduction zone that was initiated in the Cenomanian–Turonian; this blocked further movement and initiated obduction that culminated in thrusting of the Hawasina Nappes and the Samail Ophiolite onto the Arabian platform during the Campanian to Early Maastrichtian. This thrusting, although initiated under a compressive tectonic regime, appears to have been achieved mainly by gravitational mechanisms. It is important to emphasise that, the breccias and megabreccias within the Hawasina Nappes (Graham 1980; Searle *et al.* 1982; Robertson 1987) are not chaotic sedimentary deposits formed in front of an advancing nappe. The ages of their radiolarian matrices show that these breccias were emplaced during the Late Permian, the Late Triassic, the Tithonian–Berriasian, the Early Cretaceous and the Late Cretaceous, in the Hamrat Duru Basin, the Al Aridh Trough and the Umar Basin. Their formation often relates to rifting and active faulting along the margins of both the Arabian Platform and the Baid and Misfah horsts.

The Pichakun Trough (Ricou *et al.* 1980; Kazmin *et al.* 1986) has been recognized as an integral part of the south-Tethyan continental margin. However, it shows important differences from the Hawasina Basin. It appeared only in the Middle–Late Triassic, as a basin < 70 km wide (Ricou 1976), in which sedimentation ceased from the Cenomanian onwards, following a reversal in the direction of clastic influx during the Aptian. Despite these differences, the history of the Pichakun Trough and the Hawasina Basin ended during the same period, with thrusting onto the Arabian Platform and obduction of ophiolites from the Neo-Tethyan ocean.

References

BÉCHENNEC, F. 1987. Géologie des Nappes Hawasina dans les parties orientale et centrale des Montagnes d'Oman. *Thèse Doctorat d'Etat*, Université Pierre et Marie Curie, Paris 6. *Documents du Bureau de Recherches Géologiques et Minières* **127**, 474.

——, BEURRIER, M., RABU, D. & HUTIN, G. 1986a. *Geological map of Barka. Sheet NF 40–3B. Scale 1:100 000. Explanatory notes* – Directorate General of Minerals, Oman Ministry of Petroleum and Minerals.

——, ——, —— & —— 1986b. *Geological map of Bahla. Sheet NF 40–7A. Scale 1:100 000. Explanatory notes* – Directorate General of Minerals, Oman Ministry of Petroleum and Minerals.

——, LE MÉTOUR, J., RABU, D., VILLEY, M. & BEURRIER, M. 1988. The Hawasina Basin: a fragment of a starved passive continental margin, thrust over the Arabian Platform during the obduction of the Samail Nappe. *Tectonophysics*, **151**, 323–343.

BERNOULLI, D. & WEISSERT, H. 1987. The upper Hawasina nappes in the central Oman Mountains: stratigraphy, palinspastics and sequence of nappe emplacement. *Geodynamica Acta*, **1**, 47–58.

——, —— & BLOME, CH. D. 1988. Evolution of the Triassic Hawasina Basin. *In*: ROBERTSON, A. H. F., SEARLE, M. P. & RIES, A. C. (eds) *The Geology and Tectonics of the Oman Region*. Geological Society, London, Special Publication.

BEURRIER, M. 1987. Géologie de la Nappe ophiolitique de Samail dans les parties orientale et centrale des Montagnes d'Oman. *Thèse de Doctorat d'Etat*, Université Pierre et Marie Curie, Paris 6. *Documents du Bureau de Recherches Géologiques et Minières*, **128**, 459.

COOPER, D. J. W. 1987. Hamrat Duru Group: revised stratigraphy of a Mesozoic deep-water passive margin in the Oman Mountains. *Geological Magazine*, **124**, 157–164.

DAHLSTROM, C. D. A. 1969. Balanced cross sections. *Canadian Journal Earth Sciences*, **6**, 743–757.

DE WEVER, P., BOURDILLON-DE GRISSAC, Ch. &

BÉCHENNEC, F. 1988. Découverte de radiolarites permiennes au bord sud de la Tethys (nappes d'Hawasina, Sultanat d'Oman). *Comptes Rendus de l'Académie des Sciences de Paris*, **307**, série II, 1383–1388.

——, —— & —— 1988. A Permian age from radiolarites of the Hawasina Nappes, Oman Mountains. *Geology* **16**, 912–994.

——, —— & —— 1990. Radiolarian biostratigraphic data (Permian to Cretaceous) from the Hawasina complex (Oman Mountains) *In*: ROBERTSON, A. H. F., SEARLE, M. P. & RIES, A. C. (eds) *The Geology and Tectonics of the Oman Region*. Geological Society, London, Special Publication, **49**, 225–238.

GLENNIE, K. W., BOEUF, M. G. A., HUGHES CLARKE, M. W., MOODY-STUART, M., PILAAR, W. F. H. & REINHARDT, B. M. 1974. Geology of the Oman Mountains. *Verhandelingen Van het Koninklijk Nederlands geologisch Mijnbouwkundig Genootschap.* **31**, part 1, 2, 3.

GRAHAM, G. M. 1980. Evolution of a passive margin and nappe emplacement in the Oman Mountains. *In*: PANAYIOTOU, A. (ed.) *Ophiolites*, Proceedings of an International Ophiolite Symposium, Cyprus 1979. 414–423.

HOSSACK, J. R., 1979. The use of balanced cross-sections in the calculation of orogenic contraction: a review. *Journal of the Geological Society London*, **136**, 705–711.

KAZMIN, V., RICOU, L. E. & SBORTSHIKOV, J. M. 1986. Structure and evolution of the passive margin of the Eastern Tethys. *Tectonophysics*, **123**, 153–179.

LE METOUR, J. 1987. Géologie de l'Autochtone des Montagnes d'Oman: la fenêtre du Saih Hatat. *Thèse de Doctorat d'Etat* Université Pierre et Marie Curie, Paris 6, *Documents du Bureau de Recherches Géologiques et Minières*, **129**, p. 425.

——, RABU, D., TEGYEY, M., BÉCHENNEC, F., BEURRIER, M. & VILLEY, M., 1986. Le métamorphisme régional crétacé éclogites–schistes bleus sur la bordure omanaise de la plate-forme arabe: conséquence d'une tectogenèse précoce anté-obduction. *Comptes Rendus de l'Académie des Sciences Paris*, **302**, Ser. II, 905–910.

——, ——, ——, —— & ——. 1988. Subduction and obduction: two stages in the Eo–Alpine tectonometamorphic evolution of the Oman Mountains *In*: ROBERTSON, A. H. F., SEARLE M. P. & RIES, A. C. (eds) *The Geology and Tectonics of the Oman Region*, Geological Society, London, Special Publication, **49**, 327–339.

LESCUYER, J. L., OUDIN-DUNLOP, E. & BEURRIER, M. 1986. Review of the different types of mineralization related to the Oman ophiolite volcanism. *I.A.G.O.D. Congress proceedings Stockhölm*.

MERLE, O. 1984. Déplacement et déformation des nappes superficielles. *Revue de Géologie Dynamique et de Géographie Physique*, **25**, Fasc. **1**, p. 3–17.

MURREL, S. A. F. 1981. The rocks mechanics of thrust and nappe formations. *In*: MC CLAY K. R. &

PRICE N. J. (eds) *Thrust and Nappe tectonics* Geological Society, London, **9**, p. 99–109.

MURRIS, R. J. 1980. Middle East: Stratigraphic evolution and oil habitat. *American Association of Petroleum Geologists Bulletin*, **64**, 597–618.

RABU, D. 1987. Géologie de l'Autochtone des Montagnes d'Oman: la fenêtre du Jabal Akhdar. La semelle métamorphique de la Nappe ophiolitique de Samail dans les parties orientale et centrale des Montagnes d'Oman: une revue. *Thèse de Doctorat d'Etat*. Université Pierre et Marie Curie, Paris 6. *Documents du Bureau de Recherches Geologiques et Minières* **130**, p. 582.

——, LE METOUR, J., BÉCHENNEC. F., BEURRIER, M., VILLEY, M. & BOURDILLON-JEUDY DE GRISSAC, Ch. 1990. Sedimentary aspects of the Eo–Alpine cycle on the Northeast edge of the Arabian platform (Oman Mountains). *In*: ROBERTSON, A. H. F., SEARLE, M. P. & RIES, A. C. (eds) *The Geology and Tectonics of the Oman Region*. Geological Society, London, Special Publication, **49**, 49–68.

RICOU, L. E. 1976. Evolution structurale des Zagrides. La région-clef de Neyriz (zagros iranien). *Mémoire de la Société Géologique de France*, **125**, p. 140.

—— & MARCOUX, J. 1980. Organisation générale et rôle structural des radiolarites et des ophiolites le long du système alpino-méditerranéen. *Bulletin de la Société Géologique de France*. T. XXII, 7, p. 1–14.

ROBERTSON, A. H. F. 1987. The transition from a passive margin to an upper Cretaceous foreland basin related to ophiolite emplacement in the Oman Mountains. *Bulletin of the Geological Society of America*, **99**, 633–653.

SEARLE, M. P. 1985. Sequence of thrusting and origin of culminations in the northern and central Oman Mountains. *Journal of Structural Geology*, **7**, 129–143.

—— & COOPER, D. J. W. 1986. Structure of the Hawasina window culmination, Central Oman Mountains. *Transactions of the Royal Society of Edinburgh: Earth Sciences*, **77**, 143–156.

—— & GRAHAM, G. M. 1982. 'Oman exotics': oceanic carbonate build-ups associated with the early stages of continental rifting. *Geology*, **10**, 43–49.

——, LIPPARD, S. J., SMEWING, J. D. & REX, D. C. 1980. Volcanic rocks beneath the Samail Ophiolite nappe in the northern Oman Mountains and their significance in the Mesozoic evolution of Tethys. *Journal of Geological Society, London*. **137**, 589–604.

WATTS, K. F. & GARRISON, R. E. 1986. Sumeini Group, Oman–Evolution of a Mesozoic carbonate slope on a South Tethyan continental margin. *Sedimentary Geology*, **48**, 107–168.

WHITECHURCH, H., JUTEAU, T. & MONTIGNY, R. 1984. Role of the Eastern Mediterranean ophiolites (Turkey, Syria, Cyprus) in the history of the Neo-Tethys. *In*: DIXON, J. E. & ROBERTSON, A. H. F. (eds) *'Geological evolution of the Eastern Mediterranean'*, Geological Society, London, Special Publication, **17**, 301–317.

Permian to Cretaceous radiolarian biostratigraphic data from the Hawasina Complex, Oman Mountains

P. DE WEVER[1] Ch. BOURDILLON-de GRISSAC[2] & F. BECHENNEC[3]

[1] *CNRS UR 1315, Université P. M. Curie, T 15−16 E4, F-75 252 Paris Cedex 05, France*
[2] *BRGM−SGN−GEO, F-45 060 Orléans, France*
[3] *BRGM, 10 Rue Picheri, 44300 Nantes, France*

Abstract: The analysis of foraminifera and radiolaria in 3000 carbonate and 150 siliceous rock samples from the Oman Mountains results in revision of the existing stratigraphy and supports the definition of new units. In the Hawasina allochthonous unit the main results are as follows: (i) Permian bedded chert exists near the base of the sequence and is thus the first Permian bedded chert occurrence reported from the Tethyan region; (ii) an important volcanic event is dated as Triassic; (iii) bedded chert horizons are dated as Liassic; (iv) the thick turbiditic sequence has been divided into several units of Middle and Late Jurassic age. In the Samail ophiolite: (i) the ages of four tectonic episodes were established from the beginning of oceanic spreading (Albian−Early Cenomanian), to the obduction of the ophiolitic nappe (Campanian).

Around 3000 limestone and chert samples were collected for palaeontological analysis during the BRGM mapping project (1/100 000) in the Central Oman Mountains. Carbonate rocks yielded foraminifera, ostracods, algae; also macrofauna; while the siliceous rocks yielded identifiable radiolarians.

Radiolarians were extracted from rock samples with established techniques (De Wever *et al.* 1979b; 1982b) that use extremely dilute hydrofluoric acid (1 to 0.1%), and successive etching. The ages of samples were established using different sets of data handled by microcomputers. (Vrielynck & Granlund 1988, Vrielynck 1989) and from published biozonations or unpublished data (Pessagno 1977; De Wever *et al.* 1979a; Baumgartner *et al.* 1980; De Wever, 1981a,b,c, 1982 a,b; Blome, 1983; Baumgartner 1984, 1987; De Wever & Miconnet, 1985; De Wever *et al.* 1985; De Wever & Cordey, 1986; De Wever *et al.* 1986; Aita, 1987; De Wever *et al.* 1987a,b, 1988a,b; Pessagno *et al.* 1984, 1987). For each species we used the range of its acrozone, and for each sample we used the concurrent range zone.

Geological setting

The Oman Mountains comprise an arcuate chain (700 km long × 50−140 km wide), from the Musandam Peninsula in northwest to the Sur region in the southeast (Fig. 1). The mountains culminate in the 3000 m high Jabal Akhdar and are flanked to the north by the Gulf of Oman or by the Batinah plain, and to the south by the deserts of interior Oman. The mountains were uplifted mainly during Mio-Pliocene.

The following main units are recognized from the bottom to the top: Upper Proterozoic crystalline basement in the southeast (Jabal Ja'alan and Qahlat region); the 'A autochtonous unit', transgressive on the basement, this comprises volcanic and sedimentary rocks, deformed during late Panafrican and Hercynian orogenic events; and the 'B autochtonous unit', mainly composed of transgressive carbonates dated as Permian to Cretaceous. The carbonates were deposited on the northeast edge of the Arabian platform and were deformed and locally metamorphosed during the Eo−alpine orogenesis; the Hawasina nappes are composed of mainly deep-water sedimentary and volcanic rocks of Permian to Cretaceous age. They represent a fragment of the passive margin of the Southern Tethys that was overthrust onto the Arabian platform during Late Cretaceous time. The Samail ophiolite formed during Albian, Cenomanian to Senonian times (De Wever *et al.* 1988b), and was also obducted onto the Arabian platform during Campanian−Early Maastrichtian time (Beurrier *et al.* 1987). The 'Neo-Autochthonous unit' is transgressive on all the previous units. Sedimentation began during Middle to Late Maastrichtian and continued until Miocene time (Burdigalian). The eastern and central outcrops of these units, were studied by the

From ROBERTSON, A. H. F., SEARLE, M. P. & RIES, A. C. (eds), 1990,
The Geology and Tectonics of the Oman Region.
Geological Society Special Publication No 49, pp 225−238

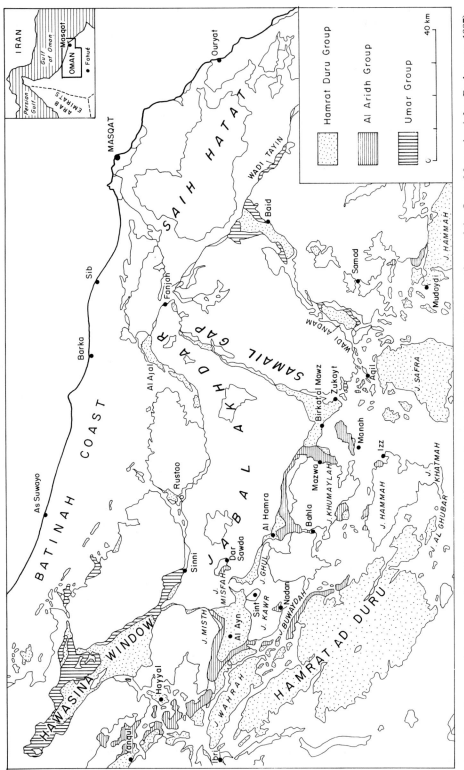

Fig. 1. Location map of the area studied (Central Oman Mountains). a Location map; b Simplified map of part of the Oman Mountains (after Bechennec, 1987), showing the main outcrops of the Al Aridh, Hamrat Duru and Umar Groups

Bureau de Recherches Géologiques et Minières (Bechennec 1987; Bechennec et al. 1990).

The Hawasina nappes are sandwiched between the overlying Samail ophiolite nappe and the underlying 'autochthonous' sequences of the Arabian platform (Jebel Akhdar and Saih Hatat) (Fig. 1). The sedimentary rocks of the Hawasina nappes document the Mesozoic evolution of the northeastern Arabian continental margin and the adjacent Tethys ocean. During Mezosoic time the Hawasina basin was flanked to the northeast (oceanwards) by carbonate platform build-ups, termed the Oman Exotics (Glennie et al. 1974; Graham 1980a,b;

Searle & Graham 1982; Kasmin et al. 1986; Watts & Garisson 1986; Bernoulli & Weissert 1987). Associated with these units are Permian and Mesozoic shelf-edge and condensed seamount facies (e.g. Hallstatt Limestones; Calon & Tozer in Bernoulli & Weissert 1987. The lower Hawasina nappes include Triassic, Jurassic and Cretaceous base-of-slope bathyal sediments (e.g. Hamrat Duru, Wahrah), and are locally overlain by massive sandstone successions. Intact Mesozoic sequences including Cretaceous pelagic sediments are also found in the highest Hawasina units (Al Aridh and Oman Exotics). Here we will use the stratigraphy proposed by

HAMRAT DURU GROUP

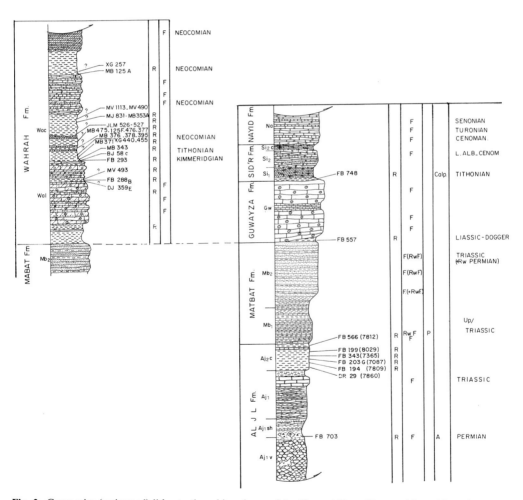

Fig. 2. Composite (estimated) lithostratigraphic column of the Hamrat Duru Group with position of productive radiolarian samples (numbers) (and "R" on columns), and other palaeontological groups (Foraminifera: "F", Pelecypods: "P", Calpionellids: "Calp", Ammonites: "A")

Béchennec (1987), as depicted on the Geological maps of Oman (Béchennec *et al.* 1986; Villey *et al.* 1986), comprising the Hamrat Duru, Al Aridh and Umar Groups:

Hamrat Duru Group

Two main types of facies exist in the Hamrat Duru Group; siliceous (i.e. Wahrah Formation) and calcareous (i.e. Guwayza Formation) (Fig. 2).

Siliceous facies of the Hamrat Duru Group (including the Wahrah Formation). The Wahrah Formation mainly comprises siliceous sediments (originally siliceous or diagenetically silicified). Most of the siliceous horizons have been dated by radiolarians. Also, Callovian–Oxfordian foraminifera were found in silicified calcareous turbidites overlying the lowest silicified sequence (Bechennec 1987; Bechennec *et al.* 1990). Chert levels overlying this thick turbiditic sequence yielded the following radiolarians of mainly Late Jurassic (Malm) age.

DJ 359E: Malm to Neocomian with : *Alievium helenae* SCHAAF, *Archaeospongoprunum* sp., *Pantanellium* sp. cf. *P. ultrasincerum* PESSAGNO. *Pantanellium lanceola* (PARONA) gr., *Archaeodictyomitra apiaria* (RUST), *Hsuum* sp., *Podobursa* (form with numerous and long equatorial spines), *Saitoum elegans* DE WEVER

FB 288B: Middle Callovian to Middle Oxfordian including : *Pantanellium lanceola*, (PARONA) gr., *Tritrabs casmaliaensis*

PESSAGNO, *Archaeodictyomitra* sp., *Hsuum brevicostatum* (OZVOLDOVA), *Hsuum maxwelli* PESSAGNO gr., *Mirifusus* sp. cf. *M. fragilis* BAUMGARTNER, *Mirifusus guadalupensis* PESSAGNO, *Saitoum* sp., *Spongocapsula* sp.

MV 493: ?Callovian to Tithonian with : *Acanthocircus dicranacanthos SQUINABOL, Alievium helenae* SCHAAF, *Angulobracchia* (?) *portmani* BAUMGARTNER, *Emiluvia chica* FOREMAN, *Pantanellium lanceola* (PARONA) gr. (ancestral form), *Pantanellium* sp. (with circular polar spines), *Triactoma cornuta* BAUMGARTNER, *Triactoma tithonianum* RUST, *Zartus* ? sp., *Archaeodictyomitra apiaria* (RUST), *Bernoullius dicera* (BAUMGARTNER), *Hsuum* sp. (*H. obispoensis* gr.), *Mirifusus mediodilatatus* (RUST), *Ristola altissima* (RUST), *Parvicingula boesii* (PARONA), *Parvicingula cosmoconica* (FOREMAN), *Podobursa triacantha* FISCHLI, *Pseudodictyomitra carpatica* (LOZYNYAK), *Syringocapsa limatum* (FOREMAN), *Thanarla pulchra* (SQUINABOL); Silicified turbidites overlying this horizon yielded Callovian-Oxfordian foraminifera (Bechennec 1987) (Fig. 3).

Thick sequence of chert of the middle part of the Wahrah Formation yielded numerous radiolarians of Tithonian to Hauterivian age.

FB 293: Bathonian to middle Tithonian (possibly Kimmeridgian), with : *Acanthocircus suboblongus* (YAO), *Eucyrtis micropora* gr. (SQUINABOL), *Hsuum brevicostatum*

Fig. 3. Radiolarians from Permian to Liassic samples.
1. *Folliculus scholasticus* ORMISTON & BABCOCK (morphotype 2, sensu Ishiga *et al.* 1986), x100 (FB 703, fig. 2), Permian, Al Jil Formation, Hamrat Duru Group.
2. *Folliculus scholasticus* ORMISTON & BABCOCK (morphotype 1, sensu Ishiga *et al.* 1986), x165 (FB 703, fig. 2), Permian, Al Jil Formation, Hamrat Duru Group.
3. *Folliculus monacanthus* ISHIGA & IMOTO, x100, (FB 703, fig. 2), Permian Al Jil Formation, Hamrat Duru Group.
4. *Falcispongus* aff. *rostratus* DUMITRICA, x125 (JLM 136C, fig. 3), Triassic (Ladinian), Aquil Formation, Umar Group.
5. "*Capnuchosphaera* ? sp. B" in DE WEVER *et al.* 1979, x125 (JLM 136C, fig. 3), Triassic (Ladinian), Aquil Formation, Umar Group.
6. *Sarla* aff. *vetusta* PESSAGNO, x100, (DJ 214F, fig. 4), Triassic, Sayfam Formation, Al Aridh Group.
7. *Plafkerium cochleatum* (NAKASEKO & NISHIMURA), x80, (JLM 136C, fig. 3), Triassic (Ladinian), Aquil Formation, Umar Group.
8. *Spongostylosphaera hellenica* (DE WEVER), x120, (JLM 136C, fig. 3), Triassic (Ladinian), Aquil Formation, Umar Group.
9. *Latium* sp. x190, (JLM 136C, fig. 3), Triassic (Ladinian), Aquil Formation, Umar Group.
10. *Jacus anatiformis* DE WEVER, x200, (DJ 213D, fig. 4), Liassic Buwajdah Formation, Al Aridh Group.
11. *Napora* sp. x190, (FB 577B, fig. 2), Liassic, Guwayza Formation, Hamrat Duru Group.
12. *Trillus elkhornensis* PESSAGNO & BLOME, x230, (DJ 213D, fig. 4), Liassic, Buwajdah Formation, Al Aridh Group.

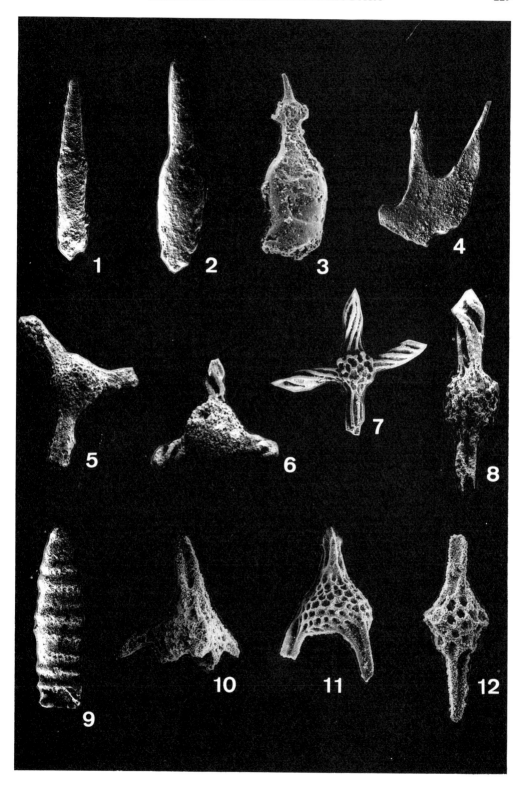

OZVOLDOVA, *Parvicingula boesii* (PAR-ONA) gr., *Podobursa triacantha* (FISCHLI) gr., *Saitoum corniculum* DE WEVER; DJ 58C: Kimmeridgian? to Neocomian, with: *Acanthocircus dicranacanthos* (SQUINABOL), *Alievium helenae* SCHAAF, *Emiluvia chica* FOREMAN, *Pantanellium lanceola* (PARONA) gr. (morphotype with thin spines), *Archaeodictyomitra excellens* (TAN), *Parvicingula boesii* (PARONA) gr., *Parvicingula cosmoconica* (FOREMAN), *Podobursa helvetica* (RUST), *Podobursa chandrika* KOCHER, *Protunuma costata* (ZITTEL), *Ristola procera* (PESSAGNO), *Saitoum corniculum* DE WEVER, *Thanarla conica* (ALIEV)

MB 343: Oxfordian to Tithonian with : *Archaeospongoprunum* sp., *Tetraditryma corralitoensis* (PESSAGNO), *Triactoma blakei* (PESSAGNO), *Triactoma jonesi* (PESSAGNO), ? *Amphipyndax* sp., *Archaeodictyomitra apiaria* (RUST), *Eucyrtis micropora* (SQUINABOL) gr., *Hsuum* sp., *Mirifusus* sp., *Podobursa spinosa* (OZVOLDOVA)

MB 371: Middle to Late Tithonian with : *Acanthocircus dicranacanthos* (SQUINABOL), *Archaeospongoprunum tehamaensis* PESSAGNO, *Emiluvia chica* FOREMAN, *Emiluvia orea* BAUMGARTNER, *Pantanellium lanceola* (PARONA), *Archaeodictyomitra apiaria* (RUST), *Parvicingula boesii* (PARONA), *Pseudodictyomitra carpatica* (LOZYNYAK), *Saitoum elegans* DE WEVER, *Sethocapsa trachyostraca* FOREMAN.

XG 440: Tithonian with : *Acanthocircus dicranacanthos* (SQUINABOL), *Alievium* sp. cf. *A. helenae* SCHAAF, *Emiluvia pessagnoi* FOREMAN, *Pantanellium lanceola* (PARONA) gr., *Archaeodictyomitra apiaria* (RUST), *Ristola altissima* (RUST)

XG 455: Tithonian to Valanginian with : *Acanthocircus dicranacanthos* (SQUINABOL), *Mirifusus* sp. cf. *M. mediodilatatus* (RUST)

MB 374: Tithonian to Berriasian with : *Acanthocircus dicranacanthos* (SQUINABOL), *Alievium helenae* SCHAAF, *Archaeospongoprunum* sp., *Emiluvia orea* BAUMGARTNER, *Pantanellium lanceola* (PARONA) gr. (ancestral morphotype), *Triactoma jonesi* (PESSAGNO), ? *Parvicingula cosmoconica* (FOREMAN), *Podobursa triacantha* (FISCHLI) gr.

MB 378: Berriasian to Middle Hauterivian with : *Acanthocircus dicranacanthos* (SQUINABOL), *Pantanellium lanceola* (PARONA) gr., *Parvicingula cosmoconica* (FOREMAN)

MB 395: Late Tithonian to Barremian with : *Archaeodictyomitra apiaria* (RUST), *A. vulgaris* PESSAGNO, *A. excellens* (TAN), *Emiluvia chica* FOREMAN, *Alievium helenae* SCHAAF, *Acanthocircus dicranacanthos* (SQUINABOL), *Pantanellium lanceola* (PARONA) gr., *Parvicingula boesii* (PARONA), *Thanarla conica* (ALIEV), *Angulobracchia* (?) *portmanni* BAUMGARTNER.

MB 475: Tithonian to Middle Valanginian with : *Acanthocircus dicranacanthos* (SQUINABOL), *Pantanellium lanceola* (PARONA) gr., *Archaeodictyomitra apiaria* (RUST), *Mirifusus mediodilatatus* (RUST), *Ristola altissima* (RUST), *Ristola* sp. cf. *R. cretacea* (BAUMGARTNER).

MB 476: Tithonian to Hauterivian with : *Acanthocircus dicranacanthos (SQUINABOL), Pantanellium lanceola* (PARONA) gr. (ancestral form), *Syringocapsa limatum* FOREMAN

MB 377: Tithonian to Hauterivian with : *Acanthocircus dicranacanthos* (SQUINABOL), *Acanthocircus trizonalis* (RUST), *Acanthocircus carinatus* FOREMAN, *Mesosaturnalis multidentatus* (SQUINABOL), *Pantanellium lanceola* (PARONA) gr., *Triactoma hybum* FOREMAN, *Eucyrtis micropora* (SQUINABOL) gr., *Pseudodictyomitra* sp.

JLM 526: Tithonian to Hauterivian with : *Acanthocircus dicranacanthos* (SQUINABOL), *Acanthocircus carinatus* FOREMAN, *Pantanellium lanceola* (PARONA) gr., *Archaeodictyomitra apiaria* (RUST), *Mirifusus* sp. cf. *M. mediodilatatus* (RUST), *Parvicingula boesii* (PARONA) gr.

JLM 527: Kimmeridgian to Tithonian with: *Emiluvia chica* FOREMAN, *Emiluvia pessagnoi* FOREMAN, *Tetratrabs bulbosa* BAUMGARTNER, *Eucyrtis micropora* gr. (SQUINABOL), *Obesacapsula rotunda* (HINDE), *Mirifusus mediodilatatus* (RUST) s.l., *Parvicingula dhimenaensis* BAUMGARTNER, *Parvicingula boesii* (PARONA), *Podocapsa amphitreptera* FOREMAN *Podobursa triacantha* (FISCHLI), *Ristola altissima* (RUST) (without nodular overgrowth), *Spongocapsula palmerae* PESSAGNO.

MV 831: Late Jurassic to Neocomian with: *Pantanellium lanceola (PARONA) gr.*, (oval central shell with thin polar spines), *Archaeospongoprunum* sp., *Ristola altissima* (RUST), *Napora* sp. cf. *N. praespinifera* (PESSAGNO)

MV 490: Berriasian to lower Valanginian with: *Acanthocircus dicranacanthos* (SQUINABOL), *Alievium helenae* SCHAAF, *Archaeodictyomitra apiaria* (RUST), *Napora bukryi* PESSAGNO;
MV 1113: Neocomian with: *Archaeodictyomitra lacrimula* (FOREMAN), *Eucyrtis* sp. cf. *E. ptyctum* RIEDEL & SANFILIPPO, *Ristola altissima* (RUST), *Parvicingula* gr. (massive form)

MB 353A: Tithonian to Neocomian with: *Acanthocircus* sp. (with two separate spines), *Archaeospongoprunum tehamaensis* PESSAGNO, *Emiluvia chica* FOREMAN, *Pantanellium lanceola* (PARONA), *Archaeodictyomitra* sp. cf. *A. lacrimula* (FOREMAN), *Archaeodictyomitra apiaria* (RUST), *Katroma* ? sp., *Parvicingula boesii* (PARONA), *Pseudodictyomitra carpatica* (LOZYNYAK), *Sethocapsa trachyostraca* FOREMAN.
Partly silicified calcareous turbidites overlying the chert sequence yielded reworked Lower Neocomian Early Cretaceous foraminifera of shallow water affinities (Bechennec 1987). The overlying sequence, composed of unsilicified turbidites was dated as late Neocomian by foraminifera (Béchennec 1987).
The upper chert sequence of the Wahrah Formation yielded radiolarians of late Neocomian (Early Cretaceous) to early Aptian (Late Cretaceous) age.

MB 125 A: Late Hauterivian to Early Aptian with: *Pantanellium lanceola (PARONA) gr.*, *Eucyrtis tenuis* (RUST), *Eucyrtis micropora* (SQUINABOL) gr., *Archaeodictyomitra lacrimula* (FOREMAN)

XG 457: Barremian to Early Aptian with: *Archaeodictyomitra lacrimula* (FOREMAN), *Eucyrtis micropora* (SQUINABOL) gr., *Crolanium pythiae* SCHAAF.

Calcareous facies of the Hamrat Duru

Group (including Guwayza Formation)
The base of the sedimentary part of the Al Jil Formation (i.e. chert overlying pillow basalt) has been dated (De Wever *et al.* 1988a) as Murghabian (Mid-Late Permian) by radio-

larians (in sample FB 703): *Follicucullus scholasticus* ORMISTON & BABCOCK (morphotypes 1 and 2 of Ishiga *et al.* 1986), *F.* sp. cf. *F. ventricosus* ORMISTON & BABCOCK, *Follicucullus monacanthus* ISHIGA & IMOTO and Triassocampe-like morphotype. This association correlates with late Gadalupian samples in Japan (Ishiga *et al.* 1986; Ishiga 1986) and those in the Urals and Texas (Nazarov & Ormiston 1985).
Some other fossils were also found in associated reworked reefal limestone blocks (De Wever *et al.* 1988a) of Late Murghabian age (= Late Kazanian within the Middle Guadalupian). These fossils are bryozoans (Fenestellidae), echinoderms (crinoids), gastropods, ostracodes corals, algae (abundant, along with *Tubiphytes obscurus* MASLOV, *Mizzia velebitana* SCHUBERT), benthic foraminifers (*Neoschwagerina margaritae, Globivalvulina vonderschmidti, Agathammina pusilla, Staffella* sp., *Geinitzina* sp., *Pachyploia* sp., *Nankinella* sp.) The base of the Aj2C (i.e. upper Al Jil Formation) locally includes limestone horizons with Triassic foraminifera and pelecypods (Béchennec 1987).
The upper part of the Al Jil (Aj2C) has been dated as Middle to Upper Triassic by radiolarians, as follows (Fig. 6).

DR 29: *Baumgartneria* sp. aff. *B. retrospina* DUMITRICA (with a central spine shorter than on holotype), *Eptingium* sp. cf. *E. manfredi* DUMITRICA, *Falcispongus calcaneum* DUMITRICA, *Plafkerium* sp.;

FB 194: *Archaeospongoprunum* sp., *Eptingium* sp. cf. *E. manfredi* DUMITRICA, ? *Plafkerium* sp.

FB 203G: *Plafkerium* sp., undescribed morphotypes belonging to the *Sarlinae* (with two spines), *Triassocampe* ? sp., Conodont fragment

FB 343A: *Capnuchosphaera lea* DE WEVER, *Capnuchosphaera mexicana* PESSAGNO, *Capnuchosphaera* sp. cf. *C. puncta* DE WEVER, *Capnuchosphaera theloides* DE WEVER, *Sarla* sp., *Triassocampe* sp.,

FB 199: *Capnuchosphaera triassica* DE WEVER, *Xiphotheca* ? sp.

FB 566: *Pseudostylosphaera* sp. cf. *P. hellenicum* (DE WEVER), *Baumgartneria* sp. cf. *B. curvispina* DUMITRICA, *Hinedorcus* sp. cf. *H. alatus* DUMITRICA,

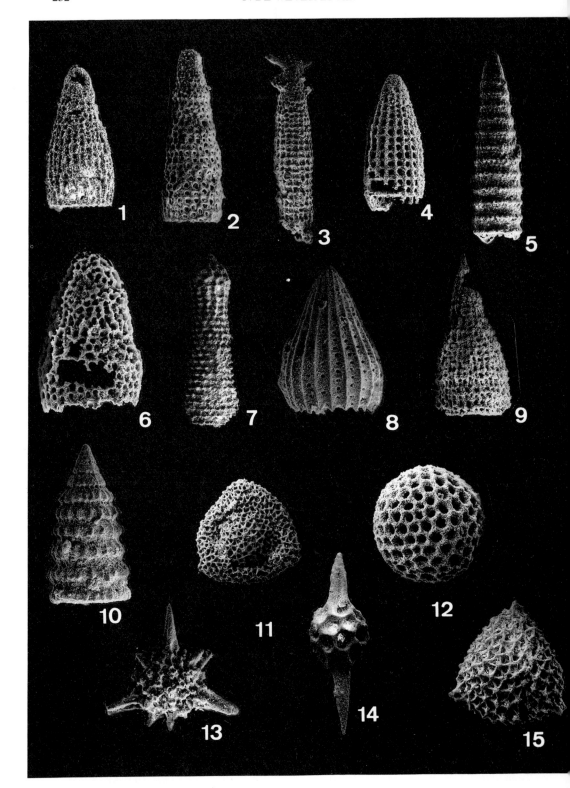

KOZUR & MOSTLER, *Plafkerium* sp., *Plafkerium hindei* PESSAGNO, *Plafkerium* sp. cf. *P. hindei* PESSAGNO, *Sepsagon longispinosum* DUMITRICA, KOZUR & MOSTLER, *Triassocampe* sp.

The lower Matbat Formation (Mb1) has been dated as Triassic by pelagic pelecypods (Halobia) in the biomicritic levels (Béchennec 1987). Some of the Permian (Upper Murghabian) microfauna are reworked.

The upper Matbat Formation (Mb1) is dated as Late Triassic (Norian−Rhaetic) by pelagic pelecypods (Halobia), Crinoidea, benthic foraminifera (from reefal, platform and deep water settings) (Béchennec 1987). Some Permian microfossils were also found in re-worked calcareous sediments throughout this sequence.

The cherts at the base of the Guwayza Formation has been dated as Late Liassic to early Dogger by radiolarians: (FB 557 B) *Bernoullius* sp. (with straight spines), *Tethis* sp. aff. *T. stolata* DE WEVER (with cephalis more clearly distinct than the holotype and with longitudinal ribs), '?*Tethis* sp.' *in* DE WEVER 1982a, *Trillus elkornensis* PESSAGNO & BLOME, and other *Nassellaria* g. sp. indet.

The siliceous base of the Sid'r Formation (base of Si1) has been dated as Kimmeridgian or Tithonian by radiolarians : (FB 748 B) *Acaeniotyle diaphorogona* FOREMAN, *Emiluvia chica* FOREMAN, *Emiluvia pessagnoi* FOREMAN, *Emiluvia sedecimporata elegans* (WISNIOWSKI), *Emiluvia sedecimporata salensis* (PESSAGNO), *Pantanellium*

lanceola (PARONA) gr., *Tritrabs worzeli* (PESSAGNO), *Tetraditryma* sp. cf. *T. pseudoplena* BAUMGARTNER, *Tritrabs casmaliensis* (PESSAGNO), *Podobursa triacantha* (FISCHLI) gr., *Podocapsa amphitreptera* FOREMAN, *Napora* sp. Neither *Higumastra imbricata* OZVOLDOVA, nor any representative of *Andromeda* were found, confirming an uppermost Jurassic age.

Some calcareous levels within this siliceous part yielded Late Tithonian−Berriasian Calpionellids (Béchennec 1987).

The silicified calcareous levels (mid and upper part) of Si1 (lower Sid'r Formation) yielded no paleontological data.

The mid Sid'r Formation (Si2) has been dated as Upper Albian to Cenomanian by foraminifera (Béchennec 1987).

The silicified calcareous horizons in the uppermost part of Sid'r Formation (Si2c) were barren.

The Nayid Formation has been dated with planktonic foraminifera (Béchennec 1987) as: mid Cenomanian to Early Turonian in the lower part; Early to middle Turonian in the middle part; Late Turonian to Early Senonian in the upper part.

The Umar group

In the upper part of the Sini Formation (UmV2) calcareous olistoliths have been dated as Triassic (Carnian) by neritic microfossils (Bechennec 1987) including algae, corals and foraminifera. No radiolaria were found in the Sini Formation (Fig. 5).

Fig. 4. Radiolarians from Liassic to Cretaceous.
1. *Parahsuum simplum* YAO, x190, (DJ 213D, fig. 4), Liassic, Buwaydah Formation, Al Aridh Group.
2. *Nassellaria* gen. et sp. indet. x150, (FB 577B, fig. 2) Liassic, Guwayza Formation, Hamrat Duru Group.
3. "Gen. sp. indet. 1" in DE WEVER, 1982, x150, (FB 577B, fig. 2), Liassic, Guwayza Formation, Hamrat Duru Group.
4. *Drulanta* sp. cf. *mostleri* YEH, x150, (DJ 213D, fig. 4), Liassic, Buwaydah Formation, Al Aridh Group.
5. *Canoptum anulatum* PESSAGNO & POISSON, x150, (FB 577B, fig. 2), Liassic, Guwayza Formation, Hamrat Duru Group.
6. *Droltus* (?) sp. x330, (FB 577B, fig. 2), Liassic, Guwayza Formation, Hamrat Duru Group.
7. *Ristola altissima* (RUST), x95, (MV 493, fig. 2), Late Jurassic to Early Cretaceous, Wahrah Formation, Hamrat Duru Group.
8. *Thanarla conica* (ALIEV), x240, (MV 841, fig. 4), Neocomian, Buwaydah Formation, Al Aridh Group.
9. *Parahsuum simplum* YAO, x190, (DJ 213D, fig. 4), Liassic, Buwaydah Formation, Al Aridh Group.
10. *Pseudodictyomitra carpatica* (LOZYNYAK), x180, (MV 493, fig. 2), Late Jurassic to early Cretaceous, Wahrah Formation, Hamrat Duru Group.
11. *Pseudoaulophacus putahensis* PESSAGNO (?), x145, (DR 40, fig. 4), Senonian, Mussalah Formation, Al Aridh Group.
12. *gen. sp. indet.*, (DJ 213D, fig. 4), Liassic, Buwaydah Formation, Al Aridh Group.
13. *Alievium helenae* SCHAAF, x250, (MV 490, fig. 2), Berriasian-Valanginian, Wahrah Formation, Hamrat Duru Group.
14. *Pantanellium lanceola* (PARONA), x150, (MV 493, fig. 2), Late Jurassic to Early Cretaceous, Wahrah Formation, Hamrat Duru Group.
15. *Alievium praegallowayi* PESSAGNO, x190, (DR 40, fig. 4), Senonian, Mussalah Formation, Al Aridh Group.

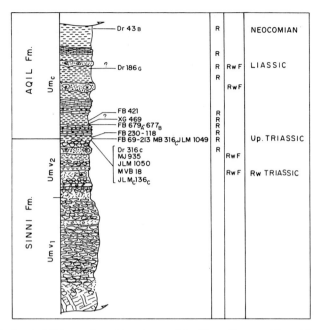

Fig. 5. Composite (estimated) lithostratigraphic column of the Umar Group with position of productive radiolarian samples (numbers) ("R" on columns), and of reworked Foraminifera "RwF"

The base of the Aqil Formation has been dated as Triassic, based on the following.

DR 316: Carnian (or Norian) with: *Capnuchosphaera deweveri* NAKASEKO & NISHIMURA, *Capnuchosphaera lea* DE WEVER

JLM 136C: Ladinian with: *Eptingium manfredi* DUMITRICA, *Falcispongus* sp. aff. *F. falciformis* DUMITRICA (spines more circular than holotype), *Pentaspongodiscus* sp. cf. *P. rarauana* DUMITRICA, *Triassocampe* sp. cf. *T. deweveri* DUMITRICA, *Capnuchosphaera* sp. (with a somewhat triangular central shell), *Pseudostylosphaera hellenica* (DE WEVER).

JLM 1050: Ladinian : *Baumgartneria* sp. aff. *B. retrospina* DUMITRICA (with somewhat shorter spines than the holotype), *Baumgartneria retrospina* DUMITRICA, *Oertlispongus* sp. aff. *O. inaequispinosus* DUMITRICA (with strongly twisted spines), *Triassocampe* sp., *Pseudostylosphaera* sp.

MV 818: Middle to Late Triassic: *Triassocampe* sp., *Plafkerium* sp. cf. *P. confluens* DUMITRICA, KOZUR & MOSTLER, *Plafkerium* sp(p), *Sarla* sp., *Spongoserrula*

rarauana DUMITRICA, *Eptingium manfredi* DUMITRICA.
MV 935: Middle to Late Triassic with: *Oertlisponginae*

FB 69: Triassic? with: *Palaeosaturnalis* sp. (or *Pseudoheliodiscus* sp.?), *Heliosaturnalis* sp.,
JLM 1049: Triassic with: *Pentaspongodiscus* sp. cf. *P. dercourti* DE WEVER (with numerous small bifidcs spines on central shell), *Capnuchosphaera* sp. (two of the coplanar arms are orthogonal, as in sample JLM 136 C)

MB 316C: Carnian to Norian with: *Pseudoheliodiscus* sp., *Triassocampe* sp., *Capnuchosphaera triassica* DE WEVER, *Heliosaturnalis* sp. and one radiolarian fragment with a spindle-shaped spine with tuberculate ribs.

The base has been dated as Late Triassic by the following.
FB 679A: Norian with: *Capnuchosphaera tricornis* DE WEVER, *Capnodoce anapetes* DE WEVER, *Capnodoce* sp. aff. *C. anapetes* DE WEVER (morphotype illustrated by Blome in Middle to Late Norian strata in North America), *Capnuchosphaera deweveri*

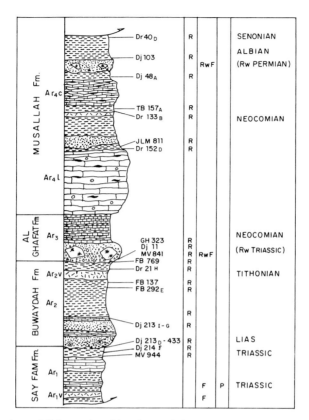

Fig. 6. Composite (estimated) lithostratigraphic column of the Al Aridh Group with position of productive radiolarian samples (numbers) (and "R" on columns), and other palaeontological groups (Foraminifera "F", Pelecypods "P", and reworked Foraminifera: "RwF")

PESSAGNO, *Perispongidium* (?) *tethyus* DE WEVER, *Syringocapsa* sp. cf. *S. batodes* DE WEVER

XG 469: Late Triassic with: *Capnuchosphaera tricornis* DE WEVER, *Capnuchosphaera concava* DE WEVER, *Capnuchosphaera* sp. cf. *C. triassica* DE WEVER, *Xiphotheca karpenissionensis* DE WEVER

The middle part of the Aqil Formation has been dated as Liassic by radiolarians.
DR 186: *Trillus elkhornensis* PESSAGNO & BLOME, *Jacus* sp. cf. *J. anatiformis* DE WEVER, *Poulpus* sp. cf. *P. keki* DE WEVER and *Thetis undulatus* DE WEVER. In this part, Late Triassic reefal microfossils (corals, algae, foraminifera) were found in limestone olistoliths.

The uppermost part of the Aqil Formation has been dated Neocomian (Hauterivian–Early Aptian) by radiolarians: (DR 43 B).

Archaeodictyomitra lacrimula (FOREMAN), *Praeconocaryomma* sp., *Pantanellium lanceola* (PARONA) gr. and *Xitus* (*Novixitus?*) sp.

Al Aridh group

Calcareous horizons in the lower part of the Sayfam Formation have been dated as Triassic by pelagic Pelecypods (i.e. *Halobia*) and Foraminifera (Fig. 6) (Béchennec 1987).

The upper part of Sayfam Formation has been dated as Late Triassic (Carnian? to Norian) by radiolarians : (MV 944) : *Parasepsagon* sp. cf. *P. robustus* KOZUR & MOSTLER, *Triassocampe* sp., *Capnuchosphaera* sp. cf. *C. triassica* DE WEVER, *Hsuum* sp. and *Sarla* sp. cf. *S. vetusta* PESSAGNO.

The lower part of the Buwaydah Formation (Ar2) has been dated as Late Liassic by radiolarians among which several species are new (work in progress): (DJ 213D, DJ 213J): *Parashuum simplum* YAO, *Pantanellidae* spp.

and (DJ 433E) : *Higumastra* sp. (fragment), ?
Pachyoncus sp., Emiluvia-like, spummellarians
with 6 orthogonal spines, and a multilayered
shell, *Pantanellinae* sp. (forms with elongated
shell) ; (DJ 213 Q) *Pachyoncus* sp., *Angulobracchia* sp., *Triactoma* sp. (morphotype with a
meshwork on the proximal part of spines), *Katroma* sp., nassellarians with a square distal
meshwork)

The upper part of the Buwaydah Formation
has been dated as Tithonian to Neocomian by
radiolarians.

FB 768: Berriasian to Early Aptian with:
Pantanellium lanceola (PARONA) gr.,
Archaeodictyomitra apiaria (RUST), *Pseudo-
dictyomitra carpatica* (LOZYNYAK),
Thanarla conica (ALIEV)

FB 292E: Tithonian to Hauterivian with:
Pantanellium lanceola (PARONA), *Archaeodictyomitra* sp., *Thanarla* sp. cf. *T. conica* (ALIEV), *Acanthocircus dicranacanthos*
(SQUINABOL)

FB 137B: Tithonian to Valanginian with:
Acanthocircus dicranacanthos (SQUI-
NABOL), *Pantanellium lanceola* (PARONA)
gr., *Podobursa polylophia* FOREMAN,
Mirifusus sp. cf. *M. mediodilatatus* (RUST),
Archaeodictyomitra apiaria (RUST)

DR 21H: Malm to Neocomian with:
Pantanellium lanceola (PARONA) gr.,
Acaeniotyle sp., *Acanthocircus* sp., *Crucella*
sp.

FB 769: Tithonian with: *Acanthocircus
dicranacanthos* (SQUINABOL), *Pantanellium lanceola* (PARONA) gr., *Podobursa triacantha* (FISCHLI), *Parvicingula cosmoconica*
(FOREMAN)

The uppermost part of the Buwaydah Forma-
tion is dated as Neocomian by radiolarians.
DJ 11: Berriasian to Cenomanian with:
Archaeodictyomitra lacrimula (FOREMAN).
Archaeodictyomitra apiaria (RUST), *Thanarla
conica* (ALIEV), *Thanarla praeveneta* PES-
SAGNO, *Eucyrtis micropora* gr. (SQUI-
NABOL)

GH 323: Neocomian with: *Ditrabs* sp. cf. *D.
sansalvadorensis* (PESSAGNO), *Eucyrtis
micropora* gr. (SQUINABOL)

MV 841: Neocomian with: *Acaeniotyle
umbilicata* FOREMAN, *Thanarla conica*
(ALIEV), *Spongocapsula palmerae*
PESSAGNO, *Archaespongoprunum* sp.; this

fauna is well preserved but specimens are
broken; several species are undescribed.

The Al Ghafat Formation (Ar3) is very
coarse-grained near its base and includes limestone olistoliths, which are dated as Late Triassic
(Norian to Rhaetian by neritic foraminifera
(Béchennec 1987).

In the Mussalah Formation, the chert overlying the limestones of the lower part (Ar41)
yielded a radiolarian fauna ranging from
Tithonian to Neocomian:

DR 152D: Late Tithonian to Hauterivian
with: *Acanthocircus   dicranacanthos*
(SQUINABOL)

JM 811: Oxfordian to Valanginian with:
Mirifusus sp., *Ristola altissima* (RUST),
Parvicingula boesii (PARONA) gr.

The middle part of the Mussallah Formation
is dated as Late Neocomian (Hauterivian to
Barremian) by radiolarians : (DR 133 B)
Pantanellium lanceola (PARONA) gr., *Cecrops
septemporatus* (PARONA), *Alievium helenae*

SCHAAF, *Thanarla elegantissima* (CITA)

Permian (Murghabian to Djulfian) horizon
limestone olistoliths with foraminifera occur in
a coarse detrital olistoliths (Béchennec 1987).

The upper part of the Mussallah Formation is
dated as Albian by radiolarians (DJ 103) with:
Thanarla conica (ALIEV), *Spongocapsula* sp.
cf. *S. perampla* (RUST), *Emiluvia* sp. cf. *E.
chica* FOREMAN, *Eucyrtis micropora* gr.
(SQUINABOL), *Napora* sp., *Mita* sp. cf. *M.
magnifica* PESSAGNO, *Acaeniotyle diaphorogona* FOREMAN (with a clear inner shell
as previously established by OZVOLDOVA
and Sykora M. (1984)

The uppermost part of the Mussallah Formation is dated as Senonian (Coniacian?) by radiolarians (DR 40 D): *Pseudoaulophacus superbus
(SQUINABOL) gr., Pseudoaulophacus flore-
sensis* PESSAGNO, *Eucyrtis micropora* gr.
(SQUINABOL), *Crucella irwini* PESSAGNO

Conclusions

The systematic collection of each bedded chert
level associated with turbidites in the Hawasina
allochthonous unit has led to greatly improved
age dating and recognition of various sedimentary and tectonic events.

The main results are as follows:
(i) Permian bedded chert exist near the base
of the Hawasina Complex. This is the first
occurrence of bedded chert of that age in
the Tethyan regions;
(ii) a volcanic event is dated as Triassic;

(iii) bedded chert horizons are dated as Liassic;
(iv) thick turbiditic sequences have been divided into a number of units of Middle and Late Jurassic age.

We thank Dr. Hilal Bin Mohd Al-Azry (Ministry of Petroleum and Minerals of Oman) for his support. The present work was financially supported by the Bureau de Recherche Géologique et Minière, Orléans and the Centre National de la Recherche Scientifique, Paris (CNRS-URA 705, GRECO n°088 and ASP EVOL. n°6374 R11). We thank A. H. F. Robertson (Edinburgh), C. Blome (USGS, Tulsa, Oklahoma), E. A. Jr. Pessagno (UTD, Texas) and R. W. Scott (Amoco Prod., Oklahoma) for their valuable comments on the manuscript. Special thanks are due to N. Kito (Paris) for his help with the work including use of the scanning electron microscope.

References

AITA, Y. 1987. Middle Jurassic to Lower Cretaceous Radiolarian Biostratigraphy of Shikoku with reference to Selected Sections in Lombardy Basin and Sicily. Science Reports of Tohoku University, Sendai, (58), Second (Geology), **1**, 1–91.

BAUMGARTNER, P. O. 1984. A Middle Jurassic–Early Cretaceous low latitude radiolarian zonation based on Unitary Associations and age of Tethyan radiolarites. Eclogae Geologicae Helvetiae, Basel, **77**, 729–837.

—— 1987. Age and genesis of Tethyan Jurassic Radiolarites, Eclogae Geologicae Helvetiae, Basel, **80**, 831–879.

—— & DE WEVER, P. & KOCHER, R. N. 1980. Correlation of Tethyan Late Jurassic-Early Cretaceous events. Cahiers de Micropaléontologie. 26e Congrès Géologique International (Paris, 7–17 Juillet 1980), Paris, **2**, 23–85.

BECHENNEC, F. 1987. Géologie des nappes Hawasina dans les parties orientale et centrale des montagnes d'Oman: Thèse Université Tierre et Marie Curie, Paris, Documents du BRGM 127.

——, BEURRIER, M., RABU, D. & HUTIN, G. 1986. Geological map of Oman, Barka, sheet NF 40–3B, Scale 1/1000000. Explanatory notes. Directorate general of Mineral, Oman Ministry of Petroleum and Minerology.

BECHENNEC, F., LE METOUR, J., RABU, D., BOURDILLON DE GRISSAC, C., DE WEVER, P., BEURRIER, M. & VILLEY, M. 1990. The Hawasina Nappes: stratigraphy and structural evolution of a fragment of the South Tethyan Passive Continental Margin. In: ROBERTSON, A. H. F., SEARLE, M. P. & RIES, A. C. (eds) The Geology and Tectonics of the Oman Region. Geological Society, London, Special Publication, **49**, 213–223.

BERNOULLI, D. & WEISSERT, H. 1987. The upper Hawasina nappes in the central Oman Mountains: stratigraphy, palinspastics and sequence of nappe emplacement. Geodinamica Acta, Paris, **1**, 47 58.

BEURRIER, M., BOURDILLON DE GRISSAC, C., DE

WEVER, P. & LESCUYER, J-L. 1987. Biostratigraphie des radiolarites associées aux volcanites ophiolitiques de la nappe de Samail (Sultanat d'Oman) : Conséquences tectogénétiques. Comptes Rendus de l'Académie des Sciences, Paris, t.**304**, ser.II, 907–910.

BLOME, C. D. 1983. Upper Triassic Capnuchosphaeridae and Capnodocidae (Radiolaria) from East Central Oregon. Micropaleontology, New York, **29**, 11–49.

DE WEVER, P. 1981a. Hagiastridae, Patulibracchiidae et Spongodiscidae (Radiolaires Polycystines) du Lias de Turquie. Revue de Micropaléontologie, Paris, **24**, 27–50.

—— 1981b. Parasaturnalidae, Pantanellidae et Sponguridae (Radiolaires polycystines) du Lias de Turquie. Revue de Micropaléontologie, Paris, **24**, 138–156.

——, 1982a. Nassellaria (radiolaires polycystines) du Lias de Turquie. Revue de Micropaléontologie, Paris, **24** 189–232.

——, 1982b. Radiolaires du Trias et du Lias de la Téthys (Systématique, stratigraphie): Publication de la Société Géologique du Nord n°7, Lille.

——, BOURDILLON DE GRISSAC, C. & BECHENNEC, F. 1988a. A Permian age from radiolarites of the Hawasina Nappes, Oman Mountains. Geology, **16**, 912–914.

——, & BEURRIER, M. 1988b. Radiolaires sénoniens de la nappes de Samail (Oman). Revue de Micropaléontologie, Paris, **31**, 166–177.

—— & CORDEY, F. 1986. Datation par les Radiolaires de la Formation des Radiolarites s.s. de la série du Pinde-Olonos (Grèce): Bajocien (?)-Tithonique. In: DE WEVER, P. (ed.) Eurorad IV – Marine Micropaleontology, Amsterdam, **11**, 113–127.

——, & DUEE, G. & EL KADIRI, KH. 1985. Les séries stratigraphiques des klippes de Chrafate (Rif septentrional, Maroc) témoins d'une marge continentale subsidente au cours du Jurassique-Crétacé. Bulletin de la Société géologique de France, Paris, **1**, **8**, 363–379.

——, GEYSSANT, J. R., AZEMA, J., DEVOS, I., DUEE, G., MANIVIT, H. & VRIELYNCK, B. 1986. La coupe de Santa Anna (zone de Sciacca, Sicile): une synthèse biostratigraphique des apports des macro-, micro- et nannofossiles du Jurassique supérieur et Crétacé inférieur. Revue de Micropaléontologie, Paris, **29**, 141–186.

—— & MICONNET, P. 1985. Datations directes des radiolarites du Bassin du Lagonegro (Lucanie, Italie méridionale). Implications et conséquences. Revista Espanola de Micropaleontologia, Madrid, **17**, 373–402.

——, RIEDEL, W. R., BAUMGARTNER, P. O., DUMITRICA, P., BJORKLUND, K., CAULET, J-P., DROBNE, K., GRANLUND, A., KOCHER, K. N. & SCHAAF, A. 1979b. Recherches actuelles sur les Radiolaires en Europe. Annales de la Société géologique du Nord, Lille, t.XCVIII, 205–222.

—— & SANFILIPPO, A., RIEDEL, W. R. & GRUBER, B. 1979a. Triassic radiolarians from Greece, Sicily, and Turkey. Micropaleontology, New York, **25**, 75–110.

DUMITRICA, P. 1982. Triassic Oertlisponginae (Radiolaria) from Eastern Carpathians and Southern Alps. — *Dari Seama Sedintelor*, Bucarest, (LXVII), 57—74.

—— & KOZUR, H. & MOSTLER, H. 1980. Contribution to the radiolarian fauna of the Middle Triassic of the Southern Alps. *Geologisch-Paläontologische Mitteilungen*, Innsbrück, **10**, 1—46.

GLENNIE, K. W., BOEUF, M. G. A., HUGHES CLARKE, M. W., MOODY STUART, M., PILAAR, W. F. H. & REINHARDT, B. M. 1974. Geology of the Oman Mountains: Verhandelingen van het Koninklijk Nederlands Geologisch mijnbouwkundig Genootschap, Gravenhage, Transactions **31**, 1—423.

GRAHAM, G. M. 1980a. Structure and sedimentology of the Hawasina Window, Oman mountains. *PhD thesis*, Open University, Milton Keynes.

—— 1980b. Evolution of a passive margin and nappe emplacement in the Oman Mountains: Proceedings, International Ophiolite Symposium, Cyprus, 414—423

ISHIGA, H. 1986. Late Carboniferous and Permian Radiolarian Biostratigraphy of Southwest Japan: *Journal of Geosciences* Osaka City University, **29**, 89—100.

——, WATASE, H. & NAKA, T. 1986. Permian radiolarians from Nishiki group in Sangun-Chugoku Belt, Southwest Japan: Earth Science (Chikyu Kagaku), *Journal of the Association for the Geological Collaboration in Japan*, **40**, 124—136.

KASMIN, V. G., RICOU, L-E. & SBORTSHIKOV, I. M. 1986. Structure and evolution of the passive margin of the eastern Tethys. *Tectonophysics*, **123**, 153—179.

NAZAROV, B. B. & ORMISTON, A. R. 1985. Radiolaria from late Paleozoic of the southern Urals, USSR and West Texas, USA. *Micropaleontology*, New York, **31**, 1—54.

OZVOLDOVA, L. & SYKORA, M. 1984. The radiolarian Assemblage from Cachtické Karpaty Mts. Limestones (The locality Sipkovsky Hàj). *Geologica Carpathica*, Bratislava, **35**, 260—290.

PESSAGNO, E. A., Jr. 1977a. Upper Jurassic Radiolaria and Radiolarian biostratigraphy of the California

Coast Ranges. *Micropaleontology*, New York, **23**, 56—113.

—— 1977b. Lower Cretaceous Radiolarian biostratigraphy of the Great Valley Sequence and Franciscan Complex, California Coast Ranges. — *Cushman Foundation Foraminiferal Research*, Special Publication, Washington, **15**, 5—87.

—— & BLOME, C. D., LONGORIA, J. F. 1984. A Revised Radiolarian Zonation for the Upper Jurassic of Western North America *Bulletins of American Paleontology*, Ithaca, Lawrence, **87**, 1—51.

—— & BLOME, C. D., CARTER, E. S., MACLEOD, N., WHALEN, P. A. & YEH, K. Y. 1987. Preliminary Radiolarian Zonation for the Jurassic of North America. *In*: CULVER, S. J. (ed.) *Studies of North American Jurassic Radiolaria, Part II*. Cushman Foundation for Foraminiferal Research, Special Publication, Norfolk, **23**, 1—51.

SANFILIPPO, A. & RIEDEL, W. R. 1985. Cretaceous Radiolaria. *In*: BOLI, H. M. *et al*, (ed.) *Plankton Stratigraphy*. Cambridge University Press, Cambridge.

SEARLE, M. P. & GRAHAM, G. M. 1982. 'Oman Exotics' — Ocean carbonate build-ups associated with early stages of continental rifting. *Geology*, **10**, 43—49.

VILLEY, M., BECHENNEC, F., BEURRIER, M., LE METOUR, J. & RABU, D. 1986. Geological Map of Yanqul, sheet NF 40-2C, scale 1/100000. Explanatory notes: Directorate general of Minerals, Oman Ministry of Petroleum and Minerals.

VRIELYNCK, B. 1989. Biostrat: programme de traitement de données et d'édition de tableaux d'extensions stratigraphiques, *Revue de Micropaléontologie, Paris*.

—— & GRANLUND, A. H. 1989. Genetab, a basic program for editing stratigraphic range charts. *Computer and Geosciences*, Elmsford, **13** 789—797.

WATTS, K. F. & GARRISON, R. E. 1986. Sumeini group, Oman — Evolution of a Mesozoic carbonate slope on a south tethyan continental margin. *Sedimentary Geology*, Amsterdam, **48**, 107—168.

Manganese occurrences in the Al Hammah Range – Wahrah Formation, Oman Mountains

W. KICKMAIER & TJ. PETERS

Mineralogisch-Petrogr. Institut, Baltzerstrasse 1, CH-3012 Bern, Switzerland

Abstract: The host rocks of the manganese in the Al Hammah Range (125 km S of Muscat) are red radiolarian cherts of Tithonian to Neocomian age, continuously exposed over 1000 km^2. The stratigraphic sequence starts with fine-grained turbiditic limestones followed by a transition zone of coloured silt-mudstones and cherts which grade into almost $CaCO_3$- free cherts, topped by 1−5 m of silicified limestones. The base of the Wahrah Formation is unknown. Sedimentological and geochemical features indicate that the cherts are of biogenic, non-hydrothermal origin. The stratiform manganese deposits are the result of sedimentary and tectonic enrichment processes. The single Mn-layers formed during periods of condensed sedimentation at the sediment−water interface. The different Mn-chert types (disseminated and layered ore and black Mn-rich cherts) can be explained by varying sedimentation rates of radiolaria, clay and manganese precipitation. Geochemically, the manganese deposits are characterized by high Mn/Fe ratios and by an extremely low minor element (e.g. Ni, Cu, Co) content. Using geochemical discrimination diagrams, the manganese deposits of the Wahrah Formation would be of hydrothermal origin. This contrasts with the sedimentary characteristics of the manganese-bearing cherts and with the field observations. Because of the Tithonian to Neocomian age of the Wahrah Formation cherts, the manganese enrichment can not be related to the formation of the Semail ophiolite. It is proposed that they might relate to a long distance discharge from the Owen fracture zone during the formation of the Masirah ophiolite.

Stratiform manganese occurrences in cherts have generally been classified as volcano-sedimentary deposits (Roy 1981). Based on comparisons with recent submarine manganese crusts, the source of the manganese is thought to be hydrothermal (Bonatti *et al.* 1972; Crerar *et al.* 1982), originating from small or large hydrothermal convective cells. The excellent continuous exposures in the Oman Mountains of the manganese bearing cherts of the Wahrah Formation offer a unique possibility to test this model.

The Al Hammah Range, a segment of the Hawasina Complex, is situated *c.* 125 km south of Muscat (Fig. 1). It belongs to a 'chain' of Hawasina allochthonous sediments lying in front of the Semail ophiolite.

In the Al Hammah Range the Wahrah Formation (240 m) comprises a non-metamorphic sequence of fine-grained turbiditic limestones (90 m i.e. the lower limestone member of Glennie *et al.* 1974). The transition zone between the lower limestone member and the prominent red radiolarian chert is represented by a sequence of white and violet mud-silstones and cherts (30 m). The overlying chert sequence (110 m) consists of red to brown radiolarian cherts, alternating with siliceous clay interbeds.

Within the red cherts manganese is enriched in two Mn-horizons (i.e. stratiform Mn-occurrences), which can be divided into, at most, six Mn-zones. The Mn-horizons can be traced through the whole range. In the field there is no indication of volcaniclastic or hydrothermal influence which could be responsible for the manganese enrichment. In addition to this sedimentary Mn-enrichment, manganese is enriched by a tectonic process (see below). Only a few outcrops of the upper limestone member are found in the field. This limestone is coarser and more silicified than the lower limestone member.

The structure of the range is dominated by an east−west striking, double plunging, *en enchelon* fold system, disrupted by numerous reverse faults. The fold axis dip gently to the east and west; minor fold axes in the western part of the range dip to the east and vice versa. Characteristic chevron-type folds in the cherts are slightly south-vergent and are often disrupted by axial-plane, or out-of-syncline thrusts. On a regional scale the Al Hammah Range can be divided into five imbricate units, which exhibit similar fold and thrust styles. The thrust planes which separate these main units are steeply north-dipping. The coloured mudstones,

From ROBERTSON, A. H. F., SEARLE, M. P. & RIES, A. C. (eds), 1990,   239
The Geology and Tectonics of the Oman Region.
Geological Society Special Publication No 49, pp 239−249

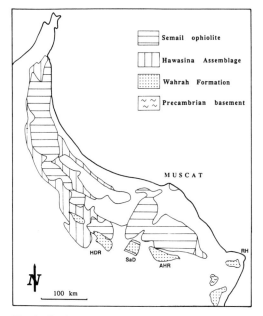

Fig. 1. Geological sketch map of Oman. (Simplified after Glennie *et al.* 1974); AHR, Al Hammah Range; SaD, Sufrad ad Dawh; HDR, Hamrat Duru; RH, Ras al Hadd.

siltstones and cherts are often tectonically reduced or completely absent, so that the lower limestones are thrust directly onto red radiolarian cherts. Due to folding and thrusting, the thickness of the Wahrah Formation sediments in the Al Hammah Range is estimated as a minimum of 1000 m.

Outside the Al Hammah Range the Wahrah Formation is exposed from Jabal Wahrah in the west to the Ras al Hadd area in the east. Most of the latter area is occupied by a Wahrah-like lithologic sequence of limestones, followed by manganese-bearing cherts and, in contrast to the map of Glennie *et al.* (1974), only sub-ordinate cherts of the Halfa Formation. Age determinations of the Ras al Hadd cherts (un-published report on the Geological Survey of the Sultanate of Oman; Sur area 1982) and preliminary dating of the Wahrah Formation in the Al Hammah Range (P. O. Baumgartner 1988, pers. comm.) based on Radiolaria indicate that they are time-equivalent units.

In comparison to the other Hawasina units, with the exception of the Umar Group, the Wahrah Formation is dominated by chert facies. Glennie *et al.* (1974) reported a regular in-crease of the pelagic to detrial sediment ratio from the Hamrat Duru, through the Wahrah Formation to the Halfa Formation (partly equiv-

alent to the Umar Group of Béchennec (1988)). In comparison to the Hamrat Duru Group, the cherts of the Wahrah Formation formed in a more distal position in the basin. This work is mainly concerned with the cherts and shales; the limestones will be the subject of a further publication.

Analytical methods

The major and trace elements were determined by an automatic XRF spectrometer. The main error in the major element analyses is SiO_2 content, since the high SiO_2 content is above the normal standardization limit. All manganese is given as MnO. The minerals were determined in thin sections, by X-ray diffractometer (XRD) and X-ray diffraction photographs using a Guninie camera.

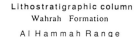

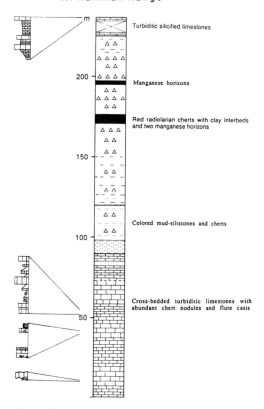

Fig. 2. Schematic stratigraphic column of the Wahrah Formation in the Al Hammah Range.

General characteristics of the radiolarian cherts

The cherts of the Wahrah Formation are typical ribbon cherts, consisting of impure radiolarian cherts and siliceous clay interbeds. The cherts lack sedimentary features typical of turbiditic cherts; e.g. graded bedding, erosional contacts between chert and shale, cross bedding or ripple marks (McBride & Folk 1979). It was possible to distinguish three basic chert types, but it is notable that they grade into each other continuously.

The chert sequence starts with muddy radiolarian cherts of brown to red colour (Fig. 2). They show parallel or flaser lamination, with a symmetrical increase in clay content towards the shale layer (i.e. triple layered cherts of Iijima (1983)). The primary contacts between shale and chert are often destroyed by shearing during folding, so that contacts are now mainly sharp.

The second chert group is found in the manganese-bearing horizons. In contrast to the other chert sequences, which are partly homogeneous, the cherts of the Mn-horizons abruptly change their lithology from one chert layer to another. Individual chert beds, however, show the same features as the basal and the uppermost chert sequences.

The third group of radiolarian cherts, the intense red cherts, lie at the top of the stratigraphic sequence (Fig. 3) and are characterized by a lower clay content. These cherts are also triple layered, although single layered beds are also common.

Within the stratigraphic succession the clay content decreases regularly upwards. At the base of the Wahrah Formation cherts, clay interbeds occupy 32% of the succession, which contrasts with 19% at the top of the sequence. Also, geochemical analyses indicate the detrital component decreases upwards. The cherts which are transitional to the upper limestones member also show a high clay content.

Manganese-bearing cherts

The stratiform sedimentary manganese enrichment in the red radiolarian cherts can be subdivided into the following zones.
(i)   brown cherts;
(ii) layered Mn-cherts;
(iii) black siliceous cherts;
(iv) nodular Mn-aggregates in red cherts.
A manganese horizon usually starts with brown cherts, followed by manganese-layered cherts, with the most manganese-rich black siliceous cherts at the top of the stratigraphic sequence. Figure 3 shows a schematic profile through a typical manganese horizon. In the field the manganese-zones are exposed continuously over several hundred metres along strike. All manganese chert types which are found in vertical sequences are also seen along strike. In a few cases black siliceous chert beds, 50 cm thick, grade continuously into 'normal' chert 5 cm thick over a horizontal distance of only 10 m. In contrast to these variably manganese-rich zones the manganese horizons are more continuous and can be correlated throughout the range.

Brown cherts. The brown muddy cherts consist of alternations of brown cherts and brown clay interbeds. Besides dispersed manganese (i.e. imparting a brown colour), manganese occurs in the finest laminae and as small nodular manganese segregations in shale partings. In contrast to the 'manganese-free' cherts, this chert type is characterized by numerous reduction haloes and fine manganese-filled joints.

Manganese-layered cherts. Within these chert beds manganese is concentrated in several layers, up to 4 cm thick. The layers are parallel to the bedding but have an irregular surface. The chert layers between the massive ore layers are typically red to brown muddy cherts with fine manganese laminae and abundant radiolaria (Fig. 4).

Black siliceous cherts. This manganese chert is striking because of its generally homogeneous texture and intense black colour in up to 60 cm thick beds. Parallel layering in the black cherts is indicated by zones which are dark brown in colour. In some cases the black part of the chert is bounded by intense red (siliceous) chert. The red cherts occur either on both sides (i.e. symmetrically) or only at the top or at the base (i.e. asymmetrically) of the black horizons.

Manganese segregations. The nodular-shaped manganese-segregations occur in muddy cherts, independently of manganese layers. These nodules reach 8 cm diameter and are slightly elongate parallel to bedding. Apart from an outer rim of amorphous manganate with abundant radiolaria and a pure pyrolusite core no concentric textures are present. These nodules occur only in a few beds and as small segregations in brown clays.

Microscopic features of the radiolarian cherts

'Manganese-free' radiolarian cherts. The radiolarian cherts are composed mainly of radiolaria, microcrystalline chalcedonic quartz

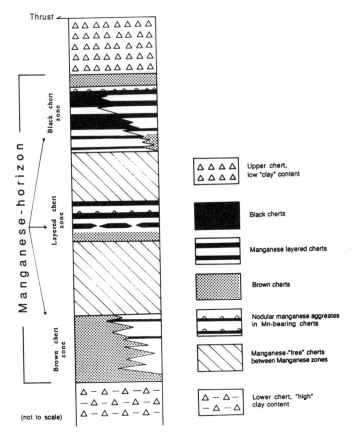

Fig. 3. Simplified profile through a manganese horizon. The figure shows the sedimentary manganese enrichment from bottom (brown cherts) to top with black siliceous cherts.

Fig. 4. Typical manganese layered chert.

(≤0.02 mm), disordered quartz, clay minerals, and in the manganese cherts pyrolusite and amorphous manganese. The clay content of cherts and shale interbeds, determined by X-ray diffraction, consists mainly of smectite, illite, and minor kaolinite. Some haematite is also present. Almost undeformed radiolaria may reach up to 70% in volume and form the groundmass, together with the calcedonic quartz. The radiolaria are homogeneously distributed in the chert and have a mean size of 0.07 mm. No enrichment or sorting is visible. The radiolaria are filled with chalcedony, microcrystalline quartz, clay or manganese.

Manganese-bearing cherts. In the brown cherts small manganese-segregations (0.02 mm) are homogeneously distributed (i.e. as disseminated 'ore' in brown cherts), or they are concentrated

Fig. 5. Manganese layer with a knobby upper surface. From field evidence the knobby surface is thought to represent the top of the layer which is supported by a sedimentary filling of the following radiolarian chert layer. (Scale bar =2 mm).

in small laminae partly replacing the clay laminae (manganese-laminated cherts). The fine internal structure of the radiolaria is well preserved through protection by a manganese infill. No sharp contacts between the manganese-rich laminae and the chert with disseminated manganese ore were observed.

Manganese-layered cherts. In the manganese-layered cherts, manganese is concentrated in 4 cm-thick layers, with none in the radiolarian chert layers between. Radiolaria are an important component of the thicker manganese layers. The manganese layers are symmetrical (i.e. they show a regular increase of manganese

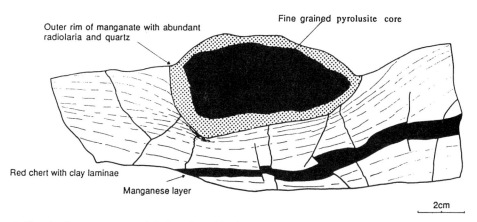

Fig. 6. Sketch of a manganese nodule in red muddy chert. The parallel lamination of the chert beneath the nodule is compressed due to selective compaction.

Table 1. *Major and trace element analyses of siliceous shales and red radiolarian cherts (three parts)*

Siliceous shales

Sample number

	1	2	3	4	5	6	7	8	9	10	11	12	13	14
Major elements (weight percent):														
SiO_2*	83.93	82.29	76.18	78.85	81.81	82.1	85.86	76.15	81.5	80.45	82.31	80.91	75.05	71.58
TiO_2	0.35	0.43	0.66	0.56	0.4	0.46	0.31	0.62	0.44	0.45	0.39	0.52	0.47	0.41
Al_2O_3	5.27	5.86	8.23	6.55	5.33	6.26	5.12	8.13	6.18	6.07	6.00	6.90	5.86	6.74
Fe_2O_3	3.1	4.56	5.71	4.26	3.25	4.20	2.38	5.54	3.85	4.23	3.88	4.00	4.21	3.78
MnO**	0.04	0.05	0.08	0.09	0.10	0.14	0.17	0.26	0.33	0.46	0.52	4.47	6.55	9.78
MgO	1.49	1.58	1.96	1.58	1.57	1.51	1.34	1.90	1.61	1.76	1.58	0.03	1.35	1.37
CaO	1.56	1.33	1.61	1.21	1.45	132	1.06	1.56	1.36	1.98	1.12	1.96	1.22	1.13
Na_2O	0.07	0.01	0.16	0.08	0.12	0.05	0.38	0.31	0.46	0.08	0.59	0.01	0.11	0.18
K_2O	0.99	0.98	1.82	1.20	0.70	0.97	0.88	1.79	1.07	1.02	1.09	1.14	1.01	0.99
P_2O_5	0.11	0.11	0.24	0.09	0.08	0.14	0.06	0.17	0.11	0.16	0.09	0.12	0.15	0.08
CO_2	0.85	0.56	0.58	0.71	1.08	0.59	0.47	0.63	0.52	1.02	0.51	1.02	0.70	0.39
Total:	97.76	97.76	97.23	95.18	95.89	97.74	98.03	97.06	97.43	97.68	98.08	101.08	96.68	96.43
Trace elements (ppm):														
Ba	136	89	175	98	85	73	103	166	97	133	115	89	131	176
Cr	51	53	77	60	37	47	40	74	40	54	45	58	55	61
Cu	31	44	216	30	74	58	37	73	49	53	61	35	83	147
Ga	6	6	9	9	7	6	6	9	5	6	6	6	4	5
Nb	9	10	18	24	19	11	8	12	15	11	7	15	10	6
Ni	41	41	57	51	44	38	33	60	46	44	43	49	83	18
Pb	1	7	2	26	24	1	2	1	1	1	4	3	1	1
Rb	36	40	61	50	36	35	28	65	40	39	38	40	43	44
Sr	130	127	159	204	142	122	152	174	138	146	123	143	408	314
Th	1	1	1	17	16	1	1	1	3	1	1	1	1	1
V	51	91	60	82	79	49	60	69	54	58	41	60	62	83
Y	24	18	45	28	28	26	11	35	22	32	19	25	21	30
Zn	47	48	80	64	46	48	31	71	47	47	42	58	63	66
Zr	69	65	119	105	91	80	67	105	97	84	62	89	80	80

* The main error in the major element analyses is SiO_2 because the high SiO_2 values are above the normal standartisation limit.
** Total Mn given as MnO.

Radiolarian cherts I

Sample number

	1	2	3	4	5	6	7	8	9	10	11	12	13	14	15	16	17	18
Majoir elements (weight percent):																		
SiO_2*	93.89	92.64	94.2	94.08	90.58	91.42	92.72	93.27	91.32	92.00	94.03	91.86	91.95	92.57	90.74	92.20	90.78	91.69
TiO_2	0.14	0.16	0.12	0.11	0.21	0.12	0.11	0.13	0.14	0.16	0.12	0.18	0.15	0.11	0.13	0.10	0.15	0.14
Al_2O_3	2.25	2.50	2.08	1.79	3.63	1.91	1.79	2.09	2.21	2.66	2.10	2.78	2.46	1.82	2.32	1.68	2.54	2.35
Fe_2O_3	1.31	1.64	1.07	0.99	1.77	1.09	1.13	1.19	1.52	1.33	1.09	1.62	1.32	1.25	1.25	0.97	1.29	1.25
MnO**	0.01	0.02	0.02	0.03	0.03	0.03	0.05	0.06	0.08	0.11	0.13	0.19	0.20	0.20	0.24	0.38	0.58	1.24
MgO	0.54	0.60	0.50	0.47	0.85	0.46	0.35	0.49	0.49	0.74	0.58	0.66	0.66	0.35	0.49	0.28	0.60	0.54
CaO	0.56	0.48	0.40	0.43	0.62	0.87	0.55	0.54	0.63	0.60	0.35	0.46	0.72	0.40	0.69	0.38	0.60	0.54
Na_2O	0.01	0.01	0.18	0.14	0.35	0.08	0.28	0.10	0.93	0.55	0.12	0.18	0.68	0.41	0.78	0.08	0.24	0.18
K_2O	0.35	0.41	0.35	0.30	0.61	0.26	0.28	0.31	0.37	0.43	0.37	0.51	0.39	0.29	0.41	0.29	0.41	0.37
P_2O_5	0.03	0.04	0.05	0.05	0.04	0.03	0.03	0.05	0.03	0.04	0.04	0.04	0.05	0.05	0.01	0.02	0.03	0.05
CO_2	0.13	0.20	0.12	0.30	0.16	0.72	0.55	0.34	0.84	0.16	0.16	0.20	0.45	0.50	0.62	0.57	0.80	0.57
Total:	99.22	98.70	99.09	98.69	98.85	96.99	97.84	98.57	98.56	98.78	99.09	98.68	99.03	97.95	97.68	96.95	96.95	98.92
Trace elements (ppm):																		
Ba	41	62	65	64	73	40	47	46	33	47	55	82	100	39	38	255	180	126
Cr	19	13	21	13	27	175	161	10	117	19	21	25	17	170	102	159	66	11
Cu	20	28	50	27	29	12	10	28	50	22	25	32	24	12	18	32	55	26
Ga	3	4	3	4	4	3	4	3	5	4	4	3	3	4	4	3	4	3
Nb	5	3	4	3	6	10	11	3	12	4	3	4	3	11	10	9	11	3
Ni	17	15	15	14	25	15	13	17	20	14	17	19	17	15	13	19	29	17
Pb	3	5	3	1	2	13	15	3	17	2	3	1	1	14	15	12	17	1
Rb	13	14	9	9	20	15	15	10	20	15	11	16	11	15	19	15	20	12
Sr	71	83	79	76	114	112	102	83	84	124	72	73	86	72	127	80	143	99
Th	1	3	1	1	1	9	8	1	9	2	1	1	1	9	12	7	12	1
V	16	38	15	21	37	10	10	16	14	22	22	16	23	10	17	10	19	30
Y	7	7	9	8	8	12	14	7	15	7	7	7	10	18	14	11	15	8
Zn	15	17	13	12	27	17	15	15	21	15	13	15	14	16	18	15	21	14
Zr	28	27	23	21	43	45	43	23	47	33	22	309	30	41	46	39	49	23

Sample 1 to 17 = Red radiolarian cherts with a "low" manganese content (MnO<1%).
* The main error in the major element analyses is SiO_2 because the high SiO_2 values are above the normal standartisation limit.
** Total Mn given as MnO.

Radiolarian cherts II

Sample number	18	19	20	21	22	23	24	25	26	27	28	29	30	31	32	33
Major elements (weight percent):																
SiO$_2$*	90.58	89.1	87.71	86.63	86.66	84.15	81.27	79.35	75.15	74.17	61.25	71.41	56.43	47.72	37.19	36.07	35.73	27.15
TiO$_2$	0.10	0.13	0.15	0.15	0.10	0.12	0.06	0.10	0.02	0.06	0.26	0.02	0.03	0.03	0.04	0.02	0.02	0.05
Al$_2$O$_3$	1.64	2.20	2.19	2.37	1.69	1.78	1.01	2.02	0.21	0.96	3.40	0.49	0.42	0.50	0.75	0.29	0.54	0.66
Fe$_2$O$_3$	1.33	1.13	1.27	1.39	1.45	1.71	0.80	1.03	0.47	0.54	2.44	0.26	0.69	0.28	0.68	0.58	0.62	0.66
MnO**	1.26	3.71	4.69	5.38	6.63	8.01	12.13	13.81	20.00	20.36	24.8	29.15	34.41	44.65	49.64	51.63	52.89	60.49
MgO	0.24	0.52	0.50	0.54	0.24	0.32	0.17	0.44	0.07	0.21	0.56	0.13	bd	0.12	0.27	0.56	0.11	0.32
CaO	0.62	0.73	0.53	0.63	0.31	0.66	0.49	0.52	0.36	0.59	0.51	0.39	0.57	1.01	0.75	1.07	0.38	1.11
Na$_2$O	0.24	0.09	0.07	0.13	0.01	0.23	bd	0.20	0.33	0.15	bd	0.07	bd	0.05	bd	bd	bd	0.01
K$_2$O	0.34	0.33	0.36	0.39	0.45	0.29	0.16	0.24	0.09	0.14	0.43	0.34	0.06	0.72	0.39	0.08	0.38	0.06
P$_2$O$_5$	0.05	0.03	0.05	0.04	0.03	0.06	0.03	0.09	0.08	0.04	0.04	0.08	0.09	0.11	0.11	0.15	0.11	0.19
CO$_2$	1.32	0.33	0.22	0.19	0.62	0.70	0.50	0.51	1.75	0.27	0.75	0.32	0.01	0.46	0.70	0.98	0.48	0.93
Total:	97.72	98.30	97.74	97.84	98.19	98.03	96.62	98.31	98.53	97.49	94.44	102.66	92.71	95.65	90.52	91.43	91.26	91.62
Trace elements (ppm):																
Ba	258	511	112	1011	1395	585	2820	139	157	1173	4128	2886	147	8439	2533	102	2491	970
Cr	146	19	19	26	135	133	169	31	238	37	67	46	151	337	171	221	190	178
Cu	32	41	40	43	78	111	25	84	4	84	253	31	10	609	19	20	32	112
Ga	2	2	2	1	4	5	2	1	2	1	4	1	2	1	2	2	2	6
Nb	9	1	3	2	17	17	12	1	17	1	22	1	15	1	18	20	21	23
Ni	14	21	31	28	25	23	28	38	31	50	58	60	81	169	129	482	171	169
Pb	26	1	1	1	22	23	8	1	6	1	6	1	6	1	6	6	12	23
Rb	13	9	11	12	18	19	10	2	11	1	25	1	9	1	8	11	10	13
Sr	101	155	159	144	317	197	411	231	343	127	565	363	231	655	435	306	451	459
Th	9	1	1	1	22	23	12	1	19	1	20	1	15	1	14	19	16	21
V	21	54	39	85	183	115	109	105	43	181	210	396	163	1153	406	191	561	564
Y	16	5	8	8	18	27	15	5	20	1	33	1	20	1	23	32	23	33
Zn	16	16	25	21	30	27	18	32	17	36	48	46	46	51	70	51	98	79
Zr	42	22	28	28	48	48	40	19	34	2	74	1	33	1	47	39	42	43

Sample 18 to 33 = Red radiolarian cherts with a "high" manganese content (MnO>1%).
* The main error in the major element analyses is SiO$_2$ because the high SiO$_2$ values are above the normal standartisation limit.
** Total Mn given as MnO.

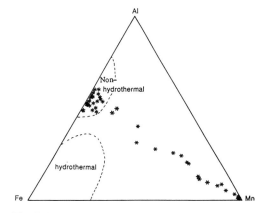

Fig. 7. Ternary plot showing Al–Fe–Mn (simplified after Adachi 1986).

content from both sides to the center), or they show asymmetrical internal structures, (i.e. an asymmetrical manganese layer with a 'sharp' basis and a colloform upper surface, Fig. 5). The base of this manganese-layer consists of

amorphous manganate, pyrolusite, microcrystalline chalcedonic quartz, abundant radiolaria and minor clay, which decreases towards the top of the layer. In the thicker manganese-layers the parallel lamination is the result of a variable SiO$_2$/MnO$_2$ ratio.

In the upper layer the space between the 'ore' is filled by microcrystalline quartz and a few radiolaria. The upper contact of the 'normal' clay-rich radiolarian chert interbed is uneven and characterized by a millimetre-wide, white, bleached zone composed of microcrystalline chalcedonic quartz.

Black siliceous cherts. The black cherts are characterized by the abundance of chalcedony-filled veinlets and primary cavities filled with macroquartz. The veinlets indicate several phases of SiO$_2$ mobilization, before and after manganese mobilization. In these cherts, well preserved radiolaria are infilled with chalcedonic quartz. The clay content in these cherts is negligible.

Nodular manganese segregations. The outer rim of the nodules consists of manganate with abundant radiolaria and chalcedonic quartz.

Table 2. Correlation matrix.

	SiO_2	TiO_2	Al_2O_3	Fe_2O_3	MnO	MgO	CaO	Na_2O	K_2O
SiO_2	1								
TiO_2	-0.197	1							
Al_2O_3	-0.161	0.988	1						
Fe_2O_3	-0.203	0.993	0.982	1					
MnO	-0.798	-0.422	-0.457	-0.415	1				
MgO	-0.127	0.974	0.983	0.970	-0.481	1			
CaO	-0.405	0.873	0.855	0.868	-0.171	0.898	1		
Na_2O	0.170	0.063	0.124	0.041	-0.224	0.126	-0.048	1	
K_2O	-0.395	0.939	0.922	0.927	-0.204	0.903	0.857	0.094	1
Ba	-0.754	-0.345	-0.387	-0.343	0.897	-0.384	-0.056	-0.194	-0.075
Cr	-0.845	0.039	0.001	0.039	0.728	-0.002	0.296	-0.161	0.294
Cu	-0.808	-0.029	-0.066	-0.033	0.732	-0.101	0.170	-0.149	0.220
Ga	0.011	0.895	0.902	0.884	-0.554	0.907	0.737	0.151	0.878
Nb	-0.144	0.939	0.913	0.918	-0.424	0.932	0.854	0.043	0.883
Ni	-0.898	0.127	0.059	0.125	0.745	0.061	0.359	-0.178	0.035
Pb	0.274	0.096	0.105	0.161	-0.307	0.152	-0.011	-0.128	0.044
Rb	-0.196	0.984	0.982	0.979	-0.417	0.956	0.834	0.102	0.951
Sr	-0.879	-0.049	-0.081	-0.050	0.838	-0.128	0.136	0.196	0.151
Th	0.149	0.018	0.024	0.018	-0.153	0.040	-0.047	-0.188	-0.131
V	-0.802	-0.287	-0.326	-0.281	0.903	-0.324	0.002	-0.202	-0.020
Y	-0.204	0.950	0.940	0.942	-0.387	0.916	0.843	0.022	0.911
Zn	-0.724	0.780	0.784	0.777	-0.211	0.705	0.782	-0.116	0.853
Zr	-0.150	0.984	0.985	0.966	-0.461	0.971	0.858	0.122	0.853

	Ba	Cr	Cu	Ga	Nb	Ni	Pb	Rb	Sr	Th	V	Y	Zn	Zr
Ba	1													
Cr	0.896	1												
Cu	0.867	0.957	1											
Ga	0.401	-0.034	-0.106	1										
Nb	-0.308	0.046	-0.031	0.857	1									
Ni	0.830	0.917	0.847	-0.038	0.141	1								
Pb	-0.199	-0.133	-0.170	0.233	0.113	-0.197	1							
Rb	-0.333	0.047	-0.022	-0.250	0.908	0.155	-0.102	1						
Sr	0.812	0.818	0.795	0.912	-0.103	0.857	-0.316	-0.330	1					
Th	-0.101	-0.119	-0.111	0.049	0.126	-0.123	0.197	0.027	-0.144	1				
V	0.993	0.923	0.888	-0.349	-0.254	0.862	-0.174	-0.277	0.841	-0.096	1			
Y	-0.319	0.052	0.025	0.873	0.883	0.860	-0.027	0.946	-0.050	-0.038	-0.296	1		
Zn	0.167	0.451	0.395	0.580	0.707	0.573	-0.116	0.776	0.485	-0.113	0.237	0.769	1	
Zr	-0.377	0.003	-0.058	0.889	0.949	0.074	0.029	0.972	-0.076	0.088	-0.321	0.947	0.739	1

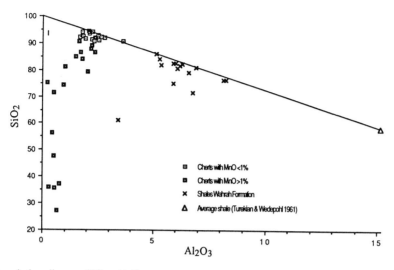

Fig. 8. Correlation diagram $SiO_2 - Al_2O_3$.

This rim resembles the manganese-rich zones of the manganese-layered cherts, or some part of the black siliceous cherts. The centre is composed of pyrolusite, with only a few radiolaria. Cavities are filled with microcrystalline or macroquartz (0.05–0.2 mm in size).

The main difference from Recent manganese nodules, as described in the literature (e.g. Glasby 1977 or DSDP reports) is the lack of concentric growth banding and the lack of any visible nucleus.

Discussion

The thickness and the lithology of limestones and cherts does not vary significantly in the Al Hammah Range. The contacts between the cherts and limestones are continuous (i.e. the transition between the coloured siltstones and the cherts), and so are the contacts between the different chert types (including manganese-cherts); this suggests slow changes in the depositional environments. The cherts of the Wahrah Formation were deposited in a wide, open ocean below the CCD (i.e. the nearly carbonate- and benthos-free cherts). No evidence of turbiditic chert deposition was found, so that the best model for these cherts is the 'double accumulation model' (i.e. detritic clay plus biogenic component), as proposed by Iijima (1983).

The only visible detrital component is fine-grained clay, indicating the cherts formed in a distal position, or the basin was protected by submarine ridges.

The manganese in the cherts of the Wahrah

Formation occurs as stratiform sedimentary enrichments in two horizons, subdivided into several manganese zones. The sedimentary features indicate manganese was concentrated during periods of reduced sedimentation of detrital clays and radiolaria, or during periods of increased manganese precipitation.

Tectonically controlled manganese enrichment

In addition to primary manganese enrichment, described above, the intense folding and thrusting lead to secondary manganese accumulation. In general two scales of 'tectonic' manganese enrichment can be distinguished.

Large-scale enrichment. This is related to folding a complete manganese horizon, with a wavelength of 40 to 100 m. The results of this folding were to form several manganese layers which can be followed up to several hundred metres along strike. In some places manganese is enriched also near the main thrust planes that duplicate the manganese-bearing cherts.

Smaller scale manganese enrichment. This is also concentrated in parasitic folds. This folding has a wavelength and amplitude of 1–20 m. Such folding in areas of maximum compression and minor thrusting leads to the most effective ore enrichment. This simple type of enrichment results in a reduction of shale or muddy chert layers. Manganese is also mobilized and redeposited in fold hinges and fills joints. A manganese-layered chert may thus change into black siliceous chert, sometimes with a pure pyrolusite layer in the centre. The primary structures are almost destroyed and are only now visible as 'ghost structures'. This type of enrichment leads to manganese-rich blocks of several cubic metres. In contrast to the large-scale enrichment, these ore bodies exhibit various shapes and pass into 'normal', relatively manganese-poor cherts after a few metres. It is not clear whether the 'symmetrical' black siliceous cherts (with a pyrolusite layer in the centre), formed by fold repetition of a layered manganese chert.

During late stages of folding and thrusting the manganese-bearing cherts were brecciated but only small amounts of manganese was mobilized.

Thin sections show different stages of manganese mobilization due to diagenesis and/or tectonism. The first primary, sedimentary and/or diagenetic manganese accumulations and radiolarian infills were described above. During the early stages of chertification, SiO_2 was mobilized to form chalcedony-filled veinlets; a 'centerline' of micro- or macroquartz indicates three stages of opening. These veinlets have sharp contacts and trend almost normal to bedding planes. In some cases manganese replaces these veinlets, starting in the centre of the vein; then manganese was mobilized along micro shear planes and microfissures. Beginning with the manganese-filled joints, the radiolarian chert was impregnated with manganese. The result of this process was a porous manganese layer, where 'pores' are filled with quartz and radiolaria. These manganese impregnations could be distinguished from primary manganese layers by the occurrence of numerous manganesefilled fissures. Where the manganese impregnation is intense, it is difficult in thin sections to distinguish between primary manganese layers and secondary manganese impregnations parallel to bedding.

In areas of strong tectonic influence (e.g. fold hinges or 'Mn-blocks') the primary features are destroyed. Thin sections of tectonic altered rocks are characterized by intense SiO_2 and manganese mobilization, numerous chalcedony-filled veinlets, relics of radiolarian cherts ('pseudobrecciation') and zones of pure pyrolusite.

Geochemistry

To support the petrologic evidence of element enrichment, a preliminary set of 33 chert and 14 shale samples were analyzed by XRF (Table 1). Beside samples from all over the range, 10 samples from a typical stratigraphic succession,

containing a manganese horizon were analyzed. In order to attribute the elements to different sources, a correlation matrix was calculated and different discrimination diagrams were constructed.

As the detrital influx consists mainly of clay minerals the Al_2O_3 content represents mainly this factor. Also the other elements like Ti, Zr, Fe_2O_3, K_2O, Rb, Y, and Ga, showing a strong positive correlation with Al_2O_3, must be attributed to a detrital component. Among the elements positively correlated with manganese (Ba and V with a coefficient of 0.9), Ba is believed to be absorbed into tetravalent manganese oxides from sea water and is not a hydrothermal component. The strong correlation of Al_2O_3 with Fe_2O_3 (Table 2) indicates a detrital origin (e.g. in Adachi's 1986 Al, Fe, Mn discrimination diagram, Fig. 7). Thus, all the Oman analyses of the manganese-poor cherts fall into the non-hydrothermal field and the manganese-rich analyses possess a constant Al/Fe-ratio. These data support the field evidence that Fe is not mobilized during diagenesis or tectonic events.

The correlation diagram $SiO_2-Al_2O_3$ (Fig. 8) shows that the cherts and shales lie approximately on the mixing line between average shale composition (Turekian & Wedepohl 1961) and pure SiO_2 (as radiolarian tests). This indicates that for the shales and cherts, detrital and biogenic (= radiolarian) components are the main contributing components to these sediments. Most of the manganese-rich samples lying on the low Al_2O_3-side (<2.5% Al_2O_3) of the diagram indicate a minimal contribution of detrital material, with influx of manganese and biogenic silica as the two main competing factors. The Al_2O_3 values in the shales are low because they are diluted by radiolaria. Furthermore, the outer Al-rich rims of the cherts were intermixed with the interbedded shale by shearing processes during folding and minor thrusting.

Conclusions

The geological and geochemical evidences indicate that the manganese enrichments in the Wahrah Formation are largely due to very low sedimentation rates of the detritally-derived material. However, enrichment has taken place due to folding, minor thrusting and mobilization into fold hinges. The source of relatively high manganese influx is not clear and must explain the extremely high Mn/Fe ratios. Cronan (1976) explains this as the result of diagenetic manganese mobilization under reducing conditions caused by high organic content of the sediment. The features observed in thin sections do not favour intense diagenetic processes for the manganese enrichments in the Wahrah Formation cherts. With intense diagenetic processes high Ni, Cu and Co contents, as in the manganese nodules of the Pacific (Halbach *et al.* 1988) would be expected. High Mn/Fe ratios are found by Scott *et al.* (1974) in the medial valley of the Mid Atlantic Ridge and by Moore & Vogt (1976) near the Galapagos spreading axis and are attributed to a hydrothermal origin. However, no evidence of large or small convective hydrothermal cells in the area of several hundred km^2 of the Wahrah Formation was detected. As manganese cherts were sedimented during Tithonian time long before the Campanian, the oceanic crust of the Semail ophiolite the oceanic crust cannot have been the source. The nearest ridge in space and time is the Owen Ridge with the Late Jurassic Masirah ophiolite. This source must have been several hundred kilometres away, implying transport of manganese-enriched sea water over large distances. Recently similar 'plumes' far away from their source have been detected in the Pacific (R. Haymons, 1987 pers. comm.). If such a mechanism is really effective it could also explain the manganese enrichment with extremely high Mn/Fe ratios as found in the Franciscan (Crear *et al.* 1982) and in the Alps (Peters 1988).

Mohamed Bin Hussain Bin Kassim, Director General of Minerals and Dr. Hilal Al Azry, Director of Geological Surveys, Ministry of Petroleum and Minerals, Sultanate of Oman are thanked for making it possible to work in Oman and for their kind help. Mr. Cherian Zachariah put his maps and knowledge of the Al Hammah Range at our disposal, for which we are grateful. A. H. F. Robertson critically read the first version of the text and made many corrections that greatly improved its style. Our field colleagues Ivan Mercolli, B. Biaggi and Ph. Steinmann contributed to the work and the discussions. The work was financially supported by the Swiss National Science foundation and the 'Hochschulstiftung'.

References

ADACHI, M., YAMAMOTO, M. & SUGISAKI, R. 1986. Hydrothermal chert and associated siliceous rocks from the northern Pacific: Their geological significance as indication of ocean ridge activity. *Sedimentary Geology*, **47**, 125−148.

BECHENNEC, F. 1988. Geologie des nappes Hawasina dans les parties orientale et centrale des montagnes d' Oman. *Documents du B.R.G.M.*, **127**, Orleans, France.

BONATTI, E., KRAEMER, T. & RYDELL, H. 1972. Classification and genesis of submarine iron-manganese deposits. *In*: HORN, D. R. (ed.) *Ferromanganese Deposits on the Pacific Floor*. National Science Foundation, Washington D. C., 149−166.

CRERAR, D. A., NAMSON, J., SO CHY, M., WILLIAMS, L. & FEIGENSON, M. D. 1982. Manganiferous cherts of the Franciscan assemblage: I. General Geology, Ancient and modern analogues, and implications for hydrothermal convection at oceanic spreading centers. *Economic Geology*, **77/3**, 519−540.

CRONAN, D. S. 1976. Manganese nodules and other ferro-manganese oxide deposits. *In*: RILLY, I. P. & CHESTER, R., (eds) *Chemical Oceanography*, **5**, Department of Oceanography, The University of Liverpool, England, Academic Press, London, 217−263.

GLASBY, G. P., (ed.) 1977. Marine Manganese deposits. *Oceanography Series*, Elsevier, Amsterdam, **15**.

GLENNIE, K. W., BOEUF, M. G. A., CLARKE, M. W., MOODY STUART, M., PILAAR, W. F. H. & REINHARDT, B. M. 1974. Geology of Oman Mountains. *Verhandelingen van het Koninklijk Nederlandse geologisch mijnbouwkundig Genootschap*, **31**.

HALBACH, P. & PUTEANUS, D. 1988. Geochemical trends of different genetic types of nodules and crusts. *In*: HALBACH, P., FRIEDERICH, G. & STOCKELBERG, U. (eds) *The manganese nodule belt of the Pacific Ocean*, Enke, Stuttgart, 61−67.

IIJIMA, A. & UTADA, M. 1983. Recent developments in sedimentology of siliceous deposits in Japan. *In*: IIJIMA, A., HEIN, J. R. & SIEVER, P. (eds) *Siliceous deposits in the Pacific region. Developments in Sedimentology*, **36**, Elsevier, Amsterdam, 45−64.

McBRIDE, E. F. & FOLK, R. L. 1979. Features and origin of Italian Jurassic radiolarites deposited on continental crust. *Journal of Sedimentary Petrology*, **49/3**, 837−868.

MOORE, W. S. & VOGT, P. R. 1976. Hydrothermal manganese crust from two sites near the Galapagos spreading axis. *Earth Planetary Science Letters*, **19**, 349−356.

PETERS, Tj. 1989. Geochemistry of manganese-bearing cherts associated with Alpine ophiolites and Hawasina Formations in Oman. *Marine Geology*.

ROY, S. 1981. *Manganese Deposits*, Academic, London.

SCOTT, M. R., SCOTT, R. B., RONA, P. A., BUTLER, L. W. & NALWALK, A. J. 1974. Rapidly accumulating manganese deposits from the Median Valley of the Mid-Atlantic Ridge. *Geophysical Research Letters*, **1/8**, 355−358.

TUREKIAN, K. K. & WEDEPOHL, K. H. 1961. Distribution of the elements in some major units of the earth's crust. *Geological Society of America Bulletin*, **72**, 175−192.

Evolution of the Arabian continental margin in the Dibba Zone, Northern Oman Mountains

A. H. F. ROBERTSON[1], C. D. BLOME[2], D. W. J. COOPER[3], A. E. S. KEMP[4] & M. P. SEARLE[5]

[1] *Department of Geology and Geophysics, University of Edinburgh, Edinburgh, EH9 3JW, UK*
[2] *United States Geological Survey, Denver Federal Center, Denver, Co USA*
[3] *Department of Geology, University of Leicester, Leicester, LEI 7RH, UK*
[4] *Department of Oceanography, University of Southampton, Southampton, S09 5NH, UK*
[5] *Department of Geology, University of Leicester, Leicester, LEI 7RH, UK*

Abstract: The Dibba Zone, Northern Oman Mountains, documents the history of an oblique-rifted (transtensional) segment of the Arabian passive margin. Unmetamorphosed Palaeozoic, pre-rift (Ordovician to ?Devonian) successions, exposed in rifted continental slivers (Oman Exotics), record stable siliciclastic and carbonate platform deposition. Early Permian rifting of the Neo-Tethys initiated a carbonate platform in the Musandam Peninsula, while shallow marine bioclastic carbonate and quartzose sediments accumulated in the subsiding axial zones (Asfar Fm., Jebel Qamar Exotics). During final continental break-up, in the Late Triassic−Early Jurassic, a carbonate platform in the Musandam Peninsula was bordered by an escarpment-bypass margin with a turbiditic apron to the southeast (Zulla Fm.). Rifted continental slivers underwent mass-wasting, giving rise to detached blocks, or olistoliths that slid into organic-rich muds and turbiditic sands (Kub Melange). During the Jurassic, the subsiding Musandam carbonate platform was bordered by a steep slope (Sumeini Gp.) and redeposited carbonates accumulated on the continental rise (Guweyza Limestone Fm.). A switch to mainly siliceous accumulation, from Late Jurassic to Early Cretaceous (Tithonian−Berriasian Sid'r Fm.) ensued, mainly in response to tensional faulting, combined with eustatic sea level rise. Following re-establishment of the platform, carbonate sediment was again shed into the basin in the Early Cretaceous (Nayid Fm.). During Cenomanian time, tholeiitic and alkaline basalt extrusions formed seamounts that locally built-up into shallow water (99−92 Ma). Platform deposition halted in the Turonian (c. 90 Ma), with flexural upwarp and erosion, followed by subsidence and slumping of shelf edge and upper slope sediments into a syntectonic foredeep, accumulating siliceous sediments and redeposited lithoclastic carbonates (Riyamah unit, Muti Fm.). Associated with emplacement of the Semail ophiolite, the passive margin successions were then imbricated by foreland-progagating thrusts (76−65 Ma), modified by the effects of possible oblique convergence, sidewall ramping and late-stage (dorsal) culmination collapse. Following erosion in the Campanian−Maastrichtian (Juweiza Fm.), platform deposition was reestablished in Palaeocene−early Oligocene. Renewed compression after mid-Eocene resulted in folding and reverse faulting of the Dibba Zone and thrust culmination of the Musandam shelf carbonates, driven by incipient continent−continent collision in the Zagros area.

The Dibba Zone in the Northern Oman Mountains (Fig. 1) exposes a transition between a Late Palaeozoic−Mesozoic continental margin and an ocean basin. This critical area links a continent−ocean boundary to the southeast in the Gulf of Oman to a continent−continent collision zone to the northwest in the Zagros area (Falcon 1967; Stocklin 1968, 1974; White & Ross 1979). Following reconnaissance studies (Hudson *et al.* 1954a,b; Allemann & Peters 1972; Glennie *et al.* 1974; Lippard *et al.* 1982), several recent papers have focussed on specific aspects of the Dibba Zone, including the sedimentology of the carbonate platform (Searle *et*

From ROBERTSON, A. H. F., SEARLE, M. P. & RIES, A. C. (eds), 1990,
The Geology and Tectonics of the Oman Region.
Geological Society Special Publication No 49, pp 251−284

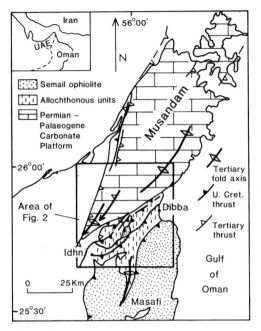

Fig. 1. Outline tectonic map of the Dibba Zone, Northern Oman Mountains; study area shown in box.

al. 1983), Late Cretaceous syn-tectonic sedimentation (Robertson 1987), and the structure and emplacement history (Searle et al. 1983; Searle 1988 a,b). Here we summarize and interpret the history and tectonic development of the continental margin in this area, concentrating on the basinal units, particularly those of the inferred continental rise, off-margin basement horsts (Oman Exotics), and Late Cretaceous volcanic seamounts. We also compare the evolution of the Dibba Zone with other areas of the Oman Mountains, and stress the role of this area as an oblique-rifted (transtensional) segment of the Arabian passive margin.

Structural setting

The Dibba Zone is an elongate, c. 10 km wide, northeast–southwest-trending topographic depression between the carbonate successions of the Musandam shelf to the northwest and the Semail ophiolite to the southeast (Figs 1 & 2). Five major thrust units are recognized: (1) the Musandam shelf carbonates, an allochthonous Late Palaeozoic–Mesozoic carbonate platform unit; (ii) the Sumeini Group, relatively large, intact thrust sheets of Mesozoic carbonate slope

facies; (iii) the Hawasina Complex, a complicated stack of thrust sheets of Mesozoic deepwater carbonate platform slope, continental rise and abyssal plain sediments; (iv) the Haybi Complex, comprising sedimentary and tectonic melange, up to mountain-sized limestone units ('olistoliths', or Oman Exotics), alkaline and tholeiitic volcanics, and greenschist and amphibolite facies metamorphic rocks forming the sole of the Semail ophiolite (Searle & Malpas 1980, 1982); (v) the overriding Late Cretaceous Semail ophiolite thrust sheet. The thrust stack is assumed to have been assembled by continentward-migrating thrusting, with originally more distal (outboard) units located at progressively higher structural levels (Fig. 3). Complexities in thrusting include oblique ramping, thrust breaching and normal faulting related to culmination collapse (Searle 1988a,b). During mid-Tertiary time, a c. 3.5 km thick sheet of Musandam shelf carbonates was thrust about 15 km westwards, along the Hagab thrust giving rise to huge domal culminations (Searle et al. 1983; Searle 1988a,b; Fig. 1). Along the southeast edge of the Musandam Peninsula a major culmination apparently collapsed southeastwards along an important normal fault (Fig. 3a), explaining the presence of a large Semail ophiolite slice well down in the structural stacking order in the north of the area (Fig. 3a). In the Dibba Zone deformation of assumed mid-Tertiary age gave rise to large, asymmetrical, west-facing 'whaleback' folds, accompanied by reverse faulting and limited out-of-sequence thrusting (Searle et al. 1983; Fig. 3b).

Palaeogeographic framework

The complexities of thrusting, including out-of-sequence thrusting, re-thrusting and the effects of a possible oblique component of convergence in the Dibba Zone mean that it is now impossible to accurately restore the lateral distribution of thrust sheets to their pre-emplacement configuration. However, generalized reconstructions can be based on the recognition of more 'proximal' and 'distal' lithofacies that can then be restored in a manner that makes palaeogeographic sense. Accordingly, during the Late Palaeozoic and Mesozoic a carbonate platform was bordered to the southeast by a deep-water basin, and this, in turn, was separated from the Mesozoic Tethys ocean by a basement ridge (Oman Exotic limestone). Each of these palaeogeographic units will now be discussed in turn, beginning with the platform exposed in the Musandam Peninsula.

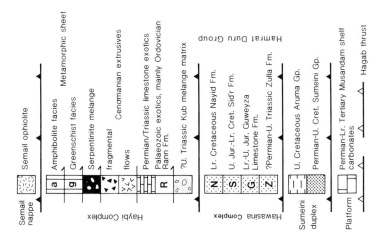

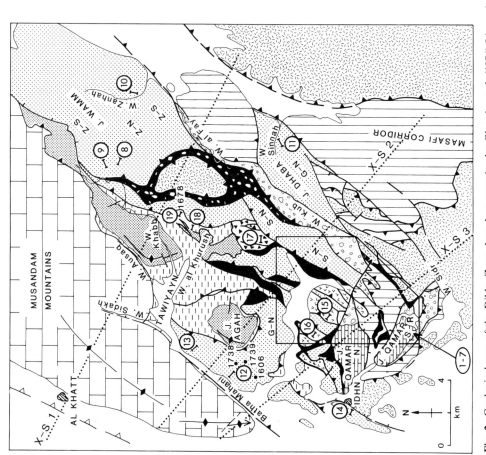

Fig. 2. Geological map of the Dibba Zone, based on mapping by Glennie *et al.* (1974) Lippard *et al.* (1982); Searle *et al.* (1983); Searle, (1988) and this work. Locations: measured successions circled; radiolarians determined marked as points. Area mapped in more detail in Fig. 9 is boxed. Lines of cross sections in Fig. 3 are also shown; for key see Fig. 2b.

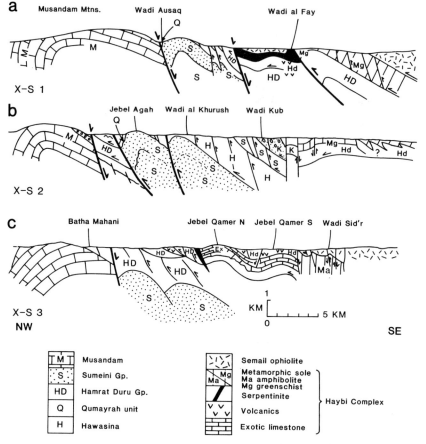

Fig. 3. Sections across the Dibba Zone, simplified from the sections of Searle (1988). See Fig. 2 for locations and Fig. 2b for key.

Hajar Supergroup: Mesozoic−Early Tertiary carbonate platform

The *c.* 3500 m thick Musandam shelf succession from Ras al Khaimah and Oman is already well documented (Fig. 1; Lees 1928; Hudson *et al.* 1954a,b; Hudson & Chatton 1959; Hudson 1960; Allemann & Peters 1972; Glennie *et al.* 1973, 1974; Biehler *et al.* 1975; Ricateau & Riche 1980; Rabu *et al.* 1990). Salient features will only be briefly summarized here, as follows:

The mainly dolomitic Permian and Triassic platform sediments (Bih, Hagil, Ghail and Milaha Fms.) consist of shoaling-upwards inter-tidal to supratidal cycles that pass laterally into higher-energy facies towards the shelf edge. In the Late Triassic, fore-reef talus conglomerates were developed around Wadi Ausaq (Fig. 2) and comprise boulders and blocks of coral, grainstone, oolite and wackestone, up to 40 m

in diameter. End-Triassic time was marked by emergence of the platform, with ferruginous deposition and progradation of quartzose sands (Ghalilah Fm.) towards, but not as far as, the shelf edge. The controls were probably uplift related to final continental break-up of Gondwana, combined with eustatic sea-level fall (Vail *et al.* 1977).

Re-establishment of shallow-water conditions gave rise to the Jurassic Musandam Group 1, 2 and 3 carbonate platform cycles (Glennie *et al.* 1974; Richateau & Riche 1980), which pass into deep open-marine thin-bedded lime mudstones of Late Jurassic−Early Cretaceous age (e.g. Miaolica facies). These grade laterally into upper slope facies containing slumps and con-glomerates in the Batha Mahani and Wadi Ausaq area, that are correlated with Tithonian to Early Cretaceous cherts in basinal sequences, and represent the response to an eustatic sea-level rise, augmented by tectonic extension and subsidence.

The upper platform slope is well exposed in the northwestern Dibba Zone, in Wadi Ausaq and Batha Mahani (Figs 2; 3a,c). Shallow-water platform carbonates, with *Kornubia*, are overlain by deeper water, well-bedded porcellaneous calpionellid limestones, radiolarian lime mudstones, and red to pink marls, interbedded with slump beds and conglomerates with Tithonian- to Berriasian-aged clasts in a muddy matrix (Allemann & Peters 1972). The main cause of the extensive slope erosion was tectonic instability, mainly normal faulting, which resulted in drowning of the Musandam shelf in Late Jurassic−Early Cretaceous time.

Platform emergence and/or non-deposition was marked by a disconformity at the base of the Albian Wasia Group (Musandam Cycle 4). Transgressive lithofacies initially comprise argillaceous carbonates (Nahr Umr Fm.), followed by the finer-grained sediments (Mauddud Formation). Inferred shallowing-upwards then gave rise to mixed terrigenous and carbonate sequences of mid-Albian to Cenomanian age (Natih Formation) (Hughes Clarke 1988).

Flexural upwarp associated with the beginning of the ophiolite obduction episode (Robertson 1987) resulted in erosion of up to 600 m of the shelf edge and the upper slope succession, down to Albian horizons in the Batha Mahani and Wadi Ausaq areas (Fig. 2). This was followed by crustal loading and down-flexure, as the Semail ophiolite overrode the continental margin. Campanian foredeep facies (Ausaq conglomerate) comprise calcilutite, pelagic carbonate and terrigenous siltstone (Allemann & Peters 1972). As the Semail ophiolite overthrust the platform margin, inner shelf areas further northwest were loaded and subsided, giving rise to a foreland basin in which ophiolite-derived sediment accumulated rapidly (Juweiza Fm.; Glennie *et al.* 1974; Patton & O'Connor 1988). Final overthrusting of the Semail ophiolite took place in upper Campanian−lower Maastrichtian time. However, there is little evidence that the ophiolite moved far over the Musandam shelf. The most far travelled Hawasina sediments, still preserved are exposed in the Hagil window and as two very small klippen in the central Musandam Mountains (Biehler *et al.* 1975).

Following emplacement of the Semail ophiolite, a carbonate shelf was re-established, as the Paleocene−Eocene Pabdeh Group and the Oligocene Asmari Formation (Fig. 4). Regional compression during Late Oligocene−Miocene time was related to collision in the Zagros area

(Searle 1988b) and the Musandam platform underwent large-scale folding, while the higher levels of the succession were thrust at least 15 km to the west along the Hagab thrust, associated with the development of a successor foreland basin (Pabdeh basin) to the west.

Sumeini Group: carbonate slope deposition

Jurassic and Cretaceous carbonate slope facies (Sumeini Group) are well exposed in the Dibba Zone (Figs. 2, 3 & 5). The Jurassic succession in the north, in Wadi Khabb (Fig. 6a) is dominated by *c.* 700 m of dark grey to black, decimetre-bedded, unburrowed lime mudstones and minor grainstones that contain calcified radiolarians, rare crinoids and small shell fragments, but are otherwise mainly unfossiliferous (A Member of Mayhah Fm.; Glennie *et al.* 1974). Slump scars are common. They are up to 30 m long by up to 5 m deep. Submarine slopes were steep and unstable for long periods. The Jurassic−mid Cretaceous limestones represent Bahama-type periplatform ooze. The setting was similar to the gullied by-pass slope inferred for the Jurassic A Member of the Mayhah Formation further south, in the Jebel Sumeini area (Watts & Garrison 1986; Fig. 5). However, the large channels seen in the Sumeini area were not observed in the Dibba Zone, possibly because slopes were unusually steep, with very extensive slumping and sediment by-passing. The succession in the Dibba Zone then passes upwards into 100−300 m of limestone-conglomerates and slumps, followed in turn by shale and thin-bedded limestone of the Qumayrah unit (Muti Formation).

Further south, similar limestone debris flows are exposed in the Jebel Agah window (Figs 2, 3b). Platform lime mudstone of Jurassic−Early Cretaceous age there are transgressively overlain by thin-bedded micritic limestone, with planktonic foraminifera of lower Albian to lower Cenomanian age (Allemann & Peters 1972). Overlying thin-bedded deep water limestones, marls and conglomerates are dated as Santonian−Coniacian (Allemann & Peters 1972), to probably early Campanian (M. P. Harte; in Robertson 1987). The succession records collapse and mass-wasting of the upper parts of the carbonate slope in early Late Cretaceous time, and is equivalent to the C Member of the Mayhah Formation in the Sumeini area (Watts & Garrison 1986). Similar fault-bounded conglomerates of Aptian−Albian age occur below the Hagab thrust in the Hagil window (Lakshaifa Fm. of Hudson *et al.* 1954b). Other smaller bodies of Sumeini Group-like carbon-

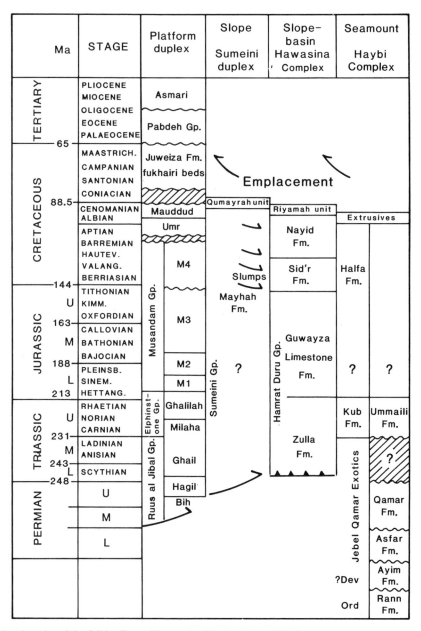

Fig. 4. Stratigraphy of the Dibba Zone. Time scale: Harland *et al.* (1982).

ates (e.g. south of Wadi al Khurush; Figs 2 & 3b) are interbedded with Late Cretaceous syn-tectonic radiolarian facies, and are correlated with the Riyamah unit of the Muti Formation.

The stratigraphically highest redeposited carbonates (slumps and debris flows) of the Late Cretaceous part of the Sumeini Group are disconformably overlain by up to 300 m of sheared imbricated, non-calcareous brown mudstone and shale, thin-bedded calciturbidites and minor rudites, that are collectively assigned to the Late Cretaceous Qumayrah unit of the Muti Formation (Glennie *et al.* 1974; Robertson 1987; Watts 1990; Fig. 2). The Qumayrah unit is folded around thrust culminations cored by the Sumeini Group (e.g. north of Tawiyayn and

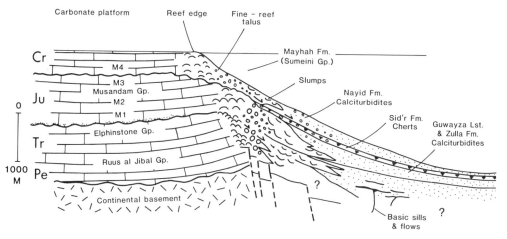

Fig. 5. Reconstruction of the Musandam shelf edge and slope.

Fig. 6. Field photographs of the Sumeini Gp. slope facies. a, typical Jurassic rippled and finely-laminated, organic-rich periplatform micrite, Wadi Ausaq; b, west-facing recumbent megascopic fold of Tertiary? origin in Late Cretaceous slope carbonates, Jebel Agah.

southwest of Jebel Agah; Fig. 6b) and is also sandwiched between these thrust sheets and the overlying carbonates of the Musandam shelf (e.g. Wadi Ausaq−Wadi Khabb; Figs 2 & 3a). The Qumayrah unit is attributed to flexural downwarp and collapse of the edge of the carbonate platform to form a foredeep that developed prior to overthrusting (Robertson 1987).

Hawasina Complex: deep water passive margin sediments

Mesozoic deep-water successions of the Hawasina Complex are exposed in generally structurally higher thrust sheets. The sedimentary structures in all the successions are consist-

ent with deposition from high- to low-density turbidity currents (cf. Bouma 1962; Hiscott & Middleton 1979; Lowe 1982), superimposed on a 'background' input of hemipelagic mud, fine-grained carbonate and true pelagic sediment, that was mainly radiolarian. In the tectonostratigraphic scheme of Glennie et al. (1973, 1974), only a small outcrop of the Hamrat Duru Group was identified in Batha Mahani (Fig. 2). Other successions were assigned by Glennie et al. (1974) to the structurally lower and coarser-grained Dibba Formation, and to the higher and more distal calcareous Dhera Formation and the siliceous Shamal Formation (Fig. 2). Cooper (1986, 1987) made the minimum necessary changes to bring the stratigraphy into line with international useage (Hedberg 1976; Holland *et al.* 1978; Fig. 4) and the terms Dhera, Dibba and Shamal Formations are now abandoned. In the Dibba Zone, deep-water platform-derived sediments are placed in the Hamrat Duru Group and comprise: the Late Permian? to Late Triassic Zulla Formation, mainly shale and limestone; the Late Triassic to mid Jurassic Guweyza Limestone Formation (revised name), mainly redeposited limestone; the Late Jurassic–Early Cretaceous (Tithonian–Barremian) Sid'r Formation, mainly chert; and lastly, the Early–mid Cretaceous (Albian–Cenomanian) Nayid Formation, mainly redeposited limestone. The Guweyza Sandstone Formation (Late Triassic) is not recognized in this area.

Triassic Zulla Formation: starved base of slope

In the central and northern Oman Mountains, the Zulla Formation is widely exposed and comprises mostly shale and muddy limestone (e.g. in the Hawasina window; Glennie *et al.* 1974; Graham 1980; Cooper 1990). In the Dibba Zone local recognition of the Zulla Formation (Fig. 2 is based on limited age data and lithological correlation.

In the northwestern area of the Dibba Zone, intact successions mapped as the Dibba Formation by Glennie *et al.* (1974) are exposed on Jebel Wamm (logs, Yamahah 1 and 2, Fig. 7). They comprise 120 m of reddish calcareous shales and thin-bedded platy lime mudstones and minor oolitic calcarenites, also rare intraformational limestone conglomerates. Bivalve fragments are common in the upper levels of the Zulla Formation. Two basic lava flows, each 9 m thick were observed and these comprise elongate 'bolster' pillows. At Wadi Zanhah (Fig. 7), laterally equivalent silicified lime mudstone turbidites were apparently deposited in deeper water close to the carbonate compensation depth (CCD). Instability of the platform edge area resulted in increased coarse-grained input, with the deposition of a 50 m thick sequence of channellized limestone conglomerates (Fig. 8a) that are interbedded with grainstones, lime mudstones and shales. Numerous bivalve fragments were again noted in the upper levels of the Zulla Formation. In general, the bedding thins and becomes finer grained from north to south across the Jebel Wamm massif.

In the southwest, in Batha Mahani (Fig. 7), the Zulla Formation comprises a 15 m thick succession of shale that passes up into thin- to medium-bedded calcilutite, silicified limestone and oolitic calcarenite, containing curved, thin-shelled pelagic bivalve fragments. Nodular silicification is ubiquitous. Radiolarians from red cherts immediately above yield upper Norian to Hettangian ages (see the Appendix). Three kilometres north of the village of Idhn (Fig. 7), a poorly exposed succession comprises 'exotic' limestone conglomerates weathered volcanics, shale and thin calcarenite (Hawasina unit 2 of Searle *et al.* 1980).

The Zulla Formation comprises shallow-water carbonate sediments derived from the Musandam shelf, particularly oolite that was redeposited down a steep escarpment margin and accumulated as small clastic wedges (Fig. 5). Slope areas (e.g. Yamahah) were largely by-passed. The newly rifted slope was unstable and repeatedly slumped, giving rise to intraformational platy-limestone breccias. Widespread tectonic instability in the Late Triassic triggered the development of lenticular conglomerates composed of reef edge-derived material. Fine-grained terrigenous background sediments accumulated under oxidizing conditions. Base of slope areas remained volcanically active. Slope-like units were covered by a wedge of finer-grained sediments, similar to those of the Hamrat Duru Group in the Hatta Zone *c.* 60 km to the south (Robertson *et al.* 1990).

Late Triassic–Jurassic Guweyza Limestone Formation: redeposited deep-sea carbonates

Time-equivalent sediments of the Early Jurassic Guweyza Sandstone Formation that are exposed elsewhere in the Oman Mountains are represented by redeposited oolitic limestones in the Dibba Zone. They are assigned to the Guweyza Limestone Formation which conformably overlies the Dibba Formation. Successions crop out on the Jebel Wamm massif, Jebel Dhaba, east Batha Mahani and near Idhn (Figs 2 & 7).

The type section of the now-discarded Dibba Formation, in Wadi Zanhah (Fig. 7) is disturbed by small- to medium-scale thrusting, which may account for the apparent absence of Middle and Late Jurassic facies (Glennie *et al.* 1974). The succession comprises decimetre-bedded oolitic, occasionally fetid, calcarenites with grey or green shale partings. Lithologically similar, but more dismembered, successions occur elsewhere in the area (e.g. Wadi Zinhah, Fig. 7).

On the north side of Jebel Wamm (Fig. 7), the formation is represented by over 50 m of

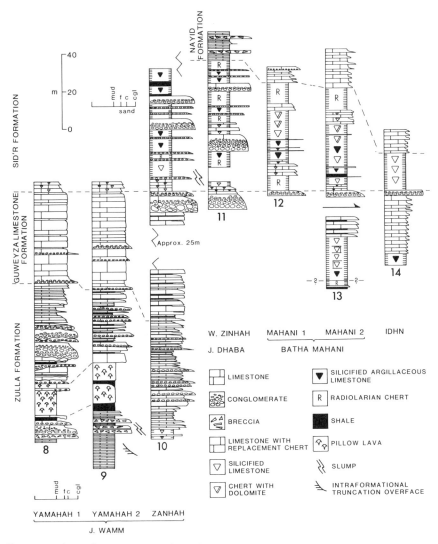

Fig. 7. Representative sedimentary successions of the continental rise Hamrat Duru Group; see Fig. 2 for locations.

metre-bedded, light grey-weathering, oolitic calcarenite, with minor pebble conglomerate, and includes intraformational clasts, as well as rarer shelf-derived sediment.

In Batha Mahani (Fig. 7), a small outcrop, previously mapped as the Hamrat Duru Group (Glennie *et al.* 1974) comprises decimetre- to metre-bedded oolitic calcarenite that is interbedded with red shale, mainly low in the succession. The lithofacies appear to be transitional between the coarse-grained Jebel Wamm successions and more easterly exposures in the Batha Mahani (Fig. 7). There, the Zulla Formation is locally conformably overlain by intact

sequences, comprising 25 m of silicified limestone, chert and shale, that then pass up into 10 m of decimetre-bedded oolitic limestone, with interbedded green shale.

At Idhn (Fig. 7), the Guweyza Limestone Formation comprises 33 m of centimetre-bedded, fine-grained, rippled calcarenite. Each bed passes into structureless, chalky weathering, wackestones in which chert nodules are preferentially concentrated in the finer grained fractions.

Throughout the Dibba Zone, the Guweyza Limestone Formation is capped by a conglomeratic horizon, except locally in the north in the

Yamahah section (Fig. 7), where there is a rapid transition to silicified limestones and cherts of the Sid'r Formation. The conglomerate contains up to 5 m-sized clasts of reefal boundstone, dolomitic grainstone, yellow and pink micrite, algal limestone, shale, green silt, rare quartzarenite and well-rounded granitic boulders.

Unlike other areas of the Oman Mountains siliciclastic input to the young rift basin was minimal in the Late Triassic. Shelf-derived sediment, largely oolitic, by-passed the slope in gullies and accumulated as small carbonate fans and/or wedges at the base of the slope and beyond (Fig. 5). Fetid lime muds were first deposited up-slope within the oxygen minimum zone, then reworked into a deeper setting. The dominance of green shale and cherts in deeper water, basinal areas (e.g. Batha Mahani) suggests that diagenetic conditions were mainly reducing; more oxidizing settings were apparently confined to lower slope and upper continental rise areas. Probably due to continued tectonic subsidence, the basin gradually subsided below the CCD and fine-grained background sediments were by then non-calcareous. The conglomerates record extensional faulting, collapse of the platform edge and erosion of submerged basement outcrops. The abundance of conglomerates contrasts with equivalent stratigraphic levels further south in the central mountains, as in the Hawasina window and the Hamrat ad Duru (Cooper 1990). From this it is concluded that the Dibba Zone was particularly tectonically active throughout much of Mesozoic time.

Late Jurassic–Early Cretaceous Sid'r Formation: siliceous deposition

The Sid'r Formation is dominated by distinctive red radiolarites of Late Jurassic (Tithonian) to Early Cretaceous (late Valanginian) age (see Appendix). In the northern Oman Mountains, the formation is subdivided into a lower calcareous unit and an upper shale unit (Cooper, 1986, 1990).

Successions at Jebel Wamm and Jebel Dhera (Fig. 7) start with silicified radiolarian wackestone and interbedded shale. Tithonian radiolarian cherts (see Appendix) and lenticular pebble conglomerates (Fig. 8b) are augmented at Jebel Wamm (Wadi Zanhah, Fig. 7) by pink slump-folded radiolarian wackestone. Five measurements of fold-facing direction indicate south-directed transport. A massive, up to 8 m thick limestone conglomerates is also regionally developed towards the middle of the formation, and defines a gradational boundary with more shale-rich successions in the upper part of the Sid'r Formation. In this, the abundance of coarse- and fine-grained carbonate and radiolarian chert is reduced.

In Batha Mahani (Fig. 7), the base of the Sid'r Formation (Unit 2 of Searle *et al.* 1983) comprises a 1–2 m thick interval of recessive-weathering shales, silicified marls and red and green radiolarian cherts, passing up into 35 m of variably silicified radiolarian wackestones and marls, with thin partings of red chert. Pebble conglomerates, 5–10 cm thick, are distinctly lenticular over 10–30 m laterally. Upwards, white-weathering, cliff-forming, medium-

Fig. 8. Field photographs of the base of slope Hamrat Duru Group. a, Late Triassic conglomerates (Zulla Formation) with sub-rounded carbonate and granitic clasts; b, Late Jurassic-Early Cretaceous slope-derived debris flows with a red shaly matrix (Sid'r Formation).

bedded silicified limestones contain abundant replacement dolomite. They are then overlain by 3 m of relatively unsilicified, coarse-grained, 30-cm thick beds of graded calcarenites, with granule-grade bases. The succession finally passes into a 5−15 m thick interval of recessive-weathering, brick red radiolarian chert and shale.

Near Idhn (Fig. 7), the Sid'r Formation is composed almost entirely of 2−10 cm-bedded, variably silicified, graded radiolarian wacke-stones. Parallel laminated, and/or rippled bed bases are common. Replacement chert accounts for 50−90% of the bed thickness. Shale is almost completely absent and is restricted to thin partings.

The Sid'r Formation records a combination of enhanced radiolarian productivity, raised sea-level (Vail et al. 1977; Ager 1981) and/or a raised CCD. Associated tectonic subsidence and faulting gave rise to the numerous platform-derived rudaceous intercalations. Drowning of the platform in Late Jurassic−Early Cretaceous time then greatly reduced carbonate input to the basin. In Northern Oman this reduction occurred in two stages (Cooper 1990). Initial input was channelized to form laterally discon-tinuous sediment bodies. Increased subsidence of the margin is recorded by conglomerates at the top of the lower unit; carbonate largely ceased to be transported into the basin and fine-grained turbidites were restricted to the base of the slope. 'Background' shale deposition then dominated and red cherts accumulated from radiolarian fall-out (upper unit) in areas shielded from shale accumulation. Much of the chert formed diagenetically by the dissolution of radiolarian tests and the replacement of the fine-grained and thin-bedded calcareous sedi-ments by silica.

Cretaceous Nayid Formation: renewed deep-sea carbonate redeposition

Successions in the Dibba Zone are dominated by two distinct lithofacies. These comprise redeposited shallow-water and hemipelagic carbonate.

The first association occurs in the north, in the Jebel Dhaba and Jebel Wamm areas (Fig. 2). It comprises platy-weathering, graded wackestone, with subordinate decimetre-bedded channelized calcarenite, fine-grained conglomerate and intraformational breccia. Weathered mafic igneous extrusives and/or sills are quite numerous.

The second association crops out further south, in the west of Batha Mahani (Figs 2 & 7)

and comprises fine- to medium-grained litho-clastic calcarenite, grading into wackestone that is locally clay-rich. Associated radiolarian cherts, 1 km south of Jebel Agah (Fig. 2), yield early Cenomanian radiolarians. This suggests that the top of the Nayid Formation is essentially coeval with the Riyamah unit of the Muti Formation.

To the west of Idhn (Fig. 7), local lithological variants include a coarse-grained calcarenite-rich base to the Nayid Formation, and the devel-opment of platy-weathering limestone, with occasional 'floating' slabs up to 4 m long.

The Nayid Formation records increased car-bonate input from the Musandam shelf that was by then re-established, with a corresponding switch from shale- to micrite-dominated back-ground deposition. Carbonate-producing organ-isms were also by then more productive (e.g. Bosellini & Winterer 1975). The platy hemi-pelagic lime-mudstones, with subordinate lenticular conglomerates composed of shelf edge-derived material and intraformational breccia (at Jebel Dhaba and Jebel Wamm) indicate a base-of-slope bypass setting. Further south, in Batha Mahani copious fine-grained and thin-bedded calciturbidites were laid down in a more distal setting further from the platform source.

Structurally-higher Hawasina units

Several large slices of Hawasina sedimentary rocks are located high in the structural stack between outcrops of the Haybi Complex to the west and the Semail ophiolite, and its metamor-phic sole to the east (Figs 2 & 3b). Proximal base of slope facies includes shelf-derived con-glomerate and reef limestone blocks, up to 10 m in size. These are unlikely to be distal units formed far from the Arabian continent, but probably came to be in their present high struc-tural position as a result of complex 'out-of-sequence' thrusting (i.e. with proximal over distal units) (Searle 1985; Bernoulli & Weissert 1987; Cooper 1988; Barrette & Calon 1987). Alternatively, these units were initially emplaced 'in sequence', but were later downthrown by normal faults located along the northwest side of the Musandam shelf succession (Searle 1988a; Fig. 3a).

In the Jebel Dhaba area, the inferred out-of-sequence unit is sandwiched between out-crops of melange (Kub Melange, see below), and the Semail nappe and its metamorphic sole (Fig. 2). Lithofacies are sheared and disrupted (i.e. as broken formation) (Fig. 9), and comprise shale, radiolarite, thin-bedded lime mudstone,

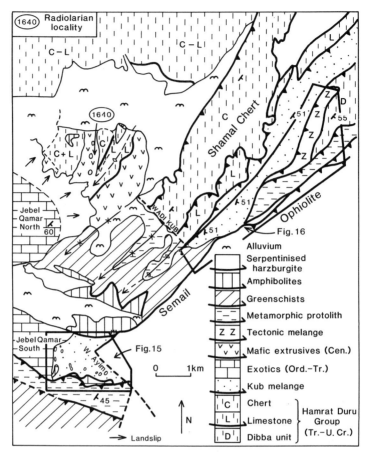

Fig. 9. Outline geological map of the Haybi Complex, showing the Kub melange, Late Cretaceous mafic extrusives and the metamorphic protolith, also distal Hawasina units (e.g. Sid'r Formation; the Shamal Chert of Glennie *et al.* 1974) and the Semail nappe in the east. Detailed maps of the Kub Melange in Figs 14 & 15 are delineated by boxes.

turbiditic calcarenite, channelized calcirudite and scattered, metre-size detached blocks of reefal limestone. The lithologies can be correlated with all four formations of the Hamrat Duru Group (Zulla, Guweyza Limestone, Sid'r and Nayid). Diabase sills are quite numerous. At the extreme southern end of this thrust-bounded unit (Fig. 9), very deformed successions of calciturbidites in beds up to 0.25 m thick, are interbedded with ribbon chert that contains radiolarians of mid-Triassic (late Ladinian) to Late Triassic (Carnian) age (see Appendix).

Northeast of Wadi Kub (Figs 2 & 9), another major duplex is mainly composed of radiolarian chert of the Sid'r Formation (Shamal chert of Glennie *et al.* (1974). This is sandwiched between volcanics of the Haybi Complex,

sheared serpentinite below, and broken formation of the Hawasina Complex above. In detail, this unit comprises tightly imbricated ribbon radiolarian chert, subordinate shale and relatively rare, thin- to medium-bedded silicified calciturbidites, with Calpionnelids (Glennie *et al.* 1974). In the north, near Wadi al Khurush (Fig. 2), the chert (Shammal chert) locally passes into redeposited limestone typical of the Nayid Formation elsewhere. This confirms a correlation with the Sid'r Formation, rather than with the Halfa, or Haliw Formations, as exposed in the central mountains (Bernoulli & Weissert 1987; Bernoulli *et al.* 1990).

The Sid'r Formation, as exposed north of Wadi Kub (Shamal chert) is structurally overlain by an elongate, c. 500–1000 m, thrust-bounded outcrop, comprising broken formation (Fig. 9).

This includes part of the 'sedimentary melange' outcrop mapped by Lippard *et al.* (1982). It is made up of lenticular slices of Hawasina rocks up to 3 km long by 0.5 km wide. These are often bounded by thin strands of steeply inclined, sheared serpentinite that increase in number and thickness northwards. Local sedimentary successions, up to 60 m thick comprise bioclast-rich calciturbidite, with rare calcirudite beds up to 0.3 m thick, containing clasts up to 0.3 m in size, and short intervals of ribbon radiolarite. The broken formation can be lithologically correlated with more distal successions of the Sid'r and Nayid Formations and contains no sedimentary matrix.

Late Cretaceous Riyamah unit: foredeep accumulation

In the central Oman Mountains, the Nayid Formation is disconformably overlain by Late Cretaceous (Cenomanian−Santonian?) siliceous facies, the Riyamah unit of the Muti Formation (Allemann & Peters 1972; Glennie *et al.* 1974; Robertson 1987; Fig. 2). The type section of the Riyamah unit was defined in the Dibba Zone (Allemann & Peters 1972). In this area a normal contact with the Nayid Formation has not yet been identified. Robertson (1987) established that certain outcrops, mainly east of Jebel Agah (Fig. 2) were correctly mapped as the Riyamah unit by Glennie *et al.* (1974), although subsequently they were not distinguished from the Hawasina Complex by Lippard *et al.* (1982) and Searle *et al.* (1983).

Near its structural base, the Riyamah unit comprises tightly-imbricated successions, metres to tens of metres thick that are composed of radiolarian chert and mudstone with shaly partings and subordinate thin-bedded, redeposited limestones. Upwards, lithoclastic calcarenites, calcirudites and slump sheets are numerous. There are also substantial masses of slope carbonates up to several kilometres long by a kilometre thick that belong to the Sumeini Group. These were previously mapped as olistoliths (Allemann & Peters 1972), or thrust sheets (Searle *et al.* 1983), but were later interpreted as slump sheets and debris flows within the Riyamah unit (Robertson 1987). The slump sheets are both underlain and overlain by shaly radiolarian facies, with depositional contacts. They mainly comprise thin- to medium-bedded successions of fetid lime mud, chaotic slump sheets and debris flows (e.g. in Wadi al Khurush; Fig. 2).

The structurally highest levels of the Riyamah unit contain relatively larger volumes of non-calcareous shale, mudstone, siltstone and fine-grained quartzose sandstone, with rarer detached blocks of mafic lava.

During Cenomanian time the input of calcareous sediment to the basin greatly diminished, probably related to flexural uplift of the platform that accompanied the initial stages of ophiolite emplacement. In the basin there was a switch to non-calcareous radiolarian accumulation below the CCD. Further uplift of the platform edge area ensued and large volumes of lithoclastic limestone were eroded and redeposited at the base of the slope as debris flows and turbidites. The carbonate slope (Mayhah Fm.) was oversteepened, failed *en masse* and slump sheets piled up at the base of the slope and then prograded into the more distal siliceous facies of the Riyamah unit. Finally, the siliceous Riyamah basin was itself flexurally downwarped to create a foredeep, accumulating shale and detached lava blocks, presumably derived from the advancing thrust load.

Haybi Complex: more outboard units

Throughout the Oman Mountains, the Haybi Complex as a whole is very heterogeneous in age, structure and lithology (see Searle & Malpas, 1980, 1982; Searle *et al.* 1980; Searle & Graham 1982; Lippard & Rex, 1982; Béchennec *et al.* 1990). In the Dibba Zone (Fig. 9) notable differences exist however. First, in some places extrusives of the Haybi Complex are thrust between deep-sea sediments of the Hawasina Complex and the metamorphic sole of the Semail ophiolite. Elsewhere the Haybi Complex is generally located at the highest structural level below the metamorphic sole. Secondly, available dates on the extrusives are all Late Cretaceous, rather than Permian or Late Triassic, as in most other areas. Thirdly, the Permian and Late Triassic limestones of the Oman Exotics in the Dibba Zone (at Jebel Qamar) are underlain by Ordovician to Permian successions; elsewhere Late Triassic extrusives are exposed. Fourthly, the Oman Exotics are associated with a distinctive sheared sedimentary melange that has not so far been reported from other areas and is here termed the *Kub Melange*.

Oman Exotic succession

The Lower Palaeozoic substratum of the Oman Exotics in the Dibba Zone yields rare insights into the evolution of the Oman area prior to rifting of the Neo-Tethys. Sequences exposed in melange blocks near Jebel Qamar (Fig. 10) were measured and correlated to give a com-

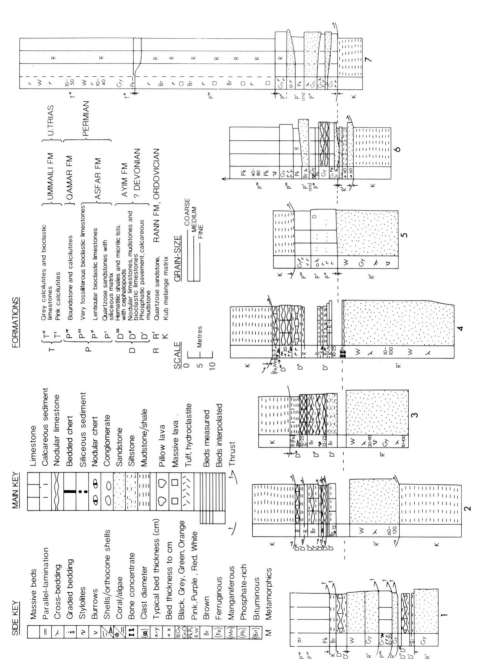

Fig. 10. Fragmentary measured successions of Palaeozoic sediments measured in individual detached blocks in the Kub Melange. See Fig. 2 for locations.

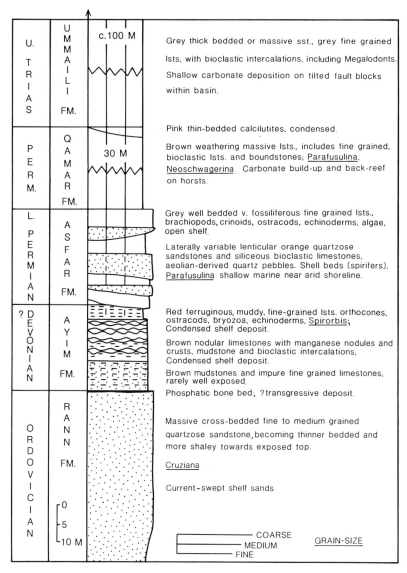

Fig. 11. Composite succession of the Palaeozoic sediments exposed in exotic blocks in the vicinity of Jebel Qamar.

posite succession (Fig. 11). The thicknesses of individual formations given by Hudson *et al.* (1954b) include what is now recognized as melange matrix and are thus very excessive.

Ordovician Rann Formation: stable continental shelf

The Ordovician Rann Formation comprises up to 80 m thick continuous successions within individual melange blocks that are composed of

fine- to medium-grained, relatively homogeneous, white to pale grey, orthoquartzite (Figs 10, 12a & 13a). The lower stratigraphical levels are thinly-bedded, often lenticular (lenses 5 m by 0.4 m) and cross-bedded, with foresets up to 1.8 m high and muddy intercalations up to 0.4 m thick. The higher intervals are thicker-bedded, more massive and mud-free. The sandstones exhibit common triliobite trace fossils (e.g. *Cruziana*). Coarser-grained sandstones are very well-sorted, almost matrix-free, and com-

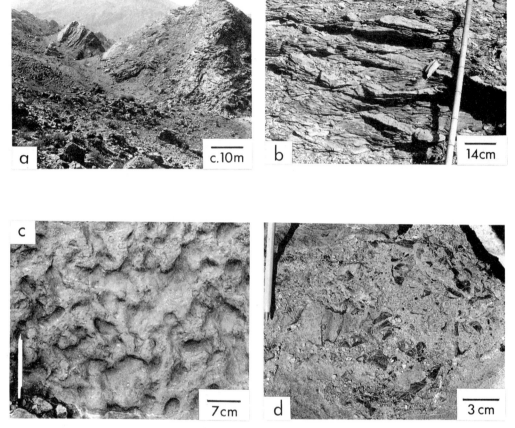

Fig. 12. Field photographs of Palaeozoic sediments in the Kub Melange. a, detached blocks of Ordovician Rann quartzite, SE of Jebel Qamar south; b, shales and thin-bedded limestones, Devonian ? Ayim Fm.; c, nodular Fe/Mn-rich micritic, limestone, Devonian? Ayim Fm.; d, shell concentrate, Permian Asfar Formation; locations all SW of Jebel Qamar south.

prise sub-angular, to very well-rounded grains of mainly plutonic and/or vein-type quartz, with minor orthoclase, plagioclase, zircon and tourmaline (Fig. 13a). More muddy sandstones higher in the succession are composed of grains of angular to sub-angular single-crystal quartz, with minor polycrystalline quartz, plagioclase and microcline in a recrystallized calcareous matrix (Fig. 13b).

The Rann Formation records current-influenced deposition on a stable siliciclastic shelf, with a continental, mainly granitic igneous provenance. The succession is similar to the 805 m thick Upper Siltstone Member of the Early and Mid-Ordovician Amdeh Formation in the Saih Hatat window (Lovelock *et al.* 1981).

Ayim Formation: condensed shelf deposition

The base of the conformably overlying *Ayim Formation* (new name) is a 0.15 m thick, Fe-Mn-rich phosphatic pavement, comprising bone material, fish teeth, broken fish scales (Fig. 13c), preferentially orientated *Orthocones* and well-rounded honey-coloured quartz grains in a siltstone matrix (Figs 10, 11). Scattered, well-rounded phosphatic lumps contain terrigenous silt. The pavement is overlain by up to 5 m of finely-laminated, thinly-bedded brown shale (Fig. 12b), argillaceous calcilutite and calcareous siltstone (Fig. 10). The succession passes upwards into rubbly, stylolitic con-

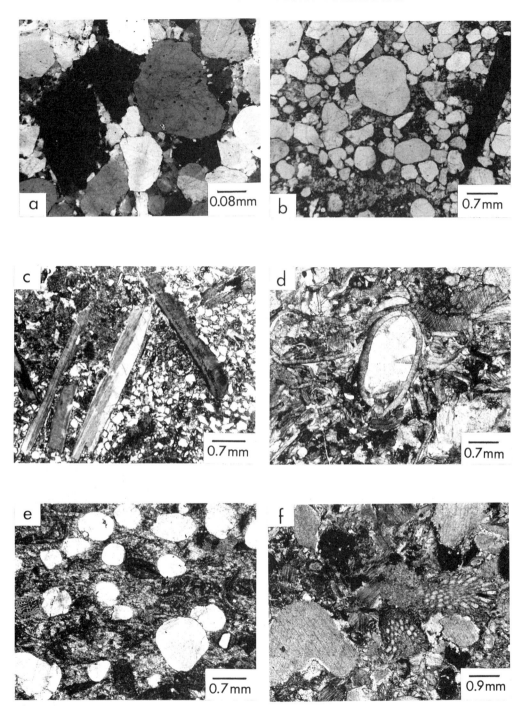

Fig. 13. Photomicrographs of Palaeozoic sediments in Oman Exotics. a, protoquartzite, Rann Formation; b, quartzose sandstone near top of the Rann Formation; note the well-rounded quartz grains; c, siltstone with fish scales from condensed interval above the Rann Formation; d, Devonian? ostracod-rich limestone (Ayim Formation); e, Early Permian calcareous sandstones: note the very well rounded aeolian-derived? grains; Asfar Formation; f, typical Early Permian bioclastic limestone containing broken pelecypod and bivalve shells, echinoderm plates and polyzoan debris; a–f from the vicinity of Jebel Qamar south.

cretionary limestone, with bioclastic limestone lenses up to 0.25 m thick (Fig. 10). There is then a 3 m thick, distinctive horizon of fine-grained nodular limestone, with manganese crusts and nodules, up to 0.2 m in diameter (Fig. 12c). The manganese occurs in an argillaceous lime-mud matrix, with numerous large burrows, that are mainly orientated parallel to bedding. The formation terminates with up to 3.5 m of brick-red argillaceous micritic limestone and hematitic shale, with numerous randomly orientated Orthocones. In addition to cephalopod remains, the limestone contains large shell and echinoderm fragments, ostracods and polyzoans in a variably recrystallized micritic matrix that is impregnated with opaque oxide (Fig. 13d). The fauna are apparently not age-diagnostic and the Ayim Formation presently can be constrained only between Ordovician and Early Permian. A Devonian age is possible as the formation, particularly the pelagic limestone and manganese nodules, resembles the Devonian Griotte and Cephalopodenkalk of the Western European Variscan (Tucker 1974).

Five samples of the reddish, Orthocone-bearing muddy limestone and associated ferro-manganese crusts and nodules were analysed for major and trace elements by X-ray fluorescence (Table 1). Fe_2O_3 in the crusts and nodules ranges up to 21.71% and MnO up to 3.07%. The metal-rich sediments contain relatively high contents of lithogenous elements (e.g. Al, K, Rb, Zr), and show enrichment of Ce relative to other Rare Earth Elements (REE) (e.g. Nb). Trace metals are not significantly enriched (e.g. Cu, Ni, Zn) in contrast to deep ocean manganese crusts and nodules (e.g. Cronan 1980). The chemical composition is consistent with slow accumulation of ferro-manganese oxide on the floor of a muddy shelf, with no detectable volcanogenic input.

The siliciclastic shelf deposition of the Rann Formation culminated in a hiatus, marked by emergence and erosion. Fish debris and aeolian-derived sand were winnowed and concentrated on the disconformity surface. The Fe- and Mn-rich muddy calcareous sediments of the Ayim Formation then accumulated on a stable submerged shelf.

Permian Asfar Formation: early rift sedimentation

The Asfar Formation comprises up to 25 m of lenticular-bedded, calcareous sandstone, sandy bioclastic limestone, and fossiliferous fine-grained limestone. Whilst successions are

Table 1. *Chemical analyses of metalliferous carbonates in the Exotic succession (Devonian? Ayim Formation).*

| Wt% | Sample Number | | | |
	1523	1524	1524A	1755
SiO_2	33.56	22.77	27.82	10.54
$Al2O_3$	9.84	7.03	6.12	3.94
Fe_2O_3	6.62	13.22	14.51	21.71
MgO	1.12	1.33	1.23	0.59
CaO	41.24	38.98	43.18	60.17
Na_2O	0.50	0.06	0.05	0.24
K_2O	2.80	2.10	1.84	0.97
TiO_2	0.42	0.54	0.46	0.42
MnO	2.81	2.92	3.07	0.58
P_2O_5	0.08	0.20	0.30	0.26
TOTAL	98.99	99.15	98.58	99.42

Trace-elements (p.p.m.)

Ni	45	183	154	43
Zn	32	26	24	8
Pb	14	13	15	35
Rb	124	94	78	46
Sc	551	440	490	373
Y	40	34	38	30
Zr	107	126	112	88
Cr	40	41	36	29
Ce	110	130	133	77
Nd	39	40	42	28
V	65	56	63	148
Ca	4	5	6	11
Ba	752	1122	1336	142

usually fragmentary and commonly inverted due to megascopic folding, an intact right-way-up sequence was logged along the southeast flank of Jebel Qamar south (Fig. 14a). There, the Asfar Formation overlies the Ayim Formation with an irregular erosional contact. Basal facies comprise fine-to medium-grained quartz-cemented siltstone and fine-grained sandstone. The succession passes into lenticular grey, cross- and wavy-bedded, fossiliferous limestone, with abundant shell fragments (Fig. 12d). This is followed by a distinctive lenticular wavy- and rubbly-bedded bioclastic limestone interval that is variably recrystallized. The upper levels of the formation comprise alternating lenses of bioclastic sandstone, pink stylolitic micritic limestone that is partly recrystallized, quartzose sandstone and well-bedded dark grey, highly fossiliferous calcilutite. Locally the Ayim Formation is condensed, or absent and there the Asfar Formation unconformably overlies the Rann Formation, with a *c.* 15° angular discordance.

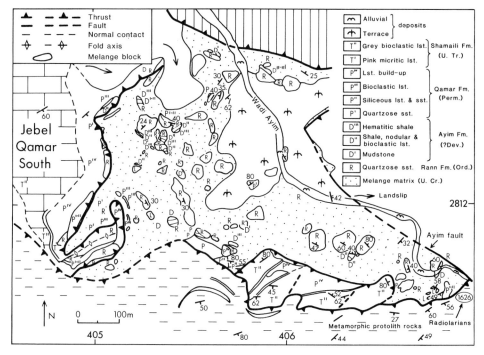

Fig. 14. Detailed geological map of the Kub Melange exposed southeast of Jebel Qamar south. See Fig. 9 for location.

Fossiliferous limestones collected southeast of Jebel Qamar south contain crinoids, gastropods, bryozoans, oysters and numerous brachiopods that R. E. Grant (pers. comm. 1982) provisionally identified as *Costiferina* sp., *Linoproductus* sp., *Marginifera*, and *Bilotina*? ('*Juresania*'), also Spirifers akin to *Licharewia*, *Pseudosyrinx* and/or *Asyrinx*. The bryozoans are probably referable to the genus *Polypora*. The entire fauna are similar to that described from Haushi in southern Oman and is Early Permian in age, if the correlation is correct (see Lee 1990). The fauna are also similar to the Early? Permian Amb Formation ('Lower Productus limestone') in the Salt Ranges of Pakistan (R. E. Grant, pers. comm. 1982).

Shelly limestone intercalations largely comprise tightly packed bivalve and brachiopod shell fragments, echinoderm plates and spines, benthic foraminifera and abundant polyzoan debris in a microspar matrix (Fig. 13f). Chemical analysis confirms the presence of abundant dolomite, often as late diagenetic rhombs. Pelagic limestone intraclasts were possibly derived from the subjacent Ayim Formation. One

oyster-rich shelly limestone horizon is packed with both broken and intact ostracod carapaces, together with scattered quartz grains and rare chloritic lumps. Interbeds comprise poorly-sorted biomicrite with abundant echinoderm plates, shells, coralline algae, benthic foraminifera, micritic intraclasts and scattered quartz grains in a partly recrystallized micritic matrix. Siliciclastic grains in sandy limestone interbeds are very well rounded, and include both strained and unstrained quartz of plutonic and/or vein-type, together with minor plagioclase and alkali feldspar (Fig. 13e).

Neo-Tethyan rifting apparently had commenced by the Early Permian (Blendiger *et al.* 1990). In the Dibba Zone, following tilting and erosion, aeolian-derived quartzose sands were reworked into the incipient rift zone. Sedimentation mainly involved mobile quartzose sand waves, and carbonate shoals, with periods of lower-energy more muddy accumulation. During Middle to Late Permian time a carbonate shelf become established in the Musandam Peninsula area to the northwest (Bih and Ghalilah Formations).

Qamar Formation: patch-reefs on rift blocks

The Asfar Formation is disconformably overlain by *c.* 60–100 m of brown-weathering, mainly fine-grained limestone that is mostly recrystallized (Figs 10 & 11). Massive to weakly-bedded, or rubbly boundstones predominate, with coral, brachiopods, and fusulinids (*Parafusulina* and *Neoschwagerina*; Hudson *et al.* 1954a). In thin section, samples are mainly composed of recrystallized micrite, with scattered dolomite rhombs.

The Permian Qamar limestones, like their coeval counterparts elsewhere in the Oman Mountains (Glennie *et al.* 1974; Searle & Graham 1982) are interpreted as patch-reefs that colonized fault blocks. Sabkhas were developed contemporaneously on a broad subsiding platform to the northwest in the Musandam Peninsula (the Hagil and Bih Fms.). The Jebel Qamar reefs apparently formed in the axial zones of the rift away from the Musandam shelf.

Late Triassic Ummaili Formation: carbonate platform deposition

Following a depositional hiatus, the Qamar Formation was unconformably overlain by pink and grey, thin-bedded lime mudstones, marking the base of the Late Triassic Ummaili Formation (Figs. 10 & 11). The contact is sharp and locally irregular. The basal 1–3 m of the overlying succession comprises laterally continuous, pink micritic limestone, locally cherty and radiolarian-bearing, and then passes into thicker-bedded grey dolomite lime-mudstone, with lenticular bioclastic limestone intercalations, including Megalodonts.

The Late Triassic Ummaili Formation is thin and pelagic, unlike the coeval, thick shallow-water successions of the Oman Exotics in the central mountains (Glennie *et al.* 1974; Searle & Graham 1982; Blendiger *et al.* 1990). Deposition there was mainly in a back-reef setting. Accumulation kept pace with subsidence until foundering took place at the end of Triassic, to Liassic time (Glennie *et al.* 1974). This subsidence is attributed to cooling, following onset of seafloor spreading in the adjacent Tethys ocean (Searle & Graham 1982). In the Dibba Zone, Early Permian reef formation was followed by emergence and/or non deposition. A further phase of rifting in the Late Triassic then led to subsidence. The site of deposition by then was a submerged off-margin platform,

probably much larger than the present Jebel Qamar outcrop.

In this study depositional successions above the Ummaili Formation were not confirmed. Late Triassic to Rhaetic sandstones and marls with *Dicerocardium* (Shamali Formation), reported by Hudson *et al.* (1954a) appear to be mostly sheared sedimentary melange and/or broken formation. The sandstones are compositionally very similar to those of the Kub Melange.

Kub Melange: rift-related sedimentary melange

The *Kub Melange* (new name) comprises detached blocks (olistoliths) of all levels of the Palaeozoic succession described above that are set in a matrix of siliciclastic shale and sandstone. The Kub Melange differs strongly from the adjacent broken formation that is derived from Hawasina Complex lithologies without a sedimentary matrix (cf. Lippard *et al* 1982). The melange crops out: (i) in the vicinity of Jebel Qamar; (ii) and further north, as an elongate outcrop between Wadi Kub and Wadi al Fay (Fig. 9). Attempts to the date the melange matrix using plant material (e.g. spores) were unsuccessful due to low-grade metamorphism.

In the south (Fig. 14), near Jebel Qamar south, the structurally higher levels of the melange, near Wadi Ayim, are dominated by quartzose sandstone interbedded with siltstone and siliceous shale. Relatively rare blocks are mostly composed of the Ordovician Rann Formation. The sandstone is brownish-grey, thin- to medium-bedded (0.05–0.5 m), medium- to very fine-grained, and commonly micaceous. The sandstone/shale ratio is < 0.5. On fresh surfaces the shale is black and contains abundant finely-divided, poorly preserved plant material. In thin section, the melange sandstone comprises angular to sub-angular, and subrounded, to occasionally very well rounded grains of plutonic and/or vein-type quartz, subordinate polycrystalline quartz, schist, plagioclase, muscovite and unstrained biotite. Scattered bioclasts include echinoderm and shell fragments. The matrix is comprised of microspar and dolomite rhombs. A mainly plutonic igneous and psammitic metamorphic provenance is inferred.

Individual sandstone beds are commonly disrupted to form elongate, lozenge-shaped masses (phacoids), mostly < 3 m long, in a sheared shaly matrix. Extension was achieved by way of layer-parallel extension, with brittle low-angle normal faulting of already-lithified sediments.

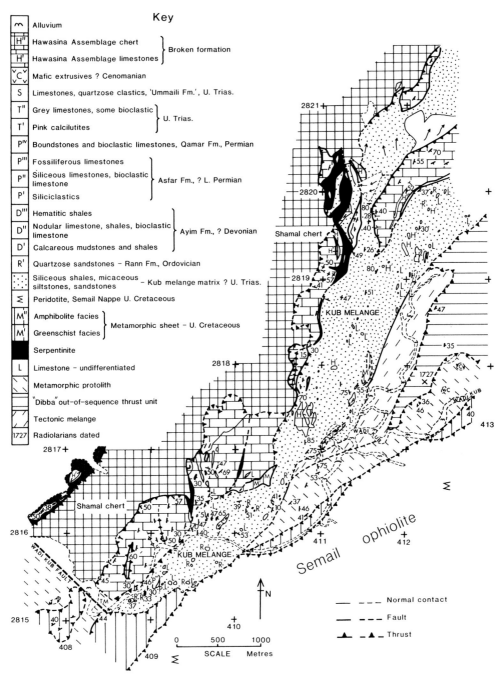

Fig. 15. Detailed geological map of the Kub Melange and adjacent units near Wadi Kub. See Fig. 9 for location by A. H. F. Robertson & A. E. S. Kemp.

The phacoids occasionally preserve isoclinal fold hinges, and rare more intact northwest-facing folds, consistent with formation during the Late Cretaceous thrusting. To the east, the Kub Melange terminates against the near vertical Ayim fault (Fig. 14), interpreted as a lateral ramp structure that was reactivated by normal faulting.

Numerous detached blocks, forming up to several kilometre-long trails particularly occur in the structurally lower levels of the melange, notably southeast of Jebel Qamar south (Fig. 14). Most of these blocks range from 1–50 m in size, as exposed 400 m south of Wadi Ayim. The margins of original blocks commonly correspond to incompetent horizons in the original stratigraphy (e.g. argillaceous Ayim Fm.). Some blocks are internally thrust-repeated (e.g. in Wadi Ayim; Fig. 14). Most blocks are correlated with the lower levels of the Palaeozoic succession (Rann, Ayim and Asfar Fms.), butu some are from the Permian and Triassic limestones (Qamar and Ummaili Fms.). Blocks of Hawasina and Haybi Complex lithologies were not observed.

The northern outcrop of the Kub Melange, from northwest of Wadi Kub to Wadi al Fay (Fig. 15) is dominated by sheared shale, with small mainly Palaeozoic-aged detached blocks, mostly 1–5 m, to rarely 15 m in size. Shearing is intense towards the margins of the melange unit. Serpentinite, basic extrusives, and amphibolite facies metamorphics locally occur as lenticular tectonic inclusions up to 300 m long. Small slices of Hawasina rocks include radiolarian chert and turbiditic calcarenite that is correlated with the Sid'r and Nayid Formations.

Genesis of the melange

The melange was previously assigned to the Late Cretaceous syntectonic Aruma Group (Searle *et al.* 1983). However, the Kub Melange shows the following significant differences from Late Cretaceous olistostromes in the central Oman Mountains (Buday'ah unit, Muti Formation; e.g. Hawasina window; Graham, 1980a,b; Robertson 1987): (i) the matrix of the Kub Melange is composed of organic-rich, siliciclastic sandstone, siltstone and shale, rather than more radiolarian and shaly sediments, as in the Late Cretaceous Muti Formation; (ii) the blocks are Palaeozoic in age, without Mesozoic Hawasina and Haybi Complex rocks (other than as localized thrust inclusions); (iii) the melange blocks occur individually within the matrix rather than being associated with debris flows (olistostromes) as in the central mountains; (iv) the quartzose sandstones are petrographically similar to Late Triassic sandstones elsewhere in the northern Oman Mountains and possibly may be coeval with the Zulla Formation in the Dibba Zone.

Possible interpretations of the Kub Melange are that: (i) the Kub Melange is tectonic in origin; (ii) it is a sheared sedimentary melange

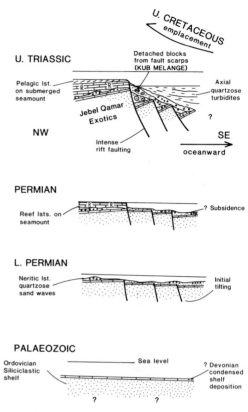

Fig. 16. Inferred Palaeozoic–Late Triassic history of the Oman Exotics exposed on Jebel Qamar north and south.

('olistostrome'). In the first scenario, the Jebel Qamar exotic ridge was sliced-off its basement and tectonically mixed with associated siliciclastic sediments during the Late Cretaceous thrusting. In the second, favoured model (Fig. 16) the origin of the melange is sedimentary. During the Late Triassic rifting, the Palaeozoic succesions were faulted, allowing olistoliths to slide off scarps. Quartzose sand, derived from rifted continental basement was redeposited as turbidites, together with abundant plant material. During the Late Cretaceous thrusting, local slivers of the overriding metamorphic sole of the Semail ophiolite and sediments of the Hawasina Complex were tectonically incorporated into the melange.

Late Cretaceous volcanics: Tethyan seamounts

The extrusives of the Haybi Complex in the Dibba Zone mainly crop out southeast of Jebel

Qamar north, as discontinuous pods up to several kilometres long. Further north, extrusives are also exposed structurally below thrust sheets of the Sid'r Formation (Shamal chert of Glennie *et al.* 1974) (Fig. 9). Biotite-bearing, fragmental extrusives exposed on the southeast flank of Jebel Qamar north (Figs 2, 3c, 9) have yielded a whole-rock K/Ar age of 96 ± 4 Ma (Cenomanian; D. C. Rex, in Searle *et al.* 1983), and extrusives elsewhere gave an age of 92 ± 6 Ma (K−Ar age on biotite; Allemann & Peters 1972). Also, fragmental extrusives in the Hagil window contain well preserved Dasycladacean algae of Aptian age (c.f. *Hensonella cylindrica*; J. D. Smewing, pers. comm. 1981).

Near Jebel Qamar north (Figs 2, 3c, 9), thrust sheets of Hawasina rocks (Nayid Fm.) are structurally overlain by a volcano-sedimentary unit up to 110 m thick, locally dated as Late Cretaceous (Fig. 17). Sixty to 80 m of ribbon radiolites, correlated with the Haliw Formation of Glennie *et al.* (1974) are depositionally overlain by clinopyroxene-plagioclase-phyric lavas, sedimentary rock inclusions and minor lava breccia (Fig. 18c). The lower *c.* 50 m of the volcanic succession contains numerous detached sedimentary blocks of recrystallized calcarenite and red ribbon chert, up to 100 m long by 15 m thick. Intercalations of pink fossiliferous biomicrite, up to 10 m long by 1 m thick appear higher in the succession (Fig. 18b), together with recrystallized boundstone blocks, up to 4 m in size. Interbedded limestones are strongly stylolitized and contain dark brown chalcedonic quartz chert of replacement origin.

Further north, in Wadi al Khurush (Fig. 2), the volcano-sedimentary succession (Fig. 17) is represented by a melange that is composed of blocks of plagioclase-phyric and aphyric pillow basalt up to 200 m in diameter, in a fine-grained shaly matrix. Interbedded pink calcareous chert lenses, up to 8 m long, contain well preserved early Cenomanian−Turonian radiolarians (see Appendix). This melange is correlated with the structurally upper part of the Late Cretaceous Riyamah unit (Robertson 1987).

A separate outcrop of mafic extrusives is exposed between Wadi al Khurush and Wadi Mu'arida (Figs 9, 18c,d). This is separated from the surrounding Sid'r and Nayid Formations by sheared serpentinite, containing marble blocks. To the northwest, near Wadi al Khurush, the volcanic succession is in fault contact with limestone slump sheets (Riyamah unit) (Fig. 2). The extrusives comprise vesicular massive and pillow basalt, ankaramite, bedded lava breccias, hyaloclastite (Fig. 18d), nodules and xenolithic blocks of pyroxenite, trachyte

and syenite (Lippard *et al.* 1982), together with pink biomicrite inclusions and rare marble blocks (Fig. 17). This assemblage is lithologically similar to Late Cretaceous successions exposed both to the north and to the south and is thus assumed also to be of Late Cretaceous age.

Geochemistry

Lippard *et al.* (1982) reported both tholeiitic and titanaugite-bearing-alkaline lava types in the Dibba Zone. Fourteen samples of Late Cretaceous extrusives were analysed by X-ray fluorescence for major and trace elements. Representative analyses are given in Table 2.

The TiO_2/Zr plot (Fig. 19a) effectively filters out differentiated rocks, while the Cr/Y plot aids recognition of basalts influenced by subduction (Pearce, 1980). On both TiO_2/Zr and Cr/Y diagrams (Fig. 19b), the southern lavas (Jebel Qamar north) show affinities with Mid Ocean Ridge (MORB) and within-plate basalts, while sills and flows of the northern outcrop (Wadi al Khurush) comprise only within-plate basalts. Niobium values, a useful guide to alkalinity, in the Jebel Qamar basalts are typical of MORB tholeiites (8−10 ppm), while the sills and flows of the northern outcrop exhibit alkali basalts values (50−100 ppm). A MORB normalized plot (Fig. 19c) confirms that the tholeiites are transitional between MORB and alkali basalt. By contrast, several (undated) dolerite sills analysed from the Hamrat Duru Group (Nayid Fm.) include MORB-type tholeiites (Fig. 19).

Setting of the Late Cretaceous volcanism

Lithological comparisons, combined with the fossil and radiometric age data suggest that the volcanic-sedimentary units are mainly Late Cretaceous (Cenomanian), rather than Permian and/or Late Triassic in age, as reported elsewhere in the Oman Mountains. *Halobia*-limestones, interbedded ribbon radiolarites and Late Triassic reefal limestones blocks, features of the central mountain extrusive successions were not recognized in the Dibba Zone.

In the central Oman Mountains, the Haybi volcanics, sited high in the structural succession are interpreted as emplaced seamounts (Searle *et al.* 1980; Searle & Graham 1982; Robertson 1986). In the Dibba Zone southern outcrop, near Jebel Qamar north, the tholeiitic volcanics are located well down in the thrust stack. The enclosed blocks are correlated with the Hamrat Duru Group (including Nayid Fm. calcitur-

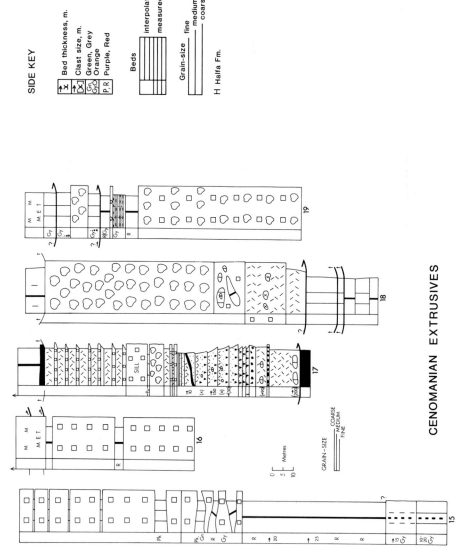

Fig. 17. Late Cretaceous extrusives, a, key to logs; b, measured logs: see Fig. 2 for locations.

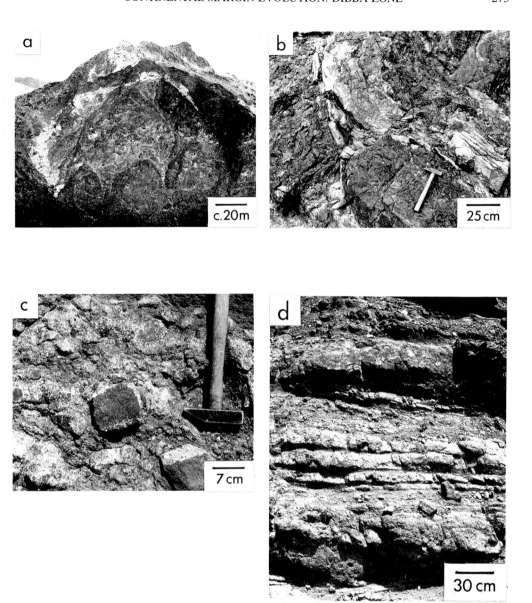

Fig. 18. Field photographs of Late Cretaceous extrusives a, basalt flows with interbedded pelagic limestone; b, detail of pelagic limestone interbedded with tholeiitic lava; a, b northeast of Jebel Qamar north; c, typical lava breccia composed of vesicular phyric alkaline basalt; d, bedded hyaloclastite; c-d, south of Wadi al Khurush.

bidites) and this suggests that eruption took place in a relative proximal continental rise, rather than an open ocean setting (Fig. 20). The recognition of sills intruded into Cretaceous proximal base-of-slope successions (Nayid Fm.) supports this interpretation. Elsewhere in the Dibba Zone, alkaline extrusives and sills crop out in a structurally higher position, near the

Semail ophiolite, for example in Wadis Ayim and Kub (Fig. 9). Lava blocks in the Late Cretaceous Riyamah unit (Wadi al Khurush) were possibly shed from these more distal volcanic units into a foredeep during the early stages of emplacement (Fig. 20).

Searle (1984) attributed the Late Cretaceous volcanism in the Dibba Zone to crustal ex-

Table 2. *Representative analyses of major- and trace-elements in the extrusives and sills from the Dibba Zone. See text for explanation.*

	Dolorite sills			Basaltic extrusives		
Sample No.	1	2	3	4	5	6
Field No.	1553	1708	1579	1645A	1645B	1662
SiO_2	41.97	47.68	40.28	48.04	52.68	45.41
Al_2O_3	14.99	15.47	15.28	16.16	13.85	13.32
Fe_2O_3	13.39	9.13	14.71	12.07	9.95	18.69
MgO	6.89	5.83	6.56	5.93	5.19	4.87
CaO	12.38	13.15	9.39	11.71	10.04	8.04
Na_2O	2.39	5.31	1.95	4.27	5.50	4.94
K_2O	2.35	0.37	4.09	0.22	0.63	0.05
TiO_2	3.81	2.60	4.57	1.56	1.84	2.03
MnO	0.20	0.11	0.19	0.19	0.15	0.30
P_2O_5	0.79	0.49	1.85	0.16	0.20	0.43
TOTAL	99.17	100.14	98.65	100.31	100.43	98.08

Trace-elements (ppm)						
Ni	72	152	33	53	49	59
Zn	133	76	177	58	95	138
Pb	–	3	–	5	5	–
Th	12	10	26	13	11	–
Rb	35	61	100	19	6	1
Sr	723	658	859	444	401	230
Y	37	27	55	3.4	25	39
Zr	380	203	486	13.6	99	189
Nb	117	45	136	9	9	15
Cr	142	282	17	11.6	137	28
Ce	218	62	583	17	14	29
Nd	81	89	189	12	10	23
Sc	21	29	16	59	41	30
V	346	257	335	292	302	607
Ca	53	77	13	9	33	10
Ba	1008	291	1869	85	48	3365
La	111	31	320	6	7	13

tension, caused by the migration of a flexural bulge towards the Arabian continent ahead of the emplacing Semail ophiolite. Alternatively, Robertson *et al.* (1990) explain comparable Late Cretaceous alkaline volcanism in the Hatta Zone, 60 km to the south in terms of extensional reactivation of a transform fault. In the case of the Dibba Zone, the MORB and within-plate volcanism is thought to relate to variable amounts of crustal stretching of older oceanic crust near the margin of the Tethyan ocean. This extension immediately preceded, or accompanied genesis of the Semail ophiolite, possibly above a northeastwards-facing subduction zone located further east.

Metamorphic protoliths

According to the Searle & Malpas (1980), the greenschist facies rocks of the metamorphic sole

exposed in the central mountains (e.g. in the Haybi corridor) show affinities with the Arabian margin successions, while the structurally overlying amphibolites formed from oceanic crust (Searle & Malpas 1982). Evidence from the Dibba Zone confirms that protoliths of the greenschist facies rocks are distal units of the Haybi Complex.

In the Dibba Zone, greenschists of the metamorphic sole are locally structurally underlain by up to several hundred metre-thick units of very deformed, recrystallized, but still recognizably sedimentary and igneous rocks that are interpreted as protoliths of the greenschist facies rocks. These are well exposed between the Kub Melange and the structurally overlying metamorphic sheet, for example near Wadi Ayim, southeast of Jebel Qamar north and in Wadi Kub (Figs 2, 9, & 15).

In Wadi Ayim (Fig. 9), the protoliths com-

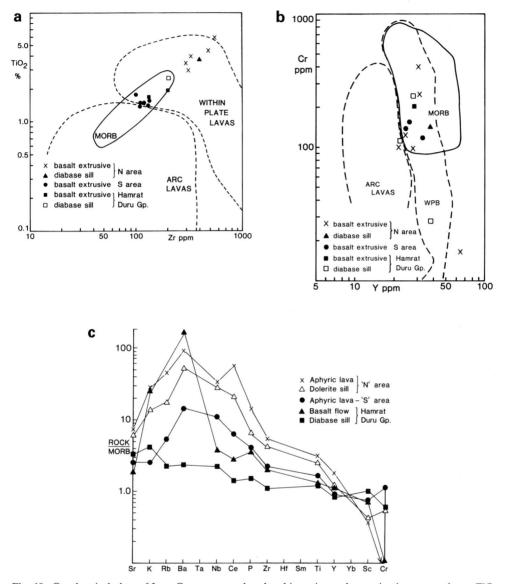

Fig. 19. Geochemical plots of Late Cretaceous and undated intrusive and extrusive igneous rocks. a, TiO_2 against Zr; b, Cr against Y; c, MORB-normalized 'spider diagram'. MORB values from Pearce (1980). See text for explanation.

prise thin-bedded siliceous mudstones and cherts, subordinate thinner-bedded (5–15 cm) chalky calcilutites, rare diabase sills and disrupted flows. The red colour of the primary oxidised pelagic sediment gives way structurally upwards to a reduced green colour, towards the greenschist facies metamorphic sole. South of Ayim, a 25 m thick dolerite sill is traceable on strike for c. 300 m and smaller sills and tectonic pods of mafic igneous rocks are common within the metamorphic protolith unit. The siliceous mudstones locally contain radiolarians of Late Jurassic (Tithonian) to Early Cretaceous (Valanginian) age (see Appendix). Further north, in Wadi Kub (Fig. 15) the metamorphic protolith comprises reddish to greenish siliceous mudstone, thin- to medium-bedded chert, pale grey-brown chalky calcilutites and local aphyric

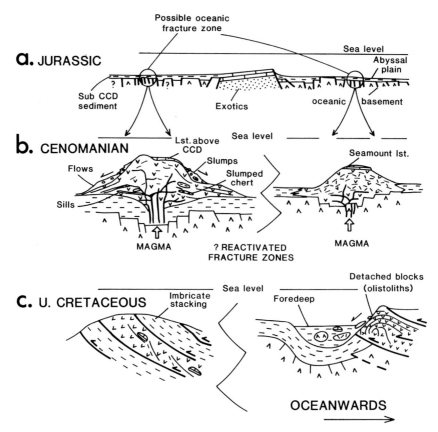

Fig. 20. Genesis of the Late Cretaceous extrusives, a, in the Late Triassic-Early Cretaceous, the Dibba Zone was cut by oceanic fracture zones; b, in Cenomanian fracture zones were crustally extended and seamounts were constructed, both inboard and outboard of a submerged Exotic ridge; c, During the Late Cretaceous emplacement more inboard lavas were incorporated in the thrust stack, while more outboard lavas were detached, slid into a foredeep, then were overridden.

to feldspar-phyric pillowed and massive basalt flows. South of Wadi Kub (Fig. 9) similar rocks become progressively more recrystallized structurally upwards over several tens of metres, and then pass with an ill-defined tectonic contact into greenschist facies metamorphics of the ophiolite sole.

Metamorphic sole

Structurally higher, greenschist facies metasediments (Lanphere 1981) and garnet-clinopyroxene-bearing amphibolites (Ghent & Stout 1981) showing polyphase deformation, and mylonitic fabrics are locally well exposed along the base of the Semail ophiolite in the Dibba Zone (Searle & Malpas 1980, 1982; Figs 2, 3, 9 & 15). Greenschists crop out extensively around the Jebel Qamar area and southwards along the Masafi corridor, and locally preserve

primary volcanic and sedimentary features, including recognizable successions of metabasalt, hyaloclastite, breccias, pillow lava, pillow breccia and other fragmental extrusives, similar to the unmetamorphosed volcanics of the Haybi Complex described above (Ziegler & Stoessel 1988). Alkaline pyroxenite-peridotite lenses are also occasionally present in the metamorphic sheet (Searle 1984).

Serpentinite and Semail ophiolite

The complete ophiolite sequence, including mantle sequence harzburgites, gabbros, sheeted dykes and pillow lavas is present in the Dibba Zone and is similar to elsewhere in Oman, where it has been studied in more detail (see Pearce *et al.* 1981; *Journal of Geophysical Research* **86**, no B4 (special issue) 1981; Lippard *et al.* 1986; *Tectonophysics* 151 No. 14 (special issue)). The ultramafic rock of the Semail ophiolite was the source of much serpentinite in the Dibba Zone. The serpentinite occurs: (i) as a matrix to tectonic melange enclosing blocks of Hawasina and Haybi Complex rocks (Fig. 15); (ii) as thin sheared strands, usually 2–5 m thick, separating Hawasina Complex thrust sheets and broken formation; (iii) surrounding a faulted oval slice of serpentinized harzburgite in the northwest, near Wadi al Fay (Fig. 3a); and (iv) as thin ductile detachment zones generally present along the base of the Semail ophiolite. The serpentinite is very sheared and commonly encloses marble and baked argillaceous sediment blocks containing actinolite, quartz and, rarely wollastonite and diopside (Allemann & Peters 1972). The serpentinite mainly comprises crysotile and lizardite and was presumably derived from the Semail ophiolite and injected into the thrust stack in relatively cool state after, initial thrust emplacement.

Late Cretaceous–?Early Tertiary thrusting

During emplacement of the Semail ophiolite, the metamorphic protolith rocks and the Exotics were overriden first and the thrust stack is then inferred to have been assembled by continentward thrusting over an evolving foredeep, represented by the Riyamah and Qumayrah units

of the Muti Formation (Fig. 21). Although the majority of faults in the Dibba Zone are thrusts related to the Late Cretaceous emplacement, a network of high-angle faults cut the thrust stack and these are related to one, or a combination of culmination collapse, normal faulting (Searle 1988), strike-slip faulting, or Tertiary reverse faulting. The uneven topography of the Semail ophiolite sole is related to a series of lateral and/or oblique ramps in the footwall, particularly in the vicinity of the Jebel Qamar Exotics (Figs 2 & 9). Specifically, major lateral ramps are inferred along Wadi Kub and to the east of Idhn village (Fig. 2). Near the Wadi Ayim fault, thrust-related shear fabrics intensify and are rotated to sub-vertical, parallel to the fault plane. The present contact between the Dibba Zone and the Musandam shelf edge along Batha Mahani is not the original platform edge, but is a normal fault formed by southeastward (dorsal) culmination collapse (Searle 1988a).

The regional, inferred tectonic transport direction is towards the west (285°) (Searle et al. 1983; Searle 1988a). Locally, however, this varies, both across the Dibba Zone and with structural depth in the thrust stack. Reconnaissance (e.g. in Batha Mahani; Fig. 2) indicates that, where developed cleavage is commonly rotated c. 10–20° anticlockwise, relative to bedding in right-way-up sequences. This could suggest a dextral strike-slip component to

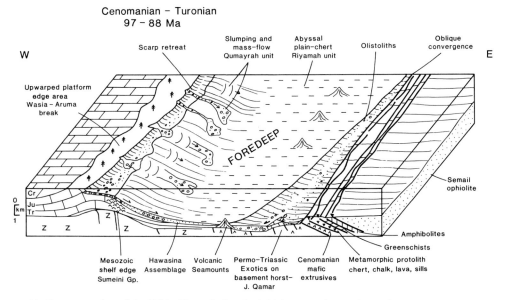

Fig. 21. Reconstruction of the Dibba Zone during the initial stages of tectonic emplacement.

the regional west-verging thrusting in the Dibba Zone. More work on this aspect would be worthwhile.

The onset of continental collision between the Arabian and central Iran plates caused large-scale folding and reverse faulting in the northern Mountains. The Musandam shelf was folded, faulted and thrust westwards *c.* 15 km along the Hagab thrust, and a clastic successor foreland basin (Pabdeh basin) formed west of the mountain front (Hudson *et al.* 1954b; Searle *et al.* 1983; Searle 1988b). The thrust stack was reverse faulted and deformed into large upright or west-facing, asymmetrical, 'whaleback' folds (e.g. Jebel Agah; Fig. 2).

Searle *et al.*'s (1983) interpretation implied that major early Tertiary rethrusting totally disrupted the original thrust geometry. However, some of the evidence for this major, restacking is now questionable. Supposedly early Tertiary successions (e.g. Jebel Hasfit) that predate culmination formation in the Musandam Peninsula have now been shown to be Late Cretaceous in age (Searle *et al.* 1989). Elsewhere, a good example of supposed major rethrusting is the Jebel Agah fold culmination, composed of limestone of the Sumeini Group (Fig. 3b). The nose of this structure (Fig. 6b) is clearly reverse faulted. However, Sumeini Group limestones exposed on the fold limbs can be seen to pass depositionally upwards into shale and muddy limestones of the Late Cretaceous Qumayrah unit (Muti Fm.; Fig. 2). This unit maps out northwards for several kilometres. Any re-thrusting in this area cannot have significantly displaced the Jebel Agah culmination from its depositional cover which is still more or less preserved. Elsewhere in the Dibba Zone many of the Sumeini Group slices in the Riyamah unit (Muti Fm.) are now interpreted as slumps, rather than as the result of re-imbrication. Also, the discovery that most of the extrusives are Late Cretaceous, rather than Late Triassic further diminishes the need for major re-thrusting to produce the present stacking geometry.

Discussion: Dibba Zone as a transtentional passive margin

The evolution of the Dibba Zone differs from other areas of Oman, as follows: (i) the thrust sheets were displaced a relatively short distance over the carbonate platform in the Musandam Peninsula; (ii) the carbonate platform slope was unusually steep and unstable, with evidence of slumping, sediment by-passing and local derivation of granitic basement clasts; (iii) the base-of-slope lithofacies are largely conglomeratic and include mega-breccias; (iv) distal Hawasina units (e.g. Wahrah and Haliw Fms.) are poorly represented; (v) Triassic volcanics are very subordinate, while Permian deep-water sediments and volcanics are, as yet unknown; (vi) the base of the Oman Exotics is interpreted as pre-rift Ordovician-Permian successions (cf. the volcanics exposed elsewhere); (vii) the Exotics are associated with the sedimentary Kub Melange that has a siliciclastic and organic-rich, shaly matrix, not reported elsewhere); (viii) Late Cretaceous extrusives are abundant and apparently were erupted in relatively inboard, as well as outboard locations; (ix) the emplacement history is more complex than elsewhere, with mid-Tertiary folding and some re-thrusting.

Many of the above features can be explained in terms of an oblique-rifted (transtensional) margin in the Dibba Zone. Regional lithofacies trends indicate that the mainly orthogonally-rifted Oman margin was offset by two major transform lineaments, the Masirah fault zone in the south and the Dibba Zone in the north, with several smaller offsets between (e.g. Semail Gap and Hatta Zone). In the Dibba Zone, the restored platform edge in the Musandam Peninsula faced southeast, then turned to more north–south further south. This area formed a major promontory with an oceanic embayment to the south, extending as far as the Hatta Zone and the Sumeini area (Robertson *et al.* 1990, Cooper, 1990).

Modern sheared (transform) passive margins (e.g. Gulf of Aqaba, and the equatorial Atlantic) exhibit a number of distinctive features (Scrutton 1979; 1982). These include: (i) a wide shelf; (ii) steep slope; (iii) a poorly developed rise; (iv) deep basins mainly located beneath the inner shelf, or along fracture zones; (v) a highly faulted continental edge with shallow ridges below the slope; (vi) horsts and grabens in the fracture zone; (vii) only limited crustal thinning and subsidence; (viii) a relatively narrow continent-ocean boundary zone < 100 km; (ix) rift volcanism that is relatively restricted and mainly occurs along fracture zones; and (x) tectonism continuing within the transform-offset zone.

Similar features exhibited by the Dibba Zone include the following: a steep slope and rise, with localized basins; continuing tectonic instability; rifted-off slivers (Jebel Qamar); rift basins with organic-rich (anoxic?) sediments; limited rift volcanism; younger, Late Cretaceous volcanism along possible reactivated fracture zones. However, the Dibba Zone shows more marked Triassic subsidence than predicted for a

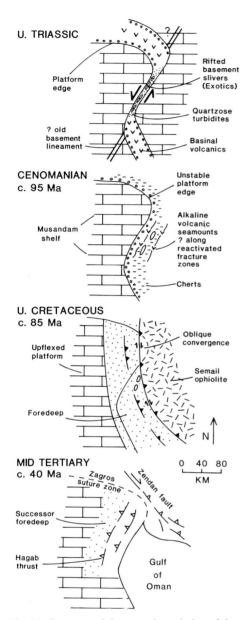

Fig. 22. Summary of the tectonic evolution of the Dibba Zone as an oblique-rifted Arabian passive margin segment. See text for further explanation.

purely transform margin, and a transtentional origin is more appropriate.

In summary, the Dibba Zone is interpreted as an oblique-rifted (transtensional) passive margin segment (Fig. 22). Shearing was apparently active during both the extensional rift and the compressional thrust-emplacement phases. Tethyan sheared passive margins elsewhere in-clude the still undeformed Levant passive margin (Garfunkel & Derin 1984) and the emplaced Antalya Complex, S. W. Turkey (Woodcock & Robertson 1982).

We thank Amoco Oman Petroleum Company for funding our study of the Dibba Zone. DWJC acknowledges the Natural Environmental Research Council for funding during the tenure of a post-graduate studentship held at Edinburgh University. John Smewing helped with logistics and discussion. Geochemical analysis was carried out in the Grant Institute, Edinburgh University, with the assistance of Mrs. D. James and Mr. G. R. Angel. We thank Mrs. D. Baty for help with drafting. The manuscript benefited from comments by P. Cawood, G. Graham and R. Nelson. The paper is published with the permission of Amoco Production Company.

Appendix

Radiolarians determined in the Dibba Zone; see Fig. 2. for locations.

Sample no: AE-81−1704
Locality: Wadi Zanhah, Sid'r Formation, radiolarite.
Radiolaria: *Archaeodictyomitra* sp.
    Praeconocaryomma sp.
    Relumbra sp.
    Stichocapsa sp. aff. *S. Cribata* Schaaf
Age: Late Jurassic (Tithonian)

Sample no: OM83−17 (MR 5866)
Locality: N of Jebel Agah, Sid'r Formation, radiolarite
Radiolaria: *Acanthocircus* sp.
    Archaeodictyomitra sp.
    Novixitus sp.
    Sethocapsa sp.
    All radiolarians very poorly preserved, casts and molds only.
Age: Probably Late Jurassic

Sample no: AE-81−1738
Locality: Jebel Agah, 2 km W of Jebel Agah, top of Sid'r Formation
Radiolaria: *Laticosta* sp.
    Novixitus rafsahensis Tippit
    Podocapsa sp.
    Stichocampium davidi Schaaf
    Thanarla brouweri (Tan Sin Hok)
    Wrangellium fisawense Tippit
Age: Early Cretaceous (late Valanginian/ Hauterivian)

Sample no: AE-81−1739
Locality: 1 km SW of Jebel Agah, Nayid Fm/ Riyamah unit
Radiolaria: *Pseudodictyomitra* sp.
    Pseudodictyomitra vestalensis Pessagno
    Stichomitra magna Squinabol
    Thanarla pulchra Squinabol
    Thanarla elegantissima Cita
Age: Late Cretaceous (early Cenomanian)

Sample no: AE-81–1606
Locality: Batha Mahani, radiolarite
             interbedded with calciturbidite, top
             of Sid'r Fm.
Radiolaria: *Archaeodictyomitra apiara* (Rust)
             Pantenellium corriganensis Pessagno
             Parvicingula boseit (Parona)
             Thanarla conica (Aliev)
Age: Early Cretaceous (late Valanginian/
             Hauterivian)

Sample no: AE-81–1640
Locality: Jebel Qamar north, below
             Cenomanian extrusives
Radiolaria: *Pseudodictyomitra* sp.
             Thanarla sp.
             Other poorly preserved Nassellarians
Age: Early Cretaceous

Sample no: AE-81–1678
Locality: 'Halfa Fm', Haybi Complex,
             interbedded with basic extrusives,
             Wadi Khurush
Radiolaria: *Dictyomitra napaensis* Pessagno
             Glennius polyaulax Tippit
             Lithostrobus punctulatus Pessagno
             Novixitus sp.
             Rhopalosyringium sp.
             Xitus sp. aff. *X. spicularis* Pessagno
             Zifondium polytretos Tippit
             Zylos sp.
Age: Late Cretaceous (Turonian)

Sample no: AE-81–1679
Locality: 'Halfa Fm'. Haybi Complex,
             interbedded with basic extrusives,
             Wadi Khurush
Radiolaria: *Archaeodictyomitra vulgaris*
             Pessagno
             Novixitus pessagnoi Tippit
             Novixitus sp.
             Pseudodictyomitra sp.
             Rhopalosyringium formanae Tippit
             Stichomitra communis Squinabol
             Thanarla sp. cf. *T. elegantissima*
             (Cita)
Age: Late Cretaceous (early Cenomanian)

Sample no: AE-81–1727
Locality: Radiolarite, associated with shale
             and redeposited limestone, Zulla
             Formation, south end of Hawasina
             thrust sheet in Wadi Khurush.
Radiolaria: *Epingium manfredi* Dumitrica
             Pseudodytlosphaera hellenica
             (DeWever)
             Staurodoras cochleata (Nakaseko
             and Nishimura)
             Triassocample scalaris (Koxur and
             Mostler)
             Yeharaia japonica Nakaseko and
             Nishimura
Age: Middle Triassic (Late Ladinian)/
             Late Triassic (early Carnian)
Remarks: Recent work has extended the ranges
             of some of the included taxa from the

late Landinian (latest Middle
Triassic) into the earliest part of the
Carnian (Late Triassic).

Sample no: AE-81–1626
Locality: Wadi Ayim 'Halfa Fm', Haybi
             Complex, radiolarite, below
             metamorphic protolith unit.
Radiolaria: *Hsuum* sp.
             Parvicingula sp.
             Stichocapsa sp. aff. *S. cribata* Schaaf
             Thanarla lacrimula (Foreman)
Age: Late Jurassic (Tithonian)/Early
             Cretaceous (Valanginian)
Remarks: Sample contains taxa too poorly
             preserved for a more precise age
             determination.

References

ALLEMANN, F. & PETERS, T. 1972. The ophiolite-
  radiolarite belt of the North Oman Mountains.
  Eclogae Geologicae Helvetiae, **65**, 657–97.
AGER, D. V. 1981. Major marine cycles in the Mesozoic. *Journal of the Geological Society*, **138**,
  159–166.
BARRETTE, P. D. & CALON, T. J. 1987. Re-imbrication
  of the Hawasina allochthons in the Sufrat and
  Dawd range, Oman Mountains. *Journal of Structural Geology*, **9**, 859–867.
BERNOULLI, D. & WEISSERT, H. 1987. The upper
  Hawasina nappes in the central Oman Moun-
  tains: stratigraphy, palinspastics and sequence of
  nappe emplacement. *Geodynamica Acta*, **1**,
  47–58.
BIEHLER, J., CHEVALIER, C. & RICATEAU, R. 1975.
  Carte géologique de la peninsula de Musandam.
  Edition B.R.G.M., Orleans, France.
BOSELLINI, A. & WINTERER, E. L. 1975. Pelagic lime-
  stone and radiolarite of the Tethyan Mesozoic: a
  genetic model. *Geology*, **3**, 279–282.
BOUMA, A. H. 1962. *Sedimentology of some flysch
  deposits*. Elsevier, Amsterdam.
CRONAN, D. S. 1980. *Underwater minerals*. Academic,
  London.
COOPER, D. J. W. 1986. *The Hamrat Duru Group:
  evolution of a Mesozoic passive carbonate margin
  in the Oman Mountains*. University of Edinburgh
  PhD thesis.
—— 1987. Hamrat Duru Group: revised stratigraphy
  of a Mesozoic deep-water passive margin in the
  Oman Mountains. *Geological Magazine*, **124**,
  157–164.
—— 1988. Structure and sequence of thrusting in
  deep-water sediments during ophiolite emplacement in the south-central Oman Mountains.
  Journal of Structural Geology, **10**, 473–485.
FALCON, N. L. 1967. The geology of the north-east
  margin of the Arabian basement shield. *Advancement of Science*, **24**, 31–42.
GARFUNKEL, Z. & DERIN, D. 1984. Permian — early
  Mesozoic tectonism and continental margin formation in Israel and its implications for the history

of the Eastern Mediterranean. *In*: ROBERTSON, A. H. F. & DIXON, J. F. (eds.) *The Geological Evolution of the Eastern Mediterranean.* Geological Society, London, Special Publication, **17**, 187–203.

GHENT, E. D. & STOUT, M. Z. 1981. Metamorphism at the base of the Samail ophiolite, southeastern Oman Mountains. *Journal of Geophysical Research*, **86**, 2557–71.

GLENNIE, K. W., BOEUF, M. G. A., HUGHES CLARK, M. W., MOODY-STUART, M., PILAAR, W. H. F. & REINHARDT, B. M. 1973. Late Cretaceous nappes in the Oman Mountains and their geologic evolution. *American Association of Petroleum Geologists Bulletin*, **57**, 5–27.

——, ——, ——, ——, —— & —— 1974. *Geology of the Oman Mountains.* Verhandelingen van het Koninklijk Nederlands geologisch Minjbouwkundig Genootschap.

GRAHAM, G. M. 1980a. Evolution of a passive margin, and nappe emplacement in the Oman Mountains. *In*: PANAYIOTOU, A. (ed.) *Ophiolites Proceeding International Ophiolite Symposium, Cyprus, 1979* 414–423.

—— 1980b. *Structure and sedimentology of the Hawasina window, Oman Mountains.* PhD thesis, Open University.

HARLAND, W. B., COX, A. V., LLEWELLYN, P. G., PICKTON, C. A. G., SMITH, A. G. & WALTERS, R. 1982. *A geologic time scale.* Cambridge University Press, Cambridge.

HEDBERG, H. D. 1976. *International stratigraphic guide: a guide to stratigraphic classification, terminology and procedure.* John Wiley, New York.

HISCOTT, R. N. & MIDDLETON, G. V. 1979. Depositional mechanisms of thick-bedded sandstones at the base of a submarine slope, Tourelle Formation (lower Ordovician), Quebec, Canada. *In*: DOYLE, L. F. & PILKEY, O. H. (eds.) *Geology of continental slopes. Special Publication of the Society of Economic Mineralogists and Paleontologists*, **27**, 307–326.

HOLLAND, C. H., AUDLEY-CHARLES, M. G., BASSET, M. G., COWIE, J. W., CURRY, D., FITCH, F. J., HANCOCK, J. M., HOUSE, M. R., INGHAM, J. K., KENT, P. E., MORTON, N., RAMSBOTTOM, W. H. C., RAWSON, P. F., SMITH, D. B., STUBBLEFIELD, C. J., TORRENS, H. S., WALLACE, P. & WOODLAND, A. W. 1978. *A guide to stratigraphical procedure.* Geological Society, London, Special report **11**.

HUDSON, R. G. S. 1960. The Permian and Trias of the Oman Peninsula, Arabia. *Geological Magazine*, **97**, 299–308.

——, BROWNE, R. N., & CHATTON, M. 1954a. The structure and stratigraphy of the Jebel Qamar area, Oman. *Proceedings of the Geological Society of London*, **1513**, xcix–civ.

—— & CHATTON, M. 1959. The Musandam Limestone (Jurassic to Lower Cretaceous) of Oman, Arabia. *Notes et Memoirs Moyen Orient*, **7**, 69–93.

——, MCGUGAN, A. & MORTON, D. M. 1954b. The structure of the Jebel Hagab area, Trucial Oman.

Quarterly Journal of the Geological Society of London, **110**, 121–52.

HUGHES CLARK, M. W. 1988. Stratigraphy of rock crust nomenclature in the oil producing area of Interior Oman. *Journal of Petroleum Geology*, **11**, 5–60.

LANPHERE, M. A. 1981. K-Ar ages of metamorphic rocks at the base of the Semail ophiolite. *Journal of Geophysical Research*, **86**, 2777–82.

LEES, G. M. 1928. The geology and tectonics of Oman and of part of southeastern Arabia. *Quarterly Journal of the Geological Society of London*, **84**, 585–670.

LIPPARD, S. J. & REX, D. C. 1982. K–Ar ages of alkaline igneous rocks in the northern Oman Mountains, N.E. Arabia, and their relation to drifting, passive margin development and destruction of the Oman Tethys. *Geological Magazine*, **119**, 497–503.

——, SHELTON, A. W. & GASS, I. G. 1986. *The ophiolite of Northern Oman.* Geological Society, London, Memoir, **11**.

——, SMEWING, J. D., ROTHERY, D. A. & BROWNING, P. 1982. The Geology of the Dibba zone, Northern Oman Mountains; a preliminary study. *Journal of the Geological Society of London*, **139**, 59–66.

LOVELOCK, P. E. R., POTTER, T. L., WALSWORTH-BELL, E. B., & WIEMER, W. M. 1981. Ordovician rocks in the Oman Mountains – the Amdeh Formation. *Geologie en Mijnbouw*, **60**, 487–495.

LOWE, D. R. 1982. Sediment gravity flows II. Deposition models with special reference to deposition of high density turbidite currents. *Journal of Sedimentary Petrology*, **52**, 279–297.

PATTON, T. L. & O'CONNOR, S. S. 1988. Cretaceous flexural history of North Oman Foredeep, United Arab Emirates. *American Association of Petroleum Geologists Bulletin*, **72**, 797–809.

PEARCE, J. A. 1980. Geochemical evidence for the genesis and eruptive setting of lavas from Tethyan ophiolites. *In*: PANAYIOTOU, A. (ed.) *Ophiolites, Proceedings International Ophiolite Symposium Cyprus 1979*, 261–273.

——, ALABASTER, T., SHELTON, A. W. & SEARLE, M. P. 1981. The Oman ophiolite as a Cretaceous arc-basin complex: evidence and implications. *Philosophical Transactions of the Royal Society, London*, **A300**, 299–317.

RICATEAU, R. & RICHE, P. H. 1980. Geology of the Musandam Peninsula (Sultanate of Oman) and its surroundings. *Journal of Petroleum Geology*, **3**, 139–52.

ROBERTSON, A. H. F. 1986. Geochemical evidence for the origins of Late Triassic melange units in the Oman Mountains as a small ocean basin formed by continental rifting. *Earth and Planetary Science Letters*, **77**, 318–32.

—— 1987. The transition from a passive margin to an Upper Cretaceous foreland basin related to ophiolite emplacement in the Oman Mountains. *Geological Society of America Bulletin*, **99**, 633–53.

SCRUTTON, R. A. 1979. On sheared passive margins. *Tectonophysics*, **59**, 293–305.

—— 1982. Crustal structure and developments of sheared passive margins. *In*: SCRUTTON, R. A. (ed.) *Dynamics of passive margins*. Geodynamics Series, American Geophysical Union, **6**, 133–140.

SEARLE, M. P. 1984. Alkaline peridotite, pyroxenite and gabbroic intrusions in the Oman Mountains, Arabia. *Canadian Journal of Earth Sciences*, **21**, 396–406.

—— 1985. Sequence of thrusting and origin of culminations in the northern and central Oman Mountains. *Journal of Structural Geology*, **7**, 129–143.

—— 1988a. Thrust tectonics of the Dibba zone and the structural evolution of the Arabian continental margin along the Musandam mountains (Oman and United Arab Emirates). *Journal of the Geological Society*, **145**, 43–54.

—— 1988b. Structure of the Musandam Culmination (Sultanate of Oman and the United Arab Emirates) and the Straits of Hormuz syntaxis. *Journal of the Geological Society*, **145**, 831–845.

—— & GRAHAM, G. M. 1982. 'Oman Exotics' — Oceanic carbonate build-ups associated with the early stages of continental rifting. *Geology*, **10**, 43–9.

——, JAMES, N. P., CALON, T. J. & SMEWING, J. D. 1983. Sedimentological and structural evolution of the Arabian continental margin in the Musandam Mountains and Dibba zone, United Arab Emirates. *Geological Society of America Bulletin*, **94**, 1381–1400.

——, LIPPARD, S. J., SMEWING, J. D. & REX, D. C. 1980. Volcanic rocks beneath the Semail Ophiolite in the northern Oman Mountains and their tectonic significance in the Mesozoic evolution of Tethys. *Journal of the Geological Society of London*, **137**, 589–604.

—— & MALPAS, J. 1980. The structure and metamorphism of rocks beneath the Semail ophiolite of Oman and their significance in ophiolite obduction. *Transactions of the Royal Society of Edinburgh: Earth Sciences*, **71**, 213–28.

—— & —— 1982. Petrochemistry and origin of subophiolitic metamorphic and related rocks in the Oman Mountains. *Journal of the Geological Society of London*, **139**, 235–48.

SEARLE, M. P., SMEWING, J. D., NOLAN, S. C., HART, M. & RAMSAY, A. T. S. 1989 Correction to Sedimentological and structural evolution of the Arabian Continental margin in the Musandam Mountains and Dibba Zone. *Geological Society*

of America Bulletin, (in press).

STOCKLIN, J. 1968. Structural history and tectonics of Iran: A review. *American Association of Petroleum Geologists Bulletin*, **52**, 1229–58.

—— 1974. Possible ancient continental margins in Iran. *In*: BURK, C. L. & DRAKE, C. L. (eds) *The geology of continental margins*. New York, Springer, 873–887.

TILTON, G. R., HOPSON, G. A. & WRIGHT, J. E. 1981. Uranium–lead isotopic ages of the Semail Ophiolite, Oman, with applications to Tethyan ocean ridge tectonics. *Journal of Geophysical Research*, **86**, 2763–76.

TIPPIT, P. R., PESSAGNO, E. A. Jr. & SMEWING, J. D. 1981. The biostratigraphy of sediments in the volcanic unit of the Semail ophiolite. *Journal of Geophysical Research*, **86**, 2756–62.

TUCKER, M. E. 1974. Sedimentology of Palaeozoic pelagic limestones: the Devonian Griotte (southern France) and Cephalopodenkalk (Germany). *In*: JENKYNS, H. C. & HSÜ, K. J. Pelagic sediments on Land and under the Sea. *Special Publication of the International Association of Sedimentologists*, **1**, 71–92.

VAIL, P. R., MITCHUM, F. M. Jr. & THOMPSON, J. III. 1977. Seismic stratigraphy and global changes in sea level, part 4: global cycles or relative changes of sea level. In: Seismic stratigraphy — applications to hydrocarbon exploration. *American Association of Petroleum Geologists Memoir*, **26**, 83–97.

WATTS, K. W. 1988. Triassic carbonate submarine fans along the Arabian platform margin, Sumeini Group, Oman. *Sedimentology*, **35**, 43–72.

—— & GARRISON, R. E. 1986. Sumeini Group, Oman — evolution of a Mesozoic carbonate slope on a South Tethyan continental margin. *Sedimentary Geology*, **48**, 107–68.

WHITE, R. S. & ROSS, D. A. 1979. Tectonics of the Western Gulf of Oman. *Journal of Geophysical Research*, **84**, 3479–89.

WOODCOCK, N. H. & ROBERTSON, A. H. F. 1982. Wrench and thrust tectonics along a Mesozoic-Cenozoic continental margin: Antalya Complex, SW Turkey. *Journal of the Geological Society*, **139**, 147–63.

ZIEGLER, U. R. F. & STOESSEL G. F. U. 1988. Metavolcanic rocks beneath the Semail Ophiolite Nappe in the United Arab Emirates: *In: The Geology and Tectonics of the Oman Region*, Abstracts of an international discussion meeting, Edinburgh, March 1988, p. 72.

Sedimentary and structural evolution of a continental margin transform lineament: the Hatta Zone, Northern Oman Mountains

A. H. F. ROBERTSON[1], A. E. S. KEMP[2], D. C. REX[3] & C. D. BLOME[4]

[1] *Department of Geology and Geophysics, West Mains Road,*
Edinburgh EH9 3JW, UK
[2] *Department of Oceanography, University of Southampton, UK*
[3] *Department of Earth Sciences, University of Leeds, Leeds, UK*
[4] *United States Geological Survey, Denver Federal Center, Denver, CO,*
USA

Abstract: The Hatta Zone, Northern Oman Mountains, is interpreted as a *c.* 50 km long left-lateral offset of the North Oman passive continental margin that was generated by right-lateral transform faulting during spreading of the Neo-Tethys ocean. During Early−Late Triassic time, slumps, debris flows and calciturbidites composed of redeposited upper slope and shelf carbonates accumulated at the base of a steep carbonate platform slope (Maqam Fm., Mayhah Fm.; Sumeini Group). Clasts in channelized conglomerates include basement-derived quartzose sandstone, schist and basic extrusives. Basaltic pillow lavas were erupted at the foot of the Late Triassic continental rise of the Hatta Zone transform lineament (Zulla Fm.). During Early to mid Jurassic time, oolitic and lithoclastic calciturbidites and debris flows accumulated on tectonically unstable base of slope (Mayhah Fm.) and continental rise (Guweyza Limestone Fm.) settings. During mid-Cretaceous time (Albian−Cenomanian), alkaline magmatism constructed seamounts along the inferred oceanward extension of the Hatta transform lineament. K/Ar ages of diabase sills range from 109 Ma ± 4 Ma, to 105 Ma ± 3 Ma on sills, while basalts gave ages of 104 Ma ± 4, to 93 Ma ± 4. During the Late Cretaceous ophiolite emplacement, abyssal plain and base of slope units were deformed into a major transverse culmination (Jebel Quimah), mainly controlled by collision with the Hatta Zone continental margin transform lineament. Hanging wall imbrication and overturning of structurally high thrust sheets occured above an inferred footwall ramp. As the Semail ophiolite overrode a north-facing transform escarpment margin, footwall slope sediments were sheared and deformed into a major lateral ramp, now represented by the Jebel Raudha−Masfut ridge. Normal faulting and deep erosion ensued, followed by Maastrichtian−early Tertiary shallow marine carbonate deposition on an unstable shelf. During renewed, mid-Tertiary deformation the Hatta Zone was reactivated, giving rise to NW−SE trending open-folding at right angles to the regional W-directed compression, followed by differential erosion to form the present lineament.

The Hatta Zone is northwest−southwest-trending, elongate window through the Semail ophiolite (Figs 1 & 2). Other windows, or corridors through the ophiolite further south (e.g. Wadis Jizi and Ahin) document dissection of the ophiolite into discrete blocks during emplacement (Robertson & Woodcock 1983). The northwestward subsurface extension of the Hatta Zone is an important depositional hinge zone (J. Jenner, pers. comm. 1982). Units exposed in the Hatta Zone, structurally below the Semail ophiolite, include platform slope carbonates (Sumeini Group), base of slope redeposited sediments (Hamrat Duru Group), and more distal, deep-sea sediments, volcanics and metamorphic rocks of the ophiolite sole (Haybi Complex) (Figs 1 & 2).

Combined lithofacies and structural evidence, discussed in this paper indicate that the Hatta Zone formed a small, left-lateral (sinistral) offset, related to *right-lateral transform faulting* of the continental margin during rifting of the Mesozoic Neo-Tethys ocean. The Hatta Zone shows some sedimentary and structural similarities with the Dibba Zone, 60 km to the north which is interpreted as a right-lateral (transtensional) offset of the continental margin in the Musandam Peninsula (Robertson *et al.* 1990).

Large-scale structure

The southeastern Hatta Zone is dominated by Jebel Quimah (Fig. 2), a northwest−southwest-

From ROBERTSON, A. H. F., SEARLE, M. P. & RIES, A. C. (eds), 1990,
The Geology and Tectonics of the Oman Region.
Geological Society Special Publication No 49, pp 285−305

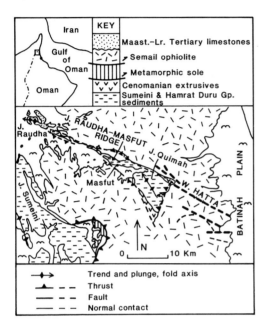

Fig. 1. Outline geological map of the Hatta Zone, northern Oman Mountains (modified after Glennie *et al.* 1974).

trending, approximately symmetrical structural culmination that trends almost at right-angles to the regional thrust-emplacement direction. Two major thrust sheets are recognized on Jebel Quimah (Figs 2, 3b,c). The lower thrust sheet is relatively intact, whereas the higher thrust sheet, exposed in the east near Wadi al Fay (Figs 2, 3c) is more internally imbricated, sheared and locally inverted. By contrast, the northwestern Hatta Zone, between Jebel Raudha and Masfut (Fig. 2) is dominated by a northwest–southwest-trending ridge, 14 km long, and up to 0.6 km wide by up to 200 m high (Jebel Raudha–Masfut ridge). Lithofacies exposed on this ridge mainly comprise steeply dipping, sheared limestones, that are unconformably overlain by little deformed Maastrichtian–Early Tertiary shallow water limestones at the northwest end, on Jebel Raudha (Figs 2, 3a).

Mesozoic passive margin history

We will first examine the sedimentary successions for evidence of a possible transform origin of the Hatta Zone. Long intact stratigraphical successions were measured in major thrust sheets that are exposed in the core and on both limbs of the Jebel Quimah culmination (Fig. 2). More fragmentary successions were

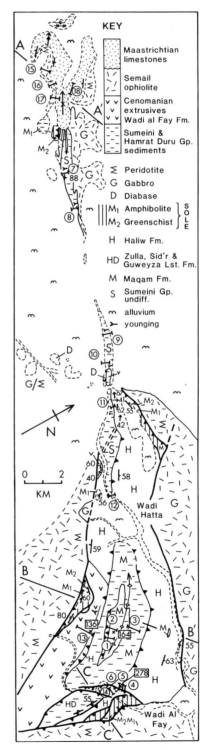

Fig. 2. Geological map of the Hatta Zone by A. H. F. Robertson and A. E. S. Kemp.

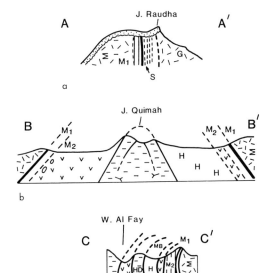

Fig. 3. Cross sections of the Hatta Zone. a, across Jebel Raudha; b, across Jebel Quimah; c, across Wadi al Fay. See Fig. 2 for locations and key to symbols.

also logged in structurally higher inverted, faulted thrust sheets located at the southeast end of Jebel Quimah and also on the Jebel Raudha-Masfut ridge further northwest (Fig. 2).

Lithostratigraphy

Glennie *et al.* (1973, 1974) originally mapped the Jebel Quimah area in the southeast of the Hatta Zone as the Sumeini Group overlain, in turn by the Dhera Formation, the Halfa Formation, and then by basic extrusives. However, in the course of remapping, it became clear that, possibly uniquely, the Sumeini Group–Dhera Formation contact is *definitely stratigraphic* rather that tectonic, thus creating a nomenclatural problem. Also, Cooper (1986, 1987) has redefined the Hamrat Duru Group, such that Glennie *et al.*'s (1974) local Dhera Formation is now abandoned.

In this study, thrust sheets mapped by Glennie *et al.* (1974) as Dhera Formation at Jebel Quimah are correlated lithologically with the Sumeini Group *and* the Hamrat Duru Group. Supporting radiolarian age data are given in the Appendix. The Hamrat Duru Group successions are assigned to the Late Triassic Zulla Formation, the Early Jurassic Guweyza Limestone Formation and the mid-Jurassic–Early Cretaceous Sid'r Formation, as redefined by

Cooper (1987). The stratigraphically higher, Cretaceous Nayid Formation and the syn-tectonic Riyamah unit (Muti Formation) were not observed.

Structurally high radiolarian cherts, south of Jebel Quimah were mapped by Glennie *et al.* (1974) as the Halfa Formation, but are here reassigned to the more 'distal' Haliw Formation (as in Bernoulli *et al.* 1990), and treated as part of the structurally high, Haybi Complex (Searle & Malpas 1980). The radiolarian cherts are locally *depositionally overlain* by basic extrusives, the *Wadi al Fay Formation* (new name), shown here to be Late Cretaceous, based on new radiometric age data (see later). The Wadi al Fay Formation is structurally overlain by small thrust intercalations, ranging from marble blocks, assigned to the Oman Exotics (Glennie *et al.* 1974), to greenschist and/or amphibolite facies metamorphic rocks of the Semail ophiolite sole.

In the northwest part of the Hatta Zone, the sheared limestones of the Jebel Raudha–Masfut ridge were mapped by Glennie *et al.* (1974) as the Late Triassic Al Aridh Formation, which includes shallow-water limestone Exotics. Here the succession is re-assigned to Early Cretaceous platform slope lithofacies of the Mayhah Formation, Sumeini Group.

Sumeini Group: Mesozoic slope and base of slope carbonates

Sumeini Group slope carbonates dominate the elongate Jebel Raudha–Masfut ridge (Fig. 3a) and also form the two major thrust sheets that dominate the Jebel Quimah culmination (Fig. 3b). We will consider the more proximal Jebel–Masfut ridge successions first.

Jebel Raudha–Masfut Ridge successions

These successions are mainly fragmentary, sheared and locally thrust imbricated, with moderate to intense pressure solution cleavage (Figs 4 & 5; logs 1–6). Lithofacies include slumped platy calcilutite, channelized limestone conglomerate (Fig. 6a,b), calcarenite, bedded replacement and primary chert and slivers of low-grade metaclastic sediment (Fig. 5, log 1). Glennie *et al.* (1974) reported an Early Cretaceous age from lithoclastic grainstone with igneous fragments, associated with the conglomerate. Protoliths similar to the low-grade schist occur in the Late Triassic D and F Members of the Maqam Formation (Sumeini Gp.) in Jebel Sumeini area (Watts & Garrison 1986; Watts 1988). Cherts stratigraphically underlying the

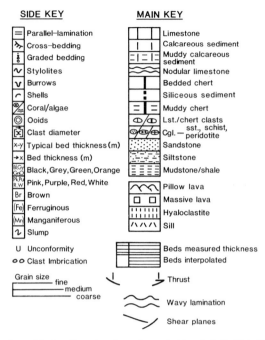

SIDE KEY

=	Parallel–lamination
⋙	Cross–bedding
⋮	Graded bedding
∿	Stylolites
v	Burrows
⌒	Shells
⊗	Coral/algae
◎	Ooids
x	Clast diameter
x-y	Typical bed thickness (m)
→x	Bed thickness (m)
B/Gy Gr/O	Black, Grey, Green, Orange
Pk/Pu R/W	Pink, Purple, Red, White
Br	Brown
(Fe)	Ferruginous
(Mn)	Manganiferous
ℒ	Slump

U   Unconformity

o o Clast Imbrication

Grain size
——— fine
—————— medium
————————— coarse

MAIN KEY

	Limestone
	Calcareous sediment
	Muddy calcareous sediment
∿∿	Nodular limestone
	Bedded chert
∴	Siliceous sediment
	Muddy chert
⊕	Lst./chert clasts
⊕	Cgl. — sst., schist, peridotite
	Sandstone
	Siltstone
	Mudstone/shale
⌒⌒	Pillow lava
□ □	Massive lava
‖‖‖	Hyaloclastite
/\/\	Sill

	Beds measured thickness
	Beds interpolated

⊥⊥ Thrust

∿∿ Wavy lamination

⟍⟋ Shear planes

Fig. 4. Key to the measured graphical sedimentary logs shown in Figs 5, 7, 9, 12 & 18. Lithology and grain-size are shown in the wider, right-hand column, while colour, bed-thickness, clast-size and a range of sedimentary structures are shown in the narrower left-hand column. Note that, for example limestone type can be identified by grain-size (e.g. calcilutite), qualified by the sedimentary structures shown (e.g. oolitic). The horizontal lines show individual measured units. More than 1 m thick beds are indicated, where measured.

conglomerate are lithologically correlated with the regionally extensive, cherty Mayhah Formation B Member (Watts & Garrison 1986), and thus the underlying platy limestones are assigned to the Jurassic Mayhah Formation A Member; however, older units (e.g. Triassic Maqam Formation) could also be present.

Most of the conglomerate is composed of subrounded, to tabular clasts of wackestone, with rare nodular chert, white crystalline reef-derived limestone, quartzose siltstone and medium-grained quartzose sandstone, up to 0.7 m long by 0.1 m wide, and are set in a siliceous, silty, and/or calcareous matrix (Fig. 5, log 1). Some, but not all of the sandstone clasts are sheared, while the matrix is commonly relatively undeformed (Fig. 6a). Other conglomerates contain clasts of limestone, black chert (Fig. 6b) and red radiolarite in a matrix of black replacement chert (Fig. 5, logs 3, 4). The exposed dimensions of the lenticular conglomerates range from 5–250 m long by 25 m thick. The majority of the smaller lenses are nearly symmetrical in outcrop (e.g. Fig. 5, logs 1, 5). Several individual conglomerate lenses comprise, at the base, coarsening-upwards, graded calci-turbidites in beds up to 0.8 m thick, passing

upwards into thick-bedded, and/or massive conglomerate. Other occurrences include en echelon lenses of bedded calcarenites, up to 30 m wide by 6 m thick (Fig. 5, log 2), and up to 30 m-thick intervals of thin-bedded calciturbidites (Fig. 5, log 5), with intercalations of thin-bedded calcilutite, largely replaced by black chert (Fig. 5, log 3).

South of Jebel Raudha, two 80–100 m wide, sub-vertical sheets of very low-grade schist are sandwiched between serpentinite of the Semail ophiolite and sheared limestones of the Jebel Raudha–Masfut ridge (Fig. 2). Thin sections show the protolith is litharenite, with abundant primary polycrystalline quartz, plagioclase and orthoclase. The texture is cataclastic with elongate metamorphic biotite laths, imparting a weak cleavage. The low-grade schist is interpreted as a quartzose unit within the Sumeini Group that was sheared and partly recrystallized during emplacement, rather than an as exotic thrust unit. Terrigenous shale and siltstone do indeed occur in the D and F Members of the Late Triassic Maqam Formation (Sumeini Group) in Jebel Sumeini area (Watts & Garrison 1986; Watts 1988).

Clasts in the channelized conglomerates were

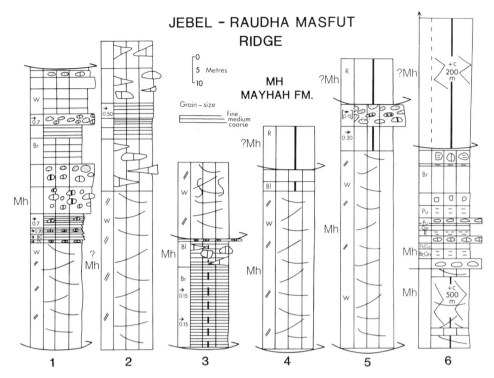

Fig. 5. Sedimentary logs of deformed slope carbonates (Sumeini Gp.) exposed on the Jebel Raudha–Masfut ridge. See Fig. 2 for location and Fig. 4 for the key.

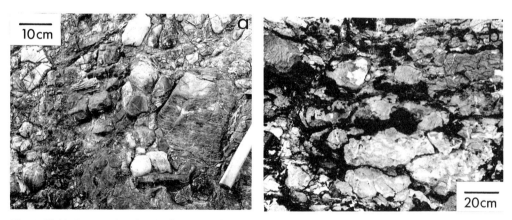

Fig. 6. Field photographs of Early Cretaceous? channelized conglomerates in the Sumeini Group. a, with well rounded clasts of crystalline limestone (white), cleaved micritic limestone and quarztzose sandstone; Jebel Masfut ridge; b, channelized conglomerate comprising platform limestone (white) and black replacement chert; Jebel Masfut ridge; both channels are located on the Jebel Raudha–Masfut ridge.

studied in thin section. Calcarenite clasts are typically carbonate platform- and/or slope-derived bioclastic packstones, with abundant pelecypod and brachiopod shells, echinoderm plates, coral, calcareous algae, benthonic foraminifera and micritic intraclasts, also polycrystalline quartz, fine-grained schist, siltstone and mudstone. Sandstone clasts comprise poorly sorted litharenite, with angular, mainly unstrained quartz, polycrystalline quartz, plagioclase, perthite, blue and/or green chlorite, muscovite, hornblende and fine-grained schist. Associated bedded litharenite is made up of grains of quartzose sandstone, siltstone, mudstone, partly recrystallized biomicrite and rare quartzite (Fig. 5, log 5). One clast contains well-rounded quartz grains, of possible aeolian origin. Permian sandstone of the Jebel Qamar exotics in the Dibba Zone is, for example petrographically similar (Robertson *et al.* 1990). The pink matrix of a thick, channelized rudite (e.g. Fig. 5, log 1) comprises biomicrite with calcite-replaced radiolarians, *Halobia?* shell fragments and small benthic foraminifera.

Jebel Quimah successions

Early Triassic? C Member Maqam Formation

More distal successions of the Sumeini Group are exposed further southeast of Jebel Quimah. The base closely resembles the Early Triassic C Member of the Maqam Formation at Jebel Sumeini 25 km to the southwest (e.g. Watts & Garrison 1986). On Jebel Quimah the succession begins with 60 m of slump sheets and mega-rudite (Figs. 7, 8a,b), that are mainly composed of calcilutite and matrix-suported intraformational calcirudite, with slightly silicified clasts, up to 4 m long (Fig. 7, log 9) and then passes into up to 200 m of mainly massive, platy calcilutite (Fig. 7, log 8).

The depositionally overlying succession comprises up to 20 m of thin- to medium-bedded redeposited wackestone and oolitic grainstone with grey shaly partings (e.g. Fig. 7, logs 7, 9). This unit can be lithologically correlated with unit (i) of the Late Triassic Zulla Formation (Hamrat Duru Group) in the Sumeini area (Cooper 1986, 1990). Syn-sedimentary layer-parallel extension is commonly observed in the form of sediment 'necking'. Individual undeformed turbidite beds can be traced up to 2 km laterally along the summit ridge of Jebel Quimah. The matrix of the oolitic limestone is silty. Many individual ooids enclose small quartz grains, together with scattered grains of quart-

zose and micaceous sandstone, siltstone, chloritized basalt and dolerite, plagioclase crystals, fine-grained schist, echinoderm plates and shells. These grains are set in recrystallized microspar.

Late Triassic? D Member Maqam Formation

The succession on Jebel Quimah continues with grey, brown, green and reddish shale and wackestone (Fig. 7, logs 7, 9), typical of the Maqam Formation D Member near Jebel Sumeini (Watts & Garrison 1986). This lithofacies can also be correlated with unit (ii) of the Late Triassic Zulla Formation in Jebel Sumeini area (Cooper 1990).

Late Triassic E Member Maqam Formation

The overlying succession in the same thrust sheet on Jebel Quimah is correlated with 'distal' lithofacies of the E Member of the Maqam Formation (e.g. section MS-2 of Watts & Garrison 1986), and with unit (iii) of the Zulla Formation (Cooper 1990), both exposed in the Sumeini area. The Jebel Quimah succession comprises up to 60 m of reddish and/or greenish ribbon radiolarian chert with shaly partings. A sample yielded poorly preserved radiolarians of Late Triassic age (late Carnian-late middle Norian; see Appendix). Stratigraphically higher shale, thin-bedded siliceous wackestone and radiolarite (Fig. 7, log 8) are correlated with the higher sedimentary levels of the Maqam Formation E Member, and with unit (iv) of the Zulla Formation, in the Sumeini area (Cooper 1990).

Jurassic? A Member Mayhah Formation

The stratigraphically overlying succession, exposed still in the same thrust sheet, on the north limb of Jebel Quimah (Fig. 7, log 9) is correlated with the Jurassic A Member of the Mayhah Formation (Watts & Garrison 1986), and with the coeval Guweyza Limestone Formation (Hamrat Duru Group; Cooper 1990). The base of the succession is defined as being just below the first major calcirudite (Fig. 7, log 9). A 9 m thick, channelized calcirudite, including occasional sandstone clasts is then overlain by up to 20 m of medium- to thick-bedded oolitic and lithoclastic calciturbidites that terminate against a major thrust. By contrast, along the south limb of Jebel Quimah (Fig. 7, log 8), the base of this unit is structurally cut-out, and the succession begins with 3 m of sheared shale and

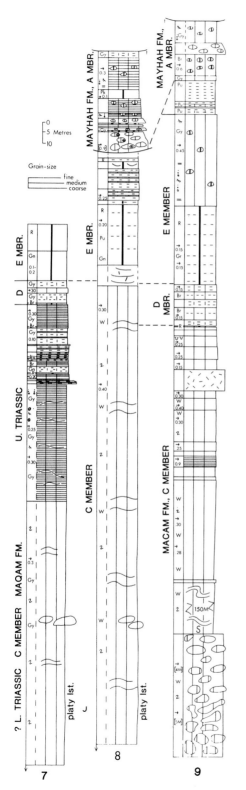

medium-bedded limestone, followed by 8 m of amalgamated calcirudites, that thin- and fine-upwards, passing into calcarenite. Subrounded clasts, up to 0.9 m in size, mainly comprise platform- and slope carbonates, again with some quartzose sandstone. Stratigraphically higher, redeposited carbonates exposed on the north limb of Jebel Quimah, include detached slabs of calcilutites, up to 1 m long, set in a green shaly and siliceous matrix, also graded lithoclastic microbreccias, up to 8 m thick.

The sandstone clasts in the channelized calcirudite are mainly litharenite and protoquartzite, with subrounded to subangular grains of plutonic and/or vein-type quartz, minor plagioclase, alkali feldspar, polycrystalline quartz, fine-grained schist, siltstone, mudstone, micritic grains, chlorite, biotite, hornblende and alkali feldspar, in a calcareous matrix. Other clasts include silicified, calcitic and/or dolomitic oolitic limestone; fine-grained calcirudite composed of silty biomicrite with abundant *Halobia*- and/or *Posidonia*- like shell fragments; and micritic limestone with scattered small shell fragments, rare calcified radiolarians and calcite-replaced quartzose grains. Less common clasts include ironstone containing iron-oxide ooids, broken and altered sponge spicules, rare small shell fragments and clay pellets, in a muddy ferruginous matrix.

Fault-controlled deposition of the Sumeini Group

The sheared successions of the Jebel Raudha−Masfut ridge accumulated on a proximal Triassic−Cretaceous? gullied carbonate slope. Palaeocurrent data from these successions are not available. However, the majority of the channels are nearly symmetrical in northwest−southeast trending outcrops, suggesting sediment transport at right-angles to this direction. Since the Jebel Sumeini area to the south is interpreted as a fault-bounded promontory (Watts 1988, 1990; Cooper 1988, 1990), it can be inferred that the Jebel Raudha−Masfut ridge marks the position of an original steep north-facing escarpment margin.

The basement clasts, including low-grade mica-schist, quartzose sediments, basic volcanics, granite and ironstone were presumably mainly eroded from the walls of channels that

Fig. 7. Graphical logs of measured sedimentary successions of the Sumeini Group on the Jebel Quimah; see Fig. 4 for the key to symbols and Fig. 2 for the locations.

Fig. 8. Field photographs. a, south side of Jebel Quimah culmination showing the Early? Triassic C Member Maqam Fm. (far right and thick-bedded unit); the shaly D Member Maqam Fm. (recessive-weathering); the ribbon radiolarites of the E Member Maqam Formation (dark, to the left); and redeposited limestones of the Mayhah Fm. A Member (far left); b, Triassic mega-rudites, Maqam Formation C Member on the south limb of Jebel Quimah (Scale bar = 1 m).

cut the escarpment margin. The sheared nature of some, but not all the clasts could relate to faulting during rifting (see below). The provenence of the clasts was probably Pre-Permian basement, Permian and Triassic rift-related quartzose sediments, rift volcanics and acidic plutons, as well as contemporaneous shelf and slope lithofacies. Basement clasts also occur in continental rise lithofacies of the Hamrat Duru Group in the Sumeini area (Cooper 1986), but were *not* observed in the more proximal slope units of the Sumeini Group in this area (K. Watts, pers. comm. 1988). A possible explanation is that the terrigenous clasts of the Hamrat Duru Group in the Sumeini area were mainly derived from basement exposed along the Hatta Zone lineament and were transported southeastwards by turbidity currents to the base of the platform slope in the Sumeini area.

On Jebel Quimah, the ?Early Triassic C Member, Maqam Formation mainly comprises more distal, slumped micrite and platform- and slope-derived calcirudite (Fig. 8a) that accumulated on a tectonically unstable base of slope area, subject to 'creep'. Similar modern settings include base of slope areas in the Bahamas (Mullins & Neuman 1979; Heath & Mullins, 1984; Schlager & Ginsburg 1981).

The overlying radiolarian sediments that are widespread in the Late Triassic distal lithofacies of the E Member Maqam Formation and in Zulla Formation unit (iii) record subsidence and drowning of the platform, related to final continental break-up and/or eustatic sealevel rise (Vail *et al.* 1977). With decreased carbonate input, the CCD rose, Later re-establishment of

the shelf allowed siliceous wackestone to prograde downslope (upper part of E Member Maqam Formation and Zulla unit (iv). The overlying shaly F Member of the Maqam Formation in Jebel Sumeini area is restricted to a thin shale unit in the Hatta Zone.

The succeeding, Early Jurassic? Mayhah Formation A member marks a return to carbonate redeposition. Platform- and slope-derived sediment was transported to the base of steep unstable slopes. Calcirudites are well represented, in keeping with an inferred escarpment margin setting. In the Hatta Zone the calcirudites are laterally continuous and were derived from linear carbonate slope areas, possibly triggered by tectonic subsidence of the margin (see later). The amalgamated lithoclastic calcirudites were mainly deposited by debris flows, following upslope collapse of lithified platform calcilutite. Lithoclasts were presumably derived from the walls of slope gullies. Interbedded shaly partings are typical of the northern mountain 'Al Ayn basin' of Cooper (1990).

Hamrat Duru Group: continental rise sediments

In the Hatta Zone more distal successions, belonging to the Hamrat Duru Group are preserved in steeply-dipping to inverted, faulted thrust sheets in the structurally higher levels of the Jebel Quimah culmination in the southeast (Figs 2, & 3b).

The stratigraphically oldest, identified successions are correlated with unit (iv) of the Late Triassic Zulla Formation (Cooper 1990).

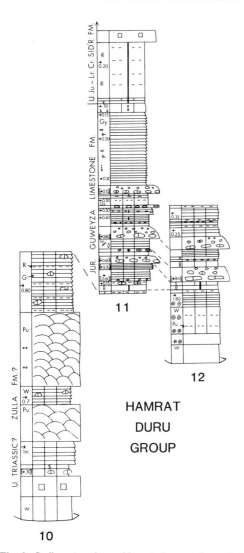

Fig. 9. Sedimentary logs of inverted successions of the Hamrat Duru Group exposed in a structurally high thrust sheet at the east end of Jebel Quimah; see Fig. 2 for location and Fig. 4 for key.

Purple, phyric, basic lavas up to 60 m thick are interbedded with oolitic grainstone turbidites (Figs 4; 9 log 10), interpreted as distal correlatives of the Late Triassic E Member Maqam Formation, discussed above; similar successions, including mafic extrusives also occur in the Zulla Formation in the Dibba Zone and in the Hawasina window (Cooper 1986, 1990).

The inverted successions, in the same thrust sheet (Fig. 9, logs 11, 12) pass stratigraphically upwards into lithofacies typical of the Guweyza

Limestone Formation in the northern Oman Mountains, as exposed in the Jebel Sumeini area and in the Dibba Zone (Copper, 1986, 1990). Medium- to thick-bedded oolitic calci-turbidites exhibit well developed large flute-casts. Interbeds comprise amalgamated, graded lithoclastic calcirudites, up to 6.5 m thick with tabular clasts of siliceous calcilutite and calcarenites, up to 8 m long by 0.8 m thick. Thin sections reveal quarzitic grains.

The Sid'r Formation comprises c. 35 m of shale and red ribbon radiolarite, in beds up to 0.2 m thick, with minor silicified calciturbidites up to 0.2 m thick (Fig. 9, log 11). A partly late Kimmeridgian or Tithonian age is indicated by radiolarians (see Appendix).

Deposition of continental rise successions

The Hamrat Duru Group successions are interpreted as distal continental rise sediments. The oolites (Zulla Fm.) were redeposited from the shelf onto a volcanically-active seafloor. Overlying Jurassic lithofacies (Guweyza Fm.) were mainly slope-derived, again with basement-derived grains. The overlying chert (Sid'r Fm.) relates to regional, tectonically-induced subsidence and/or eustatic sea-level high that flooded the platform and trapped carbonate in shelf basins (Graham 1980; Searle et al. 1983; Cooper 1986, 1990).

Hatta Zone as a transform passive margin

A number of features are suggestive of an origin of the Hatta Zone as a continental margin transform fault: (i) carbonate sediments accumulated at the base of steep, tectonically active fault scarps. This contrasts with adjacent, more orthogonally rifted margin areas where platform slopes were less steeply inclined; (ii) basement clasts are numerous in contrast to most other areas; (iii) the slope was apparently north-facing; i.e. nearly at right angles to the regional trend of the continental margin; (iv) basalts were erupted at the base of the platform slope during the Late Triassic rifting, but are rare in this setting elsewhere.

Several other features are consistent with a right-slipping transform fault: (i) the Sumeini area to the south is interpreted as a promontory with an embayment to the north of the Hatta Zone stretching as far north as the Dibba Zone (Watts 1990; Cooper 1990; Dunne et al. 1990); (ii) The successions in Wadi Mayhah, Jebel Sumeini area become more distal towards the Hatta Zone; sediment was apparently funnelled towards the Hatta Zone (Cooper 1986, 1990).

The Hatta Zone is interpreted (Fig. 10) as a

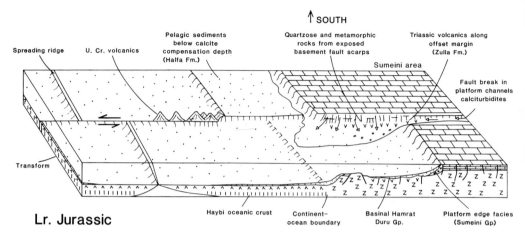

Fig. 10. Palaeogeographic model of the Hatta Zone as a small continental margin transform fault zone. See text for further explanation.

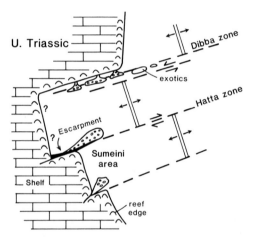

Fig. 11. Inferred palaeogeography of the Arabian continental margin in the northern Oman Mountains.

small, 50? km long transform offset of the Arabian margin (Fig. 11). Shelf-, slope- and basement-derived sediment was shed down a steep escarpment margin and accumulated in an unstable base of slope setting. Further outboard, basalts were erupted along a 'leaky transform'. The general tectonic setting is comparable with the Tamayo transform fault, where it enters the Gulf of California from the East Pacific Rise (Macdonald *et al.* 1979). There, the Baja margin is steep, and underwent normal faulting and later strike-slip and tectonic erosion. The transform zone comprises two elongate troughs separated by a 600 m high linear basement high, composed mainly of deformed turbidites.

Further comparison with modern shear passive margins (Scrutton 1979, 1982) indicates that marked subsidence begins *only* after a spreading ridge migrates beyond the transform offset zone; this event could possibly have triggered the extensive Jurassic redeposition of slope carbonates from linear slope source area (Mayhah Formation and Guweyza Limestone Formation) in the Hatta Zone.

Haybi Complex: Late Cretaceous seamount magmatism

The Hawasina Complex on the flanks of Jebel Quimah is structurally overlain by up to 300 m of tightly thrust-imbricated, sheared, 'distal' radiolarian cherts, thin-bedded wackestone and shale, with disrupted lava flows and diabase sills. These sediments are lithologically correlated with the Haliw Formation (Glennie *et al.* 1974), part of the Haybi Complex (Searle & Malpas 1980) and contain Late Jurassic–Early Cretaceous radiolarians (see Appendix). Southwest of Jebel Quimah (Fig. 2) these successions are locally *depositionally* overlain by less deformed basic extrusives and related sediments of the *Wadi Al Fay Formation* (new name), that is dated as Late Cretaceous, based on new radiometric age data. The successions mainly comprise massive and pillow flows, hyaloclastite and pyroclastic sediments that are too deformed to correlate laterally (Fig. 12). Details of individual outcrops are as follows:

Successions in the type area, Wadi al Fay, southeast of Jebel Quimah (Fig. 2) comprise up to 85 m of very vesicular, mainly aphyric pillow

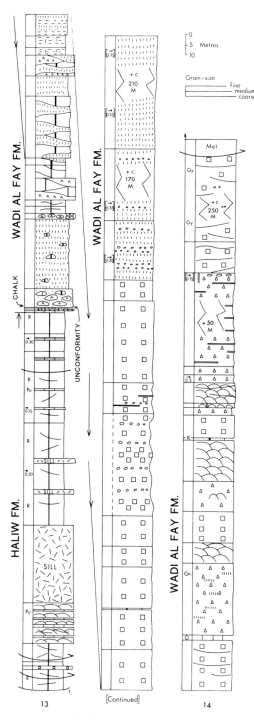

Fig. 12. Graphical logs of the extrusive successions of the Late Cretaceous Wadi al Fay Formation; see Fig. 4, for the key to symbols and Fig. 2 for the locations.

lava, overlain by 30 m of hyaloclastite, in turn passing into flattened and sheared pillow lava, with blocks of recrystallized white limestone, up to 7 m in size. Associated volcanics yielded a K/Ar hornblende age of 104 ± 4 Ma (Albian; Harland *et al*. 1882 time scale). Structurally higher, more recrystallized extrusives are overlain by the metamorphic sole of the Semail ophiolite.

Similar extrusives crop out further southwest, along Wadi Al Fay (Figs 4b, 12 log 14), an area where sheared radiolarian cherts are tectonically overlain by massive lava with rare inclusions of recrystallized limestone. Up-section, pillow lava alternates with lava breccia. The interstices of individual pillows locally contain Fe and Mn oxide-sediment and 'rosettes', mainly composed of nail-headed calcite crystals, up to 10 cm long. Higher levels of the extrusive succession comprise alternations of massive and pillow flows and pillow breccia, with clasts up to 0.5 m in size, and sand-sized hyaloclastite. Clasts include basalt with clinopyroxene phenocrysts up to 3 cm long, and numerous ultramafic nodules. Pebbles and cobbles are locally very well rounded. The softer fragmental extrusive intervals are intruded by sills, comprising up to 25% by volume. The structurally highest levels of the succession comprise 250 m of massive lava that becomes more sheared and recrystallized upwards towards the ophiolite sole.

West of Jebel Quimah (Fig. 2) radiolarian cherts are stratigraphically overlain by fragmental extrusives (Fig. 12, log 13). The volcanic succession begins with massive basalt, radiolarite, and pillow lava that are intruded by a *c*. 40 m thick pematitic dolerite sill that can be traced several kilometres laterally. K–Ar dating of hornblende in this sill yielded ages of 109 ± 4 Ma, and 108 ± 4 Ma. Biotite in another sample yielded 105 ± 3 Ma (Albian). The succession continues with sheared radiolarite, dolomitized impure limestone and small dolerite sills, less than 4 m thick. Several interbeds of soft cleaved chalk, up to 0.8 m thick (Fig. 12, log 13) contain calcite-replaced radiolarians in a micritic matrix, with scattered thin-walled shell fragments. This chalk is *depositionally* overlain, with an irregular low-angle unconformity, by a volcanic debris flow, comprising rubbly, reworked recrystallized radiolarian chert and limestone, fragmental extrusives with large biotite crystals, derived basalt and dolerite clasts. It then passes into volcaniclastic sandstones and conglomerates containing sub-rounded to well-rounded clasts of basalt (Fig. 13), diabase, and rare gabbro that is petrographically similar to the sills (Fig. 12, log 13). The lowest 10 m of the

4 cm

Fig. 13. Field photograph of well-rounded basalt clasts in volcaniclastic siltstone exposed near the base of the Late Cretaceous volcanic succession S of Jebel Quimah; scale bar = 4 cm.

overlying succession contain disrupted slump sheets of radiolarite, up to 100 m long by several metres-thick. Above is c. 30 m of hyaloclastite, rubbly lava, slumped ribbon radiolarite, rare calciturbidite interbeds and shale, then c. 300 m of deformed massive hyaloclastite comprising mainly aphyric, vesicular and angular to sub-angular mineral fragments including titanaugite, biotite and strongly zoned plagioclase. Biotite yielded K/Ar ages of 93 ± 4 Ma, and 104 ± 4 Ma (Albian–Cenomanian).

Extrusives also crop out over a wide area northeast of Jebel Quimah. For example, non-vesicular pillowed and massive lava and minor volumes of sheared recrystallized brown limestone were observed in Wadi Hatta (Fig. 2).

Geochemistry

Major- and trace-element analyses of dolerite sills and basalts from the Wadi al Fay Formation, and sills in the Hamrat Duru Group on Jebel Quimah are given in Table 1. The TiO_2/Zr diagram (Pearce 1980) (Fig. 14a) confirms the basaltic composition. On the Cr/Y diagram (Fig. 14b), samples plot in the Mid Ocean Ridge (MORB) and intra-plate fields. When normalized to MORB (Fig. 14c), samples exhibit intraplate basalt trends; anomalous K, Rb, and Ba values are attributed to weathering.

Late Cretaceous seamounts

The Late Cretaceous volcanics are interpreted as seamounts. They were constructed in deep water on the abyssal plain where radiolarites were accumulating, judging from the strati-graphically underlying deep-sea sediments (Haliw Formation). Initial volcanism was accompanied by marked uplift above the carbonate compensation depth (CCD), allowing pelagic carbonate to accumulate locally on the volcanics. Radiolarite (Haliw Fm.) slumped, giving rise to chaotic lava-chert debris flows. Polished, well rounded clasts near the base of the succession are suggestive of shallow-water deposition, or even of subaerial exposure. Massive and pillow flows erupted in topographically subdued areas (e.g. Wadi Al Fay). Pillow breccia there developed at flow fronts, and was then overridden by pillowed and massive flows, as observed on the East Pacific Rise (Ballard & Moore 1977). By contrast, the volcaniclastics apparently accumulated on steeper slopes (e.g. west of Jebel Quimah). On modern seamounts (e.g. near Hawaii; Fornari *et al.* 1978) molten lava has cascaded down steep scarps to form hyaloclastite stone-streams (Lonsdale & Batiza 1980); the Wadi Zone hyaloclastites may have formed similarly.

The local Fe–Mn interpillow oxide sediment is probably hydrothermal in origin. It filtered into cracks between pillows during breaks in eruption. The nail-head calcite crystals grew displacively in the oxide sediment. The first author has observed similar interpillow mineralization in other tectonically-emplaced lava piles, for example in Late Ordovician lavas in S. W. Scotland (at Downan Point), in the Franciscan melange in California (e.g. near the mouth of the Klamath River), and in the Late Palaeozoic Mino terrane in SW Japan.

An alkaline sill within radiolarian chert (Haliw Fm.) was dated as 105–109 Ma (Albian), while extrusions of the Wadi al Fay Formation range from c. 104–93 Ma (Albian–Cenomanian). This compares with 92–93 Ma ages of biotite pyroxenite sills and biotite wehrlite sills that intrude lavas of the Haybi Complex (on Jebel Ghawil; Lippard & Rex 1982). In the Dibba Zone, Late Cretaceous extrusives range from 92–96 Ma (Cenomanian) to Aptian? (Robertson *et al.* 1990).

The Permian and Late Cretaceous volcanism elsewhere in the Oman Mountains relates to rifting and continental break-up (Searle *et al.* 1980; Béchennec *et al.* 1990). By contrast, the Late Cretaceous magmatism of the Hatta Zone may relate to much later genesis or emplacement of the Semail ophiolite. Geochemical evidence suggests that spreading of the Semail ophiolite took place above a subduction zone (Pearce *et al.* 1981, 1984; Lippard *et al.* 1986). Searle (1984) related similar alkaline volcanism in the Dibba Zone to *emplacement* of the Semail ophiolite. In his model (Fig. 15a) volcanism was

Table 1. *Representative major- and trace-element analyses of Late Cretaceous sills and basaltic extrusives from the Hatta Zone, determined by X-ray fluorescence*

	Sills			Basaltic extrusives			
Sample No.	1	2	3	4	5	6	7
Field No.	OM8270	OM82125A	OM82163	OM82151	OM82153	OM82170	OM82171
SiO_2	43.77	45.16	45.55	41.97	43.63	43.96	42.54
Al_2O_3	12.84	8.41	13.38	15.44	13.20	12.57	12.94
Fe_2O_3	13.85	11.60	12.29	14.27	14.40	12.44	12.56
MgO	7.20	10.32	7.12	6.38	7.09	6.27	6.35
CaO	9.86	16.91	12.58	11.03	11.78	14.48	16.47
Na_2O	2.92	1.18	2.66	2.16	3.57	0.42	2.01
K_2O	2.34	1.81	2.17	3.23	0.26	5.08	2.84
TiO_2	3.92	3.41	2.72	3.48	3.74	3.19	3.24
MnO	0.21	0.15	0.16	0.20	0.21	0.19	0.21
P_2O_5	1.19	0.70	0.70	0.77	1.10	0.80	0.76
TOTAL	97.98	99.66	99.34	98.95	98.97	99.41	99.92
Trace elements (ppm)							
Ni	67	145	74	22	59	79	107
Cr	97	586	169	8	47	248	367
V	299	315	249	389	394	332	298
Sc	22	37	19	16	20	20	19
Cu	66	70	76	36	90	79	95
Zn	146	99	120	112	127	105	107
Sr	1359	446	1074	1238	1202	1025	895
Rb	65	38	35	43	5	106	50
Zr	398	225	241	305	389	343	322
Nb	92	48	59	105	117	108	96
Ba	1186	568	933	1502	378	1505	1174
Pb	9	3	2	3	1	2	2
Th	11	6	6	9	10	12	9
La	87	58	50	81	98	91	82
Ce	185	119	103	166	202	174	167
Nd	77	52	41	61	79	66	61
Y	35	25	27	30	38	32	30

1, Diabase sill in radiolarian chert (Haliw Fm.), S of J. Raudha-Masfut ridge, near Masfut; 2, dolerite sill from Wadi al Fay Formation, SE of Jebel Quimah; 3, diabase sill in Triassic succession (Maqam Fm.) near crest of Jebel Quimah; 4, 5, aphyric basalt from Wadi al Fay Fm. SE of Jebel Quimah; 6, 7, aphyric pillow basalt, Wadi al Fay Fm., close to the fault contact with metamorphic sole SE of Jebel Quimah.

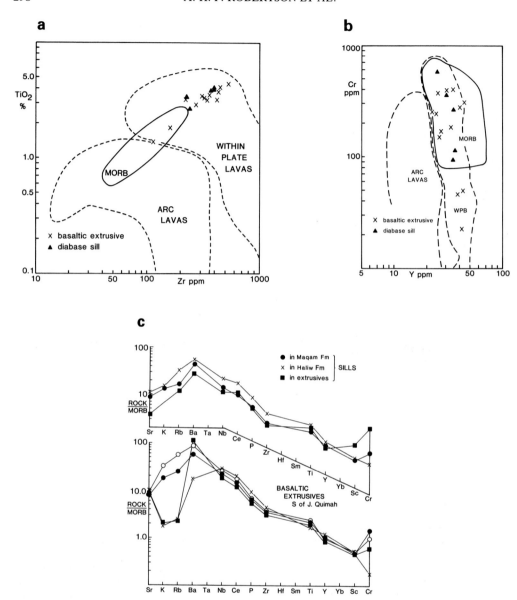

Fig. 14 Geochemistry of the Late Cretaceous lavas and sills, and other basic igneous rocks in the Hatta Zone; a, Ti–Zr; b, Y/Cr; c, MORB-normalised 'spider' diagrams, MORB values are from Pearce (1980).

activated when a peripheral bulge migrated continentwards, ahead of the overriding Semail ophiolite towards the Arabian continental margin. However, the Hatta Zone magmatism appears to *pre-date* genesis of the Semail ophiolite (i.e. 109–93 Ma K/Ar ages against 97.9–93.5 Ma for the ophiolite; Tilton *et al.* 1981). Alternatively, the alkaline magmatism may have resulted from regional crustal extension that

immediately preceded, and/or accompanied genesis of the Semail ophiolite. Extension possibly occured when old (Triassic–Jurassic?) Neo-Tethyan oceanic crust began to be consumed along a newly activated subduction zone, as shown in Fig. 15b. Pre-existing fracture zones then acted as zones of weakness and the seamounts were constructed along the Hatta Zone transform lineament.

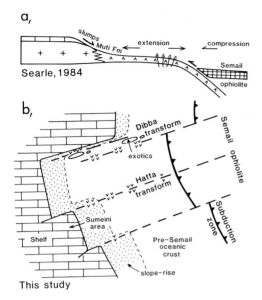

Fig. 15. Models for Late Cretaceous alkaline volcanism in Northern Oman. a, related to flexural upwarp and 'extension' in advance of the overriding Semail ophiolite (Searle, 1984); b, crustal extension on a sinking, old oceanic slab related to genesis of the Semail ophiolite above a newly initiated intra-oceanic subduction zone (preferred model).

Semail ophiolite and metamorphic sole

The Semail ophiolite and its metamorphic sole are mentioned here only in so far as they relate to the transform setting of the Hatta Zone.

At the base of the Semail ophiolite, the metamorphic sole is only locally preserved (Fig. 2). Instead, the north margin of the Jebel Raudha–Masfut limestone ridge is faulted directly against gabbro and sheared serpentinite of the Semail ophiolite. Along its southern margin, sheeted diabase is locally exposed and progressively lower stratigraphical levels of the ophiolite crop out to the southeast: i.e. gabbro (with isolated diabase dykes), then harzburgite (Fig. 1).

Along the south margin the sheeted dykes are locally exposed beneath wadi gravels. These dykes trend at 150–160° i.e. at a high angle to the more regional dyke trends in the adjacent Semail ophiolite. Smewing (1980) showed that in the Semail ophiolite to the north of the Hatta Zone, dykes trend nearly north–south, but are displaced to more westnorthwest–eastsoutheast (mean 113°) in the vicinity of the Hatta Zone, and then return to more north–south further south. He also reported vertical, ductile shear-zones and oblique compositional layering in cumulates near the Hatta Zone. Smewing (1980)

interpreted these features as evidence of an oceanic transform fault. Injection of dykes into an extensional (leaky) transform would imply a left lateral transform offset if, however the dykes were physically bulk-rotated, the opposite, right lateral displacement was implied.

The left-lateral ('leaky transform') solution favoured by Smewing (1980) is consistent with the inferred offset of the Hatta Zone (also left lateral). This could be coincidental, particularly if the ophiolite was created by conventional back-arc spreading (Pearce et al. 1981). Such a model would imply the removal of a 100–150 km wide zone of older oceanic crust from the arc-trench gap (by 'subduction erosion'?) before emplacement onto the Arabian continent (Lippard et al. 1986). Alternatively, the Semail nappe formed by incipient, 'supra-subduction zone' spreading ('pre-arc spreading' of Pearce et al. 1984). This was possibly triggered by collapse of a pre-existing spreading ridge (Coleman 1981; Robertson & Dixon 1984). In this model, the Semail ophiolite formed relatively close to the Arabian margin (within 1000 km). The formation of the inferred transform fault in the Semail ophiolite could then well have been controlled by the earlier existence of a transform fault offsetting the continental margin in the Hatta Zone (Figs 10 & 11).

Structure and emplacement history

Formation of a transverse culmination

Since the cover sediments are only mildly deformed and open-folded, the major deformation of the Hatta Zone must relate to emplacement of the Semail ophiolite in the Late Cretaceous. The southeastern area (Jebel Quimah) is dominated by several large thrust sheets that are folded into a huge northwest–southeast-trending, gently-plunging anticlinorium, or culmination, orientated almost at right angles to the regional thrust transport direction. Structurally higher sheets are folded around lower thrust sheets, consistent with a dominantly piggy-back mode of thrusting.

Thrust sheets at the southeast end of the Jebel Quimah transverse culmination are steeply-dipping, to inverted (70–45°; Figs 2, 3c). The inversion can be explained in terms of footwall imbrication and progressive rotation of thrust sheets along back-limb thrusts, above a steep ramp (e.g. Price 1970, 1972; Douglas 1984). Similar inverted zones of folding and back-thrusting occur elsewhere in Oman, for example in the eastern Hawasina window (e.g. on Jebel Abiad) and in the Haybi corridor

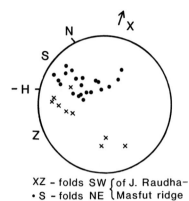

XZ – folds SW ⎰ of J. Raudha–
• S – folds NE ⎱ Masfut ridge
– H – strike of Hatta Zone

Fig. 16. Orientation of mesocopic folds axes from the sedimentary thrust sheets southwest and northeast the Jebel Raudha–Masfut ridge.

(Searle 1985; Searle & Cooper 1986). In the Hatta Zone, imbrication was possibly intensified by emplacement of the Semail ophiolite over an already steepened thrust stack. Such impedence may account for well developed tear faults along both limbs of Jebel Quimah transverse culmination, and also explain the evidence of strike-slip along the Hatta Zone.

Minor fold axes along the southeast flank of Jebel Quimah (Fig. 16) are mainly orientated northeast–southwest, consistent with regional northwest-directed nappe emplacement (Glennie *et al.* 1974). Subordinate northeast–southwest trending folds may represent folding by a combination of overthrusting and anticlinal doming. Many folds plunge steeply to the northwest, associated with locally intense northwest–southeast directed shearing, recrystallization and layer-parallel extension, features that are suggestive of strike-slip sub-parallel to the Hatta Zone. Comparable strike-slip shear is reported from another inferred culminations, in Wadi Hawasina (in Wadi Bani Umar; Searle & Cooper 1986).

Transverse culminations may relate to imbrication and/or folding of thrust sheets above lateral or oblique ramps (Dahlstrom 1970; Butler 1982; Coward 1983), controlled by footwall palaeogeography, or by thrust sheet convergence. Examples of such culminations include the Dundonnel structure, Moine thrust belt, Scotland (Elliott & Johnson 1980), and the Perivoli corridor through the Pindos ophiolite, Greece (Kemp & McCaig 1984).

An example of how such structures can develop is the Moroccan Rif (Morley 1987). There crossover elements are represented by a

lateral ramp and the northern limit of a large culmination that is developed in superimposed thrust sheets. These structures are interpreted as a transform fault that offset the early Mesozoic continent–ocean boundary in this area and was later sedimented over. During Tertiary deformation this strike-slip lineament was reactivated, giving rise to the present transverse structural elements that are similar to those of the Hatta Zone.

In the Oman Mountains the Hubat structure (central mountains) is explained either by Late Cretaceous oblique ramping at depth, or by Tertiary compression (Barrette 1988). Further south, the Ibra dome and Jebel Ma-Jhool relate to late-stage (Cretaceous) culmination collapse and gravity sliding (Cawood *et al.* 1990). By contrast, the Jebel Quimah culmination formed

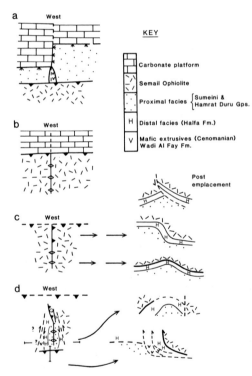

Fig. 17. Structural interpretation of the Hatta Zone. a, as a right-slipping transform (Triassic-Early Cretaceous); b, culmination formation and oblique lateral ramping. Owing to impedence by transform topography (basement ridge?, seamounts) and/or convergence of ophiolite blocks during emplacement, the overriding Semail ophiolite was folded into a transverse culmination (Jebel Quimah). Underlying units were imbricated, rotated and inverted above a large footwall ramp (SW Jebel Quimah); c setting after Late Cretaceous emplacement (plan view and sections).

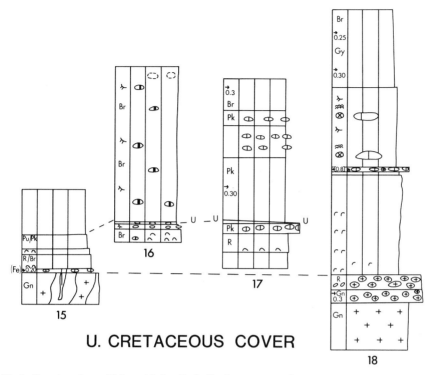

U. CRETACEOUS COVER

Fig. 18. Sedimentary logs of Maastrichtian-Early Tertiary cover sediments, Jebel Raudha. See Fig. 2 for location and Fig. 4 for key.

during the initial Late Cretaceous thrust emplacement.

Sidewall ramping

The western Hatta Zone is dominated by the 14 km long, elongate sub-vertical Jebel Raudha−Masfut ridge (Fig. 2), composed mainly of sheared limestone, in which successions invariably young northwards. Crenulation, steeply-plunging small-scale folds and localized high-angle faults (east end of Jebel Raudha, Fig. 2) indicate shear during emplacement. Also, in the northeast, Jebel Raudha is bordered by thin strands of sub-vertical sheared serpentinite, associated with slivers of deformed ophiolitic rocks, chert and basic volcanic.

The Jebel Raudha−Masfut ridge is interpreted as an oblique lateral ramp formed during Late Cretaceous emplacement. Northward younging is suggestive of a southward component of overthrusting. However, other features indicate shear (sinistral?). Ramping was thus probably oblique. Alternatively, the Jebel−Masfut ridge was once a two-sided, symmetrical culmination, more like Jebel Quimah, and the present upstanding single limb resulted

Fig. 19. Aerial view of Jebel Raudha. In the foreground Maastrichtian-Early Tertiary neritic limestone unconformably overlies sub-vertical sheared limestone of the Sumeini Group. Note the horeshoe-shaped anticline-syncline pair.

from late-stage culmination collapse. Shear-sense fabrics, however do not indicate normal faulting. Unlike the Musandam Peninsula (Searle 1988), major Tertiary culminations are absent in the Hatta Zone area and an oblique lateral origin is thus favoured. The western Hatta Zone margin was faulted, preserving higher ophiolite units (gabbro, diabase) to the south. This possibly reflects differential subsidence of loaded continental crust south of the transform.

In the favoured scenario (Fig. 17), the geometry of the transverse culmination and lateral ramp in the Hatta Zone was largely controlled by the topography of the transform lineament in the Hatta Zone. The major Jebel Quimah transverse culmination formed when the Semail ophiolite overrode the Hatta Zone transform lineament and its Late Cretaceous seamounts. The ophiolite then impinged on the inferred north-facing escarpment margin to form a >20 km-long lateral ramp. Differential subsidence ensued, such that the stratigraphically higher levels of the ophiolite are now preferentially exposed along the southern margin of the Hatta Zone in the west.

Post-emplacement sedimentary cover

At the western end of the Hatta Zone, on Jebel Raudha (Figs 2, 3a), sub-vertical limestones of the Jebel Raudha–Masfut ridge are unconformably overlain by gently-dipping ophiolite-derived conglomerate and limestone, up to 110 m thick (Fig. 18, logs 15–18). Maastrichtian and Early Tertiary ages for these limestones are inferred from study of benthonic foraminifera (A. Racey, pers. comm. 1988). The upper part of the carbonate succession on Jebel Raudha exhibits several low-angle unconformities.

At the northwest end of the Hatta Zone, the unconformable Maastrichtian–Early Tertiary carbonate cover is symmetrically open-folded on WNW-trending axes, perpendicular to the regional Tertiary NNE fold trend further west (e.g. Jebel Faiyah and Jebel Mulayhah; Glennie *et al.* 1974). In general, the NNE fold axial trend dominates to within 500 m of Jebel Raudha, then changes abruptly (Fig. 2).

Following Late Cretaceous emplacement, the ophiolite northwest of the Hatta Zone was deeply eroded and peridotite-derived sediment accumulated locally, as fluvial clastics (Qahlah Formation; Glennie *et al.* 1974). Exposed rocks surfaces were fissured, then overlain by shallow marine sand, mud and neritic algal and bioclastic carbonate, with fine-grained hemipelagic intercalations. The local low-angle unconformities in the Jebel Raudha sedimentary cover are suggestive of continuing tectonic instability along the Hatta Zone. The fact that the Tertiary fold trend locally parallels the Hatta Zone is indicative of reactivation of the transform lineament.

Conclusions: transform fault model

The Hatta Zone is interpreted as a small, *c.* 50? km long, left lateral continent margin transform that strongly influenced Mesozoic passive margin sedimentation, magmatism and Late Cretaceous emplacement, and also Tertiary deposition and folding.

The transform lineament acted as a conduit for turbidity current and mass-flow sediment transport down a steep, active escarpment margin (i.e. Sumeini Gp. of Jebel Quimah and Jebel Raudha–Masfut ridge). Basement rocks, including quartzose sandstone, mica-schist and granite were eroded from gullies incised into the carbonate platform slope. In Late Triassic time, pillow basalts were erupted on the continental rise, possibly exploiting the fracture zone (i.e. a leaky transform?). Jurassic margin deposition was punctuated by redeposition of slope-derived carbonate by slumping and mass flow (Mayhah Fm. and Guweyza Limestone Fm.). As elsewhere in Oman, the continental rise underwent radiolarian sedimentation (Sid'r Formation) during Tithonian–Early Cretaceous time. This was related to regional crustal extension and/or eustatic sealevel rise. More distal abyssal plain sediments were also mainly radiolarian (Haliw Fm.).

Early in Late Cretaceous (109–93 Ma; Albian–Cenomanian) intra-plate magmatism took place, possibly along an oceanward extension of the Hatta Zone transform and seamounts rose near, or above sealevel. The Semail ophiolite and its underplated sole were later emplaced onto the Arabian margin. The transverse Jebel Quimah culmination apparently formed by ramping over a transform ridge and the Late Cretaceous seamounts. Structurally higher thrust sheets underwent imbrication, backfolding and inversion above an inferred major lateral ramp. Carbonate platform-slope sediments were also deformed into a >20 km long lateral ramp, as the ophiolite overode a north-facing transform escarpment margin.

Erosion of the ophiolite gave rise to fluvial clastic deposition, that was then followed by shallow marine carbonate sedimentation on an unstable shelf in Maastrichtian-early Tertiary time. Deviation from the regional Tertiary fold trend indicates later reactivation of the Hatta Zone lineament.

We thank Dr J. D. Smewing for help with logistics. The fieldwork was financially supported by AMOCO Oman Petroleum Company. Mrs D. James assisted with the X-ray fluorescence analysis, Mrs. D. Baty with drafting and Mrs. Y. Cooper with photography.

The paper benefited from discussion with D. Cooper, M. Searle, and R. Haymon and from the reviewers' comments (K. Watts and C. Farmer). The paper is published with the permission of AMOCO Production Company.

Appendix

Radiolarian faunas identified

OM82–136   Haliw Fm. SE flank Jebel
(MR5869)   Quimah, deformed radiolarites
             immediately below mafic
             extrusives dated radiometrically
             as Late Cretaceous,
             (Cenomanian).
Radiolaria: *Archaeodictyomitra* sp.
             Hsuum (?) *mclaughlini* Pessagno
             Novixitus sp.
             Parvicingula sp.
             Saitoum sp.
             All radiolarians very poorly
             preserved, mostly casts and molds
Age: Late Jurassic

OM82–166   Zulla Fm. Radiolarites on ridge,
(MR5881)   Jebel Quimah, above thick
             sequence of limestone slide sheets
             (Maqam Fm.)
Radiolaria: *Acanthocircus* (?) *usitatus* Blome
             (fragment)
             Capnodoce sp.
             Corum perfectum Blome
             Sarla sp.
             All radiolarians are very poorly
             preserved, mostly casts and
             molds.
Age: Late Triassic (late Karnian to late
             middle Norian)

OM82–278   Sid'r Fm., Wadi Al Fay;
(MR5879)   radiolarite near base of
             succession mostly composed of
             redeposited limestones.
Radiolaria: *Archaeodictyomitra excellens*
             (Tan Sin Hok)
             Novixitus sp.
             Praeconocaryomma sp. cf. P.
             immodica Pessagno and Poisson
             Ristola sp. aff. R. boseii (Parona)
             Sethacapsa sp. (undescribed)
             Stichosapsa cribata (Schaaf)
Age: Late Jurassic (late Kimmeridgian
             or Tithonian)

References

BALLARD, R. D. & MOORE, J. G. 1977. *Photographic atlas of the Mid-Atlantic Ridge Rift Valley*, New York, Springer.

BARRETTE, P. D. 1988. Internal geometry and origin of the Hubat structural culmination, Oman Mountains. *Journal of Structural Geology*, **10**, 383–391.

BUTLER, R. W. H. 1982. A structural analysis of the Moine Thrust zone between Eriboll and Foinaven, NW Scotland. *Journal of Structural Geology*, **4**, 19–29.

COLEMAN, R. G. 1981. Tectonic setting for ophiolite obduction in Oman. *Journal of Geophysical Research*, **86**, 2497–2508.

COOPER, D. W. J. 1986. *The Hamrat Duru Group: evolution of a Mesozoic passive carbonate margin in the Oman Mountains*. PhD Thesis University of Edinburgh.

—— 1987. Hamrat Duru Group: revised stratigraphy of a Mesozoic deep water passive margin in the Oman Mountains. *Geological Magazine*, **124**, 157–164.

—— 1988. Structure and sequence of thrusting in deep-water sediments during ophiolite emplacement in the south-central Oman Mountains. *Journal of Structural Geology*, **10**, 473–485.

COWARD, M. P. 1983. The crust and shear zones of the Moine Thrust zone and NW Scottish Caledonides. *Journal of the Geological Society, London*, **140**, 755–811.

DAHLSTROM, C. D. A. 1970. Structural geology in the eastern margin of the Canadian Rocky Mountains. *Bulletin of Canadian Petroleum Geology*, **18**, 332–406.

DOUGLAS, R. J. W. 1984. Callum Creek, Langford Creek and Gap Map areas, Alberta. *Geological Survey of Canada, Memoir*, **402**.

ELLIOTT, D. W. & JOHNSON, M. R. W. 1980. The structural evolution of the northern part of the Moine thrust zone. *Transactions of the Royal Society of Edinburgh: Earth Sciences*, **71**, 69–96.

FORNARI, D. J., MALAHOFF, A. & HEEZEN, B. C. 1978. Volcanic structure off the crust of the Puna Ridge, Hawaii, *Geophysical implications of submarine volcanic terrane*, **89**, 605–616.

GLENNIE, K. W., BOEUF, M. G. A., HUGHES-CLARK, M. W., MOODY-STUART, M., PILAAR, M. F. & REINHARDT, B. M. 1973. Late Cretaceous nappes in the Oman Mountains and their geologic evolution. *American Association of Petroleum Geologist Bulletin*, **57**, 5–27.

—, —, —, —, —, — 1974. *Geology of the Oman Mountains*. Verhandelingen van het Koninklijk Nederlands geologisch Minjbouwkundig Genootschap.

GRAHAM, G. M. 1980. Evolution of a passive margin, and nappe emplacement in the Oman Mountains. Proceeding International Ophiolite Symposium, Cyprus, 1979, PANAYIOTOU, A. (ed.) 414–423.

HARLAND, W. B., COX, A. V., LLEWELLYN, P. G., PICKTON, C. A. G., SMITH, A. G. & WALTERS, R. 1982. *A geologic time scale*. Cambridge University Press, Cambridge.

HEATH, K. & MULLINS, H. T. 1984. Open-ocean off bank transport of fine-grained carbonate sediments in northern Bahamas. *In*: STOW, D. A. V. & PIPER, D. J. W. (eds). *Fine Grained Sediments:*

Deep Water Processes and Environments. Geological Society, London, Special Publication **15**, 199–208.

KEMP, A. E. S. & McCAIG, A. M. 1984. Origins and significance of rocks in an imbricate thrust zone beneath the Pindos ophiolite, northwestern Greece. *In*: DIXON, J. E. & ROBERTSON, A. H. F. (eds). *The Geological Evolution of the Eastern Mediterranean*, Geological Society, London, Special Publication **17**, 569–580.

LANPHERE, M. A. 1981. K-Ar ages of metamorphic rocks at the base of the Samail ophiolite. *Journal of Geophysical Research*, **86**, 2777–82.

LIPPARD, S. J. & REX, D. C. 1982. K–Ar ages of alkaline igneous rocks in the northern Oman Mountains. N.E. Arabia, and their relation to drifting, passive margin development and destruction of the Oman Tethys. *Geological Magazine*, **119**, 497–503.

——, SHELTON, A. W. & GASS, I. G. 1986. *The ophiolite of Northern Oman*. Geological Society, London, Memoir, **11**.

LONSDALE, P. & BATIZA, R. 1980. Hycloclastite and lava flows on young seamounts examined with a submersible. *Geological Society of America Bulletin*, **91**, 545–554.

MACDONALD, K. C., KASTENS, K., SPIESS, F. N. & MILLER, S. P. 1979. Deep tow studies of the Tamago transform fault. *Marine Geophysical Researches*, **4**, 37–70.

MORLEY, C. K. 1987 Origin of major cross-element zone: Moroccan Rif. *Geology*, **15**, 761–764.

MULLIS, H. T. & NEUMANN, A. C. 1979. Deep carbonate bank margin structure and sedimentation in the northern Bahama. *In*: DOYLE, L. J. & PILKEY, O. H. (eds) *Geology of continental slopes Special Publication, Society of Economic Paleontologists and Mineralogists, Tulsa*, **27**, 165–192.

PEARCE, J. A. 1980. Geochemical evidence for the genesis and eruptive setting of lavas from the Tethyan ophiolites. *In*: PANAYIOTOU, A. (ed.), *Ophiolites Proceeding International Ophiolite symposium, Nicosia Cyprus, 1979*, 261–273.

——, ALABASTER, T., SHELTON, A. W. & SEARLE, M. P. 1981. The Oman ophiolite as a Cretaceous arc-basin complex: evidence and implications. *Philosophical Transactions of the Royal Society, London*, **A300**, 299–317.

——, LIPPARD, S. J. & ROBERTS, S. 1984. Characteristics and tectonic significance of supra-subduction zone ophiolites. *In*: KOKELAAR, B. P. & HOWELLS, M. F. (eds) *Marginal basin geology. Geological Society, London, Special Publication*, **16**, 7–97.

PRICE, R. A. 1970. Geology, Canmore (East Half), Alberta, Geological Survey of Canada Map, 1265A.

—— 1972. The Canadian Rockies and tectonic evolution of the South eastern Cordillera. *In*: GLASS, D. J. (Ed.) *Guide Book AC1J, 24th International Geological Congress, Montreal, Quebec.*

ROBERTSON, A. H. F. & DIXON, J. E. 1984. Introduction: aspects of the geological evolution of the Eastern Mediterranean. *In*: DIXON, J. E. &

ROBERTSON, A. H. F. (eds), *Geological Society, London, Special Publication*, **17**, 1–74.

—— & WOODCOCK, N. H. 1983. Genesis of the Batinah Melange above the Semail ophiolite, Oman. *Journal of Structural Geology*, **5**, 1–17.

SCHLAGER, W. & GINSBURG, R. N. 1981. Bahama carbonate platforms – the deep and the past. *Marine Geology*, **44**, 1–25.

SCRUTTON, R. A. 1979. On sheared passive margins. *Tectonophysics*, **59**, 293–305.

—— 1982. Crustal structure and development of sheared passive margins. *In*: SCRUTTON, R. A. (ed.) *Dynamics of passive margins. Geodynamics Series, American Geophysical Union*, **6**, 133–140.

SEARLE, M. P. 1984. Alkaline peridotite, pyroxenite and gabbroic intrusions in the Oman Mountains, Arabia. *Canadian Journal of Earth Sciences*, **21**, 396–406.

—— 1985. Sequence of thrusting and origin of culminations in the northern and central, Oman Mountains. *Journal of Structural Geology*, **7**, 129–143.

—— 1988. Thrust tectonics of the Dibba zone and the structural evolution of the Arabian continental margin along the Musandam mountains. (Oman and United Arab Emirates). *Journal of the Geological Society of London*, **154**, 43–54.

—— & COOPER, D. J. W. 1986. Structure of the Hawasina Window Culmination, Central Oman Mountains. *Transactions of the Royal Society of Edinburgh: Earth Sciences*, **77**, 143–156.

——, JAMES, N. P., CALON, T. J. & SMEWING, J. D. 1983. Sedimentological and structural evolution of the Arabian continental margin in the Musandam Mountains and Dibba zone, United Arab Emirates. *Geological Society of America Bulletin*, **94**, 1381–1400.

——, LIPPARD, S. J., SMEWING, J. D. & REX, D. C. 1980. Volcanic rocks beneath the Semail Ophiolite in the northern Oman Mountains and their tectonic significance in the Mesozoic evolution of Tethys. *Journal of the Geological Society of London*, **137**, 589–604.

—— & MALPAS, J. 1980. The structure and metamorphism of rocks beneath the Semail ophiolite of Oman and their significance in ophiolite obduction. *Transactions of the Royal Society of Edinburgh: Earth Sciences*, **71**, 213–28.

SMEWING, J. D. 1980. An Upper Cretaceous ridge-transform intersection in the Oman Ophiolite. *In*: A. PANAYIOTOU (ed). Ophiolites. Proceedings, International Ophiolite Symposium, Nicosia, Cyprus. 407–413.

TILTON, G. R., HOPSON, G. A. & WRIGHT, J. E. 1981. Uranium-Lead isotopic ages of the Semail Ophiolite, Oman, with applications to Tethyan ocean ridge tectonics. *Journal of Geophysical Research*, **86**, 2763–76.

VAIL, P. R., MITCHUM, F. M. Jr. & THOMSON, J., III 1977. Seismic stratigraphy and global changes in sea level, part 4: global cycles and relative changes of sea level. *In*: Seismic stratigraphy – applications to hydrocarbon exploration. *American Association of Petroleum Geologists*

Memoir, **26**, 83−97.

WATTS, K. F. 1988. Triassic carbonate submarine fans along the Arabian platform margin, Sumeini Group, Oman. *Sedimentology*, **35**, 43−72.

—— & GARRISON, R. E. 1986. Sumeini Group, Oman − evolution of a Mesozoic carbonate slope on a South Tethyan continental margin. *Sedimentary Geology*, **48**, 107−68.

The tectonic evolution of pre-Permian rocks, Central and Southeastern Oman Mountains

A. MANN[1] & S. S. HANNA [2]

Earth Resources Institute, University College of Swansea, Singleton Park, Swansea, SA2 8PP, UK
[1] *Present address: Robertson Group plc, Llandudro, Gwynedd LL30 ISA, UK*
[2] *Present address: Department of Earth Sciences, Sultan Qaboos University, P.O. Box 32486, Sultanate of Oman*

Abstract: The structural history of pre-Permian basement rocks exposed in the domal uplifts of Jebel Akhdar, Jebel Nakhl and Saih Hatat, central and southeastern Oman mountains, is dominated by Late Palaeozoic and Late Cretaceous deformation and metamorphism. In Jebel Akhdar pre-Permian rocks have been deformed by large NE–SW trending thrusts and folds and intense cleavage during Late Palaeozoic compression. Later reactivation of these structures accompanied by a major flattening deformation caused by loading may be related to thrusting and folding in the overlying Permian to Cenomanian platform carbonates. These structures are ascribed partly to Late Cretaceous deformation. The complex internal structure of Saih Hatat is attributed to overprinting of possible Proterozoroic and Late Palaeozoic tectonic events by Late Cretaceous thrusting, folding and associated blueschist metamorphism. The identification of a major basement-cover duplex involving pre-Permian rocks and platform carbonates in Saih Hatat suggests that the pre-Permian basement and platform carbonates did not remain as autochthonous units during Late Cretaceous deformation. Instead, both basement and cover have been thrust southwards during emplacement of the Tethyan thrust sheets onto the Arabian continental margin. Sedimentological evidence from the Tertiary sequence reinforces the development of the Saih Hatat dome as a Late Cretaceous culmination above a deep seated thrust which may have been rejuvenated during the Tertiary. In Jebels Akhdar and Nakhl there is no evidence of a basement-cover duplex. Nevertheless, reactivation of pre-Permian structures and imbrication of cover rocks (Mesozoic platform carbonates) in Jebel Akhdar has important implications to the timing of its structural growth. An alternative model of under-thrusting of the N Arabian margin beneath a subduction trench is also proposed to explain the formation and subsequent elevation of the Oman blueschists.

The Oman Mountains are located in the SE part of the Arabian Peninsula and form an arcuate belt parallel to the Gulf of Oman. The mountains extend for approximately 700 km NW−SE and have a width of 30−130 km.

The central and southeastern Oman mountains comprise three major tectonostratigraphic units (Fig. 1). The oldest is a pre-Permian sequence, unconformably overlain by middle Permian to Cenomanian platform carbonates (Hajar Supergroup). These rocks form the basement to a second allochthonous unit consisting of deep oceanic sediments (Hawasina Complex and Haybi Complex) and the Semail ophiolite, which was emplaced onto the Arabian continental margin in Late Cretaceous times. The third unit is a neo-autochthonous sedimentary cover

to the Oman Mountains, of Late Campanian-Maastrichtian to Tertiary age (Nolan *et al.* 1990).

Little structural data have been published on the rocks beneath the middle Permian unconformity in the central Oman Mountains. This paper is an attempt to determine the structural evolution of pre-Permian rocks with particular emphasis on the extent of Late Cretaceous deformation and metamorphism. New data is put forward in this paper, based on field mapping and structural profiles in Jebel Akhdar and Saih Hatat to show that the pre-Permian rocks of the central Oman Mountains have been affected by at least two major tectonic events; a Late Palaeozoic deformation, and a Late Cretaceous thrusting which emplaced the Semail

From ROBERTSON, A. H. F., SEARLE, M. P. & RIES, A. C. (eds), 1990,
The Geology and Tectonics of the Oman Region.
Geological Society Special Publication No 49, pp 307−325

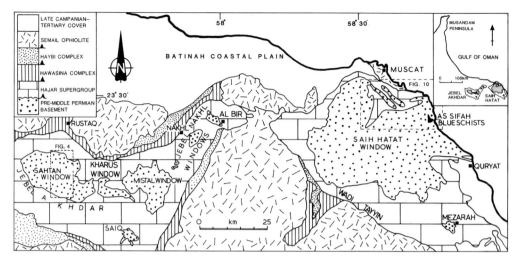

Fig. 1. Simplified geological map of the central Oman Mountains showing the distribution of pre-Permian rocks (after Glennie *et al.* 1974).

ophiolite and Tethyan thrust sheets onto the Arabian continental margin. A conceptual model for the formation and elevation of the Oman blueschists is also proposed.

Geological background

Pre-Permian rocks are exposed in a series of erosional windows beneath the platform carbonates of the Hajar Supergroup in the central Oman Mountains. From east to west these are (1) the Saih Hatat Window, (2) a number of smaller windows at the core of Jebel Nakhl and (3) the Mistal, Kharus, Sahtan and Saiq Windows at the core of Jebel Akhdar (Fig. 1). The pre-Permian formations are the oldest rocks in the mountain belt, comprising thick sequences of shallow marine and terrestrial sediments of Late Proterozoic to Early Palaeozoic age, and a group of schists and mylonites of various origins (Lees 1928; Tschopp 1967; Glennie 1977; Glennie *et al.* 1974; Lovelock *et al.* 1981; Gorin *et al.* 1982; Lippard 1983; Le Métour *et al.* 1986a,b; Villey *et al.* 1986a,b).

Late Palaeozoic deformation and metamorphism affected the pre-Permian rocks prior to the deposition of the middle Permian–Cenomanian Hajar Supergroup. In the Jebel Akhdar windows, pre-Permian sediments are deformed by large NE–SW trending folds, whereas in Saih Hatat, NNE trending structures have been recorded (Glennie *et al.* 1974; Hopson *et al.* 1981). The internal structure of Saih Hatat is very complex, involving several phases of tectonism. Possible Precambrian

deformation (Glennie 1977) has been overprinted by a Late Palaeozoic tectonic event (Glennie *et al.* 1974; Michard 1982) and Late Cretaceous thrusting and metamorphism (Glennie *et al.* 1974; Lippard 1983; Hanna 1986, 1990; Le Métour *et al.* 1986c). The deformation and metamorphism increases in intensity towards the E and NE of the Oman Mountains.

During Late Permian to middle Cretaceous times, Oman formed part of a large carbonate platform on the passive southern continental margin of the Tethyan Ocean (Fig. 2). Upwarping and subsidence associated with the formation of the Aruma/Oman foreland basin terminated the development of the carbonate platform in Oman (Glennie *et al.* 1974).

A NE dipping subduction zone is thought to have developed in the Tethyan ocean during the Late Cretaceous (Pearce *et al.* 1981). As the Arabian plate moved progressively northwards it collided with this subduction zone, resulting in the obduction of a thrust slice of Tethyan ocean floor (Semail ophiolite) onto the eastern continental margin (Glennie *et al.* 1973, 1974; Graham 1980; Coleman 1981; Lippard & Rex 1982). The collision also caused an intense imbrication of oceanic and slope sediments (Hawasina Complex and Sumeini Group), originally developed on the Oman continental margin, with Tethyan ocean floor (Glennie *et al.* 1973, 1974; Watts & Garrison 1986).

The structure of the central Oman Mountains is dominated by the Jebel Akhdar, Jebel Nakhl and Saih Hatat domes (Fig. 1). The Hawasina Window forms another major structure to the

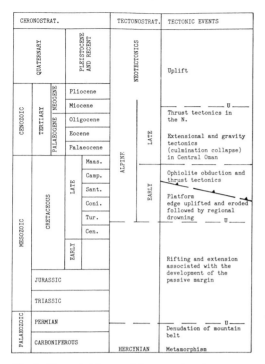

Fig. 2. Tectonic history of the central and northern Oman Mountains from Late Palaeozoic to Recent (after Hanna 1986, 1990).

NW. The origin of these structures is somewhat controversial. At first it was proposed that these major structures were a result of Tertiary compression (Glennie *et al.* 1974; Glennie 1977; Graham 1980; Searle 1980, 1985). However, later field mapping and examination of thrust tectonic relationships in the Oman Mountains led Hanna (1986, 1990) and Bernoulli & Weissart (1987) to reinterpret the Saih Hatat dome as a major culmination developed above deep seated thrusts during Late Cretaceous times. A number of important extensional structures at the peripheries of the Saih Hatat and Jebel Akhdar/Nakhl culminations were attributed to collapse of the culminations in latest Cretaceous and Tertiary times (Hanna 1986, 1990). This extensional regime was continuous throughout the Tertiary period (Mann *et al.* 1990).

This study has implications to the problems of the age of the Jebel Akhdar and Saih Hatat structures. Whereas there is no doubt as to the allochthonous nature of the Semail ophiolite and Hawasina sediments, controversy still exists as to whether the carbonate platform exposed in the domal uplifts of Jebel Akhdar and Saih Hatat has been thrust southwards during the obduction of the Semail ophiolite in Late Cre-

taceous time. If these structures developed as Late Cretaceous culminations above deep seated thrust ramps as proposed by Hanna (1986, 1990) and Bernoulli & Weissart (1987), then the thinly bedded pre-Permian sediments being of a less competent nature than the dominantly massive platform carbonates, should record this event. Alternatively, evidence of large scale folding could be found in these sequences to support the hyphothesis of Glennie *et al.* (1974), that the platform carbonates remained autochthonous during nappe emplacement and that the present day domal uplifts of Jebel Akhdar and Saih Hatat are due to Tertiary compression and uplift.

The style and orientation of structures in pre-Permian rocks are therefore described and a comparison is made with structures developed in the overlying Permian and Mesozoic platform carbonates.

Pre-Permian stratigraphy and age data

The lithological and sedimentological features of the pre-Permian rocks have been described by Glennie *et al.* (1974) and Glennie (1977) and useful correlations have been made between the sediments in the Oman Mountains and rocks from other parts of Oman (Gorin *et al.* 1982).

The oldest rocks in the Jebel Akhdar area belong to the glaciogenic Mistal Formation. This unit is a diamictite, comprising shales and siltstones, alternating with conglomerates which contain exotic clasts of granite, grandiorite and metamorphic schists similar to the crystalline basement in S Oman (Glennie *et al.* 1974; Glennie 1977). The glaciogenic unit is terminated by 5 m of laminated brown dolomite, which is in turn overlain by thick siltstones. The overlying Hajir Formation is a unit of black fetid carbonates containing distinctive layers of cross bedded lithoclastic grainstones and laminations of possible stromatolite origin (Gorin *et al.* 1982). Above the carbonates, is a thick sequence of alternating fine grained siltstones, sandstones and calcareous mudstones named the Mi'aidin Formation. The youngest member of the pre-Permian sequence in Jebel Akhdar is the Kharus Formation. The lower part of the Kharus Formation consists of laminated, partly recrystallized lime mudstones and its upper part is more massive with stratiform and locally domal stromatolites, chert nodules and intercalations of oolitic beds.

The dating of the Huqf Group in SE Oman and subsequent correlation with the lithologically similar Jebel Akhdar sequence (Gorin *et al.* 1982) has enabled tentative dating of the

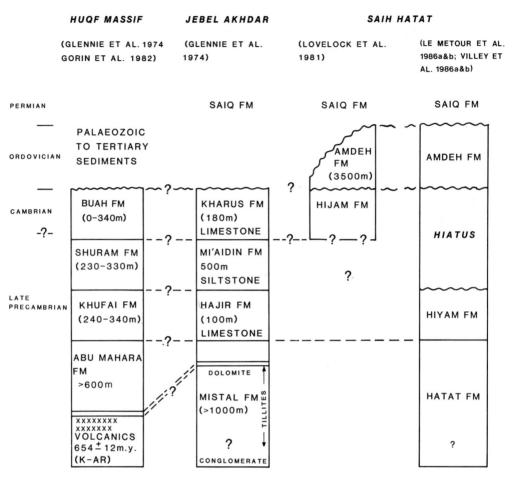

Fig. 3. Pre-Permian stratigraphy of the central Oman Mountains; correlation with the Huqf Group, south Oman.

pre-Permian rocks of the central Oman Mountains (Fig. 3). Additional age evidence is provided by Late Proterozoic–Cambrian stromatolites discovered in the Hajir Formation of Jebel Akhdar and the thin dolomite bed capping the glacial interval in the Mistal Formation which is characteristic of many Late Proterozoic tillites (Gorin *et al.* 1982).

In Saih Hatat the pre-Permian rocks can be divided into two sedimentary units (Hijam and Amdeh Formations; Glennie *et al.* 1974) and a group of schists and mylonites (Hatat Formation; Le Mètour *et al.* 1986a,b). The relationship between the dolomitic Hijam Formation and the clastic Amdeh Formation is uncertain. Glennie *et al.* (1974) believed that the Amdeh Formation was unconformably overlain by the Hijam dolomite, whereas Bailey (1981) and Le

Mètour *et al.* (1986a,b) suggested that the contact was thrust.

The Amdeh Formation contains an Early to Middle Ordovician shelly fauna (Lovelock *et al.* 1981). This more recent dating creates a problem with respect to earlier correlations of the pre-Permian rocks of Saih Hatat with other parts of Oman. Originally it was proposed that the pre-Permian Mistal and Mi'aidin Formations in Jebel Akhdar represented a lateral facies change from the Amdeh Formation (Glennie *et al.* 1974). However, the identification of Ordovician fossils in the Amdeh Formation and the discovery of possible Late Precambrian–Cambrian stromatolites in the Jebel Akhdar sequence (Gorin *et al.* 1982) must throw doubt on this correlation. It would appear that the Amdeh Formation has no lateral equivalent in Jebel

Akhdar, although the Hijam Formation may have equivalents in both Jebel Akhdar and S Oman (Fig. 3).

It would appear that two metamorphic events are recorded by the Hatat Formation in Saih Hatat. A gradual increase in metamorphic grade is seen towards the N and NE where K-Ar dates of 327 ± 16 Ma (Glennie *et al.* 1974) and 101 ± 4, 100 ± 4 and 80 ± 2 Ma have been recorded by Lippard (1983). The earlier date was interpreted as an 'Hercynian' metamorphic event, whilst the younger ages are believed to represent a mid- to late Cretaceous metamorphism during which blueschists were generated in eastern Saih Hatat (Lippard 1983). The uncertain origin of the Hatat Formation presents a stratigraphic problem which has led to a number of different stratigraphic schemes. Glennie *et al.* (1974) proposed that the schists may represent a metamorphosed equivalent of the Amdeh sediments, whereas Hopson *et al.* (1981) and Lovelock *et al.* (1981) suggested that an older, previously deformed protolith may be involved. Metamorphosed pre-Permian limestones in NE Saih Hatat (Wadi Mayh) have been assigned a possible Proterozoic age (M. Hughes Clarke, pers. comm. in Hanna 1986) and recent mapping by Le Mètour *et al.* (1986a,b) has correlated the Hatat Formation with the Late Proterozoic Mistal Formation in Jebel Akhdar (Fig. 3). It is concluded here that the Hatat schists may comprise a number of different protoliths, the nature of which requires further investigation.

Deformation of pre-Permian rocks in Jebel Akhdar

Structural mapping over an area of approximately 160 km^2 was undertaken to separate the tectonic events which have affected the pre-Permian sediments in the westernmost and largest of the erosional windows (Sahtan Window) at the core of the Jebel Akhdar structure (Fig. 1).

The structural complexity of the window has necessitated detailed stereographic analysis of minor structures. Statistical methods outlined by Watson (1966) and Woodcock (1977) are used in the description of structural orientation data. This facilitates identification of clusters and girdles and comparison of data sets. The stereographic analysis has helped to classify the relationship of folds, cleavages and thrusts, and to distinguish between different periods of deformation recorded by the pre-Permian sediments (Fig. 4).

In the S of the window the major structure is dominated by a series of large NE–SW trending asymmetrical folds and associated NW dipping thrusts, whereas in the north, the structural trend swings into an ENE–WSW orientation (Figs 4 & 5). The thrusts (T1P) have developed along limbs of the asymmetric folds and within the Hajir Formation. T1P thrust surfaces dip mainly NW and NNW and show an approximate NNW to SSE transport direction. A second thrusting event (T2P) is represented by major SW dipping backthrusts which splay off a flat decollement surface in the southern part of the window. They are associated with NW verging folds and intersections with T1P thrusts form localized triangle zones and pop-up structures (Fig. 5).

Within the hangingwall sequence of this backthrust system (T2P), is a footwall syncline (marked S on Figs 5 & 6) related to a NW dipping thrust which is one of a number of splays off the main backthrust. This is different in origin from the earlier NNW dipping forward thrust package (T1P) which occurs in the N of the window and below this major backthrust.

Below the footwall syncline (marked S on Figs 5 & 6), the Hajir limestone is deformed by a complex fold with a curved axial surface. The curvature could be due to refolding of an earlier fold, or alternatively, it may represent a hinge collapse structure within the competent Hajir limestone (Fig. 6). This could be due to the absence of the incompetent shale horizons which would have accomodated the space in the crest of the fold (cf. Ramsay 1974).

Thrust surfaces are clearly exposed within the limestones of the Hajir Formation in Wadi Bani Awf, where flats, ramps, minor cut offs and slickensides have been measured (Fig. 7a–c). Evidence of two phases of movement has been recorded on the thrust surfaces. One event is associated with NW to SE plunging slickensides and NE–SW trending folds and a second is defined by NNE–SSW plunging slickensides (Fig. 7c).

Thrusting within the Mistal and Mi'aidin Formations is more difficult to recognize, although the frequent repetition of the conglomerate lenses in the Mistal Formation suggests that thrusting has taken place within the intervening shales and slates. However, a sedimentary alternation of the repeated conglomerate horizons cannot be ruled out.

Fold wavelengths are of 1–3 km, the plunge is consistently to the NE and with one exception the facing direction is SE. Aerial views of the fold closures are highlighted by the competent Hajir Formation. Parasitic folds affecting beds

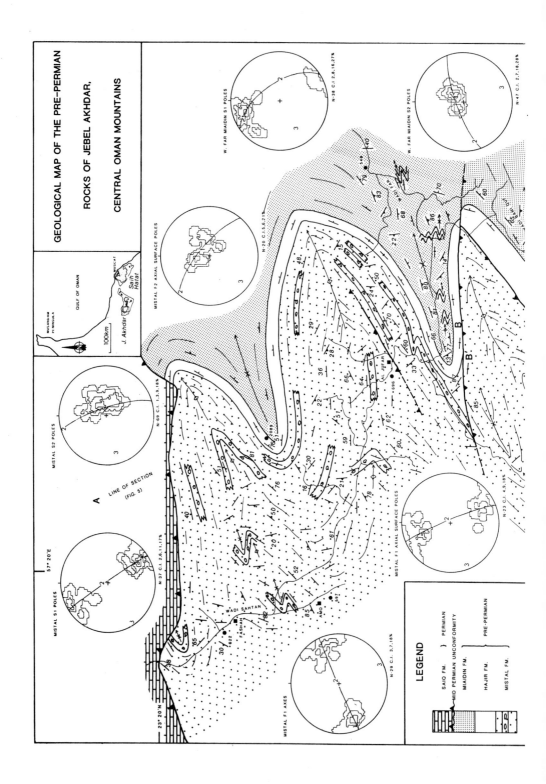

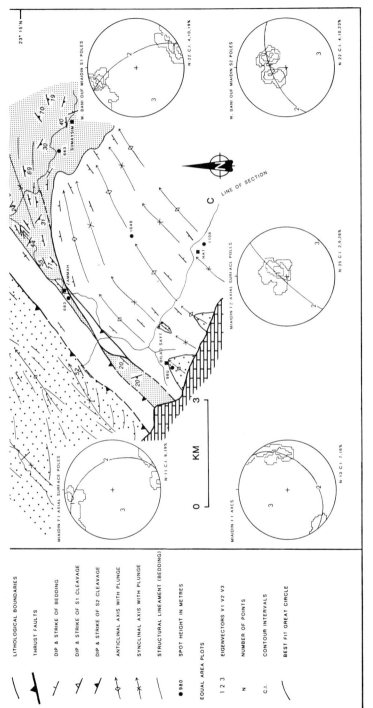

Fig. 4. Geological map of the Sahtan Window, Jebel Akhdar, central Oman Mountains. N = number of points; C. I. = contour interval; 1 = distribution mean; 2 = orthogonal point to 1 and 3 ; 3 = pole to best fit great circle.

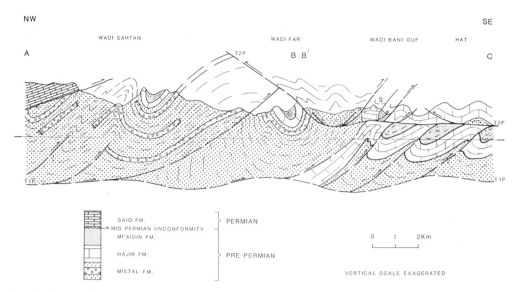

Fig. 5. Structural cross section through the Sahtan Window. Line of section shown in Fig. 4. S = syncline illustrated in Fig. 6.

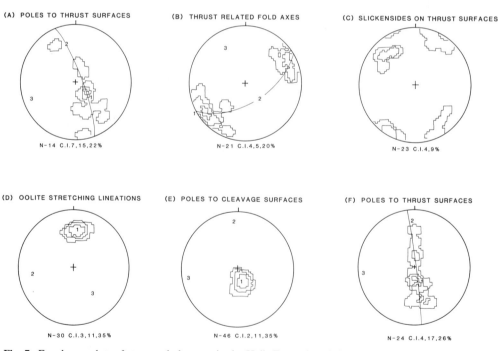

Fig. 7. Equal area plots of structural elements in the Hajir Formation, Sahtan Window (a–c) and in the Cretaceous carbonates of the Hajar Supergroup, Wadi Sahtan (d–f). See Fig. 4 for equal area plot abbreviations.

Fig. 6. Complex thrust related structures in limestones of the Hajir Formation; Wadi Bani Awf, Sahtan Window. Location shown in Fig. 5 (S).

of coarse conglomerate in the Mistal Formation and bands of competent calcareous siltstones within the Mi'aidin Formation usually display a NE—SW axial planar cleavage (S1). However, equal area plots show that on a larger scale this cleavage fans around the major structures (Fig. 4). Further plots of minor folds in the Mistal and Mi'aidin Formations show consistent NE—SW trending axes and axial surfaces which dip steeply to the NW and SE (Fig. 4). The distributions of S1 cleavage surfaces and fold axial surfaces are very similar, showing well defined clusters in most areas. However, there is a slight tendency towards a girdle distribution in the Mistal Formation.

Superimposed upon these folds is a flat lying cleavage (S2) which cuts across the earlier cleavage (S1) in the Mistal and Mi'aidin Formations. Associated with this second deformation are a number of minor structures including kinks, mullions, crenulations and poorly defined flat lying folds with wavelengths of several metres. Clustered distributions of poles to these fold axial surfaces on equal area plots indicate shallow dips to the SW in the northern part of

the Sahtan Window, a SSW dip in the centre and a change to a southerly dip in the S of the area (Fig. 4). There is a similar swing from WSW to S of the S2 cleavage surfaces.

The major structures in the pre-Permian rocks are truncated by a middle Permian unconformity at the periphery of the Sahtan bowl (Fig. 8). Evidence of tectonic movement along the unconformity surface is seen in Wadi Sahtan and Wadi Far where there is a marked overstep and discordance between the steeply dipping and folded pre-Permian rocks and the N dipping Permian Saiq Formation. Close examination of the contact shows tectonic brecciation of both the overlying massive carbonates and the underlying silty limestones and shales. This detachment horizon does not obey the thrust tectonic rule, since younger middle Permian rocks are thrust over older pre-Permian rocks (Fig. 5).

Movement along the middle Permian unconformity surface is also seen to the E of the Sahtan Window in Wadi Bani Kharus (Fig. 1) where there is a continuation of the structural style and orientation recorded in the pre-Permian rocks further west. The Hajir Forma-

Fig. 8. Pre-Permian limestones and siltstones of the Kharus Formation unconformably overlain by the middle Permian Saiq Formation, Sahtan Window.

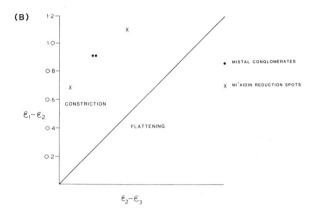

(A)

NO.	LOCALITY	FORMATION	STRAIN MARKER	METHOD	XY	YZ	XZ
1	J.AKHDAR AMQ W.SAHTAN	MISTAL	CONGLOMERATES	RF/φ	2.50	1.30*	3.25
2	AL JUFAR W.SAHTAN	MISTAL	CONGLOMERATES	RF/φ	2.50	1.30*	3.25
3	W.FAR	MI'AIDIN	REDUCTION SPOTS	RF/φ	2.00	1.63*	3.25
4	W.FAR	MI'AIDIN	REDUCTION SPOTS	RF/φ	3.00	1.08*	3.25

* - strain value estimated

Fig. 9. Strain data for pre-Permian rocks, Sahtan Window. (a) Strain ratios. (b) Logarithmic strain plot.

tion is also affected by large NE−SW striking folds and thrusts in the SE part of the Kharus Window.

Pre-Permian windows are also exposed in the core of Jebel Nakhl E of Nakhl village and W of Al Bir, in the large Mistal bowl and beneath the Saiq plateau (Fig. 1). The pre-Permian rocks in these windows have also suffered two periods of deformation, similar in style to those recorded in Jebel Akhdar.

Quantitative strain studies

Quantitative strain studies have been undertaken to determine the strain histories of pre-Permian rocks in Jebel Akhdar. Strain measurements were made at four localities in the Sahtan Window (Fig. 9) using the Rf/φ technique (Dunnet 1969; Dunnet & Siddans 1971). This method was applied to conglomerate pebbles in the Mistal Formation and to reduction spots in the siltstones of the Mi'aidin Formation. Measurements were made on surfaces which closely parallel the principal planes of the strain ellipsoid and the cleavage plane (S2) was taken as the XY principal plane with the long axis of the deformation ellipse (ex-

tension direction approximately E−W) as the X direction (after Ramsay 1967). Measurement of conglomerates and reduction spots was carried out directly in the field from ground sections. Due to poor exposure of the plane (YZ), measurements could only be taken in two planes (XY and XZ).

The results have been plotted onto a logarithmic version of the Flinn plot (Flinn 1962; Ramsay 1967). All the points lie in the constriction field (Fig. 9) which is consistent with the development of intense pencil cleavage in the pre-Permian siltstones and boudinage of the Hajir limestone in many parts of the Sahtan Window. The pencils are also parallel to the extension direction defined by reduction spots in the Mi'aidin Formation. These observations are consistent with the findings of Graham (1978) and Ramsay (1981) who have shown that pencil cleavage is usually associated with uniaxial prolate ellipsoids (K =α) and that pencil elongation is parallel to the total maximum principal extension direction (X). The prolate ellipsoids can be attributed to the two phases of approximately N to S compression resulting in the observed E−W extension.

It is therefore conceivable that quantitative

strain results in pre-Permian rocks may represent a genuine horizontal extension with strong vertical compression. This may have been produced by the load of the overlying Semail ophiolite.

Deformation of the Hajar Supergroup in Jebel Akhdar

Late Cretaceous thrusting in the Hajar Supergroup platform carbonates on the N side of Jebel Akhdar has been described by Hanna (1986, 1990). Structural elements related to this deformation have been measured in Wadi Sahtan to the N of the pre-Permian window and plotted on equal area diagrams to enable a comparison with structures developed in the pre-Permian rocks (Fig. 7d−f).

Deformed elliptical ooids from the Lower Cretaceous Habshan Formation on the N flank of Jebel Akhdar define N plunging lineations (Fig. 7d) and in places, well developed cleavage surfaces dip at shallow angles to the N (Fig. 7e). Bedding also dips to the N, but more steeply than cleavage. Sedimentological and stratigraphic evidence suggests that the limestones are right-way-up and therefore the cleavage must represent a later tectonic event, postdating the thrusting. Similar cleavages have been recorded at a number of other localities around the N side of Jebel Akhdar and in Saih Hatat (J. D. Smewing pers. comm.).

The oolite stretching lineations appear to define the N to S movement of the Late Cretaceous thrust sheets, whereas the cleavage may be related to gravity sliding of the Semail ophiolite northwards, off the Jebel Akhdar structural high (i.e. dorsal culmination collapse structure of Hanna 1986, 1990).

Comparison of certain structural elements of the pre-Permian rocks and Mesozoic platform carbonates of the Wadi Sahtan area shows significant geometrical similarities. Equal area plots of the shallow S2 cleavage surfaces developed in the Mistal and Mi'aidin Formations and the cleavage developed in the Cretaceous carbonates both show well defined clustered distributions (cf. Figs 4 & 7e). Variations in the attitude of S2 cleavage planes and related fold axial surfaces in parts of the pre-Permian window (Fig. 4) may be due in part to the incompetent nature of the pre-Permian rocks and also to differential slip of the Semail ophiolite in the centre of the Jebel Akhdar culmination.

Further comparison using equal area plots of thrust surface orientations in the Cretaceous carbonates of the Hajar Supergroup and in the pre-Permian Hajar Formation shows a similar girdle distribution in both units. It is difficult to distinguish between pre-Permian and possible Late Cretaceous thrusts in the basement, but the greater spread of points in the pre-Permian rocks, define a broad NW−SE girdle and can be explained by two phases of thrusting. Thrusts in Cretaceous rocks define a narrow N−S girdle (cf. Fig. 7a,f). Furthermore, slickenside striated thrust surfaces in the pre-Permian Hajir limestone show evidence of two phases of movement (Fig. 7c), suggesting possible Late Cretaceous reactivation of earlier pre-Permian thrusts. The NNE−SSW trend of one set of slickenside striations is consistent with the thrusting direction in the platform carbonates (Fig. 7c,f).

Deformation and metamorphism in Saih Hatat

The Saih Hatat area represents the largest structural domain in the central and southeastern Oman Mountains. Occupying an area of approximately 3250 km^2 it extends from the northern coastline near Muscat to Wadi Tayin in the S and Quryat in the E (Fig. 1). In general, Saih Hatat is a major box shaped, domal structure. It exposes the main tectonostratigraphic units of the Oman Mountains, including the lowest unit of pre-Permian basement and Hajar Supergroup platform carbonates; the unit comprising Hawasina, Oman melange and ophiolite; and the Late Campanian-Maastrichtian to Tertiary sequence (Fig. 1).

The internal structure of Saih Hatat is very complex, involving several phases of deformation previously ascribed to Precambrian (Glennie 1977) and Late Palaeozoic tectonic events (Glennie et al. 1974; Lovelock et al. 1981). Despite a marked lithological contrast between the fissile, thinly bedded pre-Permian sequences and the more massive Permian and Mesozoic shelf carbonates in Saih Hatat, many of the structures appear to involve both units.

In NE Saih Hatat, the pre-Permian Hatat Formation consists of thick units of quartz-mica schist, garnet-phengite schist, blue amphibole-bearing greenschist and meta-limestone of possible Proterozoic age (M. Hughes Clarke pers. comm. in Hanna 1986). Sheets of blueschist, garnet-bearing blueschist and eclogite (Le Mètour et al. 1986b,c) occur W and NW of As Sifah (Fig. 10). Lawsonite schists crop out in NW Saih Hatat (Michard 1983; Michard et al. 1984).

The structural relationship between the dolomites of the Hijam Formation and the Hatat schists is not clear. Glennie et al. (1974) believed

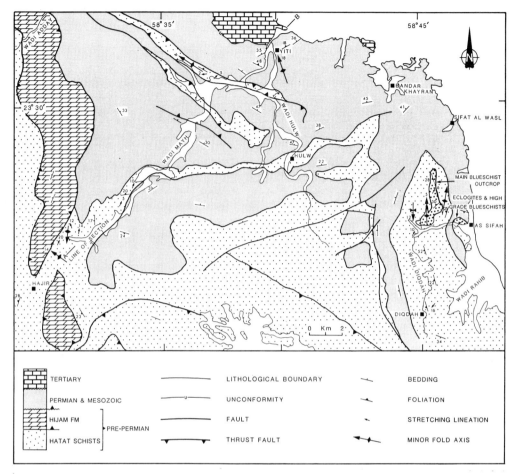

Fig. 10. Simplified geological sketch map of northeast Saih Hatat, based on maps by Glennie *et al.* (1974), Bailey (1981), Le Mètour *et al.* (1986a,b), aerial photograph interpretation and field mapping.

that the schists were unconformably overlain by the dolomite, but later mapping by Bailey (1981) shows that the schists are overthrust by the dolomite. The contacts examined in this study were tectonic (Fig. 10). However, in parts of NE Saih Hatat Le Mètour *et al.* (1986a,b) have mapped both the dolomites originally assigned to the pre-Permian Hijam Formation by Glennie *et al.* (1974) and the protolith of some Hatat schists (including the blueschists) as Permian Saiq Formation.

The unconformity separating Permian and Mesozoic rocks from the pre-Permian sequence, locally shows evidence of representing a detachment horizon. Permian rocks are folded immediately above the unconformity plane along N–S fold hinges in Wadi Aday (Hanna 1986). Small-scale thrusts, striking N–S, rep-

resent lateral ramps branching off the unconformity surface.

The northern part of the Saih Hatat Window is dominated by N-verging back folds and thrusts. The largest of these structures is a N-verging fold to the SW of Wadi Mayh which can be mapped for several kilometers eastwards in NE Saih Hatat. The fold has an overturned northern limb indicated by bedding/cleavage relationships and also by asymmetrical parasitic folds. East of Wadi Mayh, in Wadi Hulw, back thrusting and back folding are the dominant structural features of the pre-Permian sequences (Fig. 10).

In this study, structural data were collected in Wadi Mayh and As Sifah (Fig. 10) to determine the effects of Late Cretaceous deformation and metamorphism on pre-Permian basement and

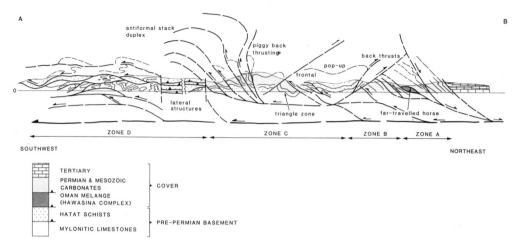

Fig. 11. Schematic cross section through Wadi Mayh, Saih Hatat. Line of section shown in Fig. 10.

Permian and Mesozoic cover rocks in NE Saih Hatat. A schematic cross section through Wadi Mayh illustrates the most complex structure seen in the internal zone of the Oman Mountains (Fig. 11). It is a major basement cover duplex in the sense of Boyer & Elliot (1982), involving rocks of possibly Proterozoic age (M. Hughes Clarke pers. comm. in Hanna 1986), younger pre-Permian rocks (basement) and Permian and Mesozoic platform carbonates of the Hajar Supergroup (cover). In Wadi Mayh, the basement-cover duplex can be described in terms of four tectonic zones (Fig. 11).

Zone (a) is restricted to an imbricate slice of red radiolarian Hawasina chert with Triassic dolomites of the Hajar Supergroup.

Zone (b) involves Mesozoic platform carbonates which show a tectonic thickening caused by numerous duplex structures. Each horse within the duplex is accreted to the overriding thrust, thus increasing the thickness of the hangingwall.

Zone (c) involves imbrication of the pre-Permian Hatat schists with Permian and Mesozoic carbonates in a pop-up structure. The schists are back thrust northwards onto Triassic dolomites. At the frontal end of the pop-up, a series of frontal imbricate stacks involve both the schists and the Permian Saiq Formation. To the S of this structure piggy-back style thrusting has developed a major duplex structure in the Permian carbonates and Hatat schists. The northernmost thrust dips very steeply to the N and is associated with a N verging fold. The thrusts dip more gently near the leading edge of the structure in the south. The northern imbricate is thought to have been back-steepened by

the development of the progressively southerly propagating thrusts assembled downwards in the direction of transport. Between the southern end of the pop-up structure and the northern end of the piggy-back structures, a triangle zone has developed mainly in the Permian Saiq Formation.

Zone (d) involves complex folding and thrusting within the pre-Permian sequence. Boudinage structures, shear zones, sheath and interference folds and flat-lying thrusts affect pre-Permian mylonitic limestones. A series of tight to isoclinal folds with sub-horizontal axial surfaces lie in the hangingwall of a low-angle out-of-sequence thrust (Fig. 12a). Other folds with complex geometries are exposed in cliff sections along both sides of Wadi Mayh. They are characterized by complex closures with meandering fold hinges plunging in different directions and display mushroom-like geometries (Fig. 12b).

A high degree of internal deformation and recrystallization is seen in the pre-Permian schists in NE Saih Hatat. This is shown by the development of mylonitic fabrics in many schists, widespread dynamic grain size reduction in the quartz-albite-mica schists and thick bands of carbonate mylonite within the metalimestones adjacent to the blueschists. These features and the development of sheath folds associated with intense NNE–SSW trending stretching lineations are all characteristic of high strain ductile deformation within deep seated shear zones.

Examination of the As Sifah blueschists has shown that they occur as highly deformed and disseminated W and SW dipping backthrust

Fig. 12. Complex folding in pre-Permian mylonitic limestones; Wadi Mayh, Saih Hatat. (a) Isoclinal fold structures in the hangingwall of an out-of-sequence thrust. (b) Mushroom fold.

sheets and pods, interleaved with quartz-mica and calc-mica schists and mylonites. Intense stretching lineations have been recorded sub-parallel to the axes of sheath folds with variable trends (Fig. 10). High pressure assemblages in the blueschists show that the peak metamorphic conditions in NE Saih Hatat reached 450−500°C and 10−13 kbars in the glaucophanic eclogite facies (Le Mètour *et al.* 1986a) to 430−600°C and 9.5−13 kbars (El-Shazly 1987). Complex disequilibrium metamorphic textures are seen in the greenschists and blueschists. The rimming of porphyroblasts of blue amphibole by Na−Ca amphibole and the breakdown of garnet to chlorite, and clinopyroxene to albite, are indicative of later retrogression. The epidote blueschist zone extends across central, SW and SE Saih Hatat at $P > 4-5$ kbars, $T > 400°C$ (Le Mètour *et al.* 1986c). It would appear, therefore, that metamorphic grade does fall rapidly towards the S and W in Saih Hatat as originally proposed by Glennie *et al.* (1974) and that the intense deformation and metamorphism recorded in NE Saih Hatat is a localized feature related to the partial subduction of the NE Oman continental margin during the initial stages of ophiolite obduction as outlined by Lippard (1983).

Discussion

Differences in dip and erosional truncation of major NE−SW trending thrusts and folds by the overlying Permian and Mesozoic platform carbonates in Jebel Akhdar suggest that the pre-Permian rocks of the central Oman Mountains have undergone a period of pre- middle Permian deformation. In Saih Hatat more than one pre-Permian tectonic event may have taken place, including Precambrian deformation (Glennie 1977). These have largely been obscured by Late Cretaceous deformation and metamorphism. The presence of complex interference folds in Wadi Mayh also suggest refolding of earlier structures.

Fossil evidence from the Amdeh Formation in Saih Hatat (Lovelock *et al.* 1981) shows that the latest of these pre-Permian events must have taken place between early Ordovician and middle Permian times. This is in agreement with a K/Ar age of 327 ± 20 Ma obtained from the Hatat schists (Glennie *et al.* 1974). Ordovician fossils have not been recorded in Jebel Akhdar, although the discovery of Late Proterozoic−Cambrian stromatolites in the upper part of the pre-Permian sequence (Gorin *et al.* 1982) narrows the age of the deformation to between Cambrian and middle Permian times.

It seems most likely that Late Palaeozoic deformation in Jebel Akhdar and Saih Hatat were synchronous. Pre-Permian rocks therefore record a period of Late Palaeozoic deformation and metamorphism that is unknown to the rest of the Arabian Peninsula. Michard (1982) proposed that the pre-Permian rocks formed part of a post-Ordovician, Late Palaeozoic fold belt continuing to N Africa.

Glennie *et al.* (1974) attributed the Akhdar−Nakhl−Saih Hatat structures in the Oman mountains to Tertiary (Oligo−Miocene) compression and regarded the pre-Permian sequence and Permian and Mesozoic platform carbonates as autochthonous units during the Late Cretaceous deformation. However, the tectonic evidence is consistent with the development of the Saih Hatat structures as Late Cretaceous culminations above a deep seated thrust (see Hanna 1986, 1990) which suggests an earlier age of structural development. Structural and sedimentological evidence from the Tertiary sequence flanking Saih Hatat reinforces this hypothesis. The younger rocks have not been affected by a major compressional event; on the contrary, the Tertiary sediments appear to have been deformed within an extensional regime (Mann *et al.* 1990) and sedimentological evidence suggests that Saih Hatat was a positive area throughout the Palaeogene period (Nolan *et al.* 1986).

In Jebel Akhdar and Jebel Nakhl there is no evidence of a basement-cover duplex. Nevertheless, the identification of Late Cretaceous structures in the pre-Permian sequences and imbrication of Mesozoic platform carbonates in Jebel Akhdar suggest that the pre-Permian basement has been deformed during the Late Cretaceous thrusting and that the structural growth of Jebel Akhdar may have initiated at this time. The Late Cretaceous deformation of pre-Permian rocks in Jebel Akhdar may be shown by possible reactivation of earlier thrusts, accompanied by a major flattenning deformation caused by loading of the overlying thrust sheets.

Although Jebel Akhdar may have formed a structural low in Tertiary times (Nolan *et al.* 1986), there is no evidence to refute its initiation at that time (Nolan pers. comm.). Furthermore, it is difficult to envisage that the Jebel Akhdar structure was formed by a separate thrusting event. The structure may have been topographically enhanced at a later stage than Saih Hatat, possibly by rejuvination of a deep seated thrust.

Tertiary collapse of these culminations is recorded by cleavages observed in the platform carbonates on the north side of Jebel Akhdar

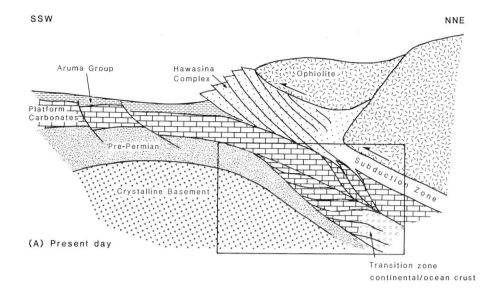

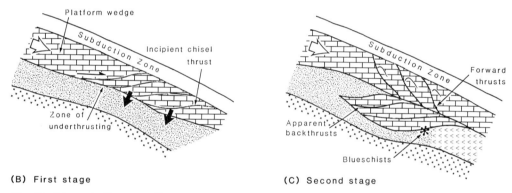

Fig. 13. Schematic diagram to illustrate the stages of development of the Oman blueschists. (a) The present day situation (see Fig. 11). (b) Emplacement of platform wedge between subduction zone and duplex. Initial slicing of toe of underthrust slab. (c) Continued chiselling of platform slab between horse and subduction zone, causing uplift of the imbricated toe. Basement-cover duplex develops at this stage.

and in Saih Hatat in addition to the culmination collapse structures described by Hanna (1986, 1990).

A critical and yet unsolved problem in the Oman Mountains is the mechanism of formation of the blueschist and glaucophane eclogites at considerable depth and their later uplift to the present erosion level without obliteration or strong overprinting. A model is proposed in which the continental margin consisting of the platform carbonates and underlying pre-Permian sequences have been underthrust beneath a subduction trench. Fig. 13 illustrates the stages by which a high P/T ductile shear zone has developed by the chiselling effect of

the continental wedge between the duplex developed in the toe of the underthrust slab and the subduction zone. The wedging causes uplift of the metamorphic slab. This kinematic model may explain the 9−13 kbar pressure estimates by Le Mètour *et al.* 1986a and El-Shazly (1987) without invoking a considerable overburden. Later elevation of the blueschists within an extensional tectonic regime (described above) may have contributed to their final uplift from considerable depth. Major footwall uplift related to extensional faults around the margins of the Saih Hatat culmination on the NE side of Saih Hatat (see Mann *et al.* 1990, Fig. 10) is shown by the absence of ophiolite and oceanic sediments which presumably have been buried (downfaulted) beneath younger Tertiary sediments. In the Mazarah area of SE Saih Hatat (Fig. 1) there is a sequence of undeformed terraces of possible Quaternary age at a topographic height of approximately 600 m above sea level. This may demonstrate that uplift of Saih Hatat (including the blueschists) continued into the Quaternary Period. Continuous isostatic uplift to the present day is demonstrated by neotectonics elsewhere in the Oman Mountains along the Maradi Fault Zone (Hanna & Nolan, 1989).

This work was funded by Amoco Oman Production Company through the Earth Sciences and Resources Institute, University of South Carolina. The authors would also like to thank the Ministry of Petroleum, Sultanate of Oman for supporting this work. We are grateful to Dr. J. D. Smewing of the Earth Resources Institute, Dr. J. Le Métour and A. El-Shazly for their constructive criticism of the manuscript. The paper is published with the permission of Amoco Production Company.

References

BAILEY, E. H. 1981. Geologic map of Muscat-Ibra area, Sultanate of Oman. *Journal of Geophysical Research. Special Issue on 'Oman Ophiolite'*, **86**.

BERNOULLI, D. & WEISSERT, H. 1987. The upper Hawasina nappes in the central Oman Mountains: Stratigraphy, palinspastics and sequence of nappe emplacement. *Geodynamica Acta (Paris)*, **1**, 47–58.

BOYER, E. S. & ELLIOTT, D. 1982. Thrust systems. *Bulletin of the American Association of Petroleum Geologists*, **66**, 1196–1230.

COLEMAN, R. G. 1981. Tectonic setting for ophiolite obduction in Oman. *Journal of Geophysical Research*, **86**, 2497–2508.

DUNNET, D. 1969. A technique of finite strain analysis using elliptical particles. *Tectonophysics*, **7**, 117–36.

—— & SIDDANS, A. W. B. 1971. Non-random sedimentary fabrics and their modification by strain. *Tectonophysics*, **12**, 307–25.

EL-SHAZLY, A. K. 1987. High pressure metamorphism in northeastern Oman and its tectonic implications. *MSc thesis, Stanford University, U.S.A.*

FLINN, D. 1962. On folding during three-dimensional progressive deformation. *Quarterly Journal of the Geological Society Of London*, **118**, 385–433.

GLENNIE, K. W. 1977. Outline of the geology of Oman. *Mèmoirs de la Sociète Gèologique de France*, **8**, 25–31.

——, BOUEF, M. G. A., HUGHES CLARK, M. W., MOODY-STUART, M., PILAAR, W. F. H. & REINHARDT, B. M. 1973. Late Cretaceous nappes in the Oman mountains and their geologic evolution. *Bulletin of the American Association of Petroleum Geologists*, **57**, 5–27.

——, ——, ——, ——, —— & —— 1974. The geology of the Oman mountains. *Verhandelingen van het Koninklijk Nederlands geologisch Mijnbouwkundig Genootschap*, **31**.

GORIN, G. E., RACZ, L. G. & WALTER, M. R. 1982. Late Precambrian–Cambrian sediments of Huqf Group, Sultanate of Oman. *Bulletin of the American Association of Petroleum Geologists*, **66**, 2609–27.

GRAHAM, G. M. 1980. Structure and sedimentology of the Hawasina Window, Oman mountains. *PhD thesis, Open University, Milton Keynes, UK.*

GRAHAM, R. H. 1978. Quantitative deformation studies in the Permian rocks of Alpes-Maritimes. *Goguel Symposium, B.R.G.M.*, 220–38.

HANNA, S. S. 1986. The Alpine (Late Cretaceous and Tertiary) tectonic evolution of the Oman mountains: A thrust tectonic approach. *Symposium on the hydrocarbon potential of intense thrust zones*, **2**, OAPEC, Kuwait, 125–174.

—— 1990. The alpine deformation of the Central Oman Mountains. *In*: ROBERTSON, A. H. F., SEARLE, M. P. & RIES, A. C. (eds) *The Geology and Tectonics of the Oman Region*. Geological Society, London, Special Publication **49**, 341–359.

—— & NOLAN, S. C. 1989. The Maradi Fault Zone: evidence of Late Neogene in the Oman Mountains. *Journal of the Geological Society of London*, **146**, 867–871.

HOPSON, C. A., COLEMAN, R. G., GREGORY, R. T., PALLISTER, J. S. & BAILEY, E. H. 1981. Geological section through the Semail ophiolite and associated rocks along a Muscat-Ibra transect, South-eastern Oman mountains. *Journal of Geophysical Research*, **86**, 2527–2544.

LEES, G. M. 1928. The geology and tectonics of Oman and parts of SE Arabia. *Quarterly Journal of the Geological Society of London*, **84**, 585–670.

LE MÉTOUR, J., GRAMONT de, X., VILLEY, M. & BEURRIER, M. 1986a. Geological map of Masqat. Sheet NF, 40–4A. Scale 1:100000. Explanatory notes. *Directorate General of Minerals, Oman Ministry of Petroleum and Minerals.*

——, VILLEY, M. & GRAMONT de X. 1986b. Geological map of Quryat. Sheet NF 40–4D. Scale 1:100000. Explanatory notes. *Directorate General of Minerals, Oman Ministry of Petroleum and Minerals.*

——, RABU, D., TEGYEY, M., BECHENNEC, F., BEURRIER, M. & VILLEY, M. 1986c. Le mètamorphisme règional crètacè de facies èclogites – schistes bleus sur la bordure omanaise de la plate-forme arabe: consèquence d'une tectogenese prècoce antè-obduction. *Compte Rendu Acadèmie Sciences, Paris*, **302**, 905–910.

LIPPARD, S. J. 1983. Cretaceous metamorphism in NE Oman and its relationship to subduction and ophiolite nappe emplacement. *Journal of the Geological Society, London*, **140**, 97–104.

—— & REX, D. C. 1982. K–Ar ages of alkaline igneous rocks in the northern Oman mountains, NE Arabia, and their relations to rifting, passive margin development and destruction of the Oman

Tethys. *Geological Magazine*, **119**, 497–503.

LOVELOCK, P. E. R., POTTER, T. L., WALSWORTH-BELL, E. B. & WEIMER, W. M. 1981. Ordovician rocks in the Oman Mountains: the Amdeh Formation. *Geologie en Mjnbouw*, **60**, 487–96.

MANN, A., HANNA, S. S. & NOLAN, S. C. 1990. Post-Campanian tectonic evolution of the central Oman Mountains: tertiary extension of the eastern Arabian Margin. *In*: ROBERTSON, A. H. F., SEARLE, M. P. & RIES, A. C. (eds) *The Geology and Tectonics of the Oman Region*. Geological Society, London, Special Publication, **49**, 549–563.

MICHARD, A. 1982. Contribution à la connaissance de la marge nord du Gondwana: une châine plissèe palèozique, vraisemblablement hercynienne, en Oman. *Compte Rendu Hebdomadairedes sèances de l'Academie des Sciences, Paris*, **295**, 1031–1036.

—— 1983. Les nappes de Mascate (Oman), rampe èpi-continentale d'obduction a facies schiste bleu et la dualitè apparente des ophiolites omanaises. *Sciences Gèologiques Bulletin, Strasbourg*, **36**, 3–16.

——, BOUCHEZ, J. L. & OUAZZANI-TOUHAMI, M. 1984. Obduction related planar and linear fabrics in Oman. *Journal of Structural Geology*, **6**, 39–50.

NOLAN, S. C., CLISSOLD, B. P., SMEWING, J. D. & SKELTON, P. W. 1986. Late Campanian to Tertiary palaeogeography of the central and northern Oman mountains. *Symposium on the hydrocarbon potential of intense thrust zones*, **2**, OAPC, Kuwait, 175–200.

——, SKELTON, P. W., CLISSOLD, B. P. & SMEWING, J. D. 1990. *In*: ROBERTSON, A. H. F., SEARLE, M. P. & RIES, A. C. (eds) *The Geology and Tectonics of the Oman Region* Geological Society, London, Special Publication **49**, 495–519.

PEARCE, J. A., ALABASTER, T., SHELTON, A. W. & SEARLE, M. P. 1981. The Oman ophiolite as a Cretaceous arc-basin complex: evidence and implication. *Philosophical Transactions of the Royal Society of London*, **A300**, 299–317.

RAMSAY, J. G. 1967. Folding and fracturing of rocks. McGraw-Hill, New York.

—— 1974. Development of chevron folds. *Bulletin of the Geological Society of America*, **85**, 1741–1753.

—— 1981. Tectonics of the Helvetic Nappes. *In*: McCLAY, K. R. & PRICE, N. J. (eds) *Thrust and Nappe Tectonics*. Geological Society, London, Special Publication **9**, 293–309.

SEARLE, M. P. 1980. The metamorphic sheet and underlying volcanic rocks beneath the Semail ophiolite in the Northern Oman mountains of Arabia. *PhD thesis, Open University, Milton Keynes, U.K.*

—— 1985. Sequence of thrusting and origins of culminations in the Northern and Central Oman mountains. *Journal of Structural Geology*, **7**, 129–1431.

TSCHOPP, R. H. 1967. The general geology of Oman. *Proceedings of the 7th World Petroleum Congress, Mexico*, **2**, 243–50.

VILLEY, M., LE METOUR, J. & GRAMONT, X. de. 1986a. Geological map of Fanjah. Sheet NF 40–3F. Scale 1:100 000. Explanatory notes. *Directorate General of Minerals, Oman Ministry of Petroleum and Minerals*.

——, —— & —— 1986b. Geological map of Sib. Sheet NF 40–3C, Scale 1:100 000. Explanatory notes. *Directorate General of Minerals, Oman Ministry of Petroleum and Minerals*.

WATSON, G. S. 1966. The statistics of orientation data. *Journal of Geology*, **74**, 786–97.

WATTS, K. F. & GARRISON, R. E. 1986. Sumeini Group, Oman — evolution of a Mesozoic carbonate slope on a south Tethyan continental margin. *Sedimentary Geology*, **48**, 107–168.

WOODCOCK, N. H. 1977. Specification of fabric shapes using an eigenvalue method. *Bulletin of the Geological Society of America*, **83**, 1231–36.

Subduction and obduction: two stages in the Eo−Alpine tectonometamorphic evolution of the Oman Mountains

J. LE MÉTOUR[1], D. RABU[1], M. TEGYEY[2], F. BÉCHENNEC[1], M. BEURRIER[2] & M. VILLEY[2]

[1] *Service Géologique National, B.R.G.M., 10 rue Henri Picherit, 44300 Nantes, France*
[2] *Service Géologique National, B.R.G.M., B.P. 6009, 45060 Orléans Cedex, France.*

Abstract: The platform unit of the Oman Mountains is composed of shelf sedimentary and volcanic rocks, ranging in age from late Proterozoic to late Turonian−Coniacian, that were deformed mainly during the polyphase Eo−Alpine tectogenesis.

In the late Turonian−Coniacian tangential shearing deformation with NE (oceanward) vergence occurred under HP/LT conditions of regional metamorphism. This tectonic phase was largely responsible for the structural and metamorphic zonation of the platform unit. A SW−NE gradient from external to internal zones has been recognized from the south flank of Jabal Akhdar, where fracture cleavage appears, to the eastern part of Saih Hatat, where schistose glaucophane ecologites are preserved. This tectonometamorphic event was related to partial subduction of the northeast corner of the Arabian platform beneath the neo-Tethyan oceanic lithosphere.

A later phase of higher-level shearing deformation with SW (continentward) vergence, during the Campanian, accompanied the thrusting of the Hawasina Nappes and the obduction of the Semail Ophiolite. These tectonic units were transported SSW respectively from the Permian−Cretaceous cover of the Arabian continental margin and from the oceanic floor of the Semail marginal basin that opened during the Albian−Cenomanian. Tectonic slicing and strike-slip faulting within the platform unit, on the northern margins of Jabal Akhdar and Saih Hatat, formed frontal and lateral ramps during the advance of the nappes onto the Arabian Platform.

During a third phase of deformation, probably during the Campanian−Maastrichtian, large-amplitude, long-wavelength, open, near-upright folding accompanied by poorly developed, subvertical, SSW−NNE fracture cleavage indicates moderate shortening during uplift perpendicular to the earlier structures.

The resulting Eo−Alpine foreland belt of the Oman Mountains was partly covered by marine carbonate deposits during the middle Maastrichtian to late Maastrichtian or early Palaeogene before being affected by Alpine tectonics during the Miocene.

The work of Lees (1928), Allemann & Peters (1972) and Glennie *et al.* (1973, 1974) showed that late Cretaceous tectonics in the Oman Mountains involved essentially southwestward thrusting of the Hawasina Nappes and the Semail Ophiolite onto the Arabian Platform. Until recently, deformation in the autochthonous platform units exposed in the updomed areas of Jabal Akhdar and Saih Hatat, that took place in the late Cretaceous, was considered to be directly related to obduction (Coleman 1981) during which the autochthon played a more or less passive role, except in the northeast of Saih Hatat, where overthrust sheets of blueschist of limited extent occur (Boudier & Michard 1981; Lippard 1983). In this region the structural and metamorphic evolution has been linked either to partial subduction of the northeastern edge of the Arabian continental margin (Lippard 1983; Lippard *et al.* 1986) or directly to obduction (Boudier & Michard 1981; Michard 1981, 1983; Michard *et al.* 1984). The large domal structures of the Jabal Akhdar and Saih Hatat tectonic windows have been explained by Tertiary compression (Glennie *et al.* 1974; Glennie 1977; Graham 1980; Searle 1985). However, these major structures have recently been interpreted by Hanna (1986) as major culminations developed during Late Cretaceous times above hypothetical deep-seated thrusts and uplifted during the Tertiary in an extensional tectonic setting. Hanna (1986) suggests that the foreland succession exposed in the Oman Mountains may in fact be far from autochthonous.

The 1:100 000 scale mapping of 13 sheets

From ROBERTSON, A. H. F., SEARLE, M. P. & RIES, A. C. (eds), 1990,
The Geology and Tectonics of the Oman Region.
Geological Society Special Publication No 49, pp 327−339

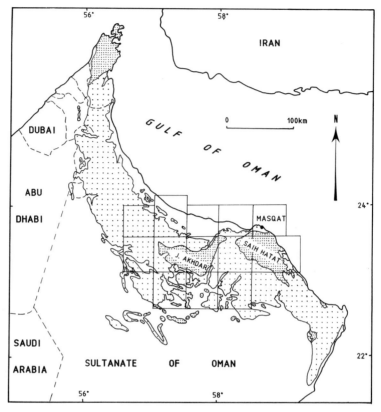

Fig. 1. Location map of the Oman Mountains autochthon (close stippled areas) and of the area studied and mapped at 1:100 000 scale (13 sheets).

covering 28 000 km^2 in the southeastern and central Oman Mountains (Fig. 1) (Béchennec *et al.* 1986a,b; Beurrier *et al.* 1986a,b; de Gramont *et al.* 1986; Hutin *et al.* 1986; Janjou *et al.* 1986; Le Métour *et al.* 1986b,c; Rabu *et al.* 1986; Villey *et al.* 1986a,b,c) and study of the autochthonous rocks exposed in the Jabal Akhdar (Rabu 1988) and Saih Hatat (Le Métour 1988) windows led to a modified interpretation of the late Cretaceous (Eo–Alpine) tectonometamorphic evolution of the area, underlining the polyphase character of the tectogenesis (subduction-related followed by obduction-related tectonics) and the synchroneity of subduction and HP/LT metamorphism, and to a new interpretation of the geodynamic evolution of the southern margin of Neo-Tethys.

From the Late Cretaceous to the present the construction of the Oman mountain chain has taken place in the context of the closure of eastern Neo-Tethys, linked to the more or less N–S convergence of the Eurasia-Iran and Africa-Arabia continental blocks (Patriat *et al.*

1982; Dercourt *et al.* 1986). The geodynamic evolution of the region can be separated into three stages: (i) ocean-ocean plate subduction and continental underthrusting, (ii) obduction and Eo-Alpine orogenesis, (iii) uplift during the Alpine orogenesis. This paper deals only with the first two of these stages, presenting first the structural and metamorphic features attributed to the early Eo–Alpine, subduction-related tectonics and then those interpreted as due to the Eo–Alpine thrust, or obduction-related tectonics. Finally a model is proposed for the geodynamic evolution of this part of the Neo-Tethyan margin during the Late Cretaceous.

Subduction-related tectonics

Two autochthonous units outcrop in the Jabal Akhdar and Saih Hatat windows (Fig. 2), a pre-Permian sequence known as Autochthonous Unit A unconformably overlain by a sequence of Permian-Cretaceous age referred to as Autochthonous Unit B (Le Métour 1988;

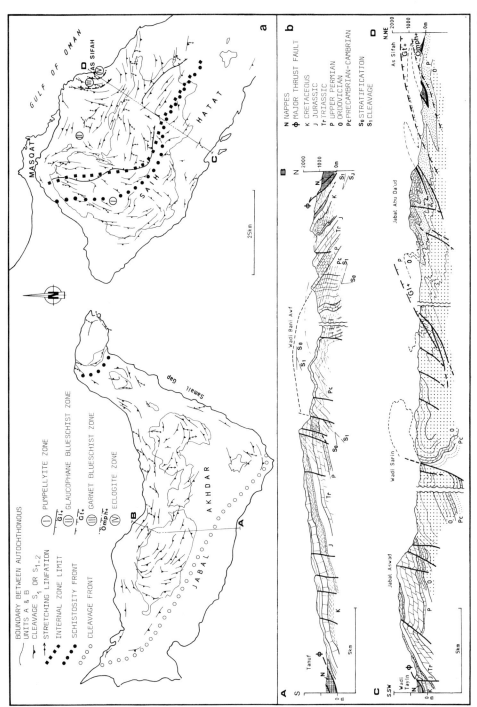

Fig. 2. Subduction tectonics in the Oman Mountains autochthon. a: structural and metamorphic zoning – b: geological sections, see location on (a)

Rabu 1988). Within these units, four features characterize the subduction tectonics (i) a sub-horizontal cleavage (simple S_1 or composite S_{1-2}, with later undulatory deformation), (ii) a C (shear)-plane, always associated with the cleavage, (iii) a lineation, L_1 within the S_1 (or S_{1-2}) cleavage, and (iv) F_1 (or F_{1-2}) folds. The origin of the first cleavage S_1 in the pre-Permian rocks is somewhat controversial. At first it was proposed that this slaty cleavage was a result of a Palaeozoic (Hercynian ?) folding event (Glennie *et al.* 1974; Glennie 1977; Michard 1982). However, detailed structural analysis in the pre-Permian Amq window (western Jabal Akhdar) led Rabu (1988) to demonstrate that the Palaeozoic folds are not associated with an axial plane cleavage. Finally, throughout the Jabal Akhdar and Saih Hatat windows, the first cleavage S_1 was the first penetrative structure to have affected the entire autochthonous sedimentary pile, from the late Proterozoic base of Autochthonous Unit A to the late Coniacian-Santonian Muti Formation at the top of Autochthonous Unit B (Le Métour 1988; Rabu 1988).

Cleavage zonation

Fracture cleavage S_1 first appears along the southwest edge of Jabal Akhdar, and northeast from here a broad zone of fracture cleavage covers most of Jabal Akhdar and the southwestern third of Saih Hatat (Fig. 2). Simple schistosity S_1 appears at the northeast extremity of Jabal Akhdar and in the central part of Saih Hatat (Fig. 2). These regions together constitute the external zone of the Eo−Alpine orogen, affected by a single early phase of deformation. To the northeast of this, stretching across the eastern half of Saih Hatat as far as the Gulf of Oman, is the polyphase-deformed internal zone (Fig. 2). In this zone are two superimposed planar structures, the S_1 schistosity and a cleavage, S_2, which in many places form a single composite structure S_{1-2}. In the centre and east of the internal zone the early schistosity commonly becomes a metamorphic foliation in the metabasites and mica schists derived respectively from dolerite sills and dykes and from acid tuffs, intercalated with the late Permian carbonates. Here the S_1 foliation is folded and cut by a second schistosity or transposed into a strain-slip cleavage (S_2).

Relations between structures

External zone. A sigmoidal cleavage, S_1, develops in association with C(shear)-planes and asymmetrical F_1 folds that deform the stratification. The C-planes make an angle of 15°−30° with the cleavage, and are parallel with the stratification in Unit B and at an angle to stratification in Unit A, owing to the differing attitudes of bedding above and below the angular unconformity that separates the two units. The intersection of the S_1 and C planes (Berthé *et al.* 1979) indicates a constant dextral sense of SW to NE shearing parallel to the L_1 lineation, defined by clasts, pebbles and asymmetrical pressure-shadows extension. The F_1 folds are inclined northeast in the direction of vergence (indicated by the polarity of the folded beds), confirming the sense of shearing inferred from the cleavage/shear plane relationship in the autochthonous pile. There is a clear cleavage-intensity gradient, within similar lithologies, increasing northeastward across the external zone. Along this gradient, in the direction of increasing intensity, F_1 fold axes gradually change their orientation into parallelism with the stretching lineation L_1, and from the front where schistosity appears the two structures are parallel.

Thus the structures in this zone indicate over all SW to NE ductile shearing deformation in the autochthonous pile, parallel to stratification in Autochthonous Unit B.

Internal zone. Subduction-related tectonism in this zone is represented by two main phases of folding, F_1 and F_2, and a late phase of large-scale upwarping, F_3. The abundance and size of the F_1 and F_2 folds increase markedly into the internal zone; with amplitudes of up to ten kilometres or more they are responsible for the main mappable large-scale structures. This is especially the case for the large-scale, asymmetric, overturned to recumbent F_2 folds, with an axial-plane crenulation cleavage to schistosity S_2, that deform the stratification and the schistosity S_1.

Recumbent F_1 folds can still be seen in the long limbs of the F_2 folds. They are tight to isoclinal large folds with an axial-plane foliation (metamorphic banding) that is locally well preserved and is associated with close-spaced, fairly flat-lying C-planes. A mineral and stretching lineation within S_1 trends SW−NE, and is highly oblique or perpendicular to the F_1 fold axes. Thus the north to northeast direction of overturning of the F_1 folds, indicated by the polarity of the deformed beds throughout the internal zone, is also the direction of vergence.

The F_2 folds are overturned or recumbent towards the northeast or east. Their curved and shallowly plunging axes trend N−S to NE−SW, parallel to a new stretching lineation that itself has the same attitude as the earlier lineation, L_1. The S_2 cleavage is commonly associated with closely-spaced, shallowly south- to south-west-dipping C(shear)-planes, whose intersection with the cleavage, observed in outcrop and in oriented thin sections, indicates a dextral SW to NE sense of shearing.

Deformation phases F_1 and F_2 are consistent with a continuum of ductile tangential deformation during which the autochthon was sheared in a SW to NE direction. The same non-coaxial tangential deformation affected both the external and internal zones, but this was expressed in the latter by more intense folding, involving much greater shortening and doubling of the thickness of autochthonous pile. No major tectonic discontinuity was produced between the external and internal zones during this continuous deformation.

Metamorphism related to subduction

Metamorphic zoning

The structures formed during early ductile shearing deformation are marked by recrystallization whose intensity varies with the SW−NE structural gradient. The present mineral associations commonly represent at least two parageneses, the earlier representing the peak of metamorphism and the others being secondary, syn- to post-tectonic assemblages.

On the scale of the Jabal Akhdar and especially the Saih Hatat window, the mineralogy of the metabasic autochthonous rocks enables four metamorphic zones to be distinguished as shown in Table 1 and on Fig. 2:

Zone 1. This is at the lowest metamorphic grade and corresponds almost exactly to the external structural zone. Chlorite, albite and white mica are ubiquitous, but pumpellyite and epidote only appear in Saih Hatat, in places associated with rare blue amphibole (magnesio-riebeckite) or actinolite. Practically pure, poikiloblastic jadeite is known from a single outcrop of Permian meta-trachyandesite (Saiq Fm.) on the west flank of Saih Hatat (Tegyey & Le Métour 1987).

Zone 2. The blueschist (glaucophane) zone covers practically the internal structural zone. Glaucophane (and/or crossite), chlorite, albite and epidote are common. Lawsonite, however, has been seen only in samples of meta-basalt and metasediment of probable Turonian age from Ruwi (Muti Fm.). The degree of recrystallization of quartz-mica, feldspathic and calcareous metasediments increases markedly from the beginning of this zone. The common mica schists show the assemblage phengite−quartz−albite (± biotite, epidote, calcite and sphene). In more micaceous phengite−paragonite−quartz rocks, chloritoid occurs locally in the middle of Zone 2. In calcschists and calcareous metasandstones, carpholite, previously described by Michard (1983) and Ouazzani−Touhami (1986) in the Masqat area, is common as radiating clusters.

Zone 3. This is a zone of glaucophane-almandine blueschist of limited extent on the coast of the Gulf of Oman (Fig. 2a), and is distinguished by the gneissic structure of the amphibolites.

Zone 4. In this zone the association of omphacite and chloromelanite with almandine and glaucophane indicate the glaucophane-eclogite facies (Le Métour *et al.* 1986a).

Mapping of the metamorphic zones shows the importance of the blueschist belt, within which a metamorphic gradient, increasing from southwest to northeast, is parallel to the structural gradient. The high-temperature blueschist facies are characterised by a paucity of lawsonite and an abundance of glaucophane-epidote associations, the latter passing to glaucophane eclogites.

Relationships between metamorphism and deformation

In the external structural zone, relations between deformation and metamorphism are simple. The low-grade metamorphic parageneses here, indicating that Zone 1 is in the pumpellyite/lawsonite−albite−chlorite zone (Miyashiro 1973; Winkler 1974), are synchronous with F_1 folds and S_1 cleavage.

In the internal structural zone, however, the polyphase character of the deformation is reflected in a succession of higher-grade parageneses. The primary parageneses indicate the glaucophane blueschist zone (Zone 2), the glaucophane−almandine zone (Zone 3) and the glaucophane eclogite zone (Zone 4). The primary parageneses are synchronous with the first stage of deformation (S_1/F_1) and mark the end

Table 1. *Mineral assemblage in the metabasites from Saih Hatat area*

	Zone 1	Zone 2	Zone 3	Zone 4
Pumpellyite	———	- - -		
Chlorite	————————————————————			- -
Lawsonite		- - -		
Na amphibole		-- ————————	————	
Ca amphibole	- ----------	----------	- - -	
Na cpx			———————	
Garnet			———————	
Epidote	- ————————————————			
Biotite		- - - - - - - ----------	----------	

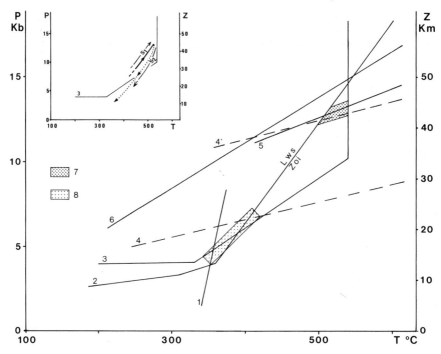

Fig. 3. Pressure — temperature — depth conditions of metamorphism in the Oman Mountains autochthon; estimated P-T-deformation paths of eclogites. 1: lower temperature limit of epidotte + actinote, after Liou *et al.* (1985); 2: stability field of lawsonite, after Nitsch (1972); 3: stability field of glaucophane, after Maresch (1977); 4 and 4': progressive variation of Si^{4+} content in phengite, after Massonne & Schreyer (1987), (4: Si^{4+} = 3.3, 4': Si^{4+} = 3.5); 5: minimal pressure for 50% jadeite content in omphacite, after Holland (1980); 6: reaction jadeite + quartz = albite, after Holland (1980); estimated fields of formation of the glaucophane — eclogite (7), and of transition between greenschist and blueschist (8).

of prograde metamorphism, at least insofar as pressure is concerned. The secondary parageneses are synchronous with or slightly later than the second phase of deformation (S_2/F_2), and indicate blueschist or blue-green schist facies conditions. The late parageneses, commonly poorly developed and static in character, mark post S_2/F_2 retrograde metamorphism in the chlorite–actinolite greenschist facies, probably accompanying uplift and cooling. It was only at the end of this late stage that the upper levels of the autochthon were affected by obduction-related shearing associated with the thrusting of the nappes. The mylonitic cleavage that developed at this stage on either side of the basal contact of the Hawasina Nappes is everywhere a fracture cleavage that may or may not be accompanied by weak recrystallization (Béchennec 1988; Le Métour 1988; Rabu 1988).

Physical conditions of metamorphism

Interpretation of the temperature and pressure conditions of the various stages of metamorphism is made using the stability curves for the main metamorphic minerals and parageneses (Fig. 3). The time parameter on this diagram is controlled by the structural evolution and enables the P−T paths of the glaucophane schists and eclogites to be estimated. K−Ar mineral ages of 80 ± 2 Ma on phengite (Lippard 1983) and 78 ± 5 Ma on glaucophane (Le Métour *et al.* 1986b) are compatible with the regional geological history and approximately calibrate the cooling history of the glaucophane eclogites and almandine−glaucophane schists.

The peak of metamorphism is reasonably established for the glaucophane eclogites at a minimum of 12 kbar and 500°C. The prograde evolution of these rocks is assumed to have taken place in the field of high-temperature blueschists, outside the lawsonite field. Elsewhere the transition from pumpellyite-chlorite schist (Zone 1 without lawsonite) to glaucophane-epidote blueschist (Zone 2 without lawsonite) probably implies a prograde path with a very steep positive slope for the entire blueschist belt (Fig. 3). The convexity of the prograde P−T path towards the high temperature field implies the underthrusting of the autochthonous protolith beneath a hot overload such as oceanic lithosphere. The conditions of crystallization of the eclogites correspond to a marked overloading, with burial to a depth of at least 35−40 km and a low geothermal gradient (12°−15°C/km). Such conditions can only be realized in a subduction setting (Ernst 1971, 1973; Miyashiro 1973). The same convexity of the retrograde path implies rapid uplift and decompression with high thermal inertia, which would account for the preservation of the HP/LT parageneses.

Obduction-related tectonics and the Eo−Alpine orogenesis

Deformation related to the obduction of the Hawasina Nappes (lower allochthonous unit) and the Semail Ophiolite (upper allochthonous unit) has imposed two types of structure on the autochthonous terrains, a mylonitic or crenulation cleavage in which lies a stretching lineation and which is developed only in the upper part of the autochthon, beneath the thrust contact with the overlying Hawasina Nappes, and intra-autochthon imbricates. These two structures are commonly associated with asymmetrical folds that deform S_1 and S_{1-2} with amplitudes up to about 100 m, verging south to southwest in the direction of movement of the nappes.

The obduction-related structures, which were also imprinted upon the Hawasina Nappes during the Campanian or Campanian-lower Maastrichtian (Glennie et al. 1974) have been recognized everywhere around the borders of the Jabal Akhdar and Saih Hatat windows, independently of the structural and metamorphic zoning described above, and are thus clearly unrelated to and later than the structures formed during subduction.

The mylonitic cleavage, developed during overthrusting, is at its most intense in the ultramylonites developed on either side of the thrust contact between the autochthon and the Hawasina Nappes, the intensity decreasing rapidly within a few metres or tens of metres away from the contact. On the regional scale, the mylonitic cleavage represents the effect of the N−S gravitational displacement of the Hawasina Nappes over the autochthon (Béchennec 1988; Béchennec et al. 1988), and occurs all around the periphery of the autochthonous massifs, notably on the southern border of Jabal Akhdar that was not affected by the earlier deformation imposed during subduction.

This cleavage and its associated stretching lineation have often been the main structures to be described in the upper part of the autochthon (e.g. Michard et al. 1984), and the characteristics of this deformation, in particular the southward vergence, mistakenly extended to the whole of the autochthonous pile. This is probably one of the main reasons why the finite deformation of the autochthonous massifs has until recently been attributed to the overthrusting of the Hawasina and Samail nappes.

The intra-autochthonous imbricates, although they are the most striking synobduction structures, do not occur throughout the autochthonous massifs, but are limited to the northern border of Jabal Akhdar and the northern and western borders of Saih Hatat (Fig. 4a). Their abundance and the intensity of the associated deformation increase north−northeastwards in both windows. They affect in particular the Permian−Cretaceous of the autochthon, but, at least locally, penetrate into the pre-Permian along the northern borders of the windows. The internal geometry of the thrust sheets and the basal thrust surfaces have been analyzed, with the following principal results.

(i) Most of the intra-autochthon imbricates correspond to tangential décollements or to initially low- to medium-angle thrusts parallel or at a very low angle to the stratification. Younger rocks are, at least locally, thrust over older, tending to decrease the exposed area of the affected units. The thrust-planes are less steeply inclined than the bedding, at least locally (Fig. 4b).

(ii) Certain imbricates, localised on the northern and western borders of the autochthonous massifs, have incorporated slices of serpentinite torn from the base of the Semail Ophiolite. In these instances the thrust surface is also, at least locally less steeply inclined than the stratification in the autochthon (Fig. 4b). The presence of these slices of serpentinite implies the juxtaposition of the ophiolite and the autochthon, and thus the tectonic thinning and suppression of the Hawasina Nappes during obduction. The basal thrust surface of the nappes upon the autochthon has thus itself been deformed and cut by the intra-autochthonous thrust surfaces. This late feature of the obduction history was responsible for the imbricated slices of autochthon and allochthon seen on the northern border of Jabal Akhdar and on the north and west of Saih Hatat.

These observations on the geometry and chronology of these structures are consistent

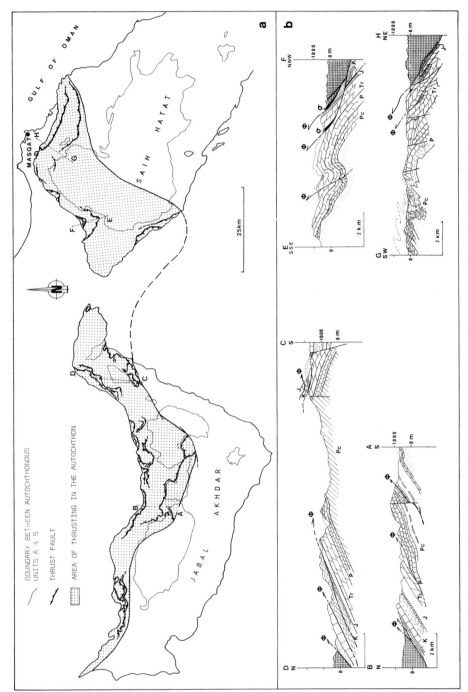

Fig. 4. Obduction tectonics in the Oman Mountains autochthon. a: location map of the intra-autochthonous imbricates b: geological sections of imbricate zones, see location on (a) — same symbols as fig. 2; σ: serpentinite.

with the formation of frontal and lateral ramps produced by anticlinal folding of the autochthon at a late stage during obduction (Fig. 4b). The geographical distribution of the intra-autochthonus imbricates and the kinematics of obduction make it possible to locate these two types of ramp accurately (Fig. 5). The development of these ramps and the associated imbricates indicates a NNE–SSW compressive tectonic régime during the static uplift of the autochthon.

To summarize, obduction tectonics in the Oman Mountains were characterized by two phases of deformation: (i) an early phase of gravity tectonics during which the Hawasina Nappes and part of the Semail Ophiolite were emplaced south–southeastwards onto the autochthon, and (ii) a late phase of compressive tectonism during which the ramps and imbricates were formed in the autochthon. The second of these phases contributed to the slowing down and stopping of Semail obduction.

When the tectonic piling-up of the various units came to an end, a last phase of regional folding deformation completed the construc-

tion of the Eo–Alpine chain of the Oman Mountains. This gave rise to a poorly developed, subvertical fracture cleavage axial planar to broad open folds with amplitudes and wavelengths of several kilometres, whose axes trend N30°–N60°, markedly oblique to the earlier structural directions (Le Métour 1988; Rabu 1988). This latest, compressive tectonic phase acompanied the uplift of the Eo–Alpine chain. Subaerial erosion ensued at once, and during the middle to late Maastrichtian the marine carbonate deposition began that was to cover the Eo–Alpine orogen, at least in the southwestern part of the chain.

Conclusions: geodynamic evolution

In the Late Cretaceous the northeast edge of the Arabian Platform, on the site of the present Oman Mountains, was deformed and metamorphosed in the course of two major tectonic episodes that resulted in the formation of the Eo–Alpine mountain chain. This involved overall NNE–SSW shortening with the closure of the Cenomanian–Turonian submarine horst-

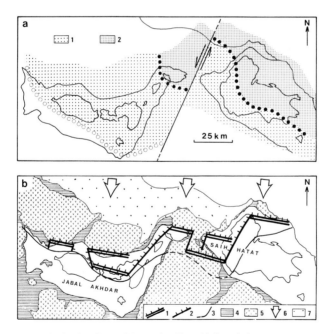

Fig. 5. Superimposed tectonics in the Oman Mountains Eo–Alpine chain.
a: Coniacian to Early Campanian — Structural sketch map of the autochthonous massifs showing, along the Samail Gap fault, the dextral strike slip displacement of the subduction related structural zones (1 — external zone; 2 — internal zone)
b: Campanian — Sketch map of frontal (1) and lateral (2) ramps, developed in the autochthon during obduction — 3: front of thrusting in the autochthon; 4: Hawasina Nappes; 5: Semail Nappe; 6: displacement vector of nappes; 7: post-nappe autochthonous.

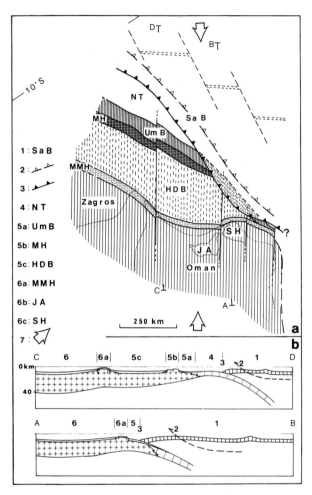

Fig. 6. Geodynamic setting of the southern Neo-Tethyan margin between Oman and the Zagros during the late Turonian–Coniacian.
a: palaeogeographical map — 1: Semail oceanic basin; 2: intra-oceanic detachment; 3: subduction; 4: Neo-Tethys (Triassic to Jurassic); 5: Hawasina Basin; 5a: Umar Basin: 5b: Misfah horst; 5c: Hamrat Duru Basin; 6: Arabian platform and intrashelf Muti Basin; 6a: (Masqat-) Musandam high; 6b: Jabal Akhdar; 6c: Saih Hatat; 7: African — Eurasian plate convergence.
b: Schematic cross-sections illustrating intraoceanic subduction, and continent-ocean subduction (see location on a).

and-trough basin on the Arabian continental margin and of the Semail marginal basin (Fig. 6), and terminated with the piling-up of the allochthonous Hawasina Nappes and Samail Ophiolite on the Oman autochthon.

In the late Turonian–Coniacian (90–86 Ma) the northeast corner of the Oman platform, an integral part of the Arabian continental plate, was loaded to a depth of at least 35–40 km beneath a wedge-shaped slab of Neo-Tethyan oceanic lithosphere, with resulting structural and metamorphic zoning of the autochthonous rocks. No major tectonic discontinuity ap-

peared within the upper part of the continental crust, that was metamorphosed up to the low-temperature eclogite facies ($P > 12$ kb; $500°C < T < 530°C$), and the oceanward vergence of the subduction-related structures is consistent with a dextral shearing couple (SSW to NNE) within continental crust drawn into NNE-directed subduction (Fig. 7).

On a broader scale, the partial subduction of this part of the Arabian plate can be attributed to the intra-oceanic subduction that had been operating in the closing Tethyan ocean-floor since at least the Turonian (Pearce *et al.* 1981;

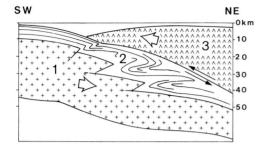

Fig. 7. Schematic cross-section illustrating the kinematics of the subduction-related tectonics in the Oman Mountains autochthon. 1: basement; 2: autochthonous units A and B; 3: Neo-Tethyan lithosphere.

Dercourt *et al.* 1986). The subduction zone was oblique to the Cenomanian–Turonian isopic (i.e. tectonostratigraphic) zones on the Arabian continental margin (Fig. 6).

It was in this geodynamic setting that a wedge of oceanic and thinned Arabian continental lithosphere was drawn into the subduction zone beneath the Neo-Tethyan oceanic lithosphere. From north to south this wedge was composed of fragments of old Arabian oceanic crust (Triassic, Jurassic and Early Cretaceous), up to the northeast corner of the Oman platform (Saih Hatat and the northeast part of Jabal Akhdar; Fig. 6). The subduction of a thinned part of the Arabian continental margin is argued by the presence of crustal biotite granites intrusive into the Samail Ophiolite (Browning & Smewing 1981; Beurrier 1988). The genesis of these magmas by partial fusion of subducted continental crust immediately preceded the intra-oceanic detachment of the Semail Nappe in the rear of the subduction zone that took place at about 90 Ma.

It is probable that the forced introduction of the continental crust into the subduction system provoked its blockage, in the Coniacian–early Campanian (*c.* 88–80 Ma) as far as the underthrust part of the Oman platform was concerned. The arrest of subduction entrained the rapid rise of the metamorphosed autochthon, and its release from the load of Neo-Tethyan oceanic lithosphere, the decompression being marked by the phase of retrograde HP/LT metamorphism at about 80 Ma. Nowhere in the Oman Mountains have the nappes been affected by the HP/LT metamorphism nor by the deformation related to the subduction of the autochthon, so its uplift must have occurred before the thrusting of the Hawasina and Semail nappes onto the former Oman platform. Fur-

thermore the advance of the nappes across the autochthon can be dated, by the sedimentation of nappe debris at their fronts (Juweiza Foration), as having occurred during the late Campanian (Glennie *et al.* 1974).

Thus, the obduction-related deformation that has been imprinted on the Oman Mountains autochthon occurred during the Campanian. This deformation affects equally the structural and metamorphic zones developed during subduction. The zoning has been offset by a sinistral strike-slip fault along the extension of the Semail Gap (Fig. 5a), that may have occurred before or at an early stage of obduction. During the SSW gravitational transport of the nappes, mylonitic deformation affected the upper few tens of metres of autochthon. This was followed by the development of SSW-verging intra-autochthon imbricates over the frontal and lateral ramps formed by the folding of the autochthon. The ramps and associated overthrusting contributed to the slowing down and stopping of obduction at about the time of the passage from the Campanian to the Maastrichtian.

During the early Maastrichtian a last phase of compressive folding deformation when they were being uplifted and subjected to erosion completed the series of deformations that formed the Eo–Alpine chain of the Oman Mountains.

The Oman Mountains constitute a favoured part of the Alpine mountain system in which the record of the polyphase Eo–Alpine (Turonian–Maastrichtian) tectonometamorphic history has been perfectly preserved. It is possible here to follow in detail the geodynamic evolution, through about 20 Ma, of a platform-continental margin-ocean transect during the closure of the eastern Neo-Tethys. Subduction, with ocean-ocean and continent–ocean convergence, followed by the obduction of a large fragment of young oceanic lithosphere were the two main stages in the Eo–Alpine tectogenesis. The features of each stage are preserved and can still be seen in the Oman Mountains due to their situation away from the Zagros–Himalaya zones of continental collision.

This paper has been written in the framework of the Bureau de Recherches Géologiques et Minières' programme for mapping in Oman. We would like to express our gratitude to Mr. Mohammed H. Kassim, Director, Directorate General of Minerals, Oman Ministry of Petroleum and Minerals, for his warm reception and the constant help throughout the mapping project. John Kemp, Service Géologique National, France, translated the text.

References

ALLEMANN, F. & PETERS, T. 1972. The ophiolite-radiolarite belt of the Northern Oman Mountains. *Eclogae geologicae Helvetiae*, **65**, 657–697.

BECHENNEC, F. 1988. Géologie des Nappes Hawasina dans les parties orientale et centrale des Montagnes d'Oman. *Documents du Bureau de Recherches Géologiques et Minières*, Orléans, **127**.

——, BEURRIER, M., RABU, D. & HUTIN, G. 1986a. Geological map of Barka. Sheet NF 40–3B. Scale 1:100 000. Explanatory Notes. *Directorate General of Minerals, Oman Ministry of Petroleum and Minerals*.

——, ——, —— & —— 1986b. Geological map of Bahla. Sheet NF 40–7A. Scale 1:100000. Explanatory Notes. *Directorate General of Minerals, Oman Ministry of Petroleum and Minerals*.

——, LE METOUR, J., RABU, D., VILLEY, M. & BEURRIER, M. 1988. The Hawasina Basin: a fragment of starved passive continental margin thrust over the Arabian Platform during obduction of the Sumail Nappe. *Tectonophysics*, **151**, 323–343.

BERTHE, D., CHOUKROUNE, P. & JEGOUZO, P. 1979. Orthogneiss, mylonite and non coaxial deformation of granites: the example of the South Armorican shear zone. *Journal of Structural Geology*, **1**, 31–42.

BEURRIER, M. 1988. Géologie de la Nappe Orthogneiss, mylonite and non coaxial deforet centrale des Montagnes d'Oman. *Documents du Bureau de Recherches Géologiques et Minières*, Orléans, **128**.

——, BECHENNEC, F., RABU, D., & HUTIN, G. 1986a. Geological map of Rustaq. Sheet NF 40–3D. Scale 1:100000. Explanatory Notes. *Directorate General Of Minerals, Oman Ministry of Petroleum and Minerals*.

——, ——, & —— 1986b. Geological map of As Suwayq. Sheet NF 40–3A. Scale 1:100000. Explanatory Notes. *Directorate General of Minerals, Oman Ministry of Petroleum and Minerals*.

BOUDIER, F. & MICHARD, A. 1981. Oman ophiolites. The quiet obduction of oceanic crust. *Terra cognita*, **1**, 109–118.

BROWNING, P. & SMEWING, J. D. 1981. Processes in magma chambers beneath spreading axes: evidence for magmatic associations in the Oman Ophiolite. *Journal of the Geological Society of London*, **138**, 279–280.

COLEMAN, R. G. 1981. Tectonic setting for ophiolite obduction in Oman. *Journal of Geophysical Research*, **86**, 2497–2508.

DERCOURT, J., ZONENSHAIN, L. P., RICOU, L. E., KAZMIN, V. G., LE PICHON, X., KNIPPER, A. L., GRANDJACQUET, C., SBORTSHIKOV, I. M., GEYSSANT, J., LEPVRIER, C., PECHERSKY, D. H., BOULIN, J., SIBUET, J. C., SAVOSTIN, L. A., SOROKHTIN, O., WESTPHAL, M., BAZHENOV, M. L., LAUER, J. P. & BIJU-DUVAL, B. 1986. Geological evolution of the Tethys belt from the Atlantic to the Pamirs since the Lias. *Tectono-physics*, **123**, 241–315.

ERNST, W. G. 1971. Metamorphic zonations on presumably subducted lithospheric plates from Japan, California and the Alps. *Contributions to Mineralogy and Petrology*, **34**, 43–59.

—— 1973. Blueschist metamorphism and P–T regimes in active subduction zones. *Tectonophysics*, **17**, 255–272.

GLENNIE, K. W. 1977. Outline of the geology of Oman. *Mémoires hors série Société Géologique de France*, **8**, 25–31.

——, BOEUF, M. G. A., HUGHES CLARKE, M. W., MOODY-STUART, M., PILAAR, W. F. H. & REINHARDT, B. M. 1973. Late Cretaceous nappes in the Oman Mountains and their geologic evolution. *Bulletin of the American Association of Petroleum Geologists*, **57**, 5–27.

——, ——, ——, ——, & —— 1974. Geology of the Oman Mountains. *Verhandelingen van het Koninklijk Nederlands geologisch Mijnbouwkundig Genootschap*. **31**, Part 1 (text), 423 pp., Part 2 (illustrations), part 3 (enclosures).

GRAHAM, G. M. 1980. Evolution of a passive margin and nappe emplacement in the Oman mountains. *In*: PANAYIOTOU, A. (ed.) *Ophiolites*, Proceedings of the International Ophiolite Symposium, Cyprus 1979, 414–423.

GRAMONT de, X., LE METOUR, J. & VILLEY, M. 1986. Geological map of Samad. Sheet NF 40–7C. Scale 1:100000. Explanatory notes. *Directorate General of Minerals, Oman Ministry of Petroleum and Minerals*.

HANNA, S. S. 1986. The Alpine (Late Cretaceous and Tertiary) tectonic evolution of the Oman mountains: A thrust tectonic approach. *Symposium on the hydrocarbon potential of intense thrust zones*, published OAPEC, Kuwait, 2, 125–174.

HOLLAND, T. J. B. 1980. The reaction albite = jadeite + quartz determined experimentally in the range 600–1200°C. *American Mineralogist*, **65**, 129–134.

HUTIN, G., BECHENNEC, F., BEURRIER, M. & RABU, D. 1986. Geological map of Birkat al Mawz. Sheet NF 40–7B. Scale 1:100000. Explanatory notes. *Directorate General of Minerals, Oman Ministry of Petroleum and Minerals*.

JANJOU, D., MINOUX, L., LE METOUR, J., VILLEY, M. GRAMONT de, X. 1986. Geological map of Ibri. Sheet NF 40–2F. Scale 1:100000. Explanatory notes. *Directorate General of Minerals, Oman Ministry of Petroleum and Minerals*.

LEES, G. M. 1928. The geology and tectonics of Oman and of parts of South Eastern Arabia. *Quarterly Journal of the Geological Society of London*, 585–670.

LE METOUR, J. 1988. Géologie de l'Autochtone des Montagnes d'Oman: la fenêtre du Saih Hatat. *Documents du Bureau de Recherches Géologiques et Minières*, Orléans, **129**.

——, RABU, D., TEGYEY, M., BECHENNEC, M., BEURRIER, M. & VILLEY, M. 1986a. Le métamorphisme régional crétacé de faciès éclogites — schistes bleus sur la bordure omanaise de la plate-forme arabe: conséquences d'une tectogenèse précoce anté-obduction. *C.R. Acad. Sci. Paris*, **302**, 905−910.

——, VILLEY, M. & GRAMONT de, X. 1986b. Geological map of Quryat. Sheet NF 40−4D. Scale 1:100 000. Explanatory notes. *Directorate General of Minerals, Oman Ministry of Petroleum and Minerals.*

——, ——, —— & BEURRIER, M. 1986c. Geological map of Masqat. Sheet NF 40−4A. Scale 1:100 000. Explanatory notes. *Directorate General of Minerals, Oman Ministry of Petroleum and Minerals.*

LIOU, J. G., MARUYAMA, S. & CHO, M. 1985. Phase equilibria and mineral paragenesis of metabasites in low-grade metamorphism. *Mineralogical Magazine*, **49**, 321−332.

LIPPARD, S. J. 1983. Cretaceous high pressure metamorphism in NE Oman and its relationship to subduction and ophiolite nappe emplacement. *Journal of the Geological Society of London*, **140**, 97−104.

——, SHELTON, A. W. & GASS, I. G. 1986. The Ophiolite of Northern Oman. *Geological Society of London Memoir*, **11**.

MARESCH, W. V. 1977. Experimental studies on glaucophane: an analysis of present knowledge. *Tectonophysics*, **43**, 109−125.

MASSONNE, H. J. & SCHREYER, W. 1987. Phengite geobarometry based on the limiting assemblage with K-feldspar, phlogopite, and quartz. *Contributions to Mineralogy and Petrology*, **96**, 212−224.

MICHARD, A. 1982. Contribution à la connaissance de la marge nord du Gondwana: une chaîne plissée paléozoïque, vraisemblablement hercynienne en Oman. *C.R. Acad. Sci., Paris*, **295**, 1031−1036.

—— 1983. Les nappes de Mascate (Oman), rampe épi-continentale d'obduction à faciès schiste bleu et la dualité apparente des ophiolites omanaises. *Sciences Géologiques Bulletin, Strasbourg*, **36**, 3−16.

——, BOUCHEZ, J. L. & OUAZZANI-TOUHAMI, M. 1984. Obduction-related planar and linear fabrics in Oman. *Journal of Structural Geology* **6**, 39−49.

MIYASHIRO, A. 1973. *Metamorphism and metamorphic belts*. George Allen & Unwin, London.

NITSCH, K. H. 1972. Das P-T-XCO2 stabilitätsfeld von Lawsonite. *Contributions to Mineralogy and*

Petrology, **34**, 116−134.

OUAZZANI-TOUHAMI, M. 1986. *Structures et recristallisations associées dans les zones de cisaillement: Nappes de Mascate (Oman) et Nappes de Federico s.1. (Rif interne, Maroc)* PhD Thesis Louis Pasteur University, Strasbourg, France.

PATRIAT, P., SEGOUFIN, J., SCHLICH, R., GOSLIN, J., AUZENDE, J. M., BEUZART, P., BONNIN, J. & OLIVET, J. L. 1982. Les mouvements relatifs de l'Inde, de l'Afrique et de l'Eurasie. *Bulletin Société Géologique de France*, 363−373.

RABU, D. 1988. Géologie de l'Autochtone des Montagnes d'Oman: la fenêtre du jabal Akhdar. La semelle métamorphique de la Nappe ophiolitique de Samail dans les parties orientale et centrale des Montagnes d'Oman: une revue. *Documents du Bureau de Recherches Géologiques et Minières*, Orléans **130**.

——, BECHENNEC, F., BEURRIER, M. & HUTIN, G. 1986. Geological map of Nakhl. Sheet NF 40−3E. Scale 1:100 000. Explanatory Notes. *Directorate General of Minerals, Oman Ministry of Petroleum and Minerals.*

SEARLE, M. P. 1985. Sequence of thrusting and origins of culminations in the Northern and Central Oman mountains. *Journal of Structural Geology*, **7**, 129−143.

TEGYEY, M. & LE METOUR, J. 1987. Mise en évidence de jadéite dans un basalte à augite primaire préservée. Permian autochtone du Saih Hatat, Oman. *Bulletin de Minéralogie supplément*, **110**, 27 (Abstr.)

VILLEY, M., BECHENNEC, F., BEURRIER, M., LE METOUR, J. & RABU, D. 1986a. Geological map of Yanqul. Sheet NF 40−2C. Scale 1:100 000. Explanatory notes. *Directorate General of Minerals, Oman Ministry of Petroleum and Minerals.*

——, LE METOUR, J. & GRAMONT de, X. 1986b. Geological map of Fanjah. Sheet NF 40−3F. Scale 1:100 000. Explanatory notes. *Directorate General of Minerals, Oman Ministry of Petroleum and Minerals.*

——, —— & —— 1986c. Geological map of Sib. Sheet NF 40−3C. Scale 1/100 000. Explanatory notes. *Directorate General of Minerals, Oman Ministry of Petroleum and Minerals.*

WINCKLER, H. G. F. 1974. *Petrogenesis of metamorphic rocks*. 4th edn, Springer Berlin.

The Alpine deformation of the Central Oman Mountains

SAMIR S. HANNA

*Earth Resources Institute, Dept of Earth Sciences, University College,
Swansea SA2 8PP, UK Present address: Department of Earth Sciences,
College of Science, Sultan Qaboos University, P.B. No. 32486, Al-khod,
Sultanate of Oman*

Abstract: The Saih Hatat, Jebel Nakhl, Jebel Akhdar and the Hawasina Window structures of the Oman Mountains developed as culminations above a major sole thrust associated with late stage emplacement of the ophiolite from the northeast onto the Arabian margin. The outcrop of a pre-Permian sequence in the cores of Jebel Akhdar, Jebel Nakhl and Saih Hatat implies that the major sole thrust is located within the pre-Permian succession. This thrust is emergent in the southern foothills of the mountains south of the Jebel Salakh Range. In the Hawasina Window, however, the thrust is at a higher level and is located within the slope and oceanic sediments. An extensional regime due to the gravity sliding of the Semail ophiolite is recognized from the occurrence of surge zones, extensional duplexes, extensional cleavage and gravity folds. The development of the extensional faults, which occur in the frontal, dorsal, lateral and oblique walls of the above culminations, may account for the absence and locally thinning of the Tethyan thrust sheets around the flanks of these structures. The extensional tectonic regime is also believed to be responsible for the final extensional nature of the 'Semail Thrust'. The Oman Mountains foreland fold and thrust belt mostly consists of a series of thrust sheets of oceanic sediments (Hawasina) together with widespread exposures of syn-tectonic (Aruma) deposits. The belt is dominated by imbricate stacks of both Hawasina and Aruma units. These imbricate stacks have been folded around major culminations arranged in a characteristic *en echelon* pattern. Late Alpine (Tertiary) deformation is largely attributed to an extensional regime of culmination collapse. Folds and thrusts were developed at the leading edge of the extensional faults (surge zones). Tertiary folding and thrusting may reactivate the pre-existing Early Alpine (Late Cretaceous) structures.

The Oman Mountains represent part of the major Himalayan–Alpine chain. The Oman Mountains are located in the southeast part of the Arabian peninsula and form an arcuate belt parallel to the Gulf of Oman. The mountains extend for approximately 700 km N–S and have a width varying from 30 to 130 km with a topographic relief up to 3 km. This paper is concerned with the central region between the Hawasina Window in the north and Saih Hatat in the south (Fig. 1).

The Central Oman Mountains are divided into an internal zone, comprising Saih Hatat, Jebel Akhdar, Jebel Nakhl and the Hawasina Window, and an external zone, comprising the foreland fold and thrust belt and undeformed foreland (Fig. 1).

The major structural domains of the internal zone consist of the Jebel Akhdar, Jebel Nakhl and Saih Hatat domes, exposing the entire shelf succession with pre-Permian basement below and the thrust sheets above, dipping symmetrically off their flanks. In addition the Hawasina Window forms another major structure; here the upper thrust sheets dip symmetrically off a core of the lower Hawasina and Sumeini Group sediments.

Glennie *et al.* (1974) interpreted these major structures as a result of Tertiary compressional events (Oligocene to Early Miocene). In the external zone some of the domal structures (Madar structure) are attributed to diapiric salt tectonics (Glennie *et al.* 1974). The Tertiary compressional interpretation of the internal zone was later adopted by many authors, e.g. Glennie (1977), Graham (1980) and Searle (1980, 1985). However, in these various studies the role of deep-seated thrusting on the continental margin at the time of ophiolite emplacement has not been considered as an alternative mechanism for creating the major structures.

This paper is an attempt to reconcile the evolution of the mountains during the Early Alpine (Late Cretaceous) in terms of thrust tectonics involving deep thrusts. It also documents an extensional regime which is related to collapse or gravity structures.

From ROBERTSON, A. H. F., SEARLE, M. P. & RIES, A. C. (eds), 1990,
The Geology and Tectonics of the Oman Region.
Geological Society Special Publication No 49, pp 341–359

341

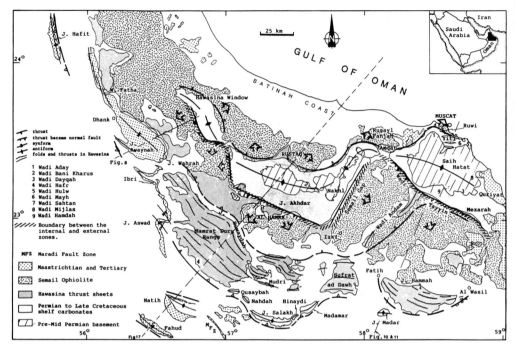

Fig. 1. Modified geological map of the Oman Mountains from Glennie *et al.* (1974), showing the boundary between the internal and external zones, ramp configuration and the location of postulated thrusts. Arrows indicate the slip direction of the ophiolite and the development of the culmination collapse structures (see the section about Late Alpine deformation for details).

Geological background

During the Middle Permian to Middle Cretaceous, SE Arabia developed as a carbonate shelf on the southern passive continental margin of the Tethyan ocean, a remnant of which now constitutes the Gulf of Oman. The shelf sequences were deposited unconformably upon pre-Permian sediments. A NE-dipping subduction zone is thought to have developed in the Tethyan ocean during the Late Cretaceous (Pearce *et al.* 1981). The Arabian plate moved progressively towards this northeasterly dipping subduction zone as Tethyan oceanic crust was consumed beneath it. Obduction of a slab of the Tethyan oceanic lithosphere (Semail Ophiolite) onto the continental margin took place above this subduction zone (Graham 1980; Coleman 1981; Lippard & Rex 1982). A syn-tectonic foreland basin developed during this emplacement event into which sediments of the Aruma Group were deposited (Glennie *et al.* 1974). Synchronous with the development of this basin was erosion of parts of the advancing Hawasina thrust sheets, the continental slope sediments and also parts of the Arabian shelf carbonates (Coleman 1981; Lippard & Rex 1982; Robertson 1987).

Outcrops of the Maastrichtian and lower Tertiary cover rocks unconformably overlie earlier structures of the internal zone. These rocks were deposited after the tectonic emplacement of the Semail ophiolite and Hawasina sediments and were folded by Middle to Late Tertiary (Late Alpine) events. The different tectonostratigraphic units which are exposed in the mountains are shown in Fig. 2 and the tectonic history of the Oman Mountains from Late Palaeozoic to Recent is summarized in Table 1.

The Oman Mountains thrust belt

The Internal Zone

Saih Hatat. The Saih Hatat occupies an area of approximately 3250 km; it extends from the northern coastline near Muscat to Wadi Tayyin in the south, and from Amqat in the West to the coastline around Quriyat in the east (Fig. 1).

In general it is a major, box-shaped, dome-like structure exposing the entire tectonostratigraphic sequence of the Oman Mountains

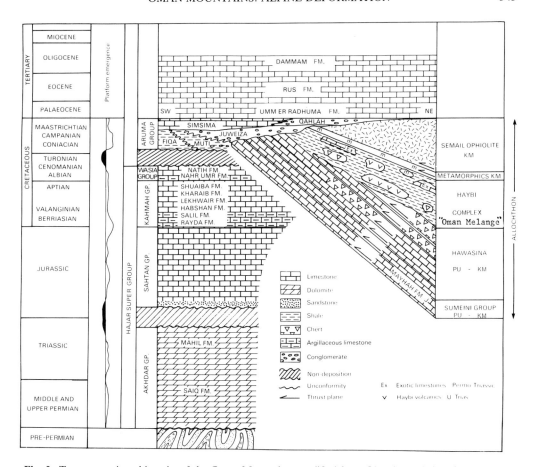

Fig. 2. Tectonostratigraphic units of the Oman Mountains, modified from Glennie *et al.* (1974).

from pre-Permian basement, shelf carbonates, Hawasina and Oman melange, and ophiolite to the unformably overlying Maastrichtian and Tertiary carbonate sequences.

The unconformity separating the Permian and Mesozoic shelf carbonates from the pre-Permian schists locally shows evidence of being a detachment horizon. Along the Wadi Aday section, the Permian shelf carbonates are folded immediately above the unconformity plane along north–south fold hinges. Small-scale thrusts, striking approximately north–south, represent lateral ramps and can be seen branching off the unconformity surface. A similar feature is also visible where Wadi Aday opens into the Saih Hatat bowl. However, Le Metour *et al.* (1986) argued that the schists beneath this unconformity plane belong to a Permian volcano–sedimentary sequence.

In the northwestern side of Wadi Aday a spectacular footwall syncline underneath a back thrust emplaced pre-Permian schists on top of the Permian Saiq Formation. The syncline verges northwards and an overturned southern limb displays overturned out-of-the syncline thrusts (Fig. 3).

A large northward-verging back fold occurs to the east of Wadi Mayh and can be mapped for a considerable distance along the Quriyat road. The fold has an overturned northern limb indicated by bedding–cleavage relationships and by asymmetrical parasitic folds. East of Wadi Mayh, along Wadi Hulw, back-thrusting and back-folding are the dominant structural features of the pre-Permian sequences.

Wadi Mayh, north of Saih Hatat, displays the most complex structures seen in the internal zone of the Oman Mountains. It is a major basement cover duplex in the sense of Boyer & Elliott (1982). It also shows imbrication between the pre-Permian sequence and the Mesozoic shelf carbonates (see Mann & Hanna 1990).

Table 1. *Tectonic history of the Central and Northern Oman Mountains from late Palaeozoic to recent.*

CHRONOSTRAT.				TECTONOSTRAT.			TECTONIC EVENTS
QUATERNARY			PLEISTOCENE AND RECENT	NEOTECTONICS			Uplift
CENOZOIC	TERTIARY	PALAEOGENE | NEOGENE	Pliocene				
			Miocene				———— U ————
			Oligocene		LATE		Thrust tectonics in the *N*
			Eocene				Extensional and gravity tectonics (culmination collapse) in Central Oman
			Palaeocene	ALPINE			
MESOZOIC	CRETACEOUS	LATE	Maas.		EARLY		Ophiolite obduction and thrust tectonics
			Camp.				
			Sant.				Platform edge uplifted and eroded followed by regional drowning ———— U ————
			Coni.				
			Tur.				
			Cen.				
		EARLY					Rifting and extension associated with the development of the passive margin
	JURASSIC						
	TRIASSIC						
PALAEOZOIC	PERMIAN						———— U ————
							Denudation of mountain belt
	CARBONIFEROUS			HERCYNIAN			Metamorphism

Some stratigraphic information from J. D. Smewing, S. C. Nolan, M. Simmons and A. H. F. Robertson (pers. comms.).

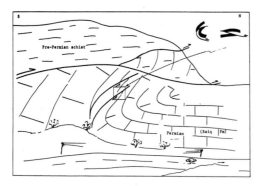

Fig. 3. Back thrust involving the pre-Permian schists and the Permian Saiq Formation, Wadi Aday, Saih Hatat note the overturned out of the syncline thrusts (traced from photograph).

Around the flanks of Saih Hatat, four major structural features are recognized as follows.

(i) *Late cleavage*. To the NE of Yiti (23° 32 N, 58° 41E), and within a highly deformed carbonate mylonite (possibly Muti Formation), bedding and cleavage dip to the north, and bedding dips steeper than cleavage. Here, bedding is the right way up. The cleavage is a later event postdating the development of the Saih Hatat structure. This feature is widely spread along the limbs of the Saih Hatat Structure.

(ii) *Gravity folds*. Around the flanks of the Saih Hatat structure, and on the coastline northeast of Yiti, a series of gravity folds can be seen affecting highly deformed rocks of the Muti Formation. They are verging away from the centre of the structure. These folds clearly have an opposite sense of vergence from the expected parasitic folds associated with the major anticline. Locally, they may be dislocated, forming

E expected parasitic folds

o observed

→ verging direction

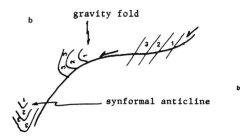

Fig. 4.(a) Schematic illustration of observed gravity folds on the flanks of Saih Hatat, Nakhl, Akhdar structures showing an opposed sense to that of the expected parasitic folds. **(b)** Gravity folds locally may be dislocated to form a synformal anticline structure.

synformal anticline structures (Fig. 4). Another example of folds which verge away from the centre of the Saih Hatat dome is in Wadi Nujum on the western flank. They form the frontal end of a surge zone in the sense of Coward (1982). The frontal end of the surge zone (thrust) has, in places brought the Jurassic rocks (lower structural unit) on top of the Oman melange or the Haybi Complex (higher structural unit) reversing the stacking order of the thrust sequence. Extension occurs at the rear of the thrusts and this balances the thrust displacement. Another example of a major gravity fold can be seen west of Ruwi where a slice of the shelf carbonate occurs on top of a schist sequence (possibly metamorphosed Muti Fm or Ruwi schists). The fold closes towards the north and interpreted as a gravity fold representing the front of a surge zone of the north Saih Hatat culmination (Fig. 5). These later gravity structures have folded rocks with an early schistosity associated with lawsonite and carpholite assemblages

(Michard 1983; Le Metour *et al.* 1986) which may had been formed during the emplacement event. Serpentine is locally injected along these early thrust faults.

(iii) Extensional faults. A series of extensional faults forming extensional duplexes can be seen on the western side of the Saih Hatat structure. Again, the sense of down-fault movement is away from the centre of the Saih Hatat structure. A series of small-scale listric normal faults occurs on the southern side of Saih Hatat and can also be seen near the top of the Mesozoic succession along Wadi Tayyin.

The normal complete tectonostratigraphic sequence is not seen around the flanks of Saih Hatat. The ophiolite is often in direct contact with the Triassic dolomites (Mahil Formation) along its northern flank (around Muscat), and is adjacent to Jurassic rocks on the western flank around Bowsher. In both localities the whole Sumeini, Hawasina and Oman melange (Haybi Complex) thrust sheets are missing. This is because of a large-scale normal fault on the north of Saih Hatat. On the southern flank of the structure, along Wadi Tayyin, the Oman melange thrust sheet and Hamrat Duru Group are partly exposed in their normal tectonostratigraphic position. However, they lie in direct contact with the Mesozoic shelf carbonates. Here, the whole Sumeini–Hawasina thrust sheets are also absent. However, in Wadi Andam these rocks are well exposed indicating that they occur underneath the ophiolite in the down-faulted hangingwall block of these extensional faults (see Fig. 1).

(iv) Back thrusting. There is a major backthrust bounding the southern side of Saih Hatat, located near the top of the shelf carbonates. The roof sequence of this thrust includes part of the Hawasina, Oman melange and the ophiolite. The underlying shelf carbonate sequence has also been affected by the back thrust and a series of layer-parallel thrusts and associated recumbent folds occur and can be seen within this sequence along Wadi Dayqah. This northwards overthrusting event extends along much of the boundary between the internal and external zones of Oman from the Saih Hatat in the south to the Hawasina Window in the north.

Tertiary relationships in Saih Hatat. A blanket of Tertiary rocks lies unconformably upon the highly folded and imbricated shelf carbonates around Saih Hatat. Their outcrop is limited to the north and southeast margins of the structure.

On the southeast flank of Saih Hatat struc-

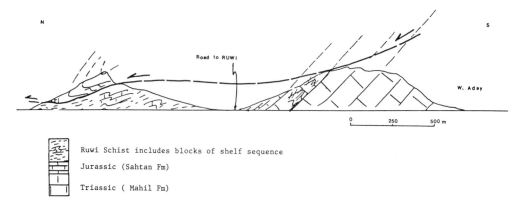

Ruwi Schist includes blocks of shelf sequence

Jurassic (Sahtan Fm)

Triassic (Mahil Fm)

Fig. 5. NS cross section showing the shelf carbonate sequence that overlies the Ruwi schist as a result of a large surge zone, thus inverting the normal tectonostratigraphic order. Ruwi area.

ture, erosion has cut through flat-lying Tertiary rocks and has exposed an intensely folded and imbricated sequence of Mesozoic shelf carbonates below. Some of these folds are isoclinal (e.g. northeast of Mezarah). Similar situations are also seen in Wadi Mijlas and Wadi Dayqah where the base Tertiary unconformity sharply truncates the folded and intensely imbricated Mesozoic shelf. North of Wadi Mayh another example of the onlap of the Tertiary cover onto the intensely imbricated sequences of the Mesozoic carbonates is seen. This relationship constrains the Early Alpine (Late Cretaceous) age of deformation in Saih Hatat.

Nevertheless, folding of the Lower Tertiary sequences does occur, e.g. around Rusayl where folding is represented by NNE–SSW steeply plunging folds. The trend of these Tertiary folds strikes perpendicular to the dip slope of Saih Hatat but plunges in the same direction as the dip slope, i.e. NNE. Around Ruwi, a steep plunging, almost neutral series of folds can also be seen plunging away from the west flank of the Saih Hatat structure.

However, around Mezarah area, a flat-lying sequence previously mapped as Tertiary is believed to be either very Late Tertiary or even Quaternary. This indicates that elevation of the Saih Hatat structure was partly at a late stage and may be still continuing.

Jebel Akhdar. The Jebel Akhdar structure is a massive (85 × 30 × 3 km) box-shaped anticline exposing the shelf carbonates above pre-Permian sediments in the core. The pre-Permian has been slightly affected by Hercynian metamorphism (Glennie *et al.* 1974). The intense imbrication described in Saih Hatat is less apparent here. However, evidence of thrusting within the shelf carbonates is represented by

imbrication and duplex structures occurring in the western side in the mouth of Wadi Sahtan, north side of Jebel Akhdar. The subsidiary faults of this duplex indicate a movement direction towards the SSW.

The Mesozoic shelf carbonates are overlain directly either by the ophiolite, Oman melange, Hamrat Duru units or by thin syn-tectonic sediments of the Muti Formation. A series of extensional faults affecting the Kahmah Group can be seen along Wadi Ghul. An extensional duplex occurs above the previously described compressional duplex in Wadi Sahtan. In Wadi Beni Kharus a major extensional fault juxtaposes the Jurassic Sahtan Formation with the Permian Saiq Formation. The Triassic dolomite of Mahil Formation is completely missing (Fig. 6). This extensional fault was interpreted as a thrust by Rabu *et al.* (1986). It is obvious that the fault cuts down section becoming layer parallel (see Fig. 6) As in Saih Hatat, much of the sequence sandwiched between the ophiolite and shelf carbonates is missing from both sides of the Jebel Akhdar structure. The thickest Hawasina sequence is exposed around the Izki area. However, Hawasina sequences are exposed again further south in the external zone (Fig. 1).

Jebel Nakhl and the Semail Gap. Jebel Nakhl (a massive flat-topped anticline) and the Semail Gap are pronounced NE–SW features that run parallel to the lineaments across Jebel Akhdar near Rustaq in the north and Al Hamra in the south, and along Wadi Andam south of Saih Hatat. This structural trend changes to NW–SE in the northern half of the central Oman Mountains, e.g. SE Hawasina Window, Jebel Buwaydah and N Hamrat Duru range.

In the Fanjah area a series of gravity folds

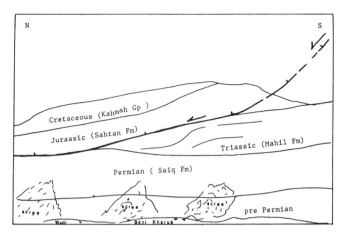

Fig. 6. Thinning of the Triassic Mahil Formation by a major extensional fault cut down section from Cretaceous to Permian to become layer parallel; Wadi Bani Kharus, J. Akhdar.

occurs verging away from the centre of the east–west nose of N Jebel Nakhl. In the north-westerly concave part of Jebel Nakhl, close to its junction with Jebel Akhdar, a series of comp-lementary faults occurs. In the southern part of the Semail Gap around Izki, there is a massive ESE verging gravity fold plunging steeply in a SSW direction. This fold can be seen from the main road before approaching Izki–Nizwa turn. On the eastern side of Jebel Nakhl (Semail Gap) it is believed that a major normal fault (lateral culmination collapse structure) may again be responsible for the absence of most of the Hawasina thrust sheets. There is a close juxtaposition of the ophiolite and Mesozoic shelf carbonates along the eastern flank of Jebel Nakhl.

The Hawasina Window. The Hawasina Window is a tectonic duplex window in the north part of the Central Oman Mountains (Fig. 1), exposing an intensely imbricated and folded sequence of Hawasina sediments beneath a cover of the upper Hawasina thrust sheets and Semail ophiolite. The window was initially mapped by Glennie *et al.* (1974) and later by Graham (1980) and Searle & Cooper (1986). The most relevant point here is that the core of the Hawasina Window includes a structurally thick sequence of Hawasina sediments compared with the pre-Permian exposed in the cores of Saih Hatat, Jebel Nakhl and Jebel Akhdar (Fig. 1). Sumeini Group rocks crop out forming several culmination structures in the window.

On the NE side of the Hawasina Window the dominant feature is the occurence of NNE verg-ing back folds affecting the Sumeini, Hawasina and ophiolite sequences (Graham 1980; Searle

& Cooper 1986). The pillow lavas of the Haybi Complex are inverted, younging north and dip-ping steeply southwards (Graham 1980). Similar structures were later described by Searle & Cooper (1986). This back fold structure may equate with the back fold and back thrust struc-tures described north of Saih Hatat.

The External Zone

The external zone of the Oman Mountains thrust belt (Fig. 1) comprises the Jebel Salakh Range, the Hawasina foreland fold and thrust belts and the overlying Maastrichtian and Tertiary.

Jabel Salakh Range. The uppermost Mesozoic shelf carbonate sequence of Cenomanian to an early Turonian age is exposed in five periclines arranged in a curvilinear form concave towards the north (Fig. 1). The trend of these periclines is approximately parallel to that of Saih Hatat, Jebel Nakhl, Jebel Akhdar and the Hawasina Window anticlinal and domal culminations and also to the distribution of the Hawasina fold and thrust belt.

The dip of their southern flanks is usually steeper than the northern limbs, particularly in Jebels Salakh, Hinaydi and Madamar, where they are locally overturned. The flanks of these structures are overlain by syntectonic sediments of the Aruma Group. Emergent thrusts can be seen in the southern flank of some of these structures, e.g. the Jebel Madamar and Jebel Salakh structures. The shelf carbonates in the latter are seen thrust southwards over the syn-tectonic Aruma shales. The thrust plane dips steeply towards the north. This thrust is believed to be arcuate and comprises frontal ramps be-

neath Jebel Salakh, Madamar and Qusaybah
and oblique to lateral ramps beneath Jebels
Hinaydi and Nahdah. Footwall synclines south
of these structures often display out-of-syncline
thrusts (Fig. 1).

The Hawasina foreland fold and thrust belt. This
belt extends some 240 km along much of the
external zone of the Oman mountains from
Jebel Hammah in the southeast to Jebel Wahrah
near Ibri in the northwest. It also includes
Hawasina sediments northeast of Wahiba Sands
outside the map area and in the Jebel Sumeini
area in the north. The width of the belt varies
from 7.5 km in the east to approximately 45 km
in the Hamrat Duru range. The belt exposes the
entire sequence of Hawasina tectonostratigraphic units.

The Hawasina sequence has been repeated
numerous times by thrusting and folding and in
places stratigraphic units of approximately 200
m thicknesses have a structural thickness of
several kilometres, covering an area of 10 or 20
km wide, e.g. the Wahrah Formation in Jebel
Wahrah and Jebel Hammah respectively.

A standard imbricate stack usually comprises
more distal units tectonically overlying more
proximal ones, e.g. Al Ayn on top of Wahrah
and Wahrah on top of the Hamrat Duru Group
However, vertical and lateral changes may com-
plicate this standard simple stacking order. For
example some formations may disappear laterally, e.g. Wahrah, so that the Al Ayn lies on
top of the Hamrat Duru. In other areas new
formations may appear, e.g. the Ibra Formation
(lateral equivalent to Al Arid). This may also
result in a change in the arrangement of individual units within an imbricate stack.

A reversal of the standard stacking order is
represented by the occurrence of more proximal
units on top of more distal ones, e.g. the Hamrat
Duru Group above the Wahran Formation in
the Sufrat ad Dawh area (Glennie *et al.* 1974).

The Hawasina sediments structurally overlie
the Coniacian to Campanian Muti Formation
and its time equivalent facies with a tectonic
(thrust) contact (Glennie *et al.* 1974). However,
in the Hamrat Duru range the Aruma sediments
locally overlie Hawasina sequence and therefore
breach the already stacked thrust sheets. Tectonic slivers of Aruma sediments between
Hawasina thrust sheets were described by
Robertson (1987).

At Wadi Hafr, in the southern margin of the
Hamrat Duru range, a new widespread melange
unit has been discovered. This unit (named in
this paper the Wadi Hafr unit) is assigned to the
Late Cretaceous Aruma Group, both on lithological and palaeontological grounds. It contains

fauna of equivalent age to the Fiqa shale of the
Aruma Group.

In the Hamrat Duru range an imbricate stack
made up of this unit, together with the Hamrat
Duru Group is folded around small scale culminations by a further thrusting event. These
small scale structures form a characteristic *en
echelon* fold pattern. Families of small folds
were folded around major antiformal structures
during an episode of thrusting involving a much
deeper crustal level. Four stages of thrusting
(T1−T4) were recognized (Fig. 7).

It has been pointed out that on a regional
scale the structural trends of these imbricates
and their co-genetic culminations display a
characteristic arcuate shape, approximately
parallel to that of the arc of Jebel Salakh Range
of the external zone and to the outcrop pattern
of the shelf carbonates in the internal zone.

In Jebel Hammah to the east of Sufrat ad
Dawh the folds and thrusts are arranged around
an arc, concave towards the north. The arc is
cut by a line joining Fatih and Al Wasil representing a possible thrust. This thrust has a
similar geometry to the re-joining splay described by Boyer & Elliot (1982) (see Fig. 1).

Tertiary deformation in the external zone. The
cover sequence that unconformably overlies the
Hawasina foreland fold and thrust belt is made
up of Maastrichtian and Early Tertiary rocks.

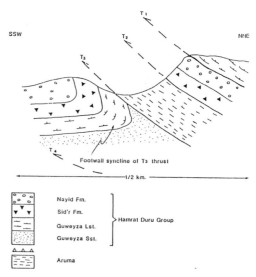

Fig. 7. Schematic section illustrating tectonic
incorporation of Aruma sediments into the Hamrat
Duru thrust sheets by sequential thrusting, central
Hamrat Duru range.

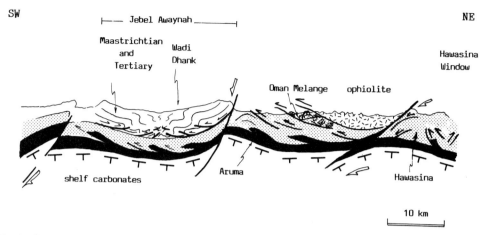

Fig. 8. Cross-section showing the Tertiary gravity folding in Jebel Awaynah. Line of section shown in Fig. 1.

Exposure of these rocks is limited to the west and southwest margin of the external zone (Fig. 1). North of Dhank, the contact between the Hawasina and the overlying Maastrichtian is a fault. This is illustrated by the highly sheared basal Maastrichtian conglomerates on the north side of Wadi Fatha. Evidence of this fault is also seen by a family of extensional faults at the base of the Maastrichtian and Tertiary sequence in this region. However, north of Ibri Simsima rocks overlying Hawasina above an irregular unconformity surface. Tertiary folding is represented by a series of anticlines and synclines arranged in an *en echelon* fold pattern. This pattern correlates structurally with the *en echelon* fold pattern described for parts of the underlying Hawasina thrust sheet (Fig. 1).

In the Dhank area itself gravity sliding was responsible for the main structural style of the Maastrichtian−Tertiary sequence which is exposed in major (45 × 24 km) NW−SE Jebel Awaynah synclinorium. Folds in the northeast flank of the major fold verge towards the southwest whilst those in the southwest flank verge towards the northeast. A complex interference zone occurs along the axis of the major synclinorium (Fig. 8). Tertiary rocks exposed around much of the south margin of the foreland are folded around monoclinal structures trending parallel to the mountain front, i.e. arcuate towards the northeast.

A characteristic Z-shaped, NW plunging fold pair forms the Jebel Aswad structure west of the northern part of the Hamrat Duru range. The northern part of the eastern limb of the syncline is a westerly-verging monoclinal structure.

Discussion

The Late Alpine (Tertiary) age for the major structures of the Oman Mountains, as proposed by Glennie *et al.* (1974) and Glennie (1977) poses several problems. Two major structural trends in the Oman Mountains can be seen. The first is a series of folds trending parallel to the general arcuate trend of the mountain belt, e.g. Saih Hatat, Akhdar, the Hawasina Window and Jebel Salakh. The second is represented by a series of folds trending in directions approximately perpendicular to the first, e.g. Jebel Nakhl, Wadi Andam folds and Jebels Nahdah and Hinaydi of the Jebel Salakh Range. Glennie *et al.*'s (1974) model did not explain the mechanism by which these trends would develop by an Oligocene−Miocene folding event. Searle (1985) has gone further and proposed that the Oman Mountains exhibit a large-scale basin-and-dome pattern resulting from biaxial interference folds. There is no evidence to suggest that the Oman Mountains (over 40 000 km²) have undergone such large scale bifolding. If Searle's (1985) model is correct, a remarkable magnitude of strain is required and should be shown within the Tertiary sequence. However, it is evident that none of the Maastrichtian and Tertiary cover has suffered such large magnitude strain or shows evidence of interference folding. In contrast, the origin of the Tertiary deformation is thought to be of extensional origin (see later sections).

Bernoulli & Weissert (1987) relate the origin of Saih Hatat and Jebel Akhdar to a Middle Tertiary (post-nappe) ramp-flat system in the Arabian foreland. They use the post-nappe deformation of the Helvetic nappes in the Swiss Alps as an analogy. However, the Late Alpine tectonic events of the Alps are not seen in the Oman Mountains. An alternative model is proposed which explains the two structural trends of the mountains in terms of thin-skinned tectonics during, and at a late stage of, the emplacement event (Early Alpine–Late Cretaceous).

Much of the evidence for the nature of thrusting at depth comes in the Oman Mountains from the internal zone, where field observations in Saih Hatat show that thrusts are much steeper dipping and involve deeper basal units than in the foreland and marginal fold belt of the external zone. The model for the Oman Mountains presented here is based on thin-skinned theory, as expounded by Rich (1934) and Dahlstrom (1970) who noted that in thrust belts structures are largely confined to upper crustal layers.

The involvement of the apparently south-westward-emplaced Tethyan oceanic sediments and the Semail ophiolite (stratigraphic thickness 14 km; Lippard et al. 1986) and their effect as a major driving force in developing imbrication of the Arabian margin has been previously underestimated. This force may relate to the collision of the Arabian margin with a subduction trench.

Early Alpine deformation

The Internal Zone. Rich (1934) demonstrated that flat topped anticline may develop above a thrust fault with a flat-ramp geometry. The Saih Hatat, Jebel Akhdar and Jebel Nakhl represent folds developed as massive flat topped anticlines. They may therefore, have formed above and ahead of a thrust ramp. The imbrication between the shelf carbonate and the pre-Permian sequence (basement–cover duplex) in N Saih Hatat suggests that a sole thrust for this duplex must occur somewhere in the pre-Permian sequence. The subsidiary faults of this duplex, which branch off the major sole thrust, were frontal ramps. They may also represent a reversal of extensional faults developed on the continental margin during earlier rifting (see Table 1). Their proximal position relative to the suture (subduction zone) implies that this major sole thrust is a deep seated one.

Structures trending subparallel to the regional NNE tectonic transport direction are interpreted as lateral structures. These include Jebel Nakhl and Semail Gap and Wadi Andam and features with similar structural trends. Northwards this approximately NE–SW structural

trend changes to NNW across the centre of Jebel Akhdar, e.g. the Hawasina Window and Jebel Buwaydah (see Fig. 1). A NNW–SSE lateral ramp is inferred between Jebel Akhdar and the Hawasina Window, representing the opposing structure to the Jebel Nakhl lateral ramp across the tectonic transport (across the centre of Jebel Akhdar). This lateral ramp,

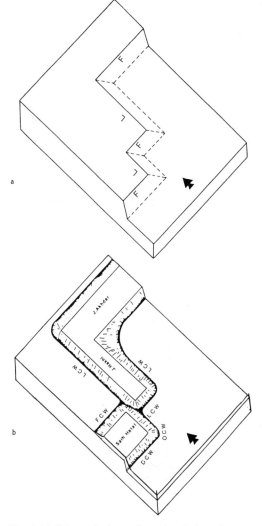

Fig. 9.(a) Schematic three-dimensional view of footwall topography of the sole thrust believed to underlie Saih Hatat, Nakhl and Akhdar of the internal zone. **(b)** Three-dimensional view of the hangingwall culminations as a result of movement across the footwall ramps in (a); FCW, frontal culmination walls; LCW, lateral culmination wall; DCW, dorsal culmination wall; OCW, oblique culmination wall.

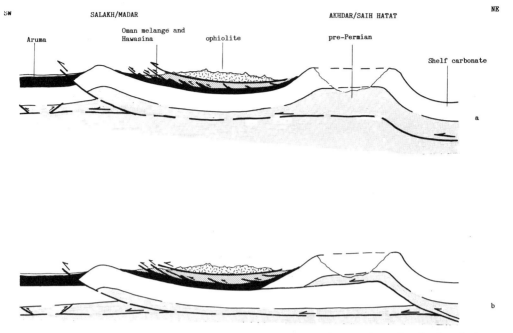

Fig. 10. Schematic structural sections across the Oman Mountains showing two alternatives for the sole thrust trajectory. In (a) the sole thrust is located within the pre-Permian sequence, whilst in (b) it cuts up section through the shelf carbonates.

however is required for the development of Jebel Akhdar culmination (see Butler 1982). Along this lateral ramp the major sole thrust may have cut up-section from the pre-Permian level below Saih Hatat, Jebel Nakhl and Jebel Akhdar to a higher level within the Hawasina sediments below the Hawasina Window. These lateral and frontal ramps are connected via oblique ramps.

Fig. 9 illustrates the three-dimensional geometry of the sole thrust that is suggested to lie beneath Saih Hatat, Jebel Nakhl and Jebel Akhdar. It also demonstrates the configuration of its frontal oblique and lateral ramps. The hangingwall sequences above the arcuate trace of this thrust are the Saih Hatat, Jebel Nakhl, and Jebel Akhdar culminations respectively.

Fig. 10 shows two possibilities for the position of the sole thrust below Saih Hatat, and Jebels Nakhl and Akhdar. In (a) it is assumed that the sole thrust lies within the pre-Permian succession. In (b) it cuts up-section to a higher level within the Mesozoic shelf. In the latter model the shelf carbonates may be duplicated beneath the pre-Permian sequence. The Mesozoic sequence is clearly involved in thrusting in the Jebel Salakh Range of the external zone

where displacement generally decreases. If either model applies, the culmination development implies that much of the exposed sequence of pre-Permian basement (partly Precambrian) and the Mesozoic shelf carbonates are not autochthonous as assumed since Glennie *et al.* (1974).

The involvement of the shelf sequence in the basement−cover duplex in Saih Hatat may suggest a breach or later out of sequence thrust penetrating the roof thrust of the basement−cover duplex and causing it to be overridden by the shelf sequence i.e. leaky duplex (Fig. 11). This figure also demonstrates an alternative model for Saih Hatat as a duplex culmination. The hinterland end of the duplex is back steepened to develop a series of back folds and back thrusts similar to those developed in the Hawasina Window within the Hawasina sequences.

Fig. 12 is a sketch block diagram illustrating a model by which it is believed the Jebel Akhdar and Jebel Nakhl culminations were formed following model (b) in Fig. 10. Two alternatives are proposed for the trajectory of the sole thrust in a direction normal to the transport direction between Saih Hatat and the Hawasina

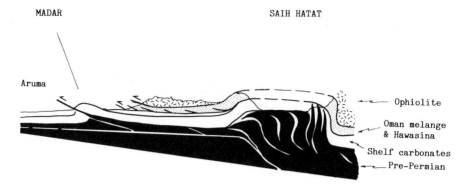

Fig. 11. Interpretive section across the mountains from Saih Hatat to Jebel Madar showing the major basement and cover duplex of the Saih Hatat culmination and the development of northward verging folds and back thrusts as a result of back steepening of earlier thrusts. This interpretive model is also applicable to the similar structural style developed in the Hawasina sediments north of the Hawasina Window.

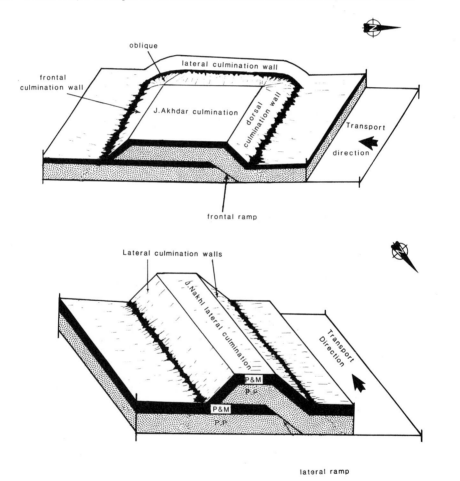

Fig. 12(a) Three-dimensional view illustrating the Jebel Akhdar culmination as a ramp anticline using model (b) of Fig. 11. Black is Permian and Mesozoic shelf carbonates, stippled is pre-Permian sequence. (b) Three-dimensional view illustrating Jebel Nakhl as a lateral culmination above a lateral culmination wall. P & M, Permian and Mesozoic shelf carbonates; P, pre-Permian.

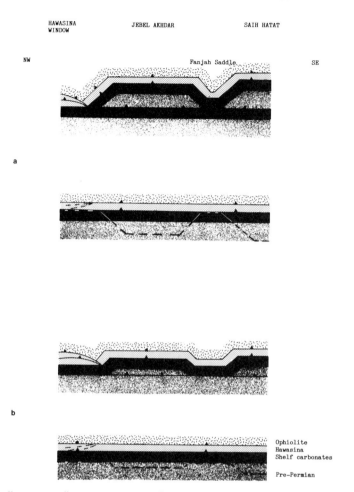

Fig.13 Hangingwall sequence diagram across tectonic transport showing the stratigraphic level of the sole thrust. In (a) the thrust cuts upsection through the shelf beneath Saih Hatat and Akhdar, and in (b) the thrust changes level within the pre-Permian sequence. Both models explain the occurrence of pre-Permian sequence in the core of the Saih Hatat and Akhdar structures but not in the Hawasina Window.

window. These two models are shown in the hangingwall sequence diagrams (Fig. 13, also Fig. 1;). The thrust may have cut up-section along the major lateral ramp between Jebel Akhdar and the Hawasina Window (Fig. 13a). Alternatively, the thrust may have changed position within the pre-Permian sequence from a much deeper level below Saih Hatat and Jebel Akhdar to a very shallow level below the Hawasina Window.

Passive-roof duplex. The boundary between the internal and external zones of the Oman Mountains is marked by a marginal back thrust. This back thrust is taken to mark a 'passive roof duplex' in the sense of Banks & Warburton (1986). It may have been developed by the

underthrusting of the front of Saih Hatat and Jebel Akhdar beneath the almost stationary ophiolite, thus developing a northwards thrusting event. Figure 14 illustrates a model explaining this concept using the duplex model for Saih Hatat. This is similar to that described by Banks & Warburton (1986) for the Kirthar and Sulaiman mountain belt, Pakistan. Note also that hangingwall collapse (overstep) is the dominant thrusting sequence in the passive roof duplex concept.

The External Zone. Glennie *et al.* (1974) explained how the standard stacking order of thrust sheets within the Hawasina belt may change or breach due to lateral facies variations. A structurally controlled breach of this usual

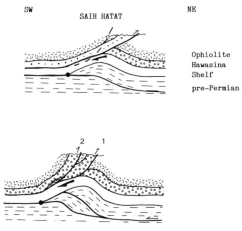

Fig. 14. The development of a 'passive-roof' duplex in front of the internal zone culminations. This diagram uses Banks & Warburton's (1986) model.

stacking order was also noticed by Glennie *et al.* (1974). They explained the occurrence of the Hamrat Duru Group above the Wahrah Formation in the Sufrat ad Dawh area by a secondary imbrication of thrusts created after the two, units had already been tectonically superimposed in the usual way (i.e. Wahrah on top of Hamrat Duru). They also suggested that a local 'envelopment' of the overlying Wahrah Formation in front of the Hamrat Duru thrust sheet was possible (Glennie *et al.* 1974). The secondary late imbricate hypothesis was adopted by Searle (1985). However, in Sufrat ad Dawh the Hamrat Duru Group may have been back thrust northwards on top of the Wahrah Formation, developing a pop-up structure.

The imbricate stack of both the syn-tectonic shales and melange (e.g. Wadi Hafr unit), together with the Hawasina sequences have been folded around major culminations in much of the Hawasina foreland belt. This structural position indicates a four stage thrust sequence (Fig. 15; see also Fig. 7), as follows:

The first phase (T1) saw the initial imbrication of the Hawasina duplex developed in the Hawasina basin during the initial emplacement of the ophiolite. The second phase (T2) rethrust the Hawasina duplex over the Aruma sediments and partly incorporated it in the thrusting. T2 is the greatest thrust displacement (150−200 km). The third phase (T3) involved both Aruma and Hawasina units in a larger scale imbrication. This T3 thrusting event penetrated up into, and breached the roof thrust of the overlying Hawasina duplex (i.e. a leaky duplex in the sense of Butler 1983, 1984). The fourth stage

(T4) thrusting event is at a much deeper level and appears to be ubiquitous. This is evident by the folding of the whole imbricate stack, developing much larger scale culminations. The imbricate stacks were initially developed as hinterland dipping duplexes and have been subsequently folded by both T3 and T4 to dip towards the foreland in what may appear as a foreland dipping duplex (Figs 7 & 15c). It is not clear what is the age of T4 thrusting event.

The gross similarities between the arcuate configuration of the Hawasina cover, the shelf carbonates of the Jebel Salakh arcuate range and the outcrop pattern of the shelf carbonates in the internal zone at Saih Hatat−Jebel Nakhl−Jebel Akhdar (Fig. 1) suggests that they are due to similar changes in the thrust geometry of the underlying major sole thrust. The arcuate shape of the master sole thrust is related to the development of frontal, oblique and lateral ramps. The thrust front is emergent to the south of the Jebel Salakh range. The map pattern and present erosion level of this thrust indicate that it may represent an isolated splay (Fig. 1). This thrust emerges at the surface south of the Jebel Salakh as a weekly emergent thrust front in Morley's (1986) classification.

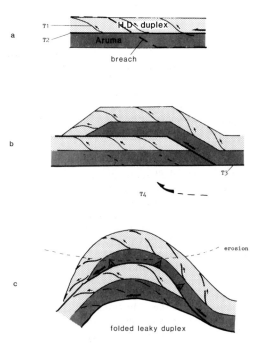

Fig. 15. Four stages of thrusting and the development of a folded leaky duplex in the Oman Mountains foreland fold and thrust belt.

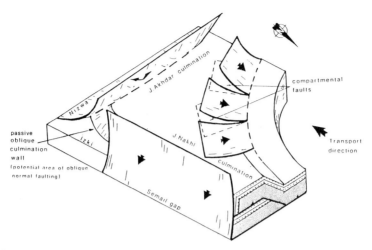

Fig. 16. Culmination collapse structures around Jebel Nakhl and Jebel Akhdar. The Semail Gap is shown here as a lateral culmination collapse structure. Note the compartmental faults between Jebel Nakhl and Jebel Akhdar.

To the east of this emergent thrust front the arcuate trend of Jebel Hammah is interpreted as a rejoining splay (cf. Boyer & Elliot 1982). The branch line of this splay intersects the map at two branch points near Fatih and Al Wasil. The ramp configuration of the Oman Mountain thrust belt is summarized in Fig.1.

Late Alpine (Tertiary) deformation: culmination collapse structures

The Early Alpine (Late Cretaceous) development of the culminations in the Oman Mountains thrust belt was followed by an extensional tectonic regime. This regime is defined by the evidence from around the flanks of the internal zone culminations, e.g. extensional faults, gravity folds, later cleavage and elimination of much of the Hawasina thrust sheets between the ophiolite and shelf sequence. Culmination collapse structures may account for the absence of some Hawasina thrust sheets around the culminations, as well as the reversal of their stacking order. However, some of the missing Hawasina may have been eroded as a result of the development of a passive roof duplex (see Fig. 14). These faults bound the major structures. The origin of the extensional structures is believed to have been initiated by a failure along the steep slopes of the culmination walls (frontal, lateral, oblique and dorsal). This is possibly due to the gliding of the ophiolite, as shown by black arrows in Fig. 1. Evidence that these culmination collapse structures occur as a back slip of the ophiolite is recorded in the northern

part of Saih Hatat and Jebel Akhdar by gravity folding, cleavage and extensional faulting.

Frontal culmination collapse structures are also seen on the southern side of Jebel Akhdar, Saih Hatat and the Hawasina Window. Fig. 16 is an interpretative model illustrating the culmination collapse structures around Jebel Akhdar and Jebel Nakhl. It shows the Semail Gap as a lateral culmination collapse feature. A series of compartmental faults also occur between the Jebel Nakhl and Jebel Akhdar structures.

It is suggested that reversal (inversion) of Triassic rift faults (see Table 1) into thrusts occurred during emplacement and that these may have been re-inverted as extensional faults during the culmination collapse (i.e. as a multiple inversion event).

The age of the extensional event is variable. Culmination collapse took place in Saih Hatat earlier than around Jebel Akhdar. There is sedimentological evidence that Saih Hatat was a positive feature during the Tertiary (Nolan et al. 1990), whilst the lack of such evidence around Jebel Akhdar may suggest that the structure only later became a positive feature (see section below). The critical stage in which the ophiolite reached an isostatic instability to initiate sliding off the culmination walls around Jebel Akhdar could, therefore have been later than that of the equivalent stage around Saih Hatat to the east and the Hawasina Window to the north.

The en echelon fold pattern described in the Tertiary rocks north of Dhank may follow or mimic similar structural patterns in the underlying Hawasina sediments. Jebel Hafit may have resulted from a rejuvenation of a passive Late Cretaceous back thrust bounding the mountain front. It is conceivable that this rethrusting event, which originated in front of these surge zones may have contributed to the development of the fourth stage of thrusting (T4) described in the Hawasina belt of the external zone (i.e. the leaky duplex structures). This may have developed as the Hawasina thrust sheets were bulldozed in front of the sliding ophiolite, thus reactivating early thrusts and structurally thickening the sequence.

It has been argued that the Jebel Salakh range developed above the Late Cretaceous frontal thrust of the Oman Mountains. However, the steeply dipping intramontane wadi gravels in the south side of Jebel Salakh indicate a much later, possibly Pliocene–Pleistocene event affecting the frontal margin of the mountains. Hanna & Nolan (1989) reported Pliocene–Pleistocene events along the Maradi Fault Zone to the south.

Fig. 17 is a cross section through the centre of the mountains from the Gulf of Oman to Natih and the Fahud oil fields showing the inferred major thrust in pre-Permian rocks underlying the major structures. Offshore information partly based on Mann *et al.* (1990).

Sedimentological evidence of Early Alpine (Late Cretaceous) age of Saih Hatat. Nolan *et al.* (1990) showed that the major culminations formed during the Late Cretaceous orogeny had a major effect upon the nature and distribution of the post-orogenic sediments. Overall, these culminations define a topographically positive belt upon and around the edges of which shallow marine to terrestrial deposits accumulated. Further away from this positive belt deeper marine sediments formed. They document the presence of a 'reverse clast stratigraphy' in the Late Campanian–Maastrichtian Al Khod Formation near Muscat. This unit records the progressive backstripping firstly of ophiolite, then of Hajar Supergroup limestones and finally of Lower Palaeozoic metamorphic quartzite, probably derived from the Amdeh Formation of Saih Hatat culmination. This evidence indicates that the Saih Hatat culmination was deeply eroded shortly after its formation. Thus the facies and thickness variations of Palaeocene and Eocene sediments indicate that in the early Tertiary the Saih Hatat culmination influenced sedimentation (Nolan *et al.* 1990).

The structural evolution of the Oman Mountains

Turonian times saw the first emplacement of the ophiolite and possibly the early stage of major thrust propagating in the pre-Permian sequence. Alternatively the development of low relief early peripheral swell (c.f. Patton & O'Connor 1988) caused increased erosion of shelf carbonates to the northeast. This also saw the development of (T1) thrusting event of the Hawasina sediments. During Coniacian–Campanian times a major translation of Hawasina 'wedge' by (T2) thrusting event took place. Some out of sequence breaching might have occurred, putting Aruma over Hawasina (leaky duplex). Structural growth of the Saih Hatat and Hawasina Window culminations by the development of duplex structure underneath them and culmination collapse (extensional gravity sliding) in Saih Hatat may also be attributed to this stage.

Maastrichtian–Oligocene carbonate sedimentation resumed over the subsided continental margin, without tectonic deformation. In Oligocene–Miocene, uplift of the new margin into a shallow marine–intertidal–evaporitic depositional setting took place.

In mid–late Miocene gravity tectonics (culmination collapse) in the Jebel Akhdar and Jebel Nakhl area occurred along major planar extensional faults bounding these structures. This was associated with elevation on deep and steep reverse faults (inversion phase). The compressional deformation increases northwards around the Oman Mountains arc with thin skin tectonics of the shelf carbonates in Musandam possibly caused by increasing proximity to the continent–content collision zone (Searle 1988).

From Pliocene–Recent, isostatic uplift in the mountains has been taking place giving rise to raised beaches of probable marine origin, as seen on the north flank of Jebel Nakhl and N Saih Hatat. Also the development of a peripheral pulge in the Musandam Peninsula (Patton & O'Connor 1988) caused eastward tilting (the e.g. of raised beaches).

Conclusions

(1) Much of the structural grain dominating both the internal and external zones is interpreted in terms of thin-skinned tectonics of Early Alpine (Late Cretaceous) age associated with emplacement of the ophiolite and Tethyan thrust sheets southwestwards onto the Arabian platform, related to attempted thrusting of the Arabian margin into a subduction trench.

(2) Saih Hatat, Jebel Nakhl, Jebel Akhdar and the Hawasina Window are inferred to be underlain by a Late Cretaceous thrust, which may be located in pre-Permian

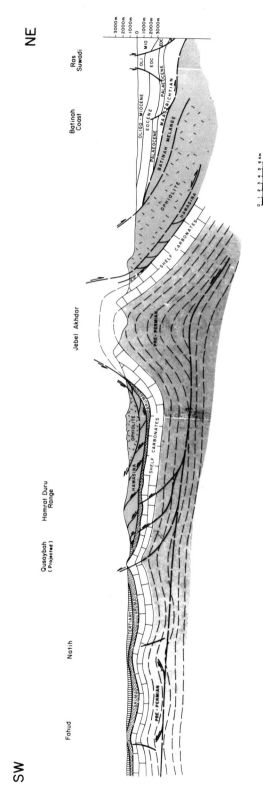

Fig. 17. Cross section across the Oman Mountains from the Gulf of Oman to Fahud Oil field. Offshore information is partly based on Mann *et al.* (1990).

sequences in the cores of the Saih Hatat, Nakhl and Akhdar culminations.

(3) The development of these culminations was followed by the major culmination collapse along the frontal, lateral, oblique and dorsal culmination walls. The Semail Gap is a lateral culmination collapse structure.

(4) The boundary between the internal and external zone is 'passive roof' duplex marked by a major back thrust. A passive back thrust also exists in the southern frontal margin of the external zone. These backthrusts later became extensional faults.

(5) Overprint of Late Alpine (Tertiary) tectonics in the Central Oman Mountains is weak, and Tertiary folding is represented either by gravity structures associated with culmination collapse or reactivation and 'mimicking' of pre-existing Early Alpine (Late Cretaceous) structures.

I thank Amoco Oman Petroleum Company for financial and logistical support. The paper is published with the permission of Amoco Production Company. The Ministry of Petroleum in Oman is also acknowledged for giving permission to work in Oman and to publish this paper. I am most grateful to J. D. Smewing of the Earth Resources Institute for first introducing me to the geology of Oman in 1982 and for his constructive criticism of this manuscript. K. W. Glennie's constructive comments were very encouraging. I also wish to thank A. H. F. Robertson (Edinburgh) and T. L. Patton (Amoco) for fruitful discussions in the field and my colleagues in the Earth Resources Institute, Swansea, particularly S. C. Nolan for help with the Tertiary stratigraphy and B. P. Clissold for co-operation in Oman. J. Warburton and the two referees, Rabu (BRGM) and Coffield (ARCO) are also thanked for their useful comments.

References

BANKS, C. J. & WARBURTON, J. 1986. 'Passive-roof' duplex geometry in the frontal structures of the Kirther and Sulaiman mountain belts, Pakistan. Journal of Structural Geology. Special Issue 'Thrusting and Deformation'. 8, 3/4, 229–237.

BARRETTE, P. D. & CALON, T. J. 1987. Re-imbrication of the Hawasina allochthans in the Sufrat ad Dawh range, Oman Mountains. Journal of Structural Geology, 9, 859–867.

BERNOULLI, D. & WEISSERT, H. 1987. The upper Hawasina nappes in the Central Oman mountains, stratigraphy, palispastics and sequence of nappe emplacement. Geodinamica Acta, 1(1), 47–58.

BOYER, E. S. & ELLIOT, D. 1982. Thrust systems. American Association of Petroleum Geologists Bulletin, 66, 1196–1230.

BUTLER, R. W. H. 1982. The terminology of structures in thrust belts. Journal of Structural Geology, 4, 4239–4245.

—— 1983. Balanced cross-sections and their implications for the deep structure of the north-west Alps. Journal of Structural Geology, 5, 125–137.

—— 1984. Balanced cross-section and their implications for the deep structure of the north-west Alps: reply. Journal of Structural Geology, 6, 601–612.

COLEMAN, R. G. 1981. Tectonic setting for ophiolite obduction in Oman. Journal of Geophysical Research, 86, 2497–2508.

COWARD, M. P. 1982. Surge zones in the Moine thrust zone of NW Scotland. Journal of Structural Geology, 4247–4256.

DAHLSTROM, C. D. 1970. Structural geology in the eastern margin of the Canadian Rocky Mountains. Bulletin of Canadian Petroleum Geology, 18, 332–406.

GLENNIE, K. W. 1977. Outline of the geology of Oman. Memoirè's hors Série géologie Societé de France, 8, 25–31.

——, BOEF, M. G. A., HUGHES CLARK, M. W., MOODY-STUART M., PILAAR, W. F. H. & REINHARDT, B. M. 1973. Late Cretaceous nappes in the Oman Mountains and their geologic evolution. Bulletin of the American Association of Petroleum Geologists, 57, 5–27.

——, BOEFF, M. G. A., HUGHES CLARK, M. W., MOODY-STUART, M., PILLAR, W. F. H. & REINHARDT, B. M. 1974. The geology of the Oman Mountains. Verhandelingen van het Koninklijk Nederlands Geologisch Mijnbouwkundig Genootschap, 31.

GRAHAM, G. M. 1980. Structure and sedimentology of the Hawasina Window, Oman Mountains. Unpublished PhD thesis, Open University, Milton Keynes, UK.

HANNA, S. S. & NOLAN, S. C. 1989. The Maradi Fault Zone: evidence of Neogene tectonics in the Oman Mountains. Journal of the Geological Society, London, 146, 867–871.

LE METOUR, J, VUKKETM, M & de GRAMONT, X. (1986). Geological map of Quryat, Sheet NF 40-4D, scale 1:100 000, explanatory notes. Directorate General of Minerals, Oman Ministry of Petroleum and Minerals.

LIPPARD, S. J. & REX, D. C. 1982. K-Ar ages of alkaline igneous rocks in the northern Oman Mountains, NE Arabia, and their relations to rifting, passive margin development and destruction of the Oman Tethys. Geological Magazine, 119, 497–503.

——, SHELTON, A. W. & GASS, I. G. 1986. The ophiolite of Northern Oman. Geological Society, London, Memoir 11.

MANN, A. & HANNA, S. S. 1990. The tectonic evolution of the pre-Permian rocks, Central and Southeastern Oman Mountains. In: ROBERTSON, A. H. F., SEARLE, M. P. & RIES, A. C. (eds) The Geology and Tectonics of the Oman Region. Geological Society, London, Special Publication, 49, 307–325.

——, —— & NOLAN, S. C. 1990. The post Campanian tectonic evolution of the Central Oman Mountains: Tertiary extension of the Eastern Arabian

Margin. *In*: ROBERTSON, A. H. F., SEARLE, M. P. & RIES, A. C. (eds) *The Geology and Tectonics of the Oman Region*. Geological Society, London, Special Publication, **49**, 549−563.

MICHARD, A. 1983. Les nappes de Mascate, Oman ramp epicontinentale d' obduction facies schiste blue et la dualite apparente des ophiolites omanaises: *Sciences Géologiques, Bulletin, Strasbourg*, **36**, 3−16.

MORLEY, C. K. 1986. A classification of thrust fronts. *American Association of Petroleum Geologists Bulletin*, **70**,(1), 12−25.

NOLAN, S. C., SKELTON, P. W., CLISSOLD, B. P. & SMEWING, J. D. 1990. Late Campanian to Tertiary palaeogeography of the central and northern Oman Mountains. *In*: ROBERTSON, A. H. F., SEARLE, M. P. & RIES, A. C. (eds) *The Geology and Tectonics of the Oman Region*. Geological Society, London, Special Publication, **49**, 495−519.

PATTON, T. L. & O' CONNOR, S. J. 1988. Cretaceous flexural history of the northern Oman mountains, foredeep, United Arab Emirates. *American Association of Petroleum Geologists Bulletin*, **72** (7), 797−809.

PEARCE, J. A., ALABASTER, T., SHELTON, A. W. & SEARLE, M. P. 1981. The Oman ophiolite as a Cretaceous arc-basin complex: evidence and implication. *Philosophical Transactions of the Royal Society, London*, A **300**, 299−317.

RABU, D., BECHENNEC, F., BEURRIER, M. & HUTIN, G. 1986. *Geological map of Nakhl, Sheet NF-40−3E, scale 1:100 000, explanatory notes*. Directorate General of Minerals, Oman Ministry of Petroleum and Minerals.

RICH, J. L. 1934. Mechanics of low-angle overthrust faulting as illustrated by Cumberland thrust block, Virginia, Kentucky and Tennessee. *American Association of Petroleum Geologists Bulletin*, **18**(12) 1584−1596.

ROBERTSON, A. H. F. 1987. The transition from a passive margin to an Upper Cretaceous foreland basin related to ophiolite emplacement in the Oman Mountains. *Geological Society of America Bulletin*, **99**, 633−653.

SEARLE, M. P. 1980. *The metamorphic sheet and underlying volcanic rocks beneath the Semail ophiolite in the northern Oman Mountains of Arabia*. Unpublished PhD thesis, Open University Milton Keynes, UK.

—— 1985. Sequence of thrusting and origins of culminations in the Northern and Central Oman Mountains. *Journal of Structural Geology*, 7, 129−143.

—— 1988. Structure of the Musandam culmination (Sultanate of Oman and United Arab Emirates) and the Straits of Hormuz syntaxis. *Journal of the Geological Society, London*, **145**(5), 831−845.

—— & COOPER, D. J. W. 1986. Structure of the Hawasina Window culmination, Central Oman Mountains. *Transactions of the Royal Society of Edinburgh: Earth Sciences*, 77, 143−156.

TSCHOPP, R. H. 1967a. The general geology of Oman. *Proc. 7th World Petroleum Congress*, 2, 231−242.

—— 1967b. Development of the Fahud field. *Proc. 7th World Petroleum Congress*, 2, 2213−2228.

Structure of the Jebel Sumeini–Jebel Ghawil area, Northern Oman

M. P. SEARLE[1], D. J. W. COOPER[1] & K. F. WATTS[2]

[1] *Department of Geology, University of Leicester, LE1 7RH, UK*
[2] *Department of Geology and Geophysics, University of Alaska,
Fairbanks, Alaska 99775, USA*

Abstract: Detailed structural mapping of the Sumeini half-window, Jebel Sumeini and
Jebel Ghawil areas in northern Oman, shows that the dominant Late Cretaceous thrusting
was a WSW-propagating piggy-back sequence modified by late-stage, deeper level thrusts
in the Sumeini slope facies carbonates which breached up into the overlying Hamrat Duru
thrust sheets. The uppermost Semail thrust carrying the complete ophiolite sequence
overlaps lower Haybi thrust sheets and inverted metamorphic isograds are displayed in the
footwall. Amphibolites and greenschists of the metamorphic sole have been subsequently
imbricated with Haybi alkaline and tholeiitic volcanics, Triassic Oman exotic limestones
and melanges of the Haybi duplex. A major E–W trending lateral ramp is inferred along
the southern edge of Jebel Ghawil downthrowing the Sharm peridotite block up to 1000 m
to the south. The basal Hamrat Duru thrust overlies Cretaceous Mayhah Formation slope
facies carbonates and has been folded around the lower, later culminations primarily of
Late Cretaceous age, enhanced by further structural growth and short-distance post-
Maastrichtian (? Eocene) thrusting. Thrusts at the base of the Sumeini Group have
breached through the overlying Hamrat Duru sheets and locally overthrust Maastrichtian
Faiyah Formation limetones along the SW margin of Jebel Wasa. Culmination of Jebel
Sumeini promoted hanging-wall drop fault development along the trailing (NE) edge of
the Sumeini duplex, down-faulting Hamrat Duru rocks to the east. The amount of
displacement of the Jebel Sumeini culmination increases towards the south, toward the
axis of the Sumeini half-window.

The Oman Mountains (Fig. 1) expose a stack of
thrust sheets composed of carbonate slope
(Sumeini Group), to continental rise and distal
basin (Hawasina Complex) Tethyan sediments,
Mesozoic volcanic rocks, Exotic limestones and
melanges (Haybi Complex), and a massive slab
of oceanic crust and mantle (Semail ophiolite
complex). These thrust sheets were emplaced
onto the passive continental margin platform
sequence of the Arabian plate during the
Turonian to Lower Maastrichtian (*c.* 93–67
Ma), before deposition of conglomerates
and shallow-marine limestones in the Upper
Maastrichtian and Lower Tertiary (Glennie *et
al.* 1973, 1974; Coleman 1981; Lippard *et al.*
1986).

The Sumeini area (Fig. 2) lies midway between the Musandam peninsula and Jebel
Akhdar on the west side of the northern Oman
Mountains (Fig. 1). Although the shelf carbonate succession is not exposed, the area does
show the complete allochthonous succession of
Late Cretaceous thrust sheets. Detailed mapping (1:20 000) and sedimentary and structural
correlations between the thrust sheets have been
made in the Jebel Sumeini area (Watts 1985)
and the Sumeini half-window–Jebel Ghawil

area (Searle 1980). This paper summarizes the
stratigraphy and describes the structure of the
Sumeini area (Fig. 2), in particular the geometry
and sequence and timing of thrusting and the
relationship between the dominant Late Cretaceous thrusting event of the Oman Mountains,
and the Tertiary re-thrusting events recorded in
the Musandam peninsula.

Stratigraphy

Stratigraphical, structural and sedimentological
features suggest that the Mesozoic Sumeini
Group formed upon the slope east of the
Arabian carbonate platform and passed basin-
wards into the Hamrat Duru Group which, in
turn, lay inboard of the Haybi Complex. The
stratigraphies of the Sumeini and Hamrat Duru
Groups are similar and reflect different stages
in the development of the Arabian carbonate
platform, the source of most of the sediment
which comprises these groups. Little platform-
derived sediment reached the deeper water,
chert-dominated formations of the distal part of
the Hawasina complex or the Haybi complex
which is dominated by Triassic rift-related volcanics and associated sediments.

From ROBERTSON, A. H. F., SEARLE, M. P. & RIES, A. C. (eds), 1990,
The Geology and Tectonics of the Oman Region.
Geological Society Special Publication No 49, pp 361–374

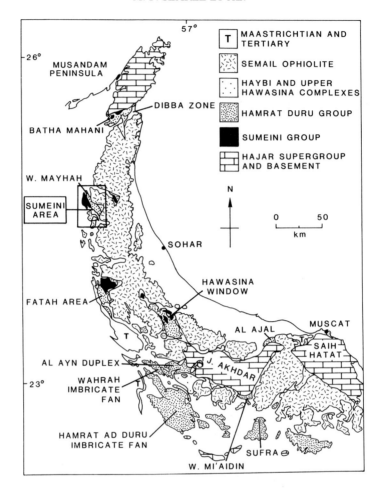

Fig. 1. Geological map of the Oman Mountains showing location of the Sumeini area.

Sumeini Group

The Sumeini Group (Fig. 3) has a total thickness of about 2500 m and is divided into two formations, namely the Permian to Triassic Maqam Formation, subdivided into Members A to F, and the Jurassic to Cretaceous Mayhah Formation, subdivided into Members A to D (Glennie *et al.* 1973, 1974; Watts & Garrison 1986; Watts 1987). These carbonate slope deposits are exposed in the Jebel Sumeini–Jebel Wasa areas in the northern part of the Sumeini half-window (Figs 2, 4 & 5).

Permian sedimentation occurred, initially, in a deep outer shelf environment (A Member, Maqam Formation), followed by shallow-water deposition of dolomitic platform carbonates with periods of gravitational instability generating calcirudites. True carbonate slope con-

ditions developed in response to rifting in the early Triassic when carbonate submarine fans composed of redeposited oolitic calcarenite and intraformational calcirudite breccias, and argillaceous periplatform limestone (C Member, Maqam Formation) formed along a distally-steepened ramp (Watts & Garrison 1986; Watts 1987).

Mid-Triassic platform emergence was accompanied by the deposition of terrigenous silts and shales on the slope (D member, Maqam Formation). This was followed by the development of a fault-bounded escarpment slope with base-of-slope calcirudite and calcarenite debris apron and associated Ladinian radiolarites forming the E member, Maqam Formation. A shelf edge reefal assemblage developed in the Norian as indicated by fore-reef talus of the Jebel Wasa Formation and coeval reef-derived

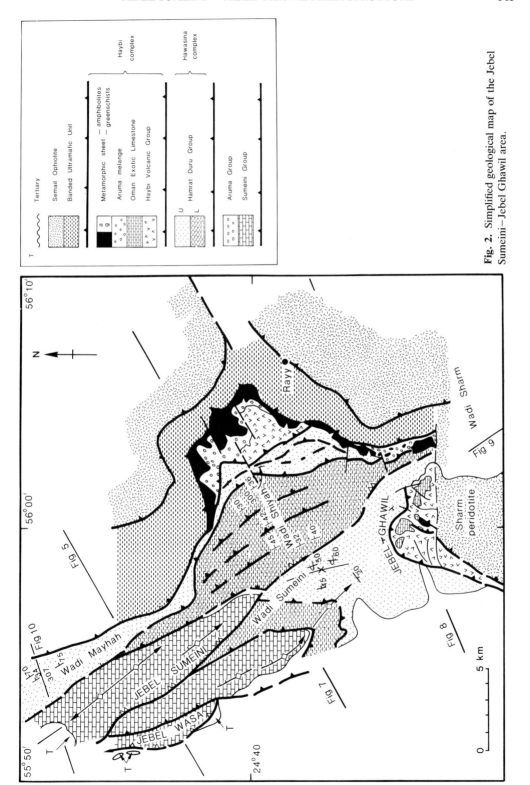

Fig. 2. Simplified geological map of the Jebel Sumeini–Jebel Ghawil area.

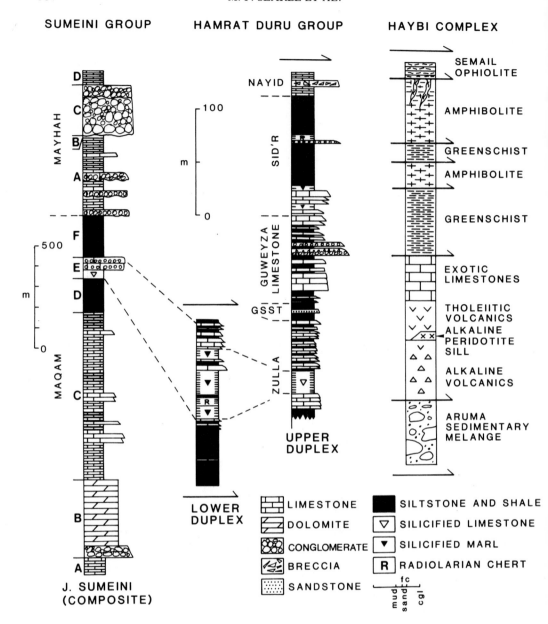

Fig. 3. Comparative stratigraphic sections through the Sumeini Group, Hamrat Duru Group and Haybi complex rocks in the Sumeini area. The Aruma sedimentary melange is equivalent of the Buday'ay unit of the Muti Formation (Robertson 1987).

debris in the E Member. Regional emergence of the shelf at the end of the Triassic prompted renewed siliciclastic sedimentation on the slope, recorded in the F Member, Maqam Formation.

The return of Jurassic carbonate platform sedimentation was marked by the deposition of periplatform lime mudstones on a slope cut by numerous channels through which oolitic and coarser-grained sediment was transported (A Member, Mayhah Formation). Such gullied bypass-slope sedimentation (Watts & Garrison 1986) ceased in the Tithonian when a high sealevel and tectonic subsidence resulted in drowning of the Arabian platform so that radiolarian

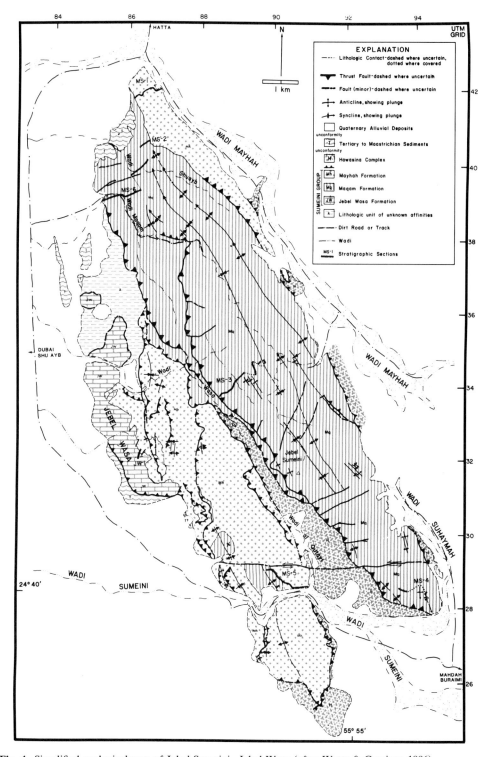

Fig. 4. Simplified geological map of Jebel Sumeini–Jebel Wasa (after Watts & Garrison 1986).

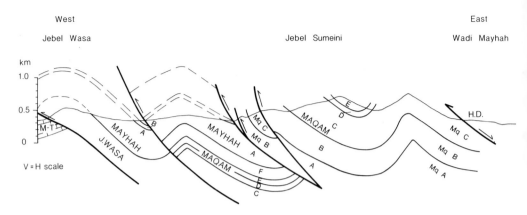

Fig. 5. Cross section across Jebel Sumeini and Jebel Wasa. See Fig. 2 for location.

cherts were deposited (B Member, Mayhah Formation).

Mid-Cretaceous instability of the platform margin, possibly an indication of the margin approaching the intra-oceanic subduction zone responsible for the generation of the Semail ophiolite, resulted in collapse of the platform margin and the generation of thick megabreccias (C Member, Mayhah Formation), followed by mixed rudite, arenite and calcilutite deposition (D Member, Mayhah Formation). Cenomanian ages from the top of this member suggests that it is transitional to the synorogenic sediments of the Qumayrah facies of the Muti Formation (Robertson 1987), deposited in a foredeep ahead of the advancing Semail ophiolite.

Hamrat Duru Group

The deep-water sediments of the Triassic to Cretaceous (Cenomanian) Hamrat Duru Group were deposited along the continental rise basin-wards from the time-equivalent Sumeini Group carbonate slope (Glennie *et al.* 1974; Cooper 1986, 1990). Following rationalization of the stratigraphical framework by Cooper (1987), in which the tectonostratigraphical Dhera Formation of Glennie *et al.* (1974) was correlated with, and assimilated into, the Hamrat Duru Group. Five formations are recognized: the Zulla, Guweyza Sandstone, Guweyza Limestone, Sid'r and Nayid (Fig. 3). Two structural units occur, a lower duplex composed exclusively of the Triassic Zulla Formation, and an upper duplex with the complete Hamrat Duru stratigraphy (Cooper 1986).

The Zulla Formation is correlated with the C and E members of the Maqam Formation. A shale-rich basal succession (unit I, Cooper 1987)

contains rare channelized conglomerates and oolitic calcarenites that represent minor influx of coarse-grained material from the distally-steepened ramp of the Sumeini Group into the basin. Terrigenous sediment, accumulating on the slope (D Member, Mayhah Formation) did not reach the basin in the Sumeini area, although it is seen elsewhere as unit II, notably in the Hawasina window (Graham 1980; Searle & Cooper 1986; Cooper 1990). Instead, a direct transition is seen to cherts and silicified marls of unit III, Zulla Formation, containing Ladinian to Norian Radiolaria (C. Blome pers. comm. in Cooper 1986), that can be correlated litho-logically and temporally with the E Member, Maqam Formation. The return to carbonate deposition (unit IV, Zulla Formation) is characterized by thin-shelled bivalves, including *Halobia*, also seen in the E Member, Maqam Formation.

Terrigenous sands and shales, correlated with the F Member, Maqam Formation, are only locally observed in discrete depocentres. They are assigned to the Guweyza Sandstone Formation.

The Guweyza Limestone Formation is, like the A Member, Mayhah Formation, characterized by redeposited oolitic limestones that were channelled into laterally discontinuous sediment bodies concentrated in the Wadi Mayhah area, with 'background' shale deposition elsewhere. However, margin destabilization in the Late Jurassic generated more widespread calcirudites from a line source of the platform margin and created more numerous sediment input points, such that subsequent carbonate input at the top of the formation was more widespread.

Drowning of the margin in the Tithonian not only resulted in chert deposition on the slope (B

Member, Mayhah Formation) but also in the basin. The Sid'r Formation contains silicified limestones at its base then, with the cut-off of carbonate input, shale deposition dominated although, where not swamped by terrigenous sediment, radiolarian cherts formed.

The return to carbonate deposition (Nayid Formation) is poorly dated, and cannot be directly correlated with the stratigraphy of the Sumeini Group. Derived microfossils and comparisons with other areas of Hamrat Duru Group exposure indicate a mid-Cretaceous age. Unlike previous perennial sedimentation patterns, shale is subordinate to platey lime mudstones. A sequence of silicified limestones at the top of some successions is tentatively correlated with the Riyamah unit of the Muti Formation (Robertson 1987).

The distal Hawasina thrust sheets exposed elsewhere in the Oman Mountains (Bernoulli & Weissart 1987) and in the adjacent Hatta Zone (Robertson et al. 1990) are not present in the Sumeini area.

Haybi Complex

The Haybi Complex (Searle 1980; Searle & Malpas 1980, 1982) structurally overlies the Hawasina thrust sheets and is overlain by the Semail ophiolite. In the Sumeini area, it is made up of four main components: the Haybi volcanic Group, Oman Exotic limestones, the metamorphic sheet and a sedimentary melange unit. The Haybi volcanics comprise titanaugite and biotite-phyric ankaramites, rare nephelinites and alkali basalts and tholeiitic pillow lavas of Late Triassic age, that are interpreted as within-plate oceanic island seamounts (Searle et al. 1980). The extensive Crataceous volcanism recorded in the Dibba Zone and Hatta zone (Robertson et al. 1990) is not present in the Sumeini area, although two small differentiated alkali periodotite sills have been mapped on Jebel Ghawil (Fig. 6). These are composed of biotite–kaersutite jacupirangites and biotite–olivine–titanaugite wehrlites and have K-Ar biotite ages 92 ± 4 and 93 ± 5 Ma (Searle 1984).

The Oman Exotic limestones are both Upper Permian and Upper Triassic although only Triassic examples are present in the Sumeini area. They conformably overlie the Haybi volcanic Group in Jebel Ghawil (Fig. 6) and are interpreted as reefal atoll cappings to the volcanic oceanic islands (Searle & Graham 1982).

The metamorphic sheet comprises hornblende and plagioclase $\pm$ garnet $\pm$ clinopyroxene amphibolites which at the highest pressures and temperatures show incipient partial melting textures immediately beneath the mantle sequence harzburgites (Searle & Malpas 1980, 1982; Ghent & Stout 1981). Geochemistry of the amphibolites suggest they are derived from MORB-related basalts and not from the Haybi alkali volcanics (Searle & Malpas 1982). The greenschists, structurally below the amphibolites, are dominantly impure quartzites with piemontite, muscovite, chlorite and rarely garnet, with less common pelites and spectacular banded marbles, interpreted as being derived largely from the Haybi Complex. Metamorphic isograds are structurally telescoped and inverted in intact sequences. High temperature, low pressure metamorphism occurred at high thermal gradients under dynamic simple shear conditions, with heat being derived from the recently formed and still hot ($>1000°C$) ophiolitic sole. Subsequent thin-skinned thrusting created imbricate slices within the Haybi duplex.

The sedimentary rocks within the Haybi Complex include relatively intact shale and chert sequences together with olistostromes or sedimentary melanges. These melanges have a multi-coloured shale or radiolarian mudstone matrix and olistoliths or slide blocks are composed of Oman Exotic limestones and Haybi volcanic rocks. The Haybi Complex sediments have been correlated with the Aruma Group; the syn-tectonic foreland basin succession above the platform carbonates (Searle et al. 1983; Searle 1985). Robertson (1987) includes these rocks in the Buday'ah unit of the Muti Formation and interprets them as the most northeasterly derived Upper Cretaceous foredeep succession now preserved.

Semail ophiolite sole thrust

The Semail thrust marks the base of the Semail ophiolite complex and shows both early ductile shearing fabrics and later brittle mylonite fabrics both in the hanging-wall (banded ultramafic unit) and footwall (metamorphic sheet). The structural telescoping of isograds indicates that shear deformation was syn-metamorphic and in a high thermal gradient. Searle (1985) noted the apparent truncation of metamorphic fabric and folds in the footwall in a few areas, and interpreted the final phase of motion along the Semail thrust as being out-of-sequence. In the northern part of the Sumeini half-window the ophiolite overlaps the Haybi duplex to rest directly on the upper Hamrat Duru duplex. The Semail ophiolite complex shows the entire oceanic mantle and crustal sequence which is

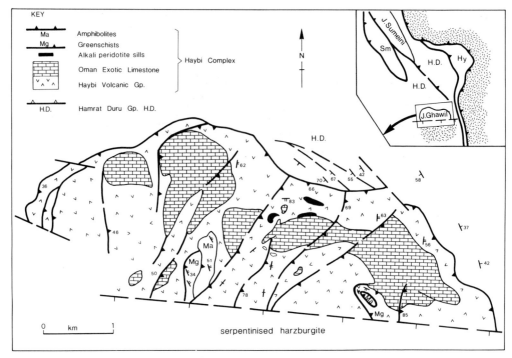

Fig. 6. Geological map of Jebel Ghawil. See Fig. 2 for location. Sm = Sumeini Group; HD = Hamrat Duru Group; Hy = Haybi complex.

over 10 km thick and is relatively intact with few internal thrusts (Lippard *et al.* 1986).

Sumeini half-window

Along Wadi Shiyah, west of Rayy Village (Figs 2 & 7) the Semail thrust has been folded and eroded to reveal the sub-ophiolite structures within the Haybi complex (Searle 1980, 1985). A relatively thick (ca. 150 m), strongly banded unit of highly sheared and serpentinized harzburgites, dunites and rare wehrlites form the base of the Semail ophiolite thrust sheet. Strong planar fabrics are evident along numerous low-temperature ductile shear zones within the ultramafics where preferential serpentinization has occurred. Along the northern edge of the Sumeini half-window the metamorphic sheet is attached to the footwall of the Semail thrust and still retains its original inverted metamorphic isograds. Garnet−clinopyroxene−hornblende−plagioclase amphibolites pass structurally downward to more homogenous garnet-free amphibolites and then a variety of greenschist facies rocks. Mylonitic fabrics are common throughout the sequence with numerous intrafolial folds and asymmetric

strain-slip folds, all indicating WSW-directed emplacement.

In the central and southern part of the Sumeini half-window, the metamorphic sheet has been disrupted by imbricate thrusting within the Haybi duplex. Amphibolites and green-schists are imbricated with alkaline and tholeiitic Haybi volcanics, Late Cretaceous sedimentary melanges and shale sequences which might be laterally equivalent of the Aruma Group fore-deep sediments on the shelf. The Haybi Complex rocks form a separate duplex bounded by the Semail thrust above and the Haybi thrust below, neither of which are breached by underlying later thrusts (Fig. 7).

Jebel Ghawil

A second area of exposure of Haybi Complex rocks form a klippe 4 km long at Jebel Ghawil (Fig. 6), structurally overlying the upper Hamrat Duru Group thrust sheet (Fig. 8). The klippe is bounded along the north side by the Haybi thrust, and along the south by an E−W aligned normal fault which has dropped the Sharm peridotite block approximately 500−1000 m down to the south. This later fault is interpreted

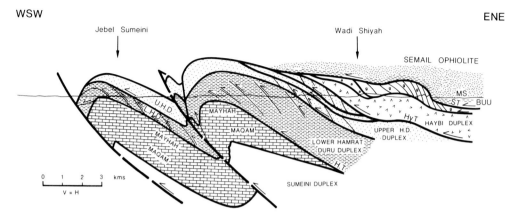

Fig. 7. Cross section from the southern end of Jebel Sumeini along Wadi Shiyah. See Fig. 2 for location. Ms = Mantle Sequence; Buu = Banded ultramafic unit; ST = Semail Thrust; HyT Haybi Thrust; H - Hawasina Thrust.

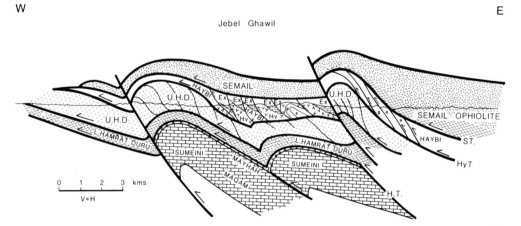

Fig. 8. Cross section across Jebel Ghawil to the base of the Semail ophiolite. See Fig. 2 for location. Abbreviations are the same as for Fig. 7.

as a hanging-wall drop fault associated with an E–W aligned lateral ramp at depth within the Sumeini slope carbonates (Fig. 9). It may reflect the southern limit of the Sumeini slope carbonates at depth and the beginning of a reentrant or embayment in the shelf edge to the south of Jebel Ghawil.

Imbricate thrusting has repeated the Haybi volcanic–Exotic limestone succession across Jebel Ghawil and in two localities amphibolites and greenschists of the metamorphic sole have been incorporated into the imbricate stack. Imbricate faults all dip eastwards and fold vergence directions consistently indicate WSW-directed transport.

Hamrat Duru Group Structure

Dominant emplacement-related fold axes and imbrication trends within the Hamrat Duru rocks are NNW–SSE with an orthogonal emplacement vector towards the WSW. Two separate duplexes of Hamrat Duru Group lithologies are recognized separating the Sumeini Group from the Haybi Complex and Semail ophiolite.

The upper Hamrat Duru duplex is concentrated along the eastern edge of the half-window, where one or two main imbricates, that are themselves internally thickened by smaller-scale structural repetitions, are com-

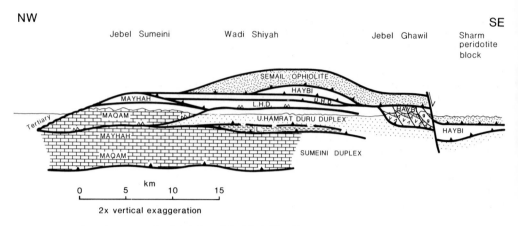

Fig. 9. Lateral section across the Jebel Sumeini–Jebel Ghawil area.

posed of the full Triassic to lower Cretaceous Hamrat Duru stratigraphic successions (Fig. 3). In the south, it lies beneath the Haybi Complex rocks of Jebel Ghawil and exposure continues along the western side of Wadi Sumeini, where folding in the Sumeini Group can be followed down-plunge into a broad anticline–syncline pair that folds the lower and upper Hamrat Duru duplex.

The upper Hamrat Duru duplex wraps around exposures of the Triassic imbricates of the lower Hamrat Duru duplex in central Wadi Sumeini. These have been structurally raised by folding of the piggy-back sequence due to culmination associated with later stage breakback thrusting in the Sumeini Group. Thrust contacts with the underlying Sumeini Group are seen around SSE-plunging antiformal folds at the southern end of Jebel Sumeini and along the southern Wadi Mayhah area (Fig. 2). Northwards, however, successively higher structural levels of the Hamrat Duru Group are juxtaposed against the Sumeini Group. The implications of this oblique contact are discussed later.

Jebel Sumeini

Mesozoic slope carbonates of the Sumeini Group are the structurally lowest units exposed in a SSE-plunging culmination which forms Jebel Sumeini (Fig. 4). The Hamrat Duru thrust sheets wrap around plunging fold noses at the south end of Jebel Sumeini, indicating that these deeper-water Tethyan sediments had been emplaced over the slope lithologies prior to thrust propagation into the lower Sumeini Group. The Hamrat Duru sole thrust overlies the Mayhah Formation where the original stacking order is

preserved; however the eastern margin of the Sumeini exposure was affected by down-to-the east normal faulting associated with culmination collapse, along northern Wadi Mayhah (Fig. 2), where the upper Hamrat Duru thrust sheet rests against Sumeini Group rocks.

Shortening within the Sumeini duplex is primarily accommodated by upright to WSW-facing folding with subordinate WSW-directed thrusting. Three major thrusts cut the Sumeini duplex into three main thrust sheets. In the west, a thrust separates Jebel Sumeini west from Jebel Wasa. Triassic fore-reef-talus facies in the footwall (J. Wasa Formation) are correlated with base of slope sediments of the upper Maqam Formation in the hanging-wall (Glennie *et al.* 1974; Watts & Garrison 1986) suggesting a major facies change across the thrust. This facies change was probably controlled by Triassic rift-related normal faulting (Watts & Garrison 1986) in which case the present thrust resulted from 'inversion' or reactivation of a pre-existing normal fault with a reversed sense of motion.

The mid-Sumeini thrust separates Jebel Sumeini west from Jebel Sumeini east. It is a late-stage breakback thrust that cuts through the Sumeini Group and breaches up into the overlying Hamrat Duru duplex placing previously lower Sumeini rocks over previously higher Hamrat Duru rocks. Folds, bedding and cleavage within the Hamrat Duru duplexes are cut by this fault which has breached through overlying thrust sheets. The south-plunging structures of the Sumeini area is such that in the north, Sumeini Group imbricates are juxtaposed, whilst towards the south a sliver of the lower duplex of the Hamrat Duru Group occurs between Jebel Sumeini east and west. A continuation of the mid-Sumeini thrust fault to the south displaces the lower Hamrat Duru duplex over the upper Hamrat Duru duplex and extends as far south as the eastern edge of Jebel Ghawil (Fig. 2), where the upper Hamrat Duru duplex is thrust over the Haybi Complex.

The structurally high position of the Sumeini culmination may indicate subsurface thrusting extending into the shelf carbonate sequence in the Jebel Sumeini area. This cannot be demonstrated from outcrop data alone since the area west of Jebel Sumeini is covered by alluvial outwash and aeolian sediments.

The timing of this late-stage thrusting is constrained by exposures of upper Late Maastrichtian and Tertiary limestones on the northern flank of Jebel Sumeini and at the northern end of the upper Hamrat Duru duplex in Wadi Mayhah (Figs 4 & 10). These sediments lie unconformably over the Sumeini Group along an erosional basal surface that truncates steeply east-dipping bedding within the Sumeini Group implying Late Cretaceous deformation. However, post-Eocene motion has tilted the upper Late Maastrichtian sediments c. 35°, dipping to the WNW indicating further uplift of Jebel Sumeini during the Tertiary. This is related to renewed thrusting along the westernmost thrust fault of the Jebel Sumeini culmination over Maastrichtian and Tertiary (Eocene?) carbonates 5 km to the south, at the western margin of Jebel Wasa. There are also isolated exposures of Maastrichtian—Tertiary limestones on the alluvial plains west of Jebel Sumeini, and conglomerates within them contain a variety of limestone clasts and some rarer granitic clasts, all of which were probably derived from weathering of the Sumeini Group or Hawasina Complex, in which basement-derived material locally occurs in other conglomerates, for examples in the Dibba zones, UAE (Searle *et al*. 1983; Searle 1988a).

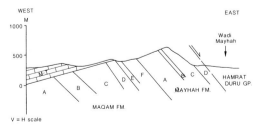

Fig. 10. Cross section across the northern part of Jebel Sumeini. See Fig. 2 for location of section.

Discussion

Sequence and timing of thrusting

The Jebel Sumeini—Jebel Ghawil area is critical for the determination of the sequence of thrusting and the style and timing of deformation during emplacement of the Semail ophiolite and the Oman Tethyan sediments within the northern Oman Mountains. In common with other culminations in the Oman Mountains (Searle 1985), the sequence of thrusting in the Sumeini area was dominantly one of foreland propagating piggy-back thrusting. Late-stage thrust faulting in the Sumeini Group was associated with deeper-level thrusting that breached the overlying Hawasina thrust sheets. Whereas the timing of growth of other culminations cored by the Sumeini Group in the Dibba zone, Asjudi half-window, Haybi corridor and Hawasina window is poorly constrained, the Jebel Sumeini culmination is unique in being associated with upper Maastrichtian and Tertiary sediments. Relationships between the allochthonous units and the post-ophiolite emplacement sediments clearly demonstrate that the development of the Sumeini culmination was primarily a Late Cretaceous event, followed by an erosional break and the deposition of upper Maastrichtian to ?Eocene conglomerates and carbonates. A second stage of small displacement thrusting and uplift is indicated by deformation affecting Maastrichtian to Eocene rocks. This late stage deformation can be related to the post-Eocene compressional event in the northern Oman foreland that was responsible for the doubly-plunging whale-back folds such as Jebel Hafit and Jebel Faiyah, both of which are associated with short-displacement reverse faults.

Detailed structural mapping in other northern Oman areas, notably the Asjudi half-window (Searle 1980, 1985), the Wadi Qumayrah area (Watts 1985), the Haybi—Hawasina window (Searle 1985, Searle & Cooper 1986), the Wadi Hatta window (Robertson *et al*. 1990) and the Dibba Zone in the United Arab Emirates (Searle *et al*. 1983; Searle 1988a; Robertson *et al*. 1990) suggests that all these culminations are cored by thrust sheets of the most proximal Sumeini Group slope sediments and formed by late-stage thrusting of these sediments.

Location of the Cretaceous shelf edge

Restoration of balanced cross-sections across all these areas allows the approximate position of the shelf edge to be determined from shortening estimates of the Sumeini Group rocks.

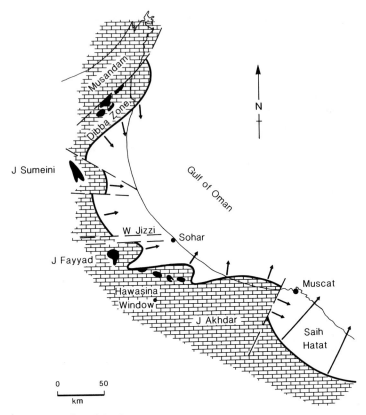

Fig. 11. Schematic reconstruction of the Oman shelf edge configuration in the Cenomanian. Black patches are the present location of Sumeini Group exposures. Short arrows depict a relatively steep shelf margin slope in the northern and central parts of the Oman Mountains. Long arrows depict a broader, gently dipping carbonate ramp in the Saih Hatat area (after Smewing & Pratt 1986).

Palaeogeographic reconstructions of the Jurassic (Watts 1990) and Lower Cretaceous (Cooper 1988, Fig. 5) shelf edge in northern Oman have been published. Fig. 11 shows a schematic reconstruction of Oman shelf edge position in the Cenomanian immediately prior to the large scale thrust emplacement of the Hawasina, Haybi and Semail ophiolite thrust sheets. Unfortunately Sumeini Group rocks are only exposed along the northern margin of the Dibba zone and in the isolated culminations mentioned above. In between these areas we have to infer the approximate position of the edge. The Cretaceous shelf edge is buried by the overlying thrust sheets along most of the length of the Oman Mountains and could only be detected by deep seismic studies which lose their precision east of the mountain front. Dunne *et al.* (1990) present a series of cross-sections across the foreland and western front of the northern Oman Mountains.

The Musandam peninsula acted as a major eastward projecting promontory of the Arabian shelf with the Dibba zone forming an oblique NE−SW striking south-facing margin to this promontory (Searle 1988a,b). A minor amount of right lateral strike-slip faulting or transtension may have occurred along the Dibba zone margin (Robertson *et al.* 1990). South of the Dibba zone no Sumeini rocks are exposed, except for isolated occurrences at Qarn Nazwa, until the Jebel Sumeini and Wadi Hatta areas. Seismic sections (Dunne *et al.* 1990) suggest that the shelf edge is structurally low and there is only evidence for short-distance thrusting as opposed to larger distances in the north (15 km westward translation) and in the Jebel Sumeini area (ca. 7 km displacement). We therefore infer that a reentrant in the Cretaceous shelf edge stretched 75 km south to a shelf edge promontory in the Jebel Sumeini−Wadi Hatta region. We infer that the Wadi Hatta transform fault also offset the shelf edge (Fig. 11).

South of the Jebel Sumeini area there is no

exposure of Sumeini rocks until we reach Jebel Fayyad–Wadi Qumayrah area where another major culmination cored by Sumeini Group rocks crops out (Searle 1985; Watts & Garrison 1986). We assume that the Wadi Qumayrah slope deposits are aligned with Jebel Sumeini although there may equally well have been a moderate embayment between the two areas because we believe that the Sumeini rocks are structurally low and translation distances are small in the area around Wadi Jizzi.

Searle & Cooper (1986) defined a major NE-facing promontory from restoration of Sumeini Group culminations in the Hawasina Window area. The position of the shelf edge must then swing to the north of the Jebel Akhdar Window where true shelf carbonate facies are exposed. The location of the shelf edge is poorly defined east of Jebel Akhdar although Smewing & Pratt (1986) have identified a broad, gently dipping carbonate ramp in the southern Saih Hatat area.

We suggest that the configuration of the Cretaceous shelf edge was not necessarily sub-parallel to the Cretaceous thrust front but consisted of a series of east or northeast facing promontories offset by minor strike slip or normal faults and separated by broad embayments. We suggest that the major Sumeini-cored culminations were a product of the interaction of the Semail ophiolite thrust sheet with an irregular continental margin profile, promoting localized footwall collapse and thrusting within the Sumeini Group along shelf-edge promontories.

Our three PhD projects were funded by an Open University Research grant (MPS), a Natural Environment Research Council grant at Edinburgh University (DJWC) and the Earth Sciences Board, University of California, Santa Cruz (KFW). Fieldwork was largely funded by AMOCO Oman Petroleum Company. We are grateful to this organization and also to J. Smewing, A. Robertson and R. Garrison for discussions and S. Hanna and P. Barette for reviewing the manuscript. This paper is published with the permission of AMOCO Production Company.

References

BERNOULLI, D. & WEISSART, H. 1987. The upper Hawasina nappes in the central Oman Mountains: Stratigraphy, palinspatics and sequence of nappe emplacement. *Geodynamica Acta*, **1**, 47–58.

COLEMAN, R. G. 1981. Tectonic setting for ophiolite obduction in Oman. *Journal of Geophysical Research*, **86**, 2497–2508.

COOPER, D. J. W. 1986. *The Hamrat Duru Group: evolution of a Mesozoic passive carbonate margin in the Oman Mountains.* Unpublished PhD thesis, University of Edinburgh, UK.

—— 1987. Hamrat Duru Group: revised stratigraphy of a Mesozoic deep-water passive margin in the Oman Mountains. *Geological Magazine*, **124**, 157–164.

—— 1988. Structure and sequence of thrusting in deep-water sediments during ophiolite emplacement in the south-central Oman Mountains. *Journal of Structural Geology*, **10**, 473–485.

—— 1990. Sedimentary evolution and palaeogeographical reconstruction of the Mesozoic continental rise of Oman Neo-Tethys evidence from the Hamrat Duru Group. *In*: ROBERTSON, A. H. F., SEARLE, M. P. & RIES, A. C. (eds) *The Geology and Tectonics of the Oman Region.* Geological Society, London, Special Publication, **49**, 161–187.

DUNNE, L. A., MANOOGIAN, P. R. & PIERINI, D. F. 1990. Structural style and domains of the Northern Oman Mountains (Oman and United Arab Emirates). *In*: ROBERTSON, A. H. F., SEARLE, M. P. & RIES, A. C. (eds) *The Geology and Tectonics of the Oman Region.* Geological Society, London, Special Publication, **49**, 375–386.

GHENT, E. D. & STOUT, M. Z. 1981. Metamorphism at the base of the Samail Ophiolite, southeastern Oman Mountains. *Journal of Geophysical Research*, **86**, 2557–2571.

GLENNIE, K. W., BOEUF, M. G. A., HUGHES CLARK, M. W., MOODY-STUART, M., PILAAR, M. F. & REINHARDT, B. B. 1973. Late Cretaceous nappes in the Oman Mountains and their geologic evolution. *American Association of Petroleum Geologists Bulletin*, **57**, 5–27.

——, ——, ——, ——, —— & ——. 1974. Geology of the Oman Mountains. *Koninklijk Nederlands. Geologisch Mijnbouwkundig Genootschap, Verhanderlingen*, **31**.

GRAHAM, G. M. 1980. *Structure and Sedimentology of the Hawasina Window, Oman Mountains.* Unpublished PhD thesis, Open University.

LIPPARD, S. J., SMEWING, J. D., ROTHERY, D. A. & BROWNING, P. 1982. The geology of the Dibba zone, northern Oman Mountains: a preliminary study. *Journal of the Geological Society, London*, **139**, 59–66.

——, SHELTON, A. W. & GASS, I. G. 1986. The ophiolite of northern Oman. *Geological Society, London, Memoir*, **11**.

ROBERTSON, A. H. F. 1987. The transition from a passive margin to an upper Cretaceous foreland basin related to ophiolite emplacement in the Oman Mountains. *Bulletin of the Geological Society of America*, **99**, 633–653.

——, BLOME, C. D., COOPER, D. W. J., KEMP, A. E. S., D. & SEARLE, M. P. 1990a. Evolution of the Arabian continental margin in the Dibba Zone, Northern Oman Mountains. *In*: ROBERTSON, A. H. F. SEARLE, M. P. & RIES, A. C. (eds) *The Geology and Tectonics of the Oman Region.* Geological Society, London, Special Publication, **49**, 251–284.

——, KEMP, A. E. S., REX D. C. & BLOME, C. D. 1990b. Sedimentary and structural evolution of a transform lineament: the Hatta Zone, Northern

Oman Mountains. *In*: ROBERTSON, A. H. F., SEARLE, M. P. & RIES, A. C. (eds) *The Geology and Tectonics of the Oman Region*. Geological Society, London, Special Publication, **49**, 285–305.

SEARLE, M. P. 1980. *The metamorphic sheet and underlying volcanic rocks beneath the Semail Ophiolite in the northern Oman Mountains of Arabia*. Unpublished PhD thesis, Open University, Milton Keynes, UK.

—— 1984. Alkaline peridotite, pyroxenite and gabbroic intrusions in the Oman Mountains Arabia. *Canadian Journal of Earth Science*, **21**, 396–406.

—— 1985. Sequence of thrusting and origin of culminations in the northern and central Oman Mountains. *Journal of Structural Geology*, **7**, 129–143.

—— 1988a. Thrust tectonics of the Dibba zone and the structural evolution of the Arabian continental margin along the Musandam mountains (Oman and United Arab Emirates). *Journal of the Geological Society, London*, **145**, 43–53.

—— 1988b. Structure of the Musandam culmination (Sultanate of Oman and United Arab Emirates) and the Straits of Hormuz syntaxis. *Journal of the Geological Society, London*, **145**, 831–845.

—— & COOPER, D. J. W. 1986. Structure of the Hawasina Window culmination, central Oman Mountains. *Transactions of the Royal Society of Edinburgh*, **77**, 143–156.

—— & GRAHAM G. M. 1982. 'Oman Exotics' — Oceanic carbonate build-ups associated with the early stages of continental rifting. *Geology*, **10**, 43–49.

——, JAMES, N. P., CALON, T. J. & SMEWING, J. D. 1983. Sedimentological and structural evolution of the Arabian continental margin in the Musandam Mountains and Dibba zone, United Arab Emirates. *Bulletin of the Geological Society of America*, **94**, 1381–1400.

——, LIPPARD, S. J., SMEWING, J. D. & REX, D. 1980. Volcanic rocks beneath the Oman ophiolite and their significance in the Mesozoic evolution of Tethys. *Journal of the Geological Society, London*, **137**, 589–604.

—— & MALPAS, J. 1980. The structure and metamorphism of rocks beneath the Semail ophiolite of Oman and their significance in ophiolite obduction. *Transactions of the Royal Society of Edinburgh*, **71**, 213–228.

—— & —— 1982. Petrochemistry and origin of sub-ophiolitic metamorphic and related rocks in the Oman Mountains. *Journal of the Geological Society, London*, **139**, 235–248.

SMEWING, J. D. & PRATT, B. R. 1986. Jurassic continental margin configuration, central Oman mountains — evidence from facies trends in the Hajar Super Group. *In: Hydrocarbon Potential of Intense Thrust Zones — Abu Dhabi Conference*, **1**, 201–226.

WATTS, K. F. 1985. *Evolution of carbonate slope facies along a south Tethyan continental margin: the Mesozoic Sumeini Group and the Qumayrah Facies of the Muti Formation, Oman*. Unpublished PhD thesis, University of California, Santa Cruz, California, USA.

—— 1987. Triassic carbonate submarine fans along the Arabian platform margin, Sumeini Group, Oman. *Sedimentology*, **34**, 43–71.

—— 1990. Mesozoic carbonate slope facies marking the Arabian platform margin. *In*: ROBERTSON, A. H. F., SEARLE, M. P. & RIES, A. C. (eds) *The Geology and Tectonics of the Oman Region*. Geological Society, London, Special Publication, **49**, 139–159.

—— & GARRISON R. E. 1986. Sumeini Group, Oman — evolution of a Mesozoic carbonate slope on a south Tethyan continental margin. *Sedimentary Geology*, **48**, 107–168.

Structural style and domains of the Northern Oman Mountains (Oman and United Arab Emirates)

L. A. DUNNE[1], P. R. MANOOGIAN[1] & D. F. PIERINI[2]

[1] *Amoco Production Company, PO Box 3092 Houston TX 77253, USA*
[2] *Advantage Resources, Denver, CO, USA*

Abstract: A variation in the style of compressional deformation is observed in the northern Oman Mountains. This variation is expressed by the relationship between two major structural levels. The shallower structural level comprises Tertiary (Pabdeh Group), Late Cretaceous (Aruma Group), and Mesozoic (Hawasina and Sumeini Groups) clastics and carbonates that have been extensively deformed by closely spaced, folded duplexes and imbricate fans. In response to the same compressional events, the deformation in the deeper portion of the section is charcterized by more widely spaced, high-angle reverse faults that are interpreted to merge at depth into a decollement surface. This reverse fault system creates large hanging wall anticlines of Middle (Wasia Group) to Early Cretaceous (Thamama Group) and older platform carbonates. The major differences in the structural styles of the two levels are probably related to lithologic variations of the major tectono-stratigraphic units in response to the compression and the large-scale dynamics of the thrust belt as a whole.

Structural linkage is expressed between the two levels by the spacial correlation of the culmination axes of the two levels. The variation in this linkage between the two levels in a strike orientation defines several domains that are separated by major structural disconti-nuities. These domains are interpreted to reflect differences in the interaction between the two structural levels during several compressional events. They are postulated to have been ultimately created in response to variations in the dynamics of the thrust belt related to the emplacement of the Semail Ophiolite onto the Arabian continental margin during the Late Cretaceous and subsequent reactivation during the Tertiary.

The regional geology and compressional deformation of the Oman Mountains have been addressed by numerous investigators, including Hudson *et al.* (1954); Ricateau & Riche (1980); Searle *et al.* (1980, 1983) and Searle (1985). The general timing and sequence of thrusting has been well documented and is characterized by Late Cretaceous 'in-sequence' emplacement of the Tethyan thrust sheet onto the Arabian plat-form. Subsequent Tertiary 'out-of-sequence' and 'leap-frog' thrusting followed and signifi-cantly complicated the original structural geometries (Searle 1985).

The subsurface structural configuration along the unexposed western leading edge of the de-formed belt in the United Arab Emirates and northern Oman is less well understood than the surface relationships (Fig. 1). An understanding of the subsurface in this area is of great interest from the perspective of hydrocarbon explo-ration as there are three major condensate−gas fields along this trend; Amoco's Sajaa Field, Arco's Margham Field and IPC's Bukha Field. For this reason, analysis and modeling of well, potential field, and seismic data have been done to delineate this leading edge as it is where the

thrust-related hydrocarbon production occurs, both in this and other productive thrust belts. Many of the relationships documented from surface exposures can be identified in the sub-surface. The purpose of this paper is to docu-ment the deformation style of the Mesozoic platform carbonate section and its relationship to the shallower section, as well as to explain what factors may have influenced this deformation.

Geological setting

The Infra-Cambrian to Palaeozoic tectonic his-tory of the area now comprising the eastern Arabian continental margin was one of relative continental stability. In the Infra-Cambrian ex-tensive evaporite deposition occurred in intra-cratonic basins with mixed carbonate and clastic deposition on the adjacent platform. Clastic deposition became dominant in the Palaeozoic (Koop & Stoneley 1982). This stability was terminated in the Permo-Triassic when intra-cratonic rifting and subsequent passive margin formation occurred as the southern Neotethys, or Hawasina, Ocean basin opened (Glennie *et*

From ROBERTSON, A. H. F., SEARLE, M. P. & RIES, A. C. (eds), 1990,
The Geology and Tectonics of the Oman Region.
Geological Society Special Publication No 49, pp 375−386

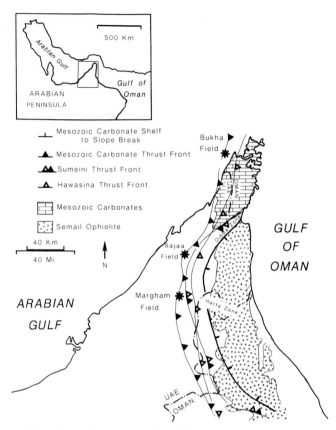

Fig. 1. Location map illustrating major tectonostratigraphic units and structural fronts of the northern Oman Mountains. Structural front positions in the subsurface identified from well, potential fields and seismic information.

al. 1973, 1974; Stocklin 1974; Koop & Stoneley 1982; Şengör *et al.* 1984; Smewing & Pratt 1986). Deposition on the Arabian platform during the Mesozoic was characterized by shallow marine carbonates of the Hajar Super-group and equivalents with concomittent slope (Sumeini Group) and basinal (Hawasina Group) deposition in the Neotethys Ocean (Glennie *et al.* 1973, 1974; Murris 1980; Koop & Stoneley 1982; Watts & Garrison 1986; Smewing & Pratt 1986; Watts 1990) (Fig. 2). Formation of an intra-oceanic subduction zone and the Semail island arc backarc complex in the Middle Cretaceous (Albian–Cenomian) initiated the closure of this ocean basin (Pearce *et al.* 1981; Gass & Shelton 1986). This was accompanied by a distinct change in depositional style on the platform as it became internally differentiated, resulting in deposition of the mixed shale–carbonate sequence of the Wasia Group (Patton & O'Connor 1986, 1988).

The subsequent impingement of this subduc-

tion-arc complex with the eastern margin of Arabia resulted in flexural loading of the margin and development of a peripheral swell and associated regional erosional unconformity during the latest Cenomanian through Turonian (Patton & O'Connor 1986). The incomplete subduction of Arabian continental crust beneath the Semail arc complex resulted in detachment and obduction of oceanic crust onto the Arabian margin. This obduction created the widespread compressional deformation that characterizes the Oman Mountains as well as the flexural foredeep of the Late Cretaceous Aruma Basin (Glennie *et al.* 1974; Pinnington *et al.* 1981; Searle *et al.* 1983; Harris *et al.* 1984; Manoogian & Dunne 1988; Nolan et al. 1990). The margin stabilized by the end of the Campanian, when obduction effectively ceased, and remained so until post-Middle Eocene time throughout the deposition of the Simsima and Umm Er Radhuma Formations (Searle *et al.* 1983; Manoogian & Dunne 1988). Evidence of post–

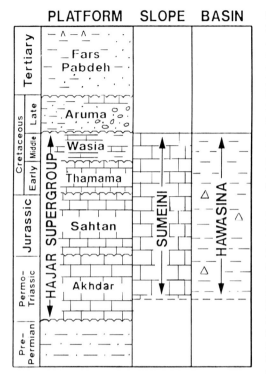

Fig. 2. Major tectonostratigraphic units in the northern Oman Mountains.

Middle Eocene compression and structural reactivation is present. This is particularly evident in the northern Oman Mountains, although the number and timing of these later events is poorly constrained. Further development of the flexural basin, the Pabdeh Basin, is associated with this reactivation, which is probably related to the closure of the northern Neotethys in the Tertiary. Since the Middle to Late Miocene, this area has been affected by isostatic equilibration of the eastern margin of the Arabian platform. Nolan *et al.* (1990) attribute the present topography to this post-Miocene uplift. Uplift has occurred along the western coast of the Musandam Peninsula with downwarping along the northern and eastern coastline (Ricateau & Riche 1980) which is being subducted beneath the Eurasian continent.

Structural levels

The predominant structural style in the Oman Mountains is compressional with a general east to west vergence in the northern mountains swinging to a north to south vergence in the southern mountains (Fig. 1). The structural fronts of the major tectonostratigraphic units are delineated by both surface and subsurface data. Based on potential field data, the Mesozoic carbonate shelf-to-slope break is interpreted to lie approximately below the frontal edge of the Semail ophiolite south of the Dibba Zone. There is progressively more overriding of this shelf to slope break to the south. Manoogian & Dunne (1988) speculate that this is related to a change from a differentiated slope margin edge, which acted as a buttress to the obducting ophiolite body in the north, to a ramp margin in the south.

The Hawasina and Sumeini thrust fronts show an interesting relationship. Both north of the Dibba Zone and south of the Hatta Zone (Fig. 1), the Hawasina front occurs more toward the foreland than the Sumeini front. This relationship is reversed in the area between the two zones where the Sumeini occupies a more foreland-ward position. This variation along strike has implications which will be discussed more fully in terms of the structural domains. The structural front of the Mesozoic carbonates is always west of that in the Hawasina–Sumeini fronts and occupies the most foreland position of all the major Mesozoic tectonostratigraphic units.

Both surface and subsurface relationships demonstrate that there are two major structural levels, and possibly a third deeper one below the resolution depth of the present data. The characteristics of the two discernable levels will be described as they are observed from both the surface and subsurface data.

Surface relationships

Two major structural levels can be identified from surface relationships in the northern Oman Mountains. The deeper level, which consists of Wasia, Thamama and older platform section (Fig. 2), is best exposed in the Musandam Peninsula. Surface mapping has delineated a series of west-vergent anticlines with steep to overturned western limbs. The faults which control this structural geometry have been interpreted to be high-angle reverse faults which sole out at depth into a horizontal detachment. Subsidiary normal faults are also present (Searle 1988). The eastern edge of the Musandam as defined in the Dibba Zone is characterized by a listric normal fault interpreted as a dorsal culmination collapse feature (Searle 1988; Robertson *et al.* 1990a).

In central Oman and the Dibba Zone of the Musandam, members of the shallower structural level include the Hawasina and Sumeini Groups. These units have been complexly deformed by thrusting (Glennie *et al*. 1973, 1974; Graham 1980; Ricateau & Riche 1980; Robertson *et al*. 1990*a*; Searle 1983; Searle 1985; Searle & Cooper 1986; Searle *et al*. 1990; Watts 1990; Watts & Garrison 1986). These units, in addition to the Aruma and Tertiary units which are less well exposed, comprise the shallowest structural level. The thrust structures within these units are characterized by eastwardly dipping thrusts that become listric with depth. Duplex formation is common. These appear to be hinterland (eastern) dipping systems (Searle 1985). The initial formation of the Hawasina, Sumeini and Aruma structures during the Late Cretaceous was likely 'normal' or in-sequence with later faults forming deeper and in a more forward or foreland position. Subsequent compression resulted in folding and rethrusting of both the deeper carbonate platform and shallower level structures giving rise to the 'out-of-sequence' and 'leap-frog' geometries of Searle (1985).

Subsurface relationships

In the subsurface, these two structural levels can also be delineated and their geometric relationships can be resolved in some detail from analysis of seismic, potential field, and well data. More than 10 000 line-kilometres of seismic, including a 3-D survey, were available for analysis. The quality of these data is variable. Selected lines were chosen for time-to-depth conversion based on both their position along the structural front and their data quality. Regional gravity and magnetic information was particularly useful in defining the leading edge of the Semail Ophiolite and its debris apron. In excess of sixty wells provided subsurface control for stratigraphic, structural and burial history data. Seven geoseismic cross-sections selected from the regional database illustrate the main features that can be observed along the leading edge of the northern Oman Mountains (Fig. 3). These sections were constructed from the depth-corrected seismic data, which were iteratively converted by an EVMIG process, as well as the other available data discussed above.

The deeper structural level consisting of Wasia, Thamama, and older platform units, is deformed into a series of west-vergent anticlines. The frontal limbs of the anticlines are steeply dipping and may become overturned in a foreland direction. The deformation of these structures is interpreted to have been caused by reverse faults which merge at depth into a decollement. This detachment is very

deep in the section and probably lies within the Palaeozoic section. It is also possible that there is a deeper structural level involving the pre-Permian section. The structural characteristics of this level are poorly understood in the northern Oman Mountains as this level is largely unexposed and below the resolution of the available seismic control. Likely speculative interpretations for the pre-Permian structure in the northern Oman Mountains may be similar to those described by Cawood *et al*. (1990), Mann & Hanna (1990), and discussed by Searle (1985) for the Jebel Akhdar area.

Although these faults have never been penetrated by a wellbore, or clearly imaged by seismic data, there are several indirect lines of evidence which suggest that they are reverse faults which may detach very deep in the section. The faults are not imaged on the seismic data as they exceed the angle of resolution of the seismic. Geometrical constraints provided by line-length balancing indicate that these faults cut the carbonate platform sequence at angles greater than 60°. There is also a significant component of vertical displacement along the leading edge of these structures. This vertical displacement certainly exceeds 1.2 km (Fig. 3, Section D−D') and may be more that 4 km (Fig. 3, Section A−A'). This occurs within a horizontal distance of 5 to 10 km.

In addition to the high-angle reverse faults, there are subsidiary thrust and normal faults within the platform sequence that have been encountered by wellbores. The thrust faults never duplicate more than 100 m of section and are more commonly associated with structures of strong west vergence. There are also normal faults that have throws of 300 to 600 m (Fig. 3, Section F−F'). Similar normal faults have been identified by Richateau & Riche (1980) and Searle (1988) in the carbonate platform sequence exposed in the Musandam. These faults are also difficult to identify from the seismic data, probably due to their interpreted high angle of dip.

Line-length balancing of the Thamama Group on dip-oriented sections was done to determine the amount of displacement at the carbonate platform level. Line-length balancing was thought to be suitable as little, if any, significant ductile behaviour or out-of-plane deformation is observed in exposures of the platform carbonates. The displacement of this level is determined by pinning the section in the western foreland autochthon with the loose line at the projected shelf edge to the east. The exact location of the shelf edge is difficult to define. Only lines of section where there is thought to

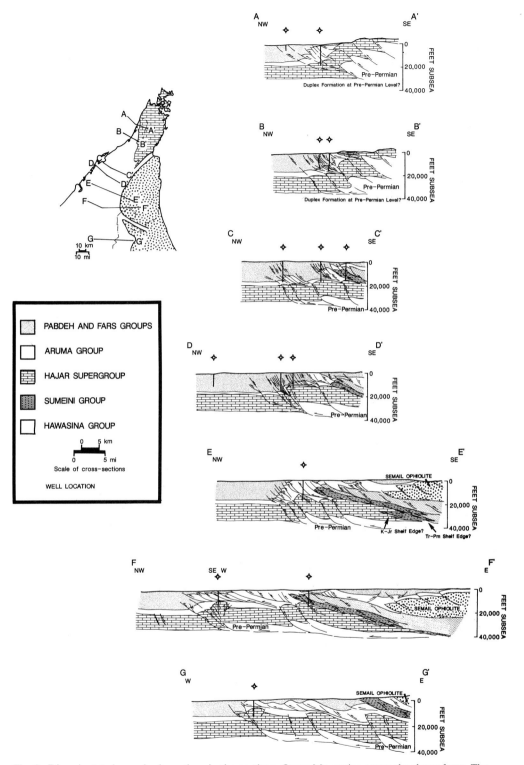

Fig. 3. Dip orientated geoseismic sections in the northern Oman Mountains across the thrust front. The sections are based on well, potential field and seismic data. Complex mesoscale structure in the Hawasina, Sumeini, Aruma, Pabdeh and Fars Groups is not illustrated. Sections have been balanced at the Mesozoic carbonate platform level only. Structure at the Pre-Permian level is highly speculative.

Table 1. *Average displacement of Mesozoic carbonate platform structures*

	Displacement	
	(km)	(miles)
Sections A−D	16	10
Sections E & F	5	3
Section G	10	6

Location of the sections is given in Fig. 3.
Displacement is determined from line-balanced sections at the Mesozoic Carbonate Platform level. The displacement is corrected to represent true dip displacement.

be good evidence as to the position of the shelf edge were used. Balancing of this deeper level results in horizontal displacements of 5−20 km, averaging 8 km.

There is an apparent change in displacement along strike with the least amount of displacement observed in Sharjah (Fig. 3, Sections D−D′ to F−F′) with greater displacement both to the north (Fig. 3, Section A−A′ and B−B′) and south (Fig. 3, Section G−G′) (Table 1). This change in displacement occurs where there is a change in the general structural configuration at the carbonate platform level. In the central portion of the study area (Fig. 3, Section C−C′), extensive well and dipmeter data indicate that the structures are relatively flat and have an abrupt frontal termination with little to no westward vergence (Fig 3, Section D−D′). To the north and south (Fig. 3, Sections A−A′, B−B′, F−F′ and G−G′) the structures have pronounce hanging-wall folds.

In the subsurface, the shallow structural level consisting of Hawasina, Sumeini, Aruma and Pabdeh Groups exhibits a style similar to that described from the surface exposures. Duplexes, as well as imbricate fans, can be interpreted from the seismic data. These appear to merge to a detachment at depth. These detachments ride above the Thamama level structures and become rooted into the block edges of these deeper structures. The Tertiary reactivation of the Aruma and older shallow structures is illustrated in Fig. 3 (Section D−D′) where an Aruma duplex cuts up through and truncates the younger Tertiary imbricate fan system. Similar relationships are common along the mountain front in the shallow level structure. We have not attempted to quantify the shortening in the shallow level because its ductile behaviour and out-of-plane deformation invalidates such balancing.

Structural domains

In the northern Oman Mountains three structural domains can be identified based on the variation in structural geometry and amount of displacement of the deep carbonate platform along strike, and the spatial relationship between the culmination axes of this deeper structural level and the shallower structural level in a vertical sense. Line-length balancing of the true dip sections of the carbonate platform level indicates a change in displacement at this level along the strike of the leading structural edge. Table 1 shows the average amount of displacement along the lines of section illustrated in Fig. 3. There is more displacement both to the north of Section D−D′ (in excess of 15 km) and to the south of F−F′ (in excess of 7 km) than the area between, which has one-half to one-third the amount of displacement (4−6 km). This spatially related variation in displacement at the deeper structural level is thought to be significant in terms of strike domains, and the implications of this will be discussed in that context in the next section.

In addition to this apparent segregation in the amount of displacement at the deeper structural level, there is a corresponding variation in culmination offsets between the deeper and shallower structural levels. This variation is defined by the position of the deeper level culminations with respect to the correlative shallower level culminations, in particular the Aruma culminations along the frontal edge. This relationship in culmination offsets is illustrated in Fig. 4. In the majority of cases, the shallower level culmination is to the west (foreland) of the corresponding platform level culmination. Variations do occur both in the sense of offset as well as distance in offset. In several cases, the Aruma culmination lies to the east of the deeper culmination (most northern structural pair and several in the southern area of the study) as shown on Fig. 4.

Several subtle but notable changes occur in the culmination offset distance along the strike of the mountain front. There is an average increase in this offset distance to the south for structural pairs where the Aruma culmination is to the west of the platform culmination. Two anomalous zones also exist where this distance exceeds 5 km, west of the southern end of the Dibba Zone and west of the Hatta Zone. There is also an area, immediately foreland of the westernmost extent of the Semail Ophiolite front, where no culmination offset occurs between the two structural levels (shallower culmi-

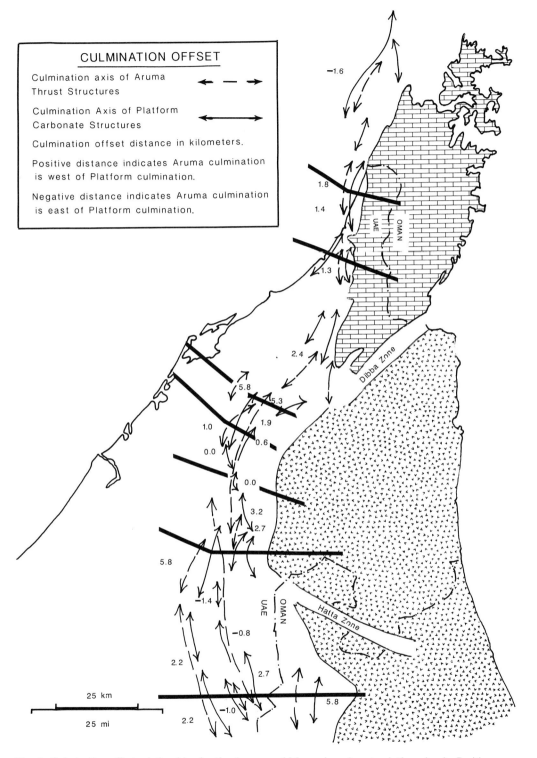

Fig. 4. Culmination offset relationships for the Aruma and Mesozoic carbonate platform levels. Positive offsets indicate the Aruma culmination is foreland of the Mesozoic carbonate culmination. Negative offsets indicate the reverse relationship.

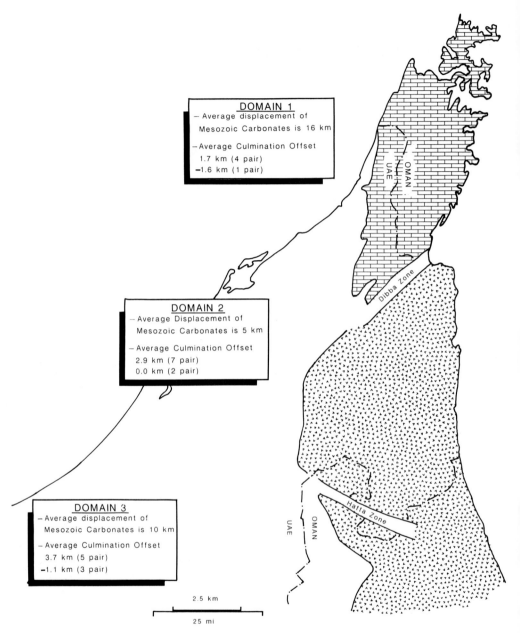

Fig. 5. Three structural domains identified from the average displacement at the Mesozoic carbonate platform level and the Aruma to Mesozoic carbonate platform culmination offset relationships.

nation is directly superimposed over the deeper culmination).

The relationship in culmination offsets that is most commonly observed is not one that would typically be anticipated in 'normal' foreland propagation of structural development, where the latest and deepest structures would occur in the more foreland position. The observed relationships lends strong support to Searle's (1985) contention that the northern Oman Mountains have a more complex deformational history than that predicted by simple foreland model of structural evolution. This complexity is interpreted to imply several discrete episodes

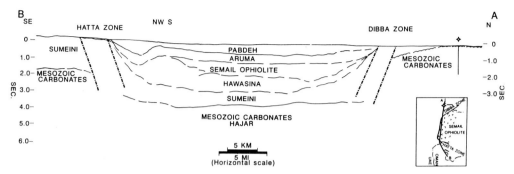

Fig. 6. Sketch section of seismic line oriented in strike direction illustrating the structural discontinuities of the Dibba and Hatta Zones as projected to the west from their surface expressions. The western subsurface limit of the Semail is based on potential field and seismic data.

of compression accompanied by rethrusting of previously formed structures.

The apparent variation and segregation both in displacement at the platform level and in the vector and magnitude of culmination offset delineate three structural domains along the strike of the northern Oman Mountains (Fig. 5). These three domains are separated by two zones that show major changes in the nature of the deeper platform carbonate level along strike (Fig. 6). The two zones are located where the greatest amount of culmination offset distance is observed along the trend, 5.8 km and 5.3 km west of the Dibba Zone, and 5.8 km west of the Hatta Zone (Fig. 4). There is a third zone at the southern limit of the study area where a similar amount of offset (5.8 km) is present. They are also associated with areas where there is a crossover between the Sumeini and Hawasina thrust fronts (Fig. 1). Of particular interest is that these two zones, which separate the three domains, are spacially linked to the surface expression of the Dibba and Hatta Zones that lie to the east.

The northernmost domain is characterized by an average displacement of 16 km at the platform level and, with the exception of one structural culmination pair, the Aruma culminations are to the west of the platform culminations. The average culmination offset distance is 1.7 km. There also appears to be greater structural relief and vertical stacking in this domain. To the south, the second domain has less displacement at the platform level, averaging 5 km. The Aruma culminations are all offset to the west of the platform culminations with the exception of two pairs which are coincident. The average offset distance is 2.9 km. The southern domain is characterized by an average displacement at the platform level of 10 km. There is a mixture in the sense of culmination offsets with the

Aruma culminations being offset both to the west and to the east of the platform culminations. For those culminations offset to the west, the average offset distance is 3.7 km. For those offset to the east, that distance averages 1.1 km.

Structural domain significance

The presence of three domains and the change in structural style which occurs at the Dibba and Hatta Zones suggests that these zones were involved in the segregation of the deformation resulting from the obduction of the Semail Ophiolite. This segregation, or compartmentalization, is thought to be related to the original continental margin morphology and its response during the obduction of the Semail Ophiolite. North of the Dibba Zone, the continental margin was differentiated with a narrow but well-developed slope morphology which acted as a buttress during the obduction event. To the south, a ramp margin with a more subtle gradient existed as suggested by the facies distribution (Watts & Garrison 1986; Watts 1990) and strike geometry as illustrated in Fig. 6. This area was subsequently more overridden by the Semail Ophiolite and associated accretionary prism.

Additionally, the Dibba Zone is interpreted to have acted initially as a transform offset in the margin during the formation of the Neotethys ocean. It also appears to have served as a transform along which the Semail Ophiolite was later emplaced. Subsequent culmination collapse in this zone, as documented by Searle (1988) and Robertson *et al.* (1990a), resulted in the present geometry of the zone. The Hatta Zone is also interpreted to have served as a transform offset in the Mesozoic continental margin along which later segmentation and rotation of the Semail took place during its emplacement (Robertson *et al.* 1990b). This margin configuration controlled by transform offsets is similar to that described for the Jurassic Omani margin to the south by Smewing & Pratt (1988). We believe that the original margin morphology significantly controlled and accommodated the deformation which occurred during the obduction event and is reflected today by the discontinuities of the Dibba and Hatta Zones which are interpreted as lateral ramps and/or transfer zones (Searle 1988). It appears that the pre-existing discontinuities of the transform offsets in the extensional margin exerted a strong control on where the later discontinuities formed during the compression resulting from the obduction of the Semail Ophiolite.

In many respects, our observations and interpretations for the geometry and development of the northern Oman Mountains are similar to those proposed by Searle (1988). We would differ with his interpretation regarding the diachronous south to north nature of the obduction and subsequent collision of Arabia and Eurasia as it is reflected in the changes which occur at the Dibba Zone. Although we observe the same geometrical characteristics, our data do not suggest that the Dibba Zone demarcates a change in the timing of structural development as suggested by Searle. Instead, the area to the south of the Dibba Zone, our Domains 2 and 3, appear to have the same temporal history as the area north of the Dibba Zone, our Domain 1, suggesting that the time of structural activity was synchronous in the northern Oman Mountains. Resolution of the ambiguities in the timing and number of structural reactivation events in the northern Oman Mountains may clarify this issue.

Conclusions

Three structural domains can be identified along the leading edge of the northern Oman Mountains. These domains are separated by the major discontinuities of the Dibba and Hatta Zones. The obduction of the Semail Ophiolite in the Late Cretaceous onto the existing continental margin and subsequent structural reactivation in the Tertiary is responsible for the present compressional geometries and variation in them along the strike of the leading edge. Although many of the general observations are not new (Glennie *et al.* 1973, 1974; Searle 1985, 1988; Searle *et al.* 1983), the identification of individual structural levels delineating the presence of three domains and their linkage in the northern Oman Mountains is significant in terms

of understanding the structural geometry along the leading edge of the mountain belt. There are still many outstanding questions, particularly in regard to the Tertiary deformation and its timing, but hopefully the data presented here and its interpretation in terms of structural evolution extends our understanding of the intricacies of the Oman Mountains.

The work presented is the result of an extensive study of the Oman Mountains done within the Africa and Middle East Region of Amoco. We thank our Amoco, as well as Chevron colleagues, P. Pickford and B. Otis, for many enlightening and spirited discussions. Special thanks to R. Nelson, T. Patton and B. Boutell of Amoco for their insights and constructive criticism regarding the ideas presented in this paper. We are indebted to the many ESRI and ERI geologists whose excellent field work provided the framework on which much of the subsurface interpretation was based. Special thanks to J. Smewing, M. Harper and S. Ali for their observations and discussions in the field. We appreciate the reviews provided by M. Harper, R. Nelson, T. Patton and B. Stoneley. In particular, many thanks to D. Boote for his thorough and thought-provoking review. We extend our appreciation to the Oman Ministry of Petroleum and Minerals, the government of Sharjah, and Amoco Production Company for their consent to publish this work. Finally, we thank A. Robertson, M. Searle, A. Ries and J. Smewing for all their efforts in convening the meeting from which this paper originated.

References

CAWOOD, P. A., GREEN, F. K. & CALON, T. J. 1990. Origin of culminations within the Southeast Oman Mountains at Jebel Majhool and Ibra Dome. *In*: ROBERTSON, A. H. F., SEARLE, M. P. & RIES, A. C. (eds) *The Geology and Tectonics of the Oman Region*. Geological Society, London, Special Publication, **49**, 419–427.

GASS, I. G. & SHELTON, A. W. 1986. Thrust tectonics of the eastern Arabian passive continental margin. *In: Hydrocarbon Potential of Intense Thrust Zones — Abu Dhabi conference 1986*, **1**, 51–73.

GLENNIE, K. W., BOEUF, M. G. A., HUGHES-CLARK, M. W., MOODY–STUART, M., PILAAR, M. F. & REINHARDT, B. B. 1973. Late Cretaceous nappes in the Oman Mountains and their geologic evolution. *American Association of Petroleum Geologists Bulletin*, **57**, 5–27.

——, ——, ——, ——, ——, —— 1974. Geology of the Oman Mountains. *Nederlands Geologisch Mijnbouwkundig Genootschap Verhandelinges*, **31**.

GRAHAM, G. M. 1980. *Structure and sedimentology of the Hawasina Window, Oman Mountains*. PhD thesis, Open University, Milton Keynes, UK.

HARRIS, P. M., FROST, S. H., SEIGLIE, G. A. and SCHNEIDERMANN, N. 1984. Regional unconformities and depositional cycles, Cretaceous of the Arabian Peninsula. *In*: SCHLEE, J. S. (ed.) *Inter-*

regional unconformities and hydrocarbon accumulations, American Association of Petroleum Geologists Memoir, **36**, 67–80.

HUDSON, R. G. S., MCGUICAN, A. & MORTON, D. M. 1954. The structure of the Jebel Hagab area, Trucial Oman. *Quarterly Journal of the Geological Society*, London, **110**, 121–152.

KOOP, W. J. & STONELEY, R. 1982. Subsidence history of the Middle East Zagros Basin. *Philosophical Transactions of the Royal Society*, London, **A305**, 149–168.

MANN, A. & HANNA, S. S. 1990. The tectonic evolution of pre-Permian rocks, Central and Southeastern Oman Mountains. *In*: ROBERTSON, A. H. F., SEARLE, M. P. & RIES, A. C. (eds) *The Geology and Tectonics of the Oman Region*. Geological Society, London, Special Publication, **49**, 307–325.

MANOOGIAN, P. R. & DUNNE, L. A. 1988. The migrating Aruma foredeep, a tool to track the obducting Semail Ophiolite. *The Geology and Tectonics of the Oman Region* Abstract, **32**.

MURRIS, R. J. 1980. Middle East – Stratigraphic evolution and oil habitat. *American Association of Petroleum Geologists Bulletin*, **64**, 597–618.

NOLAN, S. C., SKELTON, P. W., CLISSOLD, B. P. & SMEWING, J. D. 1990. Late Campanian to Tertiary palaeogeography of the Central and Northern Oman Mountains. *In*: ROBERTSON, A. H. F., SEARLE, M. P & RIES, A. C. (eds) *The Geology and Tectonics of the Oman Region*. Geological Society, London, Special Publication, **49**, 495–519.

PATTON, T. L. & O'CONNOR, S. J. 1986. Cretaceous flexural history of the northern Oman mountain foredeep, United Arab Emirates. *In: Hydrocarbon Potential of Intense Thrust Zones – Abu Dhabi Conference 1986*, **1**, 75–120.

—— & —— 1988. Cretaceous flexural history of the northern Oman Mountain foredeep, United Arab Emirates. *American Association of Petroleum Geologists Bulletin*, **72**, 797–809.

PEARCE, J. A., ALABASTER, T., SHELTON, A. W. & SEARLE, M. P. 1981. The Oman ophiolite as a Cretaceous arc-basin complex, evidence and implications: *Philosophical Transactions of the Royal Society*, London, **A300**, 299–317.

PINNINGTON, D. J, AITKEN, J., AWAD, M., BOETAL, M., DADRIAN, C., FINKLEA, E., FINNEGAN, P., HABACHI, M., HARICHANE, M., HARKINS, J. B., JEANJEAN, J., MONS, F., PELISSIER-COMBESCURE, J., TAUVEL, P., WEISS, K. & YVER, J. P. 1981. *Schlumberger well evaluation conference, United Arab Emirates, Qatar*.

RICATEAU, R. & RICHE, P. H. 1980. Geology of the Musandam Peninsula (Sultanate of Oman) and its surroundings. *Journal of Petroleum Geology*, **3**(2), 139–152.

ROBERTSON, A. H. F., BLOME, C. D., COOPER, D. W. J., KEMP, A. E. S. & SEARLE, M. P. 1990a. Evolution of the Arabian continental margin in the Dibba Zone, Northern Oman Mountains. *In*: ROBERTSON, A. H. F., SEARLE, M. P. & RIES, A. C. (eds) *The Geology and Tectonics of the*

Oman Region. Geological Society, London, Special Publication, **49**, 251–284.

——, KEMP, A. E. S., REX, D. C. & BLOME, C. D. 1990b. Sedimentary and structural evolution of a transform lineament: the Hatta Zone, Northern Oman Mountains. *In*: ROBERTSON, A. H. F., SEARLE, M. P. & RIES, A. C. (eds) *The Geology and Tectonics of the Oman Region*. Geological Society, London, Special Publication, **49**, 285–305.

SEARLE, M. P. 1985. Sequence of thrusting and origin of culminations in the northern and central Oman Mountains. *Journal of Structural Geology*, **7**, 129–143.

—— 1988. Thrust tectonics of the Dibba zone and the structural evolution of the Arabian continental margin along the Musandam mountains (Oman and United Arab Emirates). *Journal of the Geological Society*, London, **145**, 43–53.

—— & COOPER, D. J. W. 1986. Structure of the Hawasina Window culmination, central Oman Mountains. *Transactions of the Royal Society of Edinburgh*, **77**, 143–156.

——, —— & WATTS, K. 1990. Structure of the Jebel Sumeini–Jebel Ghawil areas, Northern Oman. *In*: ROBERTSON, A. H. F., SEARLE, M. P. & RIES, A. C. (eds) *The Geology and Tectonics of the Oman Region*. Geological Society, London, Special Publication, **49**, 361–374.

——, LIPPARD, S. J., SMEWING, J. D. & REX, D. 1980. Volcanic rocks beneath the Oman ophiolite and their significance in the Mesozoic evolution of Tethys. *Journal of the Geological Society, London*, **137**, 589–604.

——, JAMES, N. P., CALON, T. J. & SMEWING, J. D. 1983. Sedimentological and structural evolution of the Arabian continental margin in the Musandam Mountains and Dibba zone, United Arab Emirates. *Bulletin of the Geological Society of America*, **94**, 1381–1400.

SENGOR, A. M. C., YILMAZ, Y. & SUNGURLU, O. 1984. Tectonics of the Mediterranean Cimmerides – nature and evolution of the western termination of the Paleo-Tethys. *In*: DIXON, J. E. & ROBERTSON, A. H. F. (eds) *The Geological Evolution of the Eastern Mediterranean*. Geological Society of London, Special Publication, **17**, 77–112.

SMEWING, J. D. & PRATT, B. R. 1986. Jurassic continental margin configuration, central Oman mountains – evidence from facies trends in the Hajar Super Group. *In: Hydrocarbon Potential of Intense Thrust Zones – Abu Dhabi Conference 1986*, **1**, 201–226.

—— & —— 1988. Jurassic continental margin configuration, central Oman Mountains, evidence from facies trends in the Hajar Super Group. *The Geology and Tectonics of the Oman Region, Abstract*, **58**.

STOCKLIN, I. 1974. Possible ancient continental margin in Iran. *In*: BURK, C. & DRAKE, C. L. (eds) *The Geology of Continental Margins*. Springer, Berlin, 873–887.

WATTS, K. F. 1988. Mesozoic paleogeography of the Oman Mountains, carbonate slope facies marking the Arabian platform margin. *The Geology and Tectonics of the Oman Region, Abstract*, **65**.

—— 1990. Mesozoic palaeogeography of the Oman Mountains—carbonate slope facies marking the Arabian platform margin. *In*: ROBERTSON, A. H. F., SEARLE, M. P. & RIES, A. C. (eds) *The Geology and Tectonics of the Oman Region*. Geo-

logical Society, London, Special Publication, **49**, 139–159.

—— & GARRISON, R. E. 1986. Sumeini Group, Oman — evolution of a Mesozoic carbonate slope on a south Tethyan continental margin. *Sedimentary Geology*, **48**, 107–168.

Seismic interpretation of the structure and stratigraphy of the Strait of Hormuz

P. L. MICHAELIS[1] & R. J. PAUKEN[2]

[1] Mobil Exploration and Producing Services Inc., Dallas, P.O. Box
650232, Dallas, Texas 75265−0232 USA
[2] Mobil New Exploration Ventures, Dallas, Texas, USA

Abstract: Multifold seismic data from the Strait of Hormuz display stratigraphy and
structure typical of that found on the Musandam Peninsula to the south. The sedimentary
section seen on the seismic and tied to nearby hydrocarbon exploration wells ranges in age
from Early Cretaceous to Recent. The section is subdivided into three seismic stratigraphic
sequences by two prominent unconformities; the lowermost is at the top of the Lower
Cretaceous and the upper one is at the base of the Miocene. The unconformities appear
to have been formed as a result of two episodes of compression in the region; one during
the late Cretaceous and the other during Oligocene−Miocene time. A Prominent
'hummocky' surface is present on many of the seismic lines and is interpreted as the result
of erosion of piggy-back nappes consisting of allochthonous Musandam Limestone thrust
westward on the Tethyan continental margin, in this region, during the Late Cretaceous.
Two alternative interpretations of the 'hummocky' surface are that it is (a) composed of
Miocene Makran conglomerate and (b) Upper Cretaceous Coloured Melange. These
models and seismic data may be useful in future attempts at linking the stratigraphy and
structure of the Musandam Peninsula to that in the Zagros Fold Belt to the north as more
data become available.

The Strait of Hormuz, which separates the
Arabian Gulf from the Gulf of Oman, is surrounded by four major structural-stratigraphic
provinces: (1) the Zagros fold belt to the northwest, (2) the Arabian platform to the southwest,
(3) the Makran Basin to the east and (4) the
Oman Mountains and Musandam Peninsula to
the south (Fig. 1). Understanding how these
four provinces relate to each other, will require
additional tectonic and stratigraphic information
in the Strait of Hormuz region. Two east−west
multifold seismic lines and three structural-stratigraphic interpretations are presented in this
paper in order to provide additional information
for future studies and interpretations.

Geophysical data acquisition

During the interval from 1972 to 1974, several
seismic contractors carried out surveys in the
Strait of Hormuz, offshore southern Iran.
Approximately 3290 miles of 24 to 48 fold
seismic were shot in the area which led to the
drilling of two wells, HA-1 and HD-1 (Fig. 2).
Energy sources used by the various contractors
were Aquapulse/Maxipulse, Vaporchoc and air
guns. Record lengths recorded during these
surveys were generally six seconds, although a
few eight-second records were shot. Sample

rate was four milliseconds for the majority of
the surveys. Gravity and magnetic data were
gathered simultaneously with the recording of
the seismic data during a portion of the surveys.
Several refraction profiles were also recorded.

Regional tectono-depositional history

Regional tectono-depositional relationships in
this area provide a framework for deciphering
the geological history of the Strait of Hormuz
(e.g. Knipper *et al.* 1986). The amount of geologic data available from offshore areas surrounding Oman and the U.A.E. are limited.
Consequently, some of the interpretations partly
rely on published studies from adjacent onshore
areas.
    During the late Palaeozoic and early Mesozoic,
the eastern margin of the Arabian plate was
occupied by a shallow marine, carbonate platform. In Permo-Triassic time, a major rifting
event occurred in the area, which ultimately led
to the formation of the Tethyan seaway across
northern Africa (Robertson 1987). East of
Oman, this event led to the creation of a small
ocean basin with a passive margin setting (Searle
et al. 1983).
    A eustatic drop in sea level at the Triassic−
Jurassic boundary (Fig. 3) resulted in the devel-

From ROBERTSON, A. H. F., SEARLE, M. P. & RIES, A. C. (eds), 1990,
The Geology and Tectonics of the Oman Region.
Geological Society Special Publication No 49, pp 387−395

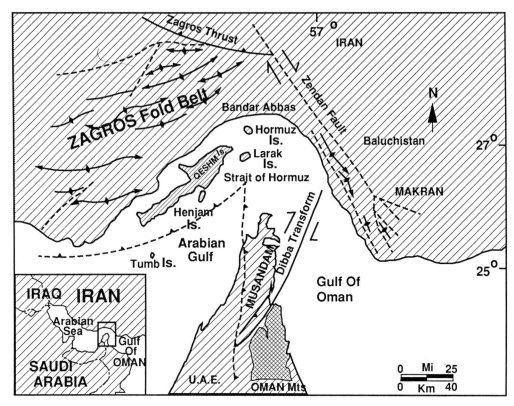

Fig. 1. Structural elements map of Oman-Iran area (partly after Searle 1988).

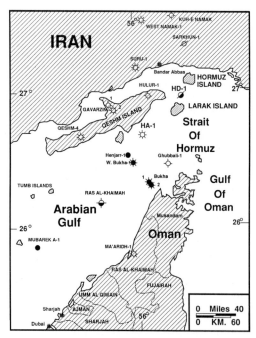

Fig. 2. Map of Strait of Hormuz region with locations of hydrocarbon exploration wells.

opment of an erosional unconformity over most of the region (Searle *et al.* 1983). Deposition of carbonates, however, continued almost uninterrupted until the late Cretaceous. A minor unconformity has been recognized in some parts of the region, separating the Aptian from the Albian. Stratigraphic sequences of early Cretaceous age outcropping in Oman and the U.A.E. display shelf, slope, and basin facies typical of a carbonate shelf setting, not unlike the modern Bahama Banks (Searle *et al.* 1983).

Carbonate deposition was terminated in the Cenomanian, with the onset of orogenesis which started with regional uplift along the axis of the present Oman Mountains (Patton & O'Connor 1988) and the development of a major erosional unconformity (Fig. 3). Collapse of the passive margin in the Turonian was followed by a major compressional event in the late Cretaceous (Turonian−early Maastrichtian) in which coastal to deep-water sedimentary facies of the Hawasina Group were thrust westward as a series of stacked nappes onto the Oman margin, forming the Oman Mountains. South of the Musandam Peninsula and Dibba Zone, this sequence of nappes is capped by over 10 km of

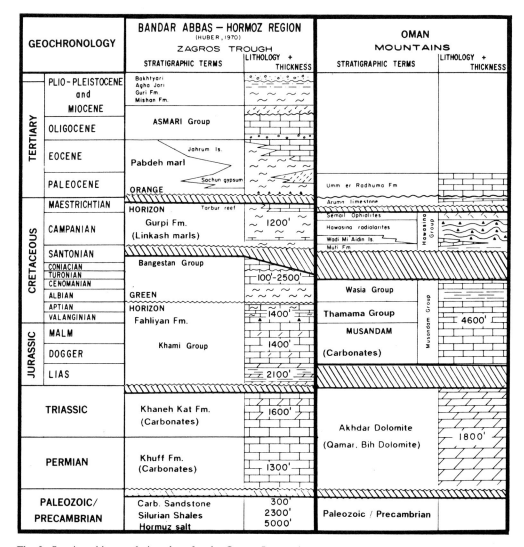

Fig. 3. Stratigraphic correlation chart for the Oman–Iran region.

Tethyan oceanic crust (Semail Ophiolites) of Cenomanian to Turonian age (95 Ma) which were also thrust onto the Arabian continental margin (Searle 1988). This event terminated nearly 160 Ma of tectonic stability in this region and was the result of opposing motions of Africa and Eurasia which closed the Tethyan seaway (Searle *et al.* 1983).

A second compressional event of lesser intensity occurred in the area during Oligocene through Miocene. During this event, short-distance thrusting of both allochthonous and autochthonous sequences occurred. No other tectonic events of significance are recognized in the Strait of Hormuz following this latter episode.

Seismic interpretation

Two time-migrated seismic lines, 399-S (Figs 4 & 5) and 321 (Figs 6 & 7) were shot in the study area and were orientated northwest–southeast (Fig. 8). Line 321 lies approximately 30 km east of Larak Island while line 399-S lies just north of a pair of small islands which are present just over 10 km north of the Musandam Peninsula. The data shown on these two seismic lines are considered to reflect the stratigraphy and structure typical of the Musandam Peninsula which plunges to the north in the direction of the lines.

Line 399-S has been tied to well HA-1 located approximately 20 km west of the line. The

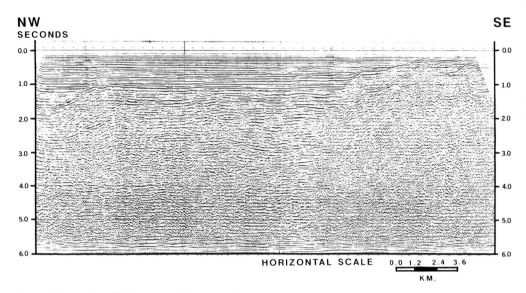

Fig. 4. Seismic Line 399-S, migrated in time, uninterpreted.

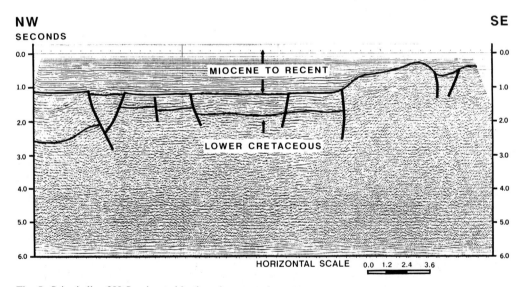

Fig. 5. Seismic line 399-S, migrated in time, interpreted.

deepest mappable reflection on this line (Fig. 5) is interpreted as the top of the Lower Cretaceous. The portion of the deeper reflection on the far-left side of the line, between 2 and 3 seconds, was tied to well HA-1 (Fig. 2). This reflection is offset by numerous faults and is truncated by a major fault bounding a prominent high block on the SE end of the line. The 'hummocky' surface on top of the high block

may also be interpreted as the top of the Lower Cretaceous, but other interpretations are possible, and will be explained below.

The upper reflection on line 399-S at 1.2 seconds has also been tied to well HA-1 and is interpreted as a Miocene unconformity. The nature of the sedimentary section between the two reflections on this line is speculative and is likely to be either Paleogene Pabdeh marls,

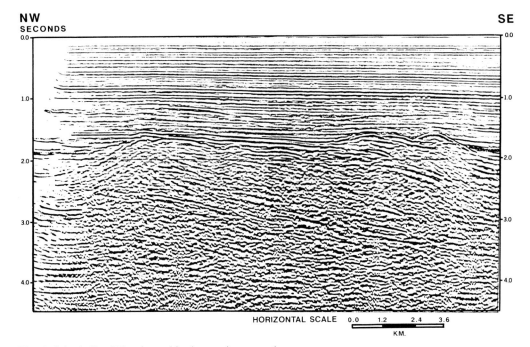

Fig. 6. Seismic line 321, migrated in time, uninterpreted.

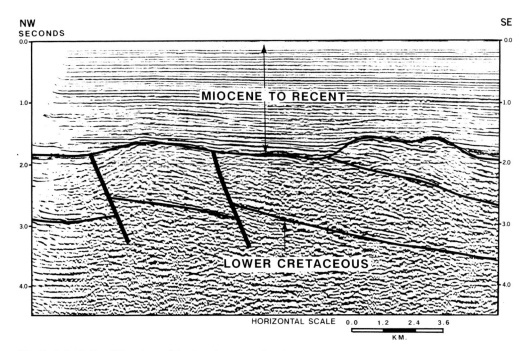

Fig. 7. Seismic line 321, migrated in time, interpreted.

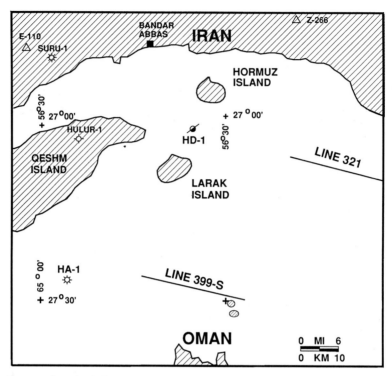

Fig. 8. Location map for seismic lines.

Upper Cretaceous Gurpi marls, or a combination of both (Fig. 3).

Line 321 (Fig. 7) lies approximately 40 km north−northeast of Line 399-S. On the left side of the line, the same two reflections interpreted on line 399-S are indicated here. To the SE, on the right-hand side of the line, an additional seismic package is present between 2.0 and 2.7 seconds and appears to be associated with the development of a 'hummocky' surface at the level of the Miocene unconformity.

The 'hummocky' surface has not been drilled, therefore, its nature and age is uncertain. Interpretation of stratigraphy and structure below the 'hummocky' surface is difficult due to poor data quality and the presence of numerous multiple reflections. Velocity determinations of the refraction data range from 18 000 to 22 000 ft s^{-1}, which is extremely high. Gravity models in this area require densities of 2.7 to 2.72 gm cm^{-3} for this material in order to match observed residual gravity to calculated curves. The Bouguer Gravity Anomaly map (Fig. 9) indicates that residual gravity anomalies exist in areas where the 'hummocky' surface is well developed. Also, the material under the 'hummocky' surface has no appreciable mag-

netic susceptibility, ruling-out the presence of ophiolites. Three-dimensional model calculations on this seismically-mapped surface, converted to depth using a density contrast of 0.4 gm cm^{-3}, result in a close match of computed and residual gravity fields.

Three interpretations are proposed for the stratigraphic age and origin of the 'hummocky' surface. These interpretations are shown diagrammatically on Fig. 10.

Interpretation I. The first interpretation is that the rock unit upon which the 'hummocky' surface is developed, is eroded, allochthonous Musandam Limestone. This interpretation is similar to that proposed by Ricateau & Riche (1980), which was based on additional seismic coverage from the southern part of the Strait of Hormuz. The surface was formed by erosion on top of a series of stacked nappes consisting of Musandam Limestone which were emplaced well above the level of the sea floor during the late Cretaceous. These nappes were then re-faulted during the Miocene compressional event. This surface was not totally buried until Neogene, as both seismic lines show onlap of the Tertiary section. The correspondence of the residual gravity anomalies with the 'hummocky'

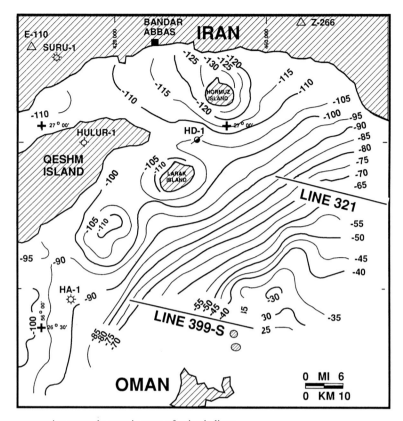

Fig. 9. Bouguer gravity anomaly map in area of seismic lines.

topography is consistent with this model, in that, the surface is underlain by rocks of laterally uniform density.

It is possible that the lower portion of the sequence of continuous seismic reflections above the 'hummocky' surface, particularly in areas of depression fill, is syn-tectonic Upper Cretaceous and/or Paleogene flysch-like deposits. Those shown on the left side of the cross-section (Fig. 10) may range in age from late Cretaceous to Miocene. The dipping reflections seen on the NW side of line 321 appear to show an onlapping relationship with the 'hummocky' surface (Fig. 6).

Interpretation II. Under the second interpretation, the 'hummocky' surface and the rocks underlying it, are composed of Makran conglomerates of early Miocene age. These rocks are exposed on the west coast of Makran (Fig. 1) and their distribution may extend as far west as the Strait of Hormuz. The section below the conglomerate and above the Musandam Limestone is interpreted as Upper Cretaceous Gurpi Formation marls which were encountered in the HD-1 well.

Residual gravity models can be constructed utilizing a density of less than 2.7 g cm^{-3} for the Gurpi Formation interval and still maintain a close match between the computed and observed residual anomalies. These models are consistent with this interpretation as well as Interpretation III, below.

Interpretation III. The third interpretation is that the 'hummocky' surface and the material composing it, is Upper Cretaceous Coloured Melange, consisting of radiolarite and exotic limestone blocks, in a shale matrix, similar to that exposed in Makran and along the coast of Oman south of the Dibba zone. The underlying stratigraphy is the same as described for Interpretation II.

Interpretation I is the preferred model because it is consistent with the observed structure in the Musandam Peninsula and Oman Mountains, where piggy-back thrusting is a common occurrence. Also, as described above, the residual gravity anomalies correspond closely with topography developed at the level of the 'hummocky' surface, interpreted here as the top of the Musandam Limestone.

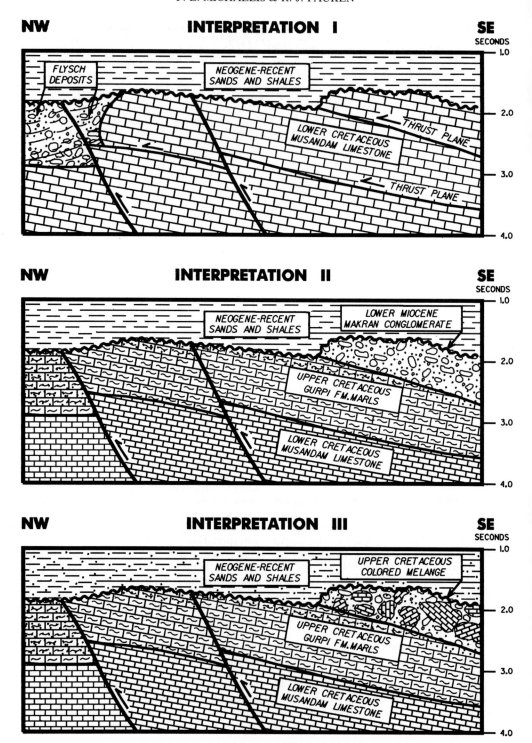

Fig. 10. Structural-stratigraphic interpretations of the Strait of Hormuz, modelled after seismic line 321.

References

KNIPPER, A., RICOU, L. E. & DERCOURT, J., 1986. Ophiolites as indicators of the geodynamic evolution of the Tethyan Ocean. *Tectonophysics*, **123**, 213–140.

PATTON, T. L. & O'CONNOR, S. J. 1988. Cretaceous flexural history of northern Oman Mountain foredeep, United Arab Emirates: *American Association of Petroleum Geologists Bulletin*, **72**, 797–809.

RICATEAU, R. & RICHE, P. H. 1980. Geology of the Musandam Peninsula (Sultanate of Oman) and its surroundings. *Journal of Petroleum Geology*, **3**, 139–152.

ROBERTSON, A. 1987. The transition from a passive margin to Upper Cretaceous foreland basin related to ophiolite emplacement in the Oman Mountains. *Geological Society of America Bulletin*, **99**, 633–653.

SEARLE, M. P. 1988. Thrust tectonics of the Dibba zone and the structural evolution of the Arabian continental margin along the Musandam Mountains (Oman and United Arab Emirates). *Journal of the Geological Society of London*, **145**, 43–53.

——, JAMES, N. P., CALON, T. J. & SMEWING, J. D. 1983. Sedimentology and structural evolution of the Arabian continental margin the Musandam Mountains and Dibba zone. United Arab Emirates. *Geological Society of America Bulletin*, **94**, 1381–1400.

Structural evolution of the Suneinah Foreland, Central Oman Mountains

D. R. D. BOOTE, D. MOU & R. I. WAITE

Occidental International Exploration & Production Co. 1200 Discovery Way, P.O. Box 12021, Bakersfield, CA 93389−2021, USA

Abstract: In the early Mesozoic, the Suneinah Foreland of the central Oman Mountains lay on the flank of a north facing Tethyan rift margin. By the end of the Middle Cretaceous, this had evolved into a carbonate dominated passive margin. Following regional uplift and erosion during the Turonian, it was downwarped, faulted and buried by a deeper water shale facies. At the beginning of the Campanian, the earlier Tethyan sea floor and continental rise prism were rapidly telescoped across the margin, loading and downflexing the crust to form the narrow Suneinah Foredeep and peripheral bulge beyond. By the end of the Cretaceous this foredeep had been filled with marls and coarse detritus shed from the adjacent allochthon, and during the Early Tertiary a transgression swept across much of the eroded nappe surface. In the Late Oligocene− Middle Miocene the Arabian plate began to separate from Africa and move northeast towards the Eurasian crustal collage. The Musandam promontory acted as a spur or indentor on this advancing plate, focussing compression and transmitting it back along deep basement fractures in the old Tethyan rift domain. Intense transpressional deformation inverted the entire margin to form the modern Oman Mountains and a new foredeep along its western flank. Reactivated Mesozoic fault blocks fringing the inversion orogen in the Suneinah area, deformed fairly rigidly, but the more plastic Late Cretaceous and Tertiary section above was squeezed into sometimes quite spectacular high amplitude folds. With the onset of sea floor spreading in the Red Sea/Gulf of Aden and northerly movement of the Arabian plate along the Dead Sea transform during the Late Miocene− Pleistocene, tectonic intensity waned in the Oman Mountains and much of its earlier sedimentary cover was stripped off.

The structural and stratigraphic development of the Suneinah Foreland on the western flanks of the Oman Mountains (Figs 1, 2 & 3) is described in this article. Its evolution is intimately related to the evolution of the mountains, which formed part of a north-facing Tethyan continental margin sequence in the early Mesozoic (Glennie *et al.* 1974; Searle *et al.* 1983). Although now obscured by younger deformation, the stratigraphic architecture of the region suggests that this margin evolved during episodic phases of rifting in the Permo-Triassic, accompanied by volcanism, post-rift subsidence and development of a deep basin, floored by attenuated continental or transitional oceanic crust (Glennie *et al.* 1974; Searle & Graham 1982; Lippard *et al.* 1986). Although oceanic crust created during the subsequent Jurassic and Early Cretaceous appears to have been entirely consumed by later subduction, contemporary facies suggest a mature passive margin had developed by mid-Cretaceous with a thick carbonate dominated platform sequence passing north into the continental slope-rise prism and abyssal plain sediment of an oceanic basin

(Glennie *et al.* 1974). Early in the Late Cretaceous, an intra-oceanic subduction zone and marginal basin formed to the northeast and began to migrate towards the Arabian craton (Gealey 1977; Pearce *et al.* 1981; Searle & Stevens 1984). Their initial collision is marked by a Late Turonian phase of emergence and erosion across much of the Middle East and Northern Somalia (Robertson 1987a,b; Murris 1980). The Oman platform margin collapsed during the later Cretaceous and was overthrust by the earlier Mesozoic slope-rise prism, abyssal plain and marginal oceanic basin beyond (Glennie *et al.* 1974; Lippard *et al.* 1986). A narrow foredeep and flanking peripheral bulge formed in the Suneinah area, at the leading edge of the allochthon (Figs 2 & 3). By the end of the Cretaceous, this had been filled by marls and coarse lithoclastics as the adjacent nappe stack was eroded and later transgressed by a carbonate dominated sequence during the Early Tertiary. In the Late Tertiary the mountain range was uplifted by a major phase of deformation, reflecting the northeastward movement of the Arabian craton and

From ROBERTSON, A. H. F., SEARLE, M. P. & RIES, A. C. (eds), 1990,
The Geology and Tectonics of the Oman Region.
Geological Society Special Publication No 49, pp 397−418

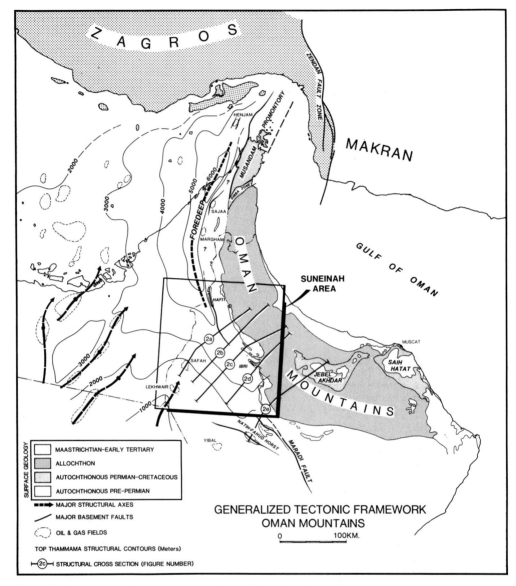

Fig. 1. Regional tectonic framework of the Suneinah Foreland Oman Mountains.

collision with the Iranian crustal collage (Searle *et al.* 1983; Lippard *et al.* 1986; Searle 1988).

As a result of this uplift its sedimentary cover was deeply eroded, and the stratigraphic record of its evolution was partially removed. However, the history of allochthon emplacement and late Tertiary deformation is chronicled quite precisely in the thick Late Cretaceous–Tertiary section still preserved in the adjacent Suneinah Foreland.

Late Cretaceous–Early Tertiary tectonostratigraphic development

The Late Cretaceous structural and stratigraphic evolution of the Suneinah Foreland can be reconstructed using the excellent control provided by several exploratory wells and extensive seismic coverage (Fig. 4). A precise biostratigraphic zonation (Fig. 5) has been developed utilizing this control. (Frost *et al.* 1980; Burrus

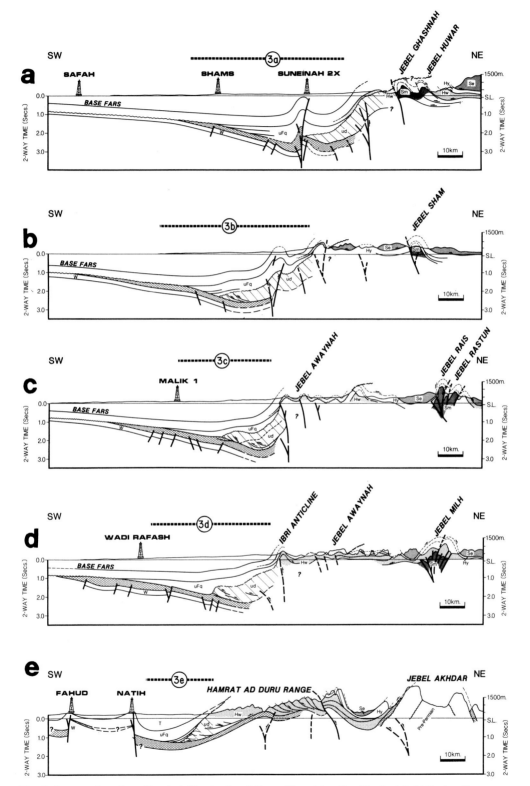

Fig. 2. Structural sections, Suneinah Foreland and Oman Mountains. See Figs 1, 4 & 14 for location. Lithology symbols as in Fig. 4. The dashed and numbered lines above each section refer to the seismic transects illustrated in Fig. 3. Partly based upon Wilson 1969; Glennie *et al.* 1974; Searle 1985; Searle & Cooper 1986.

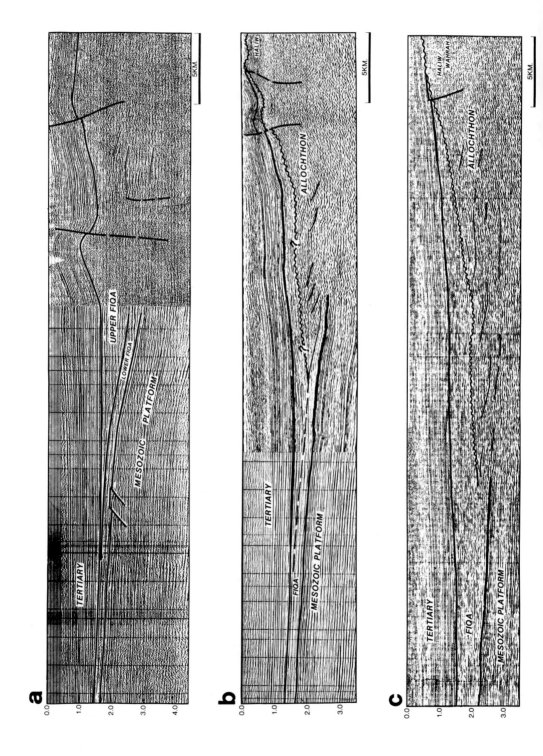

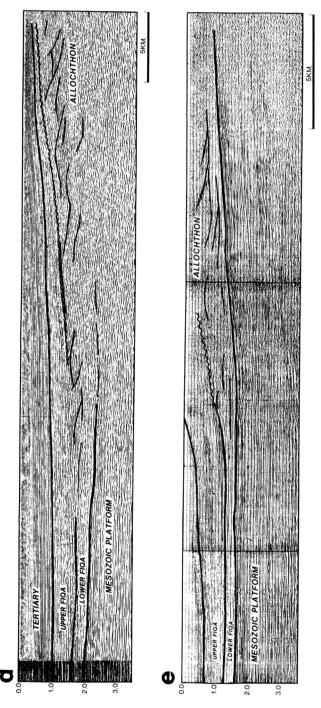

Fig. 3. Regional seismic transects, Suneinah Foreland (Figs 2, 4 & 7 for location. Vertical scale in two-way time.)

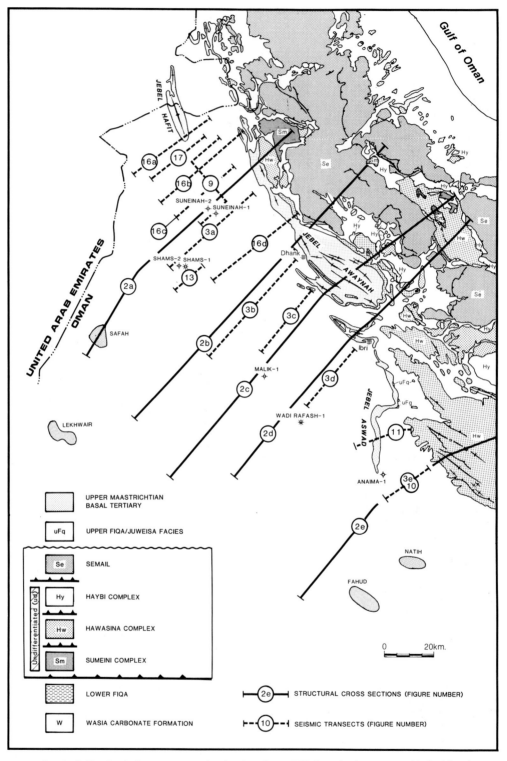

Fig. 4. Suneinah Foreland: Summary map showing locations of Wells, seismic transects (dashed lines), structural sections (solid lines) and outcrop geology.

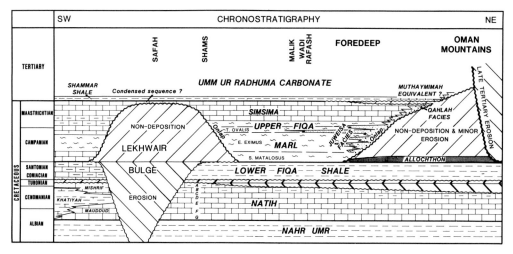

Fig. 5. Late Cretaceous Chronostratigraphy, Suneinah Foreland. The biostratigraphy is from Frost *et al.* 1980; Harris & Frost 1984; Burruss *et al.* 1985.

et al. 1985; Harris & Frost 1984). This provides a framework with which to unravel the major events leading up to and following the emplacement of the allochthon (Figs 5 & 6).

Wasia—Aruma Break

The regional Late Turonian Wasia—Aruma break is recognized as a disconformity in the southern part of the Suneinah Foreland, where Early Turonian carbonates are still preserved. However, successive units of the Middle Cretaceous Natih Formation are truncated towards the northeast (Fig. 7). The erosional break continues into the eastern United Arab Emirates and Oman Mountains where it cuts down deeply into the underlying carbonate platform (Glennie *et al.* 1974; Searle *et al.* 1983; Robertson 1987a). This period of plate margin uplift and erosional stripping has been attributed to the development of a flexural fore-bulge during the initial phases of collision between the southwesterly migrating Tethyan subduction zone and the Arabian margin (O'Connor & Patton 1985; Robertson 1987a,b).

Lower Fiqa (Coniacian—Santonian)

At the beginning of the Coniacian, attempted subduction of the Arabian plate rapidly down-flexed a wide area of the continental margin. This is reflected by rapid subsidence and deposition of the Lower Fiqa Shale in the Suneinah foreland (Figs 6 & 8). Paleobathymetric analysis (Frost *et al.* 1980) indicates water depths increased rapidly during deposition, reaching more than 300—500 m by the end of the Santonian. These shales can be traced laterally west into Abu Dhabi, where they pass into a mixed clastic—carbonate shelf sequence, and east below the allochthon into the deeper water shale and pelagic limestones of the Muti Formation (Sayja Unit; Robertson 1987a,b).

In the southern part of the Suneinah foreland, the Lower Fiqa Formation and underlying shelf carbonate rise gently east below the Hamrat ad Duru Range. In contrast, further north the platform plunges steeply towards the mountains where seismic record quality deteriorates and becomes very ambiguous (Figs 2 & 3). There are some indications of Mesozoic fault blocks upstepping back towards the mountain front. Although there is no well confirmation, locally better quality seismic data in the Hafit-Suneinah area permits a reasonable reflector character correlation, suggesting the presence of a large horst. This appears to have been partially reactivated during the Tertiary. However one segment of the bounding fault is buried by undeformed Upper Cretaceous—Lower Tertiary sediment indicating its initial formation during Lower Fiqa time (Fig. 9). Indirect support for this interpretation is provided by the existence of similar features to the north and south. Development of the Fahud—Natih horst described by Tschopp (1967a) clearly post-dates the Wasia—Aruma break with a very rapid period of growth during the Santonian. The Maradi—Haushi fault zone in Central Oman and the major, basement cored, anticlinal flexures of Saudi Arabia and Abu Dhabi were

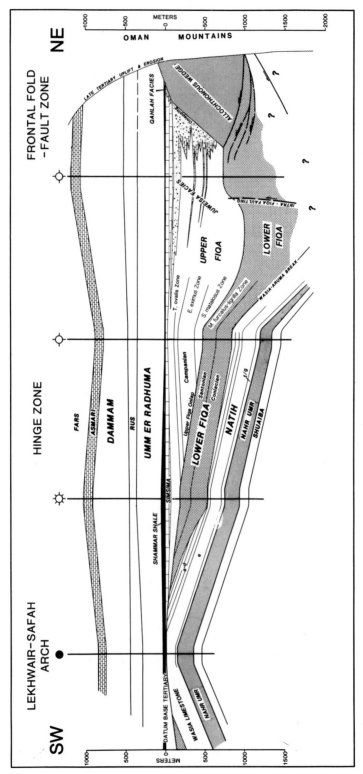

Fig. 6. Late Cretaceous stratigraphic well correlation section, Sunéinah Foredeep (base Tertiary datum).

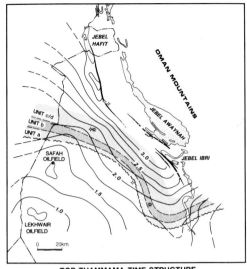

TOP THAMMAMA TIME STRUCTURE
CONTOUR INTERVAL : 250ms

PRE–FIQA (CONIACIAN) EROSION – NATIH CARBONATE SUBCROP UNITS

MAASTRICHTIAN–LOWER TERTIARY OUTCROP

Fig. 7. Generalized Top Thammama (Lower Cretaceous) Time Structure (TWT), Suneinah Foredeep. (The Middle Cretaceous carbonate units subcropping the Wasia–Aruma erosion surface are superimposed.)

all most active between the Late Turonian and Early Campanian (Murris 1980; Tschopp 1967b). Their pronounced north–south parallelism and similar growth history suggests they developed under a common stress regime, perhaps in response to a regional anticlockwise torque of the Southern Arabian platform.

Allochthon emplacement (basal Campanian)

The allochthon can be traced from outcrop into the subsurface of the Suneinah Foreland where it pinches out at the boundary between the Upper and Lower Fiqa Formations (Figs 10 & 11). Multiple imbricate thrusting within the displaced wedge suggests emplacement by a gravity driven process, sliding upon and partially incorporating the shale beneath. Equivalent Muti shales observed at outcrop in the mountains have sometimes been intensely sheared (Glennie *et al.* 1974; Robertson 1987b) and local underthrusting at the leading edge of the allochthon has tectonically thickened the shale unit to as much as twice its original thickness in some places (Fig. 10). There is only one subsurface well intersection with the displaced package but the exposed section in the adjacent

foothills (Fig. 4) suggests it is dominated by the Hawasina complex to the south and the Sumeini, Hawasina and Haybi thrust sheets in the north. Emplacement must have been an extremely rapid process as the sub-allochthonous Muti Formation (Sanja Member) in the Jebel Akhdar area appears to span the same Coniacian–Santonian time interval (Robertson 1987b) as in the Suneinah Foreland. The displaced wedge downloaded the earlier foreland basin creating a peripheral bulge to the west (Fig. 8). Because of the rapid emplacement, this bulge formed very quickly with no evidence of progressive inboard migration. Uplift, probably exaggerated by movement on pre-existing basement faults, was most pronounced along the Lekhwair Arch. This suffered quite severe erosional truncation (Fig. 8). Although there is no evidence of contemporaneous erosion beyond the Arch itself, the bulge appears to have continued north into the United Arab Emirates as a paleotopographic high.

Upper Fiqa (Campanian–Early Maastrichtian)

Lippard *et al.* (1986) suggest emplacement was terminated in the late Cretaceous as the Tethyan

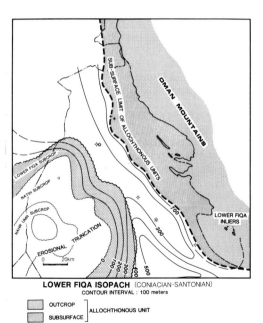

LOWER FIQA ISOPACH (CONIACIAN-SANTONIAN)
CONTOUR INTERVAL : 100 meters

OUTCROP ⎤
⎟ ALLOCHTHONOUS UNIT
SUBSURFACE ⎦

Fig. 8. Generalized Lower Fiqa Shale (Coniacian–Santonian) Isopach, Suneinah Foredeep. (The Lekhwair peripheral bulge and the units subcropping the base Campanian erosional surface are superimposed.)

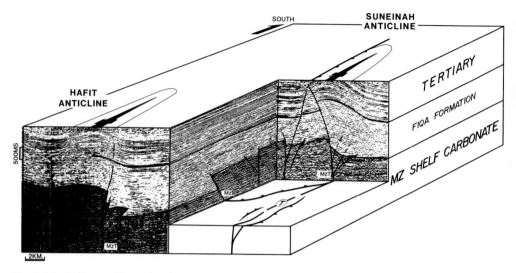

Fig. 9. Block diagram illustrating the structure of the Suneinah and Hafit Anticlines, Northern Suneinah Foredeep. (See Figs 4 & 7 for location. Vertical scale in two way time. Mz: Late Mesozoic fault movement. MzT: Late Mesozoic and reactivated Late Tertiary fault movement. T: Late Tertiary fault movement.)

subduction complex jumped back to the north. In the Suneinah Foreland, the narrow foredeep formed as a result of crustal loading, was gradually filled with marls and coarse lithoclastics (Fig. 12). These onlap both the Lekhwair Axis to the west and the allochthon to the east (Figs 6, 11 & 13). Although it is not clear whether the Lekhwair area was emergent or a site of non-deposition at this time, the allochthon was clearly exposed and suffered extensive weathering, erosion and laterization (Glennie *et al.* 1974; Hopson *et al.* 1981). Coarse detritus was shed into the Upper Fiqa foredeep as the chert-rich Juweiza turbidite facies, intercalated with Upper Fiqa marl (Fig. 6). Although thin in the Suneinah area, they are very thickly developed in the Emirates and Gulf of Oman (Glennie *et al.* 1974) suggesting erosion stripped off a significant amount of allochthon cover in some places.

Late Maastrichtian−Early Tertiary

The Oman margin subsided and was transgressed from both west and east during the Maastrichtian and later Tertiary. The Suneinah Foredeep had been largely filled by Early Maastrichtian time, and the Upper Fiqa marls pass up into shallow water limestones. These transgress and overlap the eroded allochthon surface (Fig. 12). Diachronous transgressive beach and shelf (Qahlah and Simsima facies) are now exposed along the flanks of the moun-

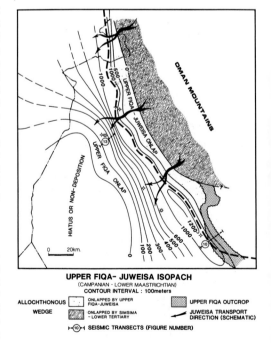

Fig. 12. Generalized (Post-Emplacement) Upper Fiqa (Campanian−Maastrichtian) Isopach map, Suneinah Foredeep.

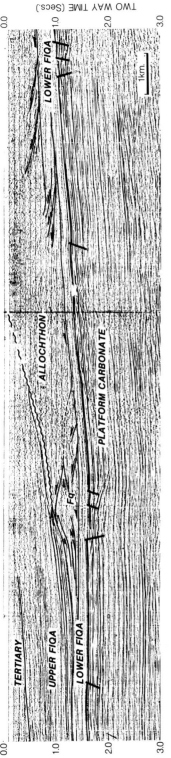

Fig. 10. Seismic Transects, South-eastern Flank (south) of the Suneinah Foredeep. (see Figs 4, 8 & 12 for location). Vertical scale in two way time. Note the tectonic thickening of the Lower Fiqa at the leading edge of the allochthon wedge, the Upper Fiqa onlaps and lack of any shallow deformation which might suggest westward late-stage/post-emplacement gravity sliding.

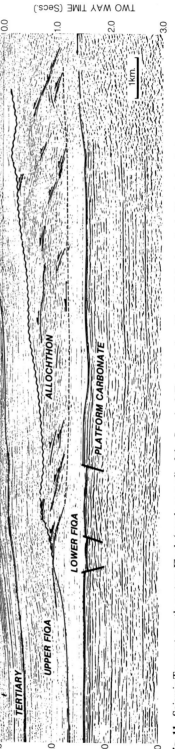

Fig. 11. Seismic Transect, south-eastern Flank (south-central) of the Suneinah Foredeep (see Figs 4 & 8 for location). Vertical scale in two way time. Note the Upper Fiqa onlap onto the allochthon surface and lack of any shallow deformation which might suggest westward post-emplacement gravity sliding.

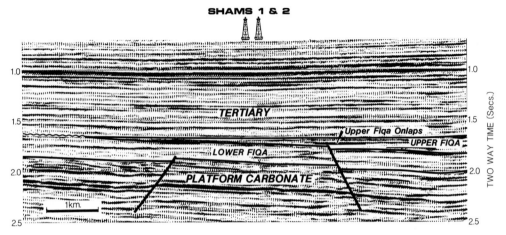

Fig. 13. Seismic Transect, Northwestern Flank of the Suneinah Foredeep (see Figs 4 & 12 for location). Vertical scale in two way time. Note the Upper Fiqa onlap onto the Lower Fiqa cover of the Shams fault block.

tains to the north and south (Glennie *et al.* 1974; Hopson *et al.* 1981; Nolan *et al.* 1989). The transgression was interrupted by a minor base Tertiary unconformity in the Hafit area (Figs 16a & 17). Although this can be correlated with a similar event to the north (Nolan *et al.* 1989), it appears to reflect rather local gravity-induced submarine erosion in the Suneinah area and may be a response to early reactivation and uplift of deep platform-cored blocks. The transgression continued into the early Tertiary. Based upon the thickness and facies organization of the truncated section along its flanks, the allochthon was probably entirely buried by the Eocene.

Late Tertiary tectonic development

The Suneinah Foreland and its regional setting

The contrasting structural elevation of equivalent Late Maastrichtian–Early Tertiary facies within the Suneinah Foreland (Figs 14 & 15) and adjacent outcrop demonstrate that the mountains experienced at least 3000 m of Late Tertiary uplift (Figs 2, 14 & 15). In the southern part of the Suneinah Foreland this was accomplished by gradual upwarping (Figs 2 & 3). Further north it appears to have been caused by thrusting along deep platform-involved faults. Seismic record quality is too poor to demonstrate this convincingly along much of the mountain front. However, it can be observed in the Hafit–Suneinah area where two shallow anti-

clines extend south from Jebel Hafit in an en echelon fashion (Fig. 16). Both are of extremely high amplitude, bounded to the east by steep west dipping fault zones with high angle reverse and extensional fault strands at shallow structural levels. The Hafit anticline is more symmetrical with a secondary bounding fault on its western flank. Both anticlines are related to the

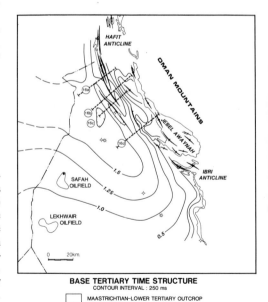

BASE TERTIARY TIME STRUCTURE
CONTOUR INTERVAL : 250 ms

☐ MAASTRICHTIAN-LOWER TERTIARY OUTCROP

├─⟨16a⟩─┤ SEISMIC TRANSECTS (FIGURE NUMBER)

Fig. 15. Generalized map showing Base Tertiary Time Structure (TWT), Suneinah Foredeep.

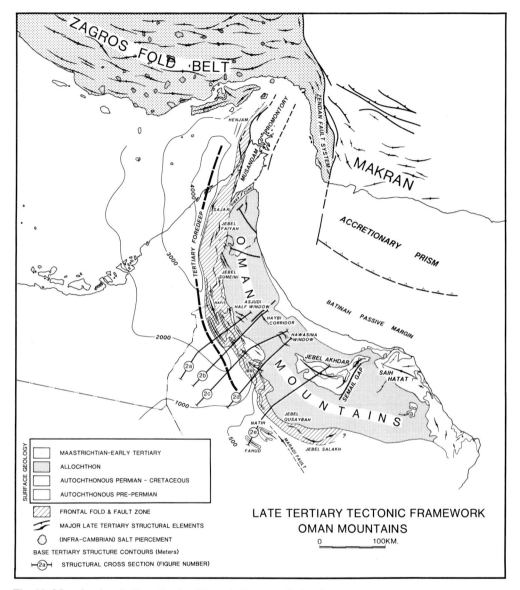

Fig. 14. Map showing the Late Tertiary Tectonic Framework, Southeastern Arabian Plate Margin and the Oman Mountains.

north–south trending segments of a deeper transverse block bounding fault (Fig. 9). The Suneinah fold extends northwards beyond the underlying horst, above a complex compressional fault zone which disrupts the Mesozoic carbonate platform with little vertical displacement (Figs 16a & 17). Although several conflicting explanations have been proposed, this structural style of deeper more rigid deformation associated with shallow plastic folding is

considered here to result from reactivated transpressional movement along old basement shears. Shallow Tertiary folding is present elsewhere fringing the mountain front of the Suneinah foreland (Fig. 15), but record quality at deeper structural levels is very poor and consequently ambiguous. Further south, the boundary faults of the Fahud–Natih horst and Maradi fault zone were reactivated in a similar fashion (Figs 2 & 14). To the north along the

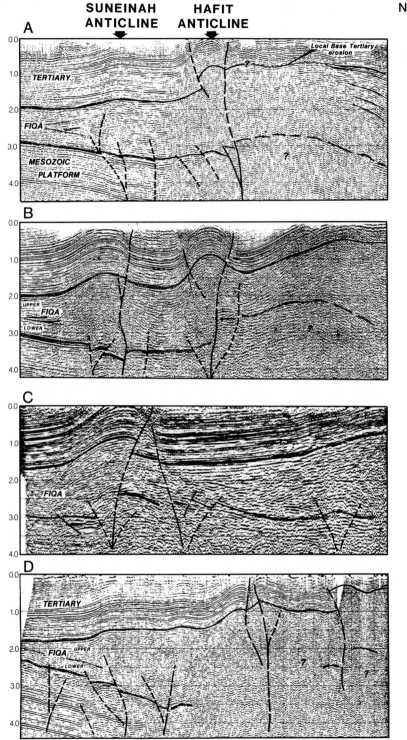

Fig. 16. Seismic Transects, Hafit and Suneinah Anticlines, Northern Suneinah Foreland (see Figs 4 & 15 for location). Note the en echelon arrangement of the Tertiary anticlines, the association of shallow folding and deep high angle reverse fault disruption of the platform and the base Tertiary truncational unconformity on section 16a.

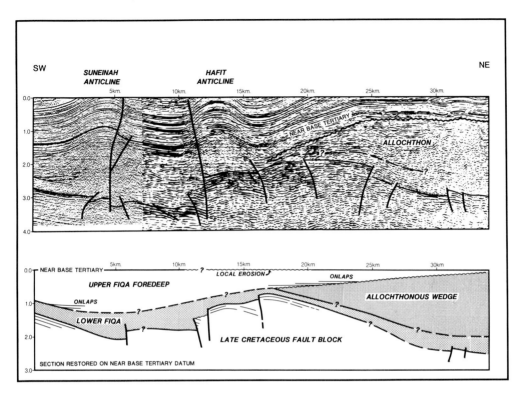

Fig. 17. Structural Transect, Suneinah−Hafit Area (see Fig. 4 for location). The seismic transect has been reconstructed in the lower panel with a pre-folding base Tertiary datum to illustrate the structural architecture of the Late Cretaceous fault block. Also note the Upper Fiqa onlap onto the allochthon surface, the local base Tertiary erosional truncation and the association of shallow plastic folding above deep compressional faulting within the more rigid platform.

flanks of the orogen, strong Tertiary deformation was responsible for a narrow zone of shallow folding with deep platform cored faulting and reactivation of pre-existing Cretaceous fault blocks. This is demonstrated by Jebel Faiyah, the Remah horst and Hagab thrust (Glennie *et al.* 1974; Searle *et al.* 1983; Searle 1988) and the spectacular high-angle reverse faulting bounding the western (Ricateau & Riche 1980) and eastern sides of the Musandam promontory.

Within the internal part of the orogen, late stage breakback thrusting has been demonstrated in the Dibba Zone, Sumeini culmination, Asjudi half-window, Haybi corridor, Hawasina Window and Jebel Akhdar culmination. (Figure 14. Searle *et al.* 1983; Searle 1985, 1988; Searle and Cooper 1986; Lippard *et al.* 1986). The age of this deformation cannot be proven directly as the original Tertiary cover has been eroded. However the association of these culminations with the intense Late Tertiary platform involved deformation, uplift and erosional truncation

along the western flanks of the mountain implies they are probably of similar age and origin. Indeed the structural style of the thrust-bounded culminations in the Haybi Corridor and Hawasina Window (Searle 1985; Searle & Cooper 1986) appears geometrically similar to the Suneinah and Hafit anticlines. Consequently it is suggested they may all represent isolated symptoms of a late-stage tectonic process responsible for uplift of the entire orogen by basement involved transpression and thrust movement.

Because of the thin late Neogene− Quaternary post deformational cover, this event can only be dated as post-early Miocene in the Suneinah area. However, further north, a major erosional unconformity is present on the western flank of the Musandam, overlain by undeformed late (?)Middle Miocene to Pleistocene sediments (Ricateau & Riche 1980). This is particularly well displayed along the northern extension of the promontory, where the upthrusted Mesozoic platform formed a pronounced paleo-

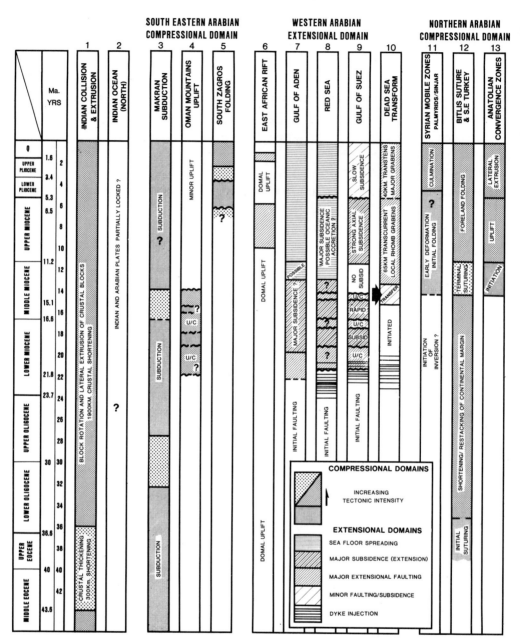

Fig. 18. Generalized Tectonic Correlation Chart, Arabian Plate Margins. Estimates of timing and intensity of the tectonic events tabulated varies from very precise in some areas to highly approximate in others. The tabulation is partly based upon the following. (1) Patriat & Achache 1984. (2) Cochran 1981; Wiens *et al.* 1985; Courtillot *et al.* 1987. (3) Farhoudi & Karig 1977; McCall & Kidd 1981; White 1981, 1984; White & Ross 1979; Ross *et al.* 1986. (5) Berberian & King 1981; Jackson 1980; Jackson *et al.* 1981; Kashfi 1976; Stocklin 1968; Tirrul *et al.* 1983. (6) Baker & Wohlenberg 1971; Baker *et al.* 1972; Noy 1978. (7) Beydoun 1970; Cochran 1981; Sahota 1985. (8) Almond 1986; Bayer *et al.* 1988; Berhe 1986; Bonatti 1987; Bonatti *et al.* 1984; Brown 1970; Crane & Bonatti 1987; Mart & Ross 1987; Montenat *et al.* 1988; Tewfik & Ayyad 1982; Schmidt *et al.* 1983; Le Pichon & Gauher 1988. (9) Evans 1988; Garfunkel & Bartov 1977; Moretti & Colletta 1987; Steckler *et al.* 1988. (10) Bartov *et al.* 1980; Eyal *et al.* 1981; Garfunkel 1981; Ron & Eyal 1985. (11) Lovelock 1984; Ponikarov *et al.* 1967. (12) Hempton 1987; Şengör *et al.* 1985. (13) Dewey & Sengor 1979; Hempton 1987; Sengor *et al.* 1985.

topographic ridge, onlapped and buried by flat-lying Late Miocene and Plio-Pleistocene sediment (White & Ross 1979; Ross *et al.* 1986). On the eastern side of the Musandam this single major unconformity is represented by at least three closely spaced compressional events of approximately Lower to lower Middle Miocene age.

A speculative model: Late Tertiary Arabian plate margin tectonics and the structural evolution of the Oman Mountains

The Late Tertiary deformation of the Oman Mountains is clearly related to the separation of the Arabian plate from Africa and its subsequent collision with the Eurasia crustal collage. An analysis of contemporary tectonism around the plate margin provides a constraining framework in which to place its structural evolution (summarized in Fig. 18).

Early–Middle Miocene (Fig. 19): Possibly as a consequence of partial locking across the Owen Fracture Zone, Arabia began to separate from Africa and move north with the Indian plate in the Oligocene (Fig. 18, Cochran 1981; Weins *et al.* 1985; Courtillot *et al.* 1987). The first major period of continental rifting and extension occurred in the Gulf of Aden during the Early Miocene (Beydoun 1966; Cochran 1981), contemporaneously with regional dyke injection along the Red Sea margin (Berhe 1986; Pallister 1987). Perhaps because of their different orientation with respect to Arabian

plate motion, rifting started later in the Red Sea (Tewfik & Ayyad 1982; Schmidt *et al.* 1983) and Gulf of Suez (Garfunkel & Bartov 1977) and culminated in the Middle Miocene.

The effect of this northerly movement of the Arabian plate is difficult to isolate within the Bitlis and Zagros compressional domains because of the contemporary closure of Neotethys. Hempton (1987) demonstrated the initial stages of collision between the Arabian and Anatolian plates occurred during this period with crustal shortening and restacking of the earlier continental margins. Although Berberian & King (1980) suggested that the High Zagros Tethyan seaway had closed by early Paleocene, the continuity of the Iranian Sanandaj–Sirjan continental sliver into the Makran (McCall & Kidd 1982), indicates it must have remained open until the Late Tertiary to accommodate the subduction responsible for the Makran accretionary prism. A mid-Miocene phase of uplift and thrusting in the Makran (McCall & Kidd 1982) correlates temporally with the Oman Mountain deformation and could reflect initial suturing between the Arabian plate and the central Iranian crustal collage. This event clearly predates the Zagros foreland folding.

As the Oman orogen is flanked by the undeformed Arabian Platform to the west and the passive Batinah continental margin and oceanic crust of the Gulf of Oman to the east, the compression responsible for its uplift must therefore have come from the north. It is suggested that the Musandam promontory formed a protruding indentor on the advancing Arabian

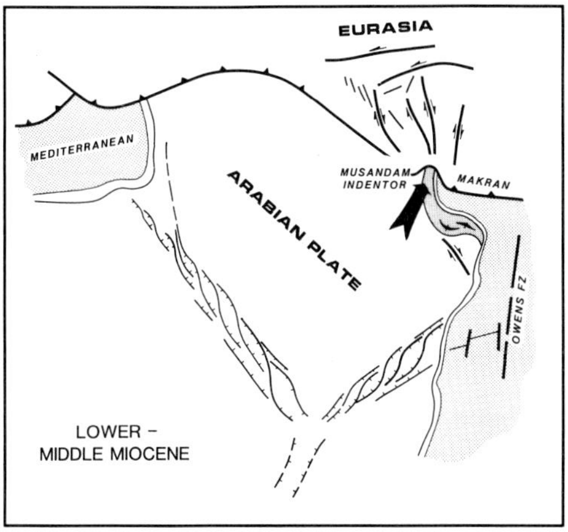

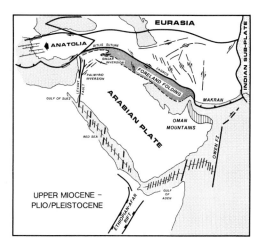

Fig. 19. Lower–Middle Miocene Arabian Plate Margin Tectonic Reconstruction. (Partly based upon Cochran 1981; Tirrul *et al.* 1983; Hempton 1987).

Fig. 20. Upper Miocene-Plio/Pleistocene Arabian Plate Margin Tectonic Reconstruction. (Partly based upon Cochran 1981; Lovelock 1984; Sengor *et al.* 1985; Crane & Bonatti 1987; Hempton 1987.)

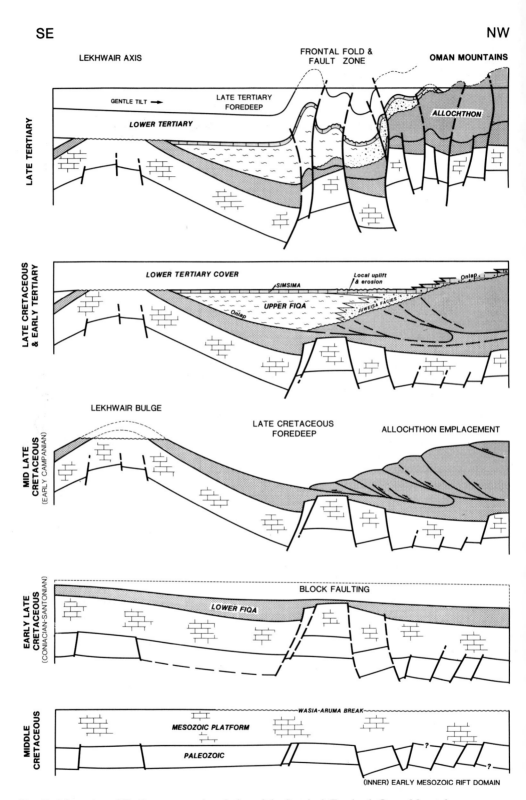

Fig. 21. Mesozoic and Tertiary structural evolution of the Suneinah Foreland, Oman Mountains.

plate. This would have focussed compression during the initial phase of collision, transmitting it back along deep basement shears, and inverting the entire mountain range by transpressional wrench faulting and thrusting (Fig. 19). Support comes from the pattern formed by several major wrench faults in central Iran. These are dispersed radially about the Musandam in a manner analogous to that caused by a rigid indentor protruding into a semiplastic medium (Tapponnier *et al*. 1982; Tirrul *et al*. 1983; Tapponnier & Molnar 1976). Although motion along these faults is sometimes very recent (Tirrul *et al*. 1983), it is quite possible they were most active during the Miocene collisional event.

The position of the Oman orogen suggests its inversion may have been confined to the fragmented and attenuated crust of the earlier Mesozoic rift domain. Certainly based upon the available seismic control, only those Late Cretaceous faults and flexures within this domain were reactivated. Similar basement-cored structures further inboard on the Arabian platform remained unaffected (Murris 1980).

Late Miocene to Plio-Pliestocene (Fig. 20): Following earlier work by Girdler & Styles (1976, 1982), Girdler (1985), Girdler & Southern (1987), Quennel (1984), Freund *et al*. (1970) and Zak & Freund (1981), Hempton (1987) suggested that the waning tectonism in the Oman Mountains during the Late Miocene could reflect a pause in the northward movement of the Arabian plate. However direct evidence of this is very ambiguous (Schulman & Bartov 1978) and contemporary sea-floor spreading in the Gulf of Aden clearly implies continual northwards motion throughout this period. Instead, the rather abrupt end to major deformation of the Oman orogen appears to correlate with a transfer of crustal extension between Africa and Arabia from the Red Sea-Gulf of Suez rift to the Red Sea—Levant axis. Subsequent northeasterly plate motion in the Late Miocene, is reflected by a major phase of collision and terminal suturing between Arabia and Anatolia and early folding in the Palmyrids along a strand of the Dead Sea Fault (Lovelock 1984). This continued with increasing intensity into the Plio-Pleistocene, contemporaneously with the lateral extrusion and escape of the Anatolian plate (Dewey & Sengor 1979; Sengör & Canitez 1982; Burke & Sengor 1986; Fig. 20). Folding in the Zagros foreland began in very late Miocene (Fig. 18) culminating in the Late Plio-Pleistocene (Stocklin 1986; Murris 1980). Associated crustal thickening was accomplished by reactivation of old extensional fractures as high-angle reverse faults (Jackson 1980; Jackson *et al*. 1981).

Deformation of the Oman margin had largely ceased by this time, apart from mild uplift of the orogen, accompanied by dextral strike slip and underthrusting of the Musandam promontory along the Zendan fault zone (White & Ross 1979; Ross *et al*. 1986). It would appear that the earlier deformation had restacked the attenuated Oman rift margin and subdued the protruding Musandam indentor. Combined with the change in plate motion following the initiation of the Dead Sea transform, this was evidently sufficient to disperse the subsequent Plio-Pleistocene compression along the length of the Zagros suture and leave the Oman Musandam in a tectonic shadow.

Summary

The Suneinah Foreland of the Oman Mountains straddles the transition between the stable Arabian platform and its continental margin. The stratigraphic architecture of the foreland basin records the evolution of this province from an early Mesozoic rifted passive margin into an active compressional margin during the late Cretaceous. Its subsequent deformation and uplift is interpreted to be a consequence of southward directed transpression and inversion of the earlier rift margin as the Arabian plate collided with the Iranian crustal collage in the Late Tertiary (summarized in Fig. 21).

Because of ambiguities in seismic and well control, several of the ideas proposed in this article are speculative and subject to significant disagreement between geoscientists in the exploration consortium operating the Suneinah Concession. The interpretation expressed here is entirely the responsibility of the authors. However, it would never have been possible without the foundation of ideas and synthesis laid by many Quintana, Gulf and Occidental geologists and geophysicists in the past. Their contribution is gratefully acknowledged. Gordon Smith's encouragement and support from Judy Yearton, Mike Chequer and Diana Monckton are especially appreciated. Several seismic records used in the illustrations were provided by BP Petroleum Development Ltd. and Japex Oman Ltd. The Ministry of Petroleum and Minerals, Sultanate of Oman and managements of Occidental International Exploration and Production Company and Chevron Overseas Petroleum Inc. are thanked for permission to publish this article.

References

ALMOND, D. C. 1986. The relation of Mesozoic–Cainozoic volcanism to tectonics in the Afro-Arabian dome. *Journal of Volcanology and Geothermal Research*, **28**, 225–246.

BAKER, B. H., MOHR, P. A. & WILLIAMS, L. A. J. 1972. Geology of the Eastern Rift System of Africa. *Geological Society of America Special Paper*, **136**.
—— & WOHLENBURG, J. 1971. Structure and evolution of the Kenya rift valley. *Nature*, **229**, 538–542.
BARTOV, Y., STEINITZ, G., EYAL, M. & EYAL, Y. 1980. Sinistral movement along the Gulf of Aqaba — its age and relation to the opening of the Red Sea. *Nature*, **285**, 220–222.
BAYER, H.-J., HOTZL, H., JADO, A. R., ROSCHER, B. & VOGGENREITER, W. 1988. Sedimentary and structural evolution of the northwest Arabian Red Sea margin. *Tectonophysics*, **153**, 137–152.
BERBERIAN, F. & KING, G. C. P. 1981. Towards a palaeogeography and tectonic evolution of Iran. *Canadian Journal of Earth Sciences*, **18**, 210–265.
BERHE, S. M. 1986. Geological and geochronological constraints on the evolution of the Red Sea — Gulf of Aden and Afar Depression. *Journal African Earth Sciences*, **5**, 101–117.
BEYDOUN, Z. R. 1966. The geology of the Arabian Peninsula, Eastern Arabian Protectorate and part of Dhofar. US Geological Survey Professional Paper 560 H. US Government Printing Office, Washington.
—— 1970. Southern Arabia and northern Somalia: comparative geology. *Philosophical Transactions of the Royal Society of London, Ser.* **A267**, 267–292.
BONATTI, E. 1987. Rifting or drifting in the Red Sea. *Nature*, **330**, 692–693.
——, COLANTONI, P., DELLA VEDOVA, B. & TAVIANI, M. 1984. Geology of the Red Sea transitional region (22°N–25°N). *Oceanologica Acta*, **7**, 385–398.
BROWN, G. F. 1970. Eastern margin of the Red Sea and coastal structures in Saudi Arabia. *Philosophical Transactions of the Royal Society of London*, **A267**, 75–87.
BURKE, K. & SENGÖR, A. M. C. 1986. Tectonic escape in the evolution of continental crust. *In*: BARAZANGI, M. & BROWN, L. D. (eds), *Reflection Seismology; the Continental Crust*. International symposium on Deep structure of the continental crust; results from reflection seismology. *Geodynamics Series*, **14**, 41–53.
BURRUSS, R. C., CERCONE, K. R. & HARRIS, P. M. 1985. Timing of Hydrocarbon Migration; evidenced from fluid inclusions in clacite cements, tectonics and burial history. *In*: SCHNEIDERMANN, N. & HARRIS, P. M. (eds), *Carbonate cements revisited; a symposium*. Society of Economic Paleontologists and Mineralogists Special Publication, **36**, 277–289.
COCHRAN, J. R. 1981. The Gulf of Aden: Structure and evolution of a young ocean basin and continental margin. *Journal of Geophysical Research*, **86**, 263–288.
COURTILLOT, V., ARMIJO, R. & TAPPONNIER, P. 1987. KINEMATICS OF THE SINAI TRIPLE JUNCTION AND A TWO PHASE MODEL OF ARABIA-AFRICA RIFTING. *In*: COWARD, M. P., DEWEY, J. F. & HANCOCK, P. L.

(eds), *Continental Extensional Tectonics*. Geological Society of London Special Publication, **28**, 559–573.
CRANE, K. & BONATTI, E. 1987. The role of fracture zones during early Red Sea rifting: structural analysis using space shuttle radar and Landsat imagery. *Journal of the Geological Society*, **144**, 407–420.
DEWEY, J. F. & SENGOR, A. M. C. 1979. Aegean and surrounding regions: Complex multiplate and continuum tectonics in a covergent zone. *Geological Society of America Bulletin*, **90**, 84–92.
EVANS, A. L. 1988. Neogene tectonic and stratigraphic events in the Gulf of Suez rift area, Egypt. *Tectonophysics*, **153**, 235–248.
EYAL, M., EYAL, Y., BARTOV, Y. & STEINITZ, G. 1981. The tectonic development of the western margin of the Gulf of Elat (Aqaba) Rift. *Tectonophysics*, **80**, 39–66.
FARHOUDI, G. & KARIG, D. E. 1977. Makran of Iran and Pakistan as an active arc system. *Geology*, **5**, 664–668.
FREUND, R., ZAK, I. & GOLDBERG, M. 1970. The shear along the Dead Sea Rift. *Philosophical Transactions of the Royal Society of London, Ser.* **A267**, 107–130.
FROST, S. H., HARRIS, P. M., BURGESS, J. D., SHAFFER, B. L., SEIGLIE, G. A. & BURRUSS, R. C. 1980. *Cretaceous geology of the Gulf/Quintana/Occidental Concession, Oman, Internal Company Report.*
GARFUNKEL, Z. 1981. Internal structure of the Dead Sea leaky transform (rift) in relation to plate kinematics. *Tectonophysics*, **80**, 81–108.
—— & BARTOV, Y. 1977. The tectonics of the Suez Rift. *Geological Survey of Israel Bulletin*, **71**, 1–44.
GEALEY, W. K. 1977. Ophiolite obduction and geologic evolution of the Oman Mountains and adjacent areas. *Geological Society of America Bulletin*, **88**, 1183–1191.
GIRDLER, R. W. 1985. Problems concerning the evolution of oceanic lithosphere in the northern Red Sea. *Tectonophysics*, **116**, 109–122.
—— & SOUTHERN, T. C. 1987. Structure and evolution of the northern Red Sea. *Nature*, **330**, 716–721.
—— & STYLES, P. 1976. The relevance of magnetic anomalies over the southern Red Sea and Gulf of Aden to Afar. *In: Proceedings International Symposium on the Afar and Related Rift Problems*, Bad Bergraben, Federal Republic of Germany, April 1–6, 1974, vol. 2, 156–170. East Schweizerbart'ische Verlagsbuchhandlung, Stuttgart, Federal Republic of Germany.
—— & —— 1982. Comments on 'The Gulf of Aden: Structure and evolution of a young ocean basin and continental margin' by J. R. Cochran. *Journal of Geophysical Research*, **87**, 6761–6763.
GLENNIE, K. W., BOEUFF, M. G. A., HUGHES-CLARK, M. W., MOODY-STUART, M., PILAAR, W. F. H. & REINHARDT, B. M. 1974. Geology of the Oman Mountains. Koninklijk Nederlands. Geologisch Mijnbouwkundig Genootschap,

Verhanderlingen, **31**.

HARRIS, P. M. & FROST, S. H. 1984. Middle Cretaceous carbonate reservoirs, Fahud Field and northwestern Oman. *American Association of Petroleum Geologists Bulletin*, **68**, 649–658.

HEMPTON, M. R. 1987. Constraints on Arabian plate motion and extensional history of the Red Sea. *Tectonics*, **6**, 687–705.

HOPSON, C. A., COLEMAN, R. G., GREGORY, R. T., PALLISTER, J. S. & BAILEY, E. H. 1981. Geologic section through the Semail ophiolite and associated rocks along a Muscat-Ibra transect, southeastern Oman Mountains. *Journal of Geophysical Research*, **86**, 2527–2544.

JACKSON, J. A. 1980. Reactivation of basement faults and crustal shortening in orogenic belts. *Nature*, **283**, 343–346.

——, FITCH, T. J. & McKENZIE, D. P. 1981. Active thrusting and the evolution of the Zagros fold belt. *In*: McCLAY, K. R. & PRICE, N. J. (eds), *Thrust and Nappe Tectonics*. Geological Society, London, Special Publication, **9**, 371–380.

KASHFI, M. S. 1976. Plate tectonics and structural evolution of the Zagros geosyncline, southwest Iran. *Geological Society of America Bulletin*, **87**, 1486–1490.

LE PICHON, X. & GAULIER, J.-M. 1988. The rotation of Arabia and the Levant fault system. *Tectonophysics*, **153**, 271–294.

LIPPARD, S. J., SHELTON, A. W. & GASS, I. G. 1986. *The Ophiolite of Northern Oman*. Geological Society, London, Memoir, **11**.

LOVELOCK, P. E. R. 1984. A review of the tectonics of the northern Middle East region. *Geological Magazine*, **121**, 577–587.

MART, Y. & ROSS, D. A. 1987. Post-Miocene rifting and diapirism in the northern Red Sea. *Marine Geology*, **74**, 173–190.

McCALL, G. J. H. & KIDD, R. G. W. 1982. The Makran, southeastern Iran: the anatomy of a convergent plate margin active from Cretaceous to present. *In*: LEGGETT, J. K. (ed.) *Trench – Forearc geology: and Forearc sedimentation and tectonics on modern and ancient active plate margins*. Geological Society, London, Special Publication, **10**, 387–397.

MONTENANT, C., OTT d'ESTEVOU, P., PURSER, B., BUROLLET, P.-F., JARRIGE, J.-J., ORSZAG-SPERBER, F., PHILOBBOS, E., PLAZIAT, J.-C., PRAT, P., RICHERT, J.-P., ROUSSEL, N. & THIRIET, J.-P. 1988. Tectonic and sedimentary evolution of the Gulf of Suez and the northwestern Red Sea. *Tectonophysics*, **153**, 161–178.

MORETTI, I. & COLLETTA, B. 1987. Spatial and temporal evolution of the Suez rift subsidence. *Journal of Geodynamics*, **7**, 151–168.

MURRIS, R. J. 1980. Middle East: Stratigraphic evolution and oil habitat. *American Association of Petroleum Geologists Bulletin*, **64**, 597–618.

NOLAN, S. C., SKELTON, P. N., CLISSOLD, B. P. & SMEWING, J. D. 1989. Maastrichtian to Early Tertiary stratigraphy and paleogeography of the Central and Northern Oman Mountains. *In*: ROBERTSON, A. H. F., SEARLE, M. P. & RIES, A.

C. *Geology and Tectonics of the Oman Region*. Geological Society, London, Special Publication, **49**, 495–519.

NOY, D. J. 1978. A comparison of magnetic anomalies in the Red Sea and Gulf of Aden. *In*: RAMBERG, I. B. & NEUMAN, E. R. (eds), *Tectonophysics and Geophysics of Continental Rifts*. D. Reidal, Hingham, Mass., 279–286.

O'CONNOR, S. J. & PATTON, T. L. 1986. Middle Cretaceous carbonate reservoirs, Fahud Field and Northwestern Oman: Discussion. *American Association of Petroleum Geologists Bulletin*, **70**, 1799–1801.

PALLISTER, J. S. 1987. Magmatic history of Red Sea rifting: Perspective from the central Saudi Arabian coastal plain. *Geological Society of America Bulletin*, **98**, 400–417.

PATRIAT, P. & ACHACHE, J. 1984. India-Eurasia collision chronology has implications for crustal shortening and driving mechanism of plates. *Nature*, **311**, 615–621.

PEARCE, J. A., ALABASTER, T., SHELTON, A. W. & SEARLE, M. P. 1981. The Oman ophiolite as a Cretaceous arc-basin complex: evidence and implications. *Philosophical Transactions of the Royal Society of London*, **A3**, 299–317.

PONIKAROV, V. P. 1967. *The Geology of Syria Exploratory notes on the geological map of Syria*. Scale 1:500 000. Ministry of Industry, Department of Geological and Mineral Research, Syrian Arab Republic.

QUENNELL, A. M. 1984. The Western Arabia Rift System. *In*: DIXON, J. E. & ROBERTSON, A. H. F. (eds), *The Geological Evolution of the Eastern Mediterranean*. Geological Society, London, Special Publication, **17**, 775–788.

RICATEAU, R. & RICHE, H. 1980. Geology of the Musandam Peninsula (Sultanate of Oman) and its surroundings. *Journal of Petroleum Geology*, **3**, 139–152.

ROBERTSON, A. H. F. 1987a. The transition from a passive margin to an Upper Cretaceous foreland basin related to ophiolite emplacement in the Oman Mountains. *Geological Society of America Bulletin*, **99**, 633–653.

—— 1987b. Upper Cretaceous Muti Formation: transition of a Mesozoic carbonate platform to a foreland basin in the Oman Mountains. *Sedimentology*, **34**, 1123–1142.

RON, H. & EYAL, Y. 1985. Intraplate deformation by block rotation and mesostructures along the Dead Sea transform, Northern Israel. *Tectonics*, **4**, 85–105.

ROSS, D. A., UCHUPI, E. & WHITE, R. S. 1986. The geology of the Persian Gulf-Gulf of Oman region: a synthesis. *Reviews of Geophysics*, **24**, 537–556.

SAHOTA, G. 1985. Evolution of the Gulf of Aden. *The Geophysical Journal of the Royal Astronomical Society*, **81**, 317.

SCHMIDT, D. L., HADLEY, D. G., & BROWN, G. F. 1983. Middle Tertiary continental rift and evolution of the Red Sea in southeastern Saudi Arabia. *USGS Open File Report*. 83–641, 1–56.

SCHULMAN, N. & BARTOV, Y. 1978. Tectonics and

sedimentation along the Rift valley. Post-Congress Excursion Y2. *10th International Congress on Sedimentology, Jerusalem, July 1978*, 36–94.

SEARLE, M. P. 1985. Sequence of thrusting and origin of culminations in the northern and central Oman Mountains. *Journal of Structural Geology*, **7**, 129–143.

—— 1988. Thrust tectonics of the Dibba Zone and the structural evolution of the Arabian continental margin along the Musandam mountains (Oman and United Arab Emirates). *Journal of the Geological Society of London*, **145**, 43–53.

—— & COOPER, D. J. W. 1986. Structure of the Hawasina Window culmination, central Oman Mountains. *Transactions of the Royal Society of Edinburg*, **77**, 143–156.

—— & GRAHAM, G. M. 1982. 'Oman Exotics' — Oceanic carbonate buildups associated with the early stages of continental rifting. *Geology*, **10**, 43–49.

——, JAMES, N. P., CALON, T. J. & SMEWING, J. D. 1983. Sedimentological and structural evolution of the Arabian continental margin in the Musandam Moutains and Dibba Zone, United Arab Emirates. *Geological Society of America Bulletin*, **94**, 1381–1400.

—— & STEVENS, R. K. 1984. Obduction processes in ancient, modern and future ophiolites. *In*: GASS, I. G., LIPPARD, S. J. & SHELTON, A. W. (eds), *Ophiolites and Ancient Oceanic Lithosphere*. Geological Society of London Special Publication, **13**, 291–303.

ŞENGÖR, A. M. C. & CANITEZ, N. 1982. The North Anatolian Fault. *In*: BERCKHEMER, H. & HSU, K. J. (eds), *Alpine-Mediterranean geodynamics*, Geodynamics Series, **7**, 205–216.

——, GORUR, N. & SAROGLU, F. 1985. Strike-slip faulting and related basin formation in zones of tectonic escape: Turkey as a case study. *Society Economic Palaeontologists and Mineralogists. Special Publication*, **37**, 227–264.

STECKLER, M. S., BERTHELOT, F., LYBERIS, N. & LE PICHON, X. 1988. Subsidence in the Gulf of Suez: implications for rifting and plate kinematics. *Tectonophysics*, **153**, 249–270.

STOCKLIN, J. 1968. Structural history and tectonics of Iran: a review. *American Association of Petroleum Geologists Bulletin*, **52**, 1229–1258.

TAPPONNIER, P. & MOLNAR, P. 1976. Slip-line field theory and large-scale continental tectonics. *Nature*, **264**, 319–324.

——, PELTZER, G., LE DAIN, A. Y. & ARMIJO, R. 1982. Propagating extrusion tectonics in Asia: New insights from simple experiments with plasticine. *Geology*, **10**, 611–616.

TEWFIK, N. & AYYAD, M. 1982. Petroleum exploration in the Red Sea shelf of Egypt. E.G.P.C. 6th Exploration Seminar, Cairo, March 1982, 30 pp.

TIRRUL, R., BELL, I. R., GRIFFIS, R. J. & CAMP, V. E. 1983. The Sistan suture zone of eastern Iran. *Geological Society of America Bulletin*, **94**, 134–150.

TSCHOPP, R. H. 1967a. Development of the Fahud Field. *7th World Petroleum Congress Proceedings*, **2**, 231–242.

—— 1967b. The general geology of Oman. 7th World Petroleum Congress Proceedings, **2**, 243–250.

WHITE, R. S. 1981. Deformation of the Makran accretionary sediment prism in the Gulf of Oman (north-west Indian Ocean). *In*: LEGETT, J. K. (ed), *Trench and Fore-arc Sedimentation*. Geological Society of London Special Publication, **10**, 69–84.

—— 1984. Active and passive plate boundaries around the Gulf of Oman, northwest Indian Ocean. Deep Sea Research, **31**, 731–745.

—— & ROSS, D. A. 1979. Tectonics of the western Gulf of Oman. *Journal of Geophysical Research*, **84**, (B7), 3479–3489.

WEINS, D. A., DeMETS, C., GORDON, R. G., STEIN, S., ARGUS, D., ENGELN, J. F., LUNDGREN, P., QUIBLE, D., STEIN, C., WEINSTEIN, S. & WOODS, D. F. 1985. A diffuse plate boundary model for Indian Ocean tectonics. *Geophysical Research Letters*, **12**, 429–432.

WILSON, H. H. 1969. Late Cretaceous eugeosynclinal sedimentation, gravity tectonics and ophiolite emplacement in the Oman Mountains, south east Arabia. *American Association of Petroleum Geologists*, **53**, 626–671.

ZAK, I. & FREUND, R. 1981. Asymmetry and basin migration in the Dead Sea Rift. *Tectonophysics*, **80**, 27–38.

The evolution of the Oman Mountains Foreland Basin

J. WARBURTON[1], T. J. BURNHILL[2], R. H. GRAHAM[2] & K. P. ISAAC[1]

[1] BP Exploration, 301 St Vincent St., Glasgow G2 5DD, UK
[2] BP Petroleum Development, Britannic House, Moor Lane, Moorgate,
London EC2Y 9BU, UK

Abstract: The Late Cretaceous fill of the Oman Mountains foredeep is subdivided into four sub-sequences using seismic stratigraphic principles based on seismic, well and outcrop data. Sub-sequence FD-a (Late Coniacian to Early Santonian) was overriden by the Hawasina allochthon on the sea bed of the foredeep. FD-b (Early to Late Santonian) was deposited during thrusting and slices of foredeep sediment were tectonically accreted onto the allochthon during the final stages of thrusting. FD-c and FD-d (Late Santonian to Late Coniacian) were deposited after the emplacement of the allochthon into the foredeep. Subsidence curves for the foredeep area show that an emergent peripheral bulge bounded the cratonic side of the foredeep throughout the Late Cretaceous. There is no evidence that the forebulge migrated with time ahead of the advancing Hawasina thrust sheets. Instead the bulge remained in situ while the basin narrowed during thrusting. During the Maastrichtian, after infill of the foredeep, the Oman Mountains area subsided beneath sea level. Clastic supply from the drowned hinterland ceased and carbonate deposition followed. The main Oman Mountain building episode was during the Late Miocene when continent-continent collision occurred in the Zagros Mountains.

The Oman Mountains are located on the eastern margin of the Arabian Platform, and form a 650 km chain of mountains stretching from the Musandam Peninsula in the NW to the Indian Ocean in the SE (Fig. 1). A well developed foredeep is present in front of the mountains which forms a belt some 50 to 100 km in width to the west of the range. Foreland basins are one of the most obvious expressions of flexure of the continental lithosphere. Downward flexing due to a tectonically emplaced load, the mountain belt, results in an adjacent depression which acts as a catchment basin for orogenic detritus. A gentle upwarp, or peripheral bulge, generally bounds the cratonic side of the foreland basin (Jacobi 1981).

The Oman Mountains provide a classic example of a marine foreland basin because the sedimentary fill of the foredeep is well documented. Much of the foredeep and underlying succession is exposed in outcrop in the Oman Mountains, and excellent correlation into the subsurface is provided by good quality seismic and well data. This contribution describes the sequence stratigraphy of the foreland basin fill using these data, and summarizes the Late Cretaceous burial and tectonic history of the foredeep and peripheral bulge. The main area described is the featureless gravel plain immediately to the southwest of the Hamrat ad Duru Range (Fig. 1).

Regional geology

The Oman Mountains are the product of two distinct orogenies. The first of these occurred during the Senonian (Late Cretaceous) when the formerly passive, northeastern margin of the Tethys ocean became compressive. The sediments of the continental slope and adjacent ocean floor, together with a considerable volume of oceanic crust, were obducted onto the eastern margin of the Arabian Platform. As a consequence of the loading of the Arabian Platform a foredeep developed in the depression between the obducted allochthon and an emergent peripheral bulge to the west.

Although the allochthon was subject to intense deformation, the underlying platform carbonates remained undeformed except for a minor extensional faulting associated with the flexure.

The second orogeny, which began in the Miocene and continued to the present day, was related to the Zagros collision in Iran (Searle 1985, 1988). In Oman this compression is manifest in a series of basement involved 'thick skinned' elevations which fold the older allochthon but do not appear to have resulted in further significant horizontal shortening. The timing of elevation of the Jebel Akhdar and Saih Hatat domes is proven in outcrop by the tilting of Late Miocene sediments parallel to the

From ROBERTSON, A. H. F., SEARLE, M. P. & RIES, A. C. (eds), 1990,
The Geology and Tectonics of the Oman Region.
Geological Society Special Publication No 49, pp 419–427

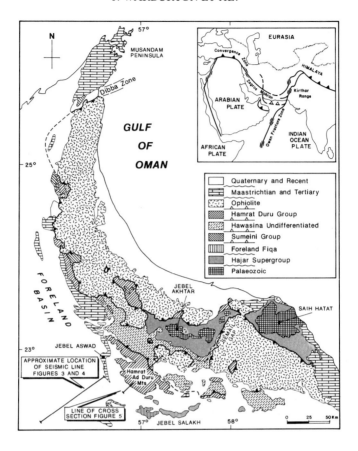

Fig. 1.

flanks of the domes. We do not believe that the major hiatus at the base of the Aruma Group (the Mahil/Aruma break of Glennie *et al.* (1973)) on the flanks of the domes records the timing of final thick-skinned elevation. Rather, it records an earlier event on the platform margin, possibly related to Late Cretaceous flexure ahead of the advancing allochthon (Patton & O'Connor 1986).

Stratigraphy

The stratigraphy of the Late Mesozoic of northern Oman is given in Fig. 2. The lithostratigraphy of the succession has been described in detail by Glennie *et al.* (1974) and more recently by Robertson (1987a,b), and Warburton *et al.* (1986).

We have used the sequence stratigraphic approach described by Vail *et al.* 1977, and Hubbard *et al.* (1985), which, by integrating field, well and seismic data allows the stratigraphy of the Oman Mountains foredeep to be described in a more dynamic fashion. The foredeep seismic sequences are bounded by unconformities and we describe their character in terms of the angular relations between internal seismic events and sequence boundaries, for example onlap, downlap and toplap (Mitchum & Vail 1977). In a complex compressional geological province, such as the Oman Mountains, the sequence boundaries are likely to record local tectonic events. We have not attempted to reconcile our sequence interpretation by inferring eustatic sea-level changes which are of global significance.

We have subdivided the succession into three megasequences, which equate to the precursor, foredeep and successor stages of the development of the Late Cretaceous orogeny.

Precursor Basin (Shelf Carbonate Megasequence)

The eastern margin of the Arabian Platform was the site of passive carbonate deposition from the Early Permian to the Late Cretaceous. This succession is collectively referred to as the Hajar Supergroup (Glennie *et al.* 1973, 1974).

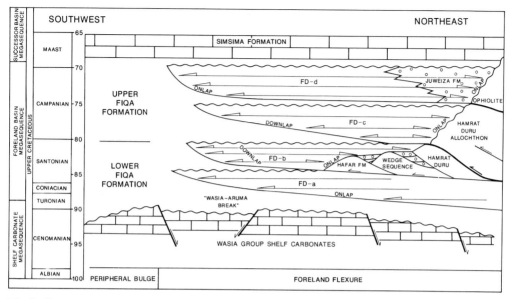

Fig. 2. Chronostratigraphic diagram for the Oman Foredeep (based on seismic well and outcrop data).

The Early Jurassic to Late Cretaceous part of the supergroup was deposited following the breakup of Gondwanaland and the opening of the Neotethys Ocean. Prior to breakup the Arabian margin rifted during the Late Permian and Triassic. Clearly the Hajar Supergroup records at least two major tectonic events, however for simplicity in this paper, we refer the entire supergroup loosely to a single Shelf Carbonate Megasequence. The distal equivalents of this Megasequence are preserved in the allochthonous units of the Oman Mountain Fold Belt. These comprise slope and oceanic sediments of the Hawasina Complex together with a complete ophiolite suite (Semail Complex). The youngest (Late Albian to Earliest Cenomanian) part of the Shelf Carbonate Megasequence, the Wasia Group (Glennie *et al.* 1973), was deposited immediately prior to the development of the foredeep. It comprises a basal transgressive clastic unit (Nahr Umr Formation), which is succeeded by thick carbonates deposited as an accreting sequence (Natih Formation). The uppermost part of the Natih Formation is locally eroded and in places karstified, testifying to the emergence of the platform at the end of the Cenomanian.

Foreland Basin

The Oman Mountains foreland basin is filled by Late Cretaceous marine sediments onto which was emplaced a thrusted wedge of allochthonous units of the Hawasina Group (Fig. 2).

The Foreland Basin Megasequence is defined by the unconformity at the base of the sedimentary fill of the foredeep. The top of the megasequence is defined by the base of the overlying Successor Basin Megasequence.

The oldest sediments in the foredeep yield Late Coniacian planktonic microfaunas. Turonian and Early Coniacian sediments are almost entirely absent on the eastern margin of the Arabian platform, and the time interval is represented by a hiatus or condensed facies.

Although onlap and downlap relationships are seen throughout the foredeep succession angular unconformities are rate. For this reason the Foreland Basin Megasequence contains only one sequence which is itself subdivided into four sub-sequences (FD-a to d). The four sub-sequences are continuous over large areas of the foredeep in the vicinity of the Hamrat ad Duru. Their internal geometry provides strong evidence for the tectonic and sedimentary response of the Arabian margin to emplacement of the allochthon. These sub-sequences are the sedimentary manifestation of several processes:
(i)   development of the foredeep as a response to loading;
(ii) emplacement, and erosion of the allochthon and deformation of the foredeep sediments;
(iii) the final erosion of the allochthon;
(iv) passive infill of the foredeep.

Sub-sequences

Examples illustrating the seismic expression of the foredeep sub-sequences are given in Figs 3 & 4.

Age determinations for the sub-sequences are based on several data sets. The chief data source is unpublished oil company biostratigraphic reports for exploration wells drilled in the foredeep area.

Numerous outcrops of foredeep lithologies were sampled for biostratigraphy by the authors in the mountains and several age determinations have been published (e.g. Glennie *et al.* 1974; Murris, 1980; Harris and Frost, 1984).

FD-a

Age: Late Coniacian to Early Santonian

The base of this sub-sequence is coincident with the base of the Foreland Basin Megasequence, which is marked by a major angular unconformity expressed on seismic data by both truncation of the underlying sequence and pronounced onlap. The sub-sequence is exposed in outcrop and has been penetrated by numerous wells. In the distal part of the foredeep it comprises a monotonous succession of hemipelagic and pelagic mudstones (Lower Fiqa Formation). In more proximal sections the upper part of the Lower Fiqa is replaced by the Muti Formation (Sayja and Hanya Members of Robertson 1987a) which comprise more coarse clastic detritus.

FD-b

Age: Early Santonian to Late Santonian

The base of this sub-sequence is marked by a minor low-angle unconformity expressed on seismic data by local truncation of the FD-a sub-sequence. The base of the sub-sequence exhibits pronounced downlap onto the unconformity in the area ahead of the emplaced wedge of allochthonous units. The sub-sequence appears to merge into the front of the wedge and becomes affected by the thrust structures which deform the wedge. There the base of FD-b becomes coincident with the base of the allochthon which directly overlies FD-a. The sub-sequence is also present above the allochthon, where it initially 'ponds' the topography between the thrust culminations and eventually blankets the wedge.

In the distal part of the foredeep sub-sequence FD-b does not exhibit downlap and is characterized by parallel strong high-amplitude reflec-

tors. Here the boundary with the underlying FD-a becomes indistinct and probably passes into a correlative conformity. Sub-sequence FD-b has only been penetrated by an exploration well in the internal eastern part of the foredeep where it contains the same hemipelagic mudstone facies as developed in FD-a (Lower Fiqa Formation). A slightly more proximal equivalent of this facies (Lusyal Formation, Warburton *et al.* 1986) may be exposed at outcrop where the foredeep sediments have been involved in the final phases of thrusting (see following section on the development of the foredeep). The sediments which 'pond' in between the thrust culminations are not exposed at surface but the seismic character suggests they are similar fine grained facies to the Lusyal Formation. The extensive succession of shallow water boulder beds (Hafar Formation, Warburton *et al.* 1986) which unconformably overlie the Hawasina Group thrusts in the southern part of the Hamrat Duru range may well be the proximal equivalents of the Lusyal Formation.

FD-c

Age: Late Santonian to Early Campanian.

In the internal eastern part of the foredeep FD-c sub-sequence conformably overlies the preceding FD-b sub-sequence. The base of the sub-sequence exhibits pronounced downlap in the area ahead of the emplaced wedge of allochthonous units. Here distinctive clinoforms are seen prograding into the foredeep, the toes of which occur at several downlap surfaces within the sub-sequence. Unlike the preceding FD-b sub-sequence, FD-c does not merge into the deformed allochthon, clearly indicating that this sub-sequence post-dates the emplacement of the Hawasina nappes.

This sub-sequence is not exposed at surface. Well penetrations in the eastern part of the foredeep near the mountains encountered hemipelagic mudstones (Upper Fiqa Formation).

FD-d

Age: Mid to Late Campanian

The FD-d sub-sequence conformably overlies the FD-c sub-sequence in the distal regions of the foredeep. However, in the proximity of the allochthon, the base of the sub-sequence onlaps the remnant clinoform topography of the underlying sub-sequence.

Well penetrations in the western distal part of the foredeep encountered hemipelagic mudstones (Upper Fiqa Formation) throughout the sub-sequence. In the eastern internal part of the foredeep, near the mountains, the well and outcrop data suggest that the Late Campanian Juweiza Formation (Glennie *et al.* 1974) interdigitates with the Upper Fiqa Formation within sub-sequence FD-d.

Successor Basin

By the end of the Late Cretaceous orogeny the Arabian continental margin was passive, and the remaining emergent allochthon was subject to gradual marine transgression. During this period of quiescence deposition of the shallow marine Simsima Formation carbonates prevailed across the whole of the Arabian Platform.

In the distal western parts of the foredeep basin the Simsima Formation is comfortable with sub-sequence FD-d, however when traced into the mountains, the base of the sequence oversteps the Hawasina wedge, and eventually the Semail ophiolite, with profound angular unconformity (Fig. 2).

Structural geometry of the frontal thrusts

The Hawasina and deformed part of the foredeep basin fill (Sub-sequence FD-b) are visible at outcrop in the Hamrat Duru range. The structure of this region has been described by Glennie *et al.* (1974) and more recently by Hanna (1986), Warburton *et al.* (1986) and Cooper (1988). Fig. 5 is a cross section across the Hamrat Duru derived from our own surface geological mapping which has been integrated with sub-surface data.

The Hamrat Duru range is a thin skinned imbricate stack which formed during the Late Cretaceous compression. Palinspastic restoration of the passive margin suggests that the displacement on the basal detachment must be of the order of 200 km (cf. Glennie *et al.* 1973). Presumably the Hawasina was stacked and shortened before it was emplaced en masse into the foredeep basin and over the Lower Fiqa Formation (subsequence FD-a).

The Hawasina thrust stack is itself deformed over a major northward verging anticline (the Hamrat Duru Dome). Upper Cretaceous and Lower Tertiary limestones are deformed around the dome and form the Jebel Aswad outcrop (Fig. 2). The Miocene succession is tilted in the sub-surface adjacent to the Jebel Aswad outcrop demonstrating a Late Miocene age for the Hamrat Duru Dome. The frontal part of the deformed Hawasina wedge is only visible on seismic data. At first sight the frontal geometry resembles a triangle zone of 'Alberta Syncline' type (Jones 1982; Banks & Warburton, 1986) beneath a frontal backthrust. However, although minor backthrust related structures of Miocene age are seen in outcrop, the fundamental structure cannot involve a major Late Miocene age backthrust because:

(i) the wedge is onlapped by undeformed beds of sub-sequence FD-c;

(ii) the thrusts of the wedge loose displacement towards the foreland through the same stratigraphic unit (sub-sequence FD-b).

This demonstrates that the already deformed Hawasina was emplaced onto the sea bed of the foredeep following the deposition of sub-sequence FD-a. Debris shed from the wedge (proximal sub-sequence FD-b) during its emplacement then became itself deformed as the thrusts propagated into the foredeep basin (see also Warburton *et al.* 1986).

Evolution of the Oman Mountains foredeep

During the Early Turonian the passive margin carbonate platform became emergent and the top of the Natih Formation was truncated. This relative fall in sea level has been attributed to a migrating peripheral bulge ahead of the developing foredeep (Patton & O'Connor, 1986). As a result Turonian and Early Conician sediments are commonly absent on the eastern margin of the Arabian Platform.

The platform was drowned during the Late Coniacian such that deep marine mudstones (Lower Fiqa Formation, sub-sequence FD-a, Fig. 6) were deposited in the distal parts of the foredeep, no intermediate facies are present. The transgression onto the platform carbonates is clearly seen on seismic data (Fig. 4) where the base of sub-sequence FD-a shows pronounced onlap to the west. This transgression must have been extremely rapid as the younging of the base of the Fiqa Formation cannot be resolved by biostratigraphy.

The drowning occurred as the carbonate platform was loaded by the obduction of Hawasina and Semail nappes on its eastern margin. A series of extensional faults developed in the upper part of the platform in response to this flexure.

Exploration wells drilled on carbonate platform tilted blocks in the foredeep show that the Fiqa Formation commonly thickens in the hanging wall. In the proximal part of the foredeep, moderately deep water limestone (Lower Sayja Member of Robertson (1987a)) deposition was

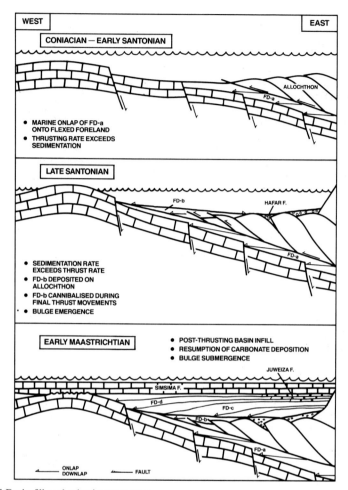

Fig. 6. Foreland Basin fill and seismic sequences

replaced by turbidites and debris flows shed off the advancing thrust sheets (Upper Sayja Member). These units were eventually overidden by, and incorporated into, the thrust wedge as it propagated into the foreland basin.

Deposition of sub-sequence FD-b occurred during the final stages of the emplacement of the wedge. Although the frontal thrusts of the wedge involve the foredeep sediments of FD-b, the sub-sequence beneath the sole thrust shows downlap relationships. These appear to be 'toe sets', suggesting that sediments shed off the wedge prograded into the foredeep before they were deformed in turn. As the 'top sets' are truncated the height of the prograding units and the water depth of the foredeep during the deposition of sub-sequence FD-b cannot be accurately established.

The involvement of foredeep sediments in thrusting probably began towards the end of thrust sheet emplacement. Over a particular period, the rate of thrust transport would have decreased relative to the background rate of foredeep sedimentation. Sediments would then be deposited onto the thrust wedge and have been 'cannibalized' and involved in thrusting before final cessation of thrust transport (Warburton *et al.* 1986).

Sub-sequence FD-c was deposited following the emplacement of the wedge. Distinct prograding units can be seen within this subsequence and both toe sets and top sets are clearly present (Fig. 4). These prograding units probably represent coarse clastic detritus shed off the emergent wedge. The nearest wells to the toe sets (approximately 10 km) encountered hemipelagic mudstones throughout the Fiqa Formation suggesting that the coarse detritus formed a narrow apron ahead of the wedge. The height of the clinoforms in the prograding units suggest water depths in the foredeep were in the order of 1000 m.

In the distal western region of the foredeep sub-sequence FD-d progressively oversteps sub-sequences FD-c to FD-a before eventually it overlies the truncated platform carbonates (close to the present-day border with the U.A.E.). In the proximal, eastern, part of the foredeep the sub-sequence onlaps the remnant clinoforms of the underlying sub-sequence FD-c. Sediments within this sub-sequence are composed entirely of hemipelagic mudstones and represent the final passive infill of the foredeep.

Subsidence history of the foredeep

In order to illustrate the subsidence history of the foredeep burial history curves have been generated from exploration well data for the mountain front, foreland basin and peripheral bulge (Fig. 7). Subsidence in the mountain front was extremely rapid in the Late Cretaceous when the Arabian margin was loaded by the emplacement of the Hawasina and Semail thrust sheets. Gentle subsidence occurred after thrusting ceased and as the foreland basin was filled. The Zagros orogeny caused rapid elevation in the mountains during the Late Miocene (Fig. 7c).

On the foreland flexure (Fig. 7b) the erosion of the extensional tilted fault blocks (Harris & Frost 1984) is recorded as an uplift event prior to the main phase of Late Cretaceous subsidence. The foredeep subsided more gradually than in the overthrust mountain front area.

The peripheral bulge (Fig. 7a) formed during the Late Cretaceous at the same time as erosion of the shelf carbonate fault blocks occurred on the foreland depression. The peripheral bulge only began to subside during the Tertiary and remained emergent throughout the Late Cretaceous.

Bulge propagation

Robertson (1987a) has suggested that the stratigraphy of the Muti Formation is compatible with the thermal model of a passive margin to foreland basin transition which involves an old rift and a submerged load (Stockmal et al. 1986). The model predicts that as the overthrust load moved over the Oman Margin the hinge point of the foreland flexure, the forebulge and the associated unconformity migrated with it.

There is however little hard, published data to support the view that the forebulge migrated. Robertson (1987a) states 'Biostratigraphic res-

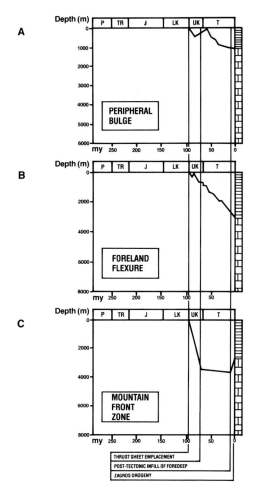

Fig. 7. Burial history curves for the Oman Foredeep

olution is inadequate to detect any time difference between the Wasia-Aruma break for example between the Semail Gap, and Jebel Salakh located 50–75 towards the foreland' (Fig. 1).

A comparison of the magnitude of the Wasia–Aruma break on the peripheral bulge and on the foreland flexure clearly demonstrates that the forebulge existed in its present location throughout thrusting. The burial curves (Fig. 7a,b) clearly show that the bulge grew in its present location during the time when the foreland panel to the east was being flexed. Had the bulge migrated over the foreland flexure, the Wasia–Aruma break would be a significantly bigger hiatus closer to that which exists at the bulge today. The entire Natih Formation would be expected to be absent throughout the foredeep. A major stratigraphic hiatus does however occur beneath the Aruma Group foredeep sediments on the northern margins of the Jebel Akhdar and Saih Hatat domes. The reason why the shelf margin was greatly elevated just prior to deposition of the Aruma Group in that area is not clear (see discussion of Regional Geology earlier).

It is probable therefore that the peripheral bulge formed in-situ and that it acted as a fixed hinge for the progressive flexure of the foreland beneath the allochthon to the east. This is also suggested by the onlap of sub-sequence FD-a which clearly demonstrates a continuous, yet very rapid, younging of the Wasia–Aruma break from east to west. This onlap relationship would not be seen above a migrating peripheral bulge.

The reason why the peripheral bulge should have formed in its present location is not clear. It is conceivable that it 'nucleated' on an earlier crustal weakness within the Arabian plate. It would be an interesting exercise to attempt flexural modelling of the Oman margin, assuming a fixed forebulge, particularly since the Late Cretaceous to Tertiary history is so well constrained.

Summary

We have provided a summary of the Late Cretaceous and Tertiary evolution of the Oman Mountains foredeep by integrating good quality seismic, outcrop and well data. The subsurface data are critical to understanding how the Hawasina allochthon relates to the foredeep sediments because nowhere is the frontal part of the thrust stack exposed.

It has been demonstrated that the allochthon was emplaced onto, and depressed, the carbonate platform margin during Coniacian to Late Santonian times. The thrusted imbricate stack advanced rapidly towards a stationary forebulge which bounded the progressively narrowing foredeep flexural basin. During the latest thrust movements slices of foreland basin sediments were accreted onto the thrust front and transported along with the Hawasina allochthon. The allochthon was buried by detritus from the elevated allochthon, and the foredeep basin was eventually filled with fine grained clastic sediments during Campanian times. Resumption of carbonate deposition during the Maastrichtian demonstrates that the clastic hinterland became submerged after the foredeep was infilled. This suggests that the Late Cretaceous proto-Oman Mountains were of relatively low relief. The present-day mountain belt was built after the Mid-Miocene during continent-continent collision in the Zagros Mountains to the north.

The evolution of the Oman foredeep and adjacent mountains is well constrained. However, two major problems deserve further attention. Firstly, why was the northern margin of the carbonate platform elevated and eroded during Turonian times such that the oldest beds of the foredeep Aruma Group rest on Permian and Triassic rocks of the Shelf Carbonate Megasequence? Secondly, what is the mechanism of formation of an in situ forebulge? Why does this appear to be the case in Oman compared with other foreland basin examples where the forebulge appears to have migrated cratonwards with time?

Conclusions

The Late Cretaceous Foredeep Megasequence comprises only one main seismic sequence representing the basin fill. Four seismic stratigraphic sub-sequences have been recognized within it. FD-a is Late Coniacian to Early Santonian in age and was overriden by the Hawasina allochthon on the sea bed of the foredeep. FD-b is Early to Late Santonian in age and was deposited during emplacement of the Hawasina thrust sheets into the foredeep basin. Slices of basinal sediment within sub-sequence FD-b were accreted onto the allochthon during the final stages of thrusting. FD-c and FD-d record the post-tectonic infill of the foredeep and burial of the allochthon during Late Santonian to Late Coniacian times.

Carbonate deposition during the Maastrichtian shows that the Oman Mountains area was not providing clastic sediments into the basin and was therefore mostly below sea level. This has important implications for the timing of the main orogenesis in the Oman Mountains and agrees with the Late Miocene age implied by tilting of the Upper Tertiary succession away from the major domes of Jebel Akhdar, Saih Hatat and Hamrat ad Duru.

Subsidence curves show that the peripheral bulge was emergent throughout the Late Cretaceous. The bulge suffered erosion at the same time that tilted fault blocks on the down-flexed carbonate platform to the east were being eroded. The forebulge formed in situ and behaved as a fixed hinge whilst the platform to the east was depressed beneath the advancing allochthon. There is no evidence of forebulge migration with time.

We thank the Chairman and Board of Directors of British Petroleum Company Ltd and the Ministry of

Petroleum and Minerals of the Sultanate of Oman for permission to publish the work. We are grateful to many of our colleagues for their individual contributions to BP's Oman Mountains project; in particular we wish to thank R. J. Fredsted and T. P. C. Thackeray. M. Hughes Clark and Samir Hanna are thanked for their ever sound discussions, and Peter Cawood and Dana Coffield made numerous helpful comments on the original manuscript.

References

BANKS, C. J. & WARBURTON, J. 1986. "Passive Roof" duplex geometry in the frontal structures of the Kirthar and Sulaiman mountain belts, Pakistan. *Journal of Structural Geology*, **8**, 3/4, 229–237.

COOPER, D. J. W. 1988. Structure and sequence of thrusting in deep water sediments during ophiolite emplacement in the South-Central Oman Mountains. *Journal of Structural Geology*, **10**, 473–485.

GLENNIE, K. W., BOEUF, M. G. A., HUGHES-CLARK, M. W., MOODY-STUART, M., PILAAR, M. F. & REINHARDT, B. B. 1973. Late Cretaceous Nappes in the Oman Mountains and their geologic evolution. *American Association of Petroleum Geologists Bulletin*, **57**, 5–27.

——, ——, ——, & REINHARDT, B. B. 1974. Geology of the Oman Mountains. *Geol. Mijnbouwkd. Genoot. Verh.*, **31**.

HANNA, S. S. 1986. The Alpine (Late Cretaceous and Tertiary) tectonic evolution of the Oman Mountains: A thrust tectonic approach. *In: Technical papers and Case Studies presented at the Symposium of intense thrust zones, Abu Dhabi*, **2**, 127–174.

HARRIS, P. M. & FROST, S. H. 1984. Middle Cretaceous carbonate reservoirs, Fahud Field, North-Western Oman. *American Association of Petroleum Geologists Bulletin*, **68**, 649–658.

HUBBARD, R. J., PAPE, J. & ROBERTS, D. G. 1985. Depositional Sequence mapping as a technique to establish tectonic and stratigraphic framework and evaluate hydrocarbon potential on a passive continental margin. *In:* BERG, O. R. & WOOLVERTON, D. G. (eds). *Seismic Stratigraphy II, an integrated approach.*

JACOBI, R. D. 1981. Peripheral bulge – a causal mechanism for the Lower/Middle Ordovician unconformity along the western margin of the Northern Appalachians. *Earth and Planetary Science Letters*, **56**, 245–251.

JONES, P. B. 1982. Oil and gas beneath east-dipping underthrust faults in the Alberta Foothills. *In:* POWERS, R. B. (ed.) *Geological Studies of the Cordilleran Thrust Belt*. Rocky Mountain Association of Petroleum Geologists, **1**, 61–74.

MITCHUM, R. M. & VAIL, P. R. 1977. Seismic stratigraphy and global changes in sea level, part 7: Seismic stratigraphic interpretation procedure. *In:* PAYTON, C. E. (ed.) *Seismic Stratigraphy – applications to hydrocarbon exploration.* American Association of Petroleum Geologists Memoir, **26**.

MURRIS, R. J. 1980. Middle East stratigraphical evolution and oil habitat. *American Association of Petroleum Geologists Bulletin*, **64**, 597–618.

PATTON, T. L. & O'CONNOR, S. J. 1986. Cretaceous flexural history of the Northern Oman Mountain Foredeep, United Arab Emirates. *In: Technical Papers and Case Studies presented at the Symposium on the hydrocarbon potential of intense thrust zones, Abu Dhabi.* **1**, 77–120.

ROBERTSON, A. H. F. 1987a. Upper Cretaceous Muti Formation: transition of a Mesozoic carbonate platform to a foreland basin in the Oman Mountains. *Sedimentology*, **34**, 1123–1142.

—— 1987b. The transition from a passive margin to an Upper Cretaceous foreland basin related to ophiolite emplacement in the Oman Mountains. *Geological Society of America Bulletin*, **99**, 633–653.

SEARLE, M. P. 1985. Sequence of thrusting and origin of culminations in the Northern and Central Oman Mountains. *Journal of Structural Geology*, **7**, 129–143.

—— 1988. Structure of the Musandam culmination (Sultanate of Oman and United Arab Emirates) and the Straits of Hormuz Syntaxis. *Journal of the Geological Society, London*, **145**, 831–845.

STOCKMAL, G. S., BEAUMONT, C. & BOUTILIER, R. 1986. Geodynamic models of convergent margin tectonics: transition from rifted margin to overthrust belt and consequences for foreland basin development. *American Association of Petroleum Geologists Bulletin*, **70**, 181–190.

VAIL, P. R., MITCHUM, R. M., TODD, R. G. WIDMIER, J. M., THOMPSON, S., SANGREE, J. B., BUDD, J. N. & HATLELID, W. G. 1977. Seismic stratigraphy and global changes in sea level, *In:* PEYTON, C. E. (ed.) *Seismic Stratigraphy – Applications to Hydrocarbon Exploration.* American Associations of Petroleum Geologists, Memoir 26.

WARBURTON, J., GRAHAM, R. H. & ISAAC, K. P. 1986. The Sedimentology and Structural Geology of the Hamrat ad Duru Range of the Sultanate of Oman. *In: Technical Papers and Case Studies presented at the Symposium on the hydrocarbon potential of intense thrust zones, Abu Dhabi*, **1**, 123–153.

Origin of culminations within the Southeast Oman Mountains at Jebel Ma-jhool and Ibra Dome

P. A. CAWOOD, F. K. GREEN & T. J. CALON

Department of Earth Sciences, Memorial University of Newfoundland,
St. John's, Nfld. Canada A1B 3X5

Abstract: Structural culminations within the southeast Oman Mountains at Jebel Ma-jhool and the Ibra Dome developed through a process of multistage thrusting. This involved assembly and emplacement of the Semail and Hawasina thrust sheets over a footwall sequence of shelf carbonates and their pre-Permian basement, followed by progressive footwall collapse and breaching of the Hawasina thrust stack producing a hanging-wall anticline cored by shelf carbonates at Jebel Ma-jhool. At the Ibra Dome, foreland- and hinterland-dipping thrusts developed during the latter stages of thrusting forming a pop-up structure. Structural relations at Jebel Ma-jhool provide conclusive evidence that culminations within the Hawasina Complex are related to a decollement surface which lies at least as deep as the level of the shelf carbonates. Formation of the Ibra Dome and Jebel Ma-jhool structures was part of a widespread re-imbrication and culmination forming episode within the Oman Mountains. Major culminations, such as the Jebel Akhdar—Jebel Nakhl—Saih Hatat structures form significant morphological as well as structural highs. Slippage of the upper level Semail Ophiolite and Oman Melange sheets off these structures has resulted in truncation of the underlying Hawasina Complex thrust stack at Ibra Dome and Jebel Ma-jhool producing a break-back thrust sequence. The timing of initial thrusting, subsequent re-imbrication and culmination formation, and gravity-driven slippage of surficial thrust sheets is constrained to a 5 Ma period between the late Campanian and early Maastrichtian. This is based on the Coniacian to Campanian age of Aruma Group strata, the youngest rock unit affected by thrusting and the presence of the Maastrichtian Qahlah Formation unconformably overlying the flanks of both the Jebel Ma-jhool and Ibra Dome culminations. Broad scale folding and high-angle faulting of Maastrichtian and Tertiary strata in the southern Oman Mountains formed through regional mid-Tertiary compression and reactivation of Late Cretaceous culminations.

In the Oman Mountains closure of the southern Tethys and collapse of the associated passive margin in the Late Cretaceous is recorded by the emplacement onto the Arabian platform of a series of thrust sheets of slope and deep water continental margin and ocean basin sequences (Sumeini Group and Hawasina Complex) and an overlying ophiolite slab (Semail Ophiolite; Glennie *et al.* 1974). The thrust sheets are folded into a number of structural culminations (Fig. 1), of which the Jebel Akhdar—Jebel Nakhl—Saih Hatat culminations are the most prominent and form the backbone of the Oman mountain chain. This belt of culminations extends for some 300 km along strike and has a half-wavelength and amplitude of approximately 50 km and 5 km, respectively.

The platform sequences of the Arabian peninsula consist of Permian to Early Cretaceous shallow marine carbonates and their underlying pre-Permian basement. They are exposed in the cores of the major culminations, and were considered by Glennie *et al.* (1974) and most subsequent workers (e.g. Searle & Graham 1982) to be largely unaffected by thrusting and nappe emplacement and thus, autochthonous.

Glennie *et al.* (1974) believed culmination development to be a response to regional compression and uplift of the mountain chain in the mid-Tertiary, in association with deformation in the Zagros Fold Belt of Iran. Recently, however, Hanna (1986) and Bernoulli & Weissert (1987; see also Searle 1985) have proposed that the Jebel Akhdar—Jebel Nakhl—Saih Hatat culminations represent hanging-wall anticlines formed by ramping over a major sole thrust lying within the pre-Permian basement and extending beneath the entire Oman Mountains. The thrust front lies on the foreland side of the Jebel Salakh—Jebel Madar culminations (Fig. 1). Searle (1985), Searle & Cooper (1986), Barrette & Calon (1987) and Cooper (1988) have established that the numerous culminations within the Hawasina Complex and Sumeini Group thrust sheets along the foreland side of the mountain range also represent hanging-wall anticlines, and formed during the later part of a multistage thrusting history.

From ROBERTSON, A. H. F., SEARLE, M. P. & RIES, A. C. (eds), 1990,
The Geology and Tectonics of the Oman Region.
Geological Society Special Publication No 49, pp 429—445

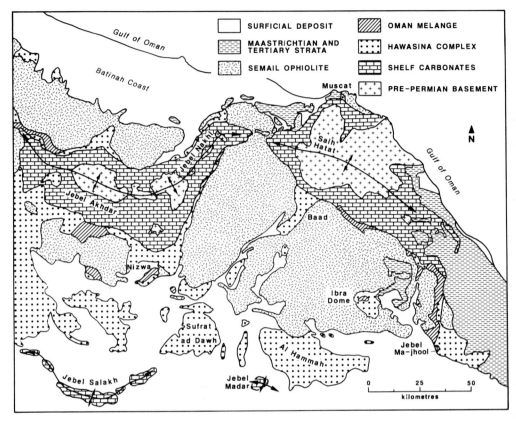

Fig. 1. Simplified geologic map of the central and southern Oman Mountains (after Glennie *et al.* 1974) showing the location of Ibra Dome and Jebel Ma-jhool with respect to the Jebel Akhdar—Jebel Nakhl—Saih Hatat and Jebel Salakh—Jebel Madar culminations.

However, these studies did not resolve if the sole thrust responsible for culmination formation lies at the base of the Hawasina Complex or penetrates into the underlying shelf carbonates and whether it forms part of the same deep basement decollement plane responsible for the Jebel Akhdar—Jebel Nakhl—Saih Hatat structures.

The absence of Tertiary strata in the vicinity of most Hawasina culminations prevents an accurate assessment of their age of formation. Hanna (1986) proposed that culmination formation took place in the Late Cretaceous. Searle *et al.* (1983) showed that mid-Tertiary deformation in the Musandam Peninsula resulted in thrusting of shelf carbonates over the Hawasina Complex and Bernoulli & Weissert (1987) suggest that the major culminations in the southern Oman Mountains could also have formed at this time.

To try to resolve problems of depth and age

of late-stage thrusting and culmination formation in the Hawasina Complex of the Oman Mountains we have focussed on two culminations within the southeastern part of the mountain range at Ibra Dome and an isolated unnamed dome of shelf carbonate (latitude 22°32′N, longitude 58°56′30″E) located on the SW margin of Al Hajar Ash Sharqi, and here referred to as Jebel Ma-jhool (Fig. 1; Ma-jhool means unknown, S. S. Hanna 1988 pers. comm.). These two areas show the possible range of rock units involved in culmination structures with the latter locality consisting of a core of shelf carbonates enveloped by thrust sheets of the Hawasina Complex, whereas the former represents a window through the Semail Ophiolite into the underlying Hawasina Complex. Both culminations are flanked by Tertiary sediments, allowing a direct assessment of the mid-Tertiary Zagros event on structural styles and timing of culmination formation.

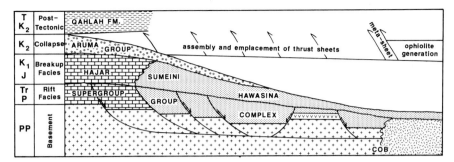

Fig. 2. Paleogeographic relationships of the major rock units in the Oman Mountains (after Glennie *et al.* 1974, Bernoulli & Weissert 1987). COB, continent ocean boundary.

Tectonostratigraphy

Glennie *et al.* (1974) demonstrated that structural telescoping of the Late Permian to Early Cretaceous Arabian passive continental margin sequence during Late Cretaceous ophiolite emplacement resulted in a consistent ordering of thrust sheets. They proposed that each thrust sheet contains approximately time equivalent strata with the strata in each structurally higher sheet originally situated at progressively more distal sites on the margin (Fig. 2). Recent work by Bernoulli & Weissert (1987) has shown that the lower thrust sheets contain only Jurassic and Cretaceous strata representing breakup-facies sedimentation (Fig. 2) and are younger that the upper thrust sheets which contain mainly rift-facies strata of Triassic age. These authors suggest that the lower thrust sheets originally formed the cover for the upper thrust sheets and that the present stacking order is a consequence of multistage thrusting. The lower thrust sheets containing the younger breakup-facies sequences of Bernoulli & Weissert (1987) are absent from the Ibra Dome and Jebel Ma-jhool areas. The Ibra Formation of largely Triassic age is the lowest unit of the Hawasina thrust stack preserved at both localities. At the Ibra Dome the base of the Hawasina thrust stack is not seen, but at Jebel Ma-jhool, the Ibra Formation directly overlies and underlies shelf carbonates and foreland basin sediments along late-stage thrust contacts.

Shelf Carbonates of the Hajar Supergroup are only exposed in the core region of the Jebel Ma-jhool culmination and belong to the Early Cretaceous Kahmah Group (Glennie *et al.* 1974; Hughes Clarke 1988), a correlative of the Thamama Group which is recognized throughout the Arabian Peninsula (Alasharhan & Nairn 1986). Early Cretaceous shelf carbonates of the upper Kahmah Group and the unconformably overlying Wasia Group are absent at Jebel Majhool. This stratigraphic gap could be due to either structural decapitation of the upper parts of the platform sequence by the Hawasina thrust sheets and/or the effect of uplift and erosion during disruption and collapse of the platform prior to accumulation of the foreland basin strata of the Aruma Group (Wasia–Aruma break of Glennie *et al.* 1974). The amount of downcutting through the shelf carbonates at the Wasia–Aruma break increases northwards and on the north side of Saih Hatat, Aruma Group strata overlie Triassic dolostone of the Mahil Formation and Jurassic limestone and sandstone of the Sahtan Formation (Robertson 1987a,b).

Aruma Group (Glennie *et al.* 1974) strata are restricted to a melange zone along the eastern and northern sides of Jebel Ma-jhool and lie along the contact between the shelf carbonates and the overlying Hawasina thrust sheets. This zone consists of red shales tectonically admixed with blocks of the structurally overlying Ibra Formation and underlying shelf carbonates.

The Ibra, Halfa and Haliw Formations (Glennie *et al.* 1974) represent deep-water, passive margin sequences which lie in internally imbricated thrust sheets of the Hawasina Complex. They consist of redeposited carbonate (grainstone grading to lime mudstone), siltstone, and red and green radiolarian cherts. Mafic volcanics and shallow intrusives occur at the base of the more complete thrust slices in the Halfa and Haliw Formations.

The Oman Exotics (Glennie *et al.* 1974) consist of large blocks of white recrystallized reefal limestone. The largest block forms the summit and south face of Jebel Hawrah, the main peak within the Ibra Dome. There appears to be no matrix to the blocks, but locally the blocks are conglomeratic containing a variety of tightly packed exotic clasts in a sparitic cement. Oman Exotic-type limestone also occurs as clasts in redeposited sediments in the Ibra, Halfa and Haliw thrust sheets. Along the eastern and southeastern sides of Jebel Hawrah occur sequences of basaltic breccia at least 75 m thick (cf. Hopson *et al.* 1981). The breccias probably represent the top of the volcanic edifice on which the Exotics accumulated (Glennie *et al.* 1974; Searle & Graham 1982).

Sandwiched between the Haliw Formation and the Oman Exotics at Ibra dome and between the ophiolite and Hawasina thrust sheets at Jebel Ma-jhool is a unit of Oman Melange (Glennie *et al.* 1974). At Ibra Dome it has a block on block structure containing a jumbled assemblage of quartz-mica phyllites, interbedded red chert and silicified limestone, shale, serpentinized peridotite and gabbro. At Jebel Ma-jhool the melange zone has an across strike width of up to 5 km and contains blocks of Oman Exotic limestone, bedded red chert and shale, serpentinized peridotite and gabbro, locally embedded in a red shale matrix. The lithologies in the melanges at both locations indicate that they represent a tectonized ophiolite–Hawasina contact zone. Along the northwestern rim of Ibra Dome the Semail Ophiolite is separated from the Hawasina Complex by the metamorphic sheet (Searle & Malpas 1980; Ghent & Stout 1981) consisting of a thin (<50 m) sequence of quartz-rich phyllites. The metamorphic sheet locally contains unmetamorphosed inclusions of the adjacent Haliw Formation suggesting some additional late-stage movement along the contact between these two units. Serpentinized peridotite and gabbro of the Semail Ophiolite (Glennie *et al.* 1974) form the highest slice of the thrust stack.

Along the eastern flank of both culminations the allochthonous units are overlain with pronounced angular unconformity by the Maastrichtian Qahlah Formation and shallow-marine Early Tertiary carbonates. The Qahlah Formation (Glennie *et al.* 1974) is composed of thick-bedded conglomerate and sandstone containing chert and some ophiolitic debris derived from the underlying Hawasina and Semail thrust sheets. Rare cross-bedding indicates a source area to the northwest. The formation is generally 5–15 m thick but sections up to 30 m thick were observed on the northeast side of the Ibra Dome.

Early Tertiary carbonates ranging in age from Paleocene to Eocene disconformably overlie the Qahlah Formation. They consist of shallow marine limestones, dolomites and marls with locally interstratified quartz sandstones and evaporites.

Jebel Ma-jhool

Jebel Ma-jhool represents the only locality in the Oman foreland fold and thrust belt where rocks of the Mesozoic carbonate platform are exposed in the core of a Hawasina Complex culmination. Thus, the structural setting of the jebel is of crucial importance in establishing the level of the basal decollement and degree of shelf involvement in the origin of the thrust-generated culminations which are widespread in the Hawasina Complex.

Glennie *et al.* (1974, enclosure 5, section 11) considered the shelf carbonates at Jebel Ma-jhool, as elsewhere in the Oman Mountains, to be autochthonous and to lie in the core of an antiformal window beneath the folded Hawasina sole thrust. However, the present detailed mapping of the jebel and its environs has established that the shelf carbonates lie in a thrust sheet which is both overthrust by and thrust over the Hawasina Complex (Figs 3 & 4).

Detailed structural framework

Exposure of shelf carbonates is largely restricted to a 1 km² doubly plunging anticline surrounded on three sides by imbricated Hawasina Complex thrust sheets and on the fourth unconformably onlapped by wadi alluvium (Figs 3 & 4). The axis of the culmination trends NW–SE and bedding dips regularly away at low to moderate angles in all directions.

Along the southwestern margin of the culmination the shelf carbonates are thrust over the Ibra Formation (Figs 3 & 4) along a decollement surface striking NW–SE and dipping at between 30–50° NE. Slickensides show large pitch angles on southeasterly dipping bedding and subsidiary fault planes within the shelf carbonates in the hanging-wall of the thrust indicating that the direction of movement was orthogonal to strike of the fault surface.

Slickensides on bedding surfaces exposed on the southwesterly and northeasterly dipping limb segments of the culmination trend perpendicular to the hinge line of the anticline. The parallel style of the fold profile, the slickenside orientation patterns, the presence of hanging-wall cutoffs of bedding in the southwestern part of the culmination, and the truncation of folds at the floor thrust indicate that the shelf carbonates were folded by flexural slip in a hanging-wall anticline related to movement over a ramp during thrusting. The surface trace of the bedding planes in the shelf carbonates on the southwestern limb of the culmination define a number

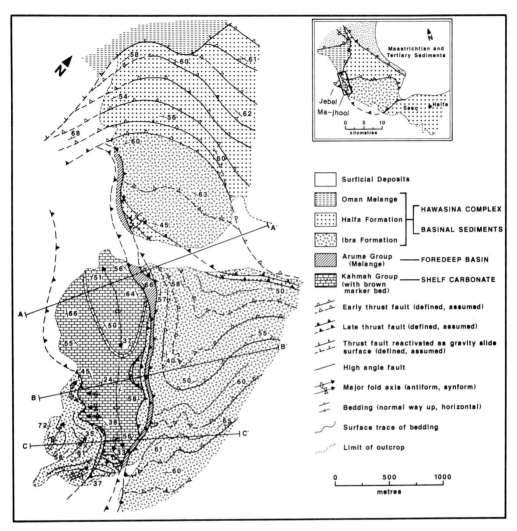

Fig. 3. Geologic map of Jebel Ma-jhool region. Base map prepared from air photographs. Inset shows regional setting of the jebel (compare with Fig. 1).

of smaller, open cross-folds (Boyer & Elliot 1982) which plunge gently to the southwest. This indicates that the floor thrust of the culmination did not only cut up-section along a single, large frontal ramp dipping to the northeast, but also involves a number of smaller northerly dipping lateral ramps.

The overall structure of the culmination thus results from bending of the hanging-wall in relation to the presence of a geometrically complex pattern of bedding cutoffs in the hanging-wall above the northeast dipping floor thrust. The structure is best interpreted as a trailing

edge ramp anticline according to Boyer's (1986) classification of fold styles in thrust sheets.

Further evidence for the involvement of the shelf sequence in thrusting in the vicinity of Jebel Ma-jhool is provided by: small isolated slivers of shelf carbonate within the footwall of the culmination along splays of the main floor thrust; a small lens of shelf carbonate thrust over Aruma melange along the SE margin of the culmination; a sliver of Ibra Formation sandwiched between shelf carbonates along a thrust plane on the NE margin of the culmination; a small anticlinal lens of shelf car-

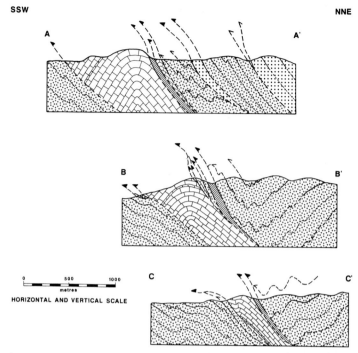

Fig. 4. Structural cross-sections through the Jebel Ma-jhool region (see Fig. 3 for location).

bonates just off the northern flank of the culmination which occurs either as a block within the melange zone or as a thrust-bound sliver along the contact between this zone and the overthrust Ibra Formation (Fig. 3).

The footwall of the culmination consists of Ibra Formation and is structurally complex (Figs 3 & 4). Bedding is tightly folded about a number of north plunging fold axes with moderate to steep dipping axial surfaces. Imbricate boundaries within this unit are hard to recognize but seem to be aligned parallel to axial planes of the folds (Fig. 3).

Most of the Hawasina Complex exposed in the environs of Jebel Ma-jhool structurally overlies the shelf carbonate sequence and consists of internally imbricated thrust sheets of the Ibra and Halfa Formations. Thrust surfaces within both the Ibra and Halfa sheets dip at around 60–70° to the NNE (Fig. 3). Imbricate surfaces and bedding within these units are folded on mesoscopic and macroscopic scales about broadly north plunging fold axes with east to northeast dipping axial surfaces. In the chert-rich Halfa thrust sheet folds tend to be disharmonic and highly non-cylindrical with chevron folds dominating, whereas in the limestone-rich Ibra thrust sheet folds of bed-

ding show a more cylindrical form with concentric type folds dominating.

The orientation of the axial plane of the Hawasina folds parallels that in the shelf culmination, implying generation during the same thrusting event. The major, but discontinuous, synform in the Ibra thrust sheets, immediately overlying the shelf carbonates (Fig. 3), appears to form a pair with the hanging-wall anticline in the shelf carbonates (Fig. 4) suggesting a fault bend fold origin (cf. Suppe 1981).

Structurally overlying the Hawasina Complex are the Oman Melange and Semail Ophiolite. Although the ordering of these units is consistent with that observed elsewhere in the Oman Mountains (Fig. 2), the sole thrust of the Oman Melange shows evidence of late-stage movement truncating the footwall Halfa imbricates (Fig. 3). Blocks of Halfa Formation are incorporated into the melange adjacent to the basal thrust surface.

Discussion

Figure 5 compares the observed stacking order in the Jebel Ma-jhool region with that established by Glennie *et al.* (1974). All tectonostratigraphic boundaries in the area show some

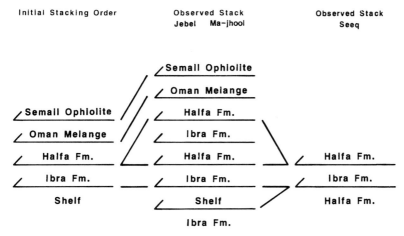

Fig. 5. Comparison of the observed stacking order of thrust sheets at Jebel Ma-jhool and Seeq with the generalized thrust stack for the Oman Mountains.

evidence of late-stage movement and re-imbrication. The thrust faults bounding each of the tectonostratigraphic units at Jebel Ma-jhool truncate internal imbricates within each of these units causing footwall cutoffs and indicating a major thrusting event after initial imbrication of the Hawasina thrust stack. The repetition of tectonostratigraphic units within the thrust stack and the resulting out-of-sequence relationships such as thrusting of shelf carbonates over a lower Ibra thrust sheet and the thrust-bound belt of Halfa Formation within the upper Ibra thrust sheet, are further effects of major late-stage thrusting within a thrust stack initially assembled in piggy-back fashion according to the lithotectonic sequence outlined by Glennie et al. (1974).

Additional evidence for late-stage reversals in the stacking order is found in the vicinity of Seeq, a village some 12 km east southeast of Jebel Ma-jhool (Fig. 3, inset). At this locality, Ibra Formation structurally overlies Halfa Formation with the intervening thrust truncating early, locally folded imbricates in these units. Regional geological relationships (Fig. 3, inset) suggest that the late-stage thrust mapped at Seeq may correlate with the thrust plane at the base of the shelf carbonates at the Jebel Ma-jhool culmination (Fig. 5).

Ibra Dome

The Ibra Dome (Fig. 1) consists of a window some 100 km^2 in area of Hawasina Complex enclosed by peridotite and gabbro of the overlying Semail Ophiolite. Mineral layering in the ophiolite dips regularly away from the Hawasina core. Dips are moderate to gentle around the eastern, southern and western margins of the culmination, but sub-vertical along the northern margin (Bailey 1981; Fig. 6).

Glennie et al. (1974) and Hopson et al. (1981; see also Bailey 1981) in their reconnaissance investigations of the structural geometry of the Ibra Dome considered it to be a gently dipping symmetrical culmination formed by late stage regional warping of the assembled thrust stack. Both groups of authors dated deformation as taking place after the cessation of early Tertiary sedimentation. Hopson et al. (1981) suggested that it may have been caused by salt protrusion at depth whereas Glennie et al. (1974) favoured a compressional model associated with deformation in the Zagros Fold Belt to the northwest.

The geologic maps and cross sections of the dome presented in Figs 6 & 7 indicate that structural relations are much more complex than previously envisaged. The Hawasina Complex within the core of the dome forms a major thrust-generated culmination, the form of which is unrelated to the simple sub-circular pattern outlined by the Semail Ophiolite–Hawasina Complex contact at the margin of the dome.

Detailed structural framework

On the basis of lithologic association and structural style, the Hawasina Complex at the Ibra Dome is subdivided into two structural blocks (Fig. 6, insert). The boundaries of the blocks are late-stage faults and at least in the western parts of the dome the blocks are separated by a unit of Oman Melange.

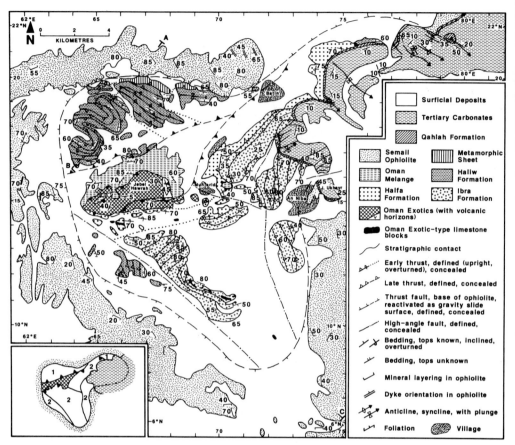

Fig. 6. Geologic map of Ibra Dome. Mineral layering and dyke orientation data in ophiolite from Bailey (1981). For simplicity recent landslide deposits which in part cover Oman Melange on the north face of Jebel Hawrah are not shown. Base map prepared from air photographs. Grid data refer to the Universal Transverse Mercator Grid Zone 40 and are taken from the Ibra 1:100 000 sheet (NF-40−081). Inset shows distribution of structural blocks within the Hawasina Complex (see text for discussion).

Block 1 lies in the northern part of the dome and consists largely of Haliw Formation but also includes along the northern margin a sliver of schists of the metamorphic sheet. The Haliw Formation is repeated by a number of thrust faults and in the southwest these are folded about near vertical NW−SE trending axial planes with fold axes plunging moderately to the southeast (Fig. 6). These folded imbricates are truncated (footwall cutoffs) and separated from the remainder of the block by a later thrust.

Scattered outcrops of limestone and chert, often contorted and sheared, occur along the northwest margin of the dome. They are mapped as Haliw Formation and included in Block 1, but exposure is poor, and where strongly deformed they more closely resemble the Oman Melange.

All structural elements are truncated at the margin of the block by the Semail Thrust in the north and northwest and by a steep late-stage hinterland dipping thrust along the southern boundary with the Oman Melange.

Block 2 incorporates the major part of the Hawasina Complex and occupies the north-eastern, central and southern parts of the dome. It contains segments of the Ibra Formation, Halfa Formation and Oman Exotics, which together behave as a coherent structural unit, and a sliver of Haliw Formation, the latter isolated from the other rock units by a late stage high-angle fault.

The Haliw Formation is internally imbricated

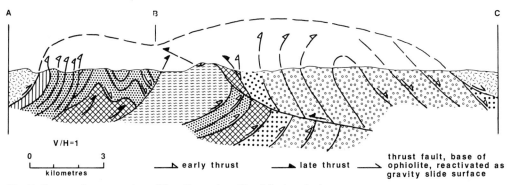

Fig. 7. Structural cross-section of Ibra Dome (see Fig. 6 for location).

along N−S to NW−SE trending and westerly dipping thrusts. Slivers of serpentinized peridotite and sheared gabbro lie along, and help define, some thrust surfaces.

The remainder of the Block 2 consists of an imbricate thrust stack of Ibra Formation, Halfa Formation and Oman Exotics folded into an asymmetric N to NW verging culmination breached on its north side by a foreland dipping back thrust (Figs 6 & 7). This hanging-wall culmination is thrust over a footwall sequence of Oman Melange. The culmination is disrupted by a number of high-angle faults trending NW−SE and N−S to NE−SW.

Bedding along the northern limb of the culmination is overturned, generally dipping at 20−30° south but consistently younging northwards. Locally on Jebel Hawrah dips may be as low as 5° south. A small window (g.r. 705152) through the northern limb of this north verging structure occurs just to the west of the village of Munjarid where an overturned hanging-wall sequence of Ibra and Halfa Formations surrounds a small, 50 m diameter, semi-circular footwall outcrop of Oman Melange. Striations developed in recrystallized sheared limestone around the margin of the window consistently indicate a N−S direction of movement.

East of Munjarid (g.r. 695150) the axis of the culmination swings abruptly from E−W to NE−SW and is offset to the northwest along a high-angle fault. The fault is truncated by the back thrust and marks the eastern limit of exposure of the Oman Exotics. The abrupt change in hanging-wall lithologic association and structural style indicates that the cross fault represents a tear fault formed during back thrusting.

All structural elements within the Hawasina Complex are truncated by the basal detachment

of the Semail Ophiolite indicating late-stage movement of the ophiolite sheet.

Discussion

Figure 8 compares the stacking order of thrust sheets observed at Ibra Dome with that established by Glennie *et al.* (1974) for the Oman Mountains as a whole. The Oman Melange, which on the basis of its constituent lithologies was generated at the Semail Ophiolite−Hawasina Complex boundary, now forms the lowest structural unit within the dome. It is overthrust by the Haliw thrust sheets in the north and the combined Ibra, Halfa and Oman Exotics thrust sheets in the south.

Overprinting relationships demonstrate that assembly of the thrust stack at the Ibra Dome is a multistage process involving initial assembly and folding of imbricates, followed by disruption of the stacking order by later stage thrusting. Thus, the discrepancies between the stacking order observed here with that established by Glennie *et al.* (1974; Fig. 8) are not a function of localized differences in palaeogeography or the method of initial stacking at the Ibra Dome but reflect modification of the initial thrust stack by later events (Searle 1985).

The Oman Melange is presently squeezed between two structural blocks of Hawasina Complex. Overall kinematic relations within the Hawasina Complex suggest that asymmetric folding and back thrusting within the southern block and frontal ramping of the Haliw Formation in the northern block form part of the same late-stage re-imbrication event. The Oman Melange lies in a triangle zone between these two blocks and the asymmetric hanging-wall culmination in the southern blocks is interpreted as a pop-up structure (Butler 1982). Back thrust-

Initial Stacking Order Oman Mountains	Observed Stacking Order Ibra Dome
Semail Ophiolite	Semail Ophiolite
Oman Melange	Oman Exotics
Hallw Fm.	Halfa Fm.
Oman Exotics	Ibra Fm.
Halfa Fm.	Hallw Fm.
Ibra Fm.	Oman Melange

Fig. 8. Comparison of the observed stack of tectonostratigraphic units at Ibra Dome with the generalized stacking order established by Glennie *et al.* (1974) for the whole of the Oman Mountains.

ing probably developed in response to difficulties in the foreland propagation of the deformational front. A similar origin was proposed by Searle & Cooper (1986) for back thrusting in the Hawasina Window. A possible frontal ramp to the back thrusting and pop-up structure at Ibra Dome lies in the northern part of the Al Hammah range (Fig. 1) where a major late-stage thrust re-imbricates the thrust stack.

Maastrichtian and Tertiary structure

Structural style of the Maastrichtian and Tertiary cover sequence at Ibra Dome and Jebel Ma-jhool contrasts markedly with that in the underlying imbricated Tethyan continental margin sequences. The cover sequence unconformably overlies the flanks of the culminations and is deformed into a series of broad open folds cut by minor high-angle faults. Thrust faults are absent. Hanna (1986) has proposed that deformation of the Maastrichtian and Tertiary strata took place in an extensional regime and reflects renewed uplift of, and slippage off, the major structural culminations. He noted that in the central Oman Mountains the basal unconformity surface of the Maastrichtian clastics is reactivated as a slide surface and that the axes of the Tertiary folds are aligned parallel to those of the major culminations with the fold structures draped over and mimicking structure in the underlying Hawasina thrust sheets. Structural styles at Ibra Dome and Jebel Ma-jhool conform, in part, to this

model with the Maastrichtian and Tertiary strata folded into a series of broad open folds that have axial planes trending parallel to that of the Saih Hatat culmination. However, the basal Maastrichtian unconformity surface shows no evidence of reactivation as a slide surface and this surface, if it exists, must lie at an as yet unrecognized level within the underlying Hawasina and Semail thrust sheets.

Numerous high-angle E–W and NE–SW trending faults cut the unconformity surface along the flank of Ibra Dome (Fig. 6). Contrasts in the character and thickness of the Maastrichtian and Tertiary rock units offset by the high-angle fault along the ophiolite-Hawasina contact at An Niba indicate that at least some of these faults show multiple phases of movement and that at least one of these phases was synchronous with sedimentation. Fig. 9 shows two measured sections through the Maastrichtian and immediately overlying Tertiary sequence at An Niba: in section A the Qahlah Formation overlies the Ibra Formation and in secion B, 2 km to the SE, the Qahlah rests on Semail Ophiolite. The upper 25 m of both sections, commencing with a thin quartz-bearing lithoclastic limestone show near identical sequences. The lower parts of the two sections are markedly different in thickness and lithologic character (Fig. 9). In section B, and elsewhere where the Qahlah Formation overlies the ophiolite, it is pervasively impregnated with hematite which, as noted by Hopson *et al.* (1981), indicates subsequent exposure and laterization of this part of the sequence. The along-strike change in the character of the Maastrichtian and lower Tertiary rock units is not a gradational feature. Rock units in section A can be traced along strike to the southeast, towards section B, as far as the Hawasina–ophiolite contact, with little if any change in character. Southeast of this contact however, the rock units take on the thickness and lithologic character seen in section B. These relationships suggest that the Hawasina–ophiolite contact was possibly reactivated along a high-angle fault after deposition of the Qahlah Formation resulting in uplift, erosion and leaching of the ophiolite block relative to the Hawasina block. The ophiolite block probably remained a positive tectonic element, perhaps through continued movement on the fault surface during accumulation of the lower parts of the Early Tertiary carbonate sequence. The stratigraphically similar upper parts of the carbonate sequence in the two sections are also offset at the Hawasina–ophiolite contact indicating further reactivation of the fault after cessation

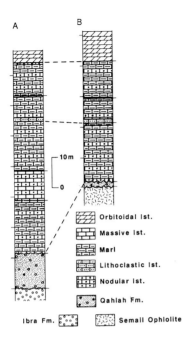

Orbitoidal lst.

Massive lst.

Marl

Lithoclastic lst.

Nodular lst.

Qahlah Fm.

Ibra Fm.   Semail Ophiolite

Fig. 9. Measured sections through Maastrichtian Qahlah Formation and the early Tertiary carbonate sequence at Ibra Dome: (A) section unconformably overlying Ibra Formation 2 km NW of An Niba (g.r. 726167); (B) section unconformably overlying Semail Ophiolite on south face of Jebel Ukhayr (g.r. 742155), immediately SE of ophiolite–Hawasina contact.

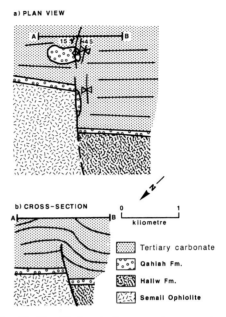

a) PLAN VIEW

b) CROSS-SECTION   0   1
                          kilometre

Tertiary carbonate

Qahlah Fm.

Haliw Fm.

Semail Ophiolite

Fig. 10. Simplified geologic map and cross-section showing development of a drape fold within Tertiary strata at the northern end of Ibra Dome (g.r. 786218) through reactivation of the Hawasina Complex– Semail Ophiolite contact. Vertical exaggeration on cross section is approximately × 10.

of Tertiary sedimentation. Offset of the Tertiary strata indicates uplift of the ophiolite block (southeast side up) relative to the Hawasina block. Additional late-stage normal faults offsetting Tertiary strata in the Hawasina block to the northeast show consistent down to the southeast sense of movement and are thus antithetic to the main fault contact.

The amount of dip–slip movement on the majority of the fault planes is no more than a few tens of metres and displacement dies out rapidly up-section. A number of these faults, particularly those associated with major basement fractures such as the Hawasina–ophiolite contact, pass along strike into small-scale asymmetric anticlines representing drape fold structures (Fig. 10).

Age of culmination formation

The Maastrichtian Qahlah Formation (Glennie et al. 1974; Nolan et al. 1986) and early Tertiary carbonates lie unconformably on the flanks of the Ibra Dome and Jebel Ma-jhool culmi-

nations. The unconformity surface truncates both imbricates within individual thrust sheets and boundaries between sheets within the thrust stack. These relationships provide an upper age limit on the time of initial thrust sheet emplacement and subsequent culmination development. A lower age limit is provided by the Semail Ophiolite which has given a uranium-lead zircon age on plagiogranite of around 95 Ma (Cenomanian, Tilton et al. 1981) and contains intercalated early Cenomanian to early Turonian sediments within the upper volcanic unit (Tippit et al. 1981). Incorporation of Aruma Group sediments, probably part of the Turonian to Campanian Muti Formation and equivalent units (Glennie et al. 1974; Robertson 1987b), within not only the Jebel Ma-jhool structure but other culmination structures elsewhere in the mountain range (Glennie et al. 1974; Searle 1985; Hanna 1986; Robertson 1987a,b), further constrains the final phase of emplacement of the thrust sheets and subsequent re-imbrication and associated culmination development to an approximately 5 Ma period between the late Campanian and early Maastrichtian (approximately 75–70 Ma).

Deformational sequence and regional relationships

Overprinting relationships between the various Mesozoic and Tertiary rock units and their associated structural elements allows the recognition of a distinct chronology of deformational events for both Ma-jhool and the Ibra Dome.

Initial imbrication

Extensive internal thrusting and associated mesoscopic and macroscopic folding within the units of the Hawasina Complex is the earliest deformational event recognized. These structures developed during initial assembly of the Hawasina Complex thrust sheets and their emplacement onto the Arabian platform and show a consistent internal ordering (Glennie *et al.* 1974). The decollement plane lies at the shelf/Hawasina interface. Bernoulli & Weissert (1987) have shown that the internal ordering is a consequence of multiphase thrusting rather than a single phase of piggy-back thrusting. They proposed that assembly of the thrust stack involved initial imbrication of the upper younger parts of the Hawasina Complex, probably by piggy-back thrusting, followed by breaching of this sequence and the imbrication and emplacement of the older and lower rift-facies sequences over the younger parts of the complex.

The lower thrust sheets of the Hawasina Complex are absent from both the Ibra Dome and Jebel Ma-jhool areas, so direct evidence of this multistage thrusting process is lacking. However, at the Ibra Dome the termination of footwall imbricates (footwall cutoffs) along some thrust planes within the Haliw Formation indicates that assembly of the thrust stack did not result from a single piggy-back thrusting event but also involved at least a second phase of thrusting which breached the imbricate stack.

Re-imbrication and culmination formation

Compression along the Arabian margin continued after initial imbrication and affected the entire crustal sequence which now consisted of the assembled and emplaced thrust sheets along with the underlying platformal carbonates and their pre-Permian basement. This event resulted in the generation of an additional set of thrusts which breached the pre-existing thrust stack (cf. Butler 1987) causing re-imbrication and reversals in the initial stacking order (Searle 1985). Structural relationships at Jebel Ma-jhool indicate that these breaching thrusts flatten out into a decollement located below the Hawasina-shelf contact resulting in the thrusting of shelf carbonates into a hanging-wall anticline over a footwall sequence of Hawasina Complex. Layer parallel shortening associated with thrusting and movement over ramps resulted in folding of the thrust stack including the formation at the Ibra Dome of a pop-up structure associated with back thrusting. This re-imbrication event corresponds with the leap-frog thrusting event described by Searle (1985), and is also responsible for the culminations in the northern and central Oman Mountains (Searle & Cooper 1986; Barrette & Calon 1987).

The axes of the Ibra Dome and Jebel Ma-jhool culminations, along with those of other culminations in the Hawasina Complex are aligned parallel to the trend of the prominent Jebel Akhdar−Jebel Nakhl−Siah Hatat and Jebel Salakh−Jebel Madar culminations. Age relationships indicate that formation of these major culminations took place during the same late Campanian to early Maastrichtian time frame as the culminations in the allochthonous thrust stack. The major culminations deform the allochthonous thrust stack indicating that their formation post-dates initial assembly and emplacement of the thrust stack. An upper age limit on formation of the major culminations is provided, as at Jebel Ma-jhool and the Ibra Dome, by unconformably overlapping Maastrichtian and early Tertiary rock units which overlap the Saih Hatat culmination (Fig. 1). Structural relations suggest that both the Hawasina culminations and the Jebel Akhdar−Jebel Nakhl−Saih Hatat and Jebel Salakh−Jebel Madar series of culminations formed above a common decollement horizion. The basal decollement responsible for the Jebel Akhdar−Jebel Nakhl−Saih Hatat culminations does not emerge on the immediate foreland margin of these structures but continues in the subsurface, either within or below the shelf carbonates, to the foreland side of the Jebel Salakh−Jebel Madar structures (Hanna 1986; Bernoulli & Weissert 1987). The Ibra Dome and Jebel Ma-jhool structures, and all other Hawasina culminations, occupy an intermediate position between the Jebel Akhdar−Jebel Nakhl−Saih Hatat and Jebel Salakh−Jebel Madar culminations, and are located structurally above the decollement horizon responsible for these structures. Thus, spatial and temporal relationships suggest that the Hawasina culminations formed above thrust splays off the same decollement system responsible for the major shelf and basement cored culminations. The involvement of shelf carbonates in the Jebel Ma-jhool structure is consistent with this interpretation.

Reactivation of high level thrust sheet

The Semail and Oman Melange sheets show extensional geometry, cutting down section through imbricates in underlying sheets. At the Ibra Dome, the Semail thrust truncates structures in the Hawasina Complex generated during culmination formation (Fig. 6). At Jebel Ma-jhool, the Oman Melange cuts down through imbricate slices of the Halfa Formation nearly to the contact with the Ibra thrust sheet (Fig. 3). The presence of blocks of serpentinized peridotite and mica schist in Oman Melange located in the core of the Ibra Dome and an imbricate of mica schist which is truncated by the Semail thrust sheet on the north flank of the dome indicates that upper-level thrust sheets, such as the Semail Ophiolite and the Oman Melange, overlay the main Hawasina Complex sequence prior to culmination formation and were not just emplaced during subsequent re-activation of the high-level sheets.

On a regional scale further evidence for reactivation of the high-level thrust sheets is found around the flanks of the Jebel Akhdar−Jebel Nakhl−Saih Hatat culminations. These structures are bounded by normal faults (Bailey 1981; Hanna 1986; Cawood 1989). The faults run parallel to, and dip away from the crest of the culminations. Sense of movement is away from the crest of the culminations. Along the northern and southern flanks of Saih Hatat, the faults lie at the Semail/Hawasina and Hawasina/shelf contact as well as within the shelf carbonates themselves (Bailey 1981; Hopson et al. 1981). Down-faulting of rock units along these structures caused extensive thinning and removal of the Hawasina Complex, and locally the upper parts of the shelf sequence are also missing. In places, this has resulted in the juxtaposition of the Semail Ophiolite against shelf carbonates as old as Late Triassic with no intervening upper shelf or Hawasina strata. Searle (1985) describes similar structural downcutting at the base of the Semail Ophiolite in the central and northern parts of the Oman Mountains with the Semail and Haybi faults cutting down section in the direction of transport. In the Hawasina Window, Searle & Cooper (1986) note that the basal detachment of the Semail Ophiolite progressively cuts down through the Hawasina Complex and Aruma Group and locally rests directly on Sumeini Group strata.

Maastrichtian and Tertiary strata unconformably overlie the reactivated higher-level thrust sheets, not only at the Ibra Dome and Jebel Ma-jhool, but also along the flank of Saih Hatat (Cawood 1989). Truncation of both re-imbrication structures and the reactivated Semail−Hawasina contact by the Maastrichtian unconformity surface indicates that the timing of both culmination formation and subsequent extensional downcutting of upper-level sheets is intimately related and hence, probably genetically linked. Growth of structural highs, especially the Jebel Akhdar−Jebel Nakhl−Saih Hatat culminations, would cause major disruption and uplift of the syn-orogenic (land) surface. Collapse of the culmination, through extensional faulting and gravity sliding, along with other processes such as gravity spreading and erosion, releases the gravitational potential energy built up through culmination formation. The upper-level thrust sheets are the most susceptible to sliding, and the sliding of these sheets is facilitated by the presence of schistose serpentinite and scaly melange along their basal detachments.

Gravity sliding of the upper-level thrust sheets off the rising culminations accounts for the extensive structural thinning and local elimination of the Hawasina Complex along the margins of the culminations below the ophiolite cap (Hanna 1986). The simple domal pattern of the Semail Ophiolite at Ibra Dome around the more complex structural pattern of the Hawasina core reflects collapse of the Semail thrust sheet off the Saih Hatat structure and its draping over the truncated structural and morphologic culmination within the Hawasina core when movement ceased. The high-angle faults disrupting the flanks of the pop-up culmination at Ibra Dome and pre-dating final major movement of the Semail thrust sheet (Fig. 6) may be localized culmination collapse features which immediately predate movement of the ophiolite thrust sheet off Saih Hatat. Although gravity slides are marked by extensional faults along the trailing margin and central parts of the slide, the leading edge of the slide will be marked by contractional faulting. The clearest example of this in the Oman Mountains is seen in the Wuqbah Block of the Semail Ophiolite. Rothery (1982) has shown that the Wuqbah Block has slid off the Haybi Corridor culmination. Movement of the block is orthogonal to the crest of the culmination and it is bounded by a listric normal fault at its trailing margin adjacent to the culmination but passes into a thrust fault at the leading edge of the block, resulting in imbrication of the ophiolite sequence. Further evidence for late-stage contractional structures related to sliding off the major structural culminations is seen in the re-imbrication and resulting out-of-sequence relationships between the Semail Ophiolite and

Hawasina Complex strata at the leading edge of the eastern part of the Ibra ophiolite block, which moved south off Saih Hatat, and also at the leading edge of the western part of this ophiolite block, which has moved east off Jebel Nakhl resulting in thrusting of the Hawasina Complex over the metamorphic sheet (see also Hanna 1986).

Maastrichtian and Tertiary sedimentation and deformation

Denudation of the morpho-structural culminations involves not only structural collapse, as evidenced by gravity sliding of the upper level thrust sheets, but also entails extensive erosion of the culminations, which resulted in the accumulation of clastic wedges such as the Qahlah Formation and related units (Nolan *et al.* 1986). At the Ibra Dome, the northerly provenance of the Qahlah Formation is consistent with derivation from the uplifted Saih Hatat culmination. Minor syn-sedimentary faulting, concentrated along pre-existing planes of weakness caused localized uplift, erosion and laterite development in the Maastrichtian strata, particularly where it rests on Semail Ophiolite on the flanks of the Ibra Dome. Evidence for emergence of Saih Hatat during the Maastrichtian, immediately following culmination formation, is best recorded in the provenance history of the Al Khawd Formation (Nolan *et al.* 1986), a time equivalent unit of the Qahlah Formation developed on the northern side of the culmination. Clast compositions within this unit record the progressive unroofing of Saih Hatat (Nolan *et al.* 1986). Ophiolite detritus dominates at the base of the formation, carbonate fragments derived from the Hajar Supergroup are common in the central parts of the unit and quartzites from the pre-Permian metamorphic basement occur at the top. As noted by Nolan *et al.* (1986), this indicates that the emergent Saih Hatat culmination was eroded down to its metamorphic core prior to the Tertiary. The distribution of Maastrichtian clastic debris around Jebels Akhdar and Nakhl indicate that they also formed major emergent areas during the Maastrichtian, though less prominent than Saih Hatat (Nolan *et al.* 1986).

The early Tertiary (Paleocene to Eocene) was marked by establishment of a widespread shallow marine carbonate bank. The lack of input of terrigenous clastic debris at this time indicates regional subsidence with the culminations no longer forming major emergent zones.

Deformation of Tertiary rock units has been dated as Oligo–Miocene by Glennie *et al.* (1974). It corresponds with uplift of the whole Oman Mountains and is synchronous with a major phase of compressive deformation in the Zagros Fold Belt of Iran (Stocklin 1974). Although this event caused substantial thrusting and associated folding in the northern parts of the Oman Mountains (Searle *et al.* 1983), its effect in the southeastern parts of the mountain range is restricted to broad scale open folding producing a number of domes and basins and normal faults with small offsets. Major fold axes within the Tertiary sequences in the vicinity of the Ibra Dome and Jebel Ma-jhool are aligned subparallel to the axis of Saih Hatat. Uplift of the central and southern parts of the Oman Mountain range during the Zagros event probably provided the driving mechanism for associated culmination collapse structures described by Hanna (1986).

The degree of uplift was not however, uniform, but rather, appears to have been concentrated at the location of the Late Cretaceous structural culminations. At the Ibra Dome, Maastrichtian and Tertiary strata lie in a broad basinal structure flanking the Hawasina culmination, suggesting further uplift of this structure during mid-Tertiary deformation. A regional culmination within the Maastrichtian and Tertiary strata east of Jebel Ma-jhool lies on the along strike extension of the Saih Hatat structure. The present elevation of this strata ranges from 1400 to 2000 m above sea level, showing an overall increase towards Saih Hatat, and is up to 1550 m above the 450–500 m average elevation of time and facies equivalent strata on the flanks of the Ibra Dome. This observation requires extensive selective uplift of the Saih Hatat structure. Selective resurgence of the Late Cretaceous structural culminations during mid-Tertiary deformation suggests regional reactivation of the decollement horizons responsible for initial culmination formation. Thus, although at the present level of erosion the mid-Tertiary deformational event is locally characterized by extensional structures related to gravity sliding and culmination collapse (Hanna 1986; Mann *et al.* 1990), this is a response to regional compression at depth which was manifest by renewed uplift of the Late Cretaceous structural culminations. The reactivated culminations provided the potential energy for driving renewed gravity sliding.

Conclusions

Similarities in the sequence of deformational events recognized at Jebel Ma-jhool and Ibra

Dome indicate a closely interrelated history of Late Cretaceous thrusting and culmination development followed by gravitational collapse off the rising culminations.

The culminations are floored by late-stage thrusts and represent hanging-wall anticlines. Formation of the culminations in Late Cretaceous time above a decollement plane located within the Arabian platform indicates that these structures formed during, and are probably part of, the same event that was responsible for the initial Jebel Akhdar–Jebel Nakhl–Saih Hatat and Jebel Salakh–Jebel Madar series of culminations.

Figures 11 & 12 present a series of schematic cross-sections showing the inter-relationship of the Saih Hatat structure to the Ibra Dome and Jebel Ma-jhool culminations, respectively. Each diagram presents two possibilities for the level of the sole thrust on the foreland side of Saih Hatat (cf. Hanna 1986; Bernoulli & Weissert 1987). In Figs 11a and 12a the sole thrust merges with and reactivates the Hawasina sole thrust. If this configuration is correct it requires a second thrust to develop within or below the shelf carbonates to explain the shelf cored culminations at Jebels Madar and Ma-jhool. In Figs 11b and 12b the sole thrust rises to the shelf-

basement interface below Saih Hatat and finally to the syn-orogenic surface on the foreland side of Jebels Madar and Ma-jhool. Assuming that the late-stage culmination collapse and gravity-sliding structures are confined to the high-level Semail and Oman Melange sheets, then the reactivation of the Hawasina-shelf contact observed at Jebel Ma-jhool favours the first configuration.

It is important to note that although these later thrusts result in an apparent out-of-sequence relationships through reversals in the stacking order (e.g. Figs 5 & 8), they are part of an overall foreland propagating thrust sequence developed through progressive footwall collapse. Reversals in the ordering of the tectono-stratigraphy reflect development of a breach thrust sequence involving propagation of foot-wall thrusts through the assembled thrust stack rather than a piggy-back thrust sequence in which these thrusts merge with the Hawasina sole thrust. Thus, although thrusting related to culmination development has overprinted features associated with emplacement of the Semail and Hawasina thrust sheets, both events probably form part of a continuous phase of Late Cretaceous compression of the Arabian margin.

The major culminations form pronounced

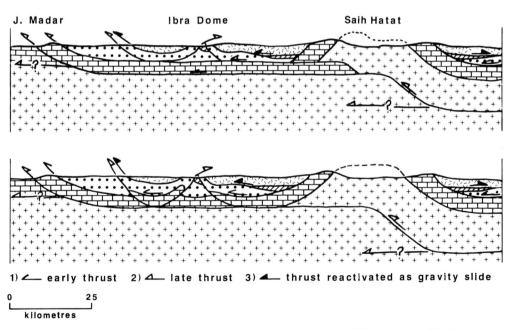

Fig. 11. Schematic cross sections showing relationship of Ibra Dome to Saih Hatat and Jebel Madar. Alternative sections reflect possible differences in the level of the sole thrust on the foreland side of Saih Hatat (cf. Hanna 1986; Bernoulli & Weissert 1987). Legend as for Fig. 1. Numbers 1–3 for the types of thrust faults corresponds with stages 1–3 of the deformational sequence discussed in text.

444   P. A. CAWOOD *ET AL.*

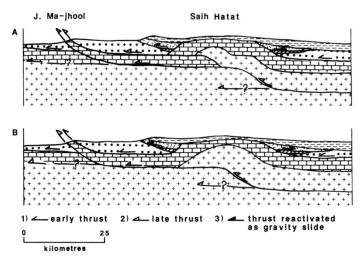

1) ◄— early thrust   2) ◄— late thrust   3) ◄— thrust reactivated as gravity slide

0 _____ 25
      kilometres

Fig. 12. Schematic cross-sections showing relationship between the Saih Hatat and Jebel Ma-jhool culminations. Alternative sections reflect possible differences in the level of the sole thrust on the foreland side of Saih Hatat (cf. Hanna 1986; Bernoulli & Weissert 1987). Legend as for Fig. 1. Numbers 1–3 for the types of thrust faults corresponds with stages 1–3 of the deformational sequence discussed in text.

morphologic as well as structural highs resulting in the generation of a number of Late Cretaceous and Tertiary gravity driven culmination collapse structures. The truncation of culmination structures along the sole thrusts of the Semail Ophiolite and Oman Melange at Ibra Dome and Jebel Ma-jhool respectively, probably reflects slippage of these surficial thrust sheets off the flank of Saih Hatat. Reactivation of these thrust sheets pre-dates Maastrichtian sedimentation.

We would like to thank Samir Hanna and John Smewing for sharing with us their knowledge of Oman geology and along with Dan Bernoulli and Mike Searle for their reviews of the manuscript. Steve Nolan made available preprints of his work on the Maastrichtian and Tertiary sequences of the Oman Mountains. We are grateful to Amoco Oman Petroleum Company for financial support. We also thank the Ministry of Petroleum and Minerals Sultanate of Oman for the opportunity to work in Oman. This paper is published with the permission of Amoco Production Company.

References

ALSHARHAN, A. S. & NAIRN, A. E. M. 1986. A review of the Cretaceous Formations in the Arabian Peninsula and Gulf: Part 1. Lower Cretaceous (Thamama Group) stratigraphy and paleogeography. *Journal of Petroleum Geology*, 9, 365–392.
BAILEY, E. H. 1981. Geologic map of Muscat-Ibra area, Sultanate of Oman, pocket map. *Journal of Geophysical Research*, 86.
BARRETTE, P. D. & CALON, T. J. 1987. Re-imbrication of the Hawasina allochthons in the Sufrat ad Dawh Range, Oman Mountains. *Journal of Structural Geology*, 9, 859–867.
BERNOULLI, D. & WEISSERT, H. 1987. The upper Hawasina nappes in the central Oman Mountains: stratigraphy, palinspastics and sequence of nappe emplacement. *Geodinamica Acta*, 1, 47–58.
BOYER, S. E. 1986. Styles of folding within thrust sheets: examples from the appalachians and Rocky Mountains of the U.S.A. and Canada. *Journal of Structural Geology*, 8, 325–339.
—— & ELLIOT, D. 1982. Thrust Systems. *Bulletin of the American Association of Petroleum Geologists*, 66, 1196–1230.
BUTLER, R. W. H. 1982. The terminology of structures in thrust belts. *Journal of Structural Geology*, 4, 239–245.
—— 1987. Thrust sequences. *Journal of the Geological Society of London*, 144, 619–634.
CAWOOD, P. A. 1989. Late-stage gravity sliding of ophiolite thrust sheets in Oman and western Newfoundland. *In: Proceedings of the Symposium on Ophiolites and Oceanic Lithosphere-TROODOS 87.* Geological Survey of Cyprus.
COOPER, D. J. W. 1988. Structure and sequence of thrusting in deep-water sediments during ophiolite emplacement in the south-central Oman Mountains. *Journal of Structural Geology*, 10, 473–485.
GHENT, E. D. & STOUT, M. Z. 1981. Metamorphism at the base of the Semail Ophiolite, southeastern Oman Mountains. *Journal of Geophysical Research*, 86, 2557–2571.
GLENNIE, K. W., BOEUF, M. G. A., HUGHES CLARK,

M. W., MOODY-STUART, M., PILAAR, W. F. H. & REINHARDT, B. M. 1973. Late Cretaceous nappes in the Oman Mountains and their geologic evolution. *Bulletin of the American Association of Petroleum Geologists*, **57**, 5−27.

——, ——, ——, —— & —— 1974. *Geology of the Oman Mountains*. Verhandelingen van het Koninklijk Nederlands Geologisch Mynbouwkundig Genootschap. Volume 31: The Hague, Martinus Nijhoff.

HANNA, S. S. 1986. The Alpine (Late Cretaceous and Tertiary) tectonic evolution of the Oman Mountains: a thrust tectonic approach. *In*: *Symposium on the hydrocarbon potential of intense thrust zones*. O.A.P.E.C. conference, Kuwait, **2**, 125−174.

HOPSON, C. A., COLEMAN, R. G., GREGORY, R. T., PALLISTER, J. S. & BAILEY, E. H. 1981. Geologic section through the Semail Ophiolite and associated rocks along a Muscat-Ibra transect, southeastern Oman Mountains. *Journal of Geophysical Research*, **86**, 2527−2544.

HUGHES CLARKE, M. W. 1988. Stratigraphy and rock unit nomenclature in the oil-producing area of Interior Oman. *Journal of Petroleum Geology*, **11**, 5−60.

LIPPARD, S. J., SHELTON, A. W. & GASS, I. G. 1986. *The ophiolite of northern Oman*. The Geological Society, London Memoir, **11**.

MANN, A., HANNA, S. S. & NOLAN, S. G. 1990. The post-Campanian tectonic evolution of the central Oman Mountains: Tertiary extension of the eastern Arabian Margin. *In*: ROBERTSON A. H. F., SEARLE, M. P. & RIES, A. C. (eds) *The Geology and Tectonics of the Oman Region*, **49**, 549−563.

NOLAN, S. C., SKELTON, P. W., CLISSOLD, B. P. & SMEWING, J. D. 1986. Late Campanian to Tertiary paleogeography of the central and northern Oman Mountains, *In*: *Symposium on the Hydrocarbon potential of intense thrust zones*. O.A.P.E.C. conference, **2**, 177−200.

POWERS, R. W., RAMIREZ, L. F., REDMOND, C. D. & ELDBERG, E. L. 1966. Geology of the Arabian Peninsula: sedimentary geology of Saudi Arabia. United States Geological Survey Professional Paper 560D.

ROBERTSON, A. H. F. 1987a. The transition from a passive margin to an Upper Cretaceous foreland basin related to ophiolite emplacement in the Oman Mountains. *Geological Society of America Bulletin*, **99**, 633−653.

—— 1987b. Upper Cretaceous Muti Formation: transition of a Mesozoic carbonate platform to a foreland basin in the Oman Mountains. *Sedimentology*, **34**, 1123−1142.

ROTHERY, D. A. 1982 *The evolution of the Wuqbah Block and the applications of remote sensing in the Oman Ophiolite*. PhD thesis, Open University, Milton Keynes, UK.

SEARLE, M. P. 1985. Sequence of thrusting and origin of culminations in the northern and central Oman Mountains. *Journal of Structural Geology*, **7**, 129−143.

—— & COOPER, D. J. W. 1986. Structure of the Hawasina Window culmination, central Oman Mountains. *Transactions of the Royal Society of Edinburg: Earth Sciences*, **77**, 143−156.

—— & GRAHAM, G. M. 1982. The 'Oman Exotics': Oceanic carbonate build-ups associated with the early stages of continental rifting. *Geology*, **10**, 43−49.

——, JAMES, N. P., CALON, T. J., & SMEWING, J. D. 1983. Sedimentological and structural evolution of the Arabian continental margin in the Musandam Mountains and Dibba zone, United Arab Emirates. *Geological Society of America Bulletin*, **94**, 1381−1400.

—— & MALPAS, J. 1980. The structure and metamorphism of rocks beneath the Semail Ophiolite of Oman and their significance in ophiolite obduction. *Transactions of the Royal Society of Edinburg: Earth Science*, **71**, 247−262.

STOCKLIN, J. 1974. Possible ancient continental margins in Iran, *In*: BURK, C. L. & DRAKE, C. L. (eds) *The geology of continental margins*. Springer, New York, 873−887.

SUPPE, J. 1981. Geometry and kinematics of fault-bend folding. *American Journal of Science*, **283**, 684−721.

TILTON, G. R., HOPSON, C. A. & WRIGHT, J. E. 1981. Uranium-lead isotopic ages of the Semail Ophiolite, Oman, with application to Tethyan ocean ridge tectonics. *Journal of Geophysical Research*, **86**, 2763−2775.

TIPPIT, P. R., SMEWING, J. D. & PESSAGNO, E. A. 1981. The biostratigraphy of sediments in the volcanic unit of the Semail Ophiolite. *Journal of Geophysical Research*, **86**, 2756−2762.

Structures associated with nappe emplacement and culmination collapse in the Central Oman Mountains

D. Q. COFFIELD

ARCO International Oil and Gas Company, P.O. Box 260888, Plano, TX 75026−0888, USA

Abstract: The Fanjah Saddle, in the Central Oman Mountains, forms a structural and topographic depression between two major culminations which expose parautochthonous rocks in windows through the overlying allochthon. Two styles of normal faulting are present in the culminations: high-angle faults which dip toward the saddle core and cut the plunging noses of the culminations, and low-angle faults around the culmination flanks which include bedding-parallel detachments, reactivated thrust planes and surge zones. This second set of faults verge down-dip radially away from the culmination flanks.

The high-angle normal faults are interpreted to be accommodation structures resulting from the differential uplift of the parautochthon between the culminations and the saddle. The low-angle normal faults are interpreted to be gravity-driven culmination collapse structures resulting from oversteepening of the culmination flanks.

Post-orogenic late Campanian to Maastrichtian sediments adjacent to the culminations indicate that the culminations were initialy emergent during this time, acting as a clastic source. These same sediments, and the underlying nappe pile, are folded by compression from displacements on the normal faults which implies culmination uplift was reactivated after the Maastrichtian, possibly during post-middle Eocene Zagros orogeny.

The bulk of the Oman Mountains consist of a nappe pile emplaced southwestward onto the northeast facing Mesozoic Arabian platform margin during the late Cretaceous (Glennie *et al.* 1973, 1974; Gealey 1977) (Fig. 1). The allochthonous section consists of imbricated and telescoped Permian to Cretaceous abyssal-plain, continental rise and slope facies rocks of the Hawasina complex (Glennie *et al.* 1973, 1974; Cooper 1987) and Sumeini Group (Watts and Garrison 1986), syn-orogenic sediments (Robertson 1987a,b), exotic limestones with volcanic substrates (Graham 1980; Searle & Graham 1982), metamorphic sheets of the Haybi complex (Searle & Malpas 1980, 1982; Ghent & Stout, 1981), and the Semail Ophiolite, a relatively intact section of oceanic lithosphere (Journal of Geophysical Research 1981; Lippard *et al.* 1986). The Oman allochthon is unconformably overlain by neo-autochthonous Maastrichtian and Paleogene shallow-marine sediments (Montenat & Blondeau 1977; Nolan *et al.* 1986).

The central Oman Mountains are dominated by several major structural culminations aligned along a NW−SE trending axis with a NE−SW trending offset at midlength (Fig. 1). The allochthon has been breached by the two largest culminations, Jebel Akhdar and Saih Hatat, exposing Paleozoic basement (Lovelock *et al.* 1981), Mesozoic platform rocks of the Hajar

Supergroup (Glennie *et al.* 1973, 1974), and syn-orogenic foreland basin sediments of the Muti Formation (Robertson 1987a,b). A domain of relatively low structural and topographic relief, the Fanjah Saddle (Fig. 2), is situated between these two culminations and provides a unique perspective on structures related to the development of the culminations and constraints on timing of deformation in the region (Coffield 1984a,b).

Tectonostratigraphy

Parautochthon

The bulk of the culminations flanking the Fanjah Saddle are composed of the Hajar Supergroup (Figs 2 & 3). The crest of the culminations are composed of the Permian Saiq and conformably overlying Triassic Mahil formations of the Akhdar Group. The Jurassic Sahtan Group and conformably overlying Late Jurassic to Lower Cretaceous Kahmah Group are juxtaposed against the Akhdar Group by normal faults dipping towards the saddle core (Figs 2 & 3). They form the bulk of the plunging noses of the culminations flanking the Fanjah Saddle. The Sahtan Group west of the saddle exposes low-energy carbonate platform facies, in contrast to exposures on the eastern side which contain higher-energy slope facies in the upper part of

From ROBERTSON, A. H. F., SEARLE, M. P. & RIES, A. C. (eds), 1990,   447
The Geology and Tectonics of the Oman Region.
Geological Society Special Publication No 49, pp 447−458

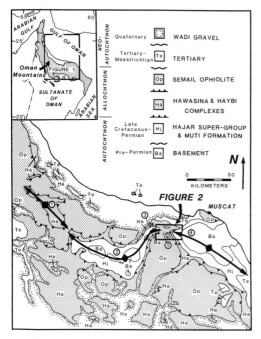

Fig. 1. Location map and simplified geologic map of the Oman Mountains with major culminations and the Fanjah Saddle indicated. 1, Hawasina Window; 2, Jebel Akhdar culmination; 3, Jebel Nakhl culmination; 4, Saih Hatat culmination; 5, Fanjah Saddle.

the section, indicating the mid- to late- Jurassic shelf-slope break of the Arabian platform margin bisected the Fanjah Saddle (Coffield 1984b). Exposures of the Kahmah Group is restricted to the western side of the saddle.

The rest of the Cretaceous section, including the upper Kahmah and conformably overlying Wasia Group, is missing on the culminations. This may be due to several factors. Glennie *et al.* (1973, 1974) described a stratigraphic thinning due to erosion and non-deposition of the Kahmah and Wasia groups to the east and northeast of Jebel Nakhl and Saih Hatat (cf. Robertson 1987a,b). In addition, tectonic scraping and accretion of the Mesozoic platform by the Oman allochthon, as has occured in northeastern Saih Hatat (Hopson *et al.* 1981; Michard *et al.* 1984), may have removed a significant portion of the section. Finally, normal faulting around the flanks, and erosion of the crests, of the culminations may have cut out the section (Hanna 1986).

Allochthon

The nappe pile encompassed in the Oman allochthon occupies the trough in between the

plunging crests of the Jebel Nakhl and Saih Hatat culminations (Figs 2 & 3). The Semail ophiolite dominates the aerial extent of the outcrop. Exposures of subophiolite thrust sheets are relatively thin and discontinuous, and are limited to the perimeters of Saih Hatat and Jebel Nakhl, and to a window through the ophiolite in the center of the Fanjah Saddle.

The Muti Formation is the lowest tectonic unit in the Fanjah Saddle and crops out as discontinuous fault-bound slices around the flanks of Jebel Nakhl. Whether the Muti Fm is actually part of the allochthon or was detached from the shelf succession by late stage normal faulting is ambiguous. The section consists of up to 50 m of highly cleaved and sheared, red, argillaceous, interbedded mudstones and shales with rare lithoclastic lime packstones that probably represent the Buday'ah unit (Robertson 1987a).

The Hawasina complex is not present in the Fanjah Saddle. This, and the relatively thin sub-ophiolite nappe pile, may be due to thinning at the trailing edge of the accretionary complex in front of the obducting Semail ophiolite (e.g. Bernoulli & Weissert 1987) or to normal faults around the perimeters of the culminations.

The Haybi Complex is exposed around the flanks of the culminations and in the window through the ophiolite in the saddle core. It forms a distinct tectonostratigraphic package enclosed by major thrust planes which separate it from the underlying Muti Formation and Sahtan Group and the overlying Semail ophiolite. Considerable internal imbrication has disrupted and repeated the melange and metamorphic sheet within the complex.

The melange consists of discontinuous slices of argillaceous, calcareous mudstones and shales interbedded with cherts, lenses of limestone conglomerates, and lenticular turbidites. Rare blocks of deformed chert, pillow basalts, exotic limestones and basalt are also present. Fault-bound units of phyllite are found at the top of the section.

Discontinuous metamorphic sheets with an inverted metamorphic grade lie structurally above the melange. Internal imbrications have thickened and repeated much of the section to a maximum of 100 m. The lithologies are dominated by greenschist quartzites which passes upward into amphibolites. Fault-bound white marble sheets are found near the top of the section.

The Semail Ophiolite tectonically overlies the Haybi Complex and occupies the topographically lowest, and structurally highest, position in the core of the Fanjah Saddle (Figs 2

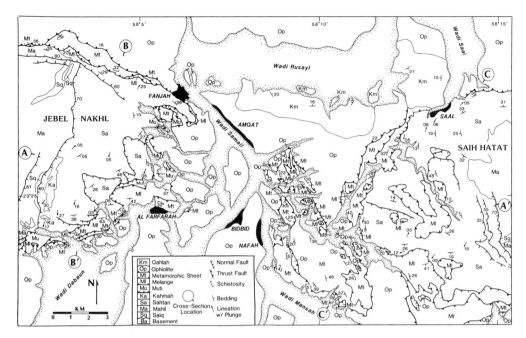

Fig. 2. Geologic map of the Fanjah Saddle with culminations exposing the Hajar Supergroup (Ka, Sa, Ma and Sq) on the east and west plunging beneath the Oman allochthon in the center. Note the folding of thrust planes in the nappe pile and the post-orogenic Maastrichtian sediments (Km) in the central saddle, and the reactivation of thrust faults as normal faults around the culmination margins.

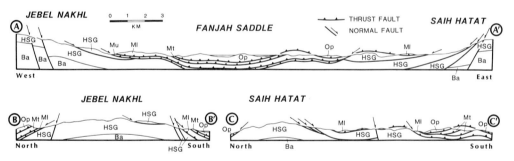

Fig. 3. Near-surface cross sections of the Fanjah Saddle illustrating the distribution and attitudes of normal faults around the culmination margins and open folding of the nappe pile in the saddle core (See Fig. 2 for locations and legend. HSG, Hajar Supergroup).

& 3). The basal portion of the Semail Ophiolite is composed of a narrow zone of intensely serpentinized peridotite with a weak planar fabric parallel to the sole thrust of the nappe. Above this lies up to 100 m of massive harzburgite and peridotite exhibiting varying degrees of serpentinization. A transitional zone containing 70 m of layered dunite lenses lies between the peridotites and the overlying gabbros which represent the highest unit preserved. A crust of orange, massive, silica-rich laterite separates partly serpentinized peridotite from the unconformably overlying late Campanian to Maastrichtian sedimentary section.

Neoautochthon

A limited exposure of post-orogenic late Campanian and Maastrichtian sediments lies unconformably over the Semail Ophiolite in the north–central portion of the study area (Figs 2 & 3). The basal section belongs to the Qahlah

Formation (Glennie *et al.* 1974; Nolan *et al.* 1986) and is composed of 50 m of fluvial sandstones and conglomerates with indications of northward transport. Conformably above this is a 100 m section of transgressive, shallow-marine limestones.

Structural geometries

Parautochthon

The culminations on either side of the 10 km wide Fanjah Saddle consist of broad open symmetrical ESE-trending anticlines which rise 1300 m above the saddle floor (Fig. 4a). They are approximately 10 km wide (N−S) with steep limbs (~40°) and plunge beneath the saddle at 20−40°. The folding has been accommodated by flexural slip along bedding surfaces as evidenced by slickensides on bedding planes orientated approximately parallel to the dip of these planes. The slip on these planes is often high lighted by thin fibrous calcite sheets less than 1 cm thick with calcite long-axes oriented parallel to slickensides.

An increasingly complex and inhomogeneous strain record is preserved in the section as one approaches the basal detachment of the overlying Oman allochthon (Coffield 1984b; Michard *et al.* 1984). An S1 pressure-solution schistosity subparallel to bedding (SO) becomes evident appoximately 100 m down section from the detachment. This planar pressure-solution flattening fabric dips to the NNE relative to SO with an acute angle of less than 10°. A spaced S2 refracted dissolution cleavage becomes prominent higher in the section and offsets S1. This fabric also dips to the NNE relative to SO with an acute angle varying from 30−35° in less competent lithologies to 50° in more competent lithologies. Calc-mylonites parallel to SO are distributed within the more competent units proximal to the basal detachment of the allochthon. These zones contain F1 intrafolial isoclinal folds with an axial-planar dissolution cleavage that is indistinguishable from S1 found elsewhere in the section. The F1 fold axes have a wide trend scatter but show a consistent SSW directed vergence (Fig. 4b). Rotated augens within the calcmylonite also indicate a SSW vergence.

An L1 lineation defined by recrystallized carbonate grains in the calc-mylonite zones are oriented along a SSW−NNE axis (Fig. 4b). Long-axes of ellipsoidal oolites and stretched sedimentary clasts in the section are also oriented parallel to this trend. Syntectonic sigmoidal veins developed in competent lith-

ologies, both singularly and in en echelon arrays, consistently indicate a translation of overlying units to the SSW. Boundinage, with boudin long-axes oriented WNW−ESE, have been rotated about their long axes with the sense of shear indicating structurally higher units moving SSW over lower units.

The strain magnitude in the carbonate succession generally increases towards the basal detachment of the allochthon but the strain distribution varies with ductility contrasts in lithology through the section. The one consistent characteristic relating these ductile structures is the south−southwest verging shear imposed on the section by the emplacement of the allochthon, considered collectively as D1 structures for the purpose of this paper.

Overprinting and cross-cutting these ductile structures is a suite of brittle structures which are generally confined to the culmination flanks. The plunging noses of the culminations on either side of the Fanjah Saddle are cut by north–south trending, high-angle normal faults, with throws exceeding 200 m, which dip towards the saddle (Figs 2 & 3). Those on Saih Hatat consist of several en echelon arcuate faults with decreasing dips progressing towards the saddle, gentle roll-over in their hanging walls, and drag features adjacent to the fault planes while Jebel Nakhl contains a single normal fault with a roll-over in the hanging wall (Fig. 5). The fault zones vary from one to ten metres in width, and contain macroscopic fault breccia and slip surfaces with slickensides plunging parallel to the dip of the fault planes. The roll-overs imply the dip of the fault planes shallow at depth (e.g. White *et al.* 1981).

Surge zones (Coward 1982) are common around the flanks of both culminations and involve rocks of the parautochthon (Fig. 6). They are characterized by extensional trailing edges defined by listric normal faults (Fig. 7), decollements in relatively incompetent units with movement down bedding planes, and compressional fronts defined by flexural slip and flexural flow asymmetric F2 folds (Fig. 8). The F2 fold axes trend parallel to the strikes of the culmination flanks, the axial planes are subhorizontal or gently dipping down into the culminations, and the fold vergences are orientated radially away from the culminations (Fig. 4e). A refracting fracture cleavage, approximately axial planar to F2, is associated with this folding (Fig. 8).

The radial distribution of these structures, grouped collectively along with the high-angle normal faults as D2 structures (Fig. 9), has resulted in variable overprinting relationships

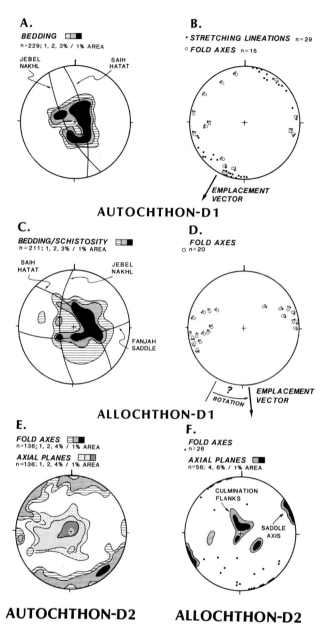

Fig. 4. Lower-hemisphere equal-area stereonet projections of structural data. A: Poles to bedding in the Hajar supergroup with great circles illustrating the gentley plunging noses of the culminations. B: Asymmetric fold axes (F1), with sense of shear around fold axes indicated by arrows, and lineations (L1), both measured in the top of the Hajar Supergroup section exposed in the culminations and together indicating SSW emplacement of the overlying allochthon. C: Poles to bedding and schistosity in the nappe pile exposed in the saddle with great circles illustrating folding around the plunging noses of the culminations and the synform of the saddle axis. D: Asymmetric fold axes measured in the nappe pile (F1 in the sedimentary melange, F1 and F2 in the metamorphic sheet), with arrows indicating sense of shear around fold axes and illustrating southward emplacement of the nappe pile. E: Fold axes (F2) and poles to axial planes measured in the culminations illustrating the sweep of fold axes around the culmination flanks. F: Fold axes (F2 in the sedimentary melange, F3 in the metamorphic sheet) and poles to axial planes illustrating two trend concentrations, one representing open upright folds within and parallel to the saddle axis, and the other representing asymmetric folds with variable orientations adjacent to the culmination margins.

Fig. 5. View north of rollover against normal fault in Jebel Nakhl juxtaposing Kahmah Group on the right against Akhdar Group on the left. The fault plane dips to the right towards the Fanjah Saddle. Mirror images of this fault cut the plunging nose of Saih Hatat on the opposite side of the Fanjah Saddle.

Fig. 6. Surge zone exhibiting compressional leading edge and extensional trailing edge. Note that this field photograph was shot within a shear zone and is not a geomorphic surface feature.

Fig. 7. View west of north-dipping arcuate normal faults located on the north side of Jebel Nakhl. Quartzites of the Haybi Complex lie to the right (north), the Sahtan group is in the centre, and the Akhdar Group is on the left. Normal faults with similar vergences are present on the north side of Saih Hatat, and occur on the southern side of Jebel Nakhl and Saih Hatat but with southward displacements.

Fig. 8. View west of north-verging fold with refracting axial-planar fracture cleavage at the leading edge of a surge zone in the Sahtan Group on the north side of the Saih Hatat culmination. Folds with similar geometries are found around, and verging away from, the flanks of both culminations. Maastrichtian sediments in the core of the Fanjah Saddle in the background are folded into open upright folds, also with fold axes paralleling the adjoining culmination flanks.

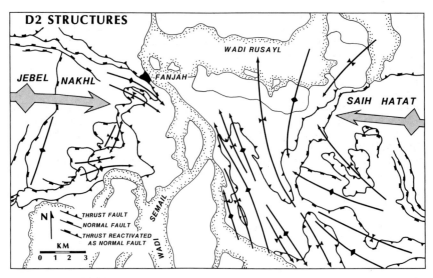

Fig. 9. Structure map of D2 faults and folds related to culmination collapse. Note the parallelism between structures and adjacent culmination flanks. Folds adjacent to the culminations are asymmetric and verge away from the culminations whereas those in the saddle are open and upright.

with D1 structures. To the south of the culminations, they have similar vergences, to the north they are opposing, and on the noses adjacent to the saddle they are orthogonal.

Allochthon

The discontinuous Muti Formation outcrop is bound on top and bottom by faults. The shales contained in this tectonic package are highly cleaved and sheared. Distinguishing the orientations of the separate cleavages or kinematic indicators was problematic due to the incompetent and disrupted nature of the unit.

The overlying Haybi Complex records a polyphase D1 deformational history related to the obduction and emplacement of the allochthon (Searle & Malpas 1980). All boundaries between major lithologic units are thrust faults, with thickening of the section by structural repetition common. The complex is bounded above and below by thrusts which truncate all internal lithologic units, fold axes, schistosities, and imbrications.

A bedding-parallel S1 schistosity is present in the melange section (Fig. 4c). Folding (F1) in the sedimentary melange is typified by tight to isoclinal SSE verging flexural flow folds (Fig. 4d). An axial planar S2 cleavage is common and is subparallel to S1. Associated L1 stretching lineations include stretched conglomerate clasts and elongate ooids aligned along an SSE–NNW axis.

Imbrication and structural thickening of the metamorphic sheet on south directed thrusts is also common. Rare F1 fold hinges with irregular orientations preserve an early S1 fabric and exhibit ductile flow deformation. A recumbent F2 flexural flow folding phase with a south-directed vergence has resulted in a prominent axial-planar S2 foliation which now defines the fabric of the metamorphic sheet. Original protolith bedding has been entirely transposed.

D2 structures have been superimposed over D1 structures in the Haybi Complex. Asymmetric flexural-slip F2 folds are found in the sedimentary melange around the perimeters of Saih Hatat and Jebel Nakhl culminations, generally in a position proximal to the Haybi Complex décollement. The fold axes are oriented parallel to the strike of the culmination flanks (Fig. 4f), with fold vergence directed radially away from the culminations. A crenulating axial–planar cleavage is often associated with this folding. Similar folds were not observed in the discontinuous metamorphic sheets around the perimeters of the culminations.

The Haybi Complex has been folded into open parallel symmetric antiforms and synforms in the saddle core (Fig. 4f). These trend northwest–southeast, paralleling the trend of the window through which they are exposed and the adjacent flank of Saih Hatat, and represent F2 and F3 structures in the sedimentary melange and the metamorphic sheet respectively (Fig. 9).

The sole thrust of the Semail Ophiolite cuts all underlying units and contains a narrow zone of D1 deformation. The basal periodotite is highly fractured and serpentinized with a weak foliation developed parallel to the thrust. D2 structures are common and include slickensides on fault planes around the perimeters of the culminations which parallel the dips of the culmination flanks. Within the saddle, the fault plane is folded into open symmetric anticlines and synclines which parallel the axis of the window where it is exposed and the flank of the adjacent Saih Hatat (Fig. 9).

Neo-autochthon

The two outcrops of neo-autochthonous sediments above the Semail Ophiolite in the north−central portion of the Fanjah Saddle are folded into a broad open symmetric syncline in the saddle axis and into somewhat tighter folds along the flank of Saih Hatat (Fig. 9). The outcrop in the core of the Fanjah Saddle has a north−south axial trace which plunges gently to the north (Fig. 8). The second outcrop, located on the northwest flank of Saih Hatat, is also folded in a broad open syncline, but with an axial trace oriented NE−SW parallel to the strike of the culmination flank on which it lies. No internal deformation is evident in the section.

Discussion

The distribution of culminations in the Oman Mountains can be explained by thrust-fault ramp and flat geometries, with the culminations representing hanging-wall anticlines above frontal, oblique and lateral ramps (Searle 1985; Hanna 1986; Bernoulli & Weissert 1987). The platform carbonates of the Musandam Peninsula, lateral equivalents of those exposed in the Jebel Akhdar and Saih Hatat culminations, are carried to high structural levels by thrust faults (Biehler et al. 1975; Ricateau & Riche 1980; Searle et al. 1983) and may root into a sole thrust in pre-Permian basement which is also carrying the Jebel Akhdar and Saih Hatat culminations. Evaporites of the late Precambrian−Cambrian Huqf Group (Gorin et al. 1982) are a possible detachment horizon.

There is evidence that the growth of the culminations was a two-stage event. The localized beach, fluviatile and fan delta deposits of the Qahlah and Al Khawd formations around the flanks of the Jebel Nakhl and Saih Hatat culminations indicate they were emergent in the late Campanian (Nolan et al. 1986). The Al Khawd

Formation on the northern margin of Saih Hatat includes a clast composition stratigraphy reversed from that exposed in Saih Hatat, and records the progressive unroofing of the culmination down to the pre-Permian quartzites before the Tertiary (Nolan et al. 1986).

Subsidence and shallow marine carbonate deposition with limited terriginous clastic input through the Paleocene and Eocene indicates the culminations were no longer significant emergent features during this time.

The Oligo−Miocene period was a time of renewed shortening and folding in the Oman Mountains. Out-of-sequence thrusting responsible for the culminations in the Musandam Peninsula are probably latest Eocene to Oligocene in age (Searle et al. 1983), which coincides with renewed foredeep development in front of the Oman Mountains (Burruss et al. 1983), folding of the Palaeogene section in the foreland (Tschopp 1967a,b), emergence of the Oman mountains (Glennie et al. 1973, 1974) and renewed shortening and thrusting in the Gulf of Oman and the Zagros Fold Belt (Coleman, 1981). An out-of-sequence thrust event has been documented in culminations within the Oman mountains (Searle & Cooper 1986) as well as in culminations in the Oman foreland (Barrette & Calon 1987) which may be synchronous with this renewed shortening.

This two-stage evolution is supported by the structures present in the Fanjah Saddle (Coffield 1984b). D1 is polyphase and related to obduction and emplacement of the nappe pile onto the platform margin. D1 structures in the allochthon include a flattening fabric, an axial planar fabric associated with recumbent folds, internal imbrication and repetition by foreland directed thrusts, and an inverted metamorphic gradient above the sole thrust. All structures contain a consistant southward vergence. D1 structures are also preserved in the autochthon proximal to the sole thrust and include recumbent folds with an axial planar fabric, boudinage, calc-mylonites and stretching lineations. All structures in the autochthon contain a consistent SSW vergence. This was followed by the initial uplift of the culminations over inferred basement rooted thrust-fault ramps which led to their emergence and erosion, and deposition of the Qahlah Formation in the late Campanian and Maastrichtian.

The second episode is post-Maastrichtian and is related to the renewed uplift of the Saih Hatat and Jebel Akhdar culminations and collapse of the allochthon off their flanks. This collapse included a possible component of rotation of the allochthon, re-orienting D1

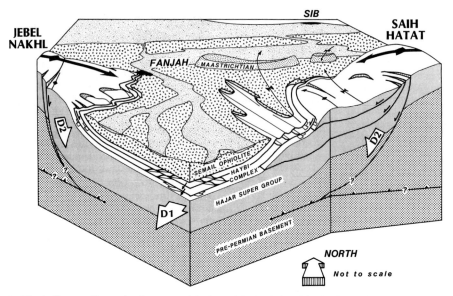

Fig. 10. Block diagram illustrating interpreted fault and fold relationships in the Fanjah Saddle. High angle normal faults cutting across the culminations root into the sole thrust beneath the culminations, accommodating the differential uplift of the Hajar Supergroup between the culminations and the saddle, whereas the low angle normal faults represent gravity-driven collapse of the nappe pile and culmination flanks on the oversteepened culmination margins.

structures to their present southward vergence from the original SSW vergence recorded in the culminations (Fig. 4d). Growth of the culminations by proposed reactivated basement involved thrusting produced high-angle normal faults rooting into the sole thrust of the culminations and accommodating the differential uplift resulting from ramp and flat geometries. Gravity-driven collapse of the overlying allochthon down-angle normal faults on the culmination flanks, and the development of associated surge zones verging away from the culminations, were contemporaneous with culmination growth. These extensional structures resulted in compression in the saddle core and the development of a D2 culmination and window in the allochthon, and folding of the late Campanian to Maastrichtian sediments along trends parallel to the culmination flanks.

Summary

Based on distinct structural styles and crosscutting relationships, two different orogenic events are recognized in the Fanjah Saddle (Fig. 10). The first is a polyphase compressional event (D1) related to the obduction and emplacement of the Oman allochthon in the Late Cretaceous and is characterized by relatively high strains and consistent southward vergence

of structures. This ended with the initial emergence of the culminations on either side of the Fanjah Saddle.

The second (D2) is related to renewed culmination uplift, the formation of normal faults around the culmination flanks, including the reactivation of D1 thrusts with normal displacements, and folding of the nappe pile and overlying late Campanian to Maastrichtian sediments adjacent to the culminations. The structures are characterized by relatively low strain extensional faults related to both differential uplift between the saddle and adjacent culminations, and gravity-driven collapse of the allochthon off the culminations. The culminations may represent ramp anticlines above basement-rooted thrusts related in time to shortening in the Gulf of Oman and Zagros folding in the latest Eocene to Oligocene.

This work was funded by Amoco Oman Petroleum Company through the Earth Sciences and Resources Institute at the University of South Carolina and formed the basis for an MSc thesis at this university. I wish to thank T. J. Calon for supervising my fieldwork and, with S. S. Hanna, S. Schamel and J. D. Smewing, for providing insights to the geology of the Oman Mountains. The paper is published with the permission of Amoco Production Company. D. Bernoulli, D. Dietrich and P. A. Cawood critically reviewed and improved the manuscript.

References

BARRETTE, P. D. & CALON, T. J. 1987. Re-imbrication of the Hawasina allochthons in the Sufrat ad Dawh range, Oman Mountains. *Journal of Structural Geology*, **9**, 859–867.

BERNOULLI, D. & WEISSERT, H. 1987. The upper Hawasina nappes in the central Oman Mountains: stratigraphy, palinspastics and sequence of nappe emplacement. *Geodinamica Acta*, **1**, 47–58.

BIEHLER, J., CHEVALIER, C. & RICATEAU, R. 1975. Geological map of the Musandam Peninsula, Sultanate of Oman: Directorate General of Petroleum and Minerals, Sultanate of Oman.

BURUSS, R. C., CERCONE, K. R. & HARRIS, P. M. 1983. Fluid inclusion petrography and tectonic-burial history of the Al Ali No. 2 well: Evidence for the timing of diagenesis and oil migration, northern Oman Foredeep. *Geology*, **11**, 567–570.

COFFIELD, D. Q. 1984a. Culmination collapse in the Fanjah Saddle, Oman (abstract): *American Association of Petroleum Geologists Bulletin*, **68**, 463.

—— 1984b. The geology of the Fanjah Saddle *MSc Thesis* University of South Carolina, Columbia.

COLEMAN, R. G. 1981. Tectonic setting for ophiolite obduction in Oman. *Journal of Geophysical Research*, **86**, 2497–2508.

COOPER, D. W. J. 1987. Hamrat Duru Group: revised stratigraphy of a Mesozoic deep-water passive margin in the Oman Mountains: *Geological Magazine*, **124**, 157–164.

COWARD, M. P. 1982. Surge zones in the Moine thrust zone of NW Scotland. *Journal of Structural Geology*, 4247–4256.

GHENT, E. D. & STOUT, M. Z. 1981, Metamorphism at the base of the Samail Ophiolite, southeastern Oman Mountains: *Journal of Geophysical Research*, **86**, 2557–2572.

GEALEY, W. K. 1977. Ophiolite obduction and geologic evolution of the Oman Mountains and adjacent areas. *Geological Society of America Bulletin*, **88**, 1183–1191.

GLENNIE, K. A., BOEUF, M. G. A., HUGHES-CLARK, M. W., MOODY-STUART, M., PILAAR, W. F. H. & REINHARDT, B. M. 1973. Late Cretaceous nappes in the Oman Mountains and their geologic evolution. *American Association of Petroleum Geologists Bulletin*, **57**, 5–27.

——, ——, ——, ——, —— & ——, 1974. Geology of the Oman Mountains (Parts one, two, and three): Verhandelingen van het Koninklijk Nederlands Geologisch Mijnbouwkundig Genootschap, Volume 31: The Hague, Martinus Nijhoff.

GORIN, G. E., RACZ, L. G. & WALTER, M. R. 1982. Late Precambrian–Cambrian sediments of Huqf Group, Sultanate of Oman: *American Association of Petroleum Geologists Bulletin*, **66**, 2609–2627.

GRAHAM, G. M. 1980. Evolution of a passive margin and nappe emplacement in the Oman Mountains.

In: Panayiotou, A. (ed.) *Proceedings of the International Ophiolite Symposium, Cyprus, 1979*, 414–423.

HANNA, S. S. 1986. The Alpine (Late Cretaceous and Tertiary) tectonic evolution of the Oman Mountains: a thrust tectonic approach, in Symposium on the Hydrocarbon Potential of Intense Thrust Zones: Organization of Arab Petroleum Exporting Countries Conference, Abu Dhabi, **2**, 125–174.

HOPSON, C. A., COLEMAN, R. G., Gregory, R. T., PALLISTER, J. S., & BAILEY, E. H. 1981. Geologic section through the Semail Ophiolite and associated rocks along a Muscat–Ibra transect, southeastern Oman Mountains. *Journal of Geophysical Research*, **86**, 2527–2544.

Journal of Geophysical Research, 1981. Oman Ophiolite special issue. **86**, 2495–2782.

LIPPARD, S. J., SHELTON, A. W. & GASS, I. G. 1986. *The Ophiolite of Northern Oman*. Geological Society, Memoir **11**.

LOVELOCK, P. E. R., POTTER, T. L., WALSWORTH-BELL, E. B. & WIEMER, W. M. 1981. Ordovician rocks in the Oman Mountains: The Amdeh Formation. *Geologie en Mijnbouw*, **60**, 487–495.

MICHARD, A., BOUCHEZ, J. L. & OUAZZANI-TOUHAMI, M. 1984. Obduction related planar and linear fabrics in Oman: *Journal of Structural Geology*, **6**, 39–49.

MONTENAT, C. & BLONDEAU, A. 1977. Premier apercu du Tertiaire d'Oman (Peninsule arabique orientale): *Bulletin de la Societe Geologique de France, 7e serie, tome XIX*, 1285–1295.

NOLAN, S. C., SKELTON, P. W., CLISSOLD, B. P. & SMEWING, J. D. 1986. Late Campanian to Tertiary Palaeogeography of the Central and Northern Oman Mountains, in Symposium on the Hydrocarbon Potential of Intense Thrust Zones: Organization of Arab Petroleum Exporting Countries Conference, Abu Dhabi, **2**, 177–200.

RICATEAU, R. & RICHÉ, P. H. 1980. Geology of the Musandam Peninsula (Sultanate of Oman) and its surroundings: *Journal of Petroleum Geology*, **3**, 139–152.

ROBERTSON, A. H. F. 1987a. The transition from a passive margin to an Upper Cretaceous foreland basin related to ophiolite emplacement in the Oman Mountains. *Geological Society of America Bulletin*, **99**, 633–653.

—— 1987b. Upper Cretaceous Muti Formation: transition of a Mesozoic carbonate platform to a foreland basin in the Oman Mountains. *Sedimentology*, **34**, 1123–1142.

SEARLE, M. P. 1985. Sequence of thrusting and origin of culminations in the northern and central Oman Mountains. *Journal of Structural Geology*, **7**, 129–143.

—— & COOPER, D. J. 1986. Structure of the Hawasina Window culmination, Central Oman Mountains: *Transactions of the Royal Society of Edinburgh: Earth Sciences*, **77**, 143–156.

—— & GRAHAM, G. M. 1982. The 'Oman Exotics': Oceanic carbonate build-ups associated with the early stages of continental rifting. *Geology*, **10**,

43–49.

——, JAMES, N. P., CALON, T. J. & SMEWING, J. D. 1983. Sedimentological and structural evolution of the Arabian continental margin in the Musandam Mountains and Dibba zone, United Arab Emirates. *Geological Society of America Bulletin*, **94**, 1381–1400.

—— & MALPAS, J. 1980. The structure and metamorphism of rocks beneath the Semail Ophiolite of Oman and their significance in ophiolite obduction. *Royal Society of Edinburgh Transactions: Earth Sciences*, **71**, p. 213–228.

—— & —— 1982. Petrochemistry and origin of subophiolitic metamorphic and related rocks in the Oman Mountains. *Journal of the Geological Society of London*, **139**, 235–248.

TSCHOPP, R. H. 1967a. Development of the Fahud field. 7th World Petroleum Congress Proceedings, Mexico, **2**, 243–250.

—— 1967b. The general geology of Oman: 7th World Petroleum Congress Proceedings, Mexico, **2**, 231–242.

WATTS, K. F. & GARRISON, R. E. 1986. Sumeini Group, Oman — Evolution of a Mesozoic carbonate slope on a south Tethyan continental margin. *Sedimentary Geology*, **48**, 107–168.

WHITE, N. J., JACKSON, J. A. & McKENZIE, D. P. 1986. The relationship between the geometry of normal faults and that of the sedimentary layers in their hanging walls. *Journal of Structural Geology*, **8**, 897–909.

The interpretation of gravity data in Oman: constraints on the ophiolite emplacement mechanism

A. W. SHELTON

*Department of Earth Sciences, Sultan Qaboos University, 32500
Al-Khod, Muscat, Sultanate of Oman*

Abstract: The results of the gravity survey which was carried out as part of the Open
University Oman Research Project and briefly reported by Lippard *et al.* are presented in
detail to further constrain the emplacement mechanism of the Semail Ophiolite. The
principal conclusions of the gravity (and magnetic) study are that (i) the Semail Ophiolite
nappe continues for a limited distance under the Batinah coastal plain and appears to have
a smoothly tapering 'trailing edge'; (ii) the lower surface of the nappe is approximately
planar; (iii) the 'leading edge' of the nappe comprises slices some 20% of the thickness of
the block to which they are attached; (iv) beneath the coastal plain, to the east of the
Hawasina Window culmination, a completely unexposed ophiolite block exists. These
conclusions favour the gravity-driven emplacement of the ophiolite nappe of Oman.

The gravity survey reported here consisted of
900 new gravity stations measured during the
field seasons of 1978 and 1979 (see Shelton
1984; Lippard *et al.* 1986). The average survey
density is one station per ten square kilometres.
The area covered (Fig. 1) lies mainly on the
Batinah Coast on the northern side of the Oman
Mountains and encompasses a previous survey
carried out for Petroleum Development Oman
(PDO) who generously made their data available in the form of a contoured map; as such the
stations were not reoccupiable or recalculable.

Great efforts were made to obtain readings
from the Oman Mountains i.e. within the
ophiolite blocks. To a limited extent this succeeded on the northern and eastern flanks of
the mountains; only the extremely rugged
harzburgite terrain resisted these efforts. Full
traverses across the mountains were, as in later
attempts (Manghnani & Coleman 1981), limited
to the wadi passes and were thus unrepresentative of the gravity field over the main body of
the blocks.

At first sight a basic and ultrabasic nappe
resting on shelf and basinal sediments would
appear an ideal subject for a gravity and magnetic investigation. In reality the complex tectonic deformation history of the ophiolite has
resulted in highly variable serpentinization
which in turn produces extreme fluctuations of
magnetic properties. These are characteristic of
ophiolites but of little interpretative use. The
accompanying density fluctuations are less disruptive and allow cautious interpretation of the
gravity data.

The aims of the gravity survey were (1) to
investigate the presence or absence of the

ophiolite beneath the Batinah coastal plain and
(2) to investigate the lower boundary of the
exposed ophiolite. It was hoped that both of
these aims would contribute to a better understanding of the emplacement mechanism of the
Semail Ophiolite and might also lead to a better
understanding of emplacement in other, less
well exposed ophiolites.

A number of emplacement mechanisms have
been put forward for the Oman Mountains.
They divide crudely into (i) oceanic-type lithosphere infilling breaks in the continental margin
during extension followed by emplacement into
its present situation during compression; (ii)
oceanic lithosphere thrust into place during
closure of, and presently rooted in, the Gulf of
Oman and (iii) oceanic lithosphere emplaced as
a result of gravity gliding from an uplifted source
area. Lippard *et al.* (1986) favour the final
mechanism and have reconstructed a sequence
of events to account for the geological and
geochemical evidence gathered in Oman. It
involves the underthrusting of marginal continental crust at a subduction zone which, on
cessation of subduction, provides the necessary
isostatic uplift to allow gravity sliding of a section
of newly-created oceanic lithosphere. Geophysical methods, described below, have been used
to test this interpretation, i.e. the gravity glide
emplacement mechanism requires at least
detachment, if not a separation from the parent
oceanic lithosphere and prior to final emplacement, a 'piggy-back' style of thrust stacking is
envisaged (e.g. Searle 1985; Hanna 1986) which
predicts a planar sole thrust for the ophiolite
nappe.

The gravity interpretation of the Batinah

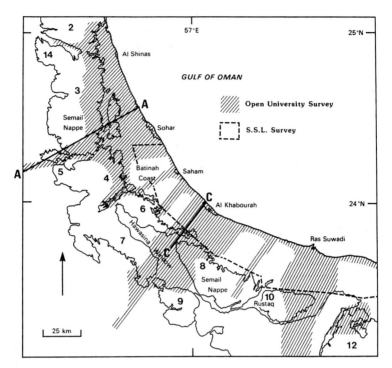

Fig. 1. Main areas covered in the Open University gravity survey and outline of earlier PDO map. A—A is the approximate line of the Fizh section described in Fig. 7; C—C is the line of the Hawasina interpretation described in Fig. 6. Numbers are the key to ophiolite block names: 2, Aswad; 3, Fizh; 4, Salahi; 5, West Jizi; 6, Sarami; 7, Wuqbah; 8, Haylayn; 9, Muqniyat; 10, Rustaq; 12, Ibra; 14, Sumeini.

coastal plain is not straightforward. Firstly, the manipulation of two unknown boundaries (upper and lower) combined with the use of uncertain density contrasts permits an unreasonably large family of solutions. Secondly, the study area is on the edge of a passive margin undergoing varying degrees of continent—continent collision. This gives rise to regional fields of the same order of wavelength and magnitude as the fields expected of the ophiolite nappe thus making the two fields difficult to separate. Thirdly there is an abrupt curtailment of gravity data at the coast; the shallow water produces a data gap of some tens of kilometres at a crucial section of the interpretation.

This paper describes the use of seismic constraints to solve the first ambiguity. The separation of regional and residual fields is more difficult but is simulated using a passive margin analogue. The data gap awaits the publication of near-shore gravity data which will either confirm or reject the assumptions built into the present modelling by the use of the margin analogues.

The gravity solution for the thickness, and

hence the lower boundary configuration, of the various ophiolite blocks depends on two things: firstly a realistic determination of the density contrast of the ophiolite with the underlying formations and secondly the collection of evenly spaced data over the entire area. The latter is extremely difficult given the rugged terrain which restricts practical surveying to unrepresentative thin sections of the nappe.

The access problem has been overcome by considering the gradients of the potential field at the limits of data collection and extending the survey to the practical limits within the block. The solution is applicable to every geological situation in which contoured information is required from unevenly spaced field data. In this case the surface fitting assumptions were not extreme and the results encouraging.

The density considerations have been carefully assessed and a strongly preferred contrast has been computed from a variety of field data. The mineral densities of the components of serpentinite and harzburgite provide the absolute limits whilst a combination of hand specimen analyses and seismic velocities give definite indications of the amount of alteration and thus the unit or 'formation' density of the ophiolite nappe.

The observed data set

Coverage was complete and intensive for the Batinah coastal plain and the eastern side of the Oman Mountains, from north of Wadi Jizi up to the borders with the UAE (Fig. 1). A swathe of measurements was taken across the central Batinah, around the Hawasina Window and into the desert beyond. A southern swathe, normal to the coastline, included the Rustaq block and crossed Jebel Akhdar to finish at the inland thrust culminations. These swathes are joined by a continuous coastal traverse and linked to the west of the mountains. Between the swathes the data are controlled by the PDO survey contour trends.

This coverage has been cautiously extended by dividing the area into panels to which a bicubic spline surface is fitted. In panels with little real data, the spline is controlled by the gradients of the surface in connecting panels. There must be, for example, data on the other side of the inaccessible part of the block or values which will continue to increase or decrease at the last known gradient. This method has to be applied judiciously but provides a better simulation of the impenetrable areas than a straightforward interpolation between data values (Fig. 2).

The data is in the form of Simple Bouguer anomalies. The indeterminate terrain corrections in the unsurveyed parts of the blocks lead to underestimates of nappe thickness by a predictable proportion. Far greater errors could result from attempts to approximate the terrain corrections and derive a complete Bouguer anomaly.

Regional residual separation

Commonly the potential field effects of deeper structures are comparatively longer in wavelength and lower in amplitude than the effects of shallow structures. However, in Oman there are slices of a relatively high-density material at the surface, with a cross section of the order 10×50 km, and this slab generates a broad anomaly which unfortunately has the same order of wavelength as anomalies due to deeper margin structures: the infamous 'shelf-edge positive' and 'continental-slope negative'. Even if the Oman margin were not under considerable stress due to its impending destruction, the rise of the Moho from continental to oceanic depths would not be compensated by the increase in depth of water and low-density sediments; a couplet of anomalies approximately +60 and − 30 Mgal within 100 km is predicted for a passive margin in perfect isostatic equilibrium. It is thus impossible to separate and remove the regional field by standard methods such as low-order surface fitting or frequency filtering. Given the lack of teleseismic data for this margin it was decided to construct a margin model, using as many local constraints as possible and observe the effect on the residual field and subsequent modelling.

The US east coast passive margin (Grow *et*

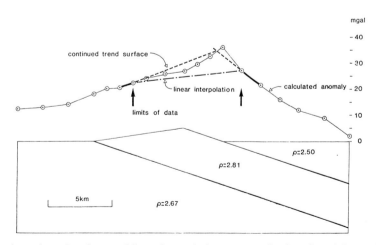

Fig. 2. Comparison of trend surfaces and linear interpolation over a stylized section of the northern Oman ophiolite. (Ophiolite portrayed as a constant thickness slab, density 2.81 Mg m^{-3}, underlying formations 2.67 Mg m^{-3} cover density 2.50 Mg m^{-3}.

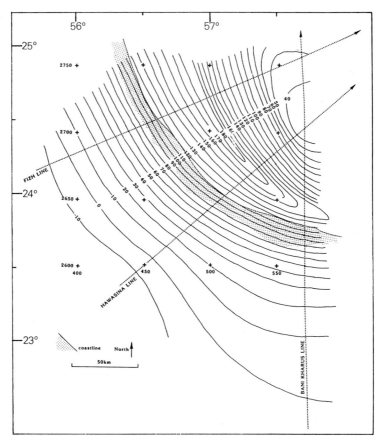

Fig. 3. Regional field for the northern Oman continental margin based on an interpolation of three modelled regional traverses detailed in Fig. 4.

al. 1979) was chosen as a simple analogue for the undoubtedly more complex situation in Oman. The entirely unknown component is the positioning of this analogue Moho geometry with respect to the present shore-line and 'shelf-edge'. It transpires that a straightforward horizontal displacement of that geometry achieves a satisfactory fit at the two sections where the regional and total field should agree. These sections lie (i) in the centre of the Gulf of Oman where the sedimentary sequence is presumed to be flat-lying and (ii) 40 to 100 km inland of the coastline.

The Gulf of Oman Free Air gravity and bathymetry are taken from White & Ross (1979). To comply with the known Gulf constraints the geometry of the 'standard' Atlantic margin requires up to 6 km of overlying sediments, a depth confirmed as reasonable by Hutchison *et al.* (1981). Considering the simple assumptions made here, the agreement in rela-

tive gravity lavels for the inland and Gulf sections gives confidence in accepting this regional for the ophiolite and coastal plain.

Using these model assumptions, two further regional lines were constructed and their values interpolated to give the resultant regional field for the area as shown in Fig. 3.

The resultant gravity field

The effect of stripping this regional from the observed data is not as extreme as might be expected. The three sections along the modelled lines illustrate this most clearly (Fig. 4). Possibly the most critical change occurs in the steepening of the gradient from the ophiolite to the Gulf. From an interpretative viewpoint this implies a more steeply dipping and more rapid pinching out of the ophiolite beneath the coastal plain than would be modelled for the observed data-set. There are also substantial influences on the

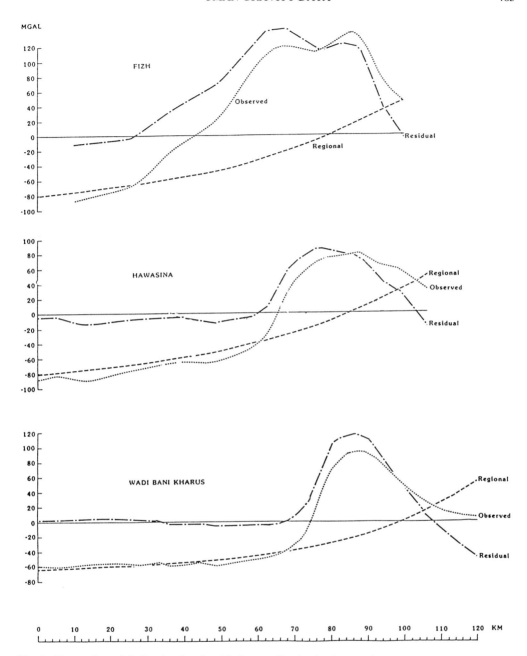

Fig. 4. Observed, modelled regional and residual anomalies for the three major traverses.

calculated thicknesses of the blocks. The assumptions of the regional field separation imply that where there is no ophiolite, there should be a zero anomaly and conversely that the residual anomaly is entirely due to ophiolite; in this context it should be noted that for the southernmost line the residual becomes negative as it approaches the shoreline. The additional thicknesses of low-density sediments in the south require that part of the ophiolite overburden be treated separately from the underlying formations, a factor that complicates the later interpretations. It is assumed that what is true for the southern traverses would also be seen to the

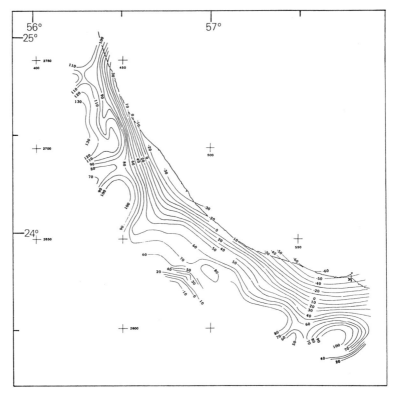

Fig. 5. Residual field for the eastern Oman Mountains and Batinah coastal plain, contour interval 10 mgal.

north if the gravity data extended farther out to sea.

Interpretation

Coastal plain solutions

The resultant field (Figs 4 & 5) shows a smooth decline from outcrop towards the Gulf of Oman. This could equally well be satisfied by a constant-dipping uniform slab or by a smoothly tapering wedge. Clearly there are no abrupt cut-offs or changes in ophiolite thickness beneath the coastal plain.

The gravity field of an ophiolite section that not only dips beneath the cover but may also thin as it does so, is controlled by a plethora of variables. These include the dips of the upper and lower surfaces of the ophiolitic slab and the density contrast of ophiolite with overlying and underlying formations. Some of this uncertainty is removed where there are coincident seismic data. Petroleum Developments (Oman) made available a seismic profile from the coastal plain opposite the Fizh block in which the upper surface of the ophiolite is clearly visible. This

surface is rough and is marked by a series of diffraction hyperbolae. Unfortunately the marked impedance contrast means that very little energy penetrates the ophiolite and there is no sign of the lower boundary.

Inspection of this time section revealed that an assumption of depth-independent velocity for the cover formations was valid. Thus if the velocity were known the dip of the upper surface could be ascertained. The empirical relationship between density and velocity provides the connection between the gravity and seismic solutions. A solution for this line was obtained in which the ophiolite has a density of 2.92 Mg m^{-3} and the mainly Tertiary cover has a formation density of 2.40 Mg m^{-3}, giving a dip for the upper ophiolite surface of 35±5°. This represents the maximum dip and cover density as the gravity solution makes no assumptions about the lower ophiolite boundary. Thinning of the ophiolite section towards the coast will force a higher density contrast and a shallower dip up to a limit of 15° dip under a cover of 1.98 Mg m^{-3} (2.07 km s^{-1}). The density measurements on Tertiary samples indicate a 'Batinah' density of not much less than 2.40 Mg m^{-3} and the seismic evidence provides a realistic unit density for the ophiolite at a dip compatible with the outcrop structure.

The density contrast accepted in the Fizh example has been used to model the sub-surface extent of ophiolite in the Hawasina region. The seismic evidence in the latter area shows only the Tertiary base reflector dipping coastwards at around 15°; the time-section should have shown the ophiolite unless it dips seawards at more than 45°. There are no structural indications of such a steep dip and furthermore, even with the contrast stretched to unrealistic limits the gravity indicates that ophiolite exists under most of the coastal plain in this region. Fig. 6a shows the iterative solution for an upper surface fixed at sea level, Fig. 6b shows the solution with the lower surface fixed at 4.7 km and Fig. 6c shows the sensible combination of the two which allows for the non-exposure of ophiolite across the coastal plain. Fig. 6c predicts unexpected high density material on the eastern (Hawasina Window) side of the ophiolite. This corresponds to outcrops of Haybi Volcanics and Metamorphic Sheet and so may not be truly representative of underlying sedimentary formations. Stripping the Tertiary prism from the data reinforces the conclusion that ophiolite exists beneath the plain and only pinches out within a kilometre of the present shoreline.

The southerly data swathe (Fig. 1) includes the Rustaq ophiolite block and a longer section of coastal plain than the northern sections. It also encompasses some of the lowest gravity values (Fig. 5) measured on the eastern side of the mountains. Here again the seismic coverage does not show any ophiolite but it is 18 km from the nearest outcrop! Both magnetic and gravity polygon models show the ophiolite pinching out before the seismic coverage begins. The lack of any seismic control means that this section is poorly constrained and the very low gravity values show the influence of low-density material on the coastal plain that invalidate the density contrasts based on a principally Tertiary limestone cover. Within these limits modelling indicates that the gravity data can be satisfied by an ophiolite nappe which has a planar lower surface and an upper surface that dips at approximately 25° beneath the coastal plain thus pinching out 15 to 16 km north of the outcrop.

Thickness of blocks

As stated in the introduction there are difficulties in providing a unit or formation density for the ophiolite to contrast with the inconvenient variety of underlying rocks. It is highly desirable to do so because iterative interpretation programmes seldom accept more than a single density contrast without vast increases in resource use. A start can be made by considering the ophiolite as a layercake of harzburgite, gabbro, dykes etc. and calculating the respective unit densities by assuming fresh rock and using mineral densities. The proportion of each layer will vary but only the large differences in the relative thicknesses of crustal and mantle rocks will make a significant contribution to the formation density.

To constrain these ideal, fresh, mineral-density derived values a large number of density measurements were made on hand samples. These samples are, of course, surface or near-surface derived and may therefore be more altered and less dense than rock at depth. Harzburgite and its alteration products offers the greatest scope for variety. The mineral density of the 'average' harzburgite described by Smewing (1980) is 3.32 Mg m^{-3}, serpentinization can lower this towards 2.62 Mg m^{-3}. To what degree is the sub-surface harzburgite altered? Seismic velocities quoted by Glennie et al. (1974) and compared with the velocity and density data of Christensen & Smewing (1981), generally suggest an overall alteration of 40%, a value in keeping with the 55 to 100% alteration observed in the majority of hand samples. At 40% alteration the bulk density of the mantle sequence is calculated to be 3.05 Mg m^{-3} and the variation in proportion of mantle sequence means that a formation density for the ophiolite nappes of between 2.84 (only crustal sequence) and 2.98 Mg m^{-3} (6 km crust + 12 km mantle) is indicated.

Set against a background which may vary from 2.20 to 2.67 Mg m^{-3} there is a possible range in density contrast of 0.17 to 0.78 Mg m^{-3}. Even if the ophiolite were completely unaltered with a unit density of 3.20 Mg m^{-3}, the maximum contrast is unlikely to exceed 0.8 Mg m^{-3}. The minimum contrast is harder to fix but is taken as 0.25 Mg m^{-3}, less than which would provide structurally unrealistic thicknesses of ophiolite nappe for this residual field. The preferred contrast is 0.52 Mg m^{-3}, coincidentally the middle of the range, because it satisfies the seismic, structural and gravity data on the coastal side of the Fizh block. Table 1 sets out the thickness range beneath the maximum gravity anomaly for the surveyed blocks. The blocks can be identified on Fig. 1.

A direct structural interpretation follows from these data in that if the ophiolite were a regularly-dipping slab beneath the coastal plain,

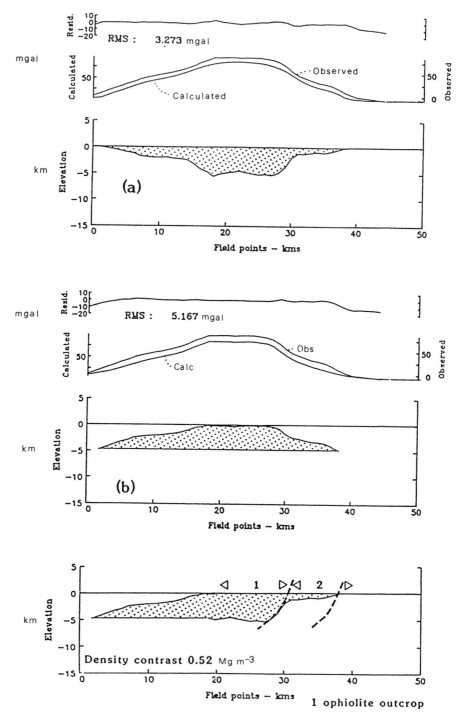

Fig. 6. Iterative solutions with density contrast 0.52 Mg m^{-3}, to the residual data through the eastern edge of the Hawasina Window. (*a*) Upper surface fixed at sea level, (*b*) lower surface fixed at 4.7 km depth and (*c*) combination of the above using outcrop constraints: 1, ophiolite outcrops; 2, Haybi volcanics and metamorphic sheet. RMS is the root mean square error in mgal between calculated and observed fields. Section located as C−C on Fig. 1 and approximately coincident with the Hawasina regional line in Fig. 3.

Table 1. *Maximum thickness of the principal ophiolite blocks.* (nomenclature following Lippard *et al.* 1986; see Fig. 1) Thickness given in km and calculated with the horizontal thin sheet approximation for an average block width of 20 km. Values are given for maximum, preferred and minimum density contrasts in Mg m^{-3}. Maximum simple Bouguer anomaly values in mgal.

Block Name	Max[1] anomaly (mgal)	U/M posn of max	Calculated thickness (km) at values (Mg m^{-3})		
			0.80	0.52	0.25
N.FIZH	131−145	2725/430	4.2−4.7	6.7−7.5	16.0−18.0
S.FIZH	121−126	2710/445	3.9−4.0	6.1−6.4	14.5−15.2
SALAHI	110−?	2680−450	3.3−?	5.5−?	12.8−?
SARAMI	73−?	2645/475	2.3−?	3.6−?	7.9−?
SHAFAN[2]	66−68	2650/490	2.0−2.1	3.2−3.3	7.1−7.3
GHUZAYN	88−92	2635/500	2.8−2.9	4.3−4.5	9.9−10.3
HAYLAYN	87−?	2610/530	2.7−?	4.2−?	9.7−?
RUSTAQ	114	2597/575	3.6	5.7	13.3

[1] SBA calculated at 2.67, less modelled regional with zero datum set equal to −62 mgal observed.
[2] Refers to unexposed (ophiolite) block under Batinah cover off Sarami Block.

its thickness could be derived from its outcrop width (neglecting tectonic repetition) and its structural dip. The thickest part of such a system is beneath the easterly or northerly exposure limits of the blocks, where the gravity coverage is most complete. In order to accommodate the known block tilts, outcrop widths and gravity data, all blocks, except Haylayn, require a density contrast between the ophiolite and its surrounding rocks of less than 0.25 Mg m^{-3}. This value, although just permissible (e.g. 2.92 against 2.67 Mg m^{-3}), is at the limits of credulity and thus suggests that the lower ophiolite boundary is a thrust plane cutting up-section.

Inspection of Table 1 shows that blocks are thinnest in the central Oman Mountains and increase in thickness to the north and south of the Hawasina culmination. In general the larger the outcrop area, the thicker the block (a sensible outcome of glide detachment). Only the Rustaq block appears to be an exception to this rule.

Trailing-edge imbricates?

Graham (1980) was one of the first to emphasize the late-stage separation of the ophiolite nappe blocks during the uplift responsible for the Hawasina Window. More recent detailed structural work (e.g. Hanna 1986) has proven late movements in the opposite sense to the emplacement direction. Most of the structural repetition is emplacement related but some extensional features are seen, particularly on the trailing-edge. Two of the sections modelled (through the Fizh and Sarami blocks) appear to show an imbricate structure on their trailing edges. This was, at first, assumed to be over-

thrusting in the emplacement sense but there were difficulties in accounting for such structures (Shelton 1984). The evidence for relatively recent detachment by back-sliding at the trailing edge provides a more convincing explanation of the structures inferred from the gravity data.

Interpretation of the Fizh section is helped by exposed rock. There are outcrops of gabbros at the eastern margin of a virtually complete ophiolite section. The contact between the lavas and these easterly gabbros is obscured in a north−south trending depression colloquially known as 'The Alley'. The structure of the trailing edge of the Fizh block has been the subject of previous studies (Smewing *et al.* 1977) but whatever the agreed solution, the gravity data predicts an equivalent structure under shallow Batinah coastal plain sediments, east of the Sarami block.

The asymmetric gravity low associated with the Fizh block 'Alley' is not centred over the axis lavas but is displaced eastwards towards the generally higher-density gabbro outcrops. This pattern is not consistent with the easterly-dipping lavas and dykes having been vertically faulted out; it suggests rather that the lower density, higher crustal units extend eastwards beneath the gabbros of Jebel Sheik indicative of low-angle faulting. The elongate positive closure east of the Sarami block outcrops (centred on UTM 489E/2653N) is a diminished version of the high associated with the 'Alley' outcrops. The Sarami block in this area shows unusually little mantle section and repetition in the dykes and lava sequence. A nearby seismic section shows the Tertiary limestones dipping at around 14° towards the coast and underlain by a kilometre thickness of sub-parallel reflectors taken to be a slice of Batinah Sheets. These seismic data were used to constrain the gravity modelling. Under the main outcrops the preferred density contrast shows a flat-lying lower surface at a depth of 4 km for 8 km of the traverse. The lower surface was fixed at this level and the model iterated with a free upper surface. This gave a solution with a 7 km section in which ophiolite shallowly (<1 km) underlies the coastal plain sediments then dips at 20° to pinch out just short of the present shoreline.

Planar lower ophiolite surfaces

The lower boundary of the ophiolite sheet cuts up-section at some of the block sides and leading edges giving an overall impression of spoon-shaped thrust slices. There is no doubt that the flatness of the base of the gravity models is partially due to the smoothing effect of extending the gravity data into the centre of the blocks. A gravity field with zero gradients in areas of low data looks appropriate and is a welcome outcome of the contouring routine; it may however be imposing an artificial geometry on the solutions.

For the coastal plain solutions, the base of the nappe is held to a plane because there are already too many variables. Except in one case, the seismic data are too tenuous to fix the upper surface and model the lower, instead the gravity solution is forced to take the alternative of fixing the lower surface. This has led to both conclusions and density contrasts compatible for the most part with the seismic data.

The section that most thoroughly tests the planar assumption is that through the southern Fizh block. These data show the greatest depth variation when allocated a single density contrast and iteratively modelled. As this is also the section with the greatest topographic range, particular care was used in the derivation of the Bouguer Anomaly residual field. The Bouguer corrections were made at 2.90 rather than the 2.67 Mg m^{-3} used without serious error in other transects. Fig. 7a shows the unconstrained single density contrast iterative solution. The model extends to depths of around 8.5 km with a prominent arch up to depths of just over 6 km coincident with the crustal outcrops and the 'Alley'. This coincidence indicates that the gravity field is being more strongly influenced by near-surface density variations rather than by abrupt changes in the lower boundary to the nappe. The effect of 'pegging' this lower surface at just under 8 km is illustrated in Fig. 7b which shows the iterative solution for the ophiolite upper surface. If the lower density components

had the full contrast, they only need extend some 1100 m below sea level to satisfy the data. If, as surface density measurements dictate, the contrast of crustal to sub-crustal rocks is more like half that with surrounding formations, then a section of over 2 km is required. Given the weathered outcrops exposed in the 'Alley' it is possible to invoke a planar basal surface for nearly 40 km across strike. However without the ameliorating effect of the near surface lower density rocks the basal plane of the ophiolite could have dips as high as 18° using the preferred density contrast.

In summary, the planar lower surface is both an artefact and a convenient method of modelling the gravity data for the Oman ophiolite. However the consequences of its assumption lead to solutions compatible with the limited seismic data and with the structures at outcrop.

Leading-edge imbricates

The Fizh section shows the most marked example of this phenomenon. The gravity data imply an irregular and markedly thinner sheet between 30−55 km in Fig. 7b. It is, at its thickest, 2.5 km compared to the 8 km depth required to satisfy the remainder of the data. The Ghuzayn (Fig. 6c) and Rustaq models both have leading edge extensions. Other central mountain traverses have these extensions separated by Hawasina sediments but the main arguments still apply.

There are two possible explanations for these features. One is that they indeed represent drastically thinned slices of normal density ophiolitic material. These require a mechanism such as diverticulation to shed parts of the main nappe leading edge and a thrust contact between the offspring and parent nappes. The mapping of the ophiolite certainly shows plenty of thrusts within the Mantle Sequence that could act in this capacity. The second alternative is that the nappe is not thinned at its leading edge but has a standard 'horse-like' cross section and is composed of highly serpentinized mantle material. The degree and extent of serpentinization required are explored below.

The sampling of harzburgite with various degrees of alteration lead directly to a density for the alteration products of 2.68 Mg m^{-3}. This density is mainly the result of admixtures of the polymorphs of serpentine with brucite. Total alteration thus lowers the density contrast of the nappe to 0.28 Mg m^{-3} and almost doubles the thickness of the leading edge slice. The 2.5 km depth would increase to 4.64 km which is, although substantial, still markedly short of

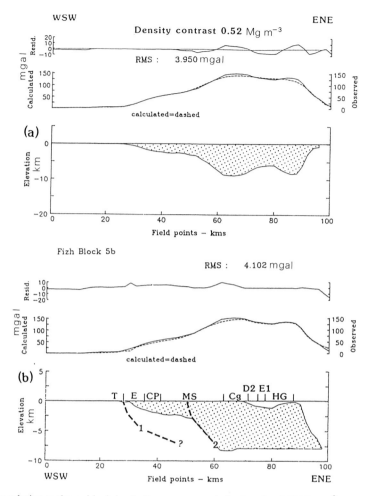

Fig. 7. Iterative solution to the residual simple Bouguer anomaly (reduced at 2.90 Mg m^{-3}) across the southern Fizh block. (a) Upper surface fixed at sea-level and vertical exaggeration ×1.25. (b) Solution obtained with a lower surface fixed at 7.9 km for km 60–100. Surface geology key: T, Tertiary; E, serpentinite; CP, scattered cumulate peridotite outcrops in alluvium; MS, Mantle Sequence; Cg, Cumulate Gabbros; D2, Sheeted dykes; E1, Pillow lavas; HG, high level and intrusive gabbros of the J. Sheik outcrops. 1, possible outline of low density material; 2, postulated major thrust. Section located as A–A on Fig. 1 and approximately coincident with the Fizh regional line of Fig. 3.

the 8 km base modelled for the main nappe. To eradicate the abrupt change in thickness of the body would require the density contrast of the leading edge to be less than a third that of the main body. Total alteration of mantle material against a background of 2.40 Mg m^{-3} implies a contrast for the main body of 0.88 Mg m^{-3}, a value which substantially exceeds the range regarded as reasonable (see earlier section). Such large thicknesses of serpentinite also contradict the field evidence which, where the base of the nappe is exposed, shows severe alteration limited to less than a kilometre and 100% serpentinite seldom exceeding 500 m thickness.

There is no doubt that the leading edge has suffered greater alteration than the main body of the nappe. The above argument seeks to show that this is a result not only of its vulnerable position in the emplacement scheme but also because it is genuinely much thinner than the main body of the ophiolite and may have originated by a glide process from the front of the main nappe.

Summary

The similarities in the field due to the passive margin and the ophiolite cause difficulties in their separation. These difficulties are overcome by using a modelled regional field which is subsequently abstracted from the observed data. The resultant residual field (shown in Fig. 5) has a steeper decline from ophiolite outcrop to the present shoreline.

Maximum use is made of a single seismic line which picks up the upper surface of the ophiolite beneath the Batinah coastal plain. It restricts the dip to less than 35° and implies a density contrast of 0.52 Mg m^{-3} with the overlying material. This contrast is used for the modelling of the nappe throughout. Solutions for upper surface dips are obtained by assuming the lower surface to be planar and horizontal. These assumptions lead to dips in agreement with outcrop measurements and predict that the ophiolite pinches out close to the present coastline in the north of the area and approximately following the zero residual contour in the wider southern Batinah plain (Fig. 5).

An inspection of the limits of possible densities shows a contrast of 0.52 Mg m^{-3} to be a median value and allows the maximum thickness of the separate blocks to be estimated from the residual anomalies. The blocks in the north are the thickest, those around the Hawasina Window thinnest and, south of that area, thickness increases once more.

There are potential field indications of repetition within the blocks, notably in the case of the Fizh block where the structure is exposed and, it is here suggested, a similar unexposed structure east of the Sarami block. The shape of the residual anomaly indicates a low-angle fault contact.

The residual field also implies thin extensions at the leading edge of the nappe (sometimes separated from the parent body by the post-emplacement culminations). The possibility that these are highly altered, low-density portions of an equivalent thickness to the rest of the nappe is considered unreasonable leaving a requirement for a forward detachment of slices from the leading edge of the ophiolite.

This interpretation of the gravity data at the Oman margin suggests that the ophiolite exposures are discrete nappes currently disconnected from their parent lithosphere which is assumed to lie beneath the Gulf of Oman. This may not be the case south of Muscat and north of the UAE border where the 'horns' of the 'Oman Embayment' (Lippard et al. 1986) would not have allowed such complete separation. For that part of the Oman margin for which gravity data are available it appears that the ophiolite is neither rooted in the upper mantle nor in the Gulf of Oman. Its emplacement must have involved the passive movement of relatively planar slabs of oceanic lithosphere.

The gravity work was carried out as part of the Open University Oman Ophiolite Project under the directorship of Professor Ian Gass. Initial funding was from the Overseas Development Administration. Later generous support was provided by the Amoco Oman Petroleum Company through a grant to Professor W. H. Kanes, Earth Sciences and Resources Institute, University of South Carolina. Petroleum Developments (Oman) provided the earlier gravity and seismic data for the Batinah Plain. The author is grateful to R. S. White, an anonymous reviewer and A. Ries for their assistance in improving the paper.

References

CHRISTENSEN, N. I. & SMEWING, J. D. 1981. Geology and seismic structure of the northern section of the Oman Ophiolite. *J. Geophysics Research* **86(B4)**, 2545–2555.

GLENNIE, K. W., BOEUF, M. G. A., HUGHES CLARK, M. W., MOODY-STUART, M., PILAAR, W. F. H. & REINHARDT, B. M. 1974. The geology of the Oman Mountains. *Konin. Neder. Geol. Mijnbouw. Genoot. Verdh.* **31**.

GRAHAM, G. M. 1980. *Structure and sedimentology of the Hawasina Window, Oman mountains.* PhD Thesis, Open University.

GROW, J. A., BOWIN, C. O. & HUTCHINSON, D. R. 1979. The gravity field of the US Atlantic continental margin. *In*: KEEN, C. E. (ed.) *Crustal properties across passive margins, Tectonophysics*, **59**, 27–52.

HANNA, S. S. 1986. The Alpine (Late Cretaceous and Tertiary) tectonic evolution of the Oman Mountains: A thrust tectonic approach. *In: Symposium on the Hydrocarbon Potential of Intense Thrust Zones.* Abu Dhabi, Volume II, 125–174.

HUTCHISON, I., LOUDEN, K. E., WHITE, R. S. & VON HERZEN, R. P. 1981. Heat flow and the age of the Gulf of Oman. *Earth and Planetary Science Letters*, **56**, 252–262.

LIPPARD, S. J., SHELTON, A. W. & GASS, I. G. 1986. *The Ophiolite of Northern Oman.* Geological Society, London, Memoir, **11**.

MANGHNANI, M. H. & COLEMAN, R. G. 1981. Gravity profiles across the Samail ophiolite, Oman. *J. Geophys. Res.* **86(B4)**, 2509–2525.

SEARLE, M. P. 1985. Sequence of thrusting and origin of culminations in the northern and central Oman Mountains. *Journal of Structural Geology*, **8**, 923–936.

SHELTON, A. W. 1984. *Geophysical studies on the northern Oman ophiolite.* PhD thesis, Open University.

SMEWING, J. D. 1980. Regional setting and petrological characteristics of the Oman ophiolite in North Oman. *In*: ROCCI, G. (ed.) *Ofioliti Special Issue on Tethyan Ophiolites*, Vol 2, *Eastern Area*, 335–378.

——, SIMONIAN, K. O., EL BOUSHI, I. M. & GASS, I.

G. 1977. Mineralized fault zone parallel to the Oman ophiolite spreading axis. *Geology*, **5**, 534–538.

WHITE, R. S. & ROSS, D. A. 1979. Tectonics of the Western Gulf of Oman. *J. Geophys. Res.* **84**, 3479–3489.

Metamorphism in the Oman Mountains in relation to the Semail ophiolite emplacement

A. K. EL-SHAZLY & R. G. COLEMAN

Geology Department, Stanford University, Stanford, CA 94305, USA

Abstract: The metamorphic rocks associated with the Semail ophiolite in the Oman Mountains represent two different facies series. Amphibolites and greenshists at the base of the Semail ophiolite constitute a metamorphic sole formed in a high-temperature, low-pressure environment. Eclogites, blueschists, lawsonite schists and other metasediments occuring at different structural levels in the basement and shelf deposits of the continental margin formed at high pressures and low temperatures. The amphibolites of the metamorphic sole formed as a result of heat transfer from the hot overthrust ophiolitic slab to the underlying oceanic sediments and volcanics shortly following intraoceanic detachment at a collapsed spreading centre about $100-90$ Ma. The underlying greenschists represent sediments and volcanics that were metamorphosed farther away from the spreading centre as the ophiolitic slab became cooler and moved closer to the continental margin. Eclogites, blueschists and crossite epidote schists formed in the Saih Hatat window as a result of A-type subduction (crustal thickening) of the basement and shelf units of the Oman continental margin in response to a change in plate motion between Africa and Eurasia and transpression or collision with a fragment of Gondwanaland about 131 Ma. A-type subduction along an east-dipping zone resulted in the burial of the eastern edge of the continental margin to a minimum depth of 30 km. High P/T metamorphic rocks formed by this process followed 'clockwise' $P-T$ paths. The Late Cretaceous emplacement of the ophiolite onto the continental margin of Oman resulted in the imbrication of the continental shelf deposits, the development of low-grade, high-P/T metamorphic rocks in the 'internal' thrust piles due to tectonic overloading and the juxtaposition of the metamorphic rocks representing different facies series. Extensional deformation associated with culmination collapse in the Late Cretaceous and Tertiary led to the exhumation of the various high P/T metamorphic rocks and the distortion of the metamorphic zones.

The emplacement of the Semail ophiolite onto the Arabian plate during the Late Cretaceous is now well documented and generally agreed upon (Glennie *et al.* 1973, 1974; Searle & Malpas 1980; Coleman 1981; Boudier *et al.* 1985; Lippard *et al.* 1986). Numerous studies that detail the igneous and structural history of the Semail ophiolite as well as the stratigraphy of the Oman continental margin have clarified the evolution and passive nature of this margin during the Permian to Late Cretaceous period. Less well documented are the metamorphic events that relate to the ophiolite emplacement and their importance in reconstructing the tectonic history of this margin as it evolved into a thrust belt during the Cretaceous.

The Semail ophiolite in Oman (SE Arabia) constitutes part of the 'croissant ophiolitique peri Arabe' of Ricou (1971) that represents ocean crust formed during the Cretaceous and emplaced as the Tethyan ocean closed. This closure can be related to an earlier fundamental change in plate motion between Africa and Eurasia (Dercourt *et al.* 1986; Boudier *et al.* 1985; Moores *et al.* 1984). During the Aptian,

the movement of the African plate changed from an eastward direction to a northward one and by the Campanian it had rotated nearly 63° counterclockwise relative to Eurasia (Dercourt *et al.* 1986). The eastern passive margin of Oman experienced crustal thickening in the Early Cretaceous as a fragment of Gondwanaland moved northward causing transpression and possibly colliding with that margin. Detachment of the oceanic crust in the Tethys at a spreading centre to the NE of the Oman margin (Boudier *et al.* 1985) initiated the obduction of the Semail ophiolite by gravity sliding across the subsiding passive continental margin. The hot base of the Semail ophiolite developed a sole of metamorphic rocks formed at high temperature (T) and low pressure (P) during intraoceanic detachment (Searle & Malpas 1980; Ghent & Stout 1981; Bucher *et al.* 1988). Emplacement of the Semail ophiolite onto the passive margin dislocated the 'autochthonous' Cretaceous–Permian shelf carbonates (Hajar SuperGroup; Glennie *et al.* 1974) by imbricate thrusting thickening the crust along the northern margin of Oman. High P/T metamorphism in

From ROBERTSON, A. H. F., SEARLE, M. P. & RIES, A. C. (eds), 1990,
The Geology and Tectonics of the Oman Region.
Geological Society Special Publication No 49, pp 473–493

the basement and shelf deposits developed concomitantly with this tectonic thickening (Michard *et al*. 1982; Michard 1983; Michard *et al*. 1984; Boudier *et al*. 1985; Montigny *et al*. 1988). Field and petrologic studies in the last decade by Searle & Malpas (1980), Ghent & Stout (1981), Lippard (1983), El-Shazly *et al*. (1987), Le Metour (1988), Bucher *et al*. (1988) and Goffé *et al*. (1988) have shown that the metamorphic rocks associated with the Semail ophiolite and representing at least two distinct metamorphic facies series were juxtaposed during the final stages of ophiolite emplacement. The present configuration of these metamorphic rocks and the exhumation of the high *P/T* metamorphics is the result of later extensional deformation developed by culmination collapse of the tectonically thickened continental margin, a process common in other orogenic zones developed during the final closure of the Tethyan ocean (Dewey 1988).

This paper is aimed at summarizing the spatial, temporal and genetic relations between the Semail ophiolite emplacement and the different metamorphic events documented in Oman. The tectonometamorphic evolution of the Oman continental margin and $P-T$ paths of the various metamorphic rocks will be discussed in detail in the light of the data of Le Metour *et al*. (1986), Goffé *et al*. (1988) and our recent petrological studies.

Tectonostratigraphy

The Semail ophiolite structurally overlies four major lithotectonic units (Glennie *et al*. 1973, 1974, Searle & Malpas 1980) which are well exposed in several tectonic windows (e.g. J. Akhdar, Saih Hatat and Hawasina windows; Figs 1 & 2). The lithotectonic units are: (1) Haybi Complex; a thrust sheet at the base of the ophiolite consisting of a metamorphic sole, a Cretaceous melange, Triassic and Cretaceous volcanics and Permo-Triassic limestones (Oman exotics; Glennie *et al*. 1974); (2) Hawasina Complex; a series of thin thrust sheets consisting of unmetamorphosed Permian to Cretaceous deep water carbonates, sandstones, turbidites and cherts, originally deposited on the continental distal slope and basin and subsequently thrust onto the margin prior to the final stages of ophiolite emplacement; (3) Mid-Permian to Upper Cretaceous shallow marine shelf carbonates (Hajar SuperGroup) unconformably or tectonically overlain by Cenomanian to Campanian conglomerates, shales, marls and limestones (Muti Formation; Robertson 1987); and (4) A pre-Permian basement of folded and

metamorphosed calcareous and arenaceous sediments, volcanics and minor granodioritic intrusions.

The high *P/T* metamorphic assemblages occur within the pre-Permian basement, the Permian to Cretaceous shelf carbonates and the Muti Formation of the Saih Hatat window in NE Oman (Figs 1 & 2; Le Metour *et al*. 1986; Goffé *et al*. 1988). The spatial and temporal evolution of the northeastern part of the Oman continental margin in relation to the stratigraphy is summarized in Fig. 11 and will be discussed in detail in the following sections.

Metamorphic rocks associated with the Semail ophiolite

The ophiolitic metamorphic sole

Geologic setting. The ophiolitic metamorphic sole crops out along the margins of several tectonic windows or culminations; e.g. Sumeini,

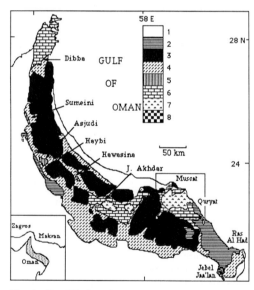

Fig. 1. Simplified geological map of the Oman Mountains (mainly from Glennie *et al*. (1974), after Lippard *et al*. (1986) and modified according to Le Metour *et al*. (1986). Inset shows the location of the Oman Mountains (stippled) relative to the Makran margin and Zagros fold belt. Square outlines the Saih Hatat area, shown in Fig. 2. Arrows point to the locations of some of the outcrops of the metamorphic aureole after Searle and Malpas (1980). 1, Recent deposits; 2, Tertiary and Maastrichtean limestones; 3, deposits; 4, Hawasina and Haybi allochthonous units; 5, Sumeini Group; 6, Hajar Supergroup; 7, Pre-Permian basement and Permian shelf deposits; 8, Jebel Jaa'lan granites and gneisses.

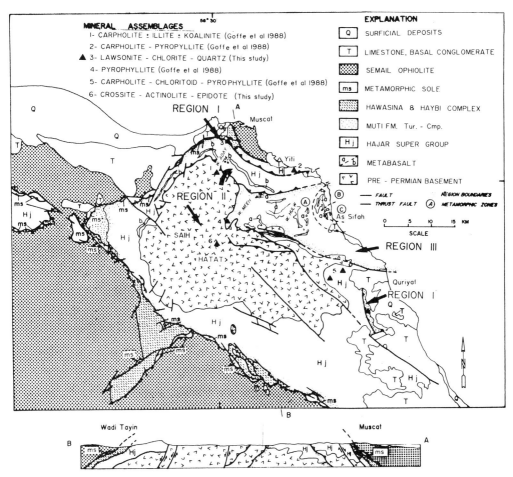

Fig. 2. Geologic map of the Saih Hatat area (simplified from Le Metour *et al.* (1986). Solid triangles and Arabic numerals show the localities of some metamorphic assemblages from regions I and II (see table 2 for details). 'a' and 'b' are metamorphosed mafic bodies in regions III and II respectively; 'a' eclogites, blueschists and crossite epidote schists. 'b' porphyritic metabasites and crossite schists. A−B is the line of cross section which shows the structural relations between the various regions (boundaries of which are in light stipple). See text for explanation of region (I, II, III) and metamorphic zone (A, B, C) boundaries.

Asjudi, Haybi, Hawasina (Wadi Hawasina, Jebel Abiad), Jebel Akhdar (Rustaq, Haylayn and Mahbab), Saih Hatat (Wadi Nujum, Awabi and W. Tayin) and several other localities in the United Arab Emirates (e.g. Dibba zone; Figs 1 & 2; Searle & Malpas 1980; Ghent & Stout 1981; Bailey 1981; Villey *et al.* 1986; Bucher *et al.* 1988; Ziegler & Stoessel 1988). This sole is composed of interbedded metavolcanic and metasedimentary units and usually has a total thickness of 150 m or less (Searle & Malpas 1980; Spray 1984). In many outcrops, the sole rocks have been completely detached from the peridotite giving rise to tectonic blocks within the Haybi Complex. Metamorphic grade de-creases down-section from the amphibolites in contact with the overlying ophiolite to green-schists and phyllites in contact with the under-lying unmetamorphosed Hawasina sediments (Ghent & Stout 1981). The mafic protoliths of some of the amphibolites and greenschists have tholeiitic, transitional or alkalic affinities charac-teristic of Jurassic basalts and Triassic Haybi volcanics (Searle & Malpas 1982; Ziegler & Stoessel 1988), whereas the protoliths of the metasediments include the Oman exotic lime-stones and Hawasina cherts and shales (Searle & Malpas 1980; Ghent & Stout 1981). The metamorphic sole rocks are characterized by a foliation or a shear fabric which in most cases is parallel to the flow fabric within the basal peridotites of the overlying ophiolite (Boudier *et al.* 1985). In most outcrops, the metamorphic sole is dissected by several thrusts that crosscut the foliation and dip towards the overlying ophiolite. In some areas, the foliation and the thrusts were rotated to a vertical or 'inverted' position by tectonic events that post-dated the emplacement of the ophiolite and were related to the development of some culminations (e.g. J. Akhdar).

Petrology and mineral chemistry. Mineral assemblages of the amphibolites and greenschists are summarized in Table 1. Amphiboles of the mafic amphibolites are hornblendes zoned from brown cores (Ti and Al^{iv}-rich?) through green to bluish green rims (Na^{M4} and Al^{vi}rich?) (Ghent & Stout 1981). Actinolite is the most common amphibole in the greenschists but hornblende (relict?) and crossite were also reported from Wadi Tayin and Dibba zone respectively (Ghent & Stout 1981; Searle & Malpas 1980). Garnets occurring in the amphibolites are almandine-rich and unzoned, whereas the less abundant garnets of the metacherts interbedded with the greenschists are more grossular-rich and zoned with lower Mg and Fe and higher Mn towards the rims (Searle & Malpas 1980, Ghent & Stout 1981). Feldspars are mostly plagioclases, with up to 48% anorthite component in some amphibolites. Ghent & Stout (1981) report K-feldspar coexisting with albite from Wadi Tayin, whereas Searle & Malpas (1980) report knots of alkali feldspar in some amphibolites which they attribute to partial melting on a local scale. Clinopyroxenes are diopside-hedenbergite solid solutions, with

a very low Na^{M2} content (0.05) (Ghent & Stout 1981). Cordierite + sillimanite and cordierite + biotite were reported from pelitic amphibolites in the northern Oman Mountains (Bucher *et al.* 1988), but no orthopyroxene or K-feldspar + sillimanite-bearing assemblages have been found. Biotite occurs in the greenschists and some amphibolites, and becomes more reddish-brown (higher in Ti?) with increasing grade (Searle & Malpas 1980).

P−T conditions of metamorphism and P−T evolution. Ghent & Stout (1981) and Searle & Malpas (1980) estimated the metamorphic temperatures of the amphibolites at 775−865°C based on Fe−Mg exchange between garnet and clinopyroxene geothermometry calibrated by Ellis & Green (1979). Ghent & Stout (1981) estimated the maximum metamorphic pressure at 6 kbar using the jadeite content of clinopyroxene coexisting with plagioclase. However, this pressure estimate is fraught with uncertainties arising from the post-amphibolite facies albitization of plagioclase and the very low jadeite content of the clinopyroxene. Peak metamorphic temperatures of the greenschists of Wadi Tayin were estimated at 400°C based on pertinent phase equilibria at 2 kbar (Ghent & Stout 1981). The greenschist assemblages do not allow for the estimation of metamorphic pressures although the occurrence of crossite in some metabasaltic rocks from the Dibba zone (Fig. 1) suggests that *P* may have exceeded 4 kbar (reaction line 6, Fig. 3; Maruyama *et al.* 1986). A detailed petrological investigation of the crossite-bearing assemblages is necessary before pressures can be confidently calculated.

The available petrologic data is not sufficient

Table 1. *Mineral assemblages of the metamorphic aureole*

	Protolith	Assemblage	Reference
Amphibolites	mafic	Hb-Cpx-Plag-Ilm-Gt±Bt±Mus ±Ep±Sph±Qz	Bucher *et al.* (1988) Searle & Malpas (1980) Ghent & Stout (1981)
	pelitic	Crd-Sill Crd-Bt	Bucher *et al.* (1988)
	calcareous	Fo-Clinohum-Cc-Sp Di-Fo-Cc Wo-Di-Gt-Cc	Bucher *et al.* (1988)
Greenschists	mafic	Act-Chl-Ep-Ab-Qz-Bt-Mus ±Gt±Hb?	Searle & Malpas (1980) Ghent & Stout (1981) Bucher *et al.* (1988)
	cherts	Qz-Pm-Cc-Ilm±Act±Chl±Mus	El-Shazly, unpublished
	quartzofeldspathic	Bt-Chl-Mus-Ab-Qz	Bucher *et al.* (1988)

Abbreviations: Ab, albite; Act, actinolite; Bt, biotite; Cc, Calcite; Chl, chlorite, Clinohum, clinohumite; Cpx, clinopyroxene: Crd, cordierite; Di, diopside; Ep, epidote; Gt, garnet; Hb, hornblende; Ilm, ilmenite; Mus, muscovite; Plag, plagioclase; Pm, piedmontite; Qz, quartz; Sph, sphene; Sp, spinel; Wo, wollastonite.

to accurately reconstruct the $P-T$ path for the metamorphic sole rocks. A speculative $P-T$ path for the amphibolites is herein proposed based on mineralogical data and the tectonic evolution of these rocks as proposed by Coleman (1981) and Ghent & Stout (1981). The albitization of plagioclase and the zoning of amphiboles in the mafic amphibolites indicate that they have been affected by a later stage of epidote—amphibolite to greenschist facies metamorphism. The development of blue—green amphibole rims on earlier brown cores suggests that the amphibolites may have undergone increased pressure or isobaric cooling during their retrogression to greenschist facies conditions. A small increase in pressure during retrogression may have resulted from shear stress induced by the gliding of the detached ophiolitic slab onto the amphibolites in the underthrust oceanic crust prior to its emplacement on the continental margin. The wedge shaped nature of the detached slab may also account for the slight increase of pressure incurred upon the subophiolitic amphibolites as the ophiolitic slab advanced towards the continental margin. An increase in pressure after peak metamorphic temperatures were attained is also consistent with the thermal model of Thompson & Ridley (1987, p. 29) for thrusting in high heat flow regimes where the heat source overlies the thrust.

Although the metamorphic pressures of the amphibolites and underlying greenschists are poorly constrained, the occurrence of cordierite in the amphibolites and crossite in the greenschists suggests that the latter formed at comparable or perhaps higher pressures than those of the amphibolites. Fig 3 shows the peak $P-T$ conditions of the amphibolites (Am) and greenschists (GS) as well as two possible $P-T$ paths for the amphibolites. Path 'A' might have been followed if retrogression of the amphibolites to greenschist facies conditions coincided temporally and spatially with the formation of the underlying greenschists. Path 'B' is a possible path if the retrogression of the amphibolites and the formation of the underlying greenschist facies metamorphics were two unrelated discrete events.

High P/T metamorphism

Geologic setting

The high P/T metamorphic rocks are restricted to the Saih Hatat window in NE Oman, where characteristic mineral assemblages occur in a variety of mafic, pelitic and calcareous units that occupy different structural levels within the

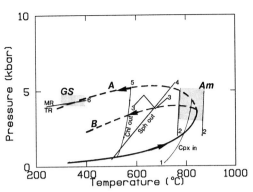

Fig. 3. $P-T$ evolution of the amphibolites in the subophiolitic metamorphic aureole. Stippled areas show the estimated $P-T$ conditions for the amphibolites (Am) and greenschists (GS). Path A is a speculative retrogressive path for the amphibolites assuming their retrogression to greenschist facies conditions coincides spatially and temporally with the greenschist facies metamorphism that took place beneath these amphibolites. Path B shows the possible evolution of the amphibolites in a situation where their retrogression is unrelated to the formation of the underlying greenschists. *Reactions*: 1, First appearance of clinopyroxenes in metabasalts (Spear 1981); 2, Range of peak metamorphic temperature for the amphibolites calculated using the garnet-clinopyroxene geothermometer of Ellis & Green (1979) from K_D^{Fe-Mg} values reported by Searle & Malpas (1980) and Ghent & Stout (1981); 3, Upper P stability limit of cordierite in 'most common pelite compositions' (Thompson 1976); 4, Upper T stability limit of sphene in metabasalts (Spear 1981); 5, Upper T stability limit of chlorite in a basaltic system (Liou *et al.* 1974); 6, The reaction: epidote + magnesioriebeckite (MR) + chlorite + quartz = tremolite (Tr) + albite + hematite + vapour (Maruyama *et al.* 1986).

continental margin sequence (Fig. 2; Le Metour *et al.* 1986). The Saih Hatat area is a structural dome flanked by the ophiolite and the underlying Hawasina sediments on the north and south. It exposes folded and metamorphosed pre-Permian and Permian basement and continental shelf deposits overlain by Mesozoic shelf carbonates in thrust contact with the overlying Hawasina sediments and the Semail ophiolite (Fig. 2). The Saih Hatat dome is one of the most complex orogenic culminations in Oman, where the stratigraphy has been complicated by several phases of folding, thrusting and normal faulting related to the ophiolite emplacement or later extensional events characteristic of culmination collapse (Hanna 1986; Searle 1985; Dewey 1988; Mann & Hanna 1990). In order to facilitate our discussion of metamorphism in

Saih Hatat, we have subdivided this area into
three regions that are separated by thrusts
mapped by Le Metour *et al.* (1986) (Fig. 2).
Each of these regions seems to have had a
distinct tectonometamorphic evolution, although a common history at some stage between
some of these regions cannot be ruled out.

Regions I and II consist of stacks of thrust
sheets and cover duplexes (Hanna 1986). In
northern Saih Hatat, these regions correspond
to the 'Muscat nappes' of Michard (1983), or
structural zones A and B of Mann & Hanna
(1990). They occupy an 'internal' position within
the Oman Mountains following the Alpine
terminology (Michard 1983). Figure 4 shows a
field view of the thrust separating regions II and
III in northern Saih Hatat.

Region I consists of unmetamorphosed Hawasina sediments and the Haybi Complex
melange thrust onto lawsonite chlorite schists,
metacherts, quartz-mica schists, calcareous
schists and carpholite-bearing metasediments
which unconformably overlie Mesozoic shelf
carbonates. Le Metour *et al.* (1986) mapped the
lawsonite chlorite schists and carpholite-bearing
metasediments of Ruwi & Quriyat (Fig. 2) as
Muti Formation; a Turonian to Campanian unit
representing the transition from a passive margin to a foreland basin (Robertson 1987a,b).
Clastic debris in the Muti Formation was derived
from the erosion of the advancing Hawasina
thrust sheets during the early stages of ophiolite
emplacement, a conclusion supported by the
occurrence of blocks of serpentinite, marble,
mafics and talc tremolite schists in the Muti unit
of Ruwi. The foliation in these blocks coincides
with that of the enclosing schists and metasediments. Region II consists of basement and cover

Fig. 4. The thrust separating the Permian to
Cretaceous shelf carbonates and interbedded
metabasalts of region II from the basement and
Permian deposits of region III. View looking west,
Wadi Meeh, Saih Hatat.

duplexes that imbricate and displace the Hajar
SuperGroup carbonates and basement sediments (Figs 2 & 4; Hanna 1986; Mann & Hanna
1990). High P/T metamorphism in this region is
manifested by crossite-bearing mafic volcanics
and carpholite-bearing metasediments contained within the basement and shelf deposits.
Region III is a structurally coherent high P/T
metamorphic terrain that has undergone the
most intense deformation and highest grade of
metamorphism. It consists of interbedded calcareous, quartzofeldspathic, mafic and Fe-rich
pelitic schists which represent the metamorphosed Permian Saiq formation (Le Metour *et
al.* 1986). The metamorphic grade decreases
from east to west where eclogites and garnet-
bearing blueschists exposed at As-Sifah grade
into crossite epidote schists that crop out from
Wadi Hulw to Wadi Meeh (Fig. 2). These units
are strongly folded with the recumbent fold
axes trending SW (Le Metour *et al.* 1986).
Boudier *et al.* (1985) report a SW-trending lineation for glaucophane which they attribute to
SW-directed thrusting. Eclogites, which are
restricted to the As-Sifah area, occur as small
pods or boudins (~25 cm in diametre) within
mafic and pelitic garnet-bearing blueschists (Fig.
5) or along the contact between the mafic and
calcareous schists. The petrology, mineral
chemistry and $P–T$ conditions of the high P/T
metamorphic rocks will be discussed in the
following section for each region separately.
Table 2 lists the mineral assemblages of the
metamorphic rocks of regions I and II. All of
the minerals discussed in the following sections
were analysed by the electron microprobe.
Representative mineral analyses and analytical
techniques will be published elsewhere (El-
Shazly *et al.* 1990) and are available from the
Geological Society Library, Burlington House,
Piccadilly, London, and the British Library Do-
cument Supply Centre, Boston Spa, Wetherly,
W. Yorks, UK, as Supplementary Publication
No SUP 18062 (15 pp).

Region I

Petrology and mineral chemistry. The lawsonite
chlorite schists of Ruwi (Fig. 2) are characterized by a nematoblastic foliation defined by
fine- to medium-grained porphyroblasts of
lawsonite that range in modal content from 20–
45%. The matrix consists of a mixture of very
fine-grained quartz and chlorite (pycnochlorite–
ripidolite). Calcite is a minor phase in some
samples. The interbedded carpholite-bearing
metasediments contain fine to medium grained
bow-tie shaped carpholite porphyroblasts that

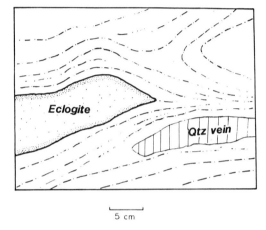

Fig. 5. A granoblastic eclogite pod in the foliated mafic and pelitic blueschists; As-Sifah (Zone C, region III).

constitute up to 40% of the rock mode. They contain abundant inclusions of quartz and in some samples pseudomorphs of amorphous iron oxides after stilpnomelane?. The ferrocarpholites contain 22−35% of the Mg-endmember and less than 1% Mn-carpholite. They have very thin inclusion-free rims that are slightly enriched in Fe. The matrix consists of very fine-grained quartz, chlorite (ripidolite) and illite. Calcite, paragonite and sphene occur in a few samples. The average K_D^{Fe-Mg} between carpholite and chlorite pairs in contact (Fe/Mg$_{car}$) (Fe/Mg$_{chl}$), is 1.3. Goffé *et al.* (1988) reported kaolinite and pyrophyllite in the carpholite-bearing metasediments of Ruwi and Yiti respectively (Fig. 2). We have only found halloysite in one sample (R-1) and believe that it may have formed as a result of post-metamorphic alteration.

P−T conditions of metamorphism of Region I.
Metamorphic $P−T$ conditions of the lawsonite chlorite schists and carpholite-bearing metasediments from Ruwi and Quriyat of region I can be

constrained by the maximum T and minimum P stability limits of lawsonite (curves 9, Fig. 6; Liou 1971; Chatterjee 1976) and the reaction ferrocarpholite = ferrochloritoid + quartz + vapour (curve 5, Fig. 6; calculated with THERMOCALC; Powell & Holland 1988). The occurrence of pyrophyllite-bearing assemblages (Goffé *et al.* 1988) suggests that metamorphism took place within the stability field of pyrophyllite defined by reactions 7 and 3 (Fig. 6, calculated with GEOCALC; Berman *et al.* 1985, 1987; Perkins *et al.* 1986). These reactions constrain the metamorphic conditions between 310°C and 340°C and $P>3$ kbar (Fig. 6) assuming that $P_{H10} = P_{total}$. Goffé *et al.* (1988) also report 'magnesiocarpholite + kaolinite + oxides' rimming the Fe carpholite, and pseudomorphs of calcite after aragonite from the 'Jurassic and Cretaceous metapelites of Ruwi' respectively. These textures suggest that metamorphic pressures may have exceeded 7.5 kbar between 310 and 340°C (Fig. 6) based on the calcite−aragonite transition (line 1, Fig. 6) of Johannes & Puhan (1971).

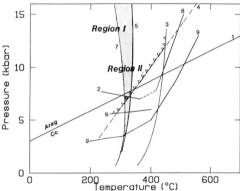

Fig. 6. $P−T$ conditions of metamorphism of regions I (stippled) and II (limited by the hachured line). *Reactions*: 1, Aragonite = calcite (Johannes and Puhan, 1971); 2, Sudoite + quartz = magnesiocarpholite (Schreyer, 1988); 3, Pyrophyllite = kyanite + quartz + vapour (calculated using GEOCALC, Berman *et al.* 1985, 1987; Perkins *et al.* 1986); 4, Crossite + actinolite = winchite (see text for explanation); 5, Ferrocarpholite = ferrochloritoid + quartz + vapour (calculated using THERMOCALC; Powell & Holland 1988; Holland, pers. comm. 1989); 6, Magnesiocarpholite (70%) + quartz = pyrophyllite + chlorite + vapour (Goffé 1982); 7, Kaolinite + quartz = pyrophyllite + vapour (calculated using GEOCALC, Berman *et al.* 1985, 1987; Perkins *et al.* 1986); 8, Magnesiocarpholite = kyanite + chlorite + quartz + vapour (Chopin & Schreyer 1983); 9, Upper T and lower P stability limits of lawsonite (Chatterjee, 1976; Liou 1971).

Table 2. *Mineral assemblages of the metamorphic rocks of regions I and II*

Region	protolith	Map unit[1]	Mineral assemblage	Locality	Reference
Region I	marl	Muti	Lw-Chl-Qz±Cc	Ruwi hills (1)	Michard *et al.* (1982) Goffé *et al.* (1988) El-Shazly *et al.* (1987)
	pelite	Muti	FeCar-Qz-Ill-Chl-Hall[2]-Pg	Ruwi hills (1)	This study
	pelite	Muti	FeCar-Qz-Cc-Ill-Chl±Sph	Ruwi hills (1)	This study
	serpentinite	Muti	Tc-Trem	Ruwi hills (1)	This study
	Al-rich pelite	Muti	Car-Kaol-Qz	Ruwi hills	Goffé *et al.* (1988)
	Al-rich pelite	Mahil?	Car-Pyr-Qz	Yitti (2)	Goffé *et al.* (1988)
	Al-rich pelite	Mahil?	MgCar-Pyr-Sud-FeCar	Al-Amarat	Goffé *et al.* (1988)
Region II	pelite	Hijam	MgCar-Qz-Ill-Hm	W. Aday (1)	This study
	pelite	Saiq?	Car-Pyr-Ctd	Quriyat (5)	Goffé *et al.* (1988)
	mafic intrusion	'Hatat amphibolites' & 'dolerites'.	Cr±Act±GAm-Ep-Ab-Chl±Ph-Sph+ Hm±Lx±Qz	Jahlut-Arqui road (6)	This study
	mafic or intermediate volcanics	Saiq	Cr-Act-Chl-Ab±Ep±Sph-Hm	W. Hulw to Bawshar (b)	Le Metour *et al.* (1986) This study

Abbreviations: Car, carpholite; Cr, crossite; Ctd, chloritoid; FeCar, ferrocarpholite; GAm, sodic-calcic amphibole; Hall, halloysite; Hm, hematite; Ill, illite; Kaol, kaolinite; Lx, leucoxene; MgCar, magnesiocarpholite; Pg, paragonite; Ph, phengite; Pyr, pyrophyllite; Sud, sudoite. See Fig. 2 for numbers in parentheses. Other abbreviations are as in table 1.

[1] Map units are after Le Metour *et al.* (1986).
[2] Weathering product.

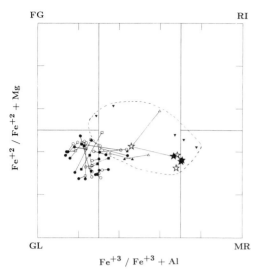

Fig. 7. Amphibole zoning patterns shown on the Miyashiro diagram. Lines connect core (solid symbols) to rim (open symbols) analyses of the same crystal. Broken line outlines the field of amphibole compositions of the crossite epidote schists of zone A, region III and the mafic rocks of region II. *Symbols*: Circles, Mafic blueschists, zones B and C; squares, pelitic blueschists, zone B; stars, Crossite-epidote schists, zone A; region III; inverted triangles, Porphyritic metabasites, triangles, Chlorite schists; Wadi Aday, region II. Gl = glaucophane, MR = magnesioriebeckite, FG = ferroglaucophane, RI = riebeckite.

Region II

Petrology and mineral chemistry. Evidence of high P/T metamorphism in this region is best seen in the mafic units and thin pelitic layers in carbonates. Metavolcanics interbedded with the Permian carbonates (Saiq Formation) of Saih Hatat (Fig. 2) are characterized by blastoporphyritic or relict volcaniclastic textures and contain the minerals: sodic amphiboles, actinolite, chlorite and albite $\pm$ epidote $\pm$ sphene $\pm$ hematite. Mafic intrusions in the pre-Permian basement (Fig. 2) also show evidence of high P/T metamorphism. They are characterized by a blasto-ophitic texture and contain the minerals: sodic amphibole, epidote, chlorite, albite, hematite $\pm$ actinolite $\pm$ sodic−calcic amphiboles $\pm$ phengite $\pm$ quartz $\pm$ sphene $\pm$ leucoxene in addition to relict igneous clinopyroxenes or amphiboles. The sodic amphiboles which occur as very fine-grained fibrous crystals are crossites or magnesioriebeckites (Fig. 7) that in many samples coexist with actinolite. The sodic-calcic amphibole species (usually

winchite) occurs as rims on crossite. Albite occurs as a fine-grained interstitial phase, as pseudomorphs after calcic plagioclase phenocrysts or fine to medium-grained rotated poikiloblasts. The carpholite-bearing metasediments of region II occur as thin layers within the basement and shelf carbonates. Carpholite (86−89% Mg end-member) constitutes up to 25% of some samples and occurs as fine- to medium-grained crystals arranged in bowtie shaped aggregates with abundant inclusions of hematite and quartz. These carpholite crystals have very thin clear rims that are slightly higher in Mg/(Mg + Fe). The matrix consists of quartz, illite and hematite.

P−T conditions of metamorphism of Region II. The coexistence of crossite and actinolite in the metabasites and the occurrence of magnesiocarpholite in the metasediments allow for a rough estimation of the metamorphic $P-T$ conditions of region II based on the stability fields of these phases shown in Fig. 6. The occurrence of magnesiocarpholite (89% Mg-end-member) suggests a minimum pressure greater than 5.5−6 kbar at temperatures between 250 and 400°C (line 6, Fig. 6, Goffé 1982). Application of the empirical geobarometer of Maruyama *et al.* (1986) to the crossite and actinolite-bearing porphyritic metabasites of Wadi Aday (Fig. 2) yields pressures of 4−6 kbar, which can only be considered minimum pressures owing to the absence of the entire buffered assemblage (sodic amphibole-actinolite-albite-chlorite-epidote-quartz). The persistence of coexisting crossite and actinolite and the development of winchite as rims on crossite indicate the incipient closure of the compositional gap between sodic and calcic amphiboles given by line 4 (Fig. 6). The empirical derivation of the $P-T$ conditions of the closure of this gap will be discussed in more detail in a later section. The occurrence of the assemblage pyrophyllite-chloritoid reported by Goffé *et al.* (1988) from several localities in region II (Fig. 2) suggests that metamorphism took place within the stability field of pyrophyllite given by reactions 7 and 3 (Fig. 6).

Region III

The mafic and Fe-rich pelitic units in the eastern part of region III near As-Sifah show clear evidence of this region having undergone the highest grade of metamorphism in the Saih Hatat window. The westward decrease in grade from eclogite to upper pumpellyite actinolite facies conditions and the structurally coherent nature of this region allow for its subdivision into metamorphic zones as pointed out by Le

Metour (1988). The mafic units of zone A consist of fine-grained, weakly foliated actinolite-bearing crossite epidote schists. Zone B is defined by the first appearance of glaucophane and garnet with the disappearance of pumpellyite in metabasites and the first appearance of chloritoid, glaucophane and garnet at the expense of chlorite and albite in metapelites. These well foliated rocks are coarser grained than zone A schists. Zone C, which consists of strongly folded garnet-bearing blueschists and eclogites, is defined by the first appearance of the garnet + clinopyroxene assemblage in metabasites, and garnet + paragonite + epidote + quartz in the rarely occurring metapelites. Although the eclogite pods occurring in this zone are volumetrically insignificant, their field relations with the interbedded garnet-bearing blueschists indicate that both rock types formed at similar $P-T$ conditions. A more detailed discussion of the petrological relations between the blueschists and eclogites of zone C will be presented elsewhere (El-Shazly *et al.* in review).

Petrology and mineral chemistry

Garnets of the eclogites and mafic blueschists of zones C and B occur as fine- to medium-grained subidioblastic crystals with a few inclusions of very fine-grained epidote, rutile and apatite in their cores or as medium-grained poikiloblasts with a helicitic texture defined by oriented inclusions of clinopyroxene, rutile, hematite and phengite. The fine-grained almandine garnets of the granoblastic eclogites and mafic blueschists are strongly zoned from Ca- and Mn-rich cores to Fe- and Mg-rich rims, whereas the medium-grained helicitic almandines are unzoned. Garnets occurring in the Fe-rich metapelites are coarse-grained unzoned almandines with inclusions of quartz, chloritoid and titanhematite giving rise to a fish-net texture which indicates rapid porphyroblast growth (Spry 1969).

Clinopyroxenes are restricted to the eclogites and high-grade mafic blueschists of zone C and to phengite−quartz−albite-bearing pods in zone B. In the eclogites of zone C, the clinopyroxenes occur as inclusions in garnet cores and rims (Cpx_I), fine-grained granular matrix crystals (Cpx_{II}) or fibrous overgrowths on matrix clinopyroxenes (Cpx_{III}). Most of the clinopyroxenes are chloromelanites according to the classification of Essene and Fyfe (1967) (Fig. 8) with a negligible amount of Ca-Tschermakite component. Within the same eclogite sample, Cpx_I crystals are more acmitic than Cpx_{II} and are often zoned towards more jadeitic rims.

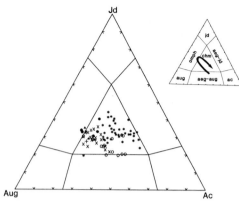

Fig. 8. Pyroxene compositions plotted on the Jadeite (Jd)−Augite (Aug)−Acmite (Ac) ternary diagram of Essene & Fyfe (1967). Inset shows the compositional evolution of the clinopyroxenes from inclusions in garnet cores to rims of matrix crystals (see text for explanation). aug, sodic augite; ac, impure acmite; jd, impure jadeite; aeg−aug, aegerine−augite; omph, omphacite; aeg−jd, aegerine−jadeite; chm, chloromelanite. ○ Inclusions in garnet (Cpx_I), As-Sifah foliated eclogites; ●, Cores of matrix Cpx crystals, As-Sifah eclogites; ×, Matrix clinopyroxene rims (Cpx_{II}), As-Sifah eclogites; *, Matrix clinopyroxene (Cpx_{II}), mafic blueschists, As-Sifah; ▲, Fracture-filling variety (Cpx_{IIb}, along fractures in garnet), As-Sifah eclogites; +, Fibrous clinopyroxene (Cpx_{III}), As-Sifah eclogites.

Cpx_I inclusions in garnet cores are also more acmitic and less jadeitic than inclusions in the rims of the same crystals. Cpx_{II} in most samples is zoned from jadeite-rich cores towards more diopside or acmite-rich rims. The evolutionary change in clinopyroxene composition is shown by an arrow on the inset of Fig. 8.

The eclogites and blueschists of zones C and B contain sodic and sodic−calcic amphiboles. The sodic amphioboles are complexly zoned from glaucophane-rich cores towards more Fe-rich rims (ferro-glaucophane or crossite; Fig. 7). Sodic−calcic amphiboles occur as outermost rims on glaucophane or crossite, as inclusions in garnet rims of some eclogites or as fine-grained fibrous crystals intergrown with albite at the expense of Cpx_{II} and Cpx_{III}. Compositionally, they are winchites, barroisites or edenites according to the classification of Leake (1978). The crossite epidote schists of zone A contain three types of amphiboles: crossite, actinolite and winchite. Crossite and actinolite occur as discrete phases in textural equilibrium whereas winchite occurs as thin rims on crossite.

Epidote (pistacite = $22-33\%$) occurs as very fine-grained inclusions in garnets, granular to columnar crystals in the matrix of mafic and pelitic blueschists or in granular clusters with hematite and phengite that pseudomorph garnet. It is unzoned or very weakly zoned with the $Fe^{3+}/(Fe^{3+} + Al)$ ratio either increasing or decreasing from core to rim.

Phengite is the most common mica in all samples. It occurs as: (1) very fine-grained inclusions in garnet, (2) fine to medium-grained oriented crystals in textural equilibrium with garnet and Cpx_{II} or sodic amphibole and epidote, and (3) coarse-grained unoriented crystals forming along garnet cracks and rims. Based on a stoichiometry of 11 oxygen atoms, the Si content of phengite ranges from 3.3 to 3.7 in the eclogites and blueschists of zones C and B and from 3.01 to 3.5 atoms/formula unit in the crossite epidote schists of zone A. The medium-grained phengites of the pelitic blueschists of zone B are zoned with the Si content decreasing from core to rim. Paragonite occurs as a minor phase in a few eclogite samples but constitutes up to 10% of some metapelites of zones B and C, where it forms at the expense of glaucophane and chloritoid. Biotite is a minor constituent of some mafic schists from zones A, B and C. It occurs as very fine- to fine-grained crystals forming at the expense of phengite or along garnet rims. Chlorite is a ubiquitous phase that forms at the expense of garnet, biotite or glaucophane in zones B and C or is intergrown with actinolite and crossite in zone A. Its modal content in the metabasites decreases from zones A to C.

Chloritoid is restricted to the pelitic blueschists of zones B and C where it occurs as fine-grained crystals commonly included in garnet. Its $Fe^{2+}/(Fe^{2+} + Mg)$ ratio ranges from 0.75 to 0.77 while its calculated Fe^{3+} content is 0.15–0.22 based on a stoichiometry of 12 oxygen atoms.

Albite constitutes up to 40% of some mafic schists from zone A but is a minor phase formed during retrogression of the blueschists and eclogites of zones B and C. Rutile is the most common accessory phase in the eclogites and blueschists of zones C and B but was not found in the crossite epidote schists of zone A, where sphene is the predominant Ti-bearing phase.

$P-T$ conditions of metamorphism

Metamorphic temperatures of the eclogites and garnet-bearing blueschists of zone C can be determined by Fe–Mg exchange geothermometry between garnet and clinopyroxene (e.g. Ellis & Green 1979). Application of the garnet-clinopyroxene geothermometer of Ellis & Green (1979) to rim pairs in the eclogites of As-Sifah yields temperatures ranging from 440 to 585°C at 10 kbar (lines 12, Fig. 9). This wide temperature range in probably due to the failure of garnet and clinopyroxene to equilibrate at the thermal peak in all samples and reflects the range over which these two phases crystallized in the different eclogite pods (El-Shazly et al., in review). Peak metamorphic temperatures are estimated at 500 to 585°C based on the reactions: glaucophane + epidote = garnet + clinopyroxene + paragonite and glaucophane + chloritoid = garnet + paragonite (reactions 10 and 9; Fig. 9). Minimum metamorphic pressures are estimated based on the jadeite content of clinopyroxene coexisting with quartz (line 1a; Fig. 9, Essene & Fyfe 1967; Newton & Smith 1967; El-Shazly 1987).

The blueschist outcrops of zone B do not contain any eclogite pods or retrograded eclogites. Their peak metamorphic temperatures could not have overstepped the reaction: glaucophane + epidote = garnet + clinopyroxene + paragonite (reaction 10, Fig. 9; Ridley 1984, Oh et al. 1988) but must have exceeded those defined by the breakdown of lawsonite in the presence of albite to zoisite and paragonite (reaction 6; Fig. 9). Their minimum pressure of metamorphism is estimated between 8 and 9.3 kbar at temperatures between 360 and 500°C respectively (Fig. 9) based on the jadeite content of clinopyroxene occurring in pods with quartz, phengite and retrograde albite (line 1b, Fig. 9).

The crossite epidote schists of zone A contain the assemblage: crossite, actinolite, albite, epidote, chlorite and quartz in some samples, which allows for the calculation of metamorphic pressures based on the Al_2O_3 content of sodic amphibole (Maruyama et al. 1986). This method yields pressures of 4.5–5.5 kbar (Fig. 9). The coexistence of crossite and actinolite in textural equilibrium and the occurrence of winchite rims on crossite indicate the incipient closure of the compositional gap between sodic and calcic amphiboles. Similar textural relations have been reported in type III metabasites of Cazadero, Franciscan Complex (Liou & Maruyama 1987) and the Aosta valley eclogites, Sesia Lanzo zone, western Alps (Reynard & Ballevre 1988), where P and T were estimated independently. These $P-T$ conditions are 7 ± 1 kbar, 270–317°C for the Franciscan type III metabasites (Maruyama & Liou 1988; Taylor & Coleman 1968) and 16 kbar, 500–550°C for the Aosta valley eclogites (Reynard & Ballevre 1988; Koons 1986). These $P-T$ estimates define the conditions of incipient closure of the

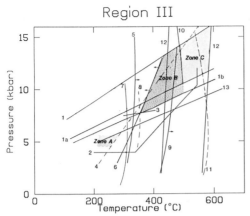

Fig. 9. $P-T$ conditions of metamorphism of zones A, B and C, region III. The small arrows on some of the reaction lines show the directions in which they will shift in $P-T$ space as extra components (e.g. Fe^{3+} or Mg) are introduced to the 'model systems'. *Reactions:* 1, jadeite + quartz = low albite (calculated using GEOCALC; Berman *et al.* 1985, 1987; Perkins *et al.* 1986). 1a, Cpx (Jd=41%) + quartz = low albite, zone C (El-Shazly 1987); 1b, Cpx (Jd=33%) + quartz = low albite, zone B (El-Shazly 1987); 2, glaucophane stability field of Maresch, (1977); 3, tremolite + chlorite + albite = epidote + glaucophane + quartz + vapour (Maruyama *et al.* 1986); 4, crossite + actinolite = winchite (see text for explanation); 5, ferrocarpholite = ferrochloritoid + quartz + vapour (calculated using THERMOCALC, Powell & Holland 1988; Holland, pers. comm. 1989), arrow shows the effect of introducing Mg to the system; 6, lawsonite + low albite = zoisite + paragonite + quartz + vapour (calculated using GEOCALC; Berman *et al.* 1985, 1987, Perkins *et al.* 1986), arrows show the effect of introducing Fe^3 into the system; 7, kaolinite + quartz = pyrophyllite + vapour (calculated using GEOCALC; Berman *et al.* 1985, 1987, Perkins *et al.* 1986); 8, low temperature stability limit of ferrochloritoid as estimated by Chopin & Schreyer (1983); 9, ferroglaucophane + ferrochloritoid = almandine + paragonite + vapour (calculated using THERMOCALC; Powell & Holland, 1988; Holland, pers. comm. 1989), arrow shows the effect of introducing Mg to the system; 10, glaucophane + clinozoisite = garnet + omphacite + paragonite + quartz + vapour (Oh *et al.* 1988); 11, the metastable reaction: clinozoisite + daphnite = almandine + grossular + vapour (calculated using THERMOCALC, Holland, pers. comm. 1989); 12, Garnet-clinopyroxene K_D values (31.46 and 14.99 respectively), plotted as a function of P and T (according to the calibration of Ellis & Green 1979); 13, phengite geobarometer for an isopleth of Si = 3.3 (Massone & Schreyer 1987).

miscibility gap between sodic and calcic amphiboles, or the reaction crossite + actinolite = winchite (line 4; Fig. 9). Extrapolating this line to the pressures estimated for the crossite epidote schists of zone A, region III (4.5–5.5 kbar) constrains their peak temperatures at about 280°C. These estimates are consistent with the occurrence of the assemblage pumpellyite, epidote, albite, chlorite and phengite in a thin metabasaltic layer inter-bedded with the crossite epidote schists in Wadi Hulw.

$P-T$ evolution of the high P/T metamorphic rocks of regions I, II and III

Regions I, II and III were metamorphosed at different $P-T$ conditions, and probably fol-lowed different $P-T$ paths prior to their juxtaposition during the final stages of ophiolite emplacement. The available petrological data can only be used to reconstruct the $P-T$ paths of the high P/T metamorphic rocks of region III. The hypothetical $P-T$ paths proposed for regions I and II (Fig. 10) are based on the inferred tectonic evolution of these thrust piles and the models of England & Thompson (1984) and Thompson & Ridley (1987).

The available data are insufficient to constrain the prograde $P-T$ path of the lawsonite chlorite schists and carpholite-bearing metasediments of region I. The formation of magnesiocarpholite at the expense of ferrocarpholite (Goffé *et al.* 1988) suggests an increase in P (Chopin & Schreyer 1983; Schreyer 1988). The retrograde path has to enter the calcite stability field at T

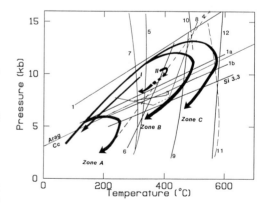

Fig. 10. $P-T$ of the high P/T rocks of regions I, II and III (zones A, B and C). Reactions 1,1a,1b,3,4,5,6,7,9,10,11 and 12 are as in Fig. 9. 8 outlines the stability field of Mg-carpholite (Fig. 6). Arag, aragonite; Cc, calcite. 'Si 3.3' is line 13, Fig. 9.

between 125 and 175°C in order to preserve aragonite or the pseudomorphs after aragonite reported by Goffé *et al.* (1988) (Carlson & Rosenfeld 1981).

The occurrence of winchite rims on crossite in the metamorphosed mafic volcanics and intrusives of region II suggests that these rocks have undergone an increase in temperature at some stage during their metamorphic evolution (Laird & Albee 1981; Holland & Richardson 1979). The absence of rims of sodic–calcic or sodic amphibole on actinolite indicates that these rocks have not undergone an increase in pressure during cooling characteristic of the 'counterclockwise $P-T$ paths' suggested by Goffé *et al.* (1988). The occurrence of chloritoid inclusions in carpholite in region II west of Quriyat (Fig. 2) can be explained by the $P-T$ path crossing the reaction carpholite = chloritoid + quartz + vapour (reaction 5; Fig. 6) during retrogression.

Textural relations and mineral zoning patterns in the mafic and pelitic units of the three metamorphic zones of region III indicate that these rocks followed a $P-T$ path of increasing P and T, followed by increasing T and decreasing P, and a final stage of retrogression (decreasing P and T; Fig. 10). The occurrence of crossite rimmed by winchite in zone A and the absence of sodic or sodic–calcic amphiboles rimming actinolite support such paths. Peak P and T estimates for the crossite epidote schists of this zone further constrain its $P-T$ path (Fig. 10). Garnets in zone B and C blueschists probably crystallized at the expense of chlorite during a stage of increasing temperature as indicated by their growth zoning patterns (Black 1973; Raheim & Green 1975; Raheim 1975; Tracy 1982). The garnet + clinopyroxene assemblage of the eclogites formed at the expense of glaucophane and epidote also during a stage of increasing T (reaction 10, Figs 9 & 10; Ridley 1984; Oh *et al.* 1988). The early stages of garnet crystal growth in the eclogites were also accompanied by an increase in pressure, indicated by the higher jadeite content of clinopyroxene inclusions in garnet rims compared to inclusions in the cores, the zoning of these inclusions towards higher jadeite at rims and by the higher jadeite content of the matrix clinopyroxenes (Cpx_{II}) compared to Cpx_I. The zoning of Cpx_{II} from jadeite-rich cores to acmite-rich rims suggests their crystallization under conditions of increasing T and/or decreasing P. The ubiquitous occurrence of quartz in the matrix and as inclusions in garnet and the decrease in the modal content of albite in the mafic rocks from zones A to C as clinopyroxene

appears (Table 3) suggest that the clinopyroxene crystallization took place at the expense of albite and support our contention that the compositional evolution of clinopyroxenes was a function of P and T. The stage of increasing T and decreasing P is marked by the development of sodic–calcic amphibole rims on glaucophane and crossite. Crystallization of garnet continued at this stage as evidenced by the occurrence of edenitic and sodic–calcic amphibole inclusions

Table 3. *Mineralogy for mafic and pelitic rocks from region III*

	Mafic rocks		
	Zone A	Zone B	Zone C
Pumpellyite	--------------		
Chlorite	———————— R ——— ---- R ----		
Epidote	———————————————		
Na-amphibole	———————————————		
Actinolite	————————— - -		
Winchite	-------------- ———————— --------------		
Barroisite			-----
Hornblende[1]			-- Tr --
Garnet		- -	
Clinopyroxene		- - - ————————	
Phengite	-------------- -------------- --------------		
Paragonite		-- ---- Tr ----	
Biotite	---- Tr ----	---- Tr ----	---- Tr ----
Albite	——————————— ---- R ----		
Quartz	———————————————		
Rutile	———————————————		
Titanite	———————— -------------- ---R---		
Hematite	———————————————		

	Pelitic rocks		
	Zone A	Zone B	Zone C
Phengite	———————————————		
Chlorite	———————————— ---- R ----		
Chloritoid		———— ----	
Paragonite		---- ————————	
Garnet		---- ————————	
Glaucophane	———————————————		
Epidote	----- ? -----	---- Tr ----	---- Tr----
Albite	————————		
Quartz	———————————————		
Biotite		---- Tr ----	---- Tr ----
Kyanite		?	----- ? -----
Rutile	———————————————		
Hematite	———————————————		

——, ubiquitous or very common phase; ---, common or rare phase; Tr, traces: R, retrograde phase phase

[1] Term includes all calcic and subcalcic amphiboles exclusive of actinolite

in the rims of some of these garnets. The zoning of medium-grained phengites in the metapelites of zones B and C suggests crystal growth during decreasing pressure (Velde 1967; Massone & Schreyer 1987). The formation of biotite at the expense of phengite in the metabasites also suggests a similar decrease in P, either at increasing or decreasing T (Powell & Evans 1983; Massone & Schreyer 1987; Bucher-Nurminen 1987). The retrogression of the eclogites and blueschists of zones C and B is marked by the formation of winchite and albite at the expense of Cpx_{II} and Cpx_{III}, the breakdown of garnet to epidote + chlorite + hematite (e.g. metastable reaction 11; Figs 9 & 10) and the chloritization of biotite. Reactions 9 and 10, which define the boundary between zones B and C for metapelites and metabasites respectively constrain the maximum temperatures of metamorphism of zone B (Fig. 9). Figure 10 shows the $P-T$ paths of the high P/T metamorphic rocks of regions I, II and III. A detailed discussion of phase relations and mineral reactions will be given elsewhere (El-Shazly et al. in review).

Discussion of P–T paths

The $P-T$ paths that we propose for region III are different from the 'counterclockwise' $P-T$ paths of Goffé et al. (1988) which they explained by the tectonic overloading and burial of an extended and heated continental crust beneath the wedge-shaped obducted ophiolite. Many of their conclusions are based on pseudomorphs after carpholite, or inclusions of chloritoid in carpholite which could have formed upon retrogression in a 'clockwise' $P-T$ loop (Fig. 9). Goffé et al. (1988) argue that the absence of pseudomorphs after lawsonite in the As-Sifah mafic blueschists forces the prograde path of these rocks to pass through pressures lower than the lawsonite stability field (reaction lines 9, Fig. 6). However, the appearance of lawsonite as apposed to epidote is a function of bulk rock composition (Maruyama et al. 1986) and oxygen fugacity (Liou, pers. comm. 1986) as well as $P-T$ conditions. The preservation of pseudomorphs after lawsonite will probably depend on reaction kinetics, temperature overstep and fluid availability. Although pseudomorphs after lawsonite were reported from the Tauern window eclogites, eastern Alps (Selverstone & Spear 1985), they have not been observed in other high P/T terrains with 'clockwise' $P-T$ paths that pass through the lawsonite stability field (e.g. Sunnfjord eclogites, W. Norway, Krogh 1982, Sanbagawa belt, Banno 1986). The couterclockwise $P-T$ paths of Goffé et al. (1988)

cannot account for the textural and mineralogical evidence presented in the previous sections, which include the zoning patterns of garnets, amphiboles and phengite, inclusions of chloritoid in garnet, and the breakdown of phengite to biotite, and garnet to epidote and chlorite. Only the zoning patterns of clinopyroxenes are equally well accounted for by a counterclockwise $P-T$ path. Goffé et al. (1988) construct a 'clockwise' $P-T$ path for the 'Al-Amarat nappe' (south of Ruwi), but their tectonic model does not explain how this nappe has had a path very different from the rest of the Muscat nappes. Furthermore, the evidence for a thin heated continental crust is based on the occurrence of pre-Permian to Permian intrusives and volcanics in the basement and it is very unlikely that their thermal effect would have continued until the Early Cretaceous.

Sequence of events and tectonic evolution

The tectonic evolution of the Saih Hatat area can be reconstructed based on the recent structural and geochronological studies of Lanphere (1981), Lippard (1983), Le Metour (1988) and Montigny et al. (1988). K–Ar and Ar^{39}/Ar^{40} dating of phengites from the eclogites and blueschists of As-Sifah (Region III, zone C) yields ages between 80 and 112 Ma (Lippard 1983; Montigny et al. 1988). Phengites from the pelitic blueschists always yield the oldest ages (107–112 Ma) which may be due to their coarser-grained nature and higher capability of Ar retention compared to the phengites of the metabasites. Montigny et al. (1988) also report a 131 Ma age on phengite from an eclogite sample, a questionable age owing to the fact that its Ar^{39}/Ar^{40} step heating spectrum does not satisfy the criteria established by Dalrymple & Lanphere (1974) for successful age plateaux. The reported phengite ages are only minimum or cooling ages since peak metamorphic temperatures of zone, C, region III (500–585°C) are higher than the blocking temperatures of phengite (314–450°C; Sisson & Onstott 1986). These ages do not record the time at which peak pressures were attained since the zoning patterns of phengite indicate their crystallization during a stage of decreasing pressure. Since some of these ages are older than the age of ophiolite emplacement and in some cases exceed the age of oceanic crust generation (Fig. 11), it can be inferred that high P/T metamorphism began in the early Cretaceous, provided that the dated minerals did not contain any excess Ar.

Our synthesis of the tectonic evolution of the

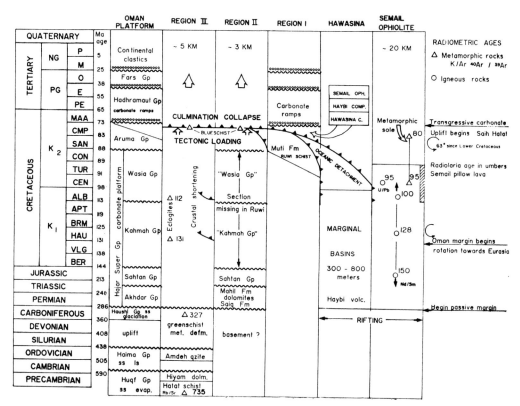

Fig. 11. The evolution of the Semail ophiolite, Hawasina sediments and the continental margin of Oman in the Saih Hatat area in space and time. See text for details.

Saih Hatat area is based on the available ages for the various high P/T metamorphic rocks and the tectonostratigraphic constraints summarized in Fig. 11. We believe that the blueschists and eclogites of region III formed in an east-dipping 'A-type subduction zone' (Bally 1975; Hodges *et al.* 1982) that developed in the lower Cretaceous. This crustal thickening event may have resulted from the northeastward rotation of Africa towards Eurasia coupled with the northward movement of a fragment of Gondwanaland causing transpression along the SE margin of Oman (Owen 1983; Dercourt *et al.* 1986; Shackelton & Ries 1988; Mountain & Prell 1990). This 'subduction' resulted in the 'tectonic burial' of zone C (region III) to a minimum depth of 30 km, whereas zones B and A were not as deeply 'subducted' (Fig. 12a).

The generation of the Semail oceanic crust took place along a NW–SE striking ridge (Boudier *et al.* 1988) between 150 and 93.5 Ma according to U–Pb dating of zircons from the ophiolitic plagiogranites (Tilton *et al.* 1981), Sm–Nd isochrons of cumulate gabbros

(McCulloch *et al.* 1981) and biostratigraphic dating of the sediments overlying the pillow lavas (Tippit *et al.* 1981), while eastward A-type subduction in the continental margin continued. The collapse of the spreading centre followed by intraoceanic detachment (Fig. 12b) took place at least $100-90$ Ma as suggested by K–Ar and Ar^{39}/Ar^{40} total fusion ages of the amphibolites in the metamorphic sole (Lanphere 1981, Montigny *et al.* 1988). This detachment must have taken place close to the spreading centre where temperatures were sufficiently high to metamorphose the sediments and volcanics of the Hawasina basin to upper amphibolite facies conditions (Ghent & Stout 1981). Heat transfer from the detached overriding ophiolitic slab to the underlying sediments and volcanics of the Hawasina basin took place mainly by conduction in a dynamic situation (Spray 1984) and possibly with the development of an 'ironing board effect' where heated sediments and volcanics are continuously being heated by the overthrust moving slab (Smith 1988). As the ophiolitic slab and the amphibolites welded to its base ad-

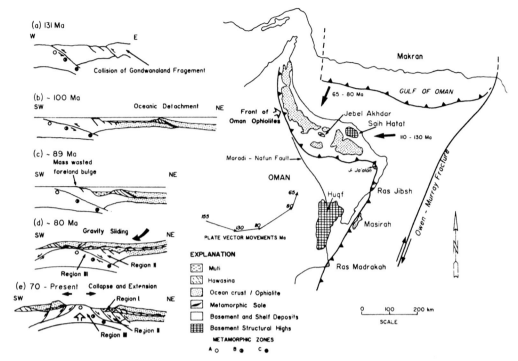

Fig. 12. Tectonic map and stages of evolution of the Oman continental margin synthesized from the data and models of Searle (1985); Lippard *et al.* (1986); Hanna (1986); Dercourt *et al.* (1986); Robertson (1987a,b); Goffe *et al.* (1988); Shackelton & Ries (1988) and Mountain & Prell (1990). Plate vector movements are after Dercourt *et al.* (1986). Cross sections are not to scale. A, B and C represent the relative depths to which the metamorphic zones of region III were buried. (a) A-type subduction (crustal thickening) and high P/T metamorphism in the basement and shelf deposits resulting from a change in plate motion between Africa and Eurasia in the early Cretaceous. (b) Intraoceanic detachment at the collapsed spreading center and imbrication of the Hawasina sediments. (c) Mass wasting of a foreland bulge and subsequent deposition of Muti sediments in a foredeep that formed in response to the impingement of the ophiolite on the northern continental margin of Oman. (d) Gravity sliding of the ophiolite and tectonic overloading of the northern continental margin resulting in the high P/T metamorphism of the Muti Formation and underlying basement and shelf deposits of regions I and II. (e) Extensional collapse of the Oman orogenic culmination caused by isostatic instability resulting in uplift and concomitant erosion. Preservation and exposure of the blueschists is the result of erosion and faulting.

vanced towards the continental margin by gravity sliding, they cooled and metamorphosed underlying sediments and volcanics to greenschist facies conditions. Ar^{39}/Ar^{40} total rock fusion of phyllites and K–Ar dating of amphiboles from the greenschists yield ages of 97.5–70.8 Ma (Lanphere 1981; Montigny *et al.* 1988) for the greenschist facies metamorphic event. The advancing ophiolitic slab also imbricated and 'bulldozed' the Hawasina sediments in front of it. As the ophiolite approached the Oman continental margin, a flexural bulge developed at the northern edge of the margin (Robertson 1987a,b) probably in response to the ophiolite impingement on that margin and continued crustal thickening along the east-

dipping A-type 'subduction zone'. The cessation of crustal thickening later led to the collapse and mass wasting of the foreland bulge in the late Turonian and the subsequent deposition of flysch-type sediments in the foredeep to form members of the Muti Formation (Fig. 12c, Robertson 1987a,b). The tectonic overloading of the continental margin (and the Muti formation) by the obducted ophiolite in the Campanian led to the generation of cover duplexes and out of sequence thrusts (Searle 1985; Hanna 1986), the inland migration of the Muti foredeep as it evolved into a foreland basin (Robertson 1987a,b) and the high P/T metamorphism of the overloaded Muti sediments (region I) and basement and shelf deposits (region II, Fig.

12d). Extensional culmination collapse followed in the early Maastrichtean as manifested by backthrusting and normal faulting, which in some cases took place along pre-existing thrusts (Hanna 1986, Dewey 1988) and resulted in the exhumation of the various high P/T rocks possibly by a mechanism similar to that proposed by Platt (1986, 1987). Thick conglomerates derived from the basement and shelf units underlying the Maastrichtean limestones mark this stage of early uplift of the unstable tectonic pile covering the Saih Hatat area (Fig. 12e).

In the Maastrichtean and Tertiary, the continental margin was partially submerged resulting in carbonate deposition on top of the ophiolite and conglomerates. Interbedded gravels in the carbonate ramps surrounding the Saih Hatat window indicate continued uplift until the late Miocene. Further unroofing of the Saih Hatat dome continues to the present time with thick pediments forming on its flanks.

We should point out that some of the ages given for the greenschists of the metamorphic sole (70−79 Ma, Lanphere 1981) and the Ruwi schists of region I (95 Ma, Montigny *et al.* 1988) are inconsistent with our tectonic reconstruction. The former ages are too young for metamorphism to have taken place in the ocean and reflect either Ar loss or a greenschist facies metamorphic event that took place after the final emplacement of the ophiolite on land. The K−Ar age of 95 Ma given for white micas from the Ruwi schists is too old for the Muti Formation to have been their protolith and may be due to excess Ar in the system. Alternatively, the protolith of the Ruwi schists may have been Hawasina sediments that were trapped beneath the ophiolite and subsequently metamorphosed instead of being bulldozed in front of the advancing ophiolite.

Conclusions

Two distinct types of Cretaceous metamorphic rock suites in the Oman Mountains formed following different $P-T-$time trajectories and developed in three different tectonic situations. The present-day structural position of these metamorphic rocks is the result of their juxtaposition during ophiolite emplacement followed by extensional tectonics associated with culmination collapse.

The amphibolites of the ophiolitic metamorphic sole formed close to the spreading centre as a result of intraoceanic detachment and metamorphism of ocean floor sediments and volcanics by heat conduction from the detached slab in a dynamic situation. The amphibolites underwent almost isobaric cooling (or a slight increase in P) during their retrogression to epidote amphibolite and greenschist facies conditions. The underlying greenschists probably represent sediments and volcanics that were metamorphosed farther away from the spreading centre and welded to the base of the detached slab as it advanced towards the continental margin.

High P/T rocks occur at different structural levels within the continental margin basement and shelf deposits in three regions that exhibit discrete $P-T-$time histories. Metamorphism of the eclogites, blueschists and crossite epidote schists of region III took place within an A-type east-dipping subduction zone that may have been initiated by the counterclockwise rotation of Africa towards Eurasia and transpression of the eastern continental margin of Oman by (or its collision with) a fragment of Gondwanaland moving north. High P/T metamorphism of region III was a protracted event and is characterized by 'clockwise' $P-T$ paths typical of thrust belts where thrusting and deformation are followed by the attainment of peak temperatures (Thompson & Ridley 1987). The late Cretaceous tectonic overloading of the continental margin by the obducted ophiolite resulted in the imbrication of the margin and high P/T metamorphism of the 'internal thrust piles' (region I and II). Although the $P-T$ paths of those regions are not well constrained, it is reasonable to assume that they followed 'clockwise' $P-T$ paths characteristic of thrust belts. Later extensional deformation associated with culmination collapse exhumed the high P/T metamorphic rocks and produced the present-day 'condensed' or distorted configuration of the various metamorphic zones (A, B and C, region III).

The conclusions of this paper are only preliminary. More work is required in order to: (1) better constrain the $P-T$ evolution of the metamorphic sole rocks and establish the relationship between amphibolite and greenschist facies metamorphism; (2) establish the temporal relationships between the various metamorphic and deformational events through rigorous age dating and field mapping, and (3) determine metamorphic grade variations in region II and establish their relationships (if any) to those of region III, and region I. Further structural studies are necessary to establish the relationship between deformation and metamorphism and to furnish evidence to support an early collision of a Gondwanaland fragment with the eastern margin of Oman.

We are grateful to Professor J. G. Liou for his advice, encouragement and review of the manuscript. Long discussions with Drs. S. Hanna, S. Maruyama, M. Lanphere, E. Krogh and C. Oh and critical reviews by Drs. S. Bohlen, J. Dixon and M. Searle are gratefully acknowledged. Pre-prints provided by Dr. Warren Prell proved important to our tectonic synthesis. This study would not have been possible without the support of the Ministry of Petroleum and Minerals, Oman, particularly Mr. M. Kassim and Dr. H. El-Azry. Financial support for this study was provided through GSA penrose, Sigma Xi, PIF and McGee grants to El-Shazly and the School of Earth Sciences, Stanford University. AKE-S wishes to acknowledge the financial support of ITT in 1986–87.

References

BAILEY, E. H. 1981. Geologic map of the Muscat-Ibra area, Sultanate of Oman. *Journal of Geophysical Research*, **86**, B-4, pocket map.

BALLY, A. W. 1975. A geodynamic scenario for hydrocarbon occurrences. *Proceedings of World Petroleum Congress*, **9**, 33–44.

BANNO, S. 1986. The high pressure metamorphic belts of Japan: A review. In: EVANS, B. W. & BROWN, E. H. (eds). *Blueschists and eclogites*. Geological Society of America, Memoir **164**, 365–374.

BERMAN, R. G., BROWN, T. H. & GREENWOOD, H. J. 1985. An internally consistent thermodynamic data-base for minerals in the system $Na_2O-K_2O-CaO-MgO-FeO-Fe_2O_3-Al_2O_3-SiO_2-TiO_2-H_2O-CO_2$. *Atomic Energy of Canada Ltd. Technical Report*, **377**.

——, —— & PERKINS, E. H. 1987. *GEO-CALC, software for the calculation and display of pressure-temperature-composition phase diagrams*. University of British Columbia.

BLACK, P. M. 1973. Mineralogy of New Caledonian metamorphic rocks: Garnets from Ouegoa district. *Contributions to Mineralogy and Petrology*, **38**, 221–235.

BOUDIER, F., BOUCHEZ, J. L., NICOLAS, A., CANNAT, M., CEULLENEER, G., MISSERI, M. & MONTIGNY, R. 1985. Kinematics of oceanic thrusting in the Oman ophiolite: model of plate convergence. *Earth and Planetary Science Letters*, **75**, 215–222.

——, CEULLENEER, G. & NICOLAS, A. 1988. Shear zones, thrusts and related magmatism in the Oman ophiolite: Initiation of thrusting on an oceanic ridge. *Tectonophysics*, **51**, 275–296.

BROTHERS, R. N. & BLAKE, M. C. 1973. Tertiary plate tectonics and high pressure metamorphism in New Caledonia. *Tectonophysics*, **17**, 337–358.

BUCHER, J., KURZ, D., PETERS, T. J. STOESSEL, F. & ZIEGLER, U. 1988. The metamorphics below the Semail nappe in the northern Oman Mountains. *The Geology and Tectonics of the Oman Region; a discussion meeting. Edinburgh. Abstracts*, 12.

BUCHER-NURMINEN, K. 1987. The recalibration of the chlorite–biotite–muscovite geobarometer. *Contributions to Mineralogy and Petrology*, **96**, 519–522.

CARLSON, W. D. & ROSENFELD, J. L. 1981. Optical determination of topotactic aragonite–calcite growth kinetics: metamorphic implications. *Journal of Geology*, **89**, 615–638.

CHATTERJEE, N. D. 1976. Margarite stability and compatibility relations in the system $CaO-Al_2O_3-SiO_2-H_2O$. *American Mineralogist*, **61**, 699–709.

CHOPIN, C. & SCHREYER, W. 1983. Magnesiocarpholite and magnesiochloritoid: two index minerals of pelitic blueschists and their preliminary phase relations in the model system $MgO-Al_2O_3-SiO_2-H_2O$. *American Journal of Science*, **283-A**, 72–96.

COLEMAN, R. G. 1981. Tectonic setting for ophiolite obduction in Oman. *Journal of Geophysical Research*, **86**, B4, 2497–2508.

DALRYMPLE, G. B. & LANPHERE, M. A., 1974. $Ar^{40}/^{39}$ age spectra of some undisturbed terrestial samples. *Geochimica et cosmochimica acta*, **38**, 715–738.

DERCOURT, J., ZONENSHAIN, L. P., RICOU, L. E., KAZMIN, V. G., LE PICHON, X., KNIPPER, A. L., GRANDJACQUET, C., SBORTSHIKOV, J. M., GEYSSANT, J., LEPURIER, C., PECHERSKY, D. H., BOULIN, J., SIBUET, J. C., SAVOSTIN, L. A., SOROKHTIN, O., WESTPHAL, M., BAZHENOV, M. L., LAUER, J. P. & BIJU-DUVAL, B. 1986. Geologic evolution of the Tethys from the Atlantic to the Pamirs since Lias. *Tectonophysics*, **123**, 241–315.

DEWEY, J. F. 1988. Extensional collapse of orogens. *Tectonics*, **7**, 1123–1139.

ENGLAND, P. C. & THOMPSON, A. B. 1984. Pressure–temperature–time paths of regional metamorphism. I — Heat transfer during the evolution of regions of thickened continental crust. *Journal of Petrology*, **25**, 894–928.

ELLIS, D. J. & GREEN, D. H. 1979. An experimental study of the effect of Ca upon garnet-clinopyroxene Fe-Mg exchange equilibria. *Contributions to Mineralogy and Petrology*, **71**, 13–22.

EL-SHAZLY, A. K. 1987. *High pressure metamorphism in NE Oman and its tectonic implications*. M.Sc thesis, Stanford University, Stanford, California.

——, COLEMAN, R. G. & LIOU, J. G., 1987. High pressure metamorphism in NE Oman and its tectonic implications. *Geological Society of America, Abstracts with programs*, **19**, 7, 853.

——, —— & —— 1990. Eclogites and blueschists from NE Oman: Petrology and P–T evolution. *Journal of Petrology*.

ESSENE, E. J. & FYFE, W. S. 1967. Omphacite in Californian metamorphic rocks. *Contributions to Mineralogy and Petrology*, **15** 1–23.

GHENT, E. D. & STOUT, M. Z. 1981. Metamorphism at the base of the Samail ophiolite, Oman. *Journal of Geophysical Research*, **86**, 2557–2571.

GLENNIE, K. W., BOEUF, M. G. A., HUGHES CLARK, M. H. W., MOODY-STUART, M., PILAAR, W. F. and REINHARDT, B. M. 1973. Late Cretaceous nappes in Oman mountains and their geologic evolution. Bulletin of the American Association

of Petroleum Geologists. **57** pp. 5−26.
——, ——, ——, —— & —— 1974. Geology of the Oman mountains. *Verh. K. Ned geol. mijnbouwkd. Genoot.* **31**, 1−423.
GOFFE, B. 1982. *Definition du facies a Fe−Mg−carpholite−chloritoide, un marqueur du metamorphisme de HP−BT dans les metasediments alumineux.* These d'Etat, Univ. Paris, Paris.
——, MICHARD, A., KIENAST, J. R. & LE MER, O., 1988. A case of obduction-related high-pressure low-temperature metamorphism in upper crustal nappes, Arabian continental margin, Oman: P−T paths and kinematic interpretation. *Tectonophysics*, **151**, 363−386.
HANNA, S. S. 1986. The Alpine (Late Cretaceous and Tertiary) tectonic evolution of the Oman mountains: A thrust tectonic approach. Symposium on the hydrocarbon potential of the intense thrust zones, *OAPEC, Kuwait*, **2**, 125−174.
HODGES, K. V., BARTELY, J. M. & BURCHFIEL, B. C. 1982. Structural evolution of an A-type subduction zone, Lofoten Rombak area, Northern Scandinavian Caledonides. *Tectonics*, **1**, 441−462.
HOLLAND, T. J. B. & RICHARDSON, S. W. 1979. Amphibole zonation in metabasites as a guide to the evolution of metamorphic conditions. *Contributions to Mineralogy and Petrology*, **70**, 143−148.
JOHANNES, W. & PUHAN, D. 1971. The calcite-aragonite transition reinvestigated. *Contributions to Mineralogy and Petrology*, **31**, 28−38.
KOONS, P. O. 1986. Relative geobarometry from high-pressure rocks of quartzofeldspathic composition from the Sesia Zone, western Alps, Italy. *Contributions to Mineralogy and Petrology*, **93**, 322−334.
KROGH, E. J. 1982. Metamorphic evolution of Norwegian country rock eclogites, as deduced from mineral inclusions and compositional zoning in garnets. *Lithos*, **15**, 305−321.
LAIRD, J. & ALBEE, A. L. 1981. Pressure, temperature and time indicators of mafic schists: their application to reconstructing the polymetamorphic history of Vermont. *American Journal of Science*, **281** 127−175.
LANPHERE, M. A. 1981. K−Ar ages of metamorphic rocks at the base of the Samail ophiolite, Oman. *Journal of Geophysical Research*, **86**, 2777−2782.
LEAKE, B. E. 1978. Nomenclature of amphiboles. *Mineralogical Magazine*, **42**, 533−563.
LE METOUR, J. 1988. Geologie de l'autochthone des montgnes d'Oman dans la fenetre du Saih Hatat. These d'Etat, Univ. Paris, Paris 6, 420 pp.
——, DE GRAMONT, X., VILLEY, M. 1986. Geological map of Masqat and Quryat, sheets NF40−4A, NF40−4D. Scale 1:100000. Ministry of Petroleum and Minerals, Directorate General of Minerals, Sultanate of Oman.
LIOU, J. G. 1971. P−T stabilities of laumontite, wairakite, lawsonite and related minerals in the system CaAl$_2$Si$_2$O$_8$-SiO$_2$-H$_2$O. *Journal of Petrology*, **12**, 297−314.

——, KUNIYOSHI, S. & ITO, K. 1974. Experimental studies of the phase relations between greenschist and amphibolite in a basaltic system. *American Journal of Science*, **274**, 613−632.
—— & MARUYAMA, S. 1987. Parageneses and compositions of amphiboles from Franciscan jadeite-glaucophane type facies series metabasites at Cazadero, California. *Journal of Metamorphic Geology*, **5**, 371−395.
LIPPARD, S. J. 1983. Cretaceous high pressure metamorphism in NE Oman and its relationship to subduction and ophiolite nappe emplacement. *Journal of the Geological Society of London*, **140**, 97−104.
——, SHELTON, A. W. & GASS, I. G. 1986. *The ophiolite of northern Oman.* Geological Society, London, Memoir, **11**.
MANN, A. & HANNA, S. S. 1990. The tectonic evolution of pre-Permian rocks, central Oman Mountains. *In*: ROBERTSON, A. H. F., SEARLE, M. P. & RIES, A. C. (eds) *The Geology and Tectonics of the Oman Region.* Geological Society, London, Special Publication, **49**, 307−325.
MARESCH, W. V. 1977. Experimental studies on glaucophane: An analysis of present knowledge. *Tectonophysics*, **43**, 109−125.
MARUYAMA, S., CHO, M. & LIOU, J. G. 1986. Experimental investigations of blueschist-greenschist transition equilibria: pressure dependence of Al$_2$O$_3$ contents in sodic amphiboles − a new geobarometer. *In*: EVANS, B. W. & BROWN, E. H. (eds). *Blueschists and eclogites.* Geological Society of America, Memoir, **164**, 1−16.
—— & LIOU, J. G. 1988. Petrology of Franciscan metabasites along the Jadeite-glaucophane type facies series, Cazadero, California. *Journal of Petrology*, **29**, 1−37.
MASSONE, H.-J. & SCHREYER, W. 1987. Phengite geobarometry based on the limiting assemblage with K-feldspar, phlogopite and quartz. *Contributions to Mineralogy and Petrology*, **96**, 212−224.
McCULLOCH, M. T., GREGORY, R. T., WASSERBURG, G. J. & TAYLOR, H. P. 1981. Sm-Nd, Rb-Sr and ^{18}O/^{16}O isotopic systematics in an oceanic crustal section: Evidence from the Semail ophiolite. *Journal of Geophysical Research*, **86**, B-4, 2721−2735.
MICHARD, A. 1983. Les nappes de Mascate (Oman), Rampe epicontinentale d'obuction a facies schiste blue, et la dualite apparente des ophiolites Omanaises. *Scientific Geology Bulletin*, **36**, 1, 3−16, Strasbourg.
——, BOUCHEZ, J. C. & OUAZZANI-TOUHAMI, M. 1984. Obduction-related planar and linear fabrics, Oman. *Journal of Structural Geology*, **6**, 39−49.
——, GOFFE, B. & OUAZZANI-TOUHAMI, M. 1982. Obduction-related high pressure-low temperature metamorphism in upper crustal materials, Muscat, Oman. *Terra Cognita*, **3**, 187.
MONTIGNY, R., LE MER, O., THUIZAT, R. & WHITECHURCH, H. 1988. K−Ar and Ar^{40}/Ar^{39}

study of metamorphic rocks associated with the Oman ophiolite: Tectonic implications. *Tectonophysics*, **151**, 345–362.

MOORES, E. M., ROBINSON, P. T., MALPAS, J. & XENOPHONOTOS, C. 1984. Model for the origin of the Troodos massif, Cyprus, and other mideast ophiolites. *Geology*, **12**, 500–303.

MOUNTAIN, G. S. & PRELL, W. L. 1990. A multiphase plate tectonic history of the Southeast continental margin of Oman. *In*: ROBERTSON, A. H. F., SEARLE, M. P. & RIES, A. C. (eds) *The Geology and Tectonics of the Oman Region*. Geological Society, London, Special Publication, **49**, 725–743.

NEWTON, R. C. & SMITH, J. V. 1967. Investigations concerning the breakdown of albite at depth in the earth. *Journal of Geology*, **75**, 268–86.

OH, C. W., KROGH, E. J. & LIOU, J. G. 1988. A petrogenetic grid for the eclogites and related facies at high pressure metamorphism. *Geological Society of America, Abstracts with programs*, **20**, 7, A344.

OWEN, H. G. 1983. *Atlas of continental displacement 200 million years to the present*. Cambridge University press, Cambridge.

PERKINS, E. H., BROWN, T. H. & BERMAN, R. G. 1986. PTX-system: three programs for calculation of P–T composition phase diagrams. *Computers and Geosciences*, **12**, 749–755.

PLATT, J. P. 1986. Dynamics of orogenic wedges and the uplift of high-pressure metamorphic rocks. *Geological Society of America Bulletin*, **97**, 1037–1053.

—— 1987. The uplift of high pressure-low temperature metamorphic rocks. *Philosophical Transactions of the Royal Society, London*, **A321**, 87–103.

POWELL, R. & EVANS, J. A. 1983. A new geobarometer for the assemblage biotite-muscovite-chlorite-quartz. *Journal of Metamorphic Geology* **1**, 331–336.

—— & HOLLAND, T. J. B. 1988. An internally consistent thermodynamic dataset with uncertainties and correlations: 3. Applications to geobarometry, worked examples and a computer program. *Journal of Metamorphic Geology*, **6**, 173–204.

RAHEIM, A. 1975. Mineral zoning as a record of pressure–temperature history of Pre-Cambrian eclogites and schists in western Tasmania. *Lithos*, **8**, 221–236.

—— & GREEN, D. H. 1975. P, T paths of natural eclogites during metamorphism; a record of subduction. *Lithos*, **8**, 317–328.

REYNARD, B. & BALLEVRE, M. 1988. Coexisting amphiboles in an eclogite from the Western Alps: new constraints on the miscibility gap between sodic and calcic amphiboles. *Journal of Metamorphic Geology*, **6**, 333–350.

RICOU, L. E. 1971. Le croissant ophiolitique peri-Arabe. Une ceinture des nappes mises en place au Cretace Superieur. *Rev. Geogra. Phys. Geol. Dyn.*, **B**, 327–350.

RIDLEY, J. 1984. Evidence of a temperature depen-

dent blueschist to 'eclogite' transformation in high pressure metamorphism of metabasic rocks. *Journal of Petrology*, **25**, 852–870.

ROBERTSON, A. H. F. 1987a. The transition from a passive margin to an Upper Cretaceous foreland basin related to ophiolite emplacement in the Oman Mountains. *Geological Society of America Bulletin*, **99**, 633–653.

—— 1987b. Upper Cretaceous Muti formation: transition from a Mesozoic nate platform to a foreland basin in the Oman Mountains. *Sedimentology*, **34**, 1123–1142.

SCHREYER, W. 1988. Experimental studies on metamorphism of crustal rocks under mantle pressures. *Mineralogical Magazine*, **52**, 1–26.

SEARLE, M. P. 1985. Sequence of thrusting and origin of culminations in the northern and central Oman Mountains. *Journal of Structural Geology*, **7**, 129–143.

SEARLE, M. P. & MALPAS, J. 1980. Structure and metamorphism of rocks beneath the Semail ophiolite of Oman and their tectonic significance in ophiolite obduction. *Transactions of the Royal Society of Edinburgh*, **71**, 247–262.

—— & —— 1982. Petrochemistry and origin of sub-ophiolitic metamorphic and related rocks in the Oman Mountains. *Journal of the Geological Society of London*, **139**, 235–248.

SELVERSTONE, J. & SPEAR, F. S. 1985. Metamorphic P–T paths from pelitic schists and greenstones from southwest Tauern window, Eastern Alps. *Journal of Metamorphic Geology*, **3**, 439–465.

SHACKELTON, R. M. & RIES, A. C. 1988. Structural evolution of NE Oman and Masirah island. *The Geology and Tectonics of the Oman region: a discussion meeting*. Edinburgh. Abstracts, p. 52.

SISSON, V. B. & ONSTOTT, T. C. 1986. Dating blueschist metamorphism: A combined Ar^{40}/Ar^{39} and electron microprobe approach. *Geochimica et Cosmochimica Acta*, **50**, 2111–2117.

SMITH, A. G. 1988. Temperatures at the base of a moving ophiolite slab. *The Geology and Tectonics of the Oman region. An International discussion meeting, Edinburgh. Abstracts*, **59**.

SPEAR, F. S. 1981. An experimental study of hornblende stability and compositional variability in amphibolite: *American Journal of Science*, **281**, 697–734.

SPRAY, J. G. 1984. Possible causes of upper mantle decoupling and ophiolite displacement. *In*: GASS, I., LIPPARD, S. J. & SHELTON, A. W. (eds). *Ophiolites and oceanic lithosphere*. Geological Society of London, Special Publication, **13**, 255–268.

SPRY, A. 1969. *Metamorphic textures*. Pergamon, Oxford.

TAYLOR, H. P. & COLEMAN, R. G. 1968. O^{18}/O^{16} ratios of coexisting minerals in glaucophane-bearing metamorphic rocks. *Geological Society of America Bulletin*, **79**, 1727–1756.

THOMPSON, A. B. 1976. Mineral reactions in pelitic rocks. II — Calculation of some P–T–X(Fe-Mg) phase relations. *American Journal of Science*, **276**, 425–454.

—— & RIDLEY, J. R. 1987. P—T-time histories of orogenic belts. *Philosophical Transactions of the Royal Society of London*, **321**, 27—45.

TILTON, G. R., HOPSON, C. A. & WRIGHT, J. E. 1981. Uranium — lead isotopic ages of the Semail ophiolite, Oman, with application to Tethyan ocean ridge tectonics. *Journal of Geophysical Research*, **86**, 2763—2775.

TIPPIT, P. R., PESSAGNO, E. A. & SMEWING, J. D. 1981. The biostratigraphy of sediments in the volcanic unit of the Semail ophiolite. *Journal of Geophysical Research*, **86**, **B-4**, 2756—2762.

TRACY, R. J. 1982. Compositional zoning and inclusions in metamorphic minerals. *In*: FERRY, J. M. (ed.), Characterization of metamorphism through mineral equilibria. *Reviews in Mineralogy*, **10**, 355—397.

VELDE, B. 1967. Si^{+4} content of natural phengites. *Contributions of Mineralogy and Petrology*, **14**, 250—258.

VILLEY, M., DE GRAMONT, X., LE METOUR, J. 1986. *Geological map of the Fanjah quadrangle*. Sheet NF40—3F. Scale: 1:100 000. Ministry of Petroleum and Minerals, Directorate General of Minerals, Sultanate of Oman.

ZIEGLER, U. R. F. & STOESSEL, G. F. U. 1988. Metavolcanic rocks beneath the Semail ophiolite nappe in the United Arab Emirates. *The Geology and Tectonics of the Oman region; a discussion meeting. Edinburgh. Abstracts*, 72.

Maastrichtian to early Tertiary stratigraphy and palaeogeography of the Central and Northern Oman Mountains

S. C. NOLAN[1], P. W. SKELTON[2], B. P. CLISSOLD[3] & J. D. SMEWING[1]

[1] *Earth Resources Institute, University Innovation Centre, Singleton Park, Swansea SA2 8PP, UK*

[2] *Department of Earth Sciences, The Open University, Milton Keynes, MK7 6AA, UK*

[3] *51 Mountain Road, Brynamman, Dyfed SA18 1AN, UK*

Abstract: Maastrichtian to Tertiary sedimentary rocks outcrop extensively around the periphery of the Oman Mountains. They form part of a geologically distinct suite of strata deposited after obduction of the Semail ophiolite and thrusting of the Hawasina and Sumeini imbricates onto the eastern edge of the Arabian plate. The lithostratigraphy of Maastrichtian and early Tertiary rocks of the central and northern Oman Mountains is revised and a number of new formations are erected. The proto-Oman Mountains were emergent in the early Maastrichtian and were subject to subaerial erosion and weathering. NW and W of the mountains, gradual subsidence followed during the Maastrichtian, allowing for formation of a transgressive, onlapping sequence represented by the Qahlah (fluviatile to shallow marine terrigenous clastics) and Simsima (shallow shelf carbonate) Formations. More rapid subsidence NE of the mountains produced fan delta and submarine debris flow/turbidite apron sequences comprising the Al Khawd and Thaqab Formations respectively. A low-angle unconformity separates Tertiary strata from older units. During the Palaeogene, basinal and slope facies with debris flows and turbidite sequences were deposited directly upon the unconformity surface in rapidly subsiding basins NW (Muthaymimah Formation) and NNE (Ruwaydah Formation) of the Oman Mountains. Elsewhere, shallow carbonate shelf facies were extensively developed in less rapidly subsiding areas during the Palaeogene. The Palaeocene and early Eocene is represented by the Jafnayn Limestone Formation. This is succeeded and overlapped by a variety of later Eocene units. ENE and E of the mountains early Eocene regression is marked by restricted facies of the Rusayl Formation. Overlying the Rusayl Formation are shallow, open shelf limestones of the Seeb Formation which is rich in alveolinid and nummulitic foraminifera. On the Arabian side of the mountains the Rusayl Formation is not developed and the Jafnayn Formation is succeeded either by the Seeb Formation or fine-grained, faunally restricted limestones and marls of the Fahud Beds, which represent intra-shelf facies.

Maastrichtian (late Cretaceous) to Eocene (early Tertiary) rocks are well exposed around the periphery of the Oman Mountains (Fig. 1). These rocks lie unconformably upon previously folded and thrusted units of the Hawasina Complex, Sumeini Group and Semail Ophiolite. They form a geologically distinct suite of strata deposited after the late Cretaceous orogenic event (Turonian to Campanian) during which the Semail Ophiolite was emplaced onto the eastern margin of the Arabian platform (Wilson 1969; Glennie *et al*. 1973, 1974; Graham 1980; Coleman 1981; Lippard & Rex 1982, and others).

Previous publications on the Maastrichtian to Eocene rocks of the central and northern Oman Mountains are few and most simply state an age and/or suggest that certain strata show broad

similarities with coeval rocks from Saudi Arabia, Qatar or Iran. The articles by Lees (1928), Glennie *et al*. (1974), Montenat & Blondeau (1977), Racz (1979), Cherif & el Deeb (1984), Nolan *et al*. (1986) and Warrak (1986) are the only previous publications to contain any stratigraphic detail on these rocks.

During reconnaissance studies by the present authors and co-workers on the post-obduction rocks of the Oman Mountains, a wide range of sedimentary facies was encountered. The existing early Tertiary lithostratigraphic framework from Saudi Arabia (cf. Steineke *et al*. 1958; Powers *et al*. 1966) could not be indiscriminately applied to the Oman Mountains without radically altering the original concepts of the existing formations.

To prevent the existing formations from

From ROBERTSON, A. H. F., SEARLE, M. P. & RIES, A. C. (eds), 1990,
The Geology and Tectonics of the Oman Region.
Geological Society Special Publication No 49, pp 495–519

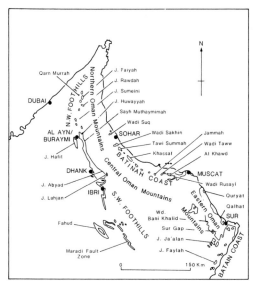

Fig. 1. Location map showing the outcrop of
Maastrichtian to Eocene rocks and the main localities
mentioned around the periphery of the Oman
Mountains.

becoming corrupted a new, local, lithostratigraphic framework for the early Tertiary is
presented.

Figure 2 illustrates this stratigraphy. For
brevity only previously unpublished palaeontological data are presented. The reader is referred to papers by Skelton *et al.* (1990) and
Montenat & Blondeau (1977) for biostratigraphical details.

The grid references given are from the 3-
GSGS edition K668 series 1:100 000 (0.63
inches to 1 mile) topographic maps of Oman
and United Arab Emirates produced by the
Military Survey, Ministry of Defence, United
Kingdom, 1963, 1964, 1967, 1970, 1971, 1975.

In many areas the Maastrichtian to Eocene
rocks of the Oman Mountains are relatively
gently deformed but locally they may be severely
folded and faulted. The reader is referred to
Warrak (1986), Mann *et al.* (1990) and Filbrandt
et al. (1990) for information regarding the structural history of these rocks. The latter also
contains stratigraphic details of these rocks in
the eastern Oman Mountains, SE of Muscat.

Stratigraphy

This section is restricted to those units which
formed after the late Cretaceous (approximately Coniacian to Late Campanian) Oman
orogenic event. It does not include the synoro-

genic Muti and Juweiza Formations (Glennie *et
al.* 1974) or the Fiqa Formation which may span
both orogenic and early post-orogenic phases.

The revised lithostratigraphy, described below
in approximate stratigraphic order, is based on
extensive outcrop studies in the northern and
central Oman mountains. All but two have
readily accessible type or reference localities at
outcrop. The revised stratigraphy is presented
in accordance with stratigraphical nomenclature by Harland *et al.* (1972); Hedburg (1976);
and the North American Commission on Stratigraphic Nomenclature (1983) (hereafter termed
'the rules of stratigraphical nomenclature').

The distribution of type areas of the named
units are shown on Fig. 3 along with important
localities mentioned in the text.

Qahlah Formation (Maastrichtian)

Author. [1] J. Horstink (unpublished report for
Petroleum Development Oman, 1967).
[2] Glennie *et al.* (1974, pp. 183–184), first
valid definition.
Derivation of Name. Unknown. The type
locality is near Qalhat and not near Qahlah.
Type Section. Glennie *et al.* (1974, p. 183) did
not present a measured section of the type area.
The one presented here (Fig. 4) from the type
section is based upon unpublished work by R.
Crawford.
Grid reference: 7 434, 25 098. 59°22′00″ E
22°46′10″ N.
Thickness: Around 140 m in the type area
(Glennie *et al.* 1974).
Description of Type Section. At the base is a
12.5 m bed of massive conglomerate with lithic
sandstone becoming proportionately more
abundant at the top. It contains clasts of red
mudstone and chert and is highly variable in
thickness. Above are 45 to 55 m of purply-red
and green lithic sandstone and conglomerate
with mudstone predominating towards the top.
Overlying is a beige marly limestone, about 4 m
thick, which contains abundant *Loftusia*, bivalves and gastropods. Above is a basalt lava
flow, between 10 and 30 m thick which is
overlain by a further 2 m of lithic sandstone.
Another, thinner flow around 2.5 m thick occurs
higher up above 10 to 15 m of dark grey claystone. The upper basalt is overlain by about 10
m of coarse lithic sandstone. There is a gap in
exposure of between 15 and 20 m to the base of
the 'Simsima' Formation.
Boundaries. At the type section the Qahlah
rests unconformably upon sub-vertical Hawasina. Nearby it also rests unconformably
upon Qalhat 'quartz porphyry' and meta-

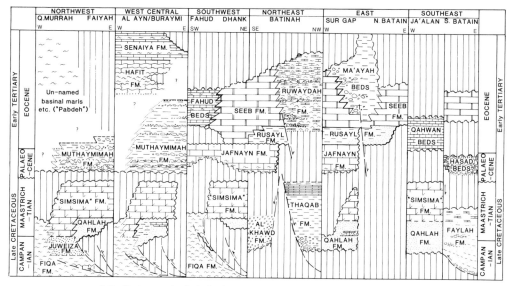

Late Cretaceous to Early Tertiary Lithostratigraphy of the Oman Mountains

Fig. 2. Lithostratigraphy of late Campanian to Eocene rocks of the Oman Mountains. Based on this paper, Filbrandt *et al.* (1990), Glennie *et al.* (1974), Cherif & El Deeb (1984) and Ries & Shackleton (1990).

Fig. 3. Distribution of type areas of named units around the Oman Mountains.

volcanics. The boundary with the overlying 'Simsima' Formation may be conformable here. Elsewhere a non-sequence is sometimes present.

Lateral Variation. The Qahlah Formation is very variable in thickness and composition as might be expected in a basal terrigenous sequence immediately overlying an unconformity.

In the southwest and northwest foothills the 'Simsima' Formation overlaps the Qahlah near Dhank (e.g. on Jebel Abyad) and near Al Ayn/Buraymi (e.g. on Jebel As Saifr).

In the eastern Oman mountains, including the type section, it is a noticeable peculiarity of the Qahlah that its clast composition is generally different to the underlying rock. In the north-west foothills between Jebels Rawdah and Faiyah the opposite is found. Red/purple coloured lenses of laterite, and possibly also saprolite, occur in a number of localities upon the Semail ophiolite. On Jebel Rawdah, palaeosols occur interbedded with sandstone and conglomerate. At Qalhat and on Jebel Huwayyah, near Al Ayn, the Qahlah Formation includes marly *Loftusia* bearing limestone.

Environment of deposition. A wide variety of non-marine fluviatile to shallow marine facies are developed in the Qahlah Formation. Fluviatile facies are well developed in the lower part of the type section. In the higher part a shallow marine influence is discernable in the presence of *Loftusia* bearing limestones and pillow basalts. A variety of beach to inshore facies are recognizable on Jebels Faiyah and Huwayyah (Skelton *et al.* 1990).

Age: The presence of *Loftusia* in the type section indicates a Maastrichtian age (Glennie *et al.* 1974). A rich fauna with abundant rudists was found in the Qahlah Formation at Jebel

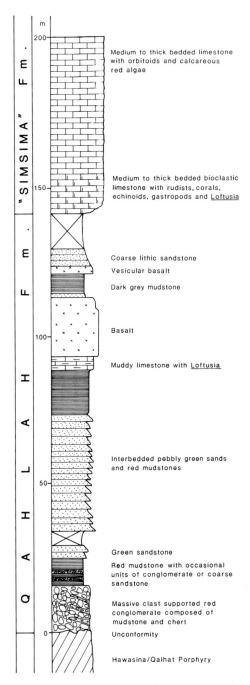

m

200—

"SIMSIMA" Fm.

Medium to thick bedded limestone
with orbitoids and calcareous
red algae

150—

Medium to thick bedded bioclastic
limestone with rudists, corals,
echinoids, gastropods and <u>Loftusia</u>

F m.

Coarse lithic sandstone

Vesicular basalt

Dark grey mudstone

100—

Basalt

Muddy limestone with <u>Loftusia</u>

Q A H L A H   F.

Interbedded pebbly green sands
and red mudstones

50—

Green sandstone

Red mudstone with occasional
units of conglomerate or coarse
sandstone

Massive clast supported red
conglomerate composed of
mudstone and chert

0—

Unconformity

Hawasina/Qalhat Porphyry

Fig. 4. Measured section from the type locality of the
Qahlah Formation, near Qalhat, east Oman
Mountains.

Huwayyah, indicating an early to 'mid' Maastrichtian age (Skelton *et al.* 1990).
Correlation and discussion. The Qahlah Formation was applied originally by Glennie *et al.*
(1974) to most post-obduction basal terrigenous
clastic facies around the Oman Mountains. Subsequent investigations revealed that this practice
meant that the unit was not allostratigraphical. For example, in the eastern mountains,
Montenat & Blondeau (1977) dated part of the
basal clastics at Quryat as early Tertiary and
north of Jebel Ja'alan the basal sandstones
belong to the Tertiary Rusayl Formation and
not the Qahlah. A number of basal clastic units
occur on the Batinah Coast which were originally included in the Qahlah, but which are
now excluded from it for stratigraphical reasons.
The basal member of the Thaqab Formation
(see section Thaqab Formation) is a deep
marine debris flow/turbidite unit differing significantly in facies from the marginal to non-
marine Qahlah. Below this is an unfossiliferous
red/orange/yellow coloured conglomerate of
possible fluviatile facies, similar to the Qahlah,
but which was deformed and in places cleaved
prior to the early Maastrichtian/end Campanian. This unit, informally termed the
'Rawdah Conglomerate' after extensive outcrops west of Rawdah village (Grid ref. 4 77 26
58) is thought to be a partly synorogenic deposit
erosively derived from the underlying melange-
like Batinah Complex of Woodcock & Robertson (1982a,b) and Robertson & Woodcock
(1983). The term 'Qahlah' has also been applied
to the Juweiza Formation by Sugden & Standing
(1975, Fig. 2).

Indiscriminate application of the term
'Qahlah' to clastics of proven, or worse, of
supposed Maastrichtian age would create a non-
allostratigraphical unit encompassing strata of
widely differing facies and ages separated by
phases of tectonism and unconformities. In
order to avoid this we recommend for the present that the term 'Qahlah' only be formally
applied to marginal to non-marine terrigenous
clastic dominated facies overlain by datable
Maastrichtian carbonates. Local terms are better for undated units of similar facies which are
overlain by Tertiary strata to avoid corrupting
the stratigraphical coherence of the Qahlah
Formation.

The lower part of the Qahlah Formation of
Jebel Huwayyah is a lateral correlative of the
'Simsima' Formation of Qarn Murrah on biostratigraphical grounds. On the Batinah coast,
it is in part a correlative of the Thaqab Formation and also probably correlates with the Al

Khawd Formation but it is not correlatable with the Rawdah Conglomerate.

'Simsima' Formation (Maastrichtian) (Fig. 5)

Author. [1] W. Sugden (1956), unpublished Qatar Petroleum report.
[2] Dominquez (1965), first published use of name but no valid definition.
[3] Hopping & Standing (1969), unpublished report to the Stratigraphic Liaison Committee.
[4] Glennie *et al.* (1974), first valid definition with a 'type' reference section in Oman.
[5] Sugden & Standing (1975), first valid definition of a type section in Qatar.

Discussion. There are a number of problems regarding the validity of the term 'Simsima'. The term was originally applied by Sugden to a section of limestone in Dukhan Well No 1, offshore Qatar, in an unpublished report: an invalid designation according to the rules of stratigraphic nomenclature. If this had subsequently been validly defined in a publication, no problem would have arisen. Unfortunately, the first valid published definition of a 'Simsima Formation' was by Glennie *et al.* (1974), who erected a 'type section' in Oman in Well Suneinah No 1 between 6470 and 6920 ft. It appears that they only meant this to be a local reference section. Subsequently a type section was designated in Qatar by Sugden & Standing (1975), but in a different well to Sugden's original, in Well Dukhan No 55, between 353 m and 502 m, at 25°24′01″N, 50°45′46″ E.

Sugden & Standing (1975) thought that long usage of the term 'Simsima' conveyed validity to it despite being a junior synonym of the Tayarat Formation (Owen & Nasr 1958) of Iraq. Both shelf limestone units could be regarded also as synonyms of the Aruma Limestone Formation (Steineke *et al.* 1958) of Saudi Arabia (not to be confused with the Aruma Group of Owen & Nasr 1958).

Despite being a well known term, the actual validity of the term 'Simsima Formation' is open to question and consequently we use it here with caution. All the designated type sections for the 'Simsima Formation' are well sections, unsuitable as reference points for most geologists because of problems of access. We designate an outcropping reference section on Jebel Faiyah which is well known to many geologists in the region, and is easily accessible.

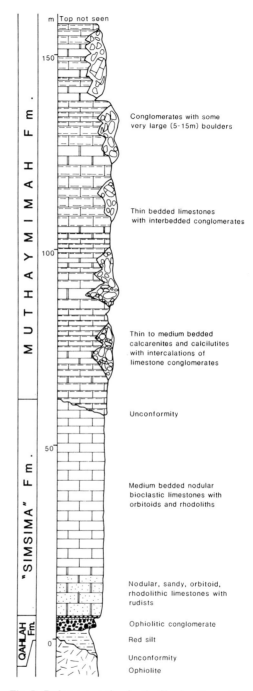

Fig. 5. Reference section for the Simsima Formation, Jebel Faiyah, NW Oman Mountains.

Thickness. 149 m in Well Dukhan No 55; 137 m in Well Suneinah No 1; up to 85 m on Jebel Faiyah; 180–200 m on Jebels Abyad and Lahjan, east of Dhank; 140 m approximately on Jebel Ja'alan.

Outcrop reference section. Central Jebel Faiyah, immediately north of a low pass, Emirate of Sharjah, United Arab Emirates. Grid reference 3810, 27735. 55°49′20″ E 25°04′30″ N.

Description of outcrop reference section. The lower 12 to 15 m consist of orange/yellow slightly dolomitic, nodular, bioturbated, orbitoid rich, foraminiferal packstone with abundant coarse rudist debris and rudists in life position (Skelton *et al.* 1990), rhodoliths, gastropods, encrusting sclerosponges and bivalves with occasional corals and echinoids. Above this is around 30 m of similar limestone with fewer macrofossils including only occasional rudist debris. The upper 40 m are finer grained, consisting of foraminiferal packstone and wackestone, with only occasional echinoids, pectinacean bivalves and naticiform gastropods.

Boundaries. At the outcrop reference section, the base of the 'Simsima Formation' is drawn at the base of the first limestone overlying Qahlah Conglomerate. Elsewhere around Jebel Faiyah the boundary between the 'Simsima' and Qahlah formations may be more transitional. Immediately adjacent to the Oman mountains (Jebel Sumeini, Jebel As Saifr and Jebel Abyad) the 'Simsima Formation' overlaps the Qahlah Formation and rests directly upon older units (Hawasina or Sumeini Group) with an angular unconformity. At such localities a very discontinuous basal layer of pebbles or cobbles of reworked pre-Maastrichtian rock is often, but not always, present. On Jebel Huwayyah, the contact between the 'Simsima' and Qahlah formations is sharp and probably represents a nonsequence (see Skelton *et al.* 1990).

Between Jebel Faiyah and Sayh Muthaymimah (Fig. 1) the 'Simsima Formation' is unconformably overlain by the Muthaymimah Formation (see later section) whilst between Wadi Khubayb (north of Dhank) and Jebel Abyad (near Yanqul) (Fig. 1) it is unconformably overlain by the Jafnayn Formation (see later section). This unconformity appears to be of regional extent in the Oman mountains. It is a low-angle feature and may not be immediately obvious at any single locality. We have nowhere found a conformable transition from the Cretaceous to Tertiary.

Lateral Variation. The formation displays wide lateral variation in shallow marine facies. Between Jebel Mulaghah (north of Faiyah) and Sayh Muthaymimah (SW of Buraymi), the basal 'Simsima Formation' is rich in rudists. South of here rudist debris becomes rarer. On Jebel Abyad (Fig. 1) the formation is dominated by foraminiferal packstones and grainstones with occasional oyster (*Exogyra sp.*, *Lopha sp.*) bands. Nearby on Jebel Lahjan (Fig. 1) the formation is very marly and unusually contains very few large benthonic foraminifera but is exceptionally rich in echinoids.

The outcrops of 'Simsima Formation' in the western inliers of Qarn Murrah (west of Faiyah) and Jebel Muhayjir (north of Buraymi) are red coloured as opposed to the usual yellow or grey colour. These are palaeontologically slightly older than the latter (Skelton *et al.* 1990).

Environment of deposition. The 'Simsima Formation' was deposited in a shallow marine environment. In most localities north of Dhank an upward deepening trend is present. Detailed sedimentological analysis of the formation between Buraymi and Jebel Faiyah indicates the presence of beach to shoreface facies, with rudists in life positions, in the basal few metres (Skelton *et al.* 1990).

Age. The 'Simsima Formation' outcropping around the Oman Mountains contains a varied fauna of molluscs, corals, echinoids and foraminifera, indicating an early to late Maastrichtian age (Skelton *et al.* 1990).

Correlation and discussion. West of the Oman Mountains in the subsurface the 'Simsima Formation' may overlie and interdigitate with the Fiqa Formation (Glennie *et al.* 1974; Harris *et al.* 1984; Burruss *et al.* 1985). The 'Simsima Formation' is correlated with the Aruma Formation (Steineke *et al.* 1958; Powers *et al.* 1966) of Saudi Arabia, and the Sharwayn Formation (Beydoun 1966; Hawkins *et al.* 1981) of Hadramawt and Dhofar.

Al Khawd Conglomerate Formation (Late Campanian?/Maastrichtian?)

Author. New Formation

Derivation of Name. Al Khawd village at the type locality.

Type Section. In low undulating ground between the Palaeogene limestone escarpment and ophiolite hills near Al Khawd village, west of Muscat (Fig. 6). Grid references 6162, 26042 to 6172, 26054. 58°08′25″ E 23°32′28″ N to 58°09′00″ E 23°33′10″ N.

Thickness. Approximately 800 m exposed at type locality, but the top contact is faulted here.

Description of type section. The Al Khawd Formation consists of interbedded polymict conglomerate, lithic sandstone and shale with rare bands (under 15 cm thick) of microcrystalline

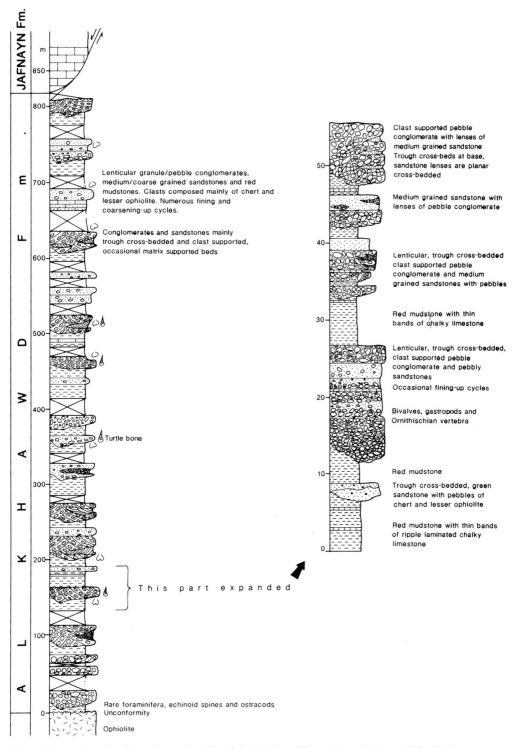

Fig. 6. Measured section from the type locality of the Al Khawd Formation, Al Khawd, S Batinah coast, near Muscat. The extract (right) shows typical details of the unit.

limestone or dolomite. Most of the detritus in the coarser beds consists of ophiolite or chert material derived from the Semail Ophiolite or Hawasina imbricates. The shales are mostly red in colour and deeply weathered. In the field these appear unfossiliferous. Marine foraminifera, echinoid spines and ostracod shells were obtained from some processed samples. The coarser beds are generally unfossiliferous but may include articulated corbiculid bivalves and gastropods.

Boundaries. The Al Khawd Formation unconformably overlies the Semail Ophiolite. Locally the boundary is usually faulted or sheared due to later tectonic movements. A strike parallel normal fault forms the boundary with the overlying Jafnayn Formation at the type locality. Elsewhere the upper boundary is unconformable.

Lateral Variation. The Al Khawd Formation has been recognized only on the Batinah Coast between Ghala and Wadi Taww. In the type area between Al Khawd and Wadi Rusayl, the formation includes a thin basal unit with coarse beds composed mostly of ophiolite derived detritus. The majority of coarse beds through the formation in this area and at Wadi Taww are composed of rounded to sub-angular clasts of Hawasina chert with smaller proportions of vein quartz and subordinate shale intraclasts and ophiolitic detritus. East of Wadi Rusayl above the basal unit of ophiolite detritus is a unit including fragments of slate and schist, possibly reworked from the metamorphic sheet, and clasts of limestone derived from the Hajar Super Group. Above this the coarse lithofacies are composed predominantly of metasedimentary quartzite, probably derived from the Lower Palaeozoic Amdeh Formation of Saih Hatat.

Environment of deposition. The sandstones and conglomerates of the Al Khawd Formation occur as lenticular channelized and semichannelized low sinuosity, fluviatile bodies which sometimes include corbiculid bivalves probably reworked from lagoonal areas. The enveloping shalier facies sometimes includes marine microfossils. The Al Khawd Formation is interpreted as a fan delta complex.

Age. The age of the Al Khawd Formation has yet to be accurately determined. It unconformably overlies the Semail ophiolite, which was finally obducted on to the Oman margin probably during the middle/late Campanian (Glennie *et al.* 1974, and others). The base of the Jafnayn Formation which unconformably overlies it is of upper Palaeocene age (Racey & White 1989, pers. comm.). A late Campanian to Maastrichtian age is, therefore, probable. This

is supported by the find of rare ornithischian and turtle bones in the type section.

Correlation and Discussion. Without more detailed palaeontological information it is not possible to accurately correlate the Al Khawd Formation with other units in the Oman mountains. It is lithologically similar to the Qahlah Formation but is assigned to a separate local unit to avoid possible confusion (see discussion in a previous section).

Thaqab Formation (Late Campanian? to Maastrichtian) (Fig. 7)

Author: New Formation.

Derivation of Name. Tawi Thaqab in Wadi Sakhin.

Type Section. On the north Batinah coast, southwest of Saham in Wadi Sakhin and a small tributary wadi, from grid reference 4 694, 26 655 to 4 748, 26 672. 56°41'00" E 24°06'30" N to 56°45'02" E 24°07'15" N, (Fig. 7).

Thickness. Approximately 1000 m. This is a conservative estimation and it may be much thicker, as the top is never seen, due to faulting or an unconformity.

Description of type section. The Thaqab Formation is intermittently exposed. It is divisible into three members. Member 1 consists of approximately 200 m of well bedded pebble and cobble conglomerate with green/khaki-coloured shale and lithic sandstone becoming volumetrically more important up sequence. Boulders are comparatively infrequent in the conglomerates. Ophiolite and Hawasina limestone and chert debris are the most frequent clast lithologies. Fragments of Oman Exotic limestone are occasionally also present. This unit passes up transitionally into Member 2; a monotonous sequence around 750 m thick (minimum) of khaki shale and mudstone, with sporadic thin (generally under 20 cm), graded beds of lithic sandstone or granule conglomerate. The shales and mudstone are very weathered at surface and include scattered crystals and veins of gypsum resulting from near-surface weathering processes. Towards the top of this unit the proportion of lithic sandstone and conglomerate slowly increases and this unit passes up transitionally into Member 3 which is around 50 m thick. Member 3 is dominated by browncoloured tabular, flaggy bedded, sandy biosparites. Interbedded with these are khaki shale and marl and occasional horizons and lithic sandstone and conglomerate including rudist and oyster debris and clasts derived from Ophiolite, Hawasina or Oman Exotic units. These pass up rapidly into a unit of khaki to

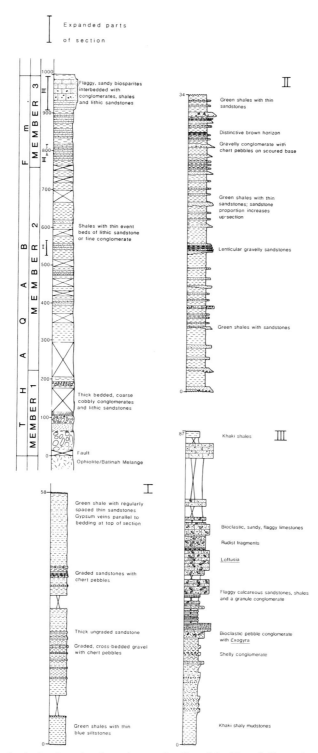

Fig. 7. Measured and calculated section from the type locality of the Thaqab Formation, Wadi Sakhin, N Batinah coast, near Saham. Sections I, II and III are detailed extracts from Members 2 and 3 (see metres for positions on summary log). Log: grid ref. 4690, 26655 to 4736, 26693. Log I: grid ref. 4710, 26681. Log II: grid ref. 4722, 26688. Log III: grid ref. 4743, 26671.

silvery coloured shales of which only 3 m are exposed.

Boundaries. The Thaqab Formation appears to be in faulted contact with underlying rocks units, the Batinah complex and Rawdah Conglomerate. At the type section the Thaqab Formation is probably in faulted or unconformable contact with the overlying Ruwaydah Formation (see late section). Further south at Khasaf (Fig. 1) it is unconformably overlain by a basal chert conglomerate of the Rusayl Formation (see later section).

Lateral variation. The lower conglomerate dominated unit (Member 1) of the Thaqab Formation has only been recognized at the type locality. The monotonous khaki shale unit (Member 2) is present from Wadi Suq. near Sohar in the north, to Doqal and Khasaf near Wadi Hawasina in the south. The limestone and overlying silvery shale units (Member 3) are present around Wadi Sakhin and Wadi Suq (Fig. 1).

Environment of deposition. Member 3 includes a diverse tracefossil assemblage, including *Scolicia* de Quatrefages, *Palaeodictyon* Meneghini and *Spiroraphe* Fuchs, similar to assemblages reported from deep water flysch sequences (Hantzschel 1975). The limestone, sandstone and fine granule conglomerate beds throughout the Thaqab Formation are generally graded and have sharp, sometimes erosive, bases. Internally these beds include structures attributable to the Bouma cycle. Ta, Tb and Td units are most frequent. These are interpreted as turbidity current deposits. The coarser conglomerate beds are chaotic and are occasionally capped by graded sandstone or limestone. They were probably deposited by debris flows. The Thaqab Formation is regarded as having formed in a deep marine slope environment.

Age. Member 3 of the Thaqab Formation contains a diverse fauna including *Durania sp.*, *Biradiolites sp.*, *Exogyra sp.*, *Lopha sp.*, *Omphalocyclus macroporus* (Lamarck), *Orbitoides media* (d'Archiac) and *Siderolites sp.* Although these are allochthonous, having been derived from an adjacent carbonate shelf, they are regarded as penecontemporaneous and not stratigraphically reworked as they are all fresh and very abundant and, despite close investigation, no reworked clasts of 'Simsima Formation' were found. This fauna indicates a Maastrichtian age. The underlying approximately 950 m of strata of the Thaqab Formation are probably early Maastrichtian to possibly late Campanian in age.

Correlation and discussion. The Thaqab Forma-

tion is superficially a possible correlative, in part at least, of the Juweiza Formation (Glennie *et al.* 1974). The Thaqab Formation is erected as a separate formation according to the rules of stratigraphical nomenclature because the Thaqab and Juweiza Formations were never laterally continuous but were separated by a positive area which supplied debris to both. The Juweiza is thought to have formed as a synorogenic deposit in front of the advancing Semail and Hawasina thrust sheets (Glennie *et al.* 1974) while the Thaqab formed on the opposite, hinterland, side of the thrust sheets and clearly, in part if not all, postdates the late Cretaceous thrusting.

The Thaqab Formation is distinguished from the Qahlah and Al Khawd Formations by its green/khaki colour and deep marine origin. Member 3 is biostratigraphically correlated with the 'Simsima Formation' at its outcrop reference section.

Jafnayn Limestone Formation (late Palaeocene to early Eocene)

Author. New Formation.
Derivation of name. Village of Jafnayn at the type section.
Type section. Southernmost limestone escarpment immediately east of the village of Jafnayn in Wadi Rusayl, west of Muscat, Oman. Grid reference 6 237, 26 020 to 6 237, 26 025. 58°13' 10" E 23°32'05" N, (Fig. 8).
Thickness. About 126 m at the type section (based on a measured section by R. Crawford).
Description of type section. Basal 3 to 4 m buff/ cream, nodular crystalline limestone with reworked chert and ophiolite clasts. Above are about 69 m of yellow marl and marly wackestone with one thick resistant nodular weathering, bioturbated crystalline limestone (mostly packstone) around 30 m in thickness containing echinoids. This lower part is variable in thickness owing, in part, to tectonically induced thickening and thinning of the marls. Their thickness at the type section appears to be about average for the area. The lower marly part is overlain by around 53 m of thickly bedded, cliff forming. grey/beige limestone (predominantly packstones and wackestones with grainstones and rudstones towards the top) which include subspherical alveolinid foraminifera, miliolids, rhodoliths and corals. Vein quartz pebbles occur in the lower 3 m of this upper unit.
Boundaries. The base of the Jafnayn Formation is seldom exposed because of scree cover at the

bottom of the escarpment it forms. At the type section about 2 m of section are unexposed between the lowest limestone with pebbles and small outcrops of Al Khawd Formation and Semail Ophiolite. The clasts in the basal Jafnayn Formation appear to be reworked from the former. Between Sunab and Lansab the boundary, where exposed, is quite sharp with a basal few centimetres or metres of yellow marl and limestone with reworked clasts lying directly upon red mudstone or conglomerate of the Al Khawd Formation. The Jafnayn Formation appears to rest upon stratigraphically higher beds in the Al Khawd Formation when traced from Lansab to Sunab. The boundary, therefore, is a low-angle unconformity. Between Jafnayn and Al Khawd villages these two formations are in contact along a large strike parallel fault.

The upper boundary with the Rusayl Formation appears conformable but it may represent a non-sequence or disconformity.

Lateral Variation. The Jafnayn Formation is present on the Batinah coast only as far north as Wadi Taww. West of the Oman mountains, the Jafnayn Formation at Jebel Abyad and Wadi Khubayb near Dhank unconformably overlies the 'Simsima Formation'. It overlaps to the northwest and southwest to rest unconformably upon Hawasina or Oman Melange in Wadi Fatah and around Ibri. South of Ibri, between Jebel Awaynah, Fahud and the Maradi Fault (Fig. 1), the Jafnayn Formation unconformably overlies the Fiqa Formation.

In the southwest Oman Mountains the Jafnayn Formation varies greatly in thickness but is remarkably constant in stratigraphical character. At Jebel Abyad the Jafnayn Formation attains around 500 m in thickness, near Ibri (25 km south) it is only 90 m, while on Jebel Fahud (100 km south again) it thickens to 130 m. Between Jebel Abyad and Fahud, west of the mountains, and between Wadi Taww and Lansab, east of the mountains, the formation is divisible into a lower marly-limestone/marl division and an upper more massive cleaner limestone division which forms cliffs. The lateral consistency is emphasized between Ibri and Fahud by the persistent occurrence of nautiloids within the upper resistant limestone division.

Environment of deposition. The Jafnayn Formation formed in a shallow shelf environment. The lower marly part includes infaunal bivalves, some in life position, gastropods and occasionally small corals. It is interpreted as having formed in a low energy environment. The upper cleaner limestone division includes winnowed horizons of alveolinid foraminifera or rhodolithic algal nodules and occasional coarse coral debris. This upper division appears to have formed in a higher-energy environment.

Age. The lower, marly units at the type locality are reported to be of late Palaeocene age (Montenat & Blondeau 1977). This is confirmed by the presence of the echinoids *Linthia cf. sudanesis* (Bather) in the basal Jafnayn Formation at Sunab and *Zuffardia rohlfsi boncarti* Lambert, *Gitolampas sp.* and *Echinolampas sweinfurthi devriesi* Roman from the Jafnayn Formation near Ibri (Dr A. Smith, British Museum of Natural History. pers. comm.).

The upper, relief forming limestone of the Jafnayn Formation at the type locality was ascribed to the lower part of the early Eocene by Montenat & Blondeau (1977).

Correlation and discussion. These age determinations correlate the Jafnayn Formation with the Umm er Radhuma Formation of Saudi Arabia (Steineke *et al.* 1958; Powers *et al.* 1966; Hasson 1985).

The Jafnayn Formation is not assigned to the Umm er Radhuma Formation to avoid confusion. The latter has been applied so widely across eastern Arabia to both shelf facies and to more basinal facies in the Pabdeh Basin (ranging from Palaeocene to late Eocene) that it cannot be said to retain a coherent lithostratigraphical character in the literature. The base of the Umm er Radhuma was originally defined partly on micropalaeontological grounds by Steineke *et al.* (1958). 'The base is at the contact of the *Lockhartia*-bearing basal dolomite and dolomitic limestone with the underlying Aruma tan dolomitic shale' (Steineke *et al.* 1985, p. 1311). In well sections referred by Hasson (1958) to the Umm er Radhuma Formation in Saudi Arabia *Lockhartia* disappears half way up the unit. In the Jafnayn Formation *Lockhartia* is absent from the basal marly unit but is present in large numbers in the upper cleaner limestone division. It is also abundant in shallow water facies of the overlying Seeb Formation. *Lockhartia* appears to be highly facies controlled in Oman and is unsuitable at a generic level for detailed biostratigraphical use.

The nature of the base of the Umm er Radhuma Formation is uncertain. Steineke *et al.* (1958) and Powers (1968) assumed it to be conformable whilst Powers *et al.* (1968), Sugden & Standing (1975) and Hasson (1985) have indicated that a disconformity may occur at the base. A low- to high-angle unconformity definitely is present at the base of the Jafnayn Formation.

Because of these ambiguities, the Jafnayn Formation is recognized as a separate local formation in the Oman mountains. This approach is justified because of its marked lateral persistence in lithostratigraphical character and is in accordance with the rules of stratigraphical procedures in that its purpose is to avoid unnecessary stratigraphical confusion. The shallow shelf Jafnayn and Umm er Radhuma Formations are separated by more basinal carbonate strata in the Pabdeh Basin and, as yet, there is no firm published evidence demonstrating that they were ever laterally joined.

Rusayl Formation (Lower Eocene)

Author. New formation.
Derivation of name. From Rusayl village.

Type section. Rusayl village, west of Muscat, Oman (Fig. 8). Grid reference 6237, 26025 to 6237, 26030. 58°13'20" E 23°32'20" N.
Thickness. 144 m measured by R. Crawford at type section but varies a lot in thickness around the type locality due to a combination of original sedimentary lenticularity and tectonic effects.
Description of type section. The basal unit consists of 52 m of poorly indurated multicoloured (red, purple, orange and yellow) shale and marl with occasional thin microcrystalline limestone and oyster bands. Patches of reddened conglomerate with chert and vein quartz clasts occur at the base, lying upon Jafnayn limestone. Above the basal unit is a prominent 6 m thick resistant, microcrystalline limestone bed. Above are 37 m of soft multicoloured shale and marl overlain by 12.5 m of interbedded multicoloured shale, sandstone and conglomerate. Towards the top of the formation are 18.5 m of multicoloured shale and marl, 18 m of interbedded marl, shale and hard orange/brown coloured well laminated grainstone and bioclastic limestone. Thin veins of gypsum transecting bedding occur within the multicoloured shales.
Boundaries. At the type section the contact between the Rusayl and Jafnayn formations is very sharp and a non-sequence is thought to be present. Around Ibri the top of the Jafnayn limestone is pitted and shows signs of possible subaerial solution. The upper contact between the Rusayl and Seeb Formations is sharp but conformable at the type locality and on a regional scale they interdigitate.
Lateral variation. Exposures of the multicoloured shales and marls, which characterize the Rusayl Formation, are all highly weathered. A number of deep road cuts in the Muscat area show that around 20 m below the surface, these

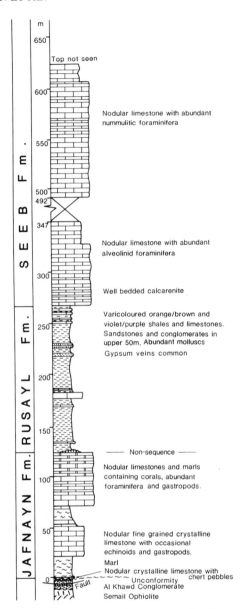

Fig. 8. Measured section from the type locality of the Jafnayn, Rusayl and Seeb Formations, Wadi Rusayl, S Batinah coast, near Muscat, from Grid Ref. 6237, 26020 to 6231, 26069.

weathered shales pass into fresh, organic-rich, black to dark grey mudstones with thin shelled bivalves, including mussels.

The Rusayl Formation is laterally highly variable. A basal conglomerate, composed of locally derived clasts, is present at a number of localities. At Medinat Qaboos, immediately east of Muscat, the Rusayl Formation rests unconformably upon sheared Ophiolite with a thin basal conglomerate of limestone and dolomite clasts derived from the adjacent northern flank of Saih Hatat. Conglomerates formed of oncolites and stromatolites occur in the Rusayl Formation to the NW around Fardah, near Khasaf (Fig. 1).

Horizons of marly oyster rudstone, laterally continuous for up to 3 km, occur at a number of localities around Fardah and Rusayl. At Jammah thick beds of pebbly sandstone and calcareous sandstone are present. Coarse bioclastic limestones comprised entirely of alveolinid and nummulitic foraminifera and of Soritidae occur at Jammah and Wadi Taww respectively.

The Rusayl Formation is recognized on the Batinah coast south of Khasaf and in the east Oman Mountains (see Filbrandt *et al*. 1990). It is absent west of the northern and central Oman Mountains.

Environment of deposition. A wide variety of sedimentary environments are represented in the Rusayl Formation, from conglomeratic beach and peritidal facies, through restricted lagoonal and mud flat facies (with autochthonous oyster beds), tidally influenced gravel bars and foraminiferal limestones, to shallow, submergent, storm bedded sandstone barrier complexes. In general the formation formed in littoral to inshore environments. Fluvial and pedogenic facies are present east of the Sur Gap.

Age. The type locality was ascribed to the lower Eocene by Montenat & Blondeau (1977). A. Smith (pers. comm.) identified the echinoids *Gitolampas? cf. enormis* Duncan and Sladen, *Schizaster sp.* and *?Linthia sp.*, indicating a lower Eocene age for the Rusayl Formation at Wadi Taww on the Batinah coast.

Correlation and discussion. The Rusayl Formation is correlated with the Rus Formation (Steineke *et al*. 1958) of Saudi Arabia. It is not included within the Rus Formation as it differs from it in a number of respects. The Rus Formation consists predominantly of poorly fossiliferous chalky limestone and gypsum/anhydrite around its type locality (Steineke *et al*. 1958; Powers *et al*. 1966; Powers 1968) while the Rusayl Formation has a noticeable terrigenous clastic content and contains diverse fossils. The gypsum present in the Rusayl Formation generally occurs as tectonic veins, not as bedded horizons as in the Rus Formation. Although these veins are most frequent in the Rusayl Formation in the Oman Mountains, post-depositional gypsum veins and crystals also

occur in exposures of shale in most of the post-Campanian succession in the area and they are not a reliable lithostratigraphical feature. Only rare thin horizons of original evaporite nodules occur in the Rusayl Formation at outcrop in the Darsayt road cut near Muscat, and north of Jebel Ja'alan (Filbrandt *et al*. 1990).

Seeb Limestone Formation (Middle Eocene)

Author. New formation.

Derivation of name. Named from the adjacent town of Seeb on the Batinah coast.

Type section. Roadside section along the main Nizwa to Muscat road through Wadi Rusayl from grid reference 6 221, 26 031 to 6 231, 26 069 on the Batinah coast west of Muscat. 58°12'00″ E 23°32'20″ N to 58°12'40″E 23°34' 90″ N, (Fig. 8).

Thickness. 356 m approximately at the type section.

Description of type section. (Based on R. Crawford unpublished section 1982). 30 m of beige, thick to moderately well bedded calcarenite with cross bedding, occasional vein quartz pebbles and common miliolids. The basal 6 m of this unit contains abundant echinoids. Overlying the basal well-bedded calcarenite unit are 51 m of beige/orange/brown coloured, medium-bedded, bioturbated, nodular weathering packstones with orbitoids, alveolinids, miliolids and occasional *Nummulites* and rhodolithic algae. The nodularity increases in intensity up from the contact with the basal well bedded calcarenite unit. Above this is a 145 m (approx) gap in exposure which elsewhere is seen to be occupied by limestone with thin marl partings. The section then continues with 130 m of bedded nodular packstones of similar aspect to those down section but with more abundant nummulitic foraminifera.

Boundaries. The contact with the underlying Rusayl Formation is sharp but conformable. The top of the Seeb Formation is unexposed. Up sequence from the Seeb Formation there are around 41 m of intermittently exposed coral rudstones of late Eocene/early Oligocene age (Montenat & Blondeau 1977). About 200 m of strata are calculated as unexposed between these and the top exposures of the Seeb Formation. A regional unconformity occurs on the Arabian Peninsula between Eocene and Oligo-Miocene strata (Steineke *et al*. 1958; Dominguez 1965; Powers *et al*. 1966; Beydoun 1966; Powers 1968; Hawkins *et al*. 1981). Such a feature may occur at the top of the Seeb Formation.

Lateral variation. In the type section and in most other localities the Seeb Formation displays a vertical trend from alveolinid/miliolid dominated limestones up to *Nummulites/Assilina* dominated limestones. From Rusayl to Wadi Taww the formation is very laterally consistent in lithostratigraphical character. On the Batinah coast the formation thins northwards and changes in facies. At Jammah and Tawi Summah a number of coral patch reef rudstones occur. Around Khasaf and Tawi Summah *Nummulites/Assilina* rudstones are developed. Grainstones dominate here, contrasting with the type section where packstones predominate. One oolitic horizon occurs at Tawi Summah.

The Seeb Formation is also present north and east of Dhank and in the eastern Oman Mountains.

Environment of deposition. The Seeb Formation formed in a shallow, open, carbonate shelf environment. A wide variety of localised facies were developed within this overall setting. High energy shoals were developed on the Batinah coast during the marine transgression at the base of the formation. The upward transition from miliolid to alveolinid and *Nummulites/Assilina* dominated lithofacies is interpreted as an upward deepening trend on comparison with published works on foraminiferal palaeoecology (Henson 1950; Wright & Murray 1972; Eva 1976; Haynes 1980). *Nummulites* and *Assilina* bank facies, similar to those described by Aigner (1983) occur around Khasaf and Tawi Summah.

Age. Montenat & Blondeau (1977) record diverse benthonic foraminifera from the Seeb Formation in its type area indicating a middle Eocene age. At Medinat Qaboos, 12 km west of Muscat, Middle Eocene echinoids, *Rhyncholampas aff. grignonensis* (Defrance) and *Ilavionia cf. beggiatoi* (Laube), were identified (A. Smith, pers. comm.) from the lower Seeb Formation between 10 and 15 m above the Tertiary basal unconformity.

Correlation and discussion. The Seeb Formation is distinguished from the Fahud Beds by its highly fossiliferous character in the field. On the north Batinah coast, the Seeb and Ruwaydah Formations may interfinger.

The Seeb Formation is correlated with the Dammam Formation (Steineke *et al.* 1958). The Seeb Formation is erected as a new local unit according to the rules of stratigraphical nomenclature because these two units appear not to have been laterally continuous with each other but were separated by finer-grained facies in the Rub'al Khali Basin and Suneinah Trough.

Ruwaydah Formation (Eocene)

Author. New formation.

Derivation of name. From Jebel Ruwaydah.

Type area. Scattered exposures between and including Jebel Ruwaydah and Al Qusayr, near Wadi Sakin, SW of Saham, on the north Batinah coast, Oman (Fig. 9). Grid reference 4762, 26656 to 4797, 26270. 56°46'10" E 24°06'28" N to 56°48'00" E 24°07'45" N.

Thickness. Approximately 900 m or more in the type area.

Description of type area. 60 m of beige, tabular, well bedded hard crystalline biosparites, with chert nodules, yellow/cream coloured shale and marl horizons and occasional lenticular beds of limestones conglomerate. The latter include pebbles, cobbles and boulders of nummulitic and alveolinid Seeb shelf limestone. Overlying this lower calcarenitic unit are around 800 m of sporadically exposed thinly interbedded, tabular, fine grained, chalky limestone and pale yellow/cream shale and marl with occasional calcarenite horizons, often with chert nodules, and lenticular limestone conglomerate beds. Above the highest conglomerate bed are about 50 m of sporadically exposed chalky limestone, marl and shale with occasional coarse bioclastic horizons rich in giant foraminifera or echinoids.

Boundaries. Neither the top nor bottom of the Ruwaydah Formation are seen. As there appear to be no Palaeocene strata present between the Ruwaydah and Thaqab Formations and the basal Ruwaydah lies adjacent to different members of the Thaqab, a strike fault or unconformity may be present.

Lateral variation. The calcarenite and conglomerate horizons wedge out laterally into chalky limestone, shale and marl. A few individual conglomerate lenses are traceable for over 5 km.

Environment of deposition. The calcarenite beds in the Ruwaydah Formation are commonly graded and may include Bouma cycles with giant foraminifera, forming Ta–Tb units. Slump folding and sole marks, such as flutes, are not common. The conglomerate beds are generally chaotic and are often capped by graded foraminiferal limestones. These are interpreted as debris flow deposits. The Ruwaydah Formation formed in a submarine slope environment. It forms a turbidity current/debris flow apron-fan complex flanking the eastern side of the north central Oman Mountains.

Age. The Ruwaydah Formation contains a diverse benthonic foraminiferal fauna including alveolinids and *Nummulites*. These appear to

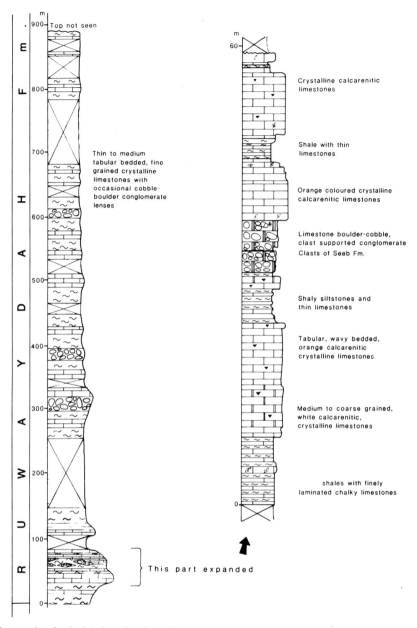

Fig. 9. Measured and calculated section from the type locality of the Ruwaydah Formation, Wadi Sakhin, N Batinah coast, near Saham (composite log grid ref. 4 762, 26 656 to 4 797, 26 279). The extract (right) shows details of the wadi section exposed on Jebel Ruwaydah, S of the ruined fort, grid ref. 4 762, 26 656 to 4 768, 26 660.

be similar to those from the Seeb Formation but palaeontological analysis is necessary to confirm this. A diverse echinoid fauna including *Coptosoma sp.*, *Echinolampas sp. cf. esnehensis* Fourtan/*cf. intermedus* Duncan and Sladen, *Linthia sp. aff. insignis* Currey/*rousseli* Cotteau, *Schizaster? africanas* de Loriol and *Macropneustes ?pellati* Cotteau/*sindensis* Lambert, indicating an Eocene age (A Smith, pers. comm.), were recorded from the upper 50 m of the Ruwaydah Formation near Al Qusayr.

Correlation and discussion. The Ruwaydah Formation is lithologically similar to the Muthaymimah Formation but differs from it in not including reworked clasts of Maastrichtian and older rocks. The Ruwaydah Formation is given a separate stratigraphical status according to the rules of stratigraphical nomenclature because the two formations were not in physical continuity, but were separated by a positive area which supplied debris for both. Like the Muthaymimah Formation, the Ruwaydah Formation differs from the Pabdeh Formation of Iran (James & Wynd 1965) on the presence of conglomerate horizons.

The Ruwaydah Formation may interfinger with the Seeb Formation north of Tawi Summah on the Batinah coast.

Fahud Beds (Middle Eocene)

Author. New informal unit.

Derivation of name. Jebel Fahud.

Type Section. Low undulating exposures on the NW flank of Jebel Fahud beginning near the base of the dip slope of Jafnayn Formation (Fig. 10). Grid reference 4 461, 24 629 to 4 452, 24 619. 56°28′20″ E 22°16′20″ N.

Thickness. About 160 m are present at the type section. The top of this unit has not been seen at surface.

Description of type section. The Fahud Beds consist of thin bedded chalky wackestone, shale and marl. It usually appears poorly fossiliferous in the field, though occasional horizons rich in alveolinid foraminifera or echinoids are discernable in most localities. At the type locality, the lower Fahud Beds consist of thin to moderately thick beds of cross bedded alveolinid calcarenite. The Fahud Beds are generally recessively weathering unit forming low outcrops and, unlike the resistant underlying Jafnayn or Seeb Formations, never forms major topographic features.

Boundaries. The base at the type locality appears to be conformable. Around Ibri, to the north, the top of the underlying Jafnayn Formation is irregular and pitted and the lower calcarenitic unit of the Fahud Beds is absent. A non-sequence or disconformity may be present.

Lateral Variation. The Fahud Beds are recognized in the SW foothills of the Oman mountains (Fig. 1) between the Maradi Fault zone and Al Mazam near Dhank. Between Al Mazam and Jebel Abyad the Fahud Beds and Seeb Formation interdigitate.

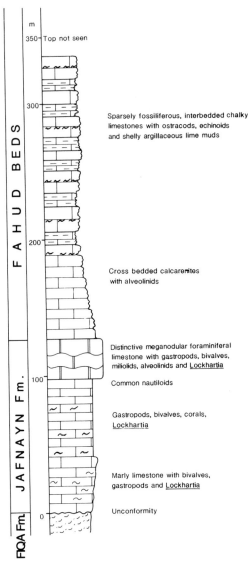

Fig. 10. Measured section from the type locality of the Fahud Beds, Jebel Fahud, SW of the Oman Mountains.

Environment of deposition. The Fahud Beds are mostly of low energy shelf facies. Its fauna generally lacks *Nummulites* and is far more restricted than the open shelf Seeb Formation. Biomodal tidally influenced shoal facies are present at Fahud and Al Mazam.

Age. Dr. A. Smith identified *Sismondia marginalis* Desor from the thin bedded wackestones and marls at the type locality and *Conoclypeus delanouei* de Loriol, *Linthia sp.* and *Echino-lampas cf. ovalis* (Bovy) from Jebel Khatmat–Dhank north of Ibri, indicating an Eocene age. *Correlation and discussion.* The Fahud Beds may be a correlative of the Dammam and/or Rus Formations of Saudi Arabia, but because of uncertainty we do not assign them to these units. The Fahud Beds lack the abundant nummulitic content of the Seb Formation and are also distinguished from the latter by their thinly bedded, recessively weathering character at surface and restricted macrofauna. At out-crop they lack the evaporitic horizons of the Rus Formation.

Muthaymimah Formation (Palaeocene to Eocene)

Author. New Formation.
Derivation of name. The Muthaymimah For-mation forms the dip slope of the hills on the northwest side of Sayh Muthaymimah, SE of Buraymi.
Type section. Hill section on the NW side of Sayh Muthaymimah (Fig. 11). Grid reference 39 980, 26 667 to 39 982, 26 670. 55°49′50″ E 24°06′30″ N.
Thickness. About 300 m at type section.
Description of type section. (After measured section by R. Crawford). 37.5 m olive green/orange brown shale, marl and thin, flaggy, argil-laceous limestone overlain by 18 m of thickly bedded limestone conglomerate including clasts of 'Simsima' limestone and reworked rudist and coral fragments, and rarer Ophiolite clasts. This is overlain by 56 m of yellow/orange, thin, platy and flaggy bedded, splintery argillaceous calculites and marl with occasional thin, len-ticular conglomerate bands. A few limestone bands contain rare subspherical alveolinids. Overlying this is a 2 to 3 m conglomerate con-taining clasts of Hawasina chert, Ophiolite and 'Simsima' limestone and reworked rudist debris. Above are 42 m of thin, flaggy, interbedded argillaceous limestone and marl which are grey in colour in the lower half and orange/yellow in colour in the upper half. Overlying these are 88 m of interbedded shale and marl with thin graded lithic sandstone and limestone bands with occasional nummulites and lenticular con-glomerates which include clasts of Hawasina chert, Ophiolite and reworked Palaeogene limestone. These are followed by 40 m of thickly bedded to massive limestone conglomerate con-taining reworked clasts of nummulitic Seeb limestone and lesser amounts of Ophiolite and Hawasina chert debris. Above this are further

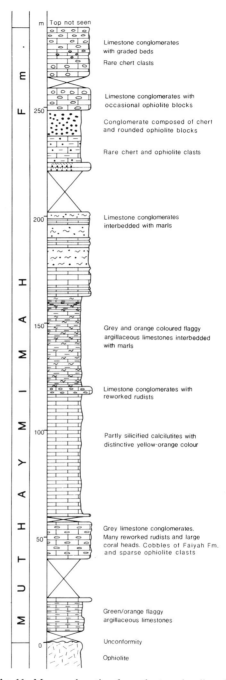

Fig. 11. Measured section from the type locality of the Muthaymimah Formation, Jebel Muthaymimah, west central side of the Oman Mountains, near Buraymi and Al Ayn.

unlogged poor exposures of thinly bedded marl and argillaceous limestone with limestone, Ophiolite and Hawasina chert clasts in the dip slope of the hill.

Boundaries. At the type section the Muthaymimah Formation lies with a sharp contact upon Semail Ophiolite. This boundary appears to be unconformable but has acted as a slip plane during later tectonic movements. On Jebel Rawdah and Faiyah the Muthaymimah Formation rests unconformably upon the 'Simsima Formation'. The Muthaymimah Formation interdigitates with and is overlain on Jebel Rawdah by un-named Eocene basinal marl, shale and limestone lacking the conglomerates typical of the Muthaymimah Formation.

Lateral variation. At the type locality, and on Jebel Mundasah immediately to the north, the formation includes a lot of pre-Maastrichtian debris. Further north on Jebels Rawdah and Faiyah and at Tawi al Harf, it includes mostly limestone debris and fragments of Ophiolite or Hawasina are rare or absent. It has only been recognized in the NW foothills of the Oman mountains.

Environment of deposition. The lenticular conglomerates in the Muthaymimah Formation were deposited by a variety of unconfined or semi-confined debris flows in a proximal submarine slope environment. Interbedded with these are graded calcareous, lithic sandstones and limestones which display units from the Bouma cycle indicating deposition from turbidity currents. Current ripples from calciturbidite beds on Jebel Rawdah indicate a palaeoflow generally from the east. The source of the clasts is presumed to have lain in the east in the Oman mountains as the Pabdeh Basin lies to the west.

The thin basal conglomerate on Jebel Thanais, just south of Jebel Faiyah, contains cobbles of 'Simsima' limestone including silicified fossils standing proud of the clast surfaces. These are enveloped by a calcilutite matrix containing planktonic foraminifera and sponge spicules. Similar features to this are also seen in the lowest limestone debris bed at the type locality. From this evidence it would appear that a brief episode of subaerial weathering may have silicified fossils in the 'Simsima' before their erosion and incorporation in relatively deep marine debris flow units of the Muthaymimah Formation. The absence of shallow marine facies at the base of the Muthaymimah Formation suggests rapid subsidence during the early Palaeogene along the NW flank of the Proto-Oman Mountain belt.

Age. The age of the Muthaymimah Formation is at present only crudely constrained. It uncon-formably overlies the Maastrichtian 'Simsima Formation' or older units and includes reworked clasts and fossils from these. Higher up it also includes occasional alveolinid and nummulitic foraminifera and reworked clasts of pene-contemporaneous Palaeogene shelf limestone. The Muthaymimah Formation appears to be of Palaeocene to (middle?) Eocene age.

Correlation and discussion. A similar conglomeratic facies, the Ruwaydah Formation exists on the NE side of the Oman mountains (see discussion in section on Ruwaydah Formation).

Hafit Formation (Eocene)

Author. Cherif & el Deeb (1984).

Derivation of name. Jebel Hafit.

Type section. Western side of Jebel Hafit, south of Al Ayn/Buraymi. Lower and Middle Members: grid reference 3 72, 26 65 to 3 73, 26 65 approx. 55°45'20" E 24°05'10" N. Upper Member: grid reference 3 72, 26 63, to 3 73, 26 63 approx. 55°45'00" E 24°04'30" N.

Thickness. 327 m maximum exposed, but the base of the Lower Member is not seen.

Description of type selection. (After Cherif & el Deeb 1984). The Hafit Formation constitutes the major relief forming units in the centre of the Hafit Pericline. The Lower Member consists of massive bedded, grey, nodular, sometimes dolomitic, wackestone with subordinate marly interbeds. It attains 111 m but its base is not exposed. This is conformably followed by the Middle Member which consists of up to 101 m of light brown marl with intercalated marly limestone bands. Following this is the Upper Member of up to 115 m of resistent pale brown/grey, nodular limestone with subordinate marly interbeds. The Upper Member is reported to rest with a low angle unconformity upon the Lower and Middle Members in southern Jebel Hafit.

Boundaries. The Upper Member is conformably overlain by the Senaiya Formation.

Lateral variation. As the Hafit Formation at outcrop is restricted to Jebel Hafit, very little lateral variation is known within the unit.

Environment of deposition. The Hafit Formation contains planktonic foraminifera and occasional large benthonic alveolinid and nummulitic foraminifera in graded calcarenite bands. In places chert filled *Thallasinoides* burrows are numerous. From this it is apparent that the Hafit Formation formed in a relatively deep, basinal, setting.

Age. Cherif & el Deeb (1984) reported a middle to early late Eocene age.

Senaiya Formation (late Eocene to early Oligocene)

Author. Cherif & el Deeb (1984).

Derivation of name. Senaiya industrial area, south of Al Ayn at the north end of the Hafit anticline.

Type sections. North and east Jebel Hafit, south of Al Ayn/Buraymi.

A and B Members: grid reference 3 74, 26 66 to 3 75, 26 67. 55°45′50″ E 24°06′10″ N.

C Member: grid reference 3 74, 26 72 approx. 55°45′20″ E 24°09′10″ N.

D Member: grid reference 3 74, 26 74 approx. 55°45′40″ E 24°09′50″ N.

E Member: grid reference 3 75, 26 74 approx. 55°45′40″ E 24°09′50″ N.

Thickness. Up to 250 m.

Description of type section. The Senaiya Formation consists of interbedded ridge forming limestones and recessive marls. Member A consists of 20 m of pale brown marl and marly limestone. The B Member is composed of up to 143 m of pale yellow, often nummulitic, limestone with marly interbeds. Marls and marly limestones up to 45 m thick constitute the C Member. These are overlain by 20 m of cross bedded miliolid calcarenite, pale yellow nummulitic limestone with dolomitic bands and marls which form Member D. Member E is composed of up to 22 m of light brown, sandy gypsiferous marl.

Boundaries. Member A of the Senaiya Formation conformably succeeds the Hafit Formation. Cherif & el Deeb (1984) noted that the E Member cuts down unconformably to overlie the B Member on the SE flank of Jebel Hafit. The Senaiya Formation is conformably overlain by the Lower Coralline Limestone Member (early middle Oligocene) or is unconformably overlain by the Upper Marly Nummulitic Member (late middle Oligocene) of the Al Jaww Formation (cf. Cherif & el Deeb, 1984).

Environment of deposition. The Eocene parts of the Senaiya Formation were deposited in a shallow to open marine carbonate shelf setting.

Age. Cherif & el Deeb (1984) report that Members A–D are of late Eocene age and suggest that Member E is of early Oligocene age.

Correlation and discussion. Mid/late Eocene to Oligocene limestones and marls of similar facies to the Senaiya formation occur in scattered outcrops along the western flank of the Oman Mountains east of Buraymi and in scattered outliers to the west of Jebel Faiyah. Further data are necessary, however, to determine their stratigraphic position.

Late Campanian to Tertiary palaeogeography of the Central and Northern Oman Mountains

Late Campanian and Maastrichtian

During the early part of this period the Oman mountains were emergent and were being actively eroded. The detritus produced was washed down onto the flanks of the mountain belt producing localized beach, fluviatile and fan delta deposits which constitute the Al Khawd and Qahlah Formations. These formations lie unconformably upon deformed pre-Campanian rocks (see Fig. 12a,b). The Al Khawd Formation, east of Wadi Rusayl, immediately north of Saih Hatat, includes a reverse stratigraphy of Saih Hatat in its clast composition. Ophiolitic debris dominates at the base, Mesozoic carbonate debris is more common higher up, and pre-Permian metamorphic quartzites predominate at the top. As this formation is unconformably overlain by late Palaeocene marls and limestones, the Saih Hatat culmination must have been breached down to the pre-Permian before the Tertiary. Late Campanian and Maastrichtian erosion elsewhere in the central and northern Oman mountains does not appear to have been as dramatic.

In a number of localities where the Qahlah Formation rests unconformably upon the Semail ophiolite, red and purple pedogenic deposits (laterites/saprolites) are developed. These are particularly well displayed around Jebel Faiyah. Their presence indicates the existence of a tropical climate with a high, possibly seasonal, rainfall by comparison with similar modern and ancient pedogenic deposits (Frakes 1979; Bardossy 1981; Leprun 1981; Schellmann 1981). Conformably overlying the Qahlah Formation on the NW and eastern flanks of the mountain belt is a sequence of shallow marine, bioclastic shelf limestones containing rudists of the 'Simsima' Formation. These generally display an upward deepening trend through the Maastrichtian (Skelton *et al.* 1990).

Deep marine basins lay to the west and NE of the mountain belt during the late Campanian and Maastrichtian. To the west lay the remnant foreland ('Aruma' or 'Fiqa') basin which filled with mudstones and shales containing planktonic foraminifera, the Fiqa Formation (Glennie *et al.* 1974; Burruss *et al.* 1985). Along the NE margin of the basin a 'flysch'-like sequence of terrigenous clastics, the Juweiza Formation, was formed during the Campanian, from detritus eroded from the advancing thrust sheets (Glennie *et al.* 1974).

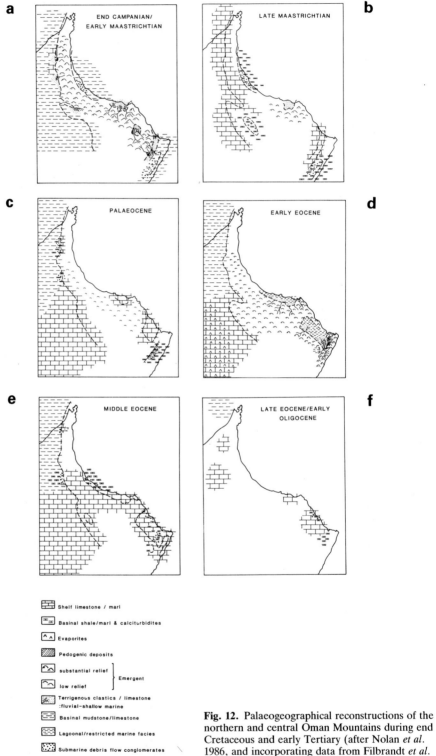

Fig. 12. Palaeogeographical reconstructions of the northern and central Oman Mountains during end Cretaceous and early Tertiary (after Nolan *et al.* 1986, and incorporating data from Filbrandt *et al.* (1990) and Ries & Shackleton (1990).

A similar sequence of basinal deposits, the Thaqab Formation, accumulated on the opposite, western, side of the north Oman mountains. At the base are cobbly and bouldery debris flow deposits. These fine upwards into a mudstone/shale sequence with episodic turbiditic sandstone beds. The sequence coarsens again towards the top with bioclastic calciturbidites containing a shallow-water fauna, derived from a shelf area to the east. The 'Simsima' limestone is, therefore, inferred to have covered much of the north Oman mountain belt during the late Maastrichtian.

Palaeocene and early Eocene (Fig. 12c)

A major regional unconformity separates Tertiary and Cretaceous strata in the Oman mountains. The 'Simsima Formation', locally up to 200 m thick, was completely eroded in patches along the western side of the mountain belt, between Ibri and Jebel Rawdah. NW of the Oman mountains the 'Pabdeh Basin' developed during the Palaeogene. Basinal marls, argillaceous limestones and calciturbidites accumulated in this basin during the Palaeocene to Oligocene (Ricateau & Riche 1980; Burruss et al. 1985). A sequence of interbedded sub-marine debris flow conglomerates, turbiditic sandstones, limestones and shales, the Muthaymimah Formation, accumulated along the steep eastern slope of this basin adjacent to the north Oman mountain belt. The conglomerates include reworked clasts of 'Simsima' limestone in the lower parts of the Muthaymimah Formation. Clasts of pre-Maastrichtian rocks and coeval Palaeogene shelf limestone become more frequent and clasts of 'Simsima' limestone become less common up sequence, indicating a progressive downstripping through the old Maastrichtian cover.

Shallow marine limestones of late Palaeocene to early Eocene age, the Jafnayn Formation, are present both NE and SW of the central Oman mountains. The lower parts of the Jafnayn Formation are marly and of low-energy facies. The higher parts consist of cleaner limestones, with abundant alveolinid foraminifera, calcareous red algae and coralline debris, which represent higher-energy facies.

Early, middle and late Eocene (Fig. 12d,e,f)

On the Batinah coast the Rusayl Formation overlies the Jafnayn Formation with a marked non-sequence and north of Wadi Taww it overlaps to rest unconformably upon older strata.

SW of the central mountains, around Ibri, the top of the Jafnayn Formation is irregular and pitted and the basal unit of the overlying Fahud Beds is absent, again suggesting the presence of a non-sequence.

During the early Eocene the central Oman mountains were probably emergent. Beach conglomerates including chert pebbles, probably eroded from the Hawasina Complex, are present at the base of the Rusayl Formation in a number of localities on the Batinah coast. South of Khasaf peritidal facies including fenestral micrites, and oncolitic and stromatolitic rudstones are associated with the basal beach facies. Overlying the basal beach facies is a sequence of mudstone and shale, with occasional oyster beds deposited in a lagoonal/tidal flat environment. Within this sequence a variety of facies are present including tidally influenced pebbly channel sandstones and wash-over lobes of foraminiferal limestone. At Jammah a number of fine-grained sandstone barrier complexes are developed.

The Rusayl Formation is absent SW of the central Oman mountains. A sequence of poorly fossiliferous, peloidal micrites, of probable lagoonal facies, overlying the Jafnayn Formation on Jebel Abyad near Dhank may be contemporary with the Rusayl Formation.

A marine transgression occurred during the middle Eocene. Open shelf limestone facies, rich in giant benthonic foraminifera, the Seeb Formation, were established across the central Oman mountains. On the Batinah coast, coral patch reefs occur at Jammah whilst to the north at Khasaf well developed nummulite bank facies, similar to those described by Aigner (1983), are present. Around Dhank, SW of the central mountains, the highly fossiliferous, open shelf limestone facies of the Seeb Formation interfingers with the Fahud Beds which consist of generally finer-grained, less fossiliferous limestones and marls. On Jebel Fahud and near Dhank, bidirectionally cross bedded calcarenite shoal facies are present in the Fahud Beds indicating deposition under a tidal influence.

In the west, deposition of the Muthaymimah Formation continued during the early to middle Eocene. In the NE a sequence of Eocene turbiditic calcarenites, shales and chalky limestones, the Ruwaydah Formation, are present. Both formations include fragments of penecontemporaneous Seeb shelf limestone eroded from the northern mountain belt. The Muthaymimah Formation also includes a lot of debris derived from pre-Maastrichtian strata. The 'Pabdeh basin' west of the northern mountains was gradually filled during the mid to late

Eocene by shallow marine shelf carbonates in the Al Ayn/Buraymi area (Cherif & el Deeb, 1984). Deposition of the basinal facies, however, continued into the Oligocene off the NW coast of the Musandam Peninsula (Ricateau & Riche 1980). NE of the central mountain belt, late Eocene/Oligocene limestones and marls with coralline patch reefs occur in Wadi Rusayl (Montenat & Blondeau 1977) indicating a regression during the late late Eocene.

Discussion

Both palaeoclimate and palaeotopography appear to have had a large influence upon the geological history of the central and northern Oman mountains during the late Cretaceous and Tertiary.

The presence of laterites/saprolites in the late Campanian/early Maastrichtian indicates the existence of a tropical climate with a high annual rainfall on comparison with ancient and modern analoges (Frakes 1979; Bardossy 1981; Leprun 1981; Schellmann 1981; Hallam 1984). A high, perhaps seasonal, annual rainfall would also allow rapid erosion of upland areas and the formation of large humid fan deltas, as at Al Khawd.

During the late Campanian/Maastrichtian, Oman was situated in the tropics in a seaward-facing position (Smith & Briden 1977) open to a prevailing easterly palaeo-wind direction (Parrish & Curtis 1982; Parrish *et al.* 1982). The rapid subaerial denudation of Saih Hatat down to the pre-Permian prior to the Palaeocene indicates that the Saih Hatat culmination probably had a very marked topography during the late Campanian/Maastrichtian. This combination of high relief and palaeo-climatical situation meant that the Oman mountains probably received a large annual rainfall and were subject to rapid erosion.

The northern Oman mountains were emergent during the end Campanian but subsided below sea level during the Maastrichtian allowing the formation of a shallow carbonate shelf (Skelton *et al.* 1990). This upward deepening, transgressive trend is at variance with the global regressive trend in sea level noted by Vail *et al.* (1977) during this period. One possible explanation is that isostatic subsidence occurred in the northern Oman Mountains due to the weight of the Semail ophiolite.

During the Palaeogene, the Oman mountains do not appear to have had as large a relief they had during the Late Cretaceous. For most of the early Tertiary the northern Oman mountains were a positive but submergent feature supply-

ing detritus to deep marine basins to the east and west. The central Oman mountains may have had a modest relief during the early Eocene allowing limited erosion of Hawasina units to form detritus for the beach conglomerates of the Rusayl Formation along the NE flank of the mountain belt. This unit also includes a small development of beach conglomerate containing limestone clasts derived from Saih Hatat in the immediate vicinity of the Saih Hatat culmination. Palaeogene sediments thin towards Saih Hatat indicating that the Saih Hatat culmination was still exerting some influence on sedimentation during the Palaeogene. From the low volumes of terrigenous detritus in the adjacent early Tertiary strata Saih Hatat and the central Oman mountains in general do not appear to have had much relief at this time (Glennie *et al.* 1974; Nolan *et al.* 1986).

The sedimentary patterns of transgression and regression noticeable in the Palaeogene strata of the mountain belt generally follow the global cycles documented by Vail *et al.* (1977). A curious anomaly within this cyclicity is present on the Batinah coast where the 'transgressive' Jafnayn limestone Formation is overlapped by the Rusayl Formation which is of 'regressive' facies. This anomaly cannot be explained by invoking substantial erosion of the Jafnayn Formation as no clasts of this unit occur reworked in the Rusayl Formation and there is only a non-sequence between them.

The lower Eocene in the central and northern Oman mountains is noticeably less evaporitic than equivalent strata in Saudi Arabia (Steineke *et al.* 1958; Powers *et al.* 1966) and interior Oman SW of the mountain belt (Glennie *et al.* 1974; Glennie 1977). This probably reflects a palaeoclimatic influence of the mountain belt as suggested by Glennie *et al.* (1974). During the lower Eocene Oman still lay in the tropics, in a similar position to that occupied during the late Cretaceous (Smith & Briden 1977) but was probably in a rain shadow because of the northwards drift of the Indian plate at this time across the line of the prevailing westerly palaeo-wind direction. Some support for this hypothesis is to be found in the numerous occurrences of Eocene bauxites in India (Bardossy 1981) which indicate a high annual rainfall in India during this period.

The present marked topographical relief of the northern and central Oman mountain belt appears to be a post-Eocene feature (Lees 1928; Glennie *et al.* 1974; Nolan *et al.* 1986). Part of this uplift may be attributed to Zagros compression in the northern Oman mountains (Ricateau & Riche 1980; Searle *et al.* 1983;

Searle 1985). Zagros effects, however, diminish southwards and the central Oman mountains appear to have been in a dominantly extensional tectonic regime since the late Campanian/Maastrichtian (Mann et al. 1990). Zagros events in the north finished during the middle Miocene (Ricateau & Riche 1980) but the Oman mountains have continued to rise from the late Miocene to the Recent (Glennie et al. 1974; Glennie 1977; Ricateau & Riche 1980). The reasons for this continued uplift are unclear at present.

Conclusions

The central and northern Oman mountains have undergone a varied geological history since the emplacement of the Semail Ophiolite and Hawasina/Sumeini thrust sheets in the late Cretaceous. Palaeoclimate and palaeotopography are seen to have had a large influence upon the type of sedimentary sequences deposited in the area from the late Campanian/Maastrichtian to the present. Tectonic structures formed during the Turonian−Campanian orogeny (Glennie et al. 1974; Hanna 1986) profoundly influenced late Campanian/Maastrichtian to Eocene sedimentation.

Amoco Oman Petroleum Company is most sincerely thanked for its help with funding this work. The paper is published with the permission of Amoco Production Company. We are grateful to R. Crawford for permission to use unpublished material collected during his time at the Earth Resources Institute.

References

AIGNER, T. 1983. Facies and origins of nummulitic buildups: an example from the Giza Pyramids Plateau (Middle Eocene, Egypt). Neues Jahrbuch fur Geologie und Palaontologie Abhandlungen, 166, 347−368.

BARDOSSY, G. Y. 1981. Palaeoenvironments of laterites and lateritic bauxites − effect of global tectonism on bauxite formation in lateritization processes. Proceedings of the International Seminar on lateritization processes, India, Dec 1979. A A Balkema, Rotterdam, 287−294.

BEYDOUN, Z. R. 1966. Geology of the Arabian Peninsula: Eastern Aden Protectorate and part of Dhufar. US Geological Survey Professional Paper, 560-H.

BURRUSS, R. C., CERCONE, R. R. & HARRIS, P. M. 1985. Timing of hydrocarbon migration: evidence from fluid inclusions in calcite cements, tectonic and burial history. In: SCHNEID-ERMANN, N. & HARRIS, P. M. (eds) Carbonate cements. Society of Economic Palaeontologists and Mineralogists, Special Publication, 36, Tulsa, 277−289.

CHERIF, O. H. & EL DEEB, W. M. Z. 1984. The

middle Eocene−Oligocene of the northern Hafit area, south of Al Ain City (United Arab Emirates). Geologie Mediterraneenne, XI, 2, 207−217.

COLEMAN, R. G. 1981. Tectonic setting for ophiolite obduction in Oman. Journal of Geophysical Research, 86, 2497−2508.

DOMINGUEZ, J. R. 1965. Offshore fields of Qatar. Institute of Petroleum Review, 19, No. 222, 198−210.

DUNNINGTON, H. V. 1967. Stratigraphic distribution of oilfields in the Iraq−Iran−Arabian Basin. Journal of the Institute of Petrology, 53, No. 520, p. 129.

EVA, A. N. 1976. The palaeoecology and sedimentology of Middle Eocene larger foraminifera in Jamaica. In: SCHAFER, C. T. & PELLETIER, B. R. (eds) First International symposium on benthonic foraminifera of continental margins, Part B, Palaeoecology and biostratigraphy. Maritime Sediments, Halifax, Canada, 467−475.

FILBRANDT, J. B., NOLAN, S. C. & RIES, A. C. 1990. Late Cretaceous and Tertiary evolution of Jebel Ja'alan and adjacent areas, NE Oman. In: ROBERTSON, A. H. F., SEARLE, M. P. & RIES, A. C. (eds) The Geology and Tectonics of the Oman Region. Geological Society, London, Special Publication, 49, 697−714.

FOX, A. F. & BROWN, R. C. C. 1968. The geology and reservoir characteristics of the Zakum Oilfield, Abu Dhabi. 2nd Regional Technical Symposium of the Society of Petroleum Engineers of AIME, Saudi Arabia section, Dhahran.

FRAKES, L. A. 1979. Climate throughout geologic time. Elsevier, Amsterdam.

GLENNIE, K. W. 1977. Outline of the geology of Oman. Memoires H. series Societie geologie France, No. 8, 25−31.

——, BOUEF, M. G. A., HUGHES-CLARK, M. W., MOODY-STUART, M., PILAAR, W. F. H. & REINHARDT, B. M. 1973. Late Cretaceous nappes in the Oman Mountains and their geologic evolution. Bulletin of the American Association of Petroleum Geologists, 57, 5−27.

——, ——, ——, ——, —— & —— 1974. The geology of the Oman Mountains. Verhandelingen van Ket Knoninklijk Nederlands geologisch Minjbouwkundig Genootschap., 31.

GRAHAM, G. M. 1980. Evolution of a passive margin and nappe emplacement in the Oman Mountains. In: PANAYIOTOU, A. (ed.) Proceedings of the International Ophiolite Symposium, Cyprus 1979, 414−423.

HALLAM, A. 1984. Continental humid and arid zones during the Jurassic and Cretaceous. Palaeogeography, Palaeoclimatology, Palaeoecology, 47, 195−233.

HANNA, S. S. 1986. The Alpine (Late Cretaceous and Tertiary) tectonic evolution of the Oman Mountains: a thrust tectonic approach. In: Symposium on the hydrocarbon potential of intense thrust zones, Ministry of Petroleum and Mineral Resources, UAE and OPEC, Kuwait, Abu Dhabi, 1986, 125−174.

HANTZCHEL, W. 1975. Trace fossils and problematica. Part W Miscellanea supplement 1, 2nd edn, Treatise on invertebrate paleontology. *Geological Society of America and University of Kansas*, Lawrence, Kansas.

HARLAND, W. B., AGER, D. V., BALL, H. W., BISHOP, W. W., BLOW, W. H., CURRY, D., DEER, W. A., GEORGE, T. N., HOLLAND, C. H., HOLMES, S. C. A., HUGHES, N. F., KENT, P. E., PITCHER, W. S., RAMSBOTTOM, W. H. C., STUBBLEFIELD, C. J., WALLACE, P. & WOODLAND, A. W. 1972. A concise guide to stratigraphical procedure. *Journal of the Geological Society of London*, **128**, 295–305.

HARRIS, P. M. & FROST, S. H. 1984. Middle Cretaceous carbonate reservoirs, Fahud field and Northwestern Oman. *Bulletin of the American Association of Petroleum Geologists*, **68**, 649–658.

HASSON, P. F. 1985. New observations on the biostratigraphy of the Saudi Arabian Umm er Radhuma Formation (Palaeogene) and its correlation with neighbouring regions. *Micropalaeontology*, **31**, 335–363.

HAWKINS, T. R. W., HINDLE, D. & STRIGNELL, R. 1981. Outlines of the stratigraphy and structural framework of the southern Dhofar (Sultanate of Oman). *Geologisch en Mijnbouw*, **60**, 247–256.

HAYNES, J. 1981. *Foraminifera*. MacMillan.

HEDBURG, H. D. (ed.). 1976. *International stratigraphic guide*. John Wiley and Sons, New York.

HENSON, F. R. S. 1950. Cretaceous and Tertiary reef formations and associated sediments in the Middle East. *Bulletin of the Association of American Petroleum Geologists*, **43**, 215–238.

JAMES, G. A. & WYND, J. G. 1965. Stratigraphic nomenclature of Iranian oil consortium agreement area. *Bulletin of the Association of American Petroleum Geologists*, **49**, 2182–2245.

LEES, G. M. 1928. The geology and tectonics of Oman and of parts of south-eastern Arabia. *Quarterly Journal of the Geological Society of London*, **84**, 585–670.

LEPRUN, J. C. 1981. Some principal features of ironcrusts in dry western Africa. *In*: *Lateritization Processes*, Proceedings of the International Seminar on lateritization processes, India, Dec 1979. A A Balkema, Rotterdam, 144–153.

LIPPARD, S. J. & REX, D. C. 1982. K-Ar ages of alkaline igneous rocks in the northern Oman Mountains, NE Arabia, and their relations to rifting, passive margin development and destruction of the Oman Tethys. *Geological Magazine*, **119**, 497–503.

MANN, A., HANNA, S. S. & NOLAN, S. C. 1990. Post-Campanian tectonic evolution of the central Oman mountains: tertiary extension of the eastern Arabian margin. *In*: ROBERTSON, A. H. F., SEARLE, M. P. & RIES, A. C. (eds) *The Geology and Tectonics of the Oman Region*. Geological Society, London, Special Publication, **49**, 549–563.

MONTENAT, C. & BLONDEAU, A. 1977. Premier apercu du Tertiaire d'Oman (Peninsule arabique orientale). *Bulletin Societie geologie France*, **19(7)**, 1285–1295.

NOLAN, S. C., CLISSOLD, B. P. SMEWING, J. D. & SKELTON, P. W. 1986. Late Campanian to Tertiary palaeogeography of the central and northern Oman Mountains. *In*: *Symposium on the hydrocarbon potential of intense thrust zones*, Ministry of Petroleum and Mineral Resources, UAE and OPEC, Kuwait, Abu Dhabi, 1986, 175–200.

NORTH AMERICAN COMMISSION ON STRATIGRAPHIC NOMENCLATURE. 1983. North American stratigraphic code. *Bulletin of the Association of American Petroleum Geologists*, **67**, 841–875.

OWEN, R. M. S. & NASR, S. N. 1958. Stratigraphy of the Kuwait-Basra area. *In*: WEEKS, L. G. (ed.) *Habitat of oil: a symposium*. Bulletin of the Association of American Petroleum Geologists, 1252–1278.

PARRISH, J. T. & CURTIS, R. L. 1982. Atmospheric circulation, upwelling and organic-rich rocks in the Mesozoic and Cenozoic eras. *Palaeogeography, Palaeoclimatology, Palaeoecology*, **40**, 31–66.

——, ZIEGLER, A. M. & SCOTESE, C. R. 1982. Rainfall patterns and the distribution of coals and evaporites in the Mesozoic and Cenozoic. *Palaeogeography, Palaeoclimatology, Palaeoecology*, **40**, 67–102.

POWERS, R. W. 1968. Saudi Arabia (excluding Arabian Shield). *Lexique Stratigraphique International*, **III**, Asie, fasc. 10b1.

——, RAMIREZ, L. F., REDMOND, C. D. & ELBERG, E. L. 1966. Geology of the Arabian Peninsula: sedimentary geology of Saudi Arabia. *US Geological Survey Professional Paper 560D*.

RACZ, L. 1979. Paleocene carbonate development of Ras al Hamra, Oman. *Bulletin Centre Recherche Exploration et Production Elf-Aquitaine*, **3**, 767–779.

RICATEAU, R. & RICHE, P. H. 1980. Geology of the Musandam Peninsula (Sultanate of Oman) and its surroundings. *Journal of Petroleum Geology*, **3**, 139–152.

SHACKLETON, R. M., RIES, A. C., BIRD, P. R., FILBRANDT, J. B., LEE, C. W. & CUNNINGHAM, G. C. 1990. The Batain Melange of NE. Oman. *In*: ROBERTSON, A. H. F., SEARLE, M. P. & RIES, A. C. (eds) *The Geology and Tectonics of the Oman Region*. Geological Society, London, Special Publication, **49**, 715–724.

ROBERTSON, A. H. F. & WOODCOCK, N. H. 1983. Genesis of the Batinah melange above the Semail ophiolite, Oman. *Journal of Structural Geology*, **5(1)**, 1–17.

SCHELLMANN, W. 1981. Consideration on the definition and classification of laterites. *In*: *Lateritization processes*. Proceedings of the International Seminar on lateritization processes, India, Dec 1979. A A Balkema, Rotterdam, 1–10.

SEARLE, M. P. 1985. Sequence of thrusting and origin of culminations in the northern and central Oman Mountains. *Journal of Structural Geology*, **7**,

129–143.

——, JAMES, N. P., CALON, T. J. & SMEWING, J. D. 1983. Sedimentological and structural evolution of the Arabian continental margin in the Musandam Mountains and Dibba zone, United Arab Emirates. *Bulletin of the Geological Society of America*, **94**, 1381–1400.

SKELTON, P. W., NOLAN, S. C. & SCOTT, R. W. 1990. The Maastrichtian transgression onto the northwestern flank of the Proto-Oman Mountains: sequences of rudist-bearing beach to open shelf facies. *In*: ROBERTSON, A. H. F., SEARLE, M. P. & RIES, A. C. (eds) *The Geology and Tectonics of the Oman Region*. Geological Society, London, Special Publication, **49**, 521–547.

SMITH, A. G. & BRIDEN, J. C. 1977. *Mesozoic and Cenozoic palaeocontinental maps*. Cambridge University Press, Cambridge.

STEINEKE, M., BRAMKAMP, R. A. & SANDER, N. J. 1958. Stratigraphic relations of Arabian Jurassic oil. *In*: *Habitat of oil*, American Association of Petroleum Geology Symposium, 1294–1329.

SUGDEN, W. & STANDING, A. 1975. Qatar Peninsula. *Lexique Stratigraphique International*, III, Asie, fasc. 10b3, 7–88.

VAIL, P. R., MITCHUM, R. M. & THOMPSON, S. 1977. Seismic stratigraphy and global changes of sea level. Part 4: global cycles of relative changes of sea level. *In*: PAYTON, C. E. (ed.) *Seismic stratigraphy — applications to hydrocarbon exploration*. Memoirs of the American Association of Petroleum Geology, **26**, 83–97.

WARRAK, M. 1986. Structural evolution of the northern Oman mountain front, Al-Ain region. *In*: *Symposium on the hydrocarbon potential of intense thrust zones*, Ministry of Petroleum and Mineral Resources, UAE & OPEC, Abu Dhabi, 375–431.

WILSON, H. H. 1969. Late Cretaceous eugeosynclinal sedimentation, gravity tectonics, and ophiolite emplacement in the Oman Mountains, SE Arabia. *Bulletin of the American Association of Petroleum Geologists*, **53**, 626–671.

WOODCOCK, N. H. & ROBERTSON, A. H. F. 1982a. The upper Batinah Complex, Oman: allochthonous sediment sheets above the Semail ophiolite. *Canadian Journal of Earth Sciences*, **19**, 1635–1656.

—— 1982b. Stratigraphy of the Mesozoic rocks above the Semail ophiolite, Oman. *Geological Magazine*, **119(1)**, 67–76.

WRIGHT, C. A. & MURRAY, J. W. 1972. Comparisons of modern and Palaeogene foraminiferid distributions and their environmental implications. *Memoires Bureau Recherche geologique Minieres*, **79**, 87–96.

The Maastrichtian transgression onto the northwestern flank of the Proto-Oman Mountains: sequences of rudist-bearing beach to open shelf facies

P. W. SKELTON[1], S. C. NOLAN[2] & R. W. SCOTT[3]

[1] *Department of Earth Sciences, The Open University, Milton Keynes, MK7 6AA, UK*

[2] *Earth Resources Institute, University College of Swansea, Singleton Park, Swansea, SA2 8PP, UK*

[3] *Amoco Production Company, 4502 East 41st Street, PO Box 3385, Tulsa, Oklahoma 74102, USA*

Abstract: The Maastrichtian Qahlah and Simsima Formations, the first autochthonous deposits on the obducted Oman ophiolite complex, crop out in a girdle of jebels around the Oman Mountains. Those around the NW flank, between Al Dhayd (Sharjah) and Al Ayn−Buraymi (Dubai−Oman) are documented to illustrate: (1) an exposed regional reference section for the widespread Simsima Formation, at Jebel Faiyah (Sharjah); (2) the marked transgressive nature of the sequence onto the obducted complex; and (3) the rich rudist faunas there, associated with various beach to shelf facies, and their palaeoecological and palaeobiogeographical implications.

'Basement' (serpentinites in the north and sedimentary nappes in the south) is overlain by locally developed laterites and the dominantly siliciclastic, marginal continental to marine deposits of the Qahlah Formation, followed, with local erosion and overlap, by the carbonate-dominated Simsima Formation. The latter continues the deepening trend, passing from basal rudist-rich inshore facies to open shelf foraminiferal packstones to wackestones. The whole sequence onlaps eastwards onto the obducted complex. Its truncated top is overlain by Palaeogene slope deposits.

In the north (Jebel Faiyah area) the Maastrichtian sequence has an open, relatively high energy aspect. A shelf margin of Simsima Formation rudist limestones briefly developed in the early Maastrichtian around Qarn Murrah. Further transgression to the southeast drowned this and, by 'mid'-Maastrichtian times, a bouldery beach conglomerate of the Qahlah Formation, with *in situ Durania*, was forming at Jebel Faiyah itself, along a cliff-backed shoreline with sandy embayments. Over this came tidally influenced rudist-rich facies and foraminiferal limestones of the Simsima Formation. In the south (Jebel Huwayyah area), in contrast, marginal fan−delta gravels and sandstones, of early Maastrichtian age, were followed by more restricted shallow marine silty marls and limestones with *Loftusia*, rudists and corals, of early to mid-Maastrichian age. These Qahlah deposits were overlapped by a relatively rudist-poor Simsima Formation sequence.

The obducted complex was thus strongly emergent at the start of the Maastrichtian, and the Aruma Sea transgressed onto its western flank, as the ophiolite subsided through that stage, forming a relatively open shelf in the north, becoming broader and more restricted further south. The rudist assemblages found on this shelf are similar to those of other open Tethyan shelves in the eastern and central Mediterranean and Middle East.

The allochthonous complex of the Semail Ophiolite and underlying sedimentary nappes, which was obducted onto the eastern Arabian continental margin in late Cretaceous times, is today widely exposed along the Oman Mountains because of post-Miocene axial uplift and erosion (Lippard *et al*. l986, and other papers in this volume). Post-emplacement autochthonous strata on the obducted complex therefore only crop out now in peripheral jebels skirting the mountain chain (Nolan *et al*. 1990, Fig. 1). The regional lithostratigraphy of these has been studied in a series of AMOCO-funded Earth Resources Institute projects, based on surface outcrop, reported by Nolan *et al*. (1990).

This paper focuses on the Maastrichtian sequence in the eastern United Arab Emirates (UAE), along the northwestern border of the Oman Mountains, from just south of Al Dhayd, in the north, to Al Ayn (UAE)−Buraymi

From ROBERTSON, A. H. F., SEARLE, M. P. & RIES, A. C. (eds), 1990,
The Geology and Tectonics of the Oman Region.
Geological Society Special Publication No 49, pp 521−547

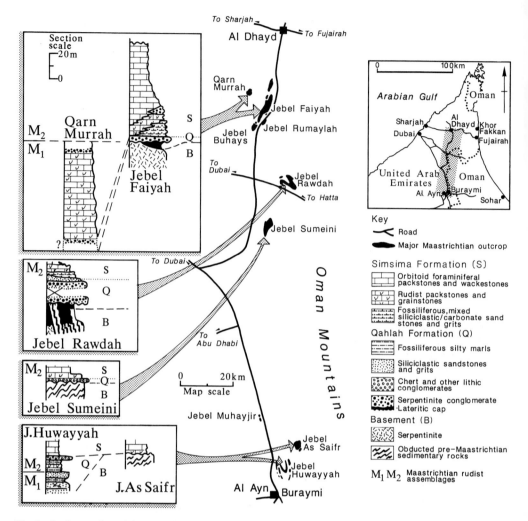

Fig. 1. Study area (top right: grey shaded rectangle), and map of Maastrichtian outcrops (black) within it, with synoptic sequences shown to the left. Note that the Qahlah/Simsima boundary and basal unconformity are diachronous.

(Oman), in the south (Fig. 1). The sequence is exposed in isolated jebels of openly folded strata, which jut out of a flattish plain of wadi−fan gravels and, further west, desert sands, flanking the mountains.

The sequence we describe has three main points of interest: first, the area includes Jebel Faiyah, selected by Nolan *et al.* (1990) to provide an accessible, exposed regional reference section for the Simsima Formation, a widespread uppermost Cretaceous shallow marine carbonate unit (see Hughes Clarke 1988; also Nolan *et al.* 1990, for discussion of problems in the use of this name); secondly, the marked transgressive character of this sequence, the first to onlap the

obducted complex, has important implications for the immediate post-emplacement history of the ophiolite; and thirdly, its rich, but hitherto scarcely documented, rudist fauna has considerable palaeoecological and palaeobiogeographical interest.

Stratigraphy and palaeoenvironmental interpretations

The same basic sequence is recognisable throughout the study area (Fig. 1). Using the formation names employed by Nolan *et al.* (1990), the sequence is: the 'basement' of obducted complex (serpentinized peridotites of the Semail Ophiolite Mantle Sequence in the north, and thrust sheets of the Hawasina Assemblage and Sumeini Group in the south) is overlain, with marked angular unconformity, by the marginal continental to shallow marine deposits of the predominantly siliciclastic Qahlah Formation; the latter is then overlain, with local minor discontinuity, and with some direct overlap onto the basement, by the shallow marine deposits of the predominantly carbonate Simsima Formation, showing a deepening trend, from shoreface to open shelf facies. A regional low-angle unconformity truncates the Simsima and is overlain by Palaeogene slope carbonates of the Muthaymimah Formation. The overall transgressive trend of the basement Qahlah Simsima sequence involves a broadly eastward onlap, towards the Oman Mountains.

The sections at the various jebels (Fig. 1) are described and interpreted in three groups below, prior to relating them to the regional stratigraphical context and summarizing the palaeogeographical implications of our work. We start with (1) the group of jebels around Jebel Faiyah, in the North, including a small hillock, Qarn Murrah, rising out of the desert sands to the West. Then we briefly consider (2) Jebels Rawdah and Sumeini, a little further south, followed by (3) Jebels Huwayyah and As-Saifr in the Al Ayn−Buraymi area.

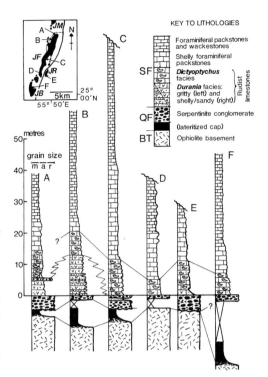

Fig. 2. Jebel Faiyah area sequence. Inset, map of Jebel Faiyah and neighbouring jebels (shown in black), showing locations of the sections A−F: JM, Jebel Mulaghah; JF, Jebel Faiyah; JR, Jebel Rumaylah; JB, Jebel Buhays. Main figure, Sections A−F, showing lateral facies variations: BT, basement; QF, Qahlah Formation; SF, Simsima Formation. Grain size grades: m, mudrock; a, arenite; r, rudite.

The Jebel Faiyah area

Jebel Faiyah (Fig. 2) comprises two connected *en echelon* anticlines trending NNE−SSW (from latitude 25°02'N and longitude 55°48'E to latitude 25°07'N and longitude 55°01'E). These have an asymmetrical, upturned boat form, verging to the west. The northern anticline continues in a small jebel just over 2 km to the north (Jebel Mulaghah), and an isolated outcrop of the eastern limb of the southern anticline forms Jebel Rumaylah. A further anticline is exposed to the southwest, forming Jebel Buhays. Hogsback exposures of the eroded limbs of these anticlines expose the full sequence reposing on the serpentine basement. Faulting disrupts the sequence here and there, particularly in the steep western limbs.

Measured sections along these jebels show considerable lateral variation in thicknesses and constituent facies of the formations (Fig. 2). Section C, the thickest, is taken as the regional reference section for the Simsima Formation. *Basement and Qahlah Formation.* At the base of the Qahlah, reddy brown, friable silty laterite and/or saprolite (yet to be analysed) caps much of the serpentine basement, forming a recessive,

commonly scree-covered horizon. No hardened pisolithic or vermiform structures were noted. The depth of this alteration varies, reaching at least 6 m around northwestern Jebel Faiyah (Section B). Locally, as in Section C, a continuous downward passage from the laterite, through greenish, sandy lithic material, into deeply weathered and brecciated serpentinite may be seen. This palaeosol lenses out southwards so that, at Jebel Rumaylah (Section E), Qahlah conglomerate directly overlies a hummocky eroded surface of fresh serpentine (Fig. 3a). Further south, at Jebel Buhays (Section F), however, the palaeosol returns, reaching some 20 m or more in thickness.

Overlying the basal palaeosol is a continuous resistant bed, up to 5 m thick, of bouldery conglomerate with a gritty sandstone matrix and with localized sandstone horizons. At Jebel Mulaghah, to the north, however, only a thin sandstone is present.

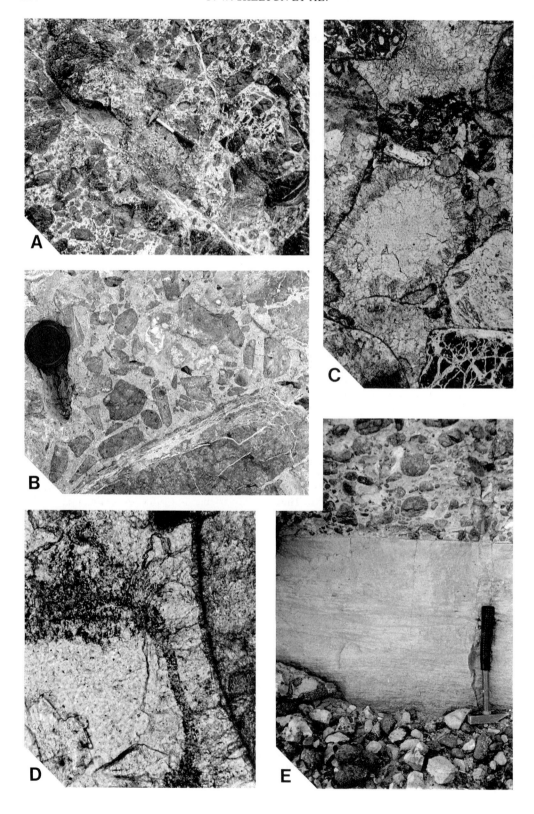

The generally well rounded clasts of the conglomerate are of serpentinized peridotite derived from the basement. The clasts show a strong preferred orientation parallel to bedding. At Jebel Rumaylah (Section E), lines of particularly large boulders (up to 1.5 m across) trace out crude bedding surfaces in the gritty matrix (Fig. 3a).

Another feature of the serpentinite boulders at some sites is syn-sedimentary arrested weathering, where the boulders have cracked and exfoliated, but have then been 'frozen' in the act of breaking up by matrix sand and thin cement rinds which have filled in the fractures (Fig. 3b).

Rounded fragments and some little worn single valves of large radiolitid and hippuritid rudists are also incorporated in the conglomerate (Fig. 3b), together with rare unworn and articulated shells of the radiolitid *Durania*.

The matrix of the conglomerate is a mixed lithic−bioclastic, medium to coarse gritty sandstone, of whitish to pale orange-brown colour. It is markedly heterogeneous, with sharp vertical changes in the relative proportions of lithic and bioclastic grains. The lithic component comprises rounded grains of serpentinized peridotite with chicken-mesh texture (Fig. 3c) and rare grains of mylonitized serpentinite containing blobs of chrome spinel, probably derived from the basal thrust zone of the ophiolite (B. Murton, 1988 pers. comm.). The bioclasts are well rounded, and most are of cloudy neomorphic calcite after aragonite or clearer, fibrous prismatic calcite (Fig. 3c). Both types are largely derived from rudist shells. Samples from Jebel Rumaylah (Section E) also include scattered spheroidal vugs, 1−2 mm across, some with arched sand rooves (Fig. 3c), conforming in shape and size to 'keystone vugs' (Emery 1945; Dunham 1970). Three generations of cement were noted here (Fig. 3c, d): (1) a thin palisade of stumpy prisms, in places holding together the sand rooves of the keystone vugs; (2) a thick isopachous fringe of elongate cloudy crystals showing a variably ghosted fibrous texture, with radiaxial extinction, lining original pores, including the keystone vugs; and (3) drusy spar, filling the remaining voids. All are now calcite, though the highly variable ghosting of (1) and (2) shows these to have been neomorphosed. The early (pre-burial) origin of these neomorphosed cements is confirmed by the lack of compactional fracturing of, or pressure solution effects between the grains. They are therefore probably derived from early marine cements of originally high Mg calcite or perhaps aragonitic (cement 2) composition (see Hollingworth & Tucker (1987), with references therein, for a discussion of similar cement fabrics). These early cements were doubtless also responsible for preventing the dolomitization, which is prevalent in the immediately overlying unit, from affecting this one. Cement (3) is presumably a later stage ?meteoric phreatic cement.

Further north (Section B) the lithic component is augmented by scattered small angular grains of chrome spinel, probably derived from the breakdown of the mylonitized serpentinite grains.

The bioclastic component includes, in addition to abundant molluscan (mainly rudist) grains, fragments of corallinacean algae (largely derived from broken rhodoliths) and abundant whole and fragmentary orbitoids and smaller benthic foraminifera. Early cement fabrics are less clearly preserved here; the primary pore spaces are filled by cloudy neomorphic calcite (? after micritic or fibrous cements).

Lithic−bioclastic sandy lenses are locally interstratified within the conglomerate. Most are rather friable and show few sedimentary structures. One in Section C, however, is better lithified and displays low-angle truncations, small scour features, climbing ripples and some small (15 cm deep) channels (Fig. 3e). Its strikingly flat top, undistorted by the overlying pebbles suggests early cementation as well. No sandstone lenses were observed at Jebel Rumaylah (Section E).

Simsima Formation. The conformably suc-

Fig. 3. Qahlah Formation serpentinite boulder conglomerate at Jebel Faiyah: (a) Outcrop at Jebel Rumaylah (Section E). Bedding dips to left (SE); serpentinite basement exposed at bottom right. Hammer shaft is 33 cms long. (b) Detail of outcrop (loose block) at northern Jebel Faiyah (Section A). Note matrix and cement filled exfoliation fractures of serpentinite boulder at base, and shell of *Biradiolites* (centre). Lens cap is 5.5 cm across. (c) Photomicrograph, in plane polarized light, of conglomerate matrix at Jebel Rumaylah. Note arched sand roof of keystone vug (centre) and lining of isopachous fibrous cement. Width of frame is 1.7 mm. Top is up. (d) Detail of another keystone vug, as in c. Note thin cement palisade of stumpy prisms around grain to right and around grains of sand roof, and much thicker isopachous fibrous fringe, in this case much neomorphosed with only weak ghosting of fibrous texture. Width of frame is 0.5 mm. Top is up. (e) Early cemented sandstone lens within Qahlah conglomerate at central Jebel Faiyah (Section C). Hammer shaft is 30 cm long.

ceeding Simsima Formation is dominated by browny yellow, patchily dolomitized bioclastic limestones, though pebbly grits and sandstones are locally interstratified in the basal few metres (especially in Section B). This local interdigitation of Qahlah-, and Simsima-type facies is lithostratigraphically resolved by arbitrarily placing the base of the Simsima Formation beneath the first limestone bed above the basal conglomerate.

Besides its localized siliciclastic content, the lower 5–20 m of the Simsima Formation has abundant coarse bioclastic rubble, amongst which rudists and orbitoid foraminifera are particularly common. These basal rudist limestones show more lateral variability than the substantially thicker upper part of the Simsima, which consists of somewhat monotonous shelly foraminiferal packstones passing up to finergrained foraminiferal packstones and wackestones (Fig. 2).

Two main facies can be discerned in the basal rudist limestones. The first is localized, immediately overlying the conglomerate in northern Jebel Faiyah (Sections A and B) and is thin to absent elsewhere. It comprises interstratified sandy rudist limestones and the gritty to pebbly sandstones mentioned above, and has a low biotic diversity, overwhelmingly dominated by *Durania* (Fig. 4a, b, c). This is termed the '*Durania* facies'. The second is present in all sections, overlying the *Durania* facies in the north, and immediately succeeding the Qahlah Formation in the south, as well as at Jebel Mulaghah, to the north of Jebel Faiyah. It comprises nodular bioclastic packstones with a much smaller and more sporadic siliciclastic content, and possesses a rich biotic diversity. It is named the '*Dictyoptychus* facies' after the large canaliculate rudist commonly associated with it (Fig. 4f). Specimens of *Durania* and

Dictyoptychus are present in both facies, though in different proportions.

Where best developed, in Section B (Fig. 2), the siliciclastic-dominated beds of the *Durania* facies are grainstones, containing rounded pebbles of serpentinite (up to 4 cm across) in grits and sandstones composed of serpentinite, with some finer, more angular grains of chrome spinel, and carbonate lithoclasts and bioclasts (as in the underlying conglomerate). The bioclasts include abundant rounded molluscan (especially rudist) grains, orbitoids and corallinacean fragments. The latter are probably largely derived from rhodoliths, and some incorporate serpentinite grains. In the thicker (several tens of centimetres) lower beds in Section B, the pebbles show a strong bedding parallel fabric, but higher up, thinner, lenticular beds of sandstone, with pebbly bases, show planar cross-stratification of decimetric scale.

The more bioclastic-rich beds of the *Durania* facies largely consist of a coarse coquinoid rubble of angular *Durania* fragments with a grainstone to packstone matrix of serpentinite–bioclastic gritty sandstone. These tend to lens out over lateral extents of only about 10 m. Here and there, upright clusters of *Durania* may be found in life position, as, for example, immediately overlying the Qahlah conglomerate at Section B (Fig. 4a). These specimens have steep inwardly inclined inner margins to their (attached) right valves, with their thin-rimmed left valves inserting in plug-like fashion (Fig. 4b), in contrast to specimens from higher in the sequence, which display the more characteristic horizontal disposition of the valve margins. Sections across the calcitic outer shell layer of these basal Simsima specimens moreover show the inclusion of sand within their cellular growth layers (Fig. 4c). Apart from *Durania*, other relatively rare, large bioclasts include fragments

Fig. 4. Simsima Formation at Jebel Faiyah (a) Cluster of upright *Durania* specimens, in life position upon the upper boundary of the Qahlah conglomerate at northwestern Jebel Faiyah (Section B), immersed in a pebbly sandstone matrix. Lens cap is 5.5 cm across. (b) Specimen of *Durania* (from locality at a, above) showing the broad inner margin of the left valve (above) fitting into the steeply inward-sloping inner rim of the right valve (below). Width of frame is 10 cm. (c) Photomicrograph, in plane polarised light, of radial section across the outer shell layer of the right valve of *Durania* (specimen shown in b, above), showing the incorporation of sand grains within the cellular growth layers. Width of frame is 1.7 mm. (d) Vertical section of acteonellid biostrome at top of *Durania* facies (Simsima Formation) at southern end of the northern anticline of Jebel Faiyah. Hammer head is 15 cm long. (e) Vertical section through part of the first rhythm in the *Dictyoptychus* facies at central Jebel Faiyah (Section C, base of Simsima). The top of the Qahlah is shown at the base; the rubbly lower unit occupies the rest of the lower half of the frame; and the nodular upper unit occupies the upper half. Height of frame about 120 cm. (f) Basal surface (underside of steeply dipping bed) of the upper unit of one of the rhythms in the *Dictyoptychus* facies at central Jebel Faiyah (Section C), showing a group of *Dictyoptychus* in life position (left: the undersides of the reclining right valves are visible) and an overturned cluster of *Durania* (right). The white lumps are rhodoliths and reworked nodules. Width of frame about 120 cm.

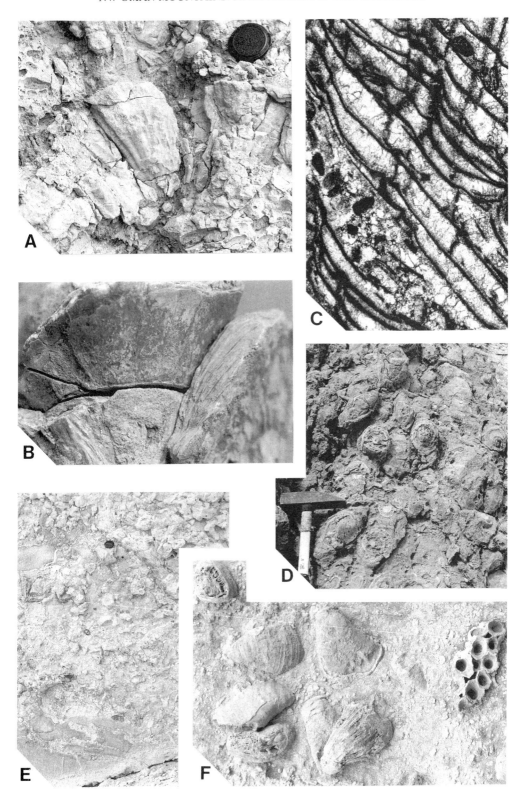

of corals, 'chaetetid' sponges, orbitoids, and other rudist genera. At the northernmost end of Jebel-Faiyah (Section A), acteonellid gastropods, large oysters and the gregarious hippuritid, *Hippurites cornucopiae* Defrance, some in life position near the top of the facies unit, join the assemblage. Here the siliciclastic content is less, and a single prominent serpentinite conglomerate interbed arbitrarily marks the top of the *Durania* facies (Fig. 2A). Acteonellids also become particularly abundant in a biostrome capping the *Durania* facies in the highly faulted sequence exposed in the southern closure of the northern anticline of Jebel Faiyah (Fig. 4d).

When traced southwards from Section B, the *Durania* facies interfingers with the *Dictyoptychus* facies (Fig. 2). Here the former shows large-scale southwardly orientated planar cross-stratification. Some of the cross-bedding is of low-angle, with concave surfaces, suggesting lateral accretion surfaces. Low relief channel forms may also be seen hereabouts.

In keeping with its more even thickness along strike, the *Dictyoptychus* facies shows rather more lateral consistency than does the *Durania* facies. At most sites it consists of massive to thickly-bedded, highly fossiliferous, medium-grained packstones (Fig. 4e). The transition to the overlying shelly foraminiferal packstones is gradational, so the boundary between them is arbitrary. Broken to whole rudists (*Dictyoptychus* and various radiolitids and hippuritids), some in life position (Fig. 4f), other bivalves [notably epifaunal forms, e.g. scallops, oysters such as *Lopha dichotoma* (Bayle) and *Exogyra* sp., and rare inoceramids], gastropods (especially large acteonellids and *Campanile*), regular echinoids and both solitary (cyclolitids) and rarer colonial corals and 'chaetetid' sponges, along with orbitoid foraminifera (Fig. 5a) and rhodoliths (Fig. 5b) are set in a matrix of poorly sorted biomicrite. Patchy ferroan dolomitization is common, and may be locally quite intense, although matrix-preferential.

A one to three metre-scale vertical rhythmicity is locally apparent (Figs 4e & 6), especially in Sections C and F. Each rhythm comprises an erosively based lower unit of rubbly grainstone to packstone, passing up, with rapid gradation, or even with minor discontinuity, to an upper unit of nodular fossiliferous packstone. This is usually capped by the erosive base of the next rhythm. Thicknesses vary, with the lower unit ranging from a few tens of centimetres (in Section C) up to about 2 m (in Section F), and the upper unit, between 0.5 and 1.5 m. The lower units of the rhythms contain a variety of broken and/or displaced shells, commonly somewhat worn and bored, and many partially encrusted by calcareous algae, together with abundant rhodoliths. Reworked nodules, serpentinite pebbles and lithic sand are also incorporated, and indeed tend to dominate in the basal rhythm (Fig. 4e). The upper units of the rhythms are characterized by a tangled network of *in situ* ramifying nodules, apparently nucleated upon branching burrow systems (Fig. 4e). Despite this extensive bioturbation, some wave ripples were noted in Section F. The body fossil content is somewhat sparser, and rhodoliths, in particular, are less common than in the lower units. However, whole *Dictyoptychus*, encrusting radiolitids and small hippuritid bouquets, with encrusting 'chaetetid' sponges and rare colonial corals, are found in life position here and there, most commonly immediately overlying the tops of the lower units (Fig. 4f). At Jebel Buhays (Section F), some thin (~5 cm) storm-generated horizons of graded sandstone, with bioturbated tops, were also noted within the rhythmic sequence.

Above the *Dictyoptychus* facies, the macrofossil content progressively decreases and the matrix becomes finer; a trend represented on Fig. 2 by the transition from 'shelly foraminiferal packstones' to 'foraminiferal packstones and wackestones'. The lower part retains some burrow-nodularity, and scattered horizons, up to a few tens of centimetres thick, containing relatively common whole shells of scallops, plicatulids (*Plicatula hirsuta* Coquand), oysters, indeterminate burrowing bivalves, gastropods, irregular echinoids, solitary corals and rhodo-

---

Fig. 5. Simsima fossils (a, b) and modern analogues for the Jebel Faiyah sequence (c–f) at Khor Fakkan, Fujairah (see Fig. 1 for locality). (a) Photomicrograph, in plane polarized light, of *Dictyoptychus* facies at northwestern Jebel Faiyah (Section B), showing sections across three orbitoids. *Omphalocyclus macroporus* (top), *Orbitoides media* (bottom right), and *Siderolites calcitrapoides* (bottom left). Width of frame is 30 mm. (b) Photomicrograph, in plane polarized light, of rhodolith in *Dictyoptychus* facies packstone at northwestern Jebel Faiyah (Section B). Width of frame is 20 mm. (c) A headland at Khor Fakkan with a serpentinite cliff flanked by a bouldery sand beach. (d) Section of eroded beachrock near back of embayment with interbedded gritty sand and shelly rubble. Hammer shaft is 33 cm long. (e) Detail of boulders and interstitial sand with rounded bioclastic rubble. Note encrusting oysters (and barnacles) at top right. (f) Photomicrograph, in plane polarised light, of beachrock (from d, above). Width of frame is 1.8 mm.

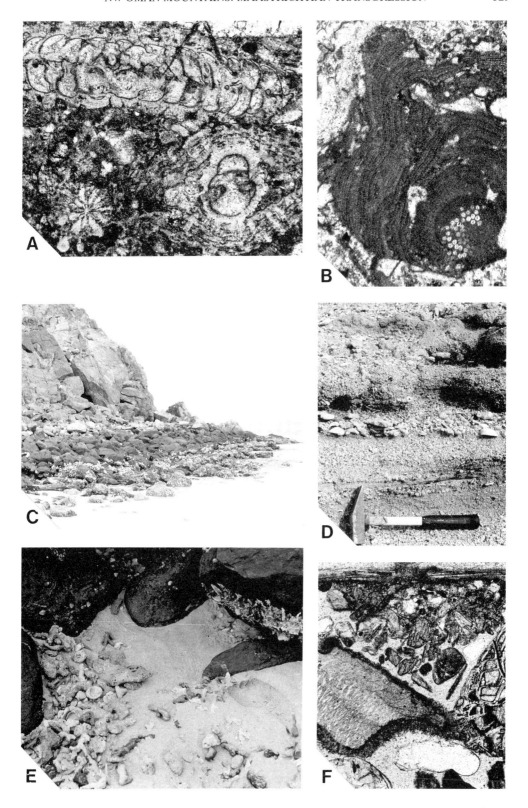

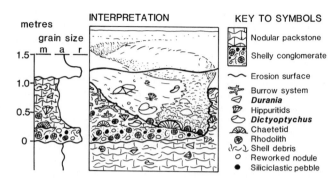

Fig. 6. Diagrammatic log of a rhythm in the *Dictyoptychus* facies of the Simsima Formation at Jebel Faiyah (left), interpreted (centre) as a tidal channel point-bar sequence.

liths, together with rare, usually fragmentary *Dictyoptychus* and *Durania*. Orbitoid foraminifera are scattered through the sequence, particularly, again, in the lower part. The foraminiferal packstones to wackestones at the top of the sequence have only rare macrofossils, but contain poorly preserved, unkeeled planktonic foraminifera and calcispheres (unidentified as yet).

Unconformity at the top of the Simsima Formation. The unconformable contact between the upper orange-yellow Simsima Formation and the overlying creamy white Muthaymimah Formation is in many places obscured by faulting. However, it is particularly well exposed on the western flank of Jebel Thanais (a small hillock just north of the western limb of Jebel Buhays). Here, the low-angle unconformity carries a thin (20–30 cm thick) conglomerate at the base of the Muthaymimah Formation. The unconformity surface itself is irregular, with scattered truncated internal moulds of shells (e.g. indeterminate nautiloids). The sub-angular pebbles of the Simsima limestone in the conglomerate are concentrated in depressions on the unconformity surface, so that, here and there, the conglomerate lenses out. The pale orange colour of the pebbles contrasts with the white matrix of the Muthaymimah Formation. The latter is a fine pelagic limestone with abundant unkeeled planktonic foraminifera and siliceous sponge spicules. Silicified shells of originally calcitic composition (particularly rudist fragments), which are scattered through the topmost part of the Simsima limestone, can also be seen incorporated in the pebbles and as isolated reworked fragments in the conglomerate.

Interpretation of the Jebel Faiyah sequences. We interpret the sequences described above as representing a sustained trend of marine transgression and deepening, passing from palaeosols to beach and shoreface facies in the Qahlah and lower Simsima, and on to open shelf facies in the upper Simsima. This trend was terminated by an erosive episode of possible emergence, marked by the unconformity. Rapid resubmergence with the deposition of pelagic slope limestones is represented by the Muthaymimah Formation.

Basement weathering and deposition of the Qahlah Formation. The locally preserved lateritic–saprolitic residual cap to the basement testifies to penetrative selective chemical mobilization under warm, wet, at least partly oxidising conditions, and thus to subaerial weathering in a warm, humid climatic regime (McFarlane 1983). The apparent lack of enriched segregation structures such as pisoliths and vermiform pipes, however, suggests only an immature stage of development.

The stratigraphical position of the bouldery conglomerate above this, and beneath the shallow marine Simsima rudist limestones, together with the admixture of locally derived, fractured and exfoliated serpentinite clasts and marine shells (Fig. 3b), point to a marginal marine origin. That this was specifically an intertidal beach deposit is indicated by aspects of its fabric. Petrographically, the well-rounded grains, the lack of compactional features, associated with the early (pre-burial) fibrous cements of marine character, and the keystone vugs (Fig. 3c, d), may together be taken as diagnostic of true beachrock (Bathurst 1971; Emery 1945; Dunham 1970). That the boulders and the shelly–gritty sand matrix accumulated together is shown by the crude stratification evident here and there (e.g. Fig. 3a), with the broad flattish surfaces of some of the boulders aligned along what would have been flat surfaces of gritty sand. The examples of early-cemented lenses of sandstone with such sedimentary structures as low-angle truncations, climbing ripples and small-scale scour features (Fig. 3e) are thus readily interpreted as representing localized patches of beach sand.

At Jebel Rumaylah (Section E), the rounding of the large boulders, the well sorted coarse matrix and the direct contact with fresh serpentinite beneath indicate persistently high energy conditions, with deposition of the beach conglomerate on a freshly eroded rock surface. Around northwestern and central Jebel Faiyah (Sections A−C) and at Jebel Buhays (Section F), in contrast, the underlay of laterite−saprolite and interbedding of sandier lenses point to somewhat less persistently high energy conditions.

A close environmental analogue for this array of beach facies is provided by the present-day Fujairah coastline at Khor Fakkan (Fig. 5c−f; locality shown on the small map in Fig. 1). Here the ophiolite mountains come down to the sea, providing an abrupt coastline of rocky headlands, which are skirted by bouldery beaches (Fig. 5c), and sandy embayments, usually backed by small wadis. We envisage that the sequence at Jebel Rumaylah corresponds to the headlands at Khor Fakkan, where the receding cliff is fronted by a zone of large, well rounded boulders with interstitial mixed siliciclastic−carbonate gravelly sand and bioclastic rubble (Fig. 5e). The other sequences may be likened to those forming in the Khor Fakkan embayments, where superficially weathered serpentinites are overlain by beach gravels and sands combining wadi-derived pebbles and sand and worn marine shells (Fig. 5d). The somewhat greater depth of serpentinite weathering in the ancient example presumably indicates rather more humid conditions. Beachrock collected from the back of one such embayment (Fig. 5f) shows a fringe of fibrous aragonite cement texturally similar to that noted (as cement generation 2) in parts of the Qahlah conglomerate (Fig. 3c). The isopachous nature of the ancient example suggests an effectively (marine) phreatic origin, however, in contrast to the vadose origin of that in Fig. 5f, suggested by its dripstone distribution. But, as Scoffin & Stoddart (1983) note, isopachous fringes are actually more common than distinctly vadose fabrics in Recent beachrocks.

The presence of unbroken, articulated shells of *Durania* within the Qahlah conglomerate and of specimens in life position at its boundary with the lithologically similar pebbly and gritty *Durania* facies of the Simsima Formation (Fig. 4a), suggest that this radiolitid was capable of

living in the foreshore zone. The sand incorporated in the growth layers of these specimens (Fig. 4c) also testifies to their survival of turbulent current activity, such as wave-swash. Like the oysters (*Saccostrea*) of the present-day beaches around Khor Fakkan (Fig. 5e), these *Durania* presumably survived tidal exposure by hermetic closure of the valves. The thin flange of fibrillar prismatic calcite, which rims the plug-like left valve, and which overlies the inner margin of the right valve in *Durania* (Fig. 4b), could well have been flexible in life, like the rubbery marginal flanges of prismatic shell layer in the living oysters, so allowing tight shell closure.

Deposition of the Simsima Formation. The continued incorporation of siliciclastics in parts of the lower Simsima (*Durania* facies) indicates sustained local siliciclastic input, presumably from small wadis debouching into the embayments. In Section B the presence of coarse, high flow regime flat-bedded, and cross-bedded grainstones in the *Durania* facies, with a finer lag component of chrome spinel, implies persisting winnowing current activity, probably in a broad lower foreshore to shallow shoreface zone. The lower, parallel-bedded units here show a striking similarity to the Recent lower foreshore facies at Khor Fakkan (Fig. 5d). The interbedded *Durania* coquinas, with scattered individuals and clusters in life position, would then represent more stabilized shell carpets colonizing the sand surface. The channel forms and possible lateral accretion surfaces of this facies are suggestive of meandering tidal channels migrating across the lower shore.

The somewhat finer-grained, packstone matrix of the *Dictyoptychus* facies and the abundance of burrows in it imply less persistent current reworking than in the *Durania* facies. Localized or spasmodic current activity is indicated by the overturning and breakage of many of the macrofossils and reworking of nodules.

The rhythmicity noted in parts of the *Dictyoptychus* facies (Fig. 6) records a repeated pattern of declining currents: the erosional base of each rhythm is followed by a coarse lag conglomerate, overlain by burrowed packstones with scattered *in situ* macrofossils. Such repetition might be attributed either to changes in the external environment (such as cycles of shallowing and deepening, or a succession of stormy, followed by quiescent episodes), or to successive lateral progradations of facies in a more or less constant setting (such as channel point-bar migration). We favour the latter interpretation (Fig. 6). If changes in sea level were the cause, we should expect the rhythms to be laterally continuous

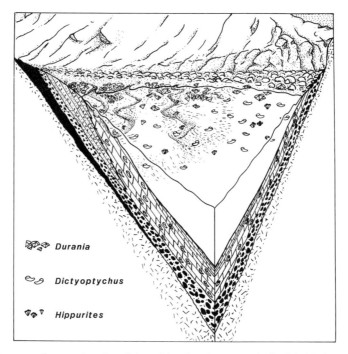

Fig. 7. Block diagrammatic reconstruction of depositional environments in the Jebel Faiyah area, in the early stages of the transgression there. Facies symbols on section faces as in Fig. 2. At the left is an embayment sequence, as at northwestern and central Jebel Faiyah: deeply laterized serpentinite is overlain by beach conglomerate (Qahlah), passing up to (Simsima) *Durania* facies pebbly, shelly sandstones and *Dictyoptychus* facies limestones, forming a small sandy lobe, traversed by meandering tidal channels. To the right, in contrast, a headland sequence (as at Jebel Rumaylah) comprises freshly eroded serpentinite directly overlain by the beach conglomerate, and the latter, in turn, by *Dictyoptychus* facies. Further offshore, the Simsima is represented by foraminiferal packstones. Clusters of *Durania* occupy the lower foreshore and upper shoreface zone in the embayment, while *Dictyoptychus*, hippuritids and associated biota flourish in the tidal channels, and more generally, in the shoreface—inshore shelf zone.

over wide areas: they are not. A storm origin for the erosion surfaces and lag conglomerates also seems unlikely as the latter appear to have accumulated slowly, as condensed deposits; the particular abundance of rhodoliths in them suggests that these actually formed there, rather than being reworked (along with the nodules) from the underlying unit. Moreover, the worn, bored and encrusted state of many of the macrofossils in the lags again testifies to slow, condensed accumulation. A meandering tidal channel origin, in contrast, would explain the lateral impersistence of the rhythms, the condensed accumulation of the (channel floor) lag conglomerates and preferential development there of rhodoliths, and the succeeding progradation across them of quieter, extensively burrowed (point-bar) deposits, with *in situ* rudists. Scoffin *et al.* (1985), working on Rarotonga in the Cook Islands, noted the for-

mation of rhodoliths along tidal channels crossing a zone of the reef flat sheltered from the ocean waves by small reef islands. In our (non-reefal) example, we envisage the tidal channels as having formed largely beyond the *Durania* facies, on the gently sloping sandy lobes developed in northwestern and central Jebel Faiyah (Fig. 7), and at Jebel Buhays. It is unlikely that *Dictyoptychus*, which had a flange of exposed mantle tissue (its right valve margin extends beyond that of the left valve), or the hippuritids, with their porous left valves, could have withstood emersion, unlike *Durania*. Their occurrence, in at least the lower parts of the point-bar units therefore implies that the channel floors and sides (at least) were fully subtidal.

The thin graded sand units noted at Jebel Buhays, which bear no clear relationship with the rhythms there, probably represent storm

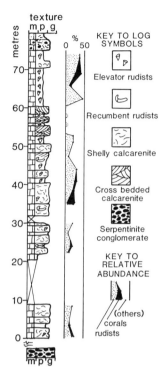

Fig. 8. The sequence of Qarn Murrah, with relative abundances (by individuals) of rudists and corals. The (matrix) textural categories are: m, mudstone; p, packstone; g, grainstone. Based on log of R. W. S. and T. C. Connolly, prepared in 1983 for an AMOCO internal report (with additions).

depositional events, sweeping thin blankets of sand offshore, into the *Dictyoptychus* facies zone.

The upward passage through the progressively finer-grained carbonates of the upper Simsima, with its diminishing benthic macrofauna and the appearance of a pelagic component, marks the transition to quieter, open shelf deposition, beyond the shoreface zone (below fair weather wave base). The unkeeled form of the planktonic foraminifera, however, indicates only moderate depths (Hart 1980). An environmental reconstruction, illustrating the succession of depositional environments in the Qahlah–Simsima transgression around Jebel Faiyah is shown in Fig. 7.

The terminal unconformity is somewhat paradoxical. The limonitic (orange) weathering of the ferroan dolomite in the Simsima Formation and the silicification of fossils near its top both predate deposition of the Muthaymimah Formation, since Simsima clasts in the basal

conglomerate of the latter show both features, while the matrix remains unaffected. These features strongly suggest sub-aerial weathering, although submarine oxidation and erosion might have been responsible. Yet the matrix of the conglomerate is a fine pelagic limestone, and so almost an extrapolation, so to speak, of the deepening trend seen in the Simsima. A short-lived regression thus seems probable, with the basal Muthaymimah conglomerate representing a thin transgressive lag, swamped by a later stage pelagic deposit. Estimation of the duration of this regressive episode could be got from the planktonic foraminifera in the uppermost parts of the Simsima and the basal Muthaymimah, and this remains a priority for future work.

The Qarn Murrah sequence. Qarn Murrah is a small hillock of gently northeastwardly dipping, deeply reddened rudist-bearing limestones projecting from the desert sands some 7 km NW of Jebel Faiyah, adjacent to the village of Tawi Murrah (latitude 25°08′N and longitude 55° 46′E). Lithologically, these may be assigned to the Simsima Formation. Our log of the sequence there (Fig. 8) includes a serpentinite conglomerate a short way beneath the visible sequence, based on occasional exposures of that lithology, through the shifting sands, to the West (S. O'Connor pers. comm.).

Over 70 m of tabular medium-bedded carbonate grainstones and medium to thick-bedded, rudist–coral biostromal packstones are exposed, the latter increasing in thickness and frequency upwards. Medium to coarse-grained bioclastic grainstones dominate the lower 40 m of the sequence, but also floor and cover the biostromes higher in the sequence. The grainstones contain moderately well sorted, rounded to subrounded bioclasts (commonly from rudists), many with micrite rims. In some beds, however, grains of serpentinite, iron-oxide and glauconite predominate. Cross-bedding is locally preserved (e.g. at 50–60 m, Fig. 8).

The biostromes in the lower 40 m of the section are 1–2 m thick with a low density of rudists (generally less than 20% of macrofossils). The large, recumbent capriniform rudist *Sabinia* is common in these, together with small radiolitids. Associated taxa are encrusting red algae, corals, orbitoids and rotaliid foraminifera, gastropods and other epifaunal bivalves, with rare echinoids.

Above 40 m, the biostromes are 10–15 m thick, with a higher density of rudists (20 to 45% of macrofossils; see Fig. 8). These are largely of bafflestone fabric, with abundant gregarious hippuritids and radiolitids of upright growth form, commonly preserved in life pos-

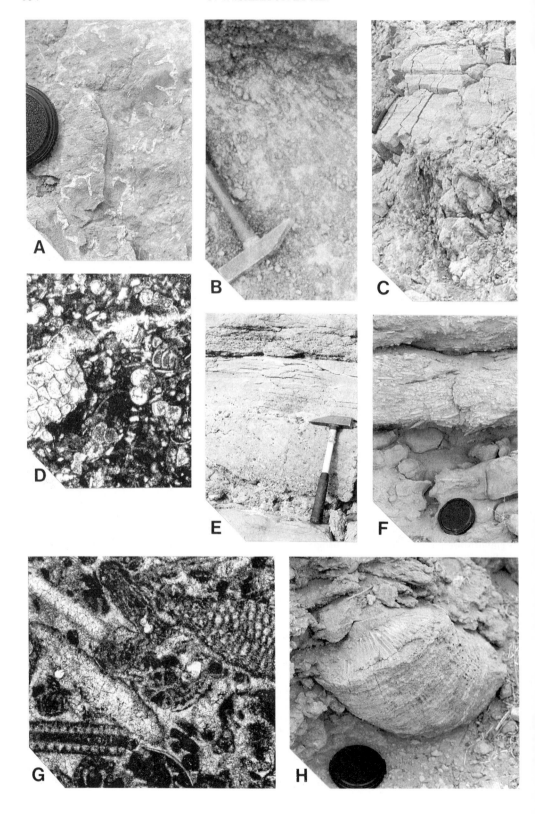

ition (Fig. 9a). They are implanted in a bioclastic packstone matrix, with a sparse admixture of rounded serpentinite grains at some levels. The uppermost thick biostrome, contains several rudist assemblages. The lower assemblage is dominated by small radiolitids (*Bournonia* and *Biradiolites*) with scarce hippuritids. The latter (*Vaccinites; Pironaea*, Fig. 9a; and *Torreites*, see Skelton & Wright 1987) then dominate in the middle part. In the upper part, radiolitids (notably the large *Vautrinia*, with *Biradiolites* and *Bournonia*) again dominate. Rarer associates here are *Sabinia* and *Pseudopolyconites*. Also present are corals, both colonial [*Meandroria konincki* (Milne-Edwards and Haime)] and solitary (a large species of *Cunnolites*, cf. *C. giganteus* d'Orbigny), orbitoids, encrusting foraminifera and rare miliolids, encrusting and bushy red algae, ostracods and gastropods. The biostrome is then capped by grainstones and medium bedded packstones with small radiolitids.

Some few hundred metres to the SE of Qarn Murrah, isolated low ridges of deeply weathered and reddened limestones are exposed. They probably represent a slightly higher part of the local Simsima succession. Large crenulate oysters [*Lopha dichotoma* (Bayle)] and other bivalves, gastropods (including acteonellids), solitary corals, stromatoporoid fingers and rare nautiloids were noted, though no rudists were observed here.

Interpretation of the Qarn Murrah sequence. The likely presence of a serpentinite conglomerate beneath the Simsima Formation at Qarn Murrah implies a transgressive trend, as at Jebel Faiyah. However, the thick rudist limestones (at least 70 m) here contrast with their thin development (5–20 m) at Jebel Faiyah. Also, the abundance of grainstone through the Qarn

Murrah sequence indicates a more sustained energetic, shallow open-marine setting, in contrast to the marked deepening trend of the Simsima at Jebel Faiyah. Nevertheless, the overall trend from grainstones to rudist bafflestones, and the progressive replacement of the recumbent *Sabinia* by hippuritids and radiolitids of 'elevator' morphology (Skelton 1979) in the biostromes, suggest an overall decline in current activity, and thus the possibility of eventual deepening and drowning of the carbonate bank. In this context, the serpentinite pebble bed at the top of the sequence might be attributed either to a storm surge or to a debris flow from a still shallower source area (to the east). The small outcrops to the SE of Qarn Murrah do hint at an upward loss of rudists and incoming of a pelagic element (the nautiloids), and the lack of outcrop, otherwise, of the upper Simsima sequence here is consistent with the expectation that it should be finer-grained and recessive.

The rich diversity and abundance of rudists at Qarn Murrah invites comparison with those documented in various platform-margin rudist buildups of similar age in the eastern and central Mediterranean area. Indeed, with the notable exception of *Torreites* (Skelton & Wright 1987), many of the same taxa feature in those examples, forming a characteristic 'Pironaean–Pseudopolyconite Senonian' assemblage (e.g. Milovanović 1960; Polšak & Mamuzić 1969; Sladić-Trifunović & Campobasso 1980; Laviano 1984; Philip 1985; Sladić–Trifunović 1987; Cestari & Sirna 1987; Negra & Philip 1987).

Stratigraphical relations of Jebel Faiyah and Qarn Murrah. Richly fossiliferous though they are, both sequences display the classic problems of uppermost Cretaceous Tethyan shelf carbonate biostratigraphy. Lacking ammonites (at these localities) and identifiable planktonic fora-

---

Fig. 9. Sedimentary and palaeontological features at Qarn Murrah (a), Jebel Rawdah (b–d) and Jebel Huwayyah (e–h). (a) Upper surface of bed of rudist bafflestone at Qarn Murrah, at about 65 m (see Fig. 8), with specimens of the multiple-fold hippuritid, *Pironaea*, in life position. Lens cap is 5.5 cm across. (b) ?Rhizoconcretionary tubules in Qahlah lateritic silts overlying the basement at the western end of Jebel Rawdah. Hammer shaft is 30 cm long. (c) Terrestrial Qahlah sandstone (below) overlain, on an erosive surface, by the basal Simsima, comprising lenticular conglomeratic sandstone passing up to mixed siliciclastic–carbonate sandstone. Western end of Jebel Rawdah. Hammer shaft is 30 cm long. (d) Photomicrograph, in plane polarised light, of the basal Muthaymimah calciturbiditic pack–wackestone at Jebel Rawdah. Note reworked (Maastrichtian) *Omphalocyclus* in addition to the Palaeogene planktonic foraminifera. Width of frame is 1.2 mm. (e) Cross-bedded pebbly sandstones in the lower Qahlah at Jebel Huwayyah, Section C. Hammer shaft is 33 cm long. (f) *Loftusia* marls in the upper Qahlah at Jebel Huwayyah, Section B. The middle bed is crammed with cigar-shaped arenaceous foraminiferan *Loftusia*. Lens cap is 5.5 cm across. (g) Photomicrograph, in plane polarised light, of poorly washed grainstone in the basal Simsima at Jebel Huwayyah, Section B. Bioclasts include orbitoids (right, centre), dasycladacean stems (lower left) and various benthic foraminifera and molluscan and echinoid grains. Width of frame is 1.8 mm. (h) A large, upwardly curved hippuritid, *Vaccinites vesiculosus*, in life position in the upper part of the *Loftusia* marls (upper Qahlah) at Jebel Huwayyah, Section B. Lens cap is 5.5 cm across.

Table 1. *Maastrichtian rudist and orbitoid assemblages from the Simsima rudist limestones of Qarn Murrah and Jebel Faiyah, Sharjah, UAE*

Qarn Murrah (M₁fauna)	Jebel Faiyah (M₂fauna)
Rudists:	Rudists:
Vaccinites braciensis Sladić Trifunović	*Hippurites cornucopiae* Defrance
Pironaea ?corrugata (Woodward)	*Hippurites* cf. *nabresinensis* Futterer
P. *?praeslavonica* Milovanović,	
Sladić- Trifunović and Grubić	*Durania* cf. *austinensis* (Roemer)
Torreites sanchezi milovanovici Grubić	*Biradiolites aquitanicus* Toucas
	Bournonia sp.
Vautrinia sp. cf. *Osculigera vautrinioides* Vogel	*Praeradiolites* cf. *aristidis* (Munier-Chalmas)
Bournonia excavata (d'Orbigny)	*Colveraia* sp.
Bournonia sp.	
Biradiolites sp.	*Dictyoptychus morgani* (Douvillé)
Pseudopolyconites sp.	*Plagioptychus* sp.
Colveraia sp.	
Sabinia sp.	
Larger Foraminifera:	Larger Foraminifera:
Orbitoides media (d'Archiac)	*Orbitoides media* (d'Archiac)
Lepidorbitoides sp.	*Omphalocyclus macroporus* (Lamarck)
	Lepidorbitoides cf. *minor* (Schlumberger)
	Siderolites calcitrapoides Lamarck
	Loftusia cf. *minor* Cox

minifera, we have had to rely on various benthic taxa, principally the rudists and orbitoids, for correlation. Yet these are commonly prone to provinciality and many may have had regionally diachronous ranges (Philip 1982; Gili *et al.* 1986; Caus & Hottinger 1986). Detailed palaeontological work is still in progress (for future publication), and we urge that our own taxonomic records would certainly be augmented by inspection of other private and institutional collections from these localities.

With these limitations, our provisional listing of rudists and orbitoids from Qarn Murrah and Jebel Faiyah (Table 1) suggests a Maastrichtian age for both sequences, with the rudist limestones of Qarn Murrah probably lowermost Maastrichtian (or perhaps even Upper Campanian), and those of Jebel Faiyah (together with the Qahlah conglomerate there) probably 'mid' (i.e. upper Lower to lower Upper) Maastrichtian (see below).

The faunas of Qarn Murrah and Jebel Faiyah listed in Table 1 are, nevertheless, strikingly different. For the following discussion it is therefore convenient to label them as the 'M₁' and 'M₂' faunas, respectively. That the difference between the two is due to age difference rather than to ecology is strongly suggested both by regional stratigraphical, and by more

general biostratigraphical considerations. At Jebel Huwayyah, to the South (discussed later), notable M₁ elements (*Torreites* and *Sabinia*) were recovered from the basal conglomerates forming the lower part of the Qahlah Formation there, while key M₂ elements (e.g. *Dictyoptychus* and *Loftusia*) make their appearance in the overlying marls of that formation (Fig. 12, Section C). The M₁ fauna thus appears to predate the M₂ fauna.

That the M₁ fauna comes from no higher than the Lower Maastrichtian is indicated by the presence of *Torreites sanchezi*; the range of this species can be bracketed within the Upper Campanian–Lower Maastrichtian (see Skelton & Wright 1987), and indeed specimens from Dhofar, in southern Oman, have been assigned to the Upper Campanian (Philip & Platel 1987). The abundance of *Orbitoides media* and paucity of *Lepidorbitoides* in the assemblage also supports this conclusion. Although *Pironaea praeslavonica* is generally described as a 'Middle' Maastrichtian form (Sladić-Trifunović 1972; Pamouktchiev 1975), the specimens at Qarn Murrah have many primitive features, and are somewhat similar to *P. corrugata*, which ranges down into the Campanian. The specimens here designated as *P. corrugata* may indeed be juveniles of this species. Moreover, Pejović &

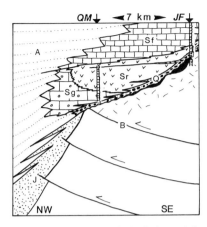

Fig. 10. Inferred stratigraphical relations of the sequences at Qarn Murrah (QM) and Jebel Faiyah (JF); B, basement (undifferentiated, with the Semail Nappe at top); J, Juweiza Flysch; A, Aruma basinal deposits(?); Q, Qahlah Formation; S, Simsima Formation, comprising outer shelf grainstones (Sg), rudist limestones (Sr) and foraminiferal packstones and wackestones (Sf).

Radoičić (1987) have recently cast doubt on the restriction of the 'more evolved' species of *Pironaea* to the Maastrichtian, and have argued that these, together with *Colveraia*, may even range from the Lower Campanian to the Maastrichtian. Only *Vautrinia*, then, still seems to indicate a Maastrichtian age (Vogel 1970), though the distribution of this genus is really not well known.

The possibility of the M_1 fauna extending down into the Upper Campanian therefore cannot be excluded. Most of the other taxa cited have Campanian–Maastrichtian ranges, and Negra & Philip (1987), for example, have assigned an assemblage from central Tunisia including *Vaccinites braciensis*, *Pironaea* cf. *corrugata*, *Sabinia* and *Pseudopolyconites* to the Upper Campanian (based on orbitoids). At a first approximation, then, the M_1 fauna is probably from (?the lower part of) the Lower Maastrichtian but may indeed range down into the Upper Campanian.

A definite Maastrichtian age for the M_2 fauna is given by *Dictyoptychus morgani* (Douvillé 1904), and, indeed, the orbitoid assemblage is typical for the high Lower to low Upper Maastrichtian (Van Gorsel 1978; Neumann 1980; with due allowance being made for the extension well into the Maastrichtian of *Orbitoides media*, Sladić-Trifunović 1972) The small size of the *Loftusia* cf. *minor* might, however, suggest a level still within the Lower

Maastrichtian (Al-Omari & Sadek 1976). It has been widely supposed that *Omphalocyclus* is restricted to Upper Maastrichtian strata, but the claim is not a strong one, since, as Van Gorsel (1978) observed, '... most of these age assignments are themselves based on the presence of this genus'. Although nothing more diagnostic was recovered by us from Jebel Faiyah, M_2-type faunas from Jebel Rawdah and Jebel Huwayyah yield ammonite evidence similarly indicative of a broadly 'mid'-Maastrichtian level. How far the rest of the Simsima, above the rudist limestones, extends into the Upper Maastrichtian, at Jebel Faiyah, is at present uncertain, although further work on the (poorly preserved) planktonic foraminifera could help.

In conclusion, the evidence currently available to us indicates a pattern of broadly eastward transgression onto the obducted ophiolite (Fig. 10). To start with, in the earliest Maastrichtian, carbonate production kept pace with the subsidence, allowing a thick development of M_1 rudist limestones at the margin of the Aruma Basin (off to the west). Later, however, sometime during the latter part of the early Maastrichtian, this became drowned, and the eastward marine onlap onto the ophiolite continued with a more markedly deepening sequence, incorporating only thin M_2 rudist limestones.

Jebels Rawdah and Sumeini

Jebel Rawdah lies to the north of the Dubai–Hatta road, some 20 km SSE of Jebel Faiyah (Fig. 1). An open syncline, flanked by minor anticlinal closures, trending NW–SE and plunging to the northwest, exposes a sequence somewhat similar to that at Jebel Faiyah. It directly overlies a narrow, steeply NE-dipping imbricate thrust stack emerging through the ophiolite at the northwestern end of the Hatta Zone. The stack forms a prominent ridge, exposing slope and basinal carbonates of the Sumeini Group and Hawasina Complex, respectively, with incorporated Albian–Cenomanian extrusives (see Robertson *et al.* 1990). This disappears beneath the imposing southeastern escarpment of Jebel Rawdah. To the south of the Dubai–Hatta road, exposures of the Simsima Formation are also present on the western flanks of the Jebel Sumeini massif, unconformably overlying Sumeini Group slope carbonates.

The Jebel Rawdah sequence. The Maastrichtian sequence shows marked variations in thickness, but broadly appears to thin towards the southeast, from at least 90 m at the western end of the jebel to little more than 30 m at its south-

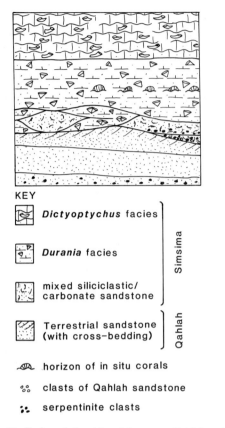

KEY

▧ **Dictyoptychus** facies ⎤
⎥
▧ **Durania** facies ⎥ Simsima
⎥
▧ mixed siliciclastic/ ⎦
carbonate sandstone

▧ Terrestrial sandstone ⎤
(with cross–bedding) ⎦ Qahlah

⌒ horizon of in situ corals

°₀° clasts of Qahlah sandstone

∴ serpentinite clasts

Fig. 11. Facies relationships of the upper Qahlah and lower Simsima on the Southfacing escarpment of western Jebel Rawdah. Some 4–5 m of sequence is represented, with vertical exaggeration ×2.

eastern end. To a large extent this appears to be due to southeastward downcutting of the basal Muthaymimah unconformity, which is noticeably more angular here than at Jebel Faiyah.

At the southeastern end of the jebel an irregular erosion surface truncates the steeply dipping thrust units. The thick volcanic unit included in these is deeply lateritized, with up to 15 m of red-purply silt grading downwards into blocky weathered rock. Above the basal Qahlah laterite here is up to 20 m of red-stained conglomerate, much of it scree covered. Its lower few metres contain brightly red-stained angular boulders and pebbles of local provenance. At the top of the conglomerate the pebbles are well rounded, in contrast, and few exceed 10 cm in diameter. A minor erosion surface on the conglomerate is then followed by about 13 m of Simsima limestones. Those of the lower 3 m are sandy, with large *in situ* hippuritids

and other broken rudists, gastropods and stromatoporoids. This is similar to the more peripheral *Durania* facies at Jebel Faiyah (e.g. in Section A). This facies is overlain by medium-grained bioclastic grainstones and finer nodular packstones with a typical *Dictyoptychus* facies assemblage (again as at Jebel Faiyah). A sharp unconformity surface capping the Simsima is overlain by thin flaggy limestones with cherts of the Muthaymimah Formation.

The Qahlah and lower Simsima have a thicker and more variegated development around the western end of the jebel (Fig. 11). At least 28 m of Qahlah basement weathering products and transported sediments are exposed here: the former comprise interbedded brick-red to purply-brown coloured ferruginous sandy-silt palaeosols with tubules (Fig. 9b) and gritty and pebbly haematitic ironstones; and the latter contains sandy serpentinite conglomerate passing up through green, coarse lithic sandstones to red, well-sorted fine-grained sandstones with cross-bedding.

The base of the Simsima in the western outcrop is again erosive, and clasts of the underlying red Qahlah sandstone, along with pebbles of Semail serpentinite and Hawasina chert, are incorporated in the lower part of a mixed lithic–bioclastic sandstone unit (Fig. 9c). The sandstone itself is well laminated, well sorted and includes numerous low angle truncations. Rudist-bearing limestones follow, passing up to finer-grained orbitoid limestones with fewer macrofossils (Fig. 11).

As at Jebel Faiyah, the rudist limestones are divisible into a lower *Durania* facies and an upper *Dictyoptychus* facies (Fig. 11). The former is locally channelized and includes numerous horizons with *Durania* in life position. Coarse shelly rudstones, grainstones and packstones dominate this facies. The overlying *Dictyoptychus* facies is bioturbated and nodular, and consists predominantly of medium-grained packstones with rhodoliths. A rich fauna is present, similar to that in the *Dictyoptychus* facies at Jebel Faiyah, though accompanied here by some nautiloids and rare ammonites. Macrofossils are commoner in the overlying orbitoid limestones than at Jebel Faiyah. For example, around the northwestern edge of Jebel Rawdah, where the highest exposures of the Simsima are found, several large hippuritids are present, in life position.

The unconformity at the top of the Simsima is highly irregular. It is overlain by localized, thin bouldery conglomerates (containing Simsima clasts and rarer serpentinite and chert clasts) immersed in, and overlain by white calciturbi-

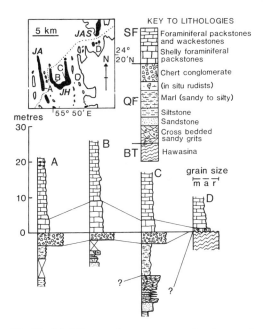

Fig. 12. Jebel Huwayyah area sequence. Inset, map of jebels, with Maastrichtian outcrops shown in black, showing locations of the Sections A–D: *JA*, Jebel Auha; *JAS*, Jebel As-Saifr; *JH*, Jebel Huwayyah. Main figures, Sections A–D, showing lateral facies variations: BT, basement; QF, Qahlah Formation; SF, Simsima Formation. The unconformity at the top of these sections (overlain by the Muthaymimah Formation) is not visible at outcrop, but may be seen elsewhere, to the South. Grain size grades: m, mudrock; a, arenite; r, rudite.

dites (Fig. 9d) with bands of chert nodules. The downward cutting of the unconformity towards the east is at its greatest a short way west of the southeastern end of the jebel, where Muthaymimah limestones locally repose directly on the basement.

The Jebel Sumeini sequence. The Maastrichtian sequence on western Jebel Sumeini (Fig. 1) was only briefly studied. Here, the Simsima Formation discordantly overlies the basement (Triassic Maqam Formation limestones of the Sumeini Group: Watts 1987). A thin and discontinuous veneer of locally derived limestone conglomerate overlies the flattish but irregular unconformity, penetrating crevices in it. Within only a few tens of centimetres this passes up to yellow (limonite-) stained nodular orbitoid limestones with abundant rudists (*Dictyoptychus*, *Durania* and large *Hippurites cornucopiae* being dominant). Lithologically this compares most closely with the *Dictyoptychus* facies of the Simsima Formation.

Interpretation of the Jebel Rawdah and Jebel Sumeini sequences. The basal ferruginous sandy silts and ironstones of the Qahlah Formation at Jebel Rawdah are interpreted as lateritic–saprolitic weathering profiles, as at Jebel Faiyah. The presence here of enriched segregations (now haematite) suggests a slightly more mature stage of development. The tubules (Fig. 9b) might represent plant rootlets (or, rather, rhizoconcretions). The overlying sandstones and conglomerates are unfossiliferous and are probably terrestrial in origin. Some of the fine, well-sorted red sandstones at the western end of the jebel show possibly aeolian dune cross-bedding.

The sedimentary structures of the basal Simsima sandstone in the western part, and its stratigraphical position, suggest a beach deposit (comparing somewhat with the sandstone lenses within the Qahlah conglomerate at Jebel Faiyah). The overlying sequence of *Durania* facies, *Dictyoptychus* facies and orbitoid limestones, again by analogy with Jebel Faiyah, may be interpreted as representing a continuing transgressive trend from locally channelized lower foreshore and shoreface deposits to quieter open shelf deposits. However, the greater persistence of rudists in the upper part of the Simsima at Jebel Rawdah may indicate a less pronounced trend of deepening than at Jebel Faiyah.

The Qahlah Formation is evidently overlapped by the Simsima at Jebel Sumeini, where a thin transgressive lag conglomerate, marking the base of the Simsima Formation, abruptly passes up to *Dictyoptychus* facies shoreface deposits.

The unconformable Simsima–Muthaymimah transition at Jebel Rawdah again bears witness to an erosive, possibly emergent episode followed by rapid drowning and the emplacement of carbonate slope deposits. Again, further work on the planktonic foraminifera is needed to date these events. The marked southeasternward (mountainward) downcutting of the unconformity here may indicate local tectonic influences at this time, as well.

Stratigraphical relations of Jebels Rawdah and Sumeini. The transgressive trend of the Maastrichtian post-obduction sequence noted at Jebel Faiyah is again represented at Jebels Rawdah and Sumeini, though with the Simsima Formation overlapping the Qahlah at the latter. The rudist limestones at both jebels yield faunal assemblages of 'M$_2$' character and so are probably more or less co-eval with those at Jebel Faiyah itself. Notable rudist constituents of the M$_2$ fauna present are *Dictyoptychus morgani* and *Hippurites cornucopiae* along with other less age-diagnostic forms such as *Durania*, *Biradiolites* and *Bournonia*. *Omphalocyclus macroporus* and *Siderolites calcitrapoides* are also present both within the orbitoid limestones of the Simsima and, reworked, in the basal conglomerate of the Muthaymimah Formation (Fig. 9d).

An important find in the rudist limestones at Jebel Rawdah was of the ammonite *Pachydiscus*. Three specimens have been determined for us by W. J. Kennedy (pers. comm.), as *P. (P.) neubergicus* (Hauer), *P. (P.)* group of *neubergicus* (Hauer) — *gollevillensis* (d'Orbigny) and *P.* sp., indicating a 'mid' (upper Lower to lower Upper) Maastrichtian level.

Further information on the age of the rudist limestones has been furnished by the echinoid fauna, which has been studied for us by A. B. Smith. He had identified the following taxa: *Orthopsis miliaris* Cotteau/*morgani* Cotteau and Gauthier, *Goniopygus superbus* Cotteau and Gauthier, *Metholectypus inflatus* Cotteau and Gauthier, *Metholectypus* sp. cf. *trechmanni* Hawkins, *Conulus orientalis* Cotteau and Gauthier and ?*Pygurostoma morgani* Cotteau and Gauthier (fragment). According to Smith (pers. comm.) the presence of *Conulus orientalis* suggests a Lower Maastrichtian fauna, though the ranges of such taxa in the eastern Tethyan Realm are only poorly constrained.

In conclusion, the sequence in this area bears witness to a marine transgression in 'mid'-Maastrichtian times, as at Jebel Faiyah, though subsidence was probably rather less marked. The preservation of a more mature weathering profile on the basement and of a relatively thick veneer of continental facies in the Qahlah Formation at Jebel Rawdah points to a more subdued, less cliff-lined coastline. The thin transgressive lag in the basal Simsima at Jebel Sumeini hints at rapid onlap over a flattish (rocky) surface, probably involving relatively little subsidence.

The Jebel Huwayyah area

A prominent concentric group of jebels emerge through the wadi gravels and sands some 8 km to the northeast of the twin towns of Al Ayn (UAE)−Buraymi (Oman). The Maastrichtian crops out (Fig. 12) around the crescentic Jebel Huwayyah, on the limbs of a broad southerly-plunging anticline, as well as along Jebel Auha, to its west, which represents a fault repetition of the western limb of Jebel Huwayyah. Another 10 km to the northeast, Maastrichtian strata recur on the southern part of Jebel As-Saifr

and, particularly, in a small cluster of hillocks immediately south of the jebel, across the vehicle track. Sections from this group of jebels show a laterally variable lithostratigraphy (Fig. 12). Isolated hillocks of reddened limestones also project from the desert sands to the west of the Dubai−Al Ayn road, some 30 km N of Al Ayn, and one of these, Jebel Muhayjir (Fig. 1), will also be briefly discussed.

Jebels Huwayyah, Auha and As-Saifr, Only the upper parts of a relatively thick Qahlah sequence are visible in Jebels Huwayyah and Auha (Sections A−C). This is overlapped to the northeast by Simsima limestones, which directly repose on an erosion surface of steep eastwardly dipping Hawasina cherts at Jebel As-Saifr. The latter form the only outcrop of the basement in the district considered here.

The thickest exposure of the Qahlah Formation is in the southeastern corner of Jebel Huwayyah (Fig. 12, Section C), where a 24 m section is visible. Overlying poorly exposed, weathered khaki-coloured shales are about 11 m of brown sandstones and chert conglomerates. These are well bedded, with minor bioturbation and some low angle truncations. Some beds show decimetric planar cross bedding, with pebbles in the lower parts of the foresets (Fig. 9e), as well as herringbone cross-bedding, wave ripples and horizons of (high flow regime) flat lamination. Approximately midway through this part of the sequence is a narrow band of marl with abundant small oysters, many of which are articulated and cemented to each other or to the top of the bed. In addition to subangular chert pebbles, the gritty sandstones and conglomerates overlying the oyster marl contain common, worn whole and fragmented valves of rudists (Table 2) as well as rare colonial corals of flat, encrusting form and some unworn oyster valves.

Above the conglomerates and sandstones is a poorly exposed 9 m sequence of thinly bedded, richly fossiliferous (Table 2) brown sandy to silty marls and bioclastic limestones. These are better exposed in Section B (Fig. 12). The giant fusiform arenaceous foraminiferan, *Loftusia*, entirely dominates some beds (Fig. 9f) and is otherwise common throughout the marly unit. Rudists are also common in some beds, many in life position (Fig. 9h). Horizontal branching burrow systems are locally preserved. The matrix of the limestones is a poorly sorted, medium-grained bioclastic packstone with abundant larger, and smaller (textulariine) benthic foraminifera, rudist and echinoid grains and coralline algal fragments.

Laterally equivalent beds to the west at Jebel

Table 2. *Fauna of the Qahlah and basal Simsima Formations of the Jebel Huwayyah area, NE of Al Ayn, UAE/ Buraymi, Oman*

Basal Simsima limestones

Rudist bivalves:
Vaccinites cf oppeli Douvillé
Durania sp.
Biradiolites ?aquitanicus Toucas
Dictyoptychus morgani (Douvillé)

Non-rudist bivalves:
Neithea regularis (E. F. von Schlotheim)
Spondylus subserratus Douvillé
unidentified scallops, oysters and burrowing bivalves

Gastropods:
Campanile ganesha (Noetling)
unidentified acteonellids
indet, internal moulds

Cephalopods:
Pachydiscus (P.) neubergicus Hauer
Neancyloceras? sp.
unidentified nautiloids

Echinoids:
Conulus orientalis Cotteau and Gauthier
Faujasia eccentripora Lees
Pygurostoma morgani Cotteau and Gauthier

Corals:
unidentified cyclolitids

Foraminifera:
Omphalocyclus macroporus (Lamarck)
unidentified orbitoids

Upper Qahlah silty marls and limestones

Rudist bivalves:
Vaccinites vesiculosus (Woodward)
V. loftusi (Woodward)
Biradiolites sp.
Bournonia sp.
Dictyoptychus morgani

Non-rudist bivalves:
Neithea regularis
Spondylus subserratus
* *Merklinia catalaunica* (Vidal)
* *Ctenoides* cf *tecta* (Goldfuss)
Granocardium productum (J. Sowerby)
unidentified scallops and oysters

Gastropods:
Campanile ganesha
Chenopus (Hippocrene)? sp.
diverse indet. internal moulds

Corals:
Cunnolites (C.) reussi (Fromental)
C. (Paracunnolites) scutellum (Reuss)
C. (Plesiocunnolites) undulata (Goldfuss)
various undetermined (small) colonial corals

Sponge:
indet. 'stromatoporoids'

Foraminifera:
Loftusia sp.
Omphalocyclus macroporus
Orbitoides ?media (D'Archiac)

Lower Qahlah conglomerates and sandstones

Rudist bivalves:
Torreites sanchezi milovanovici Grubić
Sabinia sp.
indet. lapeirousiine radiolitid

Non-rudist bivalves:
unidentified small oysters

Corals:
indet. flat colonial forms.

Ammonites identified by W. J. Kennedy. * Identified by A. V. Dhondt. Echinoids identified by A. B. Smith. Corals identified by S. F. Frost, some from his own collection. Other identifications by the authors.

Auha (Section A) are finer grained and only poorly fossiliferous. Here, soft bioturbated silt-stones, mudstones and marly limestones yield some small gastropods, bivalves (*Pinna*) and orbitoids.

The Qahlah is capped, in Sections A–C, by a 2 to 3 m thick bed of unfossiliferous, red-coloured chert pebble breccio-conglomerate.

The Simsima Formation, comprising yellow nodular limestones, abruptly, but concordantly overlies the Qahlah in Sections A–C, and the basement (discordantly) in Section D (Fig. 12). It commences with but a few metres of shelly foraminiferal grainstones to packstones, with localized assemblages of rudists (Table 2). At Jebel As-Saifr (Section D), several very large hippuritids (*Vaccinites* cf. *oppeli* Douvillé, up to 30 cm across) were found in life position, encrusting surfaces close to, or actually upon the basement. Rudists are rare in the overlying few metres and in the basal Simsima of the other sections. At Section B, for example, rare *Durania* are swamped by the other benthic taxa (Table 2). These are in a matrix of medium-grained bioclastic poorly washed grainstone to packstone (Fig. 9g), with abundant larger (orbitoid) and small benthic foraminifera, dasycladacean and corallinacean algal fragments, and molluscan and echinoid grains. Along strike to the north, rare nautiloids and ammonites are also present. Above this, the sequence rapidly passes up to finer-grained orbitoid packstones.

To the west, at Jebel Auha (Section A), the upper few metres of the Simsima comprise pale, fine-grained packstones with scattered orbitoids and horizons of chert nodules.

Although the top of the Simsima Formation is not exposed here, the terminal unconformity, overlain by the Muthaymimah Formation slope carbonates, is exposed some 25 km to the southeast of Al Ayn, at Sayh Muthaymimah.

Interpretation of the Jebel Huwayyah area sequences. The generally coarse grain size and the sedimentary structures of the lower Qahlah in Section C indicate sustained current activity, shallow channelling, braid development (Fig. 9e), wave action (wave ripples) and reversals of current flow (herringbone cross-bedding). The oyster marl horizon, presumably developed in a temporarily and locally protected area, points to marine influences, though the lack of any accompanying *in situ* fauna with the oysters hints at possibly brackish waters. The marine influence is re-inforced in the conglomerates above the oyster marl, with the introduction of the rolled (worn) rudists and corals, presumably transported in from a more open marine site.

This combination of features in the lower Qahlah suggests a fan delta depositional system of tidally influenced channels and gravelly sand braids, with localized oyster marl flats. Transgressive backstepping of facies is indicated by the increasing marine influence.

The *Loftusia* marls, with their numerous in situ rudists represent the subtidal continuation of this transgressive trend. Current energies were generally low, allowing the accumulation of silty marl, though the rich fauna, with plentiful small corals suggests slow rates of sedimentation. A quiet, inner shelf setting is envisaged. The finer-grained, less fossiliferous beds at Jebel Auha are interpreted as a more offshore (slightly deeper) equivalent.

The chert conglomerate at the top of the Qahlah is difficult to interpret. It might represent either a sharp regressive pulse, or a catastrophic depositional event (such as a flood-driven influx of gravel). It is remarkably devoid of any useful sedimentary structures or fossils to aid interpretation. Only its composition, its rather even thickness over a broad area and its wedging out towards Jebel As-Saifr (Fig. 12) provide clues. Like the chert conglomerate lower in the Qahlah, we may suppose that it was derived from the local basement of Hawasina cherts. The erosion surface on the latter, beneath the Simsima limestone at Jebel As-Saifr (and thereabouts), provides a likely source. Alternatively the ultimate source might have been yet further to the east, with erosional removal of the resulting Qahlah deposits from Jebel As-Saifr yielding the chert conglomerate prior to deposition of the Simsima. The juxtaposition of this even blanket of material over the Qahlah marls and the nearby probable source area might also suggest contemporaneous growth-faulting just to the west of Jebel As-Saifr.

One indication that some shallowing was associated with the chert conglomerate comes from the basal facies of the overlying Simsima limestone; its poorly washed grainstone to packstone texture and rounding of bioclasts (Fig. 9g) suggests rather more energetic conditions than in the preceding *Loftusia* marls. Moreover, the presence of dasycladacean algae in this facies points to shallow waters. However, the rapid transition into the finer orbitoid packstones above suggests a prompt resumption of the transgressive trend. The condensed lag-like character of the basal rudist facies at Jebel As-Saifr is similar to that at Jebel Sumeini, and again suggests rapid transgression over flattish terrain. The fine packstones with chert nodules at the top of the sequence at Jebel Auha marks the arrival of deeper-water deposits in the western part of the area.

Jebel Muhayjir. This small, isolated hillock, immediately alongside the Dubai—Al Ayn road (Fig. 1), exposes purply-red stained orbitoid packstones and grainstones with numerous oysters, small radiolitid rudists, colonial and solitary corals and *Spondylus*. Lithologically this outcrop correlates with the Simsima at Qarn Murrah, though with a rather greater abundance of corals and correspondingly fewer rudists. It may similarly be interpreted as an open shelf, shallow buildup, in this case with scattered coral patch reefs.

Stratigraphical relations of the Jebel Huwayyah area sequences and Jebel Muhayjir. The chief importance of Jebel Huwayyah is the light it throws on the stratigraphical relations of the

'M$_1$' and 'M$_2$' faunas recognised at Qarn Murrah and Jebel Faiyah, respectively (Table 1). Two of the characteristic components of the M$_1$ fauna, *Torreites* and *Sabinia*, were recovered as worn specimens in the lower, conglomeratic part of the Qahlah Formation at Section C (Fig. 12 & Table 2). Neither genus has anywhere been found alongside exclusively M$_2$ taxa, such as *Dictyoptychus*, *Loftusia* or *Hippurites cornucopiae*. The overlying *Loftusia* marls (the upper part of the Qahlah here), in contrast, contain both *Dictyoptychus* and *Loftusia*, as well as *Omphalocyclus macroporus* (cf. Table 1). The evidence of this sequence therefore points to the M$_1$ fauna predating the M$_2$ fauna.

The M$_2$ fauna persists, albeit sporadically, in the lower few metres of the overlying Simsima Formation. The ammonites from laterally equivalent beds to the North have been identified for us by W. J. Kennedy (pers. comm.) as *Pachydiscus* (*P.*) *neubergicus* (Hauer) and *Neancyloceras*? sp., indicating a Lower to low Upper Maastrichtian level. A Lower Maastrichtian level is indicated by the echinoids from the lowermost Simsima (Table 2: A. B. Smith, pers. comm.). The bivalve *Merklinia catalaunica* (Vidal), is an Upper Campanian−Maastrichtian species (A. V. Dhondt, pers. comm.). These biostratigraphical indications are therefore consistent with the 'mid-Maastrichtian' (or at least upper Lower Maastrichtian) level inferred for the M$_2$ fauna at Jebel Faiyah. How far the Simsima Formation here extends up into the Upper Maastrichtian (if indeed it does) is again uncertain.

Regrettably, no clearly age-diagnostic fossils were obtained from the brief visit to Jebel Muhayjir. Purely on the grounds of lithological similarity it may be supposed to correlate with Qarn Murrah, but this remains to be substantiated.

In conclusion, the overall transgressive trend noted at the other localities is again evident, with a possible (local) regressive pulse at the top of the Qahlah Formation. Again an early to mid-Maastrichtian age is implied, and a broadly eastward pattern of onlap is indicated both by the more offshore character of the sequence at Jebel Auha than that at Jebel Huwayyah and the offshore shoal character of Jebel Muhayjir, and by the overlap of the Qahlah by the Simsima Formation at Jebel As-Saifr (Fig. 2). The succession from fan-delta, through quiet inner shelf, to open shelf facies suggests transgression over a rather broader shelf than further north, where the marine facies have a more 'open' character at the outset. As at Jebel Rawdah, a subdued topography is also indicated.

Regional stratigraphical relationships

Further outcrops of basement and overlying neoautochthonous strata are exposed in a group of jebels around Sayh Muthaymimah, some 25 km SE of Al Ayn. The same basic sequence as before is recognisable, comprising (serpentinite) basement, Qahlah, Simsima and Muthaymimah Formations, but in a structurally complex relationship. In places the full sequence, albeit with sheared boundaries, is visible, but locally the Muthaymimah is found reposing directly on the serpentinite, suggesting some tectonic activity between the times of deposition of the Simsima and Muthaymimah Formations. The upper parts of the Qahlah Formation here include brown-grey nodular marly burrowed packstones with *Dictyoptychus*, small colonial and solitary corals, and orbitoids, similar to the *Loftusia* marls at Jebel Huwayyah. The overlying Simsima Formation comprises massive nodular, yellow-weathering foraminiferal packstones with scattered *Dictyoptychus*, small radiolitids, oysters, scallops, gastropods, orbitoids and rhodoliths in its lower few metres, again as at Jebel Huwayyah. In the southern part of Jebel Sa'ah up to 45 m of the Simsima Formation is visible. The uppermost 15 m is paler in colour, finer-grained and has bands of chert nodules, together with common irregular echinoids. This latter facies represents a continuation of the deepening trend noted elsewhere.

In the Dhank area, to the South (Nolan *et al*. 1990 Fig. 1), the Simsima Formation also becomes invaded by *Loftusia*, oyster and echinoid rich marly facies. Correspondingly, rudists, which are somewhat less diverse at Jebel Huwayyah than at Jebel Faiyah, become rare in the Dhank area. Only towards the southern end of the Oman Mountains (Jebel Ja'Alan, Nolan *et al*. 1990, fig. 1; Filbrandt *et al*. 1990 is there a return of rudist-rich, cleaner limestones in the Simsima Formation.

At a broader scale, transgressive Maastrichtian rudist and orbitoid limestones, with a basal siliciclastic component have been noted in many other areas around the margins of the Aruma Basin. In the Dhofar region of southern Oman, for example, such facies of the Sharwayn Formation unconformably overlie (and overstep) an autochthonous Cretaceous sequence (Cavelier *et al*. 1985; Philip & Platel 1987). The Sharwayn Formation is described as being probably Upper Maastrichtian; but the rudist and foraminiferal evidence cited could be equally consistent with the Lower to 'mid'-Maastrichtian assignment of the Simsima Formation in the Oman Mountains area preferred by us.

Passing to the northwestern margin of the Aruma Basin, the subsurface 'type' sequence of the Simsima Formation, in Qatar, is noted by Hughes Clarke (1988) to commence with minor basal clastics, lying disconformably upon underlying units (generally Fiqa) and to pass up to fossiliferous shallow marine limestones of Maastrichtian age. On the western flank of the Aruma Basin, in central Saudi Arabia, El Asa'ad (1983) has divided the Aruma Formation (not to be confused with the 'Aruma Group'; see Nolan et al. 1990) into a lower, Turonian to Campanian Khanasir Member (nodular, locally dolomitized marly limestones), overlain, with low angle unconformity, by the Maastrichtian Hajajah and Lina Members (oyster and cyclolitid-bearing marls passing up via orbitoid–rudist limestones to nautiloid and ammonite bearing foraminiferal limestones).

In the Aruma Basin itself, to the west of the present study area, well data show that the Simsima passes out to basinal pelagic facies.

Across the entire region the top of the Simsima Formation is erosionally truncated and unconformably overlain in many areas by Tertiary deposits: the latest Cretaceous regressive pulse was thus ubiquitous (Hughes Clarke 1988).

Palaeogeographical summary and discussion

Fig. 13 provides a block-diagrammatic reconstruction of the palaeogeography of the area studied in this paper in 'mid'-Maastrichtian times, when the Qahlah–Simsima transgression onto the obducted complex was well advanced.

During the Campanian, the leading edge of the obducted ophiolite complex became detached, uplifted and gravitationally emplaced westwards, as the Semail Nappe, over the sedimentary nappes and the easternmost basin-fill (Muti) sediments of the Aruma Basin, as a result of isostatic rebound of the Arabian continental margin, following the cessation of subduction there (Lippard et al. 1986). Thus, at the dawn of Maastrichtian times, a crescentic island of ophiolitic and underlying nappes (the 'Proto-Oman Mountains') lay emerged along the eastern Arabian margin. From then on, through the Maastrichtian, the complex was progressively onlapped by the Qahlah–Simsima sequences described in this paper. By late Maastrichtian times most, if not all the Proto-Oman Mountains had probably become drowned, but a sharp regression in ?latest Maastrichtian–early Palaeocene times may

have re-exposed large areas to subaerial erosion, prior to renewed transgression in the Palaeocene (see the synoptic palaeogeographical maps presented by Nolan et al. 1990).

During the early Maastrichtian, the emerged ophiolite was subjected to extensive weathering, in a tropical climate, forming the lateritic–saprolitic profiles noted, for example, at Jebels Faiyah and Rawdah and Sayh Muthaymimah. Elsewhere, erosion produced irregular rocky surfaces where the underlying sedimentary nappes were exposed (e.g. parts of Jebel Rawdah and Jebels Sumeini and As-Saifr).

Some continental deposits were preserved at Jebel Rawdah, but by and large the first transgressive deposits in the study area comprise various marginal marine facies. In earliest Maastrichtian times, a carbonate bank soon became established at Qarn Murrah, and initially kept pace with the subsidence. To the South, at Jebel Huwayyah, a broad gravelly fan was developing, with, perhaps, a carbonate bank forming further seawards, along the strike of Jebel Muhayjir.

As the transgression proceeded, through to 'mid'-Maastrichtian times, it covered a narrow shelf of open marine character in the north, becoming broader and more sheltered in the south. At Jebel Faiyah, a mountainous coastline of rocky headlands and shallow embayments retreated to leave a sequence of bouldery beach conglomerate and sandy foreshore deposits passing up via rudist-rich shoreface, to open shelf deposits. From Jebel Rawdah to Jebel Huwayyah, in contrast, a flatter terrain was transgressed, by beach to shoreface deposits at the former, and by quite inner shelf deposits at the latter, in both cases eventually passing up to quiet open shelf deposits.

The question naturally arises: was the Maastrichtian onlap noted here and throughout the region due to subsidence or due to a eustatic rise in sea level? Most authors have portrayed the Maastrichtian as a time of eustatic fall (e.g. Hancock & Kauffman 1979; Vail et al. 1977). In a recently refined seismic stratigraphical analysis, Haq et al. (1987) detected, within this overall trend, two 'short term' cycles of rise and fall. However, it is unlikely that these would have produced the observed pattern of consistent onlap and deepening. It is thus probable that the transgression was largely the result of continued subsidence of the ophiolite throughout the Maastrichtian. The regressive phase at the close of the stage, however, co-incides with a marked global eustatic fall and thus can be essentially attributed to that. Nevertheless, the angular form of the unconformity surface at

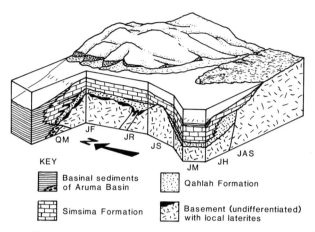

KEY

▨ Basinal sediments of Aruma Basin

▨ Simsima Formation

▨ Qahlah Formation

▨ Basement (undifferentiated) with local laterites

Fig. 13. Block diagrammatic reconstruction of palaeogeography and stratigraphical relationships of the study area in mid-Maastrichtian times. The vertical scale is highly exaggerated and the distance between the Jebels Faiyah to Sumeini area and the Jebel Huwayyah area has been shortened, for compactness. Key to localities: QM, Qarn Murrah; JF, Jebel Faiyah; JR, Jebel Rawdah; JS, Jebel Sumeini; JM, Jebel Muhayjir; JH, Jebel Huwayyah; JAS, Jebel As-Saifr.

Jebel Rawdah and Sayh Muthaymimah suggests some localized tectonic activity.

The rudist faunas of the study area are of considerable palaeobiogeographical interest, and fuller systematic treatment of them will follow in a later publication. As noted, the Qarn Murrah assemblage, in particular, shows strong affinities with the 'Pironaean–Pseudopolyconite Senonian' assemblages well known in the literature from the eastern and central Mediterranean, and Asia Minor areas (Italy, Yugoslavia, Rumania, Bulgaria, Turkey, Syria, Iran, Tunisia and, somewhat anomalously, southeastern Spain: Sladić-Trifunović & Campobasso 1980; Negra & Philip 1987). The assemblage noted here certainly extends the geographical range of this fauna much further to the southeast, along the original southern Tethyan margin, than has yet been documented. Taken together with evidence for the arrival in the Oman–UAE area of Caribbean-derived taxa (Skelton & Wright 1987), this would sugest that, in earliest Maastrichtian times at least, there was free marine communication all along the southern Tethyan margin from eastern Arabia to the eastern and central Mediterranean. That is less evident, however, for the mid-Maastrichtian, when more endemic forms such as *Dictyoptychus* and *Loftusia*, shared only with the Middle East and Asia Minor (Cox 1934; Dilley 1973) make their appearance.

We thank W. J. Kennedy, A. B. Smith and A. V. Dhondt for help with identification of ammonites, echinoids and some of the non-rudist bivalves, respectively, and T. C. Connolly, S. O'Connor and S. F. Frost for discussions on the sequences. J. Dryden is thanked for typing the manuscript. The field work was financed by Amoco Production Company, Houston and organized by the Earth Resources Institute, Swansea, UK. The paper is published with the permission of Amoco Production Company.

References

AL-OMARI, F. S. & SADEK, A 1976. *Loftusia* from northern Iraq. *Revista Española de Micropaleontología*, **8**, 57–70.

BATHURST, R. G. C. 1971. *Carbonate sediments and their diagenesis. Developments in Sedimentology*. Elsevier Publishing Co., Amsterdam, **12**

CAUS, E. & HOTTINGER, L. 1986. Particularidades de la fauna (macroforaminiferos) del Cretácico superior pirenaico. *Paleontologia i Evolució*, **20**, 115–123.

CAVELIER C., PLATEL, J.-P., ROGER, J., BERTHIAUX, A. & ROBELIN, C. 1985. Stratigraphie et histoire géologique du Dhofar (Sultanat d'Oman) depuis la transgression Crétacé. *Resumés des principaux résultats scientifiques et techniques du Bureau de Recherches Géologiques et Minières*, **RS 1976**, 50–52.

CESTARI, R. & SIRNA, G. 1987. Rudist fauna of Maastrichtian deposits in southern Salento (Puglia — Italy). *In*: COLIZZA, E., COSTA, R., CUCCHI, F. & PUGLIESE, N. (eds) *International Symposium of the "Evolution of the karstic carbonate platform: relation with other peri-Adriatic carbonate platforms"*. Abstract, Trieste.

COX, L. R. 1934. On the structure of the Persian rudist genus *Trechmannella* (formerly *Polyptychus*), with a description of a new species.

Malacological Society London, Proceedings, **21** (1), 42–66.

DILLEY, F. C. 1973. Cretaceous larger foraminifera. *In*: HALLAM, A. (ed.) *Atlas of palaeobiogeography*, Elsevier, Amsterdam, 403–419.

DOUVILLÉ, H. 1904. Mollusques fossiles. *In*: DE MORGAN, J. (ed.) *Mission scientifique en Perse, Tome 3eme, Partie 4 — Paléontologie*. Ernest Leroux, Paris, France, 191–380.

DUNHAM, R. J. 1970. Keystone vugs in carbonate beach deposits. *Bulletin of the American Association of Petroleum Geologists*, **54**, 845.

EL ASA-AD, G. M. A. 1983. Bio- and chronostratigraphy of the Aruma Formation in Central Saudi Arabia. *In*: ABED, A. M. & KHALED, H. M. (eds) *Proceedings of the First Jordanian Geological Conference, 6–8 September 1982*. Jordanian Geologists Association, Amman, 87–111.

EMERY, K. O. 1945. Entrapment of air in beach sand. *Journal of Sedimentary Petrology*, **15**, 39–49.

FILBRANDT, J. B., NOLAN, S. C. & RIES, A. C. 1990. Late Cretaceous and Tertiary evolution of Jebel Ja'alan and adjacent areas, NE Oman. *In*: ROBERTSON, A. H. F, SEARLE, M. P. & RIES, A. C. (eds.) *The Geology and Tectonics of the Oman Region*, Geological Society, London Special Publication, **49**, 697–714.

GILI, E., PONS, J.-M. & VICENS, E. 1986. Problematica del uso de los rudistas (Bivalvia) en bioestratigrafia. *In*: VILLAS, I. (ed.) *Memorias de las 1.as Jornadas de Paleontología*. Diputación General de Aragón, Zaragoza, Spain, 121–130.

HANCOCK, J. M. & KAUFFMAN, E. G. 1979. The great transgressions of the late Cretaceous. *Journal of the Geological Society of London*, **136**, 175–186.

HAQ, B. U., HARDENBOL, J. & VAIL, P. R. 1987. Chronology of fluctuating sea levels since the Triassic (250 million years ago to present). *Science*, **235**, 1156–1166.

HART, M. B. 1980. A water depth model for the evolution of the planktonic foraminiferida. *Nature*, **286**, 252–254.

HOLLINGWORTH, N. T. J. & TUCKER, M. E. 1987. The Upper Permian (Zechstein) Tunstall Reef of north east England: palaeoecology and early diagenesis. *In*: PERYT, T. M. (ed.) *The Zechstein facies in Europe*. Lecture Notes in Earth Sciences, Springer-Verlag, Berlin, **10**, 23–50.

HUGHES CLARKE, M. W. 1988. Stratigraphy and rock unit nomenclature in the oil-producing area of interior Oman. *Journal of Petroleum Geology*, **11**, 5–60.

LAVIANO, A. 1984. Preliminary observations on the Upper Cretaceous coral–rudist facies of Ostuni (southeastern Murge, Apulia). *Rivista Italiana di Paleontologia i Stratigrafia*, **90**(2), 177–204.

LIPPARD, S. J., SHELTON, A. W. & GASS, I. G. 1986. *The Ophiolite of northern Oman*. Geological Society, London, Memoir, **11**.

MCFARLANE, M. J. 1983. Laterites. *In*: GOUDIE, A. S. & PYE, K. (eds) *Chemical sediments and geomorphology — precipitates and residua in the near-surface environment*. Academic, London, 7–58.

MILOVANOVIC, B. 1960. Stratigraphie du Sénonien dans les Dinarides Yougoslaves d'après les rudistes. *Bullètin du Société géologique de France*, (7)**2**, 366–375.

NEGRA, M. & PHILIP, J. 1987. Stratigraphie et paléontologie des formations à rudistes et grands foraminifères du Campanien supérieur du Jebel Kebar (Tunisie Centrale). *Geologie Méditerranéenne*, **12/13**, 49–57.

NEUMANN, M. 1980. Répartition stratigraphique des grands foraminifères du Campanien et du Maastrichtien en Mésogée. *26ᵉ Congrès Geologique International*, p. 266. Résumés, Vol. 1, Paris, France.

NOLAN, S. C., SKELTON, P. W., CLISSOLD, B. P. & SMEWING, J. D. 1990. Maastrichtian to early Tertiary stratigraphy and palaeogeography of the central and northern Oman Mountains. *In*: ROBERTSON, A. H. F., SEARLE, M. P. &. RIES, A. C. (eds) *The Geology and Tectonics of the Oman Region* Geological Society, London, Special Publication, **49**, 495–519.

PAMOUKTCHIEV, A. 1975. Origine et phylogénie du genre *Pironaea* (Hippuritidae, Maestrichtien) de l'Europe de Sud-Est et d'Asie Mineure. *Geologica Balcanica* **5**, 81–92.

PEJOVIĆ, D. & RADOIČIĆ, R. 1987. Prilog stratigrafiji gornje krede ostrva Brača-Jadranska karbonatna platforma. (Contribution to the study of Upper Cretaceous stratigraphy of Brač). *Geologija — Razprave in Poročila*, **28/29**, 121–150. [In Serbo-Croat with English summary]

PHILIP, J. 1982. Paléobiogéographie des rudistes et géodynamique des marges mésogénnes au Crétacé supérieur. *Bullètin du Société géologique de France*, (7)**24** (5,6), 995–1006.

—— 1985. Sur les relations des marges téthysiennes au Campanien et au Maastrichtien déduites de la distribution des rudistes. *Bulletin du Société géologique de France*, (8) **1**(5), 723–731.

—— & PLATEL, J.-P. 1987. Sur la présence du genre *Torreites* (Rudiste de la Province Caraïbe) dans le Campanien du Dhofar (Sud de l'Oman); conséquences sur l'évolution paléobiogeographique du Pacifique et de l'Ocean Indien au Crétacé. *Comptes— Rendus de l'Académie des Sciences Paris*, **304**, sér. 2, 679–684.

POLŠAK, A. & MAMUZIĆ, P. 1969. Nova nalazista rudista u gornjoj kredi Vanjskih Dinarida (Les nouveaux gisements de rudistes dans le Crétacé supérieur des Dinarides Externes). *Geološki Vjesnik*, **22**, 229–245. [In Serbo-Croat, with French summary]

ROBERTSON, A. H. F., BLOME, C. D., COOPER, D. W. J., KEMP, A. E. S., & SEARLE, M. P. 1990a. Evolution of the Arabian continental margin in the Dibba Zone, Northern Oman Mountains. *In*: ROBERTSON, A. H. F., SEARLE M. P. & RIES, A. C. (eds) *The Geology and Tectonics of the Oman Region* Geological Society London, Special Publication, **49**, 251–284.

——, KEMP, A. E. S., REX, D. C. & BLOME, C. D. 1990b. Sedimentary and structural evolution of a transform lineament: the Hatta Zone, Northern Oman mountains. *In*: ROBERTSON, A. H. F., SEARLE, M. P. & RIES, A. C. (eds) *The Geology and Tectonics of the Oman Region* Geological Society London, Special Publication, **49**, 285–305.

SCOFFIN, T. P. & STODDART, D. R. 1983. Beachrock and intertidal cements. *In*: GOUDIE, A. S. & PYE, K. (eds) *Chemical sediments and geomorphology – precipitates and residua in the near-surface environment*. Academic, London, 401–425.

——, ——, TUDHOPE, A. W. & WOODROFFE, C. 1985. Rhodoliths and coralliths of Muri Lagoon, Rarotonga, Cook Islands. *Coral Reefs*, **4**, 71–80.

SKELTON, P. W. 1979. Gregariousness and proto-cooperation in rudists (Bivalvia). *In*: LARWOOD, G. & ROSEN, B. R. (eds) *Biology and systematics of colonial organisms*. Systematics Association Special Volume, Academic Press, London, **11**, 251–279.

—— & WRIGHT, V. P. 1987. A Caribbean rudist bivalve in Oman: island-hopping across the Pacific in the late Cretaceous. *Palaeontology*, **30**, 505–529

SLADIĆ-TRIFUNOVIĆ, M. 1972. Senonian limestones with orbitoides and rudists from Kozluk (north-eastern Bosnia). *Geološki Anali Balkanskoga Poluostrva*, **37**(2), 111–150 [in Serbian with English summary].

—— 1981. Discovery of Colveraias in the Maastrichtian of Yugoslavia (Islands Brač and Hvar). *Geološki Anali Balkanskoga Poluostrva*, **45**, 221–227 [in Serbian with English summary]

—— 1987. Le Senonien à Pironaea et Pseudopoly-conites de la plaque apulienne. *In*: COLIZZA, E., COSTA, R., CUCCHI, F. & PUGLIESE, N. (eds) *International Symposium of the "Evolution of the karstic carbonate platform: relation with other peri-Adriatic carbonate platforms"*. Abstract, Trieste.

—— & CAMPOBASSO, V. 1980. Pseudopolyconites and Colveraias from Maastrichtian of Poggiardo (Lecce, Puglia), Italy. *Geološki Anali Balkanskoga Poluostrva*, **43/44**, 273–286 [in Serbian with English summary].

VAIL, P. R., MITCHUM, R. M. & THOMPSON III, S. 1977. Seismic stratigraphy and global changes of sea level, Part 4: Global cycles of relative changes of sea level. *In*: PAYTON, C. E. (ed.) *Seismic Stratigraphy – Applications to hydrocarbon exploration*. American Association of Petroleum Geologists, Memoir, **26**, 83–97.

VAN GORSEL, J. T. 1978. Late Cretaceous orbitoidal foraminifera. *In*: HEDLEY, R. H. & Adams, C. G. (eds) *Foraminifera*, Academic, London, **3**, 1–120.

VOGEL, K. 1970. Die Radioliten – Gattung Osculigera Kühn: (höhere Oberkreide) und die Funktion kennzeichnender morphologischer Eigenschaften der Rudisten. *Paläontologisches Zeitschrift*, **44**, 63–81.

WATTS, K. F. 1987. Triassic submarine carbonate fans along the Arabian platform margin, Sumeini Group, Oman. *Sedimentology*, **34**, 43–71.

The post-Campanian tectonic evolution of the Central Oman Mountains: Tertiary extension of the Eastern Arabian Margin

A. MANN[1], S. S. HANNA[2] & S. C. NOLAN

Earth Resources Institute, University College of Swansea, Singleton Park, SWANSEA, SA2 8PP UK

[1] *Present address: Robertson Group plc, Llandudno, Gwynedd, LL30 1SA, UK*

[2] *Present address: Department of Earth Sciences, Sultan Qaboos University, PO Box 32486, Sultanate of Oman.*

Abstract: This paper documents the structural history of the central Oman Mountains after the obduction of the Semail ophiolite onto the eastern margin of the Arabian continent during the Late Cretaceous (Santonian/Campanian). The post-obduction history is recorded by a Late Campanian/Maastrichian–Tertiary sedimentary cover to the mountain belt. These sediments have been deformed within an extensional tectonic regime which is continuous northeastwards into the Gulf of Oman hinterland basin and southwestwards away from the SW foothills.

Large-scale down-to-the-basin normal faults have been recognized on the Batinah Coastal Plain NE of the mountain belt. Localized block-faulting and roll-over folds are associated with major faults that separate the Late Campanian to Tertiary sediments from older basement rocks of the Oman Mountains and with Late Cretaceous thrusts reactivated as normal faults. To the SW of the mountains, large NW–SE striking folds are thought to be gravity structures developed above a decollement in Late Cretaceous shales.

Syn-sedimentary tectonic influences are summarized and integrated with the structural analysis to identify the style and timing of tectonism on the S margin of the Gulf of Oman from the Late Campanian/Maastrichtian to present. There is evidence to suggest that penecontemporaneous tectonics controlled rates of subsidence and facies development during this time. A major E–W trending palaeo-high running close to the present-day shoreline affected Palaeogene sedimentation.

Unlike the northern Oman Mountains (Musandam Peninsula), there is no unequivocal evidence of mid-Tertiary (Zagros) compressional structures in the central Oman Mountains. Structural development of the cover sediments in the central mountain belt is believed to be controlled by underlying Late Cretaceous basement structures. In particular the Saih Hatat culmination was a positive structure throughout the Late Cretaceous and Early Tertiary, affecting both the stratigraphic and structural history of adjacent areas. The northern end of the Nakhl culmination seems to have had little effect on sedimentation but did influence deformation in the Tertiary.

Prior to this paper, very little structural information had been published on the Late Campanian to Tertiary rocks of the central Oman Mountains. This study is based on detailed field mapping, structural and stratigraphic analysis and cross-strike structural sections of the Late Campanian to Tertiary sediments of the Batinah Coast and SW Oman Mountains. The structural and stratigraphic studies have been combined to identify the style and timing of tectonism on the S margin of the Gulf of Oman from the Late Campanian to present. The regional implications to both the structural development of the Oman Mountains and the Gulf of Oman hinterland basin is also considered.

Late Campanian to Tertiary rocks crop out along the NE and SW flanks of the Oman Mountains in the Sultanate of Oman and the United Arab Emirates (Fig. 1). They form a cover sequence lying unconformably upon older strata which were deformed during the Turonian to Campanian (Glennie *et al.* 1974; Hanna 1986; 1990).

Geological background

During Late Permian to Middle Cretaceous times, Oman formed part of a large carbonate platform on the passive southern continental margin of the Tethyan Ocean (Fig. 2). A rem-

From ROBERTSON, A. H. F., SEARLE, M. P. & RIES, A. C. (eds), 1990, *The Geology and Tectonics of the Oman Region*. Geological Society Special Publication No 49, pp 549–563

549

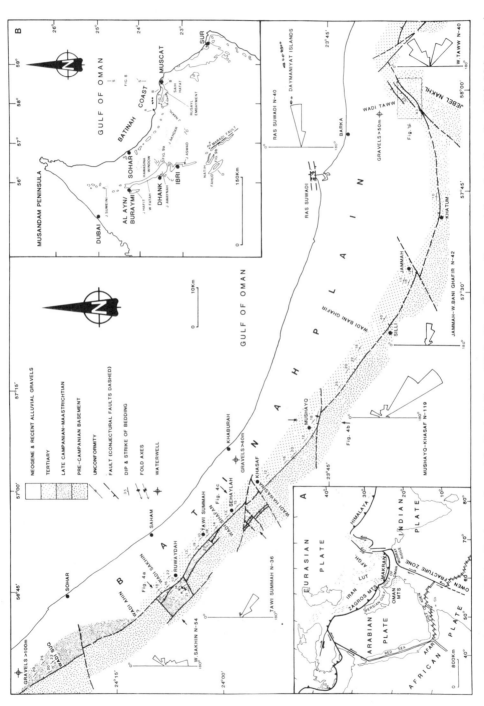

Fig. 1. Late Campanian/Maastrichtian-Tertiary geology of the Batinah Coastal Plain. Rose diagrams illustrate joint orientations. Inset (A): Major tectonic units in the Middle East region. Inset (B): Location of Late Campanian/Maastrichtian-Tertiary exposures in the Oman Mountains. Dotted lines represent the margins of the main structural domains.

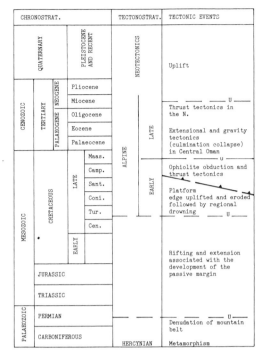

Fig. 2. Tectonic history of the central and north Oman Mountains from Late Palaeozoic to present (after Hanna 1986).

nant of this ocean now constitutes the Gulf of Oman. Upwarping and subsidence associated with the formation of the Aruma/Oman foreland basin terminated the development of the carbonate platform in Oman (Glennie *et al.* 1974; Robertson 1987).

A NE dipping subduction zone and island arc complex are thought to have developed in the Tethyan ocean during the Late Cretaceous (Pearce *et al.* 1981). As the Arabian plate moved progressively northwards it collided with this subduction zone/island arc complex, resulting in obduction of a thrust slice of Tethyan ocean floor (Semail ophiolite) onto the eastern continental margin (Glennie *et al.* 1973, 1974; Graham 1980; Coleman 1981; Lippard & Rex 1982). The collision also caused an intense imbrication of oceanic and slope sediments (Hawasina & Sumeini Group) originally developed on the Oman continental margin and Tethyan ocean floor (Glennie *et al.* 1973, 1974; Watts & Garrison 1986). Thrusting also involved the pre-Permian basement and overlying shelf carbonates (Hajar Supergroup) of the eastern margin of the Arabian continental shelf

(Glennie *et al.* 1974; Hopson *et al.* 1981; Michard 1983; Michard *et al.* 1984; Hanna 1986).

The structure of the central Oman Mountains is dominated by the domal Jebel Akhdar, Jebel Nakhl and Saih Hatat highs. The Hawasina Window forms another major structure to the NW (Fig. 1b). Initially, it was proposed that these major structures were a result of Tertiary compression (Glennie *et al.* 1974; Glennie 1977; Graham 1980; Searle 1980, 1985). However, detailed field mapping and examination of thrust tectonic relationships in the Oman Mountains led Hanna (1986) to interpret these domes as culminations developed during the Late Cretaceous above deep seated thrusts. A number of important extensional structures at the peripheries of the Saih Hatat and Jebel Akhdar/Nakhl culminations were attributed to culmination collapse during Late Cretaceous and Tertiary time (Hanna 1986).

Following a period of relative tectonic stability in the early Tertiary, N directed subduction and associated arc volcanism recommenced during the Eocene, this time N of the Gulf of Oman in the Makran and Baluchistan (White & Klitgord 1976; Farhoudi & Karig 1977; Coleman 1981). This subduction accommodated convergence between the oceanic crust of the Arabian plate beneath the Gulf and the continental Eurasian plate beneath Iran to the N (Fig. 1a).

Glennie *et al.* (1974, p. 350) recognized Tertiary compressional structures in Maastrichtian and Tertiary sediments to the W of the N Oman Mountains but suspected that the Tertiary cover rocks in the central Oman Mountains were affected by gravity tectonics. Two main compressional phases were described by Ricateau & Richè (1980) and Searle *et al.* (1983) in the Musandam Peninsula in the far northern Oman Mountains. The first was related to Late Cretaceous emplacement of Tethyan ophiolites and basinal sediments whilst the second was a later Oligo–Miocene event which produced large-scale open folds and rethrusting of earlier tectonic units. This Tertiary deformation was correlated with the Zagros fold belt of SW Iran.

The presence of Tertiary normal faults in the Musandam Peninsula was recognized by Biehler *et al.* (1975) and Ricateau & Richè (1980). They mapped a close network of NNE–SSW striking faults onshore and also detected extensional faults offshore in seismic sections. The faults affected Upper Cretaceous and Tertiary sediments and were interpreted as the youngest faults in the region, post-dating the Zagros compressional events which ended in the Lower Miocene. Later uplift rejuvenated these normal faults and continued until recent times, since a number of fluvial terraces and Quaternary raised beaches have been identified.

In this paper we extend these studies and document the tectonic evolution of the central Oman Mountains from the end Cretaceous to the present.

Late Campanian/Maastrichtian to Eocene Stratigraphy and Syn-sedimentary tectonics

The main compressional movements of the Late Cretaceous orogenic event ceased during the Late Campanian (Glennie *et al.* 1974). The post-obduction stratigraphical evolution of the Oman Mountains has recently been outlined by Nolan *et al.* (1986, 1990). Their stratigraphical scheme is used in this paper and summarized in Fig. 3. Nolan *et al.* (1986) show that structures developed during the Late Cretaceous collision and obduction phase had a pronounced effect on the distribution of sedimentary basins and facies through the Maastrichtian to Oligo–Miocene.

The lithostratigraphy of Late Cretaceous and early Tertiary strata of the Oman Mountains is more complex than the lithostratigraphy of coeval rocks in Saudi Arabia (Fig. 3). This is a reflection of the much wider variety of facies developed in the Oman mountain belt during this period. Part of this variation is due to syn-sedimentary tectonic controls on deposition in the Oman Mountains.

Late Cretaceous

During the Late Cretaceous, after the obduction of the Semail ophiolite, the eastern side of the Oman mountain belt developed as a steep margin. Terrigenous debris eroded from the newly formed mountain chain was shed eastwards into the Gulf of Oman and to a lesser extent westwards into the remnant Aruma foreland basin.

Adjacent to Saih Hatat, in the Rusayl Embayment, is a thick localized conglomerate shale unit, the Al Khawd Formation (Figs 1 & 3) which unconformably overlies the Semail ophiolite and in turn is disconformably overlain by Palaeocene limestones and marls. The age of the Al Khawd Formation has yet to be finalized, but a late Campanian–late Maastrichtian age is suggested, based on ornithischian and turtle bones. In the E of the Rusayl Embayment, the

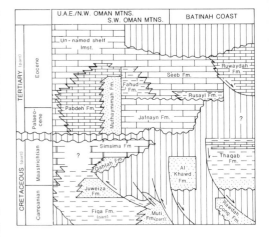

Fig. 3. Correlation of Late Cretaceous and Early Tertiary lithostratigraphy of the Eastern Arabian peninsula (after Nolan *et al.* 1986).

Al Khawd Formation includes a reverse stratigraphy of Saih Hatat in its clast composition. Ophiolite clasts dominate the basal conglomerate, carbonate fragments derived from the Late Permian to Mid-Cretaceous Hajar Super Group are more common in higher conglomerates, and metamorphic quartzite debris from the pre-Permian basement predominates in the highest conglomerates. These relationships clearly demonstrate that Saih Hatat was a major pre-existing structure which had formed during the Upper Cretaceous and had been eroded down to the metamorphic basement prior to the Tertiary.

Contrasting styles of deposition occurred on the E and W flanks of the Oman Mountains N of Tawi Summah and Dhank during the Late Cretaceous. A thick submarine turbidity current/debris flow apron sequence, the Thaqab Formation, was developed on the E side between Sohar and Khasaf (Fig. 1). This includes in its lower part terrigenous debris derived from the Batinah melange and Semail ophiolite. The upper part of the Thaqab Formation is composed predominantly of calciturbidites and debris flows consisting of bioclastic debris derived from a carbonate shelf which developed across the N Oman Mountains during the Maastrichtian. Terrigenous debris forms a relatively low proportion.

A localized submarine turbidity/debris flow unit, the Juweiza Formation, is developed on the W side of the northern Oman Mountains and consists of terrigenous debris derived from the Semail ophiolite during the Late Campanian to early Maastrichtian (Glennie *et al.* 1974).

Throughout the Maastrichtian, the N Oman mountain belt subsided and shallow shelf carbonates, the Simsima Formation, transgressed across terrigenous sandstones and conglomerates of fluviatile, beach and pedogenic deposits of the Qahlah Formation and overstepped eastwards onto the Hawasina sediments and Sumeini Group. These relationships record rapid erosion of an emergent Oman mountain belt during the Late Cretaceous.

Early Tertiary

The early Tertiary strata preserved in the foothills of the Oman Mountains are predominantly of carbonate facies and include much less terrigenous material reworked from older units than the preceding Late Campanian and Maastrichtian. This indicates that during the Early Tertiary, the Oman mountain belt was not actively eroded to the same extent as in the end Cretaceous. Lateral variation in thickness and facies in Palaeocene and Eocene strata of the foothills, however, indicate that the major structural features which controlled the Late Campanian and Maastrichtian deposition also continued to influence early Tertiary sedimentation. For example, in the Rusayl Embayment (Fig. 1b) the Palaeocene and Eocene Jafnayn, Rusayl and basal Seeb Formations (Fig. 3) all thin and become more littoral in facies towards Saih Hatat. These units include very little coarse terrigenous debris, indicating very much reduced levels of contemporary erosion of Saih Hatat compared to the Late Cretaceous.

When traced northwards on the Batinah coastal plain, the Rusayl Formation overlaps the Jafnayn Formation to rest unconformably upon either the Thaqab Formation or upon the pre-Campanian basement. Both the Eocene Rusayl and Seeb Formations also thin and become increasingly shallower shelf and littoral facies northwards towards Khasaf (Fig. 1). North of Tawi Summah (Fig. 1), the Eocene thickens considerably and changes in facies to a submarine slope basin facies constituting the Ruwaydah Formation (Fig. 3). Blocks of shallow shelf limestone were reworked from the Seeb Formation eastwards into submarine debris flow units in the coeval Ruwaydah Formation indicating instability of the NE flank of the central Oman mountains. A similar facies, the Muthaymimah Formation (Fig. 3), occurs on the W flanks of the N Oman Mountains. This includes calciturbidites and debris flows similar to those of the Ruwaydah Formation. The Muthaymimah Formation also includes debris reworked from older units,

including fragments of Hawasina sediment, ophiolite and Maastrichtian Simsima limestone.

The above relationships indicate that the N Oman Mountains and Saih Hatat remained structurally positive areas throughout the Late Cretaceous and early Tertiary.

Oligo−Miocene strata are very poorly exposed because of the unconformable overlap of Neogene to Recent wadi deposits which form plains flanking the mountain belt (Fig. 1). Oligocene strata in the Rusayl Embayment and on Jebel Hafit are predominantly of carbonate facies with coral patch reefs. Little terrigenous debris appears in the strata around the mountain belt until the Miocene. Interbedded Miocene sandstones, shales and coralline limestones occur at Suwadi on the Batinah coast (Fig. 1) and Ricateau & Riché (1980) report Miocene terrigenous deposits off the Musandam Peninsula. These relationships indicate that significant subaerial erosion of the Oman mountains belt did not recommence until Miocene times.

In summary, facies and stratigraphic analysis in the post-obduction sediments indicate that the Oman Mountains have formed a structurally positive feature since their formation in the Turonian to Campanian/early Maastrichtian. This is also reflected in the structural evolution of the mountain belt.

Evidence of extensional tectonics in the Central Oman Mountains

Batinah Coastal Plain

The Late Campanian to Tertiary sedimentary cover on the Batinah Plain generally displays a shallow NE sheet dip away from the Oman Mountains towards the Gulf of Oman (Fig. 1). The most significant and continuous structural feature present on the Batinah Plain is the fault contact between cover sediments and their basement. This 120° lineament is paralleled by well developed joint sets in all of the more competent lithologies (Fig. 1).

A variety of structural styles associated with this basement-cover contact can be related to differences in attitude of the fault and the response of the cover sediments to movement along this contact. The simplest situation is at Ruwaydah where normal faults, parallel to strike, downthrow towards the Gulf of Oman (Fig. 4a). In places, the boundary fault is listric at depth and at Mushayq rollover anticlines are developed above listric portions of the fault (Fig. 4b). Antithetic alignments of nodules in limestones of the Seeb Formation adjacent to the boundary fault are probably minor ac-

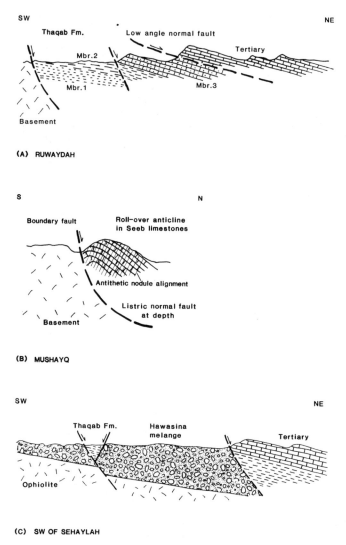

Fig. 4. Schematic cross sections illustrating structural styles associated with the basement-cover fault on the Batinah Plain. (A) Simple normal fault, (B) Listric normal fault and roll-over anticline, (C) Tilted fault block SW of the main basement-cover contact. Not to scale.

commodation structures associated with movement on the fault. Other normal faults have developed in the cover sediments parallel to the boundary faults. For example, at Ruwaydah a low-angle normal fault can be demonstrated between the Maastrichtian Thaqab Formation and Eocene Ruwaydah Formation on stratigraphical grounds, since the upper part of the Thaqab is faulted out (Fig. 4a). Cover sediments are also preserved in downfaulted blocks surrounded by basement to the SW of the boundary fault. SW of Sehaylah, sediments which belong to the Maastrichtian Thaqab Formation (Nolan

et al. 1990) form a NW−SE trending fault block to the SW of the main basement-cover contact at Sehaylah (Figs 1 & 4c). Further examples are seen in the Rusayl Embayment where outliers of late Cretaceous (probably Maastrichtian) and Tertiary sediments (Nolan *et al.* 1990) are preserved in synclinal structures downfaulted against ophiolite. Such structures may be more common along the NE of the central Oman Mountain front, but they are not recognized because of a lack of cover sequence strata to indicate their presence.

Between Khasaf and Mushayq an uncon-

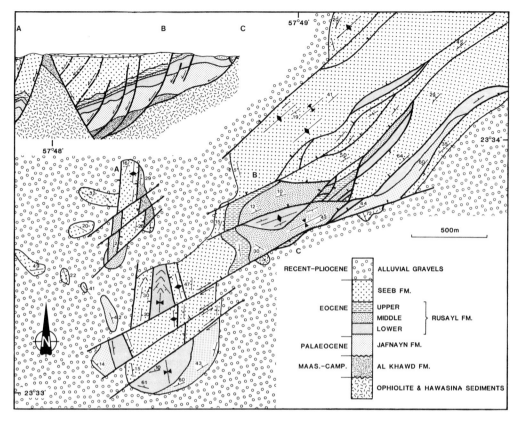

Fig. 5. Tectonic map of Late Campanian/Maastrichtian-Tertiary cover sediments at Wadi Taww, Batinah Plain. See Fig. 1 for location and structural symbols.

formity can be demonstrated between the Rusayl Formation and basement (Fig. 1). The basal conglomerate contains clasts reworked from the underlying basement and there appears to be no displacement on the main basement cover contact. Syn-sedimentary growth faults to the N of Khasaf, postulated to have been active by Nolan *et al.* (1986), explain the rapid lateral variation in facies and thickness of Eocene strata.

A more complex structural relationship is seen at Wadi Taww where extensive outcrops of late Cretaceous-middle Eocene rocks are exposed along the NW flank of the Jebel Nakhl culmination. This area provides an insight into the deformation of the cover sediments close to the mountain front and their structural relationship to the pre-Maastrichtian basement.

The Tertiary sediments dip steeply off the basement near to the contact, but bedding becomes more shallow NW towards the coast. A normal fault contact between Tertiary sediments and the basement can be demonstrated. The Jafnayn and Lower Rusayl sediments are

completely faulted out and the Middle Rusayl limestone is downfaulted against the Hawasina cherts and limestones (Fig. 5). In places, normal faults have developed in an antithetic relationship to the basement-cover contact.

Shallow roll-over folds are the major structures present in the Tertiary rocks of Wadi Taww. The fold axes trend NE−SW and N−S with wavelengths of 200−500 m. Two of the larger folds have developed close to the basement above the boundary fault. To the W of these folds a shallow N−S striking syncline has developed at an angle to the trend of the other folds, above a N−S trending cross fault (Fig. 5).

The dominant trend of other normal faults in the Tertiary rocks of Wadi Taww is NE−SW, parallel to the boundary fault. Detailed mapping of displaced units shows a component of strike-slip movement along these structures (Fig. 5). Many faults have propagated along lithological boundaries between incompetent and competent rocks, in particular, the contacts between the incompetent units of the Rusayl Formation and massive limestones of the Seeb and Jafnayn Fms. These contacts have acted as planes of considerable movement to the extent that the entire Rusayl Formation in this area displays widespread structural incompetence and represents an important zone of décollement. This is shown by a number of structural features including faulting, cleavage development and tectonic thinning of shale horizons.

Bedding parallel faults have developed within the Rusayl Formation between foraminiferal siltstones of the Lower Rusayl and the Middle Rusayl limestone. This important tectonic contact shows a number of normal fault splays emerging from the overlying beds and zones of intense brecciation. Localized compressive regimes have developed close to this fault with pressure solution layer parallel stylolites in the Middle Rusayl limestone increasing in intensity towards the fault. Similarly, the foraminiferal siltstones and overlying thinly bedded limestones locally show evidence of tectonic cleavage.

A set of N−S trending transfer faults in limestone scarps of the Seeb Formation to the W of the area have produced small horst and graben structures with displacements on individual faults of a few metres. Other N−S trending transfer faults can be demonstrated between upfaulted slivers of Al Khawd conglomerate and Seeb limestones. They also offset basement rocks and show vertical displacements of 300−400 m. Displacement of transfer faults shows a predominantly sinistral component of strike-slip movement along normal faults parallel to the basement contact (Fig. 5).

A number of other transfer faults on the Batinah Plain account for many of the basement-cover contact offsets. The largest of these structures is at Wadi Sakhin, near Ruwaydah, where a block of Thaqab sediments has been downfaulted against basement. In this area a set of NE−SW striking joints in the cover sequence lie parallel to the transfer faults (Fig. 1). Another transfer fault can be demonstrated at Tawi Summah, where the boundary fault has been displaced by approximately 800 m (Fig. 1). The transfer fault is terminated to the N by a strike parallel fault which has developed between the Thaqab shales and conglomerates and Ruwaydah limestones. Part of the Thaqab Formation is missing, presumably faulted out.

Many of the transfer faults in the Late Campanian to Tertiary sediments on the Batinah Plain also affect basement lithologies. The faults have been identified by structural mapping in the basement by the authors and by extrapolation from the map of Glennie *et al.*

(1974). Another example is S of Wadi Suq, where a major NE−SW lineament strikes NE from the basement ophiolite to displace the Thaqab Formation (Fig. 1). A similar situation is seen at Khasaf where faults mapped in the Rawdah Conglomerate (Nolan *et al.* 1990) continue NE into the cover sediments (Fig. 1). At Jammah, a major structural lineament in Wadi Far extends NE across the Batinah Plain and displaces the Tertiary rocks (Fig. 1).

The island of Suwadi, situated off the Batinah Coast NW of Barka, is of particular significance because the Miocene sediments are the closest Tertiary exposures to the offshore sequences in the Gulf of Oman. E−W trending, *en échelon* normal faults in cliffs on the S side of the island are marked by sets of S plunging slickensides (Fig. 6). Displacements on individual faults are quite small (4−5 m). In the central part of the island, however, larger structures display well developed fault breccias. These normal faults are parallel to a steep fault guided cliff line on the N side of the island and intensive sets of E−W joints and fractures (Fig. 1). The attitude of normal faults, intense jointing and the upstanding position of the island in an area of no other Tertiary exposures suggest that Suwadi may represent an important fault block or horst (Fig. 7a).

Rusayl Embayment

Maastrichtian to Tertiary rocks in the Rusayl area have developed on the NW flank of the Saih Hatat culmination in an embayment between Mesozoic carbonates to the SE and Semail ophiolite to the SW (Fig. 1b). This area provides an interesting study of structural relationships between the cover sediments and basement rocks close to the edge of a major

Fig. 6. S dipping *en échelon* normal faults in Miocene sediments; Suwadi.

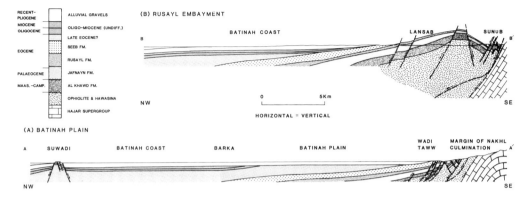

Fig. 7. Structural cross-sections through the eastern part of the Batinah Coast. For location see Fig. 1b.

culmination. The main structures are a series of large NE−SW and NW−SE striking anticlines and synclines and associated normal faults. Some of these faults are important tectonic zones which affect the basement as well as the cover sequence.

In the E part of the Rusayl area late Cretaceous (probably Maastrichtian) and Tertiary rocks form a structural bowl at Sunub. This feature is a faulted synclinal basin, slightly elongate in shape with a NNE−SSW trend (Fig. 7b). The basin margin consists of upstanding ridges of Seeb limestones which dip inwards on all sides and overlie Rusayl limestones and shales, and Jafnayn limestones. The Rusayl limestones show evidence of local tectonic thinning. Beneath the Tertiary rocks is a thick sequence of late Cretaceous (probably Maastrichtian) Al Khawd conglomerate (Nolan et al. 1990) which form low ground around the edge of the bowl and extend eastwards to rest unconformably on ophiolite. The conglomerate has been affected by a number of growth faults (B. P. Clissold pers. comm.). The cover sediments dip steeply NW near to a faulted contact with Mesozoic shelf carbonates which also involves slivers of Rusayl Formation and ophiolite in a complex NE−SW trending fault zone along the SE margin of the bowl. The Sunub bowl is affected by a number of other normal faults trending approximately NE and NW. In the centre of the bowl, a series of tilted fault blocks have developed in which Seeb limestones have been downfaulted against Jafnayn limestones and Al Khawd conglomerates (Fig. 7b).

To the NW, a large anticline cored by ophiolite strikes in a NE−SW direction, parallel to the boundary fault. Both this fold and a complimentary syncline further W tighten towards the S and open out northwards. The anticline

may have developed above an irregular fault surface which may flatten slightly at depth (Fig. 7b). The tightening appears to represent an accommodation feature produced by confining pressures associated with the Tertiary cover slipping off the boundary fault northwestwards into the confined Rusayl Embayment (see Fig. 10).

Gulf of Oman

Geophysical studies have demonstrated that the Gulf of Oman is floored by ocean crust and covered by at least 6 km of deep-marine sediment (White & Klitgord 1976). Deep drilling has shown that the sediments are underlain by Palaeocene basalts (Whitmarsh et al. 1974) which suggest that the ocean crust is at least that old. A deformed sediment prism which forms the offshore Makran continental margin and extends northwards, onshore into Iran and Pakistan accumulated above the descending plate. A model of N dipping imbricate thrusting was proposed by White & Ross (1979) to explain the development of fold ridges and basins on this margin. Towards the NE coast of Oman, the Arabian continental margin drops steeply down to the Gulf of Oman abyssal plain and in places the continental slope is so steep that the sediments have become unstable and moved downslope in large gravity slumps (White & Klitgord 1976).

The possibility of extensional faults to the N of the Batinah Coast in the offshore cover sequence (hinterland basin) is supported by seismic surveys in the Gulf of Oman (White & Ross 1979; Ricateau & Riché 1980). A reinterpretation of some seismic data can be made in the light of the new onshore structural information gathered in this study. The S part of one seismic

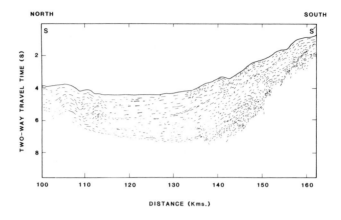

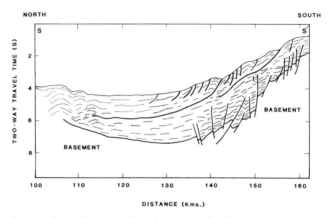

Fig. 8. Interpretive line drawing and structural section across the Oman continental margin, N of Muscat. Traced from a seismic profile in White & Ross (1979). For location see Fig. 1b.

profile N of Muscat shows a number of steeply dipping reflectors which may represent normal fault contacts between the cover sediments and their basement (White & Ross 1979, Fig. 7). Above the steep reflectors two shallow reflectors are interpreted as detachment horizons of major sediment surges off the Oman continental margin and down the continental slope. Towards the front end of the northernmost surge, northerly verging folds have developed in the hangingwall of the fault (Fig. 8). These structures show an opposed sense to the large S verging folds related to imbricate thrusting on the Makran margin to the N.

Post-Lower Miocene extensional faults have also been identified in Late Cretaceous and Tertiary sediments both onshore and in offshore sediments to the E of the Musandam Peninsula (Ricateau & Riché 1980). This suggests that the extensional regime identified at the margins of the central Oman Mountains and in the Gulf of

Oman N of Muscat shows a westward continuation. Extension in Musandam began at a later time after the Oligo−Miocene Zagros compressional event.

Southwest foothills of the Oman Mountains

Maastrichtian and Tertiary rocks form relatively low lying jebels in the outlying foothills to the southern Oman Mountains (Fig. 1b). The cover sediments overlie Semail ophiolite, sediments of the Hawasina Group and the Aruma Group (Fiqa shale).

Jebel Hafit represents the northernmost Tertiary outcrops covered by this study (Fig. 1b). Here, Tertiary sediments are folded around a N−S fold verging towards the E. The northern part of Jebel Hafit shows a more complex structural pattern, displaying a series of folds ar-

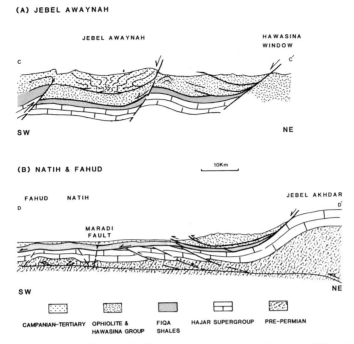

Fig. 9. Schematic cross sections to illustrate the Tertiary extensional tectonics to the SW of the central Oman Mountains. For location se Fig. 1b. The major extensional fault in section (B) is located within the Fiqa shale. Sub-surface data after Tschopp (1967).

ranged in a simple zig-zag fashion (Warrak 1986).

Southwards, in the Wadi Fatha area, the Tertiary sediments are folded in an en échelon fold pattern. This pattern is similar to that described in the underlying Hawasina foreland in that the folds are doubly plunging, elongated structures, arranged in a simple zig-zag pattern.

Further S, around Jebel Awaynah, the Maastrichtian and Tertiary cover unconformably overlies Hawasina sediments. On a regional scale they are folded around a synclinorial structure (45 km × 25 km). This synclinorium consists of a series of en échelon folds with an opposed sense of vergence across its main axial trace (Fig. 9a). On the NE side of the synclinorium, folds verge towards the SW, whilst on the SE side, a NE vergence is seen. The intervening area is a rather complex structural zone representing an interference between the opposed fold structures.

At Ibri, the cover sediments are folded into a NW−SE trending antiformal structure, with Hawasina rocks exposed in the core. Southeastwards, a major NW−SE striking fold pair forms Jebel Aswad (Fig. 1b). This structure consists of a synform to the NE and an antiform

to the SW. These relatively open folds plunge towards the NNW and extend for approximately 50 km along the central part of the SW foothills of the Oman Mountains. The dip of the NE limb of the synclinal fold becomes progressively steeper to approximately vertical. Northwards, however, the limb becomes flatter to form a monoclinal structure.

To the S, the Natih and Fahud structures are broad, open folds with opposed senses of vergence, Fahud to the S and Natih to the N (Fig. 9b). The Natih and Fahud structures are separated from flat lying Maastrichtian rocks to the E by the Maradi Fault Zone (Fig. 1b). The NW−SE fault zone has a topographic expression marked by small Tertiary ridges folded around a NW−SE trend. Hanna & Nolan (1989), concluded that the fault shows a right-lateral strike-slip component.

Basement Control

The most important influence on the depositional environments and structural development of the cover sediments is the presence of pre-existing basement structures on both sides of the Oman Mountains. From Wadi Taww to

Sunub, the boundary fault separating the cover sediments and basement also delineates the edges of the major culminations. The identification of extensional faults at the N margin of these culminations associated with culmination collapse (Hanna 1986), suggests that movement on the basement cover-fault may be related to reactivation of these basement faults. The presence of Tertiary strata associated with ophiolite in the hangingwall of the boundary fault at Sunub shows that the fault was probably developed during, and reactivated since, culmination collapse.

In these same areas it has been shown that transfer faults affect basement and cover rocks. At Sunub a bowl-like structure of fault blocks formed between the transfer faults and the basement-cover fault. Similarly, at Wadi Taww, N-trending horst blocks with displacements of 300−400 m are parallel to the adjacent transfer fault. These structures also seem, therefore, to represent reactivated basement faults.

On the SW side of the Oman mountains at Wadi Fatha, the en échelon fold pattern in the Tertiary cover is compatible with those mapped in the underlying Hawasina rocks. Their origin is related to a ramp in the basement which is concave towards the NE and described as an active oblique ramp. Gliding of the Tertiary rocks over the pre-existing en échelon fold pattern may have caused the cover sediments to mimic the underlying geometry. Elsewhere, the structural geometry in the Maastrichtian and Tertiary cover seems to be controlled by the structural grain developed during the Late Cretaceous.

Jebel Aswad is believed to overlie a fold pair representing a lateral tip of an underlying Late Cretaceous thrust. The Natih and Fahud structures are interpreted here as a pop-up and triangle zone above Late Cretaceous frontal and back thrusts (Fig. 9b). It is also suggested that the Maastrichtian and Tertiary cover may have used the underlying easy gliding Fiqa shales of the Aruma Group as a major décollement to facilitate a southward movement by a gravity gliding mechanism.

Discussion

The main extensional movement of the sedimentary cover on the Batinah Plain is consistently down towards the N and NE, away from the Oman Mountains. Structural profiling in the Rusayl Embayment, however, has identified a considerably larger number of normal faults than on the Batinah Plain and a series of folds with variable trends. Some of these structures

have also been identified by the mapping of Villey et al. (1986a, b). This more complex pattern of deformation can be explained by invoking extensional movement away from the Saih Hatat and Jebel Nakhl culminations in a direction perpendicular to the culmination walls. It may be expected that extension of the sediments into the confined Rusayl Embayment would be associated with a strike-slip component to accommodate this deformation because of the orthogonal relationship of the Saih Hatat to Jebel Nakhl culmination walls (Fig. 10). Strike-slip faulting has apparently been mapped by Glennie et al. (1974) and Villey et al. (1986a) on the E margin of the Rusayl Embayment where the basement-cover contact has been displaced in a sinistral sense. Strike-slip movement was also recorded at Wadi Taww, on the W side of the Jebel Nakhl culmination (Fig. 5).

Another important feature which may control the structural development in this area is the possibility of an irregular basement surface. This could explain the development of some of the larger structures such as the Lansab anticline (Fig. 7b). In this example the fold has developed above a bulge in the basement at depth caused by either a shallowing of the fault between the Hajar Supergroup carbonates and ophiolite or by the presence of a fault bounded wedge of Hawasina sediments between these units.

The identification of extensional structures in Miocene sediments on the island of Suwadi and on seismic sections in the Gulf of Oman has led to a prediction that the extensional style of faulting associated with the basement-cover contact is continuous across the Batinah Plain into the offshore sequence. Suwadi lies directly across strike from the Wadi Hawasina area which, on the basis of the structural mapping and sedimentological evidence, has been recognized as a palaeo-high. To the ENE of Sawadi, the Daymaniyat Islands lie along the same structural trend and may also represent an upfaulted block in the extensional system. It is therefore suggested that the Hawasina−Suwadi−Daymaniyat structure shows evidence of a prolonged structural history and influenced sedimentation from Eocene to the present along the southern margin of the Gulf of Oman.

By contrast, structures developed in the Maastrichtian and Tertiary sequence on the SW side of the Oman mountains display only the frontal ends of the extensional faults. The dominant structural style here is related to folding developed by the interference between the southward moving Tertiary cover and the underlying structures in the basement. The gross simi-

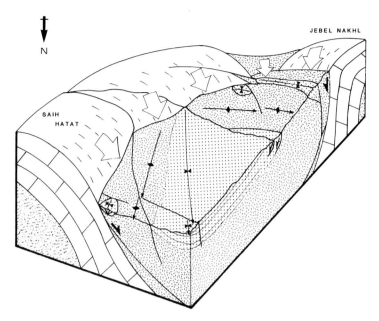

Fig. 10. Conceptual model of Tertiary extensional tectonics in the Rusayl Embayment. Based on observations by the authors, B. P. Clissold (pers. comm.) and Glennie *et al.* (1974). Ornament as Fig. 9.

larity between the tectonic style of both the basement and the Tertiary cover is additional evidence (Fig. 9b).

Implications for the Oman Mountains and Gulf of Oman

Structural mapping combined with stratigraphic studies has shown that Saih Hatat is the major structure in the E of the central Oman Mountains. Although the Nakhl culmination had less of an influence on Tertiary sedimentation, the structure clearly exerted an influence on Tertiary tectonic development.

The apparent prolonged age and timing of the extensional events in the central Oman Mountains may be a result of collapse of the main culminations at different times (Hanna 1986). It is proposed that the Saih Hatat culmination collapsed earlier than the Jebel Akhdar−Nakhl culmination; a view supported by stratigraphic and sedimentological studies and the results of structural mapping in this study. Saih Hatat formed a positive feature during the Palaeogene Period and later played a significant role in the deformation of the Rusayl area. By contrast, the Jebel Akhdar−Nakhl culmination appears to have had little effect on Palaeogene sedimentation. It is therefore possible that the Jebel Akhdar−Nakhl structure became a more positive feature at a later time and that the

extensional influence on the Late Campanian to Tertiary rocks was also a later event.

It is evident that during the early Tertiary, the Oman Mountains had a lower relief than the present elevation which must have been produced by post-Palaeogene uplift. Evidence of this uplift is shown by numerous raised beaches in the Muscat/Batinah coast area and on the Musandam Peninsula (Ricateau & Riché 1980), and by the neo-tectonic structures identified in post-Eocene sediments on the S side of the Oman Mountains (Hanna & Nolan 1989). Mapping on the Batinah Plain has shown that the displacement on the basement-cover fault decreases from Mushayq northwards, towards a high around Khasaf and Wadi Hawasina where Tertiary sediments lie unconformably upon the basement. This area has been interpreted above as an important basement structure in the S of the Gulf of Oman and Batinah Plain with a long history of tectonic prominence.

It has been predicted that extensional faults are also present beneath the Batinah Plain and the Gulf of Oman, since extensional structures have also been mapped at Suwadi on the coast. Normal faults between the basement and sedimentary cover have also been identified in the Gulf of Oman (White & Ross 1979) and large surge zones within the cover sediments have shown that the extensional regime is continuous into the offshore sequence. Similarly, the presence of post-Miocene normal faults in Musandam (Biehler *et al.* 1975; Ricateau & Riché 1980) also suggests that the Late Tertiary extensional regime continues NW in the Western part of the Gulf of Oman to the Musandam Peninsula.

The Late Campanian to Tertiary strata of the central Oman Mountains and Gulf of Oman have therefore been deformed within an extensional tectonic regime with evidence of only localized compression associated with the overall extensional setting. No evidence of Tertiary compression has been found in this study S of the Wadi Jizzi lineament and although post-Eocene thrusting was postulated in the Jebel Sumeini area N of Wadi Jizzi (Watts & Garrison 1986), this deformation could equally well represent either the frontal end of an extensional fault or a reactivated Late Cretaceous thrust within an extensional regime caused by uplift of the mountain belt. The Tertiary compressional deformation identified on the Musandam Peninsula dies out southeastwards away from the north Oman Mountains. It is, therefore, concluded that there is no evidence of a compressional Zagros event in the central Oman Mountains, and the term 'Zagros' should not be applied to this area. It is apparent from the regional tectonic setting (Fig. 1a) that the central Oman Mountains are a greater distance away from the Zagros thrust belt than the northern Oman Mountains. It is not surprising therefore, that the effects of Zagros compression diminishes southwards.

The Oman continental margin has a previous history of normal faulting during the Middle to Late Triassic and Early Cretaceous which may have controlled sedimentation at this time (Glennie *et al.* 1973, 1974; Smewing & Pratt 1986; Robertson 1987). These faults may have been later reactivated as thrusts during the Late Cretaceous ophiolite emplacement and subsequently inverted as extensional faults during culmination collapse (Hanna 1986). By contrast, the N part of the Gulf of Oman adjacent to the Makran is dominated by large compressional folds associated with thrusting; a result of subduction of ocean crust beneath the Makran (White & Ross 1979). The northward subduction of ocean floor combined with uplift of the Oman Mountains has resulted in extensional movement, by a simple gravity mechanism, of the Late Campanian to Tertiary sedimentary cover northwards, away from the Oman continental margin and into the Gulf of Oman in a typical hinterland basin geometry.

The causal mechanism behind the continued uplift of the Oman Mountains is unclear. Part of the initial Late Cretaceous uplift may have included an isostatic uplift due to early culmination collapse involving the Semail ophiolite. The more recent Late Tertiary to present-day movement involves essentially vertical uplift; the cause of which requires further investigation.

This work was funded by Amoco Oman Petroleum Company through the Earth Sciences and Resources Institute, University of South Carolina. The authors wish to thank the Ministry of Petroleum and Minerals, Sultanate of Oman. Amoco Production Company granted permission to publish this paper. We are grateful to Dr J. D. Smewing of the Earth Resources Institute, Swansea for his constructive criticism of the manuscript. We would like to thank Mr. B. P. Clissold for his helpful co-operation in Oman and for access to unpublished information on the Rusayl area.

References

BIEHLER, J., CHEVALIER, C. & RICATEAU, R. 1975. *Carte géologique de la peninsule de Musandam.* Edition B. R. G. M., Orléans (France).

COLEMAN, R. G. 1981. Tectonic setting for ophiolite obduction in Oman. *Journal of Geophysical Research*, **86**, 2497–2508.

FARHOUDI, G. & KARIG, D. C. 1977. Makran of Iran and Pakistan as an active arc system. *Geology*, **5**, 664–668.

GLENNIE, K. W. 1977. Outline of the geology of Oman. *Mémoires de la Société Géologique de France*, **8**, 25–31.

——, BOUEF, M. G. A., HUGHES CLARKE, M. W., MOODY-STUART, M., PILAAR, W. F. H. & REINHARDT, B. M. 1973. Late Cretaceous nappes in the Oman mountains and their geologic evolution. *Bulletin of the American Association of Petroleum Geologists*, **57**, 5–27.

——, ——, ——, ——, —— & —— 1974. The geology of the Oman mountains. *Verhandelingen van het Koninklijk Nederlands geologisch Mijnbouwkundig Genootschap* **31**.

GRAHAM, G. M. 1980. Structure and sedimentology of the Hawasina Window, Oman mountains. *PhD. thesis, Open University, Milton Keynes, U.K.*

HANNA, S. S. 1986. The Alpine (Late Cretaceous and Tertiary) tectonic evolution of the Oman mountains: A thrust tectonic approach. *Symposium on the hydrocarbon potential of intense thrust zones*, **2**, OAPEC, Kuwait, 125–174.

—— 1990. The Alpine deformation of the Central Oman Mountains. *In:* ROBERTSON, A. H. F., SEARLE, M. P. & RIES, A. C. (eds) *The Geology and Tectonics of the Oman Region.* Geological Society, London, Special Publication, **49**, 341–349.

—— & NOLAN, S. C. 1989. The Maradi Fault Zone: evidence of Late Neogene in the Oman Mountains. *Journal of the Geological Society of London*, **146**, 867–871.

HOPSON, C. A., COLEMAN, R. G., GREGORY, R. T., PALLISTER, J. S. & BAILEY, E. H. 1981. Geological section through the Semail ophiolite and associated rocks along a Muscat-Ibra transect, South-eastern Oman mountains. *Journal of Geophysical Research*, **86**, 2527–2544.

LIPPARD, S. J. & REX, D. C. 1982. K–Ar ages of alkaline igneous rocks in the northern Oman mountains, NE Arabia, and their relations to rifting, passive margin development and destruction of the Oman Tethys. *Geological Magazine*, **119**, 497–503.

MICHARD, A. 1983. Les nappes de Mascate (Oman), Rampe epicontinentale d'obduction a facies schiste bleu, et la dualite apparente des ophiolites Omanaises. *Bulletin des Sciences Géologiques*, **36**, 3–16.

——, BOUCHEZ, J. L. & OUAZZANI–TOUHAMI, M. 1984. Obduction-related planar and linear fabrics in Oman. *Journal of Structural Geology*, **6**, 39–49.

NOLAN, S. C., CLISSOLD, B. P., SMEWING, J. D. & SKELTON, P. W. 1986. Late Campanian to Tertiary palaeogeography of the Central and Northern Oman mountains. *Symposium on the hydrocarbon potential of intense thrust zones*, **2**, OAPC, Kuwait, 175–200.

——, SKELTON, P. W., CLISSOLD, B. P. & SMEWING, J. D. 1990. Maastrichtian-Early Tertiary stratigraphy and palaeogeography of the central and northern Oman Mountains. *In*: ROBERTSON, A. H. F., SEARLE, M. P. & RIES, A. C. 1990. *The Geology and Tectonics of the Oman Region*. Geological Society, London, Special Publication, **49**, 495–519.

PEARCE, J. A., ALABASTER, T., SHELTON, A. W. & SEARLE, M. P. 1981. The Oman ophiolite as a Cretaceous arc-basin complex: evidence and implication. *Philosophical Transactions of the Royal Society of London* **A300**, 299–317.

RICATEAU, R. & RICHE, P. H. 1980. Geology of the Musandam Peninsula (Sultanate of Oman) and its surroundings. *Journal of Petroleum Geology*, **3**, 139–152.

ROBERTSON, A. H. F. 1987. The transition from a passive margin to an Upper Cretaceous foreland basin related to ophiolite emplacement in the Oman mountains. *Bulletin of the Geological Society of America*, **99**, 633–653.

SEARLE, M. P. 1980. The metamorphic sheet and underlying volcanic rocks beneath the Semail ophiolite in the Northern Oman mountains of Arabia. *PhD. thesis* Open University, Milton Keynes, U.K.

—— 1985. Sequence of thrusting and origins of culminations in the Northern and Central Oman mountains. *Journal of Structural Geology*, **7**, 129–143.

——, JAMES, N. P., CALON, T. J. & SMEWING, J. D. 1983. Sedimentological and structural evolution of the Arabian continental margin in the Musandam Mountains and Dibba Zone, United Arab Emirates. *Bulletin of the Geological Society of America*, **94**, 1381–1400.

——, LIPPARD, S. J., SMEWING, J. D. & REX, D. C. 1980. Volcanic rocks beneath the Semail ophiolite nappe in the Northern Oman mountains and their significance in the Mesozoic evolution of Tethys. *Journal of the Geological Society of London*, **137**, 589–604.

SMEWING, J. D. & PRATT, B. R. 1986. Jurassic continental margin configuration, central Oman mountains: Evidence from facies trends in the Hajar Super Group. *Symposium on the hydrocarbon potential of intense thrust zones*, **2**, OAPEC, Kuwait, 201–226.

TSCHOPP, R. H. 1967. The general geology of Oman. *Proceedings of the 7th World Petroleum Congress, Mexico*, **2**, 243–50

VILLEY, M., LE METOUR, J. & GRAMONT, X. de. 1986a. *Geological map of Fanjah*. Sheet NF 40–3F, scale 1:100000. Explanatory Notes: Directorate General of Minerals, Oman Ministry of Petroleum and Minerals.

——, —— & —— 1986b. *Geological map of Sib*. Sheet NF 40–3C, scale 1:100000: Explanatory Notes: Directorate General of Minerals, Oman Ministry of Petroleum and Minerals.

WARRAK, M. 1986. Structural evolution of the Northern Oman mountain front, Al-Ain region. *Symposium on the hydrocarbon potential of intense thrust zones*, **1**, OAPEC, Kuwait, 375–431.

WATTS, K. F. & GARRISON, R. E. 1986. Sumeini Group, Oman — evolution of a Mesozoic carbonate slope on a south Tethyan continental margin. *Sedimentary Geology*, **48**, 107–168.

WHITE, R. S. & KLITGORD, K. D. 1976. Sediment deformation and plate tectonics in the Gulf of Oman. *Earth and Planetary Science Letters*, **32**, 199–209.

—— & ROSS, D. A. 1979. Tectonics of the western Gulf of Oman. *Journal of geophysical Research*, **84**, 3479–3489.

WHITMARSH, R. B. *et al.* 1974. *Initial reports of the Deep Sea Drilling Project*, **23**. U.S. Government Printing Office, Washington, D.C., 809–812.

Cenozoic alluvial fan systems of interior Oman: palaeoenvironmental reconstruction based on discrimination of palaeochannels using remotely sensed data

J. MAIZELS[1] & C. McBEAN[2]

[1] *Department of Geography, University of Aberdeen, Elphinstone Road, Aberdeen AB9 2UF, UK*
[2] *JARIC, RAF Brampton, Huntingdon, Cambridgeshire, PE18 8QL, UK*

Abstract: Sequences of exhumed, superimposed palaeochannel generations exposed on a Cenozoic alluvial fan in interior Oman are discriminated using a range of different remote sensing techniques. While lithological composition has been demonstrated to vary systematically with relative age of the deposit, ground radiometry has confirmed a relationship between spectral response and percentage cherts in the alluvial deposits. This relationship has allowed up to 14 palaeochannel generations to be discriminated from tonal contrasts on black and white air photographs, and up to five generations on black and white air photo mosaics and SIR-A imagery, and on Landsat MSS false colour imagery. Mapping of successive palaeochannel generations has highlighted the contrasts in channel extent, morphology and pattern during long-term evolution of the fan. These changes in palaeochannel characteristics are interpreted in terms of changes in humidity and continentality of the catchment, changes in eustatic level and in the watertable, and progressive expansion of the drainage network during the Cenozoic.

A major indicator of Cenozoic palaeoenvironments within the arid tropical zone lies in relict alluvial fan systems. These contain evidence of changing climatic, tectonic and run-off conditions during Tertiary and Quaternary times, particularly in areas adjacent to actively rising mountain chains. In many fan systems, sedimentological evidence of palaeoenvironmental changes is derived from isolated stratigraphic sections and from morphological relations between fan surfaces of different age and elevation. Only rarely are the former channel systems associated with successive stages of fan growth preserved or exposed, which is unfortunate as it is these channel systems that most closely reflect the nature of climatic, tectonic and hydrologic changes though time.

This study focuses on Cenozoic alluvial fan systems in interior Oman, which comprise up to 20 successive generations of exhumed multistorey palaeodrainage systems. Each palaeodrainage generation is characterized by a distinctive lithological composition, resulting from progressive growth of the catchment area onto a different geological substrate, and from long-term weathering of constituent sediments. While morphology and pattern of the palaeochannel systems can be accurately mapped from conventional, stereoscopic air photo cover, this is available for only a small area of the Oman fans. In addition, reliable determination of palaeochannel generation, based on morphologic and stratigraphic relations as well as on lithological composition, can only be achieved by detailed field mapping and sediment analysis. The lack of complete air photo cover and the impracticability of extensive field sampling in these relatively remote and inaccessible fan systems, precludes the extensive use of such methods in the determination of palaeochannel generation. Since each palaeochannel generation comprises a distinctive lithological suite, the only alternative means of discriminating successive palaeochannel generations for the complete fan system may lie in the use of remote sensing methods which can successfully discriminate the spectral properties of these different surface materials.

The aim of this paper is to test out the application of remote sensing methods in the discrimination of fan gravel lithologies, and of associated palaeochannel generations. This study forms part of a larger programme of palaeoenvironmental reconstruction of the Omani alluvial systems during the Cenozoic.

From ROBERTSON, A. H. F., SEARLE, M. P. & RIES, A. C. (eds), 1990, *The Geology and Tectonics of the Oman Region.* Geological Society Special Publication No 49, pp 565–582

More detailed discussion of long-term fan development and palaeohydrology is presented elsewhere (Maizels 1989 a, b).

Palaeochannel systems in environmental reconstruction

The south and southwest margins of the Oman mountains are flanked by vast relict alluvial fans, extending for >250 km beyond the mountain edge. The proximal alluvial fan deposits are >250 m thick, resting on the Miocene continental Fars group (Aubel 1983; Jones 1985), suggesting that the basal fan gravels may date from Pliocene times. The youngest surfaces are mantled with early–mid Holocene chert lithics, indicating that fan growth had ceased by early Holocene times (Edens 1989). No other dates are yet available to cover the long time span of Plio-Pleistocene time represented within the fan sequence.

The Cenozoic is characterized by global climatic, eustatic and tectonic changes, and these are reflected within all major terrestrial and marine environmental systems. Palaeodrainage courses are particularly sensitive to changes in climate which affect vegetation cover, precipitation regimes, evapotranspiration rates and catchment runoff (e.g. Schumm 1965).

Sea level during the last glaciation (25–10 ka BP) was up to 130 m lower than at present resulting in greater aridity and continentality in much of the Middle East, and stronger and more persistent winter northeast trade winds (e.g. Glennie 1970; Street & Grove 1976; Prell et al. 1980; Van Campo et al. 1982). Marked increases in aridity associated with glacial episodes are likely to be reflected in the development of more ephemeral flow regimes, associated with poorly vegetated, steep catchment slopes, low water tables, rapid transmission losses into channel bed and banks, and diminished flows downstream (cf. Riley 1977; Graf 1988). These high-power ephemeral flows from poorly vegetated catchments are likely to have transported coarse clastic sediments within low-sinuosity distributary systems (cf. Parkash et al. 1983; Nichols 1987; Reid & Frostick 1989), in which individual channel branches diminished in size downfan as flows disappeared into the substrate (e.g. cf. Friend 1978; Steel & Aasheim 1978). Short-lived episodes of stream activity are likely to have been separated by prolonged periods of eolian activity, characterized by thick accumulations of loess and/or desert sands infilling inactive channel courses, and/or by extensive deflation of fine sediments.

By contrast, interglacial episodes are likely to have been significantly more humid, leading to more widely vegetated slopes and fan surfaces, more finely graded sediment inputs, and more seasonal or even perennial flow regimes (cf. Schumm 1965). These more prolonged periods of fluvial activity are likely to have been accommodated in more stable, extensive, or continuous channel systems.

Hence, it should be possible to differentiate palaeochannel systems which developed during more arid phases from those of more humid phases of the Cenozoic, especially during the Quaternary. However, channel behaviour responds not only to external (allocyclic) controls such as climate, eustasy and tectonism, but also to intrinsic (autocyclic) controls inherent within the fluvial system itself (cf. Kraus & Middleton 1987). For example, longterm fan aggradation may gradually result in progressive steepening and coarsening of palaeochannel systems until a threshold condition is reached and fan entrenchment begins. Similarly, changes in the drainage network resulting from progressive network expansion can result in increased runoff volumes and sediment inputs to alluvial fan systems.

A major element of palaeoenvironmental reconstruction in areas of relict alluvial fan development clearly lies, therefore, in the analysis of the morphology, pattern and extent of the palaeodrainage network, as well as in the lithologies, sediment facies and stratigraphic relations both of individual palaeochannel deposits and of successive palaeochannel generations.

Geology of the alluvial source materials

The alluvial fan sediments in this study form part of the wadi Andam catchment, which covers an area of c. 4500 km². The headwaters of the wadi system originate within the Semail ophiolite nappe of the eastern Oman Mountains and drain southwards via transverse routeways through the low, WNW–ESE trending ridges of the Lower Hawasina limestones and cherts (Glennie et al. 1974; Hopson et al. 1981). Beyond this mountain edge lies a series of up-domed limestone outliers of Hajar and 'exotic' origin, such as Jebel Madar (Fig. 1). A narrow gap in these ridges marks the emergence point of the drainage system from within the massif onto the piedmont zone.

No other drainage system in this southern piedmont zone extends far enough northwards to drain the ophiolite; and the wadi Andam system is unique in its range of source rocks. The main ones include a wide variety of basic and ultrabasic igneous rocks (including serpen-

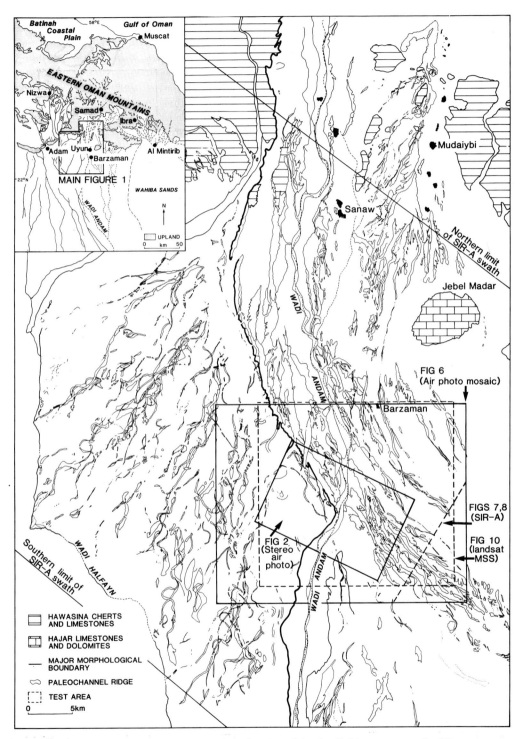

Fig. 1. The Oman palaeochannel systems and the location of the detailed test areas, south of Barzaman.

tinites, peridotites, gabbros, dolerites and basalts) as well as Hawasina cherts, and limestones from a variety of sources of different ages, ranging from the older up-domed massifs (Permian–late Cretaceous), to the foothills of Hawasina turbidite limestones and 'exotic' marbles (Hopson *et al*. 1981).

Methods of palaeochannel discrimination

Preliminary inspection of air photo mosaics of the alluvial fans in Oman indicates numerous generations of superimposed linear palaeochannel ridges, intersecting at a variety of angles and variety of elevations, and exhibiting a wide variety of morphologies, patterns, and upstream and downstream extents (Fig. 1). Contrasts in tone between successive generations are particularly conspicuous, with the older generations exhibiting the palest grey tones, the youngest appearing black.

Selection of methods and test site

The mapping project was divided into three components. First, analysis of lithological composition and particle size characteristics for the surface materials on successive palaeochannel ridges. Second, ground radiometer data were collected in the field at a number of the sites sampled for sediment type, in order to test the relationship between both surface lithology and particle size, and spectral reflectance. Finally, palaeochannel systems were mapped in a selected test site using (1) low-altitude, stereoscopic, black and white air photography; (2) high-altitude, monoscopic, black and white air photo mosaics; (3) Shuttle Imaging Radar (SIR-A); and (4) Landsat MSS imagery. Some of this analysis is still in progress, and will later be extended to include Landsat TM imagery. The differences in discrimination of successive palaeochannel generations were assessed from comparison of the four resulting interpretations.

The test site selected was covered by all four forms of imagery, and was sufficiently accessible to allow detailed sampling and radiometric measurement of surface sediments. The test site includes a large number of different palaeochannel generations as well as the present course of wadi Andam. It covers an area of *c*. 200 km^2 (*c*. 17 × 12 km) for method (1) and *c*. 650 km^2 (*c*. 28 × 23 km) for methods (2) to (4) (Fig. 1).

Lithological composition

On initial visual inspection of air photo mosaics the most conspicuous contrast between successive palaeochannel generations was tone. Tonal differences between sedimentary deposits are most likely to reflect contrasts in composition and/or size of the sedimentary particles, so in the first part of this study we looked for changes in lithological composition through the palaeochannel sequence. A change in composition of the channel sediments through time is likely to reflect either progressive long-term weathering or chemical diagenesis (e.g. Hunt & Mabey 1966; Goudie 1989) of the less resistant lithologies (such as the ophiolitic rocks), and/or changes in sources of sediment supply to the former drainage system.

Palaeochannel sediments were sampled for lithological composition at over 200 sites, selected from key areas, including the test site, for determining changes at palaeochannel intersections and multistorey sequences. At each site, surface materials were sampled from a randomly located 0.5 m × 0.5 m quadrat, from which the hundred largest clasts were collected for analysis. Clasts were initially classified into three main lithological groups: cherts and siliceous clasts, ophiolite clasts and limestones (including Hawasina and 'exotics').

Clast size variations

Since the tone is related to the reflectance properties of the surface materials, the tone recorded by the imaging system will depend both on the part of the electromagnetic spectrum used, and on the nature and composition of the target surface itself. On radar imagery, for example, surfaces of fine-grained material are smooth and appear as areas of dark tone whereas rough surfaces are more heterogeneous, due to their more complex backscattering properties.

This study examined variations in sediment size at over 200 palaeochannel sites, including those at the test site, with the aim of relating these size variations to tonal variations detected in both the visible/infrared and the radar imagery systems.

Ground radiometer measurements

Ground radiometer measurements in the test area were used to test whether reflectance represents a response to lithological composition and/or size of the palaeochannel sediments. If such relationships were established, they would indicate that (a) tonal contrasts on black and white air photos and spectral contrasts on Landsat colour composites do reflect lithological composition and/or particle size of the Oman palaeochannel deposits; and that (b) these contrasts may therefore be used to dis-

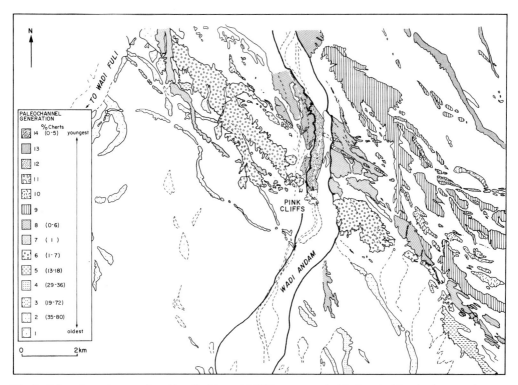

Fig. 2. Palaeochannel generations identified from 1:36 000 stereoscopic, black and white air photograph cover of the Barzaman (Pink Cliffs) test area. 14 palaeochannel generations can be distinguished.

criminate successive palaeochannel generations, by visual interpretation or digital image processing.

We used a Milton Multiband Radiometer, recording in spectral channels similar to those of Bands 2, 3, 4, and 5 of the Landsat Thematic Mapper (0.52−0.60, 0.63−0.69, 0.76−0.90 and 1.55−1.75 μm, respectively). The radiometer was mounted on the arm of a platform 2 m above the sample surface, with the platform arm directed towards the sun for each reading, while the platform was kept as vertical as possible. The sampling area has an approximate diameter of 0.5 m, and formed the basis of lithological, sediment size, and ground radiometry data. In order to determine the spectral response of the lithological suite present, the bidirectional reflectance (BDR) was determined at each of the sampling sites by means of three repeat readings corrected by a wavelength-dependent factor to compensate for the variation in reflectance from the standard Kodak Grey reference card (Milton 1980; McBean 1989).

Air photograph interpretation

Low altitude, stereo cover, air survey. Two sets of large-scale air photographs were available for selected parts of the alluvial fan systems, but concentrated in the Barzaman test area (Fig. 2). Black and white stereoscopic air photos at the scales of 1:32 000 (1981, courtesy of Public Authority for Water Resources (PAWR), Oman) and 1:30 000 (flown by BKS Surveys Ltd) were used for mapping the palaeochannel systems in the test area and where possible, for discriminating between successive palaeochannel generations.

Air photo mosaics. Air photo mosaics at the scale of *c.* 1:100 000 provided non-stereoscopic, black and white cover for the full extent of the alluvial fan system. The mosaics were used to extend the mapping of palaeochannel generations from tonal relationships established within the test area to wider areas across the fan system. However, photographic quality was generally poor, and tonal contrasts only minimal, thereby reducing the reliability of the mapping procedures.

Shuttle Imaging Radar (SIR-A)

We used part of Data Take 37a of Shuttle Imaging Radar (SIR-A). The image used data acquired in 1981 covering a swath of terrain extending south-eastwards from Jebel Madar, and crossing the northeastern part of the palaeochannel system (Fig. 1). The return radar signal is controlled by three major ground parameters: (a) the surface relief, such as macro-scale variations in slope angle, form and orientation; (b) the surface roughness, and particularly the size and spacing of micro-scale surface irregularities (see Table 1); and (c) the complex dielectric constant, which is an electrical property influenced by variations in soil moisture and salinity.

Radar backscatter is generally greatest from a surface lying perpendicular to, or sloping towards, the incident signal, whether at the macro- or micro-scale. A smooth, flat surface, on the other hand, will allow the signal to reflect away from the sensor, producing a low return, while a rough surface will result in a diffuse scattering of relatively uniform intensity (cf. Lynne & Taylor 1986). The complex dielectric constant further influences the radar backscatter by determining the amount of surface penetration of the signal. Penetration is least when the surface moisture content is high, giving greater radar reflectivity.

In this study, the SIR-A image was used as a means of interpreting morphological relations and contrasts in relief between successive palaeochannel generations, while the textural variations on a micro-scale were also tested against variations in surface sediment sizes.

Landsat imagery

The Landsat Multispectral Scanner (MSS) scans a 185 km-wide swath in four wavebands with a ground resolution of 79×79 m. The wavelength range for bands 4, 5, 6 and 7 is $0.5–0.6$, $0.6–0.7$, $0.7–0.8$, and $0.8–1.1$ μ m, respectively. The more recently established Landsat Thematic Mapper (TM) is a sensor with higher spatial resolution and more appropriate spectral coverage (e.g. Rothery 1987).

Landsat MSS imagery acquired in 1976 and 1978 was available for the eastern palaeochannel systems in this study. Because no complete Landsat cover (either MSS or TM) was available for the full extent of the alluvial fans, only the MSS digital data were used for mapping palaeo-channels, and mapping was confined to the test area. Analysis of TM imagery at a later stage should allow more complete mapping of successive palaeochannel systems across the whole area (cf. Abrams 1986; Abrams *et al.* 1988).

Discrimination of palaeochannels using ground truth and remote sensing data

Preliminary mapping from air photographs

A preliminary map of individual palaeochannel networks of apparent different generation was constructed for part of the Barzaman (Pink Cliffs) test area from black and white aerial

Table 1. *Field and image definition of surface roughness for SIR-A radar data*

Category	Image appearance	Environment	Surface grain size
Very smooth	Black	Smooth and flat with no surface perturbations. Open water, fine mud or silt.	
Smooth	Dark Grey	Smooth and flat with only minor irregularities. Sand dunes, sabkha, fine gravel with no vegetation.	< 14.6 mm
Intermediate	Mid Grey	Gravel, low vegetation on dunes.	14.6−83.1 mm
Rough	Light Grey	Small boulders, salt doming, sabkha, scrub vegetation on dunes and in wadis.	83.1−300 mm
Very rough	White	Gullying, boulders, blocky rock outcrops, e.g. aeolianite, raised channels, forest stands, urban areas.	> 300 mm

photographs at 1:36000 scale (Fig. 2). The extent of each palaeochannel course, its morphological and, where possible, its stratigraphic relations were checked in the field. This mapping phase identified 14 distinct palaeochannel generations, based on intersection, truncation or superimposition of older deposits by younger (cf. Friend *et al.* 1981). However, the relative time period represented both by the palaeochannel deposits and by the periods between those of palaeochannel activity cannot be determined solely from mapping of the palaeochannel systems.

The resulting map indicates that the oldest generation (1) in the test area forms broad, low relief, sinuous channels, while generations 2–5 form narrow (<*c*. 30 m wide), sinuous ridges, traceable for up to *c*. 10 km, and exhibiting undulating irregular crest-lines (Tables 2; Fig. 2). Generations 6 and 7 include some sinuous ridges, but are more typically characterized by broad, flat-topped gravel spreads (*c*. 1.5 km wide), rising over 35 m above the adjacent wadi floor. These ridges are locally highly dissected, and a number of isolated and short linear outliers extend southeastwards from the main ridges. The younger generations (9 to 13) lie to the northeast of the older generations, and form both low, dissected, lighter-toned spreads (older), and darker toned, low sinuosity, narrow, discontinuous ridges (younger). The youngest generation identified in the test area (generation 14) forms a broad low-level terrace, up to 500 m wide, bounding the present course of the wadi Andam (Table 2).

Lithological composition of successive palaeochannel ridges

Significant differences were found in the lithological composition of the palaeochannel deposits of different generation and hence of different relative age, both within the test area and for the alluvial fan as a whole (Fig. 3). Indeed, the relative proportions of the three dominant lithological groups, namely ophiolite debris, cherts and limestones, change systematically through the alluvial sequence. Detailed sampling of at least eight palaeochannel generations apparent in the test area (Fig. 3), indicates that the oldest palaeochannel deposits in the area contain up to 80% cherts at some sites (averaging 48%) while the third generation palaeochannels comprise 19–72% cherts (averaging 42%). These older generation ridges exhibit undulating crest lines, gravel thicknesses of <1 m, overlying pink dolomitic clays of the

Barzaman Formation, and are mantled with worked chert lithics. The cherts are generally red and orange, giving an overall reddish hue to the exposures. However, the clasts are also coated in a dark brown–black 'desert varnish', which forms a weathering surface masking the unweathered colour and modifying the reflectance properties of the rock (cf. Rothery 1984a).

Generations 4 and 5 contain only 29–36%, and 13–18% cherts, respectively, representing a highly significant reduction in the proportion of Hawasina sediments and a marked rise in concentrations of ophiolite clasts, compared with those of earlier generations. The younger generations (6 and 7) form broad, high gravel spreads dominated by ophiolite lithologies. Palaeochannel generation 6 comprises >90 per cent ophiolite, while that of generation 7 contains >98 per ophiolite. The gravel spread of the youngest generation, forming the wadi terrace deposits (generation 14) is dominated by ophiolite, generally to the exclusion of all other lithological types.

Clast size variations

Maximum clast diameters decrease systematically downfan over a distance of *c*. 220 km, although there is a marked tendency in many areas for the older palaeochannel generations to comprise significantly finer materials than those of the younger generations. The overall rates of downfan fining are therefore significantly lower in the older deposits (~1.01 mm km^{-1}) than in the younger (~4.1 mm km^{-1}) (Maizels 1989a).

At a local scale, significant differences in clast size can be found not only between deposits of different relative age, but also longitudinally within a given palaeochannel deposit. In the Barzaman test area, maximum clast diameters (averaging 16.0 cm) occur on the oldest palaeochannel ridge (generation 2), with generation 3 generally finer (averaging 13.2 cm). The high gravel sheets are also mantled with relatively coarse materials (averaging 14.7 cm), while the youngest gravels (generation 8) become finer again (12.5 cm).

Downstream fining is particularly distinctive along the ridge of generation 2, with clast sizes diminishing from 19.8 cm to 11.7 cm over a distance of *c*. 10 km (i.e. a local size decrease rate averaging *c*. 54 mm km^{-1}, with r^2= 0.63) (Fig. 4a). No other local trends of downstream fining have been identified in the Barzaman test area, perhaps because the sampling density was inadequate on some of the palaeochannel generations.

Table 2. *Morphological characteristics of successive palaeochannel generations and their palaeohydrological interpretation, Oman palaeochannel systems.*

Palaeochannel generation	Distal extent of channel system (km)	Mean sinuosity	Mean meander wavelength (km)	Amplitude of meander belt (km)	No. of active channel zones	Mean channel width (m) Proximal	Distal	Bankfull palaeodischarge estimates (m^3s^{-1}) Min.	Max.	Palaeohydrologic interpretation SH/H-subhumid/humid SA/A-semiarid/arid
1	>60	1.17	2.8	1.3	2–3	–	136	594	2239	SH-H
2	>60	1.21	4.7	3.6	~3	(304)[1]	105	424	1142	H
3	>60	prox 1.16 dist 1.47	4.2	1.9	~1	(298)[1]	102	408	4180	H-SH
4	>60	1.09	5.9	3.4	~3	(476)[1]	241	1249	7055	SA-A
5	>60	1.20	2.9	1.2	~4	(174)[1]	164	485	1180	SA
6	>60	1.18	4.5	3.2	3–5	116	164	483	4649	SH-H
7	>60	1.09	4.4	2.3	6–7	173	140	553	1368	SH-H
8	~40	1.07	3.3	1.5	~5	313	122	1755	2883	SA
9	~40	1.04	2.7	1.3	~6	148	75	663	2117	SA-A
10	~40	1.07	3.2	1.3	2–3	30	34	83	2750	SA-A
11	~40	1.07	3.2	1.4	2–3	–	23	59	2750	SA-A
12	~40	1.07	–	>6.5	1?	881	866	5750	14440	SA-A
	~30	1.09	–	>6.5	1?	2185	1114	9140	30720	SA-A

[1] Sample distances too small to be representative (after Maizels 1989b).

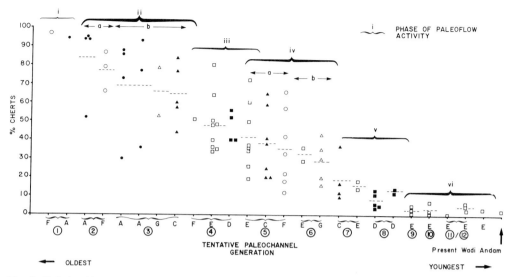

Fig. 3. Relationship between lithological composition of successive palaeochannel generations, and relative age of the deposit, for the Barzaman test area (generations indicated in bold figures), and five other field sites (after Maizels 1989). The percentage of cherts in the palaeochannel gravels generally increases with increasing age of the deposit. Each vertical line of data plotted on the diagram represents the % chert at sites within a given palaeochannel deposit. The horizontal broken lines represent the mean % chert for that palaeochannel deposit. Statistically significant differences in chert percentages have been used to discriminate groups of palaeochannel generations and separate periods of fluvial activity.

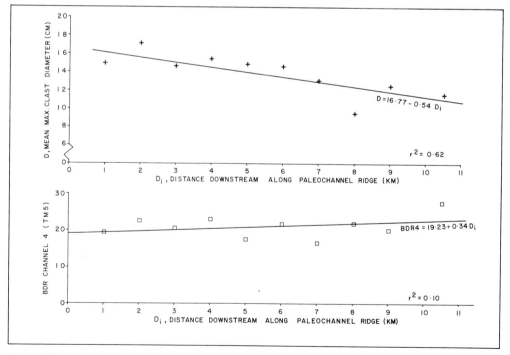

Fig. 4 (A). Downchannel decline in mean maximum clast diameter, palaeochannel generation 3, Barzaman test area. (B). Downchannel change in bidirectional reflectance (channel 4 [TM5]), for palaeochannel generation 3, Barzaman test area.

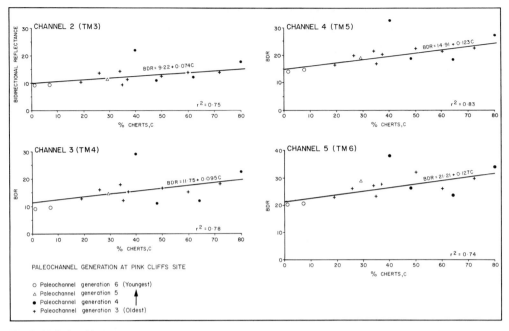

Fig. 5. Relationship between lithological composition of palaeochannel surface deposits in the Barzaman test area, and associated bidirectional reflectance for bands 1, 2, 3 and 4 (equivalent to TM bands 2, 3, 4 and 5 respectively).

Ground radiometer measurements and lithological composition

Ground radiometer measurements were taken at a number of sites on palaeochannel surfaces of generations 2, 3 and 6 in the test area. The results indicate a remarkably high correlation between BDR values and the lithological composition of the surface gravels defined in terms of the percentage cherts present (Fig. 5). With the exception of one site which is located at the southernmost tip of the oldest palaeochannel and comprises only a thin pebble lag over the widely exposed, light coloured, (i.e. bright-toned), underlying Barzaman Formation, the correlations between radiometer readings and the percentage chert are highly signficant for each wave band (Fig. 5). The results indicate a systematic and predictable increase in BDR with increasing proportions of chert present on the surface, and hence with increasing relative age of the palaeochannel deposit. The strong correlation between lithology and BDR for the selected sites suggests in turn that the degree of desert varnish development on the particle surfaces has been insufficient to mask fully the reflectance properties of the individual litho-logies (see Rothery 1984a, 1987). However, the r^2 values indicate an unexplained variance of up to 26%, suggesting that varnish development as well as the presence of ophiolite, accounts for some of the internal variability in BDR for a given lithological suite (e.g. see Rothery 1984a, 1987).

Ground radiometer measurements and clast sizes

No significant relationships emerge between ground BDR values and mean clast sizes. Although a slight inverse relationship is apparent between downstream fining and increased BDR values along the palaeochannel ridge of generation 2, the relationship is not statistically significant (Fig. 4B). The absence of a size relationship is confirmed also by the lack of correlation between clast sizes and lithological composition for the sites in the test area (Maizels 1989a). However, the range of sizes present within the data set is relatively small (10−20 cm), and the measurements are based on the size of the ten largest particles, rather than mean size and size variation within each sample quadrat, so further testing is necessary to establish the nature of any BDR-sediment size relation.

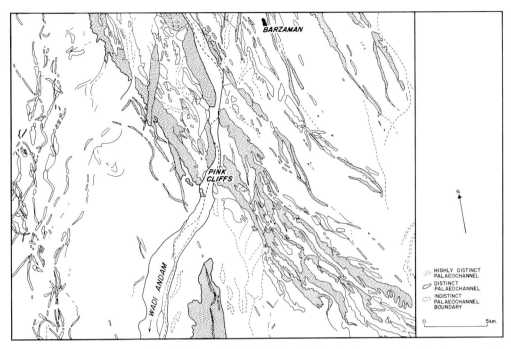

Fig. 6. Palaeochannel systems identified from 1:100 000 black and white air photo mosaic of the Barzaman test area. (See Fig. 1 for location).

Palaeochannel mapping from air photo mosaic

The major palaeochannel generations can be clearly distinguished from the 1:100 000 air photo mosaic (Fig. 6). However, the tonal contrasts are of a low order, and neither discrimination of successive generations nor correlation of generations in different parts of the mosaic can be accurately achieved. Hence, the individual generations have not been distinguished on the map interpretation, and any further interpretation would require extrapolation from the map of the test area derived from the large-scale, stereoscopic air survey. The area covered by the mosaic test area extends beyond that of the stereoscopic air photo cover, and does in fact reveal the existence of a complex multi-storey sequence of N−S trending palaeochannels lying some 10−12 km west of wadi Andam (Fig. 6). These westerly palaeochannels are likely to predate any of those found in the air photo test area, largely because they exhibit a much paler tone (i.e. richer in cherts), and because they have been truncated by the later, dark-toned (i.e. richer in ophiolites) palaeochannel systems trending NW−SE. Fig. 6 suggests that at least five of those older gener-

ations of superimposed palaeochannels are present in this westerly zone, and that these are dominated by narrow, persistent, sinuous, chert-rich courses. The northeastern half of the area is dominated by NW−SE trending broad, composite, and dissected ridges, of more recent age. However, the detail and tonal contrasts are too poorly resolved to allow accurate discrimination of more than five distinct palaeochannel generations, in addition to the 14 identified from the large-scale air photo cover. The north−south trending course of the present wadi Andam is clearly revealed, highlighted by the silts and sands deposited along its sinuous route (Fig. 6).

Palaeochannel mapping from SIR-A

The complex response of the sensor system to a wide range of ground parameters renders interpretation of the image of the palaeochannel systems particularly difficult. Five main levels of grey tone can be interpreted from work by Peake & Oliver (1971), and Stone & McBean (1987) (Table 1). The image of the Oman palaeochannel systems clearly reveals high relief palaeochannels, and especially those ridges with a northwest−southeast orientation, i.e. per-

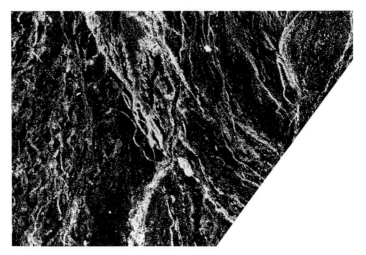

Fig. 7. Shuttle Imaging Radar (SIR-A) image of the Barzaman area, derived from Data Take 37a, 1981. Look direction is from the southwest. (See Fig. 1 for location).

pendicular to the look direction (Fig. 7). Those palaeochannel ridges stand out as the brightest features on the radar image, and particularly enhance the younger NW−SE trending palaeochannel systems in the northeast half of the image (Fig. 8). However, the many lower-relief palaeochannel ridges and gravel spreads in this area, and the older systems lying to the west, are only poorly resolved. Indeed, the majority of the palaeochannel courses cannot be clearly identified, since the radar image provides only indistinct, mottled grey toning devoid of linear features (Fig. 8). As the nominal ground resolution of the SIR-A system is c. 40 m, narrower palaeochannels cannot readily be detected, unless they exhibit a relatively high relief (e.g. >about 10 m). Generations 1 and 2 at the Pink Cliffs site, for example, are frequently less than 10 m wide, but rise 10−12 m above the surrounding gravel plains, and hence emerge as distinctive features on the image.

The radar image also reveals areas of flat, relatively smooth, low relief such as the present-day course of the wadi Andam and the smooth, fine-grained gravel plains which extend between the palaeochannel ridges. These surface characteristics produce a very low-signal (i.e. dark tone) radar image, particularly where vegetation cover is sparse or absent. The absence of vegetation allows most of the radar energy to reflect away from the sensor, so that very little information is returned on the image. With increasing distance from the wadi bed towards the adjacent flood plain and low flood plain terraces, the amount of surface vegetation

increases. This increase in vegetation is apparent in the increase in radar return from dark grey to white, with shrubs and trees acting to increase the radar backscatter.

The radar image has been successful in revealing the major palaeochannels, i.e. the largest and highest, together with the different palaeochannel systems (N−S trending and NW−SE trending systems) and the present wadi system. Only about five palaeochannel generations can be distinguished within the test area (Fig. 8), but with a low accuracy when compared with the stereoscopic air photo map interpretation (Fig. 2). In addition, the image does not appear to have been successful in discriminating between palaeochannels comprising different sediment sizes, and has only revealed differences in textural quality of palaeochannels, inter-ridge plains and present wadi courses.

Palaeochannel mapping from Landsat imagery

All the major palaeochannel systems are clearly distinguished on the MSS image (Figs 9 & 10). However, with a ground resolution of c. 80 m, many of the narrower channels are not clearly discriminated (Fig. 9). A supervised classification of palaeochannel systems in the Barzaman test area based on six test areas and four MSS bands, for example, failed to identify a number of the older palaeochannel generations (generations 1−5), largely because individual test-pixels extended well beyond the margins of a

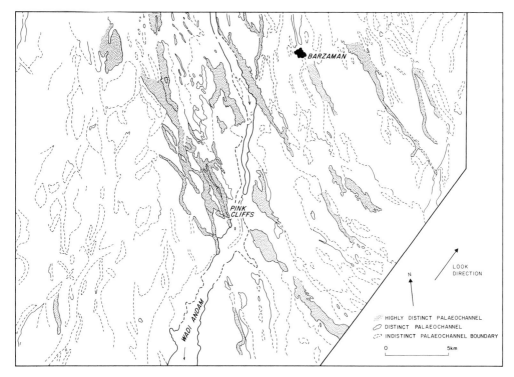

Fig. 8. Palaeochannel systems identified from the SIR-A image of the Barzaman area, based on interpretation of imagery from Data Take 37a, 1981 (from Fig.7). (See Fig. 1 for location).

given channel deposit (Figs 9 & 10). However, for the broader deposits, the supervised classification was reasonably successful in discriminating between the palaeochannels of the later generations, and between palaeochannel systems and the more recently active wadi systems. The radiometric resolution has also proved too coarse to allow accurate discrimination of successive palaeochannel generations from radiance contrasts alone. Hence, in the Barzaman test area, no more than four or five generations can be distinguished, such that the majority of palaeochannels can only be related to a particular palaeochannel system.

The contrasts in the nature of the inter-ridge plains for each palaeochannel system are also conspicuous, with the older surfaces to the southwest discriminated on the four-band, false colour composite, from the younger plains to the northeast. In the southwest, fine overbank sediments associated with the former meandering channels have been widely deflated to reveal the underlying Barzaman Formation, while in the northeast the plains comprise gravel sheet deposits associated with the former braided

river systems, and which have proved too coarse to be removed by deflation.

Discussion and interpretation

Assessment of remote sensing methods for palaeochannel mapping and discrimination

The low-altitude aerial survey cover, at scales of c. 1:30000 and 1:36000, has allowed the most accurate and detailed mapping of paleochannel systems, and the discrimination of 14 distinct palaeochannel generations (Fig. 2). In the absence of complete stereoscopic air survey cover, a combination of air photo mosaics (1:100000), Landsat MSS and SIR-A imagery can provide reasonably acceptable maps of the major palaeochannel systems, allowing identification of up to five successive generations (Figs 6, 8 & 9). However, none of these three methods can provide accurate discrimination of the many successive palaeochannel generations which are likely to be present on the fan, largely because of poor tonal contrasts, poor ground resolution and/or inadequate ground response

Fig. 9. Palaeochannel systems identified from the Landsat 1 imagery, based on interpretation of a four-band, six-class, supervised classification. (See Fig. 1 for location).

to the imaging system. The Landsat TM is likely, in the future, to provide a more reliable and rapid means of mapping and discriminating between successive palaeochannel generations.

Changes in palaeochannel pattern and morphology

The maps produced from different types of remotely sensed data for the Barzaman test area indicate that significant changes have occurred in palaeochannel characteristics through time. As shown earlier, those changes have been accompanied by a systematic and progressive change in the lithological composition of the palaeochannel gravels, from chert- to ophiolite-dominated constituents. The main changes include the following.

Palaeochannel orientation. The map interpretations demonstrate that a major change in orientation of the dominant palaeochannel systems occurred at some stage during fan formation. The older systems clearly drained southwards and were subsequently truncated by younger, southeast draining systems. Inspection of the complete drainage systems (Fig. 1) suggests that the older systems extended southwards for over 200 km, while the younger dis-

appear southeastwards into the Wahiba Sands.
Palaeochannel pattern and morphology. The older channels are significantly more sinuous, forming narrow, single-thread, meandering channels with wavelengths averaging *c.* 4.0 km. These single-thread channels also appear to have repeatedly followed established routeways, leading to the complex, multistorey sequences seen from the air photo mosaic west of wadi Andam (Fig. 6). The younger generations, by contrast, tend to form broad, multiple channel systems (e.g. generation 8, (Fig. 2), more typical of braided stream environments. Southeast of the Pink Cliffs site, for example, up to 5 to 6 anabranches of such a braided system may be identified, extending over a width of *c.* 5 km. The present wadi Andam follows a low sinuosity channel incised into the older fan deposits, and floored by a locally braided channel.

Palaeoenvironmental interpretation

The observed changes in the palaeochannel systems may be explained by a complex interaction of both allocyclic and autocyclic controls. *Precipitation regime.* Long-term changes in channel orientation, pattern and morphology

Fig. 10. False colour composite of the Barzaman test area based on a supervised classification of part of Landsat MSS image, using a four-band classification of six distinctive palaeochannel generations. (See Fig. 1 for location).

may be explained by fluctuations in climatic conditions, and particularly, the precipitation regime. During periods of increased humidity stream flows are likely to have been seasonal or even perennial. A number of the earlier palaeochannel generations exhibit characteristics which are likely to have resulted from more prolonged annual river flows than those of the later generations, and those of the present day. More perennial flows are likely to have given rise to more extensive, spatially continuous, sinuous drainage courses (cf. Jackson 1978; Arche 1983; Bridge 1985). Indeed, in order to establish highly sinuous meandering courses, it is likely that mean flows would have established equilibrium channel forms. Increased humidity would also promote more extensive vegetation cover, soil development and slope stability, thereby reducing both the quantity and calibre of sediments being input to the alluvial fan systems. Hence, the earlier palaeochannel systems developed typically meandering courses, draining through relatively fine-grained bank material, and maintaining their flow widths for prolonged distances downstream. Empirical relationships established between meander geometry and flows in present-day sinuous channels suggest that bankfull flows in the early palaeochannel generations would have averaged between c. 160 and 1400 m^3 s^{-1} (Table 2). Analysis of sediment facies (details of which are presented elsewhere (Maizels 1987, 1989a, b), indicates that these deposits are dominated by large-scale, trough cross sets composed of fine gravel and coarse sand, representing large dune bedforms characteristic of distal meandering streams. Overbank sediments may have included the fine sands, silts and clays which now form part of the thick Barzaman Formation.

By contrast, flow regimes during more arid conditions would have become increasingly ephemeral, characterized by flashy flows, and by rare high-magnitude flood events. These flows would have been accommodated by large distributary channel systems such as those of the later palaeochannel generations (esp. generation 8, Fig. 2; cf. Parkash et al. 1983; Nichols 1987). These palaeochannels narrow downfan, tapering off and disappearing into the substrate within 40 km of the mountain edge. Downstream diminution of flows would have been promoted by short-lived flood events, by high transmission losses into the dry substrate, and by high evaporation rates (cf. Schick 1988; Reid & Frostick 1989). Estimates of stream flow magnitudes suggest bankfull flows ranging from c. 13 000 to 31 000 m^3 s^{-1} (Maizels 1989 a, b; Table 2).

Periods of increased aridity may also be invoked to explain the exhumation of the alluvial fans and their long-term sequence of palaeochannel deposits. About 40 km^3 of sediment has been removed from the alluvial fan deposits to reveal the multistorey palaeochannel systems. Some of this material was probably removed by fluvial erosion during fan entrenchment, but this process would have been confined to the main wadi courses. Large interfluve areas composed of extensive and thick sequences of fine overbank sediments and interbedded eolian silts would have been exposed to the increased force of the northeast trade winds during periods of increased aridity and continentality. Largescale deflation of these inter-channel fines would have led to inversion of the alluvial fans, leaving the coarse-grained channel thalwegs as upstanding ridges capped by cemented conglomerates (see Glennie 1970; Stalder 1975; cf. Abrams et al. 1988).

Changes in relative base level. Fluctuations in humidity and aridity were closely linked with largescale fluctuations in sea-level during the Cenozoic. A sea-level fall to −130 m during the last glaciation could have been associated with low, or falling, water tables. A long-term fall in the water table would release a greater thickness of surface fines to eolian entrainment and removal, and also act to encourage entrenchment by flood events in the main wadi courses. Some evidence of periodic incision is apparent from maps of the palaeochannels which show younger generations cutting through older generations of channel (e.g. generations 2 and 3, Pink Cliffs area). However the most catastrophic episode(s) of entrenchment was associated with the formation of the wadi Andam channel, and its associated terrace sequence (cf. Abrams et al. 1988).

Expansion of the channel network. Changes in the main allocyclic controls cannot, however, explain the progressive increases in ophiolite lithologies through the palaeochannel sequence. Evidence of selective chemical alteration through hydrolysis and diagenesis of the ophiolite lithologies does exist within the older palaeochannel generations in the form of dolomite nodules, 'ghosting' of clasts, and disintegrating ophiolite fragments (Glennie et al. 1974). However, such weathering during more humid conditions cannot explain the progressive absence of all cherts within the youngest deposits. The most plausible explanation seems to lie in the gradual expansion of the drainage network northwards through the cherts and limestones of the Hawasina hills into the ophiolite outcrop of the eastern Oman Mountains.

Northward growth of the headwaters of the wadi Andam system could have resulted in capture of the headwater zone of the adjacent wadi Adam system, resulting in a dramatic rise in catchment area, in run-off volumes and in influx of ophiolite lithologies to the alluvial fans. Such a dramatic change in run-off conditions could also have triggered the large-scale entrenchment of the alluvial fans, particularly if acting in association with falling base levels.

The combination of these three main controls (precipitation regime, base level changes and network expansion), together with other complex tectonic, pedogenic and fluvial mechanisms, could have acted to promote long-term fan growth during alternating periods of increased and decreased humidity and associated fluctuations in annual flow regime, interspersed with episodes of incision and deflation during the Cenozoic. Larger-scale fluctuations in precipitation regime and persistence of eolian activity during the Pleistocene, associated with major changes in sea level and continentality, combined with dramatic expansion of the drainage area on to the ophiolite, could have acted to promote large-scale entrenchment during rare, high-magnitude flood events. Extensive deflation of the interfluve areas, particularly during the glacial episodes of the Quaternary, would have contributed to large-scale landscape inversion.

Conclusion

Mapping of palaeochannel systems using remote sensing methods has provided a crucial means of discriminating between successive generations of fluvial activity. Low-altitude aerial survey cover has provided the greatest detail and accuracy of discrimination, while black and white air photo mosaics at 1:100 000 scale and Landsat MSS data have proved the most valuable complementary methods in the identification of tonal contrasts over larger areas. These contrasts have been shown to be related to changes in lithological composition of the channel deposits, and consequently may be used in the construction of a relative chronology for long-term palaeochannel evolution. The results indicate that palaeochannel orientation, extent, pattern and morphology identified from remotely sensed data reflect changes in flow regime and sediment supply during fan development. In particular, periods of increased humidity may be invoked to explain the sinuous, persistent, fine-grained palaeochannel courses characteristic of the early drainage systems. More arid periods characterized by ephemeral

flows and prolonged episodes of eolian activity gave rise initially to limited distributary networks comprising coarse-grained, low-sinuosity, braided channels. Large-scale entrenchment and deflation occurred subsequently in association with falling base level and increased catchment area.

A detailed chronological framework is not yet available, but the major changes in palaeohydrology, and hence in overall palaeoclimatic conditions, have now been broadly established. A major element of this achievement has been the application of remote sensing methods, based initially on ground truthing of the spectral response of sediments of varying lithology. Further research of this kind needs to be extended to areas of more variable lithology, such as the limestones of the adjacent alluvial fan systems; and to more detailed mapping of palaeochannel systems within small areas exhibiting complex palaeochannel interrelationships, the results of which can then be extended to the interpretation of complete drainage systems across the alluvial fans. In particular, this research programme needs to be extended to the interpretation of Landsat TM data, which should provide both the radiometric and spatial resolution required for discrimination of the large number of palaeochannel generations identified so far. Finally, it is essential that the changes in the palaeochannel systems be linked more firmly to a chronological framework not only for Oman, but also for the Arabian peninsula, and the arid tropics in general.

The authors would like to express particular appreciation to Dr K. Glennie for many invaluable discussions, both in the UK and in the field. Thanks are also extended to P. Considine, J. R. Jones and H. Weier, of the former Public Authority for Water Resources, Sultanate of Oman; to B. Duff and Dr M. Hughes Clarke of Petroleum Development Oman, and to Dr G. Stanger, for their stimulating discussions. The logistic support of the Sultan of Oman's Armed Forces and the Coastal Security Force is also gratefully acknowledged. The authors would like to thank all members of the Royal Geographical Society Eastern Sands Project for their enthusiasm and support during the progress of this research programme. Laboratory assistance from M. Lamb is also gratefully acknowledged. The authors are also grateful to Dr J. Ford of the Jet Propulsion Laboratory, Pasadena, for supplying the SIR-A radar imagery, and to Dr D. Rothery of the Open University for his constructive comments on an earlier draft of this paper. Chris McBean was in receipt of a NERC-funded studentship.

References

ABRAMS, M. J., 1986. Mapping the Oman ophiolite using TM data. In: Proc. 5th Thematic Conference on Remote Sensing for Exploration Geology. Vol 1. Reno, Nevada, 85−95.

——, CHADWICK, O. & ROTHERY, D., 1988. Quaternary history of the Semail ophiolite along the Batinah coast, Oman. In: ROBERTSON, A. H. F., SEARLE, M. P., RIES, A. C. & SMEWING, J. D. (eds). The Geology and Tectonics of the Oman Region. Geological Society, Abstracts 4.

ARCHE, A. 1983. Coarse-grained meander lobe deposits in the Jarama River, Madrid, Spain. In: COLLINSON, J. D. & LEWIN, J. (eds) Modern and Ancient Fluvial Systems. International Association of Sedimentologists, Special Publication 6, 313−321.

AUBEL, J. W. 1983. Bajada hydrological area. In: The Hydrology of the Sultanate of Oman. A Preliminary Assessment. Public Authority for Water Resources, Report PAWR 83−1, 66−74.

BRIDGE, J. S. 1985. Palaeochannel pattern inferred from alluvial deposits: a critical evaluation. Journal of Sedimentary Petrology 55, 579−589.

EDENS, C. 1989. Prehistory. Journal of Oman Studies Special Report 3

EVERETT, J. R., RUSSELL, O. R. & NICHOLS, D. A. 1984. Landsat surveys of southeastern Arabia. In: EL-BAZ, F. (ed). Deserts and Arid Lands. Martinus Nijhoff, Netherlands, 171−194.

FRIEND, P. F. 1978. Distinctive features of some ancient river systems. In: MIALL, A. D. (ed.), Fluvial Sedimentology. Canadian Society of Petroleum Geologists, Memoir 5, 531−542.

——, ARZO, M. M., NIJMAN, W. & PUIGDEFABREGAS, C. 1981. Fluvial sedimentology in the Tertiary south Pyrenean and Ebro basins, Spain. In: ELLIOT, T. (ed.). Field Guides to Modern and Ancient Fluvial Systems in Britain and Spain. International Association of Sedimentologists, 4.1−4.50.

GLENNIE, K. W. 1970. Desert Sedimentary Environments. Elsevier, Amsterdam.

——, BOEUF, M. G. A., HUGHES CLARKE, M. W., MOODY-STUART, M., PILAAR, W. F. H. & REINHARDT, B. M. 1974. The Geology of the Oman Mountains. Transactions of the Royal Dutch Geological Mining Society, 31.

GOUDIE, A. S. 1989. Weathering processes. In: THOMAS, D. S. G. (ed.). Arid Zone Geomorphology, Belhaven/Halsted Press, London, 11−24.

GRAF, W. L. 1988. Fluvial Processes in Dryland Rivers. Springer, Berlin.

HOPSON, C. A., COLEMAN, R. G., GREGORY, R. T., PALLISTER, J. S. & BAILEY, E. H. 1981. Geologic section through the Samail ophiolite and associated rocks along a Muscat-Ibra transect, southeastern Oman Mountains. Journal of Geophysical Research, 86, 2527−2544.

HUNT, C. B. & MABEY, D. R. 1966. Stratigraphy and structure, Death Valley, California. U.S. Geological Survey, Professional Paper 494A.

JACKSON, R. G. II. 1978. Preliminary evaluation of lithofacies models for meandering alluvial streams. In: MIALL, A. D. (ed.). Fluvial Sedimentology. Canadian Society Petroleum Geol-

ogists, Memoir 5, 543−576.

JONES, J. R. 1985. Results of test drilling for water in northwestern Sharqiyah area, Sultanate of Oman, 1983−84. Public Authority for Water Resources, Report PAWR 85−21.

KRAUS, M. J. & MIDDLETON, L. T. 1987. Contrasting architecture of two alluvial suites in different structural settings. In: ETHRIDGE, F. G., FLORES, R. M. & HARVEY, M. D. (eds), Recent Developments in Fluvial Sedimentology, Society of Economic Palaeontologists and Mineralogists, Special Publication No. 38, 253−262.

LYNNE, G. J. & TAYLOR, G. R. 1986. Intergration of SIR-B imagery with geological and geophysical data in Australia. In: Proceedings of the 5th Thematic Conference on Remote sensing for Exploration Geology. Vol. 1 Reno, Nevada 179−191.

MAIZELS, J. K. 1987. Plio-Pleistocene raised channel systems of the western Sharqiya (Wahiba), Oman. In: FROSTICK, L. & REID, I. (eds). Desert Sediments: Ancient and Modern. Geological Society, London, Special Publication 35, 31−50.

—— 1989a. Palaeochannels. Journal of Oman Studies Special Report 3.

—— 1989b. Stratigraphy and history of alluvial fan development in Oman. In: RACHOCKI, A. & CHURCH, M. A. (eds) Alluvial Fans − A Field Approach. Wiley, Chichester.

MCBEAN, C. 1989. Land cover classification in the Wahiba Sands using remote sensing. Journal of Oman Studies Special Report No. 3.

MILTON, 1980. A portable multiband radiometer for ground data collection in remote sensing. International Journal of Remote Sensing, 1 153−165.

NICHOLS, G. J. 1987. Structural controls on fluvial distributary systems − The Luna system, northeastern Spain. In: FLORES, R. M. & HARVEY, M. D. (eds). Recent Developments in Fluvial Sedimentology, Society of Economic Palaeontologists and Mineralogists, Special Publication 39, 29−277.

PARKASH, B., AWASTHI, A. K. & GOHAIN, K. 1983. Lithofacies of the Markanda terminal fan, Kurukshetra district, Haryana, India. In: COLLINSON, J. D. & LEWIN J. (eds.) Modern and Ancient Fluvial Systems. International Association of Sedimentologists, Special Publication 6, 337−344.

PEAKE & OLIVER. 1971. The response of terrestrial surfaces at microwave frequencies. Ohio State Univ. Electroscience Lab. Technical Report AFAL−TR−70−30, 2440−2447.

PRELL, W. L., HUTSON, W. H., WILLIAMS, D. F., BE, A. W. H., GEITZENAUER, R. & MOLFINO, B. 1980. Surface circulation of the Indian Ocean during the last interglacial maximum, approximately 18 000 yr B. P. Quaternary Research, 14, 309−336.

REID, I. & FROSTICK, L. E. 1989. Channel form, flows and sediments in deserts. In: THOMAS, D. S. G. (ed.). Arid Zone Geomorphology. Belhaven/Halsted, London. 117−135.

RILEY, S. J. 1977. Some downstream trends in the

hydraulic, geometric, and sedimentary charac-
teristics of an inland distributary system. *In:*
GREGORY, K. J. (ed.). *River Channel Changes.*
Wiley. 337–352.

ROTHERY, D. A. 1984a. Reflectances of ophiolite
rocks in the Landsat MSS bands: relevance to
lithological mapping by remote sensing. *Journal
of the Geological Society of London,* **141,** 933–
939.

—— 1984b. The role of Landsat Multi-spectral
Scanner (MSS) imagery in mapping the Oman
ophiolite. *In:* GASS, I. G., LIPPARD, S. J. &
SHELTON, A. W. (eds) *Ophiolites and the lithosphere.* Blackwell. 405–413.

—— 1987. Improved discrimination of rock units
using Landsat Thematic Mapper imagery of the
Oman ophiolite. *Journal of the Geological Society
of London,* **144,** 587–597.

SCHICK, A. 1988. Hydrologic aspects of floods in
extreme arid environments. *In:* BAKER, V. R.,
KOCHEL, R. C. & PATTON, P. D. (eds). *Flood
Geomorphology.* Wiley. 189–203.

SCHUMM, S. A. 1965. Quaternary paleohydrology.
In: WRIGHT, H. E. and FREY, D. G. (eds) *Quatern-

ary of the United States.* Princeton University
Press. 783–794.

STALDER, P. J. 1975. Cementation of Pliocene-Qua-
ternary fluviatile clastic sediments in and along
the Oman Mountains. *Geologie en Mijnbouw,* **54**
148–136.

STEEL, R. & AASHEIM, S. M. 1978. Alluvial sand
deposition in a rapidly subsiding basin (Devonian,
Norway). *In:* MIALL, A. D. (ed), *Fluvial Sedimentology.* Canadian Society of Petroleum Geologists,
Memoir **5** 385–412.

STONE, R. J. & McBEAN, C. W. 1987. Radar discrimination of sebkha environments: A comparison of SIR-A backscatter from Tunisia and
Oman. *In: Advances in Digital Image Processing.* Proceedings of the Annual Conference of
Remote Sensing Society, Nottingham. 611–617.

STREET, F. & GROVE, A. T. 1976. Environmental and
climatic implications of late Quaternary lakelevel
fluctuations in Africa. *Nature,* **261,** 385–390.

VAN CAMPO, E., DUPLESSY, J. C. & ROSSIGNOL-STRICK,
M. 1982. Climatic conditions deduced from a
150-kyr oxygen isotope-pollen record from the
Arabian Sea. *Nature,* **296,** 56–59.

Geology and Tectonics of South Oman

Tectonics, geochronology and geochemistry of the Precambrian rocks of Oman

I. G. GASS[1], A. C. RIES[2], R. M. SHACKLETON[3] & J. D. SMEWING[4]

[1] *Department of Earth Sciences, Open University, Milton Keynes MK7 6AA, UK*

[2] *Earth Sciences and Resources Institute, University of Reading, 19 Upper Redlands Rd, Reading RG1 5JJ, UK*

[3] *The Croft Barn, Church Street, East Hendred, Oxon OX12 8LA, UK*

[4] *Earth Resources Institute, University College Swansea, Swansea SA2 8PP, UK*

Abstract: Precambrian rocks crop out in NE Oman (Qalhat and Jebel Ja'alan), in SE Oman (near Mirbat) and offshore on the Kuria Muria Islands. Similar rocks occur on Socotra and Abd el Kuri. In all these localities the Precambrian rocks include metasediments of greenschist or amphibolite facies, intruded by dolerites, granodiorites and granites and cut by doleritic and felsitic dykes which in the Mirbat area, form a dense swarm. Foliation trends vary but are predominantly ENE–WSW. Geochronological data show that the rocks are late Proterozoic (800–600 Ma) in age and are therefore chronologically and compositionally similar to the Pan-African rocks of the Afro-Arabian Shield. Unmetamorphosed, weakly deformed Infracambrian sediments in the Huqf–Haushi Uplift and in the Saih Hatat and Jebel Akhdar windows are not cut by the dyke swarms, which are therefore probably late Proterozoic in age although radiometric dating suggests a lower Palaeozoic age. These widely distributed late Proterozoic metamorphic rocks indicate that the middle Proterozoic (*c.* 1700 Ma) gneisses in the Afif Terrain in eastern Saudi Arabia do not mark the eastern limit of the Pan-African belt. Before the breakup of Gondwanaland that limit must have lain between the Oman–Somalia region and the Archaean and middle Proterozoic terranes of the Bundelkhand and Aravalli areas of India.

The Precambrian crystalline basement is well exposed in western Saudi Arabia, the Yemen Arab Republic and the People's Democratic Republic of Yemen as a result of late Tertiary to Recent uplift of the Afro-Arabian Dome. In contrast, there are very few such occurrences in the eastern part of the Arabian Peninsula. Only three small, isolated basement outcrops have so far been identified all of which occur in Oman, i.e. the Kuria Muria Islands, the Mirbat Peninsula and Jebel Ja'alan (Fig. 1), and these outcrops are the subject of this paper.

Some 25 years ago it was realized that the Afro-Arabian Precambrian basement consisted of major Archaean cratons (west African, Congo and south Africa or Kalahari Cratons) whereas the vast surrounding areas, termed Pan-African by Kennedy (1964), yielded late Proterozoic (500±100Ma) ages. Kennedy's age data were obtained by $^{40}K-^{39}Ar$ methods and many suspected that they were not original ages but reflected thermal resetting of radiometric clocks in rocks that were Archaean in age (e.g.

Kröner 1977). Subsequent extensive Rb–Sr dating showed that most ages fall in the range 450–900 Ma (e.g. Greenwood *et al.* 1976; Hashad 1980) which failed to confirm the older ages of 1000–1200 Ma identified by Egyptian workers.

In the 1970s, following regional mapping of the Western Saudi Arabian basement by the USGS and BRGM, and more detailed, localized investigations by several research teams from European and north American universities, which included Saudi nationals, two views concerning the origin of the Pan-African in western Arabia, Egypt and the NE Sudan emerged. Both groups accepted that the Pan-African terranes consisted primarily (*c.* 60%) of granitic rocks associated with intermediate to silicic volcanic rocks and volcaniclastic sediments, cut by linear or gently arcuate zones where mafic and ultramafic igneous assemblages are common. One group (e.g. Engel *et al.* 1980) interpreted these assemblages to represent unspecified, possibly Archaean, granitic terranes cut by rift

From ROBERTSON, A. H. F., SEARLE, M. P. & RIES, A. C. (eds), 1990
The Geology and Tectonics of the Oman Region.
Geological Society Special Publication No 49, pp 585–599

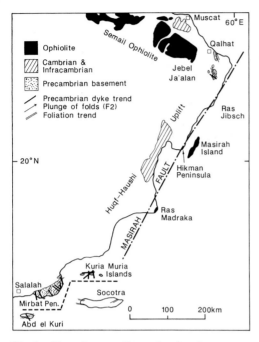

Fig. 1. Map of eastern Oman showing the outcrops of Precambrian rocks and main tectonic units. Abd el Kuri and Socotra restored to their positions before the opening of the Gulf of Aden.

systems, similar to the present-day Red Sea, along which fragments of oceanic lithosphere had been preserved. The other group, to which the present authors belong, gave more credence to the increasingly abundant geochemical data which showed that most of the granitic and volcanic rocks were calc-alkali in character and fall into the volcanic arc field on trace element discrimination plots of Pearce *et al.* (1984). Members of this group (e.g. Bakor *et al.* 1976; Neary *et al.* 1976; Gass 1977, 1981) proposed that the Pan-African originated as a series of intra-oceanic island arcs some 900 Ma ago and that they evolved through at least two stages of increasing maturity before they were finally accreted together at *c.* 600 Ma when the terranes became part of the Afro-Arabian continental crust; thereafter all igneous activity has within-plate geochemical characteristics. In this model the linear/arcuate zones of mafic and ultramafic rocks are regarded as ophiolites (e.g. Gass 1977; Shackleton 1986; Fitches *et al.* 1983), obducted fragments of the once extensive late Proterozoic oceanic lithosphere that existed between the arcs. Unfortunately, there are no palaeomagnetic data to identify the location of the

various arc systems or the ophiolites before they were accreted.

The arc systems and associated ophiolite zones trend N–S to NE–SW across Arabia and NE Africa and have been traced into northern Kenya (Shackleton 1986). From there they continue southwards into the Mozambique Belt, which yields similar Pan-African ages (older ones in Mozambique) and is regarded as a continent–continent collision zone. Although most of the specimens dated fall between the 600–900 Ma extended Pan-African time span, lead isotope evidence clearly indicates that part of the SE Arabian Shield (Zalon region) consists of rocks of middle to lower Proterozoic (1700–2300 Ma) age (e.g. Stacey & Agar 1985; Stacey & Hedge 1984). These older ages could represent either the western extremity of an extensive older continental mass or an island of Seychelles-type, within the Pan-African ocean.

The abundance of Precambrian volcanic rocks and volcaniclastic sediments in the northern part of the Afro-Arabian Shield on both sides of the Red Sea, and their absence farther south in the Mozambique Belt suggests that the erosional bevel into the Precambrian cuts progressively deeper southwards. Gass (1977) suggested that in the north the bevel was less than 1 km deep whereas in the south some 5 km of Precambrian had been removed by erosion. Hence if the Oman basement occurrences are Pan-African in age, they might be expected to represent deeper levels than those in Saudi Arabia to the northwest.

Description of the Precambrian rocks exposed in Oman is followed by a discussion of the geochronology and geochemistry of specimens collected from three areas. Finally the implications of these data for regional structure and Precambrian palaeogeography are discussed.

The Kuria–Muria islands

There are five islands within Kuria Muria group which lies off the SE coast of Oman (Fig. 1). Four of these islands lie on an 80 km long E–W trending line (17°30′N:55°36′–56°20′E and consist mainly of Precambrian crystalline rocks. During this study, the largest island, Al Hallaniyah, was visited for six days. From the air, the islands immediately east and west of Al Hallaniyah seem to consist of similar rocks with the same NE structural trends as the mixed amphibolite–granite terrane that forms the central part of the Al Hallaniyah Precambrian outcrop; the westernmost island of the line, Al Haskiyah, appears to be formed entirely of granite.

Al Hallaniyah (Fig. 2) has a surface area of *c.*

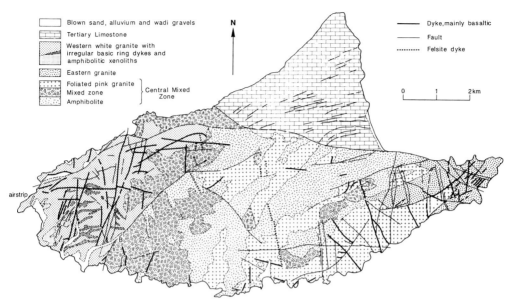

Fig. 2. Photogeological map of Al Hallaniyah Island, Kuria Muria Islands. Note the threefold division of the Precambrian into the Eastern and Western Granites and the Mixed Zone of amphibolites invaded by granodiorites. Field evidence suggests that the amphibolites have an ophiolitic protolith. The geochronology and geochemistry samples were collected from loc. B, near the faulted western margin of the Mixed Zone. Immediately west of loc. B are good exposures of a basic xenolith terrane representing a series of basic ring dykes invaded by the Western Granite.

55 km^2. The topography is directly related to the underlying geology. The northern promontory, of c. 10 km^2, terminates at Ras Hallaniyah where there are 500 m sea cliffs, formed by a gently dipping sequence of Tertiary carbonates, downthrown against Precambrian (772±8 Ma) rocks by an E–W trending fault. The east and west extremities of the island are respectively underlain by 5 km^2 and 12 km^2 granitic masses. In these areas the resultant topography is subdued with major topographic highs and relief usually <50 m. In contrast, the central 27 km^2 NE-trending spine of the island, which comprises approximately equal proportions of amphibolites intricately and complexly injected with pink foliated granite, has a rugged ridged relief that rises to an altitude of 458 m near the geographic centre of the island.

A surprising feature is that the major drainage system has its sources on the low northern promontory of down faulted Tertiary rocks. The streams have cut through the uplifted crystalline basement, to emerge on the south coast. Clearly they are antecedent relative to the faulting. Views from the air suggest that the island consists of three blocks each tilted towards the south, the low-relief sub-Tertiary berel, cuts

across the basement and is still recognizable. The faults must have moved slowly enough for erosion to keep pace. The drainage system was presumably initiated in a block tilted southwards bounded by a major fault trending about ENE, off the NW coast. A similar tilt is seen on the island immediately west of Al Hallaniyah.

Of the Precambrian rocks, the granitic complexes that form the east and west extremities of Hallaniyah Island will be described before the structurally and compositionally more complex mixed amphibolite/granitic central zone. Although the contacts observed in the present study between the two granitic masses and the central zone are either faults or thrusts, it is accepted that the Mixed Zone is older because of its more intense and complex deformation. Also basic dykes, common in both granitic areas, are less common in the Mixed Zone (see Fig. 2).

Eastern Granite

Although rock types present in the Eastern Granite range from pink leucogranite through biotite granodiorite and diorites to mafic biotite-amphibole diorites, the main rock types are a pale pink, K-feldspar-phyric granite and a less abundant, pinker syenitic facies with much less quartz. These two types interfinger. Both have locally been foliated; the porphyritic variety then has the appearance of an augen gneiss. The foliation, a strong flattening fabric, is vertical and trends between 050−060 and also cuts late pegmatitic and aplite veins. In places the foliation is restricted to narrow (1−3 m) left-lateral shear zones with a similar orientation. Although cut by numerous E−W faults, the main western contact of the granite is a steeply inclined thrust emplacing the granites over the Mixed Zone. As this contact is approached the granite becomes intensely deformed.

Among the minor rock types occurring within the Eastern Granite, is a small outcrop of fine-grained, thinly-bedded metasediments consisting of quartz, alkali feldspar and biotite and containing small garnets that are associated with calc-silicate rocks. Intrusive contacts indicate that these sediments are older than the granite. As these metasediments are structurally and compositionally similar to more extensive outcrops on Jebel Ja'alan, they are more fully described below. The other, and most obvious minor rocks in the Eastern Granite, are basaltic dykes. There are two trends, an older set trending N−S (350−010), and a younger, unde-formed set trending NE (050), parallel to the foliation in the host granite.

Western Granite

Although similar in general appearance to the Eastern Granite, the western Granite is markedly less deformed and more compositionally variable. Like its eastern counterpart, it is partly in fault contact with the central Mixed Zone, this contact being a straight NE trending, now high-angle fault, following the line of a prominent wadi. The main rock type is a white leucogranite containing quartz, alkali feldspar and biotite with abundant accessory sphene. More mafic granodioritic−dioritic xenoliths, range in size from a few cm to irregular patches, c. 0.5 km across. These more mafic masses are more strongly foliated than the leucocratic host and hence may represent an older granodioritic mass caught up in the leuco-granite melt. The foliation is so regular and the deformation of mineral phases so slight that its origin was initially considered to be igneous but was rejected in favour of a tectonic origin.

Other rock types within the Western Granite are abundant pink pegmatites. These occur in narrow E−W and N−S trending zones and are seemingly related to fracture zones allowing the permeation of late stage granitic fluids. Also present in an area of 4 km^2 in the SW is a series of intrusions, some basic but many composite, acid and basic. These have a definite arcuate pattern and seem to have been a series of inwardly-dipping cone sheets related to a centre just offshore from the south coast. Like the Eastern Granite, the Western Granite is cut by two sets of basic dykes, which also cut the cone sheets but the trends differ in that the older dykes trend c. 090 and the younger set c. 010. Some of the E−W trending dykes are markedly plagioclase-phyric.

Mixed Zone

The central part of the island is formed by a tectonically and compositionally complex terrane here termed the 'Mixed Zone'. The two dominant rock types, amphibolites and a pink, foliated granodiorite, occur as major rock masses and together as an intricate mix of the two (Mixed Zone on Fig. 2) in which the structural grain is NE and the contacts between the two rock types are commonly near-vertical (Fig. 2). But this is an intensely complex terrane that has undergone polyphase deformation and repeated plutonic magmatism. Field studies indicate that the amphibolitic rocks, most of which were originally gabbros and peridotites, were cut by basic dykes before being foliated. Subsequently they were injected, first by grey and secondly by pinkish granodiorite after which they were deformed by a second foliation before the complex was cut by unfoliated felsic and basic dykes. Foliation trends recorded within the granites range between E−W and ESE−WNW; foliation varies from very intense to almost imperceptible.

Generally the amphibolites are coarse-grained rocks consisting primarily of plagioclase feldspar, amphibole after clinopyroxene and minor quartz. Relict textures and the identification of igneous phase layering in one outcrop that dips at 15° to 220°, oblique to nearby foliation, suggests a gabbroic protolith. Other varieties include ultramafic rocks containing euhedral polymorphs of serpentinite after olivine and an altered but still identifiable inter-cumulus matrix of orthopyroxene. An isolated outcrop of fine-grained basic rocks, containing quartz-filled ovoids, probably represents deformed vesicles in a lava. The outcrop has a bulbous appearance suggesting that these volcanic rocks were originally pillow lavas. It is tentatively proposed that this association of peridotite and gabbroic cumulates, cut by basic dykes, and with possible pillow lavas, suggest that the protolith of these amphibolites could have a late Proterozoic ophiolite of the type identified elsewhere in the Afro-Arabian Shield (e.g. Bakor *et al.* 1976; Fitches *et al.* 1983).

The amphibolites are complexly interdigitated with granitoids. Although the main type is a pink foliated granodiorite, the rocks present vary widely in texture, colour and composition. Single outcrops commonly show gradations from granite (*s.s.*) through granodiorites to diorites or expose quartz or K-feldspar-rich, rapakivi-textured facies of one type. Xenoliths are abundant and are mainly of the older grey granodiorite in the younger pink variety or when present in the grey granodiorite, are mainly basic and aligned and probably represent former basic dykes. The contact between the amphibolite and the granite is sometimes marked by a 1–3 cm wide white zone of albite. This seems to be a reaction relationship and could be a variety of rodingite although this is usually found between gabbros and serpentinite.

Magmatic and tectonic evolution

The Precambrian of Al Hallaniyah Island consists of three distinct units, the Eastern and Western Granites and the spatially intervening Mixed Zone. Based on the assumption that because the Mixed Zone is relatively more deformed, it is therefore the oldest of the three units and the Rb−Sr age of 772±8 Ma represents the age of the Mixed Zone granodiorites. Also, as the amphibolite-facies rocks of the Mixed Zone seem to have an ophiolitic protolith, it is most likely that the ophiolitic slice of oceanic lithosphere had been obducted before the emplacement of the Mixed Zone granodiorites. Similarly, from the degree of deformation, the Eastern Granite is considered to be older than the Western Granite. Although mainly in tectonic contact with the Mixed Zone, both these granites−granodiorite complexes are considered to be formed from arc-type melts that invaded the ophiolitic zone after it had been obducted but whilst the genetic subduction zone was still active. The variation in foliation, fault and dyke trends between the three units, does not necessarily imply that they are not now in their original spatial distribution.

Mirbat area, South Oman

The following observations are based on a brief reconnaissance and air photograph interpretation (Fig. 3).

Metasediments

These are the oldest rocks in the Mirbat area and comprise fine-grained, well laminated quartz-feldspar-biotite schists, massive bedded quartz-rich rocks (originally impure sandstones), muscovite-rich layers (originally shales), calc-silicate bands and abundant hard amphibolite bands, often rich in biotite (originally basic sills?).

The grade of metamorphism throughout the Precambrian outcrop appears to be amphibolite

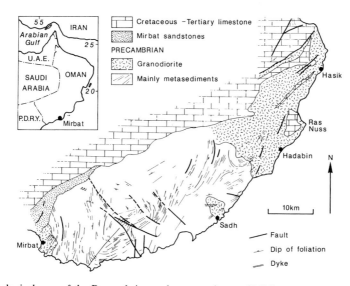

Fig. 3. Photogeological map of the Precambrian rocks exposed east of Mirbat.

590   I. G. GASS *ET AL.*

facies with garnet as the most commonly occurring index mineral. Eastwards from Mirbat the grade of metamorphism rises so that near Sadh, the metasediments are migmatitic and cut by pink granite sheets and quartz−feldspar−biotite pegmatites.

The main tectonic planar fabric (S_2) in the metasediments is picked out by biotites. This fabric is axial planar to isoclinal folds which fold the bedding, an earlier flattening fabric (S_1), early quartz-feldspar partial melt lenses and granite sheets. In some places quartz−feldspar−biotite−beryl pegmatites appear as boudins in this main fabric. Later granite sheets have been intruded along F_2 hinges. The regional strike of the S_2 fabric is NE−SW (Fig. 3) with a moderate dip to the NW or SE. An associated mineral lineation plunges at low angles mainly towards the WSW. The main flattening fabric is warped by later irregular open folds which trend c. NE−SW (Fig. 3). These folds appear to be associated with a steeply-dipping schistosity (S_3) which is apparently responsible for the second schistosity seen on the air photographs both in the metasediments and the intrusive rocks.

Intrusive rocks

The metasediments and also a sheet-like body of peridotite are intruded by post-F_2 granitoid rocks which are mostly either homogeneous granodiorites, e.g. the Mirbat and Hadabin granodiorites (Fig. 3), or pink granite sheets. The Mirbat granodiorite is cut by pink granite veins, pink quartz−feldspar−magnetite pegmatites and fine grained biotite-rich granite veins. The interior of the Mirbat granodiorite appears

to be undeformed but in the marginal zone, E of Mirbat, there is a strong planar fabric, striking NNE and dipping steeply WNW, which is probably the S_3 fabric. As on Al Hallaniyah Island, there are a few foliated basic dykes which cut the granodiorites and the pink granite sheets. Thus there seems to have been a long sequence of intrusions into the metasediments, some before, and some after, the main flattening fabric was formed.

Post-tectonic dyke swarm

The metamorphic rocks are cut by a prominent dyke swarm (Fig. 4) which is particularly well developed near Sadh. The dykes mostly trend between 130° and 160° with a vertical dip. In places the basic dykes are cut by acid dykes and the same relationship can be seen on the air photographs. Radiometric dating also shows that the basic dykes are older than the acid dykes.

Abd el Kuri

This island, west of Socotra, was studied briefly by one of us (RMS). Since it must have been situated only a short distance south of the Mirbat area before the opening of the Gulf of Aden (Fig. 1), brief mention is appropriate here.

The Precambrian basement is exposed on the island under discontinuous cover of Cretaceous sediments, now dislocated by extensional faults into a series of S-dipping tilt blocks. The tectonostratigraphy may be summarized as follows:
   Cretaceous   (peneplanation)
   Precambrian
        Dolerites

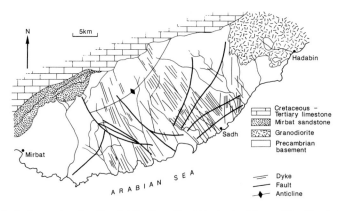

Fig. 4. Photogeological map showing the distribution of post-tectonic dykes cutting Precambrian rocks, near Mirbat.

Felsites, pink granite and quartz porphyry
Grey, probably related⎫
(intermediate), dykes   ⎬ relation
Diorite and xenolithic ⎪ uncertain
granodiorite   ⎭
    (Folding: formation of schistosity)
Granite veining
    (Deformation: formation of schistosity)
Basic complex at least partly intrusive
(including metagabbro)
Metasediments (garnetiferous petites; epidotic lenses probably represent calcareous sediments)

Statistical analysis of foliations shows a strong maximum *c*. 45° towards 115, and a mineral lineation plunging moderately to gently southeastwards. The dykes trend either *c*. NW–SE (10) or *c*. 030 (4).

Jebel Ja'alan

An inlier of crystalline basement rocks is exposed in the core of Jebel Ja'alan, *c*. 50 km SSW of Sur in NE Oman (Figs 1 & 5). The

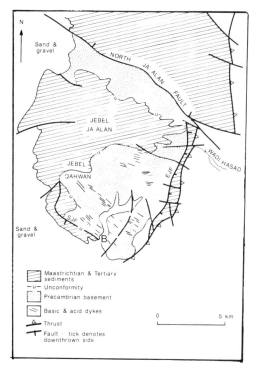

Fig. 5. Geological map of the Jebel Ja'alan area (simplified from Filbrandt *et al.* 1990). SJF — South Ja'alan Fault; EJF — East Ja'alan Fault.

geological map (Fig. 5), compiled from air photographs and field reconnaissance, shows that the basement rocks are unconformably overlain by Maastrichtian and Tertiary sediments, described by Filbrandt *et al.* (1990).

Chronologically and compositionally the Precambrian basement complex of Jebel Ja'alan comprises three components, (i) metasediments, (ii) Jebel Ja'alan plutonic complex and (iii) post-tectonic dyke swarm.

Metasediments

The metasedimentary sequence mostly comprises quartz-biotite-muscovite schists. There are some sandy units which, in places, are graded and cross-bedded, calc-silicate bands and amphibolites. Metamorphic minerals (garnet, sillimanite and possibly kyanite) indicate an upper amphibolite-facies metamorphism. Variable amounts of quartz-feldspar lenses (leucosomes), parallel to the early tectonic fabric, indicate some partial melting. The metasediments are cut by later fine-grained, garnet-biotite-bearing white granite veins which crosscut the earlier leucosomes and are themselves folded.

The metasediments, seen to the N of Jebel Ja'alan, are strongly deformed. The rarely seen sedimentary bedding, an early pressure solution fabric (S_1) which is slightly oblique to the bedding, quartz-feldspar leucosomes and fine-grained white biotite granite sheets are all affected by a strong planar flattening fabric (S_2) shown by parallel biotite flakes. The more competent granite sheets are pulled apart in the flattening fabric and the tension gashes are filled with fibres growing in the extension direction. The main metamorphism either pre-dated, or was contemporaneous with, the main flattening fabric shown by garnets which are flattened in this fabric. Sillimanite needles are aligned in the extension direction. A later phase of compression produced a heterogeneously developed crenulation cleavage (S_3). Some granite veins post-date S_2 and are affected by S_3.

Both the pressure solution fabric and the main flattening fabric are slightly oblique to, and where seen, steeper than, the bedding but the lack of convincing way-up criteria, mostly masked by the strong pressure solution fabric, made it impossible to determine the facing direction of the main folds associated with S_2.

In Wadi Hasad the metamorphic grade is higher; the rocks are migmatitic with biotite-rich layers and amphibolitic bands, cut by pink granite sheets. Tight folds are associated with the main flattening fabric (S_2) which here strikes generally WSW−ENE and dips gently NNW. This fabric is folded by open late folds which plunge to the ENE.

Jebel Ja'alan plutonic complex

The metasediments are intruded by an igneous complex which is well exposed north of Bilad Bani Bu Ali. The components of this complex vary from early heterogeneously deformed basic to late undeformed acid rocks; the more acid components often contain randomly oriented basic xenoliths. The rocks are hornblendites, diorites, xenolithic whitish biotite-rich granodiorites with small plagioclase phenocrysts and pink xenolithic biotite granites with large pink potash feldspar phenocrysts. Most of these rocks are cross-cut by later fine-grained pink granite sheets, aplites and pink quartz-feldspar pegmatites.

Post-tectonic dyke swarm

Both the metasediments and the igneous complex are cut by a swarm of porphyritic dykes of basic or intermediate composition. The width of the dykes is variable but may reach 17 m. Their trend is generally *c*. NW−SE, but tends to swing from *c*. 145 in the N to *c*. 120 in the S. The dykes mostly dip very steeply. Many can be traced for long distances on air photographs. Faulting of the dykes is rare and displacements small, in remarkable contrast to the intense faulting and deformation of the younger rocks surrounding the Jebel Ja'alan massif.

Qalhat

A narrow strip of Precambrian basement extends for *c*. 15 km SSE from Qalhat, *c*. 50 km N of Jebel Ja'alan. The rocks, briefly examined during the present study at the northern end of the inlier, consist of upper amphibolite-facies metasediments (garnetiferous gneiss; grey banded siliceous rock probably originally a sandstone); hornblende biotite gneiss; amphibolite; possibly basic igneous; foliated xenolitic diorite; pink granite; white pegmatite sheets; and red pegmatite. Foliation dips measured were irregularly oriented but when plotted define a girdle corresponding to a plane, presumably the axial surface of late folds, dipping about 30° to the south. The assemblage is similar to that seen on Jebel Ja'alan but there appear to be no basic dykes, which may be due to poor exposure. Air photos were not available for this area.

Geochronology

Analytical methods

The Rb/Sr ratios were obtained by EDXRF at the Open University. The $^{87}Sr/^{86}Sr$ ratios, normalized to a NBS 987 standard value of 0.71014 ±3, were obtained on an automated 54E mass spectrometer at the Open University. The errors quoted on ages and initial ratios are at the two sigma level. All ages have been regressed using the method of York (1969) and the decay constant for ^{87}Rb of 1.42×10^{-11} yr^{-1} as recommended by Steiger & Jaeger (1977). Where the MSWD is >1, the errors on the ages and initial ratios have been multiplied by the square root of the MSWD thus allowing for any geological errors as well as analytical errors.

The K−Ar age determinations were obtained by D. C. Rex at the University of Leeds using an AEI MS10 mass spectrometer. All the analyses were done in duplicate and the ages determined using the following constants:

$$\lambda_\beta = 0.581 \times 10^{-10} \ yr^{-1}$$
$$\lambda_\epsilon = 4.962 \times 10^{-10} \ yr^{-1}$$
$$^{40}K/K = 1.19 \times 10^{-2}.$$

Rb−Sr ages

Seven samples collected from Al Hallaniyah Island (loc. B, Fig. 2) varied in composition from diorite through granodiorite, to pink granites (see Appendix). The samples show a heterogeneous deformation with some having a strong planar fabric. A Rb−Sr whole-rock isochron age of 772±8 Ma was obtained with a $^{87}Sr/^{86}Sr$ initial ratio of 0.70250 ± 8 (MSWD = 1.6) (Fig. 6; Table 1).

In thin section all the samples of granitic composition can be seen to consist of quartz, orthoclase (microcline and perthite), plagioclase, biotite and rare amphibole with magnetite and sphene as accessories. Most commonly the mineral phases are fresh although alkali feldspars can show minor marginal kaolinization, plagioclase is sometimes mildly sericitized and biotite occasionally partly chloritized. The textures are all allotriomorphic, and the grain size is coarse and equigranular except in the K-feldspar-phyric facies in which microcline megacrysts are abundant. The metamorphic foliation, so clearly evident in the field, is identified microscopically by the crude alignment of biotite. All other minerals have intricately sutured margins and show little sign of internal deformation. Hence this statistically good isochron is interpreted to record the age of intrusion of the igneous complex.

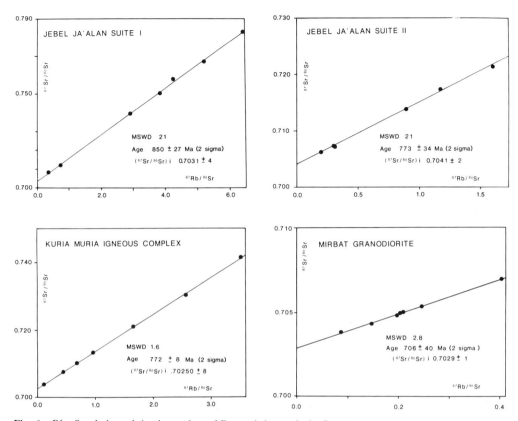

Fig. 6. Rb−Sr whole-rock isochron plots of Precambrian rocks in Oman.

Two suites of rocks were collected from the Jebel Ja'alan area. Suite I of seven samples was collected from near loc. B on Fig. 5, from an igneous complex, varying in composition from basic hornblende-rich rocks through diorites, granodiorites, biotite granites to pink granites cut by pink aplite sheets and pegmatites. These samples gave a Rb−Sr whole-rock isochron age of 850 ± 27 Ma with a $^{87}Sr/^{86}Sr$ initial ratio of 0.7031 ± 4 (MSWD = 1) (Fig. 6; Table 1). This age is interpreted as the age of crystallization of the igneous complex. The MSWD is large because most of the samples show some degree of deformation, varying from undulatory extinction in quartz grains, through a weak schistosity to partial recrystallization.

Suite II was collected from farther up the wadi from loose boulders in the wadi fill. Six samples of strongly banded and deformed igneous rocks gave a Rb−Sr whole-rock isochron age of 773 ± Ma with a $^{87}Sr/^{86}SR$ initial ratio of 0.7041 ± 2 (MSWD = 14) (Fig. 6;

Table 1). This age is interpreted as the age of the deformation and amphibolite-facies metamorphism which produced the banding in the rocks.

The basement E of Mirbat is a deeply eroded low-lying peneplain and the only fresh rock suitable for dating was seen in the blasted road cuttings, W of Mirbat. Seven samples were collected from a post-tectonic or late-tectonic granodiorite intruded into migmatitic sediments. A Rb−Sr whole-rock isochron age of 706 ± 40 Ma was obtained with a $^{87}Sr/^{86}Sr$ initial ratio of 0.7029 ± 1 (MSWD = 2.8) (Fig. 6; Table 1). This age is interpreted as an intrusion age. The large error is mostly due to the poor spread of $^{87}Rb/^{86}Sr$ ratios which results from the homogeneity in the composition of the intrusion.

K−Ar ages

One sample collected from the basic dyke swarm, cutting the metamorphic basement of

Table 1. *Rb−Sr analytical deta*

Sample No.	Rb (ppm)	Sr (ppm)	^{87}Rb/^{86}Sr ± 4%	^{87}Sr/^{86}Sr ± 0.01%
JA'ALAN SUITE I			*Age 850 ± 27 Ma*	
63D	28	251	0.318	0.70712
63C	62	267	0.666	0.71070
63E	99	61	4.711	0.75973
63H	147	73	5.853	0.77419
63A	62	68	2.640	0.73499
63I	132	111	3.452	0.74455
63F	66	50	3.836	0.75151
JA'ALAN SUITE II			*Age 773 ± 34 Ma*	
65C	163	296	1.595	0.72116
60A	145	1424	0.295	0.70721
65A	93	304	0.886	0.71392
65B	76	190	1.158	0.71732
60B	108	1089	0.287	0.70729
61	116	1750	0.192	0.70629
KURIA MURIA IGNEOUS SUITE			*Age 772 ± 8 Ma*	
KM2	79	514	0.445	0.70743
KM3	92	104	2.565	0.73039
KM4	70	58	3.504	0.74159
KM5	104	182	1.655	0.72074
KM8	77	232	0.961	0.71309
KM9	37	911	0.117	0.70378
KM10	73	278	0.760	0.71080
MIRBAT GRANODIORITE			*Age 706 ± 40 Ma*	
215D	54	388	0.403	0.70698
215C	32	631	0.147	0.70430
215A	35	515	0.197	0.70481
219	35	1173	0.086	0.70383
216B	57	673	0.245	0.70536
215B	36	510	0.204	0.70500
216A	36	499	0.209	0.70504

Table 2. *K−Ar analytical data*

Rock type	No.	%K	Vol.^{40}Ar rad.scc/g × 10^{-5}	% ^{40}Ar rad.	Age Ma
Mirbat area					
Basic dyke	210B	0.787	2.1120	81.0	604 ± 24
			2.2773	89.6	
604 ± 24					
Acid dyke	210A	1.99	4.4237	76.0	490 ± 21
			4.3159	70.0	
Jebel Ja'alan					
Basic dyke	66	0.842	1.6620	76.6	430 ± 20
			1.5188	86.7	
Lamprophyric plug	72	0.642	0.5200	56.3	197 ± 8
			0.5196	58.1	

Jebel Ja'alan, gave a K−Ar whole-rock age of 430 ± 20 Ma. Basic and acid dykes sampled from the equivalent dyke swarm in the Mirbat area gave K−Ar whole-rock ages of 604 ± 24 Ma and 490 ± 21 Ma, respectively (Table 2).

Geochemistry

Analyses of 25 samples collected from the Precambrian basement in Oman are given in Table 3. All these specimens were collected

le 3. *Major and trace element data of Precambrian samples from Oman*

c. No.	Kuria Muria									Mirbat				
	KM1	KM3	KM4	KM5	KM6	KM7	KM8	KM9	KM10	M215A	M215B	M215C	M215D	M216B
₂	55.67	78.13	75.27	72.98	68.14	65.37	70.82	56.23	68.98	71.81	67.26	70.36	59.05	58.22
₂	1.20	0.13	0.21	0.18	0.61	0.64	0.34	1.02	0.52	0.21	0.19	0.16	0.27	0.72
O₃	16.76	12.12	13.27	13.42	15.69	16.71	14.86	15.12	15.98	14.75	14.95	15.69	12.00	15.39
O₃	8.29	0.56	1.36	1.94	3.59	4.22	2.53	7.62	2.78	1.76	1.50	1.22	1.97	4.97
O	0.17	0.01	0.04	0.04	0.09	0.09	0.04	0.17	0.10	0.05	0.06	0.04	0.13	0.07
O	4.30	0.01	0.39	0.27	0.91	1.59	0.93	6.36	0.75	0.89	0.99	0.84	1.29	4.39
)	6.63	0.69	0.67	1.13	1.96	3.47	1.89	6.14	1.60	2.45	5.02	3.16	10.22	5.84
O	4.14	3.47	3.68	4.12	5.05	5.58	4.81	3.87	5.81	4.62	4.99	5.38	3.45	4.17
)	1.84	4.85	5.04	4.24	3.57	2.00	3.46	1.96	2.95	2.08	1.87	1.62	2.89	1.88
₅	0.36		0.11		0.16	0.23	0.12	0.28	0.16	0.06	0.12	0.05	0.10	0.23
)	0.08	0.05	0.07	0.08	0.31	0.03	0.15	0.06	0.11	0.17	0.11	0.08	0.13	0.09
₅	0.03			0.01	0.01	0.02	0.01	0.03	0.01				0	0.02
	0.01	0.01		0.01	0.01	0.01	0.01	0.01	0.01		0.01		0.02	0.01
.I.	1.01	0.38	0.13	0.43	0.56	0.60	0.67	1.66	0.60	1.35	3.72	1.84	8.10	4.01
TAL	100.49	100.41	100.23	98.85	100.65	100.57	100.63	100.56	100.33	100.19	100.79	100.46	99.63	100.01
	37	92	70	104	51	46	77	37	73	35	36	32	54	57
	771	104	58	182	397	481	232	911	278	515	510	631	388	673
	34	26	16	32	19	22	13	18	26	5	5	4	8	17
	196	76	142	159	411	183	131	150	344	85	72	83	76	157
	7	7	5	7	7	7	4	5	11	6	6	5	7	8
	12	20	17	20	16	17	16	11	26	14	14	13	17	13
	—	3	6	4	3	6	2	1	6	—	<1	1	—	3
	9	7	6	6	4	8	11	73	6	7	11	9	9	8
	112	13	32	32	77	67	36	108	91	42	39	32	55	81
	22	17	17	18	17	22	15	20	20	15	18	15	17	20
	29	7	—	2	6	11	6	92	8	3	8	—	12	22

	Jebel Ja'alan									
	J63A	J63B	J63C	J63D	J63F	J63G	J63H	J65A	J65B	J65C
₂	71.67	74.82	73.50	60.72	49.48	74.82	56.81	70.91	74.12	61.1
₂	0.18	0.27	0.38	1.02	1.18	0.22	0.77	0.37	0.15	0.6
O₃	15.29	11.85	12.69	15.54	14.77	12.07	14.09	12.07	13.58	13.9
O₃	1.21	3.46	2.67	7.62	11.22	3.01	5.57	5.14	2.08	8.11
)	0.03	0.06	0.04	0.12	0.20	0.06	0.09	0.06	0.04	0.3
)	0.46	0.76	0.35	3.45	7.47	1.38	1.96	2.49	0.24	4.50
)	1.24	0.37	1.36	5.29	10.01	0.50	12.94	0.86	1.28	5.43
O	4.61	4.63	2.45	3.29	2.77	3.09	1.25	2.46	3.05	2.70
	4.60	2.47	5.47	1.88	0.96	3.97	3.21	4.74	4.93	1.93
₅	0.07	0.04	0.10	0.19	0.20	0.08	0.16	0.04	0	0.13
)	0.22	0.10	0.07	0.07		0.11	0.09	0.15	0.33	0.02
₅	0	0	0	0.03	—	0	0.01	0	0	0.03
	0.01	0.01	0	0.05	0.05	0.01	0.01	0.01	0.01	0.02
.I.	0.71	0.55	0.88	1.35	0.01	0.85	1.91	1.11	0.81	1.53
TAL	100.28	99.39	99.96	100.62	1.41	100.16	98.87	100.41		100.51
	145	62	121	62	99.76	66	160	147	100.60	76
	1424	68	55	267	28	50	190	73	93	190
	7	92	90	38	251	72	34	67	304	155
	145	447	420	272	31	495	171	595	12	42
	12	17	16	7	80	16	16	37	130	12
	52	15	15	14	4	16	24	23	10	17
	17	13	19	4	12	5	20	10	29	5
	11	5	8	36	2	5	5	3	20	24
	32	98	61	79	—	131	83	159	2	118
	17	21	15	18	93	18	19	20	43	24
	5	4	5	33	19	2	43	9	14	37
					71				7	

primarily for geochronological purposes, hence the range of rock types is limited.

Although the major element abundances in granitic rocks have been used to identify their tectonic setting of origin and emplacement, e.g. Peacocks's (1931) alkali-lime index and Shand's (1951) peraluminous, meta-aluminous and peralkali subdivisions, they are poor tectonic discriminants because they rely on so few variables. Pearce *et al.* (1984) classify granitic rocks into four tectonic settings, ocean ridge granites (ORG), volcanic arc granites (VAG), within-plate granites (WPG) and collision granites (COLG) on the basis of their trace element (K, Rb, Sr, Y, Zr and Nb) abundances. Of Pearce's various discrimination plots, two are used here, Nb against SiO_2 because it has been previously used to classify Arabian Pan-African granitic rocks (e.g. Gass 1979), and Rb against Y+Nb because Pearce (pers. comm.) identifies it as one of the best discrimination plots.

Pearce & Gale (1977, Fig. 8, p. 19) plotted Nb (ppm) against SiO_2 (wt%) for granitic rocks of known tectonic setting and showed that whereas VAG has Nb contents of less than 10– 15 ppm across the entire range of SiO_2 values, that WPG Nb contents were generally greater than 20 ppm except in those with low (>53%) SiO_2 content (see Fig. 7). This plot was used by Gass (1982, Table 1, p. 594) to show that in the granitic rocks of Saudi Arabian basement there is a definite switch in granite geochemistry from those with volcanic arc to those with within-plate characteristics; the latter he termed 'Post-

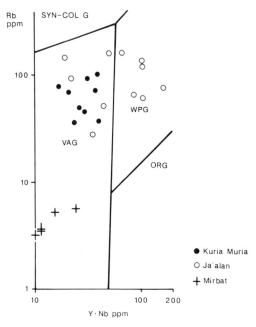

Fig. 8. Plot of Oman Precambrian specimens on a Rb against Y + Nb discrimination diagram. See text for discussion.

Pan-African'. As shown on Fig. 7 all the Oman Precambrian specimens plot within the volcanic arc field of Pearce & Gale (shaded) or Gass (solid line). Specimens from Kuria Muria and Mirbat fall well within the VAG field whereas those from Jebel Ja'alan lie in the upper part of the arc field with one specimen outside the Saudi Arabian field of Gass and one outside the global field of Pearce & Gale. However, on this plot, none are of WPG composition.

On Fig. 8, a Rb against Y+Nb plot which Pearce *et al.* (1984) regard as one of the most reliable granite discrimination diagrams, specimens from Kuria Muria and Mirbat fall in well defined clusters within the VAG field. Specimens from Jebel Ja'alan unexpectedly spread across both the within-plate and volcanic arc fields. The radiometric data identify two suites at 850 ± 27 and 773 ± 34 Ma respectively, and individual specimens from each of these suites lie in the WPG and VAG fields. There is clearly a problem that whereas the isochrons indicate isotopic homogeneity, there is a wide variation in Y+Nb (Fig. 8). When Figs 7 & 8 are compared, it is evident that the variation in Y (i.e. HREE) is causing elevated (Nb+Y) values. Insufficient field work was done to identify the relation between specimens of the two age suites or between the VAG and WPC speci-

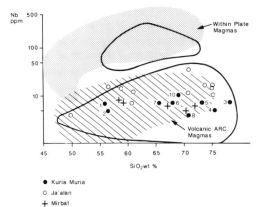

Fig. 7. Nb against SiO_2 plot showing (i) range in composition of granitic rocks of known tectonic setting (shaded areas); (ii) compositional fields of late Proterozoic–Eocambrian granitic rocks from the Saudi Arabian part of the Pan-African, Afro-Arabian Shield bounded by solid lines, (iii) specimens from Oman.

Table 4. *Tentative correlation of Precambrian rocks in Oman, Abd el Kuri and Socotra*

	Kuria Muria Islands (Al Hallaniyah)	Mirbat	Abd el Kuri	Socotra*	Huqf–Haushi	Jebel Ja'alan	Qalhat
Cambrian / Infracambrian	N–S basic & acid dykes E–W basic dykes Pegmatites, aplites Bimodal cone sheets White leucogranite S_3	Basic/acid dyke swarm S_3 Early basic dykes Microgranite	Dolerite dykes	Acid, intermed. (basic) dykes Peralkaline granite Gabbro Volcanics S_3 Folding, local Hadibu Series	Huqf Group	Basic & intermediate dyke swarm S_3	
Upper Proterozoic	Pink syenite Porphyritic granite Pink foliated granodiorite S_2 Amphibolite-facies metamorphism S_1 Ophiolite? complex Metasediments	Quartz feldspar magnetite pegmatites Pink granite sheets Granodiorite S_2 Upper amphibolite-facies metamorphism S_1 Quartz feldspar beryl pegmatites (intrusive) Metasediments	Pink granite Quartz porphyry Felsite Grey dykes Diorite Xenolithic granodiorite S_2 Granite veining – Upper amphibolite-facies metamorphism S_1 Mafic complex including metagabbro Metasediments	Gabbro Granite	Crystalline basement in subsurface	Granitic veins Pink granite sheets, aplites pink pegmatites Xenolithic granite Xenolithic granodiorite Diorite Hornblendite S_2 Amphibolite-facies metamorphism S_1 Metasediments	Red & white pegmatites Pink granite Xenolithic diorite Amphibolite-facies metamorphism Amphibolites Metasediments

[1] Modified from Beydoun & Bichan (1970) — position of Hadibu Series unchanged.

mens of each suite. As an explanation, it has been suggested (N. Harris, pers. comm.) that (i) a HREE phase, garnet or zircon, may have been entrained in the melt, (ii) some of the samples containing pegmatitic, aplitic or porphyritic phases are unsuitable for discrimination plots and (iii) a WP component was added to the melt, possibly as a result of back-arc extension.

Conclusions

The Precambrian rocks of the various areas discussed show strong similarities (Table 5). In all of the areas, metasediments and metabasites in amphibolite facies are complexly deformed and intruded by dioritic, granodioritic and granitic rocks, the youngest of which are essentially post-tectonic. All these are cut by dyke swarms, predominantly basic but with some acid dykes which, where relative ages can be seen, are slightly younger than the basic dykes. In the Mirbat area, their close association and parallelism suggests a bimodal suite. Since no such dykes are seen in the extensive expanses of Infracambrian and younger rocks in the Huqf–Haushi area (see Fig. 1), nor in rocks of similar age in the Jebel Akhdar window, it seems almost certain that the dyke swarms are Precambrian.

The geochronological data indicate clearly that the Precambrian rocks of Oman lie within the Pan-African domain (*S.l.*) and are not part of an older (early Proterozoic) basement such as that identified in eastern Saudi Arabia (Afif Terrane, Stacey & Agar 1985; Stacey & Hedge 1987). The main eastern or southeastern limit of the Pan-African domain must have lain farther east (Shackleton 1986).

The geochemical data show that most of the granitoid rocks have the signature of volcanic-arc granites, reinforcing the similarity to the Pan-African terranes of the western half of the Arabian Plate.

Perhaps the most interesting result of the present study is the recognition of a complex of mafic and ultramafic rocks on Al Hallaniyah (Kuria Muria Islands), which appear on the evidence so far available to be ophiolitic. This probably implies a suture between colliding island arcs much farther east than those recognized in Saudi Arabia.

The foliation trends in the Kuria Maria and Mirbat areas, and on Abd el Kuri and Socotra (Beydoun & Bichan 1970) are fairly consistently about ENE–WSW; data from Jebel Ja'alan & Qahhat are too scanty to decide whether these areas differ. The orientation of the dyke swarms is much less consistent suggesting that, as ap-

pears to be the case in the eastern Desert of Egypt and on Socotra, the dykes may be related to different centres and be of different ages, rather than being of regional tectonic significance.

This work was funded by Amoco Production Company (International) through an operating grant to W. H. Kanes, Earth Sciences and Resources Institute, University of South Carolina. Amoco Production Company (International) and the Oman Ministry of Petroleum and Minerals are thanked for permission to publish this paper. N. B. W. Harris is thanked for his constructive criticism of the paper.

Appendix

Petrography of samples listed in Table 3.

KM1   Fresh, undeformed granitoid igneous rock.

KM3   Large microcline crystals and quartz set in an equigranular matrix with ragged flakes of slightly chloritized biotite, plagioclase and myrmekite.

KM4   Microcline-phyric granodiorite with equidimensional groundmass of plagioclase (zoned in places), small roughly aligned biotite flakes and subordinate quartz.

KM5   Equidimensional biotite granite with large slightly chloritized flakes of biotite, plagioclase, microcline, myrmekite and quartz.

KM8   Equigranular biotite granite, with myrmekite, mica and plagioclase.

KM9   Equigranular biotite granodiorite with plagioclase, sericitized alkali feldspar, biotite and quartz.

KM10 Biotite-K-feldspar leucogranite with microline, quartz, plagioclase and biotite.

References

BAKOR, A. R., GASS, I. G. & NEARY, C. R. 1976. Jabal al Wask, NW Saudi Arabia: an Eocambrian back-arc ophiolite. *Earth and Planetary Science Letters*, **30**, 1–9.

BEYDOUN, Z. R. & BICHAN, M. R. 1970. The Geology of Socotra Island, Gulf of Aden. *Quarterly Journal of the Geological Society of London*, **125**, 413–446.

ENGEL, A. E. J., DIXON, T. H. & STERN, R. J. 1980. Late Precambrian evolution of Afro-Arabian crust from ocean arc to craton. *Bulletin of the Geological Society of America*, **91**, 699–706.

FILBRANDT, J. B., NOLAN, S. C. & RIES, A. C. 1990. Late Cretaceous and Tertiary evolution of Jebel Ja'alan and adjacent areas, NE Oman. *In*: ROBERTSON, A. H. F., SEARLE, M. P. & RIES, A. C. (eds) *The Geology and Tectonics of the Oman*

Region. Geological Society, London, Special Publication, **49**, 697−714.

FITCHES, W. R., GRAHAM, R. H., HUSSEIN, I. M., RIES, A. C., SHACKLETON, R. M. & PRICE, R. C. 1983. The late Precambrian ophiolite of Sol Hamed, NW. Sudan. *Precambrian Research*, **19**, 385−411.

GASS, I. G. 1977. The evolution of the Pan-African crystalline basement in NE Africa and Arabia. *Journal of the Geological Society of London*, **134**, 129−38.

—— 1979. Evolutionary model for the Pan-African crystalline basement. *In: Evolution and mineralization of the Arabian−Nubian Shield*. Bulletin of the Institute of Applied Geology, Jeddah, **1**, 11−20.

—— 1981. Pan-African (Upper Proterozoic) plate tectonics of the Arabian-Nubian Shield. *In:* KRONER, A. (ed.) *Precambrian Plate Tectonics*. Elsevier, Amsterdam. 387−405.

—— 1982. Upper Proterozoic (Pan-African) calcalkaline magmatism in northeastern Africa and Arabia. *In:* THORPE, R. S. (ed.) *Andesites*. John Wiley & Sons. 591−609.

GREENWOOD, W. R., HADLEY, D. G., ANDERSON, R. E., FLECK, R. J. & SCHMIDT, D. L. 1976. Late Proterozoic cratonization in southwestern Saudi Arabia. *Philosophical Transactions of the Royal Society of London, A*, **280**, 517−527.

HASHAD, A. H. 1980. Present status of geochronological data on the Egyptian basement complex. *In: Evolution and Mineralization of the Arabian-Nubian Shield*. Bulletin of the Institute of Applied Geology, Jeddah, **3**, 34−36.

KENNEDY, W. Q. 1964. The structural differentiation of Africa in the Pan-African (500 Ma) tectonic episode. *8th annual report of the Research Institute of African Geology, University of Leeds*, 48−49.

KRONER, A. 1977. The Precambrian geotectonic evolution of Africa: plate accretion versus plate destruction. *Precambrian Research*, **4**, 163−215.

NEARY, C. R., GASS, I. G. & CAVANAGH, B. J. 1976. Granitic association of northeastern Sudan. *Bulletin of the Geological Society of America*, **87**, 1501−1512.

PEACOCK, M. A. 1931. Classification of igneous rocks. *Journal of Geology*, **39**, 54−67.

PEARCE, J. A. & GALE, G. H. 1977. Identification of ore-deposition environment from trace-element geochemistry of associated igneous host rocks. *In: Volcanic processes in Ore Genesis*. Geological Society, London, Special Publication **7**, 14−24.

PEARCE, J. A. & HARRIS, N. B. W. & TINDLE, A. G. 1984. Trace element discrimination diagrams for the tectonic interpretation of granitic rocks. *Journal of Petrology*, **25**, 956−983.

SHACKLETON, R. M. 1986. Precambrian collision tectonics in Africa. *In:* COWARD, M. P. & RIES, A. C. (eds) *Collision Tectonics*. Geological Society, London, Special Publication **19**, 329−349.

SHAND, S. J. 1951. *Eruptive Rocks*. J. Wiley, New York.

STACEY, J. S. & HEDGE, C. E. 1984. Geochronological and isotopic evidence for early Proterozoic crust in the eastern Arabian Shield. *Geology*, **12**, 310−313.

—— & AGAR, R. A. 1985. U−Pb isotopic evidence for the accretion of a continental microplate in the Zalim region of the Saudi Arabian Shield. *Journal of the Geological Society of London*, **142**, 1189−1203.

STEIGER, R. H. & JAEGER, E. 1977. Subcomission on Geochronology: Convention on the use of decay constants in geo- and cosmochronology. *Earth and Planetary Science Letters*, **36**, 359−362.

YORK, D. 1966. Least-squares fitting of a straight line. *Canadian Journal of Physics*, **44**, 1079−1086.

Intraplatformal basin-fill deposits from the Infracambrian Huqf Group, east Central Oman

V. P. WRIGHT[1], A. C. RIES[2] & S. G. MUNN[3]

[1] *Postgraduate Research Institute for Sedimentology, University of Reading, Reading RG6 2AB, UK*
[2] *Earth Sciences and Resources Institute, University of Reading, 19 Upper Redlands Road, Reading RG1 5JJ*
[3] *Amoco Production Company, 501 WestLake Park Boulevard, P.O. Box 3092, Houston, Texas 77253, USA*

Abstract: The Infracambrian Huqf Group, well exposed in the Huqf−Haushi area of Central Oman, is an alternating sequence of clastic (Abu Mahara and Shuram Formations) and carbonate (Khufai and Buah Formations) sequences overlain, in the subsurface, by the evaporitic Ara Formation. The Khufai and Buah Formations are dolomites whose lowest members have previously been interpreted as lagoonal deposits; they are here reinterpreted as sub-wave base deposits which were probably formed in an intraplatformal basin. The upper parts of both formations consist of shoal and back shoal (peritidal) deposits with evaporites. The intervening Shuram Formation is a mixed siliclastic−carbonate unit deposited in an extensive shallow wave and tidally−influenced setting.

The Huqf−Haushi inlier (Fig. 1), which is surrounded by Tertiary to Recent sediments, provides the best exposed section through the Palaeozoic sequence of Oman. The latter lies in the core of a broad anticlinal structure, the Huqf−Haushi Uplift, the axial trace of which runs parallel to the SE coast of Oman (Fig. 1). This structure has been active as a structural high throughout most of the Phanerozoic. The rocks in the Huqf−Haushi Uplift have also been affected by the Masirah Transform Fault, a left-lateral, strike-slip fault zone, trending NNE/SSW, parallel to the SE continental margin of Oman (Fig. 1). The effects of these structures on the rocks in the Huqf−Haushi area are discussed in Ries & Shackleton (1990).

Stratigraphy

The sediments exposed in the Huqf−Haushi inlier range in age from late Precambrian through Late Cretaceous, although the stratigraphic sequence is not continuous. The Huqf Group (Fig. 2) is regarded as late Precambrian is age, possibly extending into the Early Cambrian, although no diagnostic fossils have been described. A trachyte in the basal part of a core through the Abu Mahara Formation gave a K−Ar age of 654±12 Ma; this age is taken as

the base of the Abu Mahara Formation (Hughes Clarke 1988). The Group contains five formations of which only the lower four formations crop out in the Huqf−Haushi region (Fig. 3). Elsewhere in the subcrop of Central Oman the uppermost unit, the Ara Formation, contains a thick interbedded unit of salt and dolomite which produces oil in the South Oman Salt Basin and is responsible for the major salt structures of Southern and Central Oman.

The Buah Formation, the uppermost unit of the Huqf Group exposed in the Huqf−Haushi area, is unconformably overlain by the Mahatta Humaid Formation, a sequence of mainly continental clastics containing a marine horizon at the top of the sequence with uppermost Cambrian trilobites.

Sedimentology of the Huqf Group

Gorin *et al.* (1982) interpreted the Khufai, Shuram and Buah Formations as essentially shallow water, marine platform deposits, forming part of the extensive southern margin of the late Precambrian−Early Cambrian Pangaea. However, within this huge platform a number of intracratonic salt basins developed, related to Early Cambrian extension in what are now Oman, Pakistan, Saudi Arabia, the Arabian Gulf and Iran (Wolfart 1981; Husseini 1988).

During the present study, the middle three

---

† Reading University, P.R.I.S. Contribution No. 009.

From ROBERTSON, A. H. F., SEARLE, M. P. & RIES, A. C. (eds), 1990,
The Geology and Tectonics of the Oman Region.
Geological Society Special Publication No 49, pp 601−616

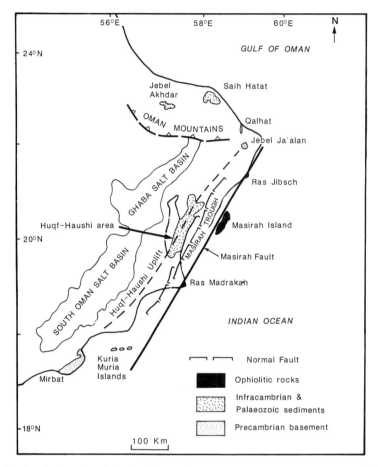

Fig. 1. Map showing the location of the Huqf−Haushi area and the main tectonic features of Oman.

formations of the Huqf Group were examined in detail. The Khufai and Buah Formations, in the Khufai (Wadi Shuram area), Buah and Mukhaibah Domes (Fig. 3), are here reinterpreted as prograding carbonate ramp sequences filling intraplatformal basins and are not regarded as shallow water platformal deposits as suggested by Gorin *et al.* (1982). This re-evaluation is based mainly on the lowest units of the Khufai and Buah Formations. The present interpretation of the upper units of both formations largely agrees with that of Gorin *et al.* (1982). The top of the Buah Formation is not exposed and it is possible that the Ara Formation was restricted to the Ghaba Salt Basin to the west (Gorin *et al.* 1982). The Shuram Formation is a red siltstone and limestone unit which is easily eroded and forms extensive, low-relief discontinous outcrops making a detailed study virtually impossible.

Khufai Formation

Three sections of the Khufai Formation were studied with the most continuous occurring in Wadi Shuram (Khufai Dome) where 290 m of dolomites are exposed. Gorin *et al.* (1982) record a thickness range of 240−340 m for this sequence; the marked local thickness variations probably reflecting structural effects, especially in the lithologically very uniform, lower part of the unit.

In the three sections studied (Fig. 4), an overall coarsening-upwards trend occurs. In the Wadi Shuram section the formation can be subdivided into four units, the lower two of which can be correlated with the other two sections.

Unit A

In Wadi Shuram and the Mukhaibah Dome the basal unit, which is transitional up from the

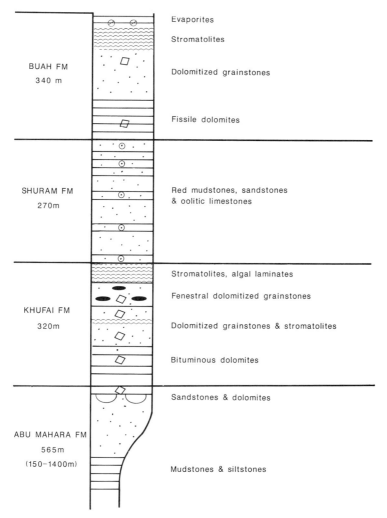

Fig. 2. Generalized lithostratigraphy for the Huqf Group exposed in the Huqf–Haushi area. Thicknesses are from the type sections and those given brackets are from other locations (data from Hughes Clarke 1988). Key to symbols shown in Fig. 4.

Abu Mahara Formation, consists of 100 m of medium- to thickly-bedded, laminated to structureless, dark bituminous dolomites. Rare grading and current ripple-lamination occur. A single 35 cm thick graded, possibly turbiditic, bed was noted in Wadi Shuram, 40 m above the base of the unit. In all the sections deformed laminations and slump structures occur, although not abundantly. A single metre-scale slump at Wadi Shuram indicates movement to the N. Chert nodules occur at several levels.

Dolomitization in the Wadi Shuram and Mukhaibah Dome sections has masked many of the finer structures. The dolomites are finely to coarsely crystalline and are locally argillaceous

and organic-rich. Ghosts allochems were not seen in thin section.

In the Buah Dome the Khufai Formation, although being intermittently exposed particularly in the upper part of the section, appears to contrast markedly with the other two sections. The exception is the lowermost part which again consists of locally vuggy, bituminous, structureless to laminated dolomites which pass up into a thick sequence of fissile dolomites and dolomitized grainstones. The fissile dolomites, which commonly form recessive units, consist of thin-bedded and laminated fissile dark grey to pink dolomitic mudstones (Fig. 5a), while the dolomitized grainstones have had their grainstone

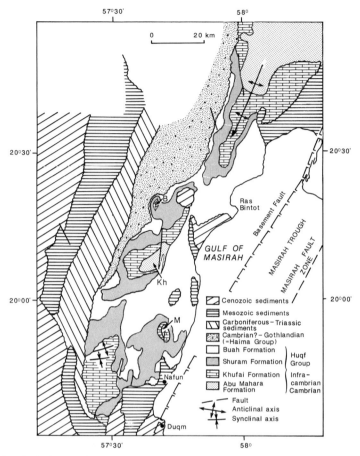

Fig. 3. Simplified geological map of the Huqf–Haushi area (modified from Gorin *et al.* 1982). M, Mukhaibah Dome; Kh, Khufai Dome; B, Buah Dome.

fabric, in places, completely obliterated. Generally the beds are thin- to medium-bedded in the lower part of the sequence but thicken up-section. The grains consist of peloids, intraclasts and quartz sand. Cross-bedding and cross-lamination are common. Some of the grainstones are graded with intraclast lags at the base and planar laminations at the top (Fig. 5b). Floating cobble-sized clasts and flame structures also occur in the upper parts of these beds. Soft-sediment deformation features are common in these graded horizons. Minor 'metre-scale' channelling is also present. The top part of the sequence consists entirely of dolomitized grainstones with numerous intraclast lag horizons and thin (up to 20 cm) lenses of conglomerates which contain well rounded cobble- and pebble-sized clasts of pink to black dolomicrite (Fig. 5c). This grainstone interval is distinctly different from that in Unit B.

Gorin *et al.* (1982) record collapse structures associated with evaporite solution breccias in the lower part of the Khufai Formation. However during this study no such features were seen, nor were typical shallow water depositional indicators, such as desiccation cracks, fenestrae or wave-generated bedform structures.

Unit B. In Wadi Shuram this unit is 54 m thick and is distinguished from Unit A by being lighter coloured, cross-bedded (Fig. 6a) and containing chertified stratiform and undulatory stromatolites. The transition from Unit A to B is well exposed in the Mukhaibah Dome where the lower 30 m of Unit B is seen.

The base is marked by lighter coloured dolomites with medium-scale planar cross-bedding. There is an upward decrease in the scale of the cross-bedding with the development of wave ripple cross-lamination and low angle

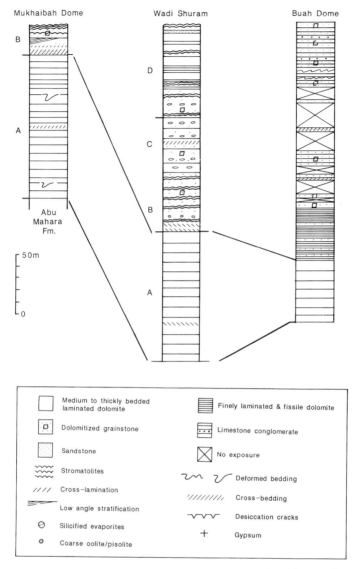

Fig. 4. Sections through the Khufai Formation in the main outcrops of the study area. Inset shows key to lithostratigraphic symbols used in this paper.

cross-lamination. These cross-lamination dolomites are overlain by chertified stratiform stromatolites.

In Wadi Shuram the basal cross-stratified sequence is only 7 m thick and is locally absent, with cherty stratiform stromatolitic dolomites overlying the laminated bituminous dolomites of Unit A. The rest of this unit consists of dolomitized grainstones, commonly cross-bedded, with cherty stratiform stromatolites. Small fenestrae, similar to those in Unit C, were seen in one horizon. In thin section many

of the cross-bedded and cross-laminated dolomites are composed of fine to coarsely crystalline dolomite with no visible grains but others show relict ooids or peloids defined by micritic-grade dolomite rims, filled by drusy dolomite cement. The cherts consist of micro- and megaquartz (in the sense of Tucker (1981) & Milliken (1979)) which has replaced micritic dolomite but no features indicating the replacement of evaporites occur and they are not chalcedonic.

Unit C. In Wadi Shuram this unit consists of 35 m of structureless, thick-bedded dolomites with

Fig. 5. (a) Fissile dolomites from Unit A, Khufai Formation, Buah Dome. (b) Graded limestones from Unit A, Khufai Formation, Buah Dome. Floating dolomite mudstone clasts and flame structures occur in the upper parts of these units with convolute lamination beneath. (c) Thin conglomerate layer, Unit A, Khufai Formation, Buah Dome. These are grain-supported, well rounded horizons and are not associated with thicker graded beds similar to that shown in (b). Scale is 1 cm long.

some minor chert horizons (Fig. 4). The dolomites are crudely laminated in part, with numerous horizons of well developed irregular fenestrae (Fig. 6b) in the sense of Grover & Read (1978) and some cross-lamination. Unit C is distinguished from Unit B by the general absence of stromatolitic cherts and by the presence of fenestrae. In thin section the dolomites are dolomitized grainstones (Fig. 6c) and packstones, the grains consisting of dolomitized peloids, ooids and less commonly, intraclasts. Many grains are defined by micritic dolomite

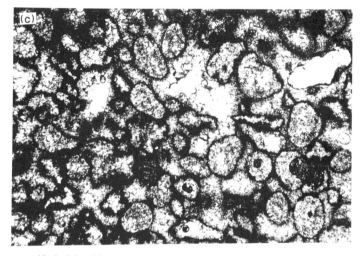

Fig. 6. (a) Cross-stratified, dolomitized coarse oolitic grainstones. Unit B, Khufai Formation, Wadi Shuram. (b) Irregular fenestrae in dolomitized packstone. Unit C, Khufai Formation, Wadi Shuram. The fenestrae are uncemented. Scale divisions are 2 cm each. (c) Dolomitized oolitic grainstone with vuggy porosity. Field of view is 3.5 mm wide. Unit C, Khufai Formation, Wadi Shuram.

rims as in Unit B. One striking feature is the abundance of dolomitized, isopachous, finely fibrous, intergranular cements.

Unit D. 74 m of Unit D were logged in Wadi Shuram (Fig. 4) but the contact with the overlying Shuram Formation is not exposed. This unit is distinguished from Unit C by the abundance of chertified stratiform and undulatory stromatolites, locally forming domal biostromes and bioherms (in sense of Preiss (1976)). This is the most heterogeneous unit. Most of it is characterized by dolomitized grainstones, minor fenestral limestones and beds of chertified stratiform stromatolites (Fig. 7a), which pass laterally

into domal stromatolites. The top 10 m of Unit D in Wadi Shuram consists of thick-bedded packets of chertified stratiform stromatolites, dolomite-cemented sandstones and two cycles of limestones, 20 cm and 1 m in thickness. These cycles, (Figs 7 & 8) begin with a cross-laminated dolomitized grainstone or a sandstone. The cross-lamination is mainly low angle but some higher-angle bipolar sets occur. This horizon is erosively overlain by a flake breccia with large platy clasts and cobble-sized fragments of the underlying grainstone-sandstone which, in the upper cycle, has a lenticular (channel) form. the overlying horizon consists

Fig. 7. (a) Laminated dolomicrites with cherty microbial laminae and stromatolites. Unit D, Khufai Formation, Wadi Shuram. (b) channel sequence from the top of Unit D, Khufai Formation, Wadi Shuram. The lower part shows planar, low-angle sandstones overlain by a lenticular mud flake (intraclast) breccia with sandstone cobbles and dolomite flakes. Above the hammer head is a stromatolitic unit (see Fig. 8). (c) Stromatolitic dome. Unit B, Buah Formation, Buah Dome.

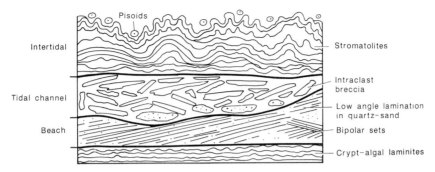

Fig. 8. Schematic diagram of a tidal channel sequence from Unit D, Wadi Shuram. These cycles range from 0.2 to 1 m in thickness.

of linked domal stromatolites (domed biostromes), up to 1 m in diameter, composed internally of small linked columns a few cm in diameter. The upper unit is capped by a discontinuous coarse pisolitic grainstone.

The transition into the Shuram Formation is exposed at the SW end of the Mukhaibah Dome (Fig. 9). The top of the Khufai Formation exhibits large, stacked domal stromatolites, 0.5 m in diameter, in beds 2 m thick. Waverippled surfaces, coated by thin stromatolitic laminae, also occur. These are overlain by 3 m of platy dolomites with rosettes of silica (lutecite), a few mm in diameter, with anhydrite

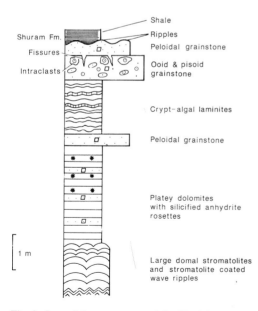

Fig. 9. Log of the upper part of the Khufai Formation in the Mukhaibah Dome (key to symbols shown in Fig. 4).

inclusions. Similar rosettes have been described and figured by Pratt & James (1986) from the St. George Group (Lower Ordovician) of Newfoundland. Between the first red siltstones of the Shuram Formation and the top cryptmicrobial laminite of the Khufai Formation, is a pisolitic–oolitic grainstone with pebble-sized clasts of oolite set in a very well sorted oolitic matrix. Small fissures filled with red dolomicrite and ooids occur in the top of this grainstone. This is overlain by a thin peloidal grainstone whose top surface displays large wave ripples.

Interpretation

Most of the finer details of the Khufai carbonates have been obliterated by dolomitization including useful sedimentary structures and grain types, especially in Unit A. Only in the coarser grained units such as B and C are the larger allochems preserved as ghosts in the dolomites.

Unit A. The presence of dolomites, lacking any dolomitized grains in the lower laminated bituminous intervals, probably reflects the dolomitization of fine-grained sediments. This finer grain size, coupled with the predominance of fine-scale lamination, suggests deposition in a low-energy setting. The presence of some current-ripple cross-lamination reflects minor current activity. The bituminous nature of this unit suggests deposition under poorly oxygenated bottom conditions, allowing organic matter to be preserved. The absence of burrowing organisms may simply reflect the age of this unit although the presence of more massive units may suggest phases of bioturbation during which the lamination was destroyed. If so, such homogenized units would reflect phases of increased oxygen levels in the bottom waters.

Periodic current activity occurred and the thin graded laminae and a possible turbidite, may represent sediment transport by turbidity flows. Further evidence of a possible slope influence comes from the occurrence of small slumps. With the limited amount of detail which can be seen in these dolomites, it is impossible to differentiate a turbidite from a graded storm-related unit.

In the Buah Dome section the presence of graded grainstone horizons further suggests sediment deposition by periodic flows (sediment gravity flows or storm deposits). Storm-related features such as hummocky cross stratification were not seen nor indeed were abundant wave-formed structures indicating deposition above fairweather wave base.

The thin conglomerate horizons are strikingly similar to deposits described from other Precambrian and Lower Palaeozoic sequences (Bertrand-Sarfati & Moussine-Pouchkine 1983; Markello & Read 1981; Ricketts 1983; Whisonant 1987). In the Cambrian sequences described by Markello & Read (1981) and Whisonant (1987), such conglomerates have been attributed to storm reworking but conclusive evidence is lacking in the case of the Khufai Formation.

An explanation for the differences between the two types of sequences in Unit A is not obvious. In the Wadi Shuram and Mukhaibah Dome sections the unit is sharply overlain by cross-bedded dolomitized grainstones or stromatolitic cherts. The Buah Dome succession indicates a gradual coarsening upwards into a grainstone-dominated setting. However, Gorin *et al.* (1982) claimed to have found evidence of evaporites in the basal Khufai Formation. They considered the lower part of Unit A to represent a supratidal sequence (sabkha), overlain by lower-energy lagoonal deposits, but gave no locality details of these occurrences. From the present study the basal Khufai Formation (Unit A) appears to have been deposited in a low-energy, low-oxygen setting, with periodic higher-energy influxes and sediment reworking, but with an absence of features indicating shallow subtidal conditions.

Unit B. The lower part of this unit, which comprises cross-bedded dolomites passing up into rippled dolomites with low-angle lamination (resembling swash lamination), may represent the progradation of a grainstone shoal. The top of the shoal was colonized by microbial mats. While such a sequence is more or less complete at the Mukhaibah Dome section, it is much thinner in Wadi Shuram. The remaining part of this unit shows evidence of stromatolites which developed on structureless grainstones. This latter feature may have been a function of a reduced energy level reflecting deposition in a

periodically stabilized sand belt area behind a series of bars. Similar zones are developed in the Bahamas today behind active oolite banks (Harris 1983). The lower energy settings in such areas allow colonization by subtidal microbial mats which form stratiform stromatolites. The low-relief forms of the stromatolites in Unit C probably represent such colonization. The occurrence of rare fenestrae (see below) is evidence of at least periodic prolonged exposure on these sand belts.

Unit C. Unit C lacks abundant stromatolites but contains prominent fenestrae (Fig. 6b). Such fenestrae (birdseye or keystone vugs) can be very useful environmental indicators but their origin needs to be carefully assessed. Similar structures can be mimicked, for example, by evaporite vugs (as in Unit C of the Buah Formation, see below). Those in Unit C, which occur within grainstones, are cavities larger than intergranular pores and show neither evidence of being after evaporites nor being of simple solutional origin. They are typical 'irregular fenestrae' (cf. Grover & Read 1978); similar fenestrae form on modern intertidal zones which are exposed for more than 60% of the time (upper intertidal-supratidal zone) (Ginsburg *et al.* 1977).

In summary, this unit was probably deposited on a series of intertidal to supratidal sand flats (beaches). The occurrence of finely fibrous, isopachous cements may reflect early beach rock lithification, hence preserving the delicate fenestral fabrics. Crude analogies could be made with the wave influenced grainy tidal flats of the central and western part of the Trucial Coast (Purser & Evans 1973) which have calcareous sands with small scale cross-stratification, abundant early cementation (beach rock) and exposure features, but lack microbial mats.

These intertidal-supratidal units possibly developed behind a prograding shoal belt (Unit B), yet are grain-dominated with the apparent absence of muddy lithologies. This must reflect an open wave and/or tidally-influenced setting, and not protected tidal mud flats.

The preservation of grains as micrite-rimmed remnants within dolomite cements (Fig. 6c) is strikingly reminiscent of dolomitized shoal deposits from the Zechstein (UK) as described by Kaldi & Gidman (1982). In such cases early meteoric leaching was followed by extensive dolomite cementation in mixing zones. However evidence of subaerial exposure within Unit C was not seen.

Unit D. The grainstones with stratiform stromatolites, fenestrae and cross-lamination in the lower half suggest a mixture of shallow subtidal and intertidal settings. The upper part contains thick units of flat laminated cherts and fine grained dolomites, lacking ghost allochems. The lutecite rosettes containing anhydrite inclusions, are replaced anhydrite rosettes, which had grown displacively within the peritidal sediments (intertidal or supratidal sediments). The cherts in the stromatolites have probably replaced organic laminae, not evaporites, as they lack any textural features associated with evaporites (cf. Milliken 1979).

The units which occur near the top of the sequence at Wadi Shuram probably represent tidal channel deposits. The lower grainstone/sandstone interval represents a beach deposit, into which broad channels were cut and filled with dolomite flake breccias (Fig. 8). Such breccias form on the upper intertidal–supratidal zones of modern carbonate tidal flats as a result of desiccation. These clasts can be transported and concentrated into channels. The filled channels were overgrown by typical intertidal domal stromatolites.

Gorin et al. (1982) interpreted the top of the Khufai Formation as representing a hardground and a break in deposition. The occurrence of intraclasts within the pisoid–ooid grainstone and subsequent fissuring indicates multiple phases of cementation and reworking, common processes in shallow marine hardgrounds associated with oolite shoals. There is, however, no evidence of any significant erosional break between the top Khufai Formation grainstones and the basal red silts of the Shuram Formation. The oolites at the top of the Khufai Formation in the Mukhaibah Dome are evidence of less protected, higher-energy conditions and herald the shallow marine clastics and oolitic carbonates above.

In summary this unit represents deposition in fluctuating low and higher energy subtidal, intertidal and supratidal environments. The Khufai Formation is a shallowing-upwards sequence from offshore, through the offshore transition zone (top of Unit A, Buah Dome), into shoal (Unit B) and beach (Unit C) and back-shoal (Unit D) environments.

Shuram Formation

Gorin et al. (1982) gave a maximum thickness for this discontinuously exposed sequence of 750 m but from the present study, the estimated thickness is <600 m. The formation has a characteristic dark red colour and forms areas of low relief. Gorin et al. (1982) divided it into a lower siltstone unit, oolitic and slightly calcareous, and an upper unit with more oolitic

and peloidal grainstones and lime mudstones. However from the present study the grainstones are more prominent in the lower part of the formation along with siltstones and sandstones, but the limestone interbeds do increase in frequency up the sequence and pass transitionally into the lower Buah Formation. The grainstones are typically lensoid, <0.5 m thick, and a few metres long. Wave ripple cross-lamination, wave and current rippled surfaces, planar cross-stratification commonly bipolar and low-angle cross-stratification are abundant. Rare small domal stromatolites, up to 0.3 m thick, also occur. The red siltstones and fine sandstones exhibit similar sedimentary features and loading features are very common.

Interpretation

The depositional setting seems to have been a very shallow (above wave base) one with no significant break in deposition between the Khufai and Shuram Formations (see above). The widespread areal monotomy of the unit suggests a uniform depositional system, predominantly receiving siliciclastic sediment. The thinness of the grainstones might suggest that they were derived from nearby oolite shoals, and subsequently wave and current reworked. However, there is no direct evidence and of the development of a large ooid bank and the exact depositional setting is uncertain. There is no comparable modern analogue.

The lack of exposure features in the siliciclastics argues against a fluvial or intertidal origin. A platform setting could be envisaged, with higher siliciclastic input than carbonate production. It must have been wave- and tidally-influenced, although not to the extent that barred shorelines or tidal sand wave complexes were allowed to develop. Storm deposits were not recognized.

Buah Formation

Although the top of this formation was not seen, the exposed sequence attains a thickness of 250 m in Wadi Shuram (Gorin et al. (1982) record of maximum thickness of 340 m). The formation is very heavily dolomitized and most of the original depositional textures have been totally obliterated. Three distinctive units can be recognized and easily correlated across the region (Fig. 10).
Unit A. This consists of 30 m to more than 60 m of very fissile, slightly silty, lime mudstones and dolomicrites (undolomitized near the base of the unit in Wadi Shuram). Many horizons are

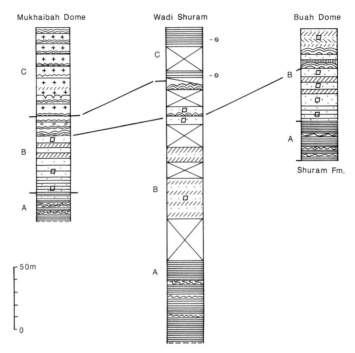

Fig. 10. Sections in the Buah Formation (key to symbols shown in Fig. 4).

highly contorted (Fig. 10) and, after weathering, look like pockets of flake breccia but lack any evidence of desiccation, such as mud cracks, fenestrae or displacive evaporites.

In the Buah Dome the base of the formation is marked by the sharp disappearance of the red siltstones and cross-bedded grainstones of the Shuram Formation. At the contact is a thin, flat-pebble conglomerate of reworked Shuram Formation lithologies but with no prominent erosion surface beneath.

Unit B. This unit consists of heavily dolomitized grainstones, which are transitional into the underlying, fissile laminites. Within the latter beds, which are up to 1 m thick, structureless coarser dolomites appear and these increase in frequency upsection. In the Buah Dome the transition exhibits thin (under 30 cm), erosive-based and lenticular, coarser structureless dolomites (dolomitized grainstones), separated by beds of fissile laminated dolomicrite.

Most of this unit consists of thin- to medium-bedded, light coloured, coarsely crystalline dolomitized grainstones. Medium scale cross-bedding is locally present. In outcrops immediately south of the Mukhaibah Dome there are packages, several metres thick, of very thinly-bedded dolomites which are cross-cut by planar

erosion surfaces, with relief of 1 m. Some of these thinly-bedded limestones exhibit faint ripple cross-lamination.

Near the top of the unit there are one, or locally two, horizons of huge stromatolites and crypt-microbial laminites, marking a transition into Unit C. In the Buah Dome, this unit is particularly well developed with thickly-bedded to massive cross-bedded dolomitized grain-stones and stromatolite units up to 4 m thick, composed of large coalescing domes 0.5−1 m in diameter (Fig. 7c). The top of the lowest biostrome is marked by a 30 cm thick layer of narrow columnar stromatolites, identified as *Gymnosolen* by Gorin *et al.* (1982, p. 2618). This lower biostrome is overlain by 5 m of dolomitized grainstones followed by a second series of larger domal stromatolites, up to 3 m thick and 4 m in diameter. These are also overlain by more dolomitized grainstones.

In Wadi Shuram two prominent stromatolite horizons also occur, although the upper group is overlain directly by Unit C. In sections south of the Mukhaibah Dome small, metre-scale stromatolites occur above the first bio-strome and are interbedded with cross-bedded grainstones.

Unit C. This unit is only seen in any thickness at

Wadi Shuram and to the south of the Mukhaibah Dome. At the former location, there are more than 50 m of intermittently exposed fine grained, fenestral cherty dolomites and heavily weathered evaporite horizons. The fenestrae, which are subspherical to lenticular in shape and have smooth walls, are either open and contain gypsum or are partially filled with mega-quartz spherules and subhedral mega-quartz with anhydrite inclusions. It was not possible to determine any primary features within these recessive units.

South of the Mukhaibah Dome the unit consists of alternating beds, up to 4 m thick, of cherty stromatolites and deeply weathered replaced evaporites. The weathering and coarse replacement has obscured the original features, making it impossible to ascertain if the former evaporites were nodular or laminated. The beds consist of irregular, very coarsely crystalline masses of sparry calcite with gypsum and nodular chert. Thin surface crusts of halite may reflect significant amounts of halite in the substrate. The chert nodules in these beds are similar to those in the Wadi Shuram section. The stromatolites, which are chert-rich, have diameters of up to 2 m and are stacked to form beds 2 m thick.

Interpretation

The extensive, fabric destructive, dolomitization of the Buah Formation makes interpretation even more difficult than in the case of the other two formations. Although the results of the present study agree with the interpretation of Gorin *et al.* (1982) for the upper two units, there is a difference of interpretation on the depositional setting for the lowest unit.

Unit A. The horizons of contorted laminae were regarded as intraclasts by Gorin *et al.* (1982) who suggested that those in the lower part, not associated with any desiccation cracks, were the products of storms while those in the upper part, associated with mudcracks, were desiccation breccias (mud-flake breccias). These authors also recorded stromatolites in this lower part of the sequence. During our studies we found no stromatolites, nor desiccation cracks. If storms had contributed to the formation of these apparent flake clusters, they left no evidence in the form of scours, graded units or other storm-related features. Furthermore these clusters of upturned laminae were never seen to have been transported, only as in situ, but deformed, bundles of laminae picked out by differential weathering. These clusters are here attributed to soft sediment deformation features, possibly related to dewatering as they have no preferred orientations.

The whole of this unit lacks any features suggesting shallow-water deposition, with no desiccation features or wave ripples. It is concluded therefore that the laminated dolomicrites were deposited in a low-energy, sub-wave base setting devoid of burrowers, possibly due to anaerobic bottom conditions.

The interfingering of lithologies from Units A & B lithologies suggests a graded facies transition. The presence of structureless beds in Unit A possibly reflects periods of dysaerobic or aerobic bottom conditions.

Unit B. The upward increase in the content of dolomitized grainstones may reflect shallowing. The erosive-based grainstones of the Buah Dome section and the small channel-fill packages of the Mukhaibah Dome area might represent storm channelling but other evidence of storm deposition is lacking. The thick cross-bedded dolomitized grainstones reflect deposition in active shoal environments.

The large stromatolite biostromes near the top of the section are thought to represent minor reef development. Similar shoal-belt reefs are common in Precambrian and Cambrian carbonate sequences (Cecile & Campbell 1978; Ricketts 1983; Grotzinger 1986) and recently Dill *et al.* (1986) have described similar sized stromatolitic bioherms from the Exuma Islands in the Bahamas. The low domal morphologies probably reflect the most stable growth forms for such high energy settings.

Unit C. The cherts display features indicating silicification of evaporites, such as flamboyant and spherulitic megaquartz (Milliken 1979). The fenestrae are smooth and regular in shape and probably reflect precursor evaporite nodules and are not keystone vugs. The abundance of preserved and calcitized evaporites also indicates extensive evaporite formation. In the Wadi Shuram section these are associated with dolomicrites and are locally nodular suggesting displacive growth, but in the Mukhaibah Dome area the thicker evaporitic beds alternate with thick stromatolites lacking any features indicating intertidal deposition. Both lithologies may represent subtidal settings. However the deep weathering precludes the recognition of the precise setting, i.e. subaqueous or supratidal. Their overall relatively well bedded nature may suggest that these were originally bedded subaqueous 'lagoonal' evaporites. In general the unit represents deposition in low-energy peritidal and lagoonal environments, presumably behind the prograding shoal-reef complex (Unit B).

Discussion

Difficult access, lack of complete sections and the wide separation of those sections studied makes a detailed regional sedimentological analysis at present impracticable. The transitions between the formations appear to be gradational. That between the top Abu Mahara and the Khufai Formations represents a transgressive phase, from non-marine clastics (Gorin *et al.* 1982) to sub-wave base, organic-rich carbonate laminites. The transgression from the Khufai Formation into the Shuram Formation reflects a minor change in sea level from protected peritidal to wave- and tidally-influenced shallow marine, the significant change being a major influx in siliciclastic sedimentation. The gradual transition through the upper Shuram Formation into the lower Buah Formation, from shallow subtidal to below wave-base low-energy conditions represents a deepening phase. Regional thickness changes must be treated with care as significant variations were noted within certain areas reflecting tectonic overprinting. The thickness of individual facies associations are anomalously high. For example, in the Khufai Formation, Units B and C probably represent prograding shoal and backshoal deposits, respectively, but their thicknesses indicate stacking and not the simple superposition of individual sequences. The occurrence of 35 m of beach deposits in Unit C is evidence of rising net sea level during accumulation. Indeed rising relative sea level is required for the progradation of thick back-shoal and peritidal deposits behind a prograding shoal complex, or else the back-shoal areas would have become isolated and filled forming strand-plains. Invoking major sea level rises poses problems regarding the possible drowning of the whole cratonic area. Considering the regional setting, i.e. adjacent to a major salt basin, and from the re-evaluation of the whole sequence presented here, a high subsidence rate is a more reasonable cause for facies stacking and back-shoal onlap.

The basal units in the Khufai and Buah Formations are critical to any interpretation of the overall sequence. The absence of any shallow water features argues against the lagoonal/shallow subtidal interpretation of Gorin *et al.* (1982, pp 2619, 2620). Instead Unit A in both formations is here regarded as sub-wave base, probably sub-storm wave base, deposits. Striking similarities exist with the basinal laminated carbonates in the European Zechstein (Permian) salt basin deposits described by Clark (1980) and Clark & Tallbacka (1980).

If this latter interpretation is correct, the two carbonate units represent shallowing-upwards sequences from sub-wave base marine to peritidal. The lack of evidence of significant slumping or sediment gravity flows in either of the lower units (A) and the generally gradational nature of the transitions into the grainstone units suggests a ramp and not a shelf margin. Carbonate ramps (Ahr 1973) have gentle slopes from shorelines to low energy deeper water settings. Read (1985) has recognized two categories: homoclinal and distally-steepened types. The former have continuous, gentle slopes from shoreline to basin while the latter have a break-of slope developed well seaward of shoal environments. The lack of evidence of any slope redeposition suggests a gentle homoclinal environment for the Huqf ramps. Although ramps occur in a variety of tectonic settings they are common features of intracratonic (intraplatformal) basins (Markello & Read 1981; Lohmann 1976; Burchette & Brittain 1985) where the gentle slopes and slow subsidence rates favour ramp development. Such a setting probably existed during deposition of the Huqf Group within the Nubo−Arabian Platform, and such intraplatformal basins are relatively common features of some lower Palaeozoic 'cratonic' sequences (Markello & Read 1981).

Intraplatformal basins are susceptible to isolation during phases of sea-level fall and may be converted into salt basins (e.g. Zechstein of NW Europe). It remains unclear how the Huqf−Haushi area relates to the development of the Ghaba Salt Basin to the west. In the case of some salt basins, ramp sequences can originate around the margins of, and prograde (centripetally) into, the basin which can later become filled by evaporites (Clark 1984). Clark refers to these prograding margins as marginal platforms, and Gorin *et al.* (1982, p 2624) also use this term but presumably regard the Huqf carbonates as wholly 'platformal' and not part of a prograding ramp margin. Whether the Huqf ramps were building westwards, towards a developing Ghaba Basin, or eastwards into what is now the Masirah Bay area is unclear, unless subsurface data becomes available and a full assessment of the relationships of the Huqf ramps of any adjacent intracratonic basins remains conjectural. The lack of reliable palaeocurrent data from the Khufai and Buah Formations also severely limits interpretation. As a result, our analysis of the Huqf Group is somewhat two-dimensional, and any assessment of the directions of progradation of the Khufai and Buah Formations is highly speculative.

The sequences in the Buah and Khufai For-

KHUFAI FORMATION

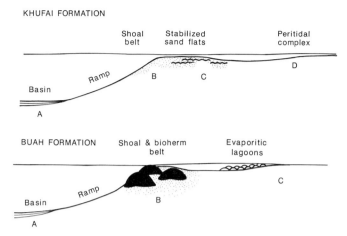

Fig. 11. Schematic models for the depositional settings of the Khufai and Buah Formations (A, B, C & D referred to in text)

mations differ in some interesting respects. The thick cross-bedded dolomitized grainstones and large stromatolite bioherms of the Buah Formation may represent a higher energy shoal zone than the Khufai Formation where stabilized sand shoals were a more prominent environment (Fig. 11). The Buah shoal belt also appears to have formed a more effective barrier system resulting in the formation of possible sub-aqueous bedded evaporites (lagoonal) in its lee. Whether such differences reflect changes in wave or tidal regimes or perhaps even the width of the ramp-margins, is unclear from the limited data available.

The apparent absence of fossils, especially in the upper units of this Cambrian sequence, requires comment. Dolomitization may have obliterated bioclastic material but alternatively the basins may have been hypersaline and so lacked any skeletal benthos. This might also explain the lack of bioturbation, perhaps linked to the development of density stratification and anoxic bottom conditions.

Conclusions

The basal units of the Infracambrian Khufai and Buah Formations in the Huqf–Haushi area consist of laminated dolomitized carbonate mudstones with minor grainstones and conglomerates representing event (storm) beds. These units are reinterpreted as distal ramp or basin deposits and not lagoonal carbonates as proposed by previous workers.

The two units represent the deposits of intra-platformal basins developed on the Nubo–

Arabian craton. They filled as ramp margins prograded into the basins to form shallowing-upwards sequences several hundred metres thick. The Buah episode may have been linked to the filling of the Ghaba Salt Basin to the west and there are striking similarities between these sequences and those of the Permian Zechstein deposits of NW Europe.

This work was funded by Amoco Production Company (International) through an operating grant to W. H. Kanes, Earth Sciences and Resources Institute, University of South Carolina. Amoco Production Company (International) and the Oman Ministry of Petroleum and Minerals are thanked for permission to publish this paper. We wish to thank David Clark and Ian Fairchild for their very constructive reviews of the manuscript.

References

AHR, W. M. 1973. The carbonate ramp: an alternative to the shelf model. *Transactions of the Gulf Coast Association of Geological Societies. 23rd Annual Convention*, 221–225.

BERTRAND-SARFATI, J. & MOUSSINE-POUCHKINE, A. 1983. PLatform to basin evolution: the carbonates of Late Proterozoic (Vendian), Gourma, west Africa. *Journal of Sedimentary Petrology*, **53**, 275–293.

BURCHETTE, T. P. & BRITTAIN, S. R. 1985. Carbonate facies analysis in the exploration for hydrocarbons: a case study from the Cretaceous of the Middle East. *In*: BRENCHLEY, P. J. R. & WILLIAMS B. P. J. (eds) *Sedimentology: Recent Developments and Applied Aspects*. Geological Society, London, Special Publication **18**, 311–338.

CECILE, M. P. & CAMPBELL, F. H. A. 1978. Regressive stromatolite reefs and associated facies, Middle

Goulburn Group (Lower Proterozoic) in Klilohigok Basin, N.W.T. *Bulletin of Canadian Petroleum Geology*, **26**, 237–267.

CLARK, D. N. 1980. The sedimentology of the Zechstein Carbonate Formation of eastern Drenthe, the Netherlands. *Contributions to Sedimentology*, **9**, 131–165.

—— 1984. The Zechstein of northwest Europe. *In*: *Carbonate Geology*. Open University Course Notes. Open University, Milton Keynes. 151–170.

——& TALLBACKA, L. 1980. The Zechstein deposit of southern Denmark. *Contributions to Sedimentology*, **9**, 205–231.

DILL, R. F., SHINN, E. A., JONES, A. T., KELLY, K & STEINEN, R. P. 1986. Giant subtidal stromatolites forming in normal salinity waters. *Nature*, **324**, 55–58.

GINSBURG, R. N., HARDIE, L. A., BRICKER, O. P., GARRETT, P. & WANLESS, H. R. 1977. Exposure index: a quantitative approach to defining position within a tidal zone. *In*: HARDIE, L. A. (ed.) *Sedimentation on the Modern Carbonate Tidal Flats of northwest Andros island, Bahamas*. 7–11. John Hopkins Studies in Geology, **22**, John Hopkins Univ. Press, Baltimore.

GORIN, G. E., RACZ, L. G. & WALTER, M. R. 1982. Late Precambrian-Cambrian Sediments of Huqf Group, Sultanate of Oman. *Bulletin of the American Association of Petroleum Geologists*, **66**, 2609–2627.

GROTZINGER, J. P. 1986. Evolution of early Proterozoic passive margin carbonate platform, Rocknest Formation, Wopmay Orogen, northwest Territories Canada. *Journal of Sedimentary Petrology*, **56**, 831–847.

GROVER, G. M. & READ, J. F. 1978. Fenestral and associated vadose diagenetic fabrics of tidal flat carbonates, Middle Ordovician New Market Limestone, South Western Virginia. *Journal of Sedimentary Petrology*, **48**, 453–473.

HARRIS, P. M. 1983. The Joulters ooid shoal, Great Bahama Bank. *In*: PERYT, T. (ed.) *Coated Grains*. Springer, Berlin, 132–141.

HUGHES CLARKE, M. W. 1988. Stratigraphy and rock-unit nomenclature in the oil-producing area of Interior Oman. *Journal of Petroleum Geology*, **11**, 5–60.

HUSSEINI, M. I. 1988. The Arabian Infracambrian extensional system. *Tectonophysics*, **148**, 93–103.

LOHMANN, K. C. 1976. Lower Dresbachian (Upper Cambrian) platform to deep-shelf transition in eastern Nevada and western Utah. An evaluation through lithologic cycle correlation. *Brigham Young University Geology Studies*, **23**, 111–122.

MARKELLO, J. R. & READ, J. F. 1981. Carbonate ramp-to-deeper shale shelf transitions of an Upper Cambrian intrashelf basin, Nolichucky Formation, Southwest Virginia Appalachians. *Sedimentology*, **28**, 573–597.

MILLIKEN, K. L. 1979. The silicified evaporite syndrome — two aspects of silicification history of former evaporite nodules from southern Kentucky and northern Tennessee. *Journal of Sedimentary Petrology*, **49**, 245–256.

PRATT, B. R. & JAMES, N. P. 1986. The St. George Group (Lower Ordovician) of western Newfoundland: tidal flat island model for carbonate sedimentation in shallow epeiric seas. *Sedimentology*, **33**, 313–44.

PREISS, W. V. 1976. Basic field and laboratory methods for the study of stromatolites. *In*: WALTER, M. R. (ed.) *Stromatolites*. Elsevier, Amsterdam. 5–13.

PURSER, B. H. & EVANS, G. 1973. Regional sedimentation along the Trucial Coast, SE Persian Gulf. *In*: PURSER, B. J. (ed.) *Persian Gulf, Holocene Carbonate Sedimentation and Diagenesis in a shallow Epicontinental Sea*. Springer, Berlin.

READ, J. F. 1985. Carbonate platform facies models. *Bulletin of the American Association of Petroleum Geologists*, **66**, 860–878.

RICKETTS, B. D. 1983. The evolution of a middle Precambrian dolostone sequence — a spectrum of dolomitization regimes. *Journal of Sedimentary Petrology*, **53**, 565–586.

RIES A. C. & SHACKLETON, R. M. 1990. Structures in the Huqf–Haushi area, east Central Oman, *In*: ROBERTSON, A. H. F., SEARLE, M. P. & RIES, A. C. (eds) *The Geology and Tectonics of the Oman Region*. Geological Society, London, Special Publication, **49**, 653–664.

TUCKER, M. E. 1981. *Sedimentary Petrology: An Introduction*. Blackwell, Oxford.

WHISONANT, R. C. 1987. Palaeocurrent and petrographic analysis of imbricate intraclasts in shallow marine carbonates, Upper Cambrian, southwestern Virginia. *Journal of Sedimentary Petrology*, **57**, 983–94.

WOLFART, R. 1981. *Lower Palaeozoic Rocks of the Middle East, Eastern and Southern Africa and Antarctica*. Wiley, London. 6–30.

Carbonate/evaporite deposition in the Late Precambrian – Early Cambrian Ara Formation of Southern Oman

B. W. MATTES[1] & S. CONWAY MORRIS[2]

[1] *Shell Western E&P Inc., P.O. Box 991, Houston, Texas 77001, U.S.A. (Present address: BHP Petroleum, 35 Collins St., Melbourne, Victoria 3000, Australia)*
[2] *Department of Earth Sciences, University of Cambridge, Downing Street, Cambridge CB2 3EQ, UK*

Abstract: The Ara Formation of southern Oman is a geological rarity — a late Proterozoic sedimentary sequence which contains rich hydrocarbon source rocks and large accumulations of oil. It consists of a cyclic sequence of carbonates and evaporites deposited in a restricted basin. The source rocks were deposited in relatively deep, anoxic parts of the basin; reservoir rocks, most of them dolomitic, were deposited in shallow water on adjacent shelf or ramp areas. Since the sedimentary sequence overlying the Ara Formation has been truncated by numerous unconformities, the Ara source rocks have never been buried very deeply and have had a long history of oil generation in many areas, they are still within the oil window. Thick evaporites provide a regional seal for the intraformational trapping of hydrocarbons. In addition, post-depositional basin inversion led to structural elevation of what had been the deeper parts of the basin along a broad NW dipping flank. Episodic down-dip salt removal along this flank allowed Ara oil to bypass the salt seal and to charge overlying reservoirs ranging in age from Cambrian to Tertiary.

The Ara Formation represents at least five third-order tectono-eustatic cycles of carbonate to evaporite sedimentation. Carbonates formed during periods of relatively high sea level; evaporites during sea level low stands, compounded by evaporative drawdown. The carbonates were deposited in a variety of marine to mesohaline environments; in addition to an abundance of cyanobacterial remains and framestone fabrics, they contain one of the earliest shelly faunas in the geologic record.

The Vendian to Early Cambrian Huqf Group is a thick sequence of mostly shallow water sediments which occurs throughout much of the Sultanate of Oman. The oldest Huqf sediments lie directly on igneous and metamorphic basement with radiometric ages of between 740 and 870 Ma (Hughes Clarke 1988) and contain terrestrial sediments and mixtites of possible glacial origin. The younger members of the Huqf Group form a sequence dominated by shallow to marginal marine carbonate and siliciclastic sediments, but containing distinct evidence that the platform upon which they were deposited was interrupted by deeper intra- and extra-platform basins. In the subsurface, the youngest unit of the Huqf Group is the Ara Formation, a carbonate/evaporite sequence with thick salt which spans the Cambrian–Precambrian boundary. It was even, at one stage, considered to be a possible candidate for the boundary type section. In outcrop areas of Oman, however, the Huqf has been deeply truncated, and the Ara Formation is missing entirely.

In the subsurface, the present distribution of Ara salt is relict of post-depositional structural inversion and salt removal. Compounding this regional 'downdip' concentration of salt was halokinetic deformation caused by sediment loading. Ara halokinesis, in fact, had a controlling influence on the tectonic style and hydrocarbon trapping potential of the oil rich post-Huqf sedimentary sequence. Internally, the Ara Formation contains a cyclic alternation of carbonate, siliciclastic and evaporitic rocks, with at least five third-order cycles recurring in sections up to 2 km in thickness. The cyclicity reflects changes which took place in the depth and salinity of water in the original depositional basin. The carbonates are of marine origin and contain some of the oldest shelly fossils known from the geologic record. The deeper parts of the basin were periodically anaerobic to dysaerobic, resulting in the preservation of profuse amounts of organic detritus and the formation of rich hydrocarbon source rocks.

Ara evaporites were deposited during periods

From ROBERTSON, A. H. F., SEARLE, M. P. & RIES, A. C. (eds), 1990,
The Geology and Tectonics of the Oman Region.
Geological Society Special Publication No 49, pp 617–636

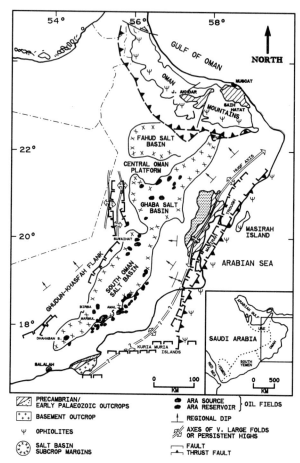

Fig. 1. Simplified geological map of Oman.

of low relative sea level when the basin, which was geographically restricted, became isolated from the open ocean. Sulphate intervals occur above and below all of the carbonate members. Periods of extreme basinwide hypersalinity are gave rise to thick intervals of halite with associated potassium salts. Red beds are also often found associated with the salt and potash — these originated from the faulted margins of the basin and from the erosion of intra-platform highs.

The carbonates and sulphates in this sequence display unique geochemical signatures which vary from cycle to cycle, and which have been used for lithostratigraphic correlation. The most important of these geochemical anomalies include high uranium concentrations in marker horizons within the carbonates, distinct carbon and oxygen isotope values in different carbonate members, and distinct sulphur isotope values in the sulphate members.

The Ara carbonates have suffered a complex diagenetic history. Platform facies, in particular, were extensively leached and dolomitized during early diagenesis, creating excellent reservoir character. Unfortunately, much of this was overprinted and reduced by later diagenetic processes, resulting in widely variable reservoir properties.

The Huqf Group has been the object of considered exploration interest in recent years in the South Oman Salt Basin, the area of this study (Fig. 1), and light, sulphurous oil has been found within a number of structures in the Ara carbonates, the oils being typed to Huqf source rocks. The Huqf has also charged giant fields in overlying reservoirs of the Cambrian Haima and Permo-Carboniferous Haushi Groups, particularly along the Eastern Flank of the South Oman Salt Basin (Al-Marjeby & Nash 1986; Heward 1990). This has occurred via long distance migration in permeable rocks

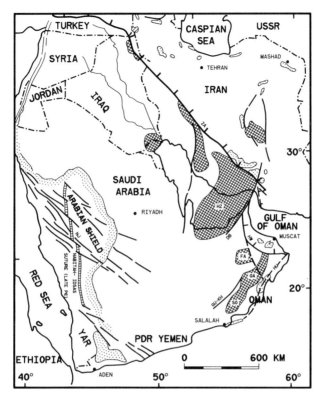

Fig. 2. Major tectonic elements of the Arabian Peninsula. Hatched areas are Infracambrian salt basins; stippled areas are outcropping Precambrian rocks. (Hz, Hormuz Salt Basin; FA/GA/SO, Fahud/Ghaba/South Oman Salt Basins; NJ, Late Precambrian Najd fault system; GU-KH, Ghudun-Khasfah & DB, Dibba fault systems, and HU, Huqf anti-clinal axis are late precambrian structural trends; ZA, Zagros and HW, Hawasina are Mesozoic thrust fronts which may be superimposed on late Precambrian structural lineaments.)

within and below the salt, and by local (vertical) migration in areas of salt removal. Over large areas of south Oman the Ara has never been buried to depths greater than 5000 m, and Ara source rocks have not only been within the oil or gas generating windows for long periods of time but may still be generating hydrocarbons.

Palaeogeography and tectonic setting

During Infracambrian time the Ara Salt Basin, of which the present-day Oman Salt Basins form a remnant (Fig. 1), appears to have been one element in a belt of restricted basins orientated roughly N−S and conformable with well defined Proterozoic N−S lineaments of the Arabian Shield.

The Ara Salt is continuous under northern Oman and is equivalent to the Hormuz Salt of the Arabian Gulf and Iran (Fig. 2). The Ara sequence is also probably equivalent in age to the Punjab Series (Salt Range) of Pakistan and

the Punjab. This system of Infracambrian evaporite basins appears to have stretched, therefore, from India and Pakistan in their pre-drift position across the eastern extremity of the Arabian Shield to central Iran and possibly beyond. Salt of broadly similar age deposited in those basins has subsequently acted as a deep seated detachment surface for foreland shortening in three mountain belts − the Himalayas, the Zagros and the Oman Mountains (e.g. Butler *et al.* 1987).

The original geometry and lateral extent of the Ara Salt Basin are not known. At present, a series of complex, fault bounded basement highs delineate the South Oman Basin (the southernmost segment of the Ara Basin) to the west (Fig. 1), but movement along these faults could have been, at least in part, post-depositional. To the east there is no evidence of salt, or its former presence, in the Huqf outcrop area (Fig. 1). On the eastern flank of the present day salt basin, however, the pattern of sediment distribution and inversion structures indicate that thick salt was originally present under much of the area, but has been removed to its present day limit as the Huqf−Dhofar Axis was repeatedly uplifted (Al-Marjeby & Nash 1986; Heward 1990).

To the south the current limit of the South Oman Salt Basin extends into Dhofar, but the presence of Infracambrian non-evaporitic platform sediments in the Yemen PDR suggests that the Ara Salt Basin may have had an open marine connection in that direction. In Iran, the Hormuz Salt Basin was linked towards the north with an open marine trough or re-entrant in the region of what is now the Caspian Sea. Kent (1979, 1987) suggested that the Hormuz Basin was isolated from the open ocean in the north by a system of NW−SE trending Precambrian structural elements which were later reactivated into structural belts such as the High and Main Zagros.

As far as the dating will allow, it appears that the period of most rapid subsidence in the Ara and Hormuz Salt Basins coincided with the last pulse of the Pan-African Orogeny in western Arabia/North Africa. In the Arabian Shield, this final pulse of collision produced a N-S trending suture and had a median age of about 590 Ma. Subsequent wrench tectonics, including up to 300 km of sinistral displacement along the NW-SE trending Najd Fault System, continued at least into the Cambrian (e.g. Jackson & Ramsay 1980). The actual extension of the Najd faults below the Phanerozoic sediment cover to the east of the Shield is uncertain. The salt basins, however, are bounded partly by a NE−SW trending system of extensional faults of probable Infracambrian vintage (the Ghudun−Khasfah faults of southern Oman, and Dibba fault system of the Gulf states). It is tempting to suggest that the extension which led to the subsidence of the salt basins (including the Salt Range) predated transcurrent motion along the Najd faults, and was caused by intraplate tensional stresses and crustal thinning directly related to the final phase of the Pan-African Orogeny. It is possible, particularly in the Hormuz Basin, that these linear, evaporitic grabens may have developed into incipient rift basins (Husseini 1988) before the stress regime changed and extension ceased, some time close to the start of the Cambrian. But direct lithologic evidence for such a geodynamic model is sparse at present.

Stratigraphy

The Late Precambrian sediments of the Huqf Group are exposed along the culmination of

the Huqf−Dhofar Axis in southern and east−central Oman and in the Oman Mountains in the north (Fig. 1), and are widely distributed in the subsurface. The Huqf Group has previously been divided into five formations (Gorin et al. 1982) based on a combination of outcrop and subsurface data which cannot, at this stage, be reliably correlated (Fig. 3). In this study, two stratigraphic schemes have been used − an outcrop scheme, comprising the Buah, Shuram, Khufai and Abu Mahara Formations or their equivalents, with type sections defined from the Huqf Axis (Hughes Clarke 1988); and a subsurface scheme which consists of the Ara Formation, with a type section 1775 m thick defined from the southern Oman well Birba-1, and an underlying, undifferentiated 'pre-Ara' Huqf succession (Fig. 4).

Apart from a number of southern Oman salt domes in which blocks of Ara Formation dolomite have been rafted to the surface, the Ara is entirely missing in surface exposures. Throughout Oman, the Buah or its equivalent formations is overlain unconformably at outcrop by Cambrian or younger sediments (Fig. 4). In the Huqf Axis area, the top surface of the Buah is deeply karstified, and the karst depressions filled with Cambrian sandstone of the Haima Group. In the subsurface of the interior of Oman, on the other hand, the Ara is well developed but its relationship with underlying units is problematic. A thick carbonate interval that contains both shallow and deep water facies and immediately underlies the Ara salt was assigned previously to the Buah Formation. In the Suwaihat area of southern Oman however (Fig. 1) the Ara Formation, *including* this thick pre-salt carbonate member, is separated from the underlying 'pre-Ara' section by an angular unconformity. Consequently, the unit previously referred to as the 'Buah' is now considered to be the basal carbonate member of the Ara Formation; everything below it is assigned to the 'pre-Ara Huqf' (Fig. 4) in the absence of reliable data to allow the subsurface sequence to be tied to the outcrops. No direct correlation should be made between the 'pre-Ara Huqf' in subcrop and the 'Huqf' as defined from outcrop at this stage (see also Hughes Clarke 1988).

Ara Formation on the Eastern Flank

On the eastern flank of the South Oman Salt Basin, the Ara Formation consists mostly of dark, finely bedded argillaceous dolomite which contains very rich hydrocarbon source rocks. This sequence was first identified in the Amal Field where it was penetrated in large, mound-like structures with chaotic dips (Fig. 5). These

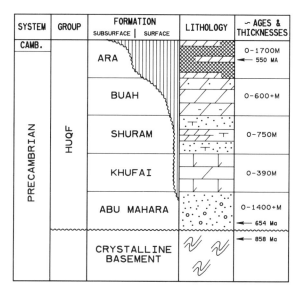

SYSTEM	GROUP	FORMATION SUBSURFACE | SURFACE	LITHOLOGY	⌐ AGES & THICKNESSES
CAMB.	HUQF	ARA		0-1700M ◄— 550 MA
PRECAMBRIAN		BUAH		0-600+M
		SHURAM		0-750M
		KHUFAI		0-390M
		ABU MAHARA		0-1400+M ◄— 654 Ma
		CRYSTALLINE BASEMENT		◄— 858 Ma

Fig. 3. Previously interpreted lithostratigraphic subdivision of the Huqf Group in southern Oman. Based on Gorin *et al.* (1982).

features were originally interpreted as shale diapirs and the sequence was consequently christened the 'Ara Shale' (= 'Remnant Ara' of Heward (1990)). Later study showed that the 'mounds' were not diapiric — they are, in fact, megabreccia bodies, collapse features formed by the progressive removal of the evaporites with which they were originally associated following structural inversion of the Ara Salt Basin. They overlie a NW-dipping ramp of undisturbed, pre-salt, basal Ara carbonate and pre-Ara Huqf sediments (Fig. 5). The geometry of these Ara collapse features has had an important influence on the formation of hydrocarbon traps in the overlying Palaeozoic clastic sequence, and the sapropelic facies which they contain has provided much of the charge for these traps. The province contains an estimated 12 billion bbl of oil in place (Heward 1990).

Sediments similar to the 'Ara Shale' facies of the eastern flank have also been encountered *in situ* in a number of wells in the South Oman Salt Basin, interbedded with salt and anhydrite.

Age of the Ara Formation

The base of the Ara Formation appears to have an age of about 550–570 Ma from the following evidence:

(a) $^{87}Sr/^{86}Sr$ analyses of the microscopic clay fraction of Ara carbonates on the eastern flank yielded an age of 550±10 Ma (see Kralik 1982 for an outline of the analytical methods).

(b) The presence of shelly faunas and bioherms suggests an uppermost Proterozoic to Early Cambrian age (say 540 to 570 Ma, although the age of the boundary is by no means uncontroversial).

(c) Very high sulphur isotope values characterize the Ara sulphate facies; these correlate with a sulphur isotope peak from elsewhere in the world (including Iran and Pakistan) dated between 530 and 570 Ma (see Holser 1977).

(d) Correlative strata from elsewhere in the Middle East are overlain by rocks bearing Early Cambrian faunas (e.g. Berberian & King 1981; Stocklin 1971).

(e) Trilobites in Haima Group sediments that overlie the Ara are Early to Middle Cambrian in age (data from Petroleum Development Oman).

Internal Stratigraphy of the Ara Formation

In the South Oman Salt Basin, the Ara Formation contains five third-order carbonate/ evaporite couplets (Fig. 6). The overall sequence consists of a basal carbonate member and four overlying carbonate units, or 'stringers', each sandwiched by thin sulphates and thick salt. The individual carbonate intervals vary in thickness from less than 10 m up to 200 m, and the associated sulphate beds are mostly less than 20 m thick. Salt thickness varies enormously due to post-depositional loading, salt movement and salt removal. The lateral con-

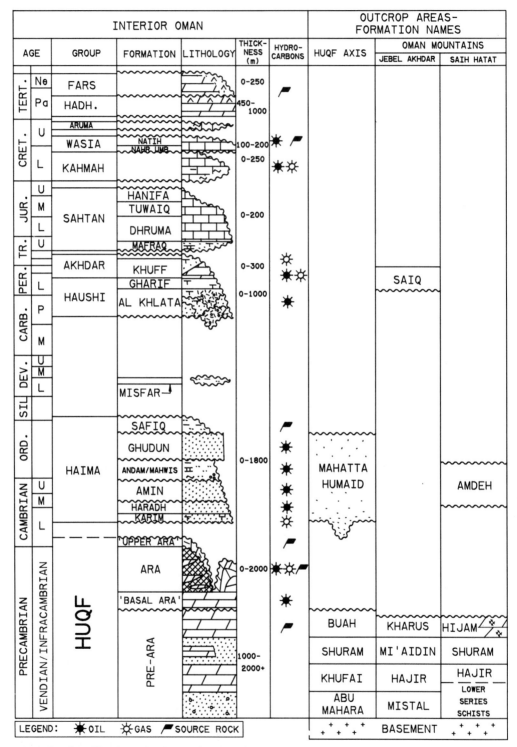

Fig. 4. Stratigraphic scheme for the Interior of southern Oman and a correlation with the outcrop stratigraphy of the Huqf Group in the Huqf area and the Oman Mountains. Complete subsurface stratigraphy is shown to highlight the gaps in the section and the rapid thickness variations — both due, in large part, to movement and removal of Ara salt.

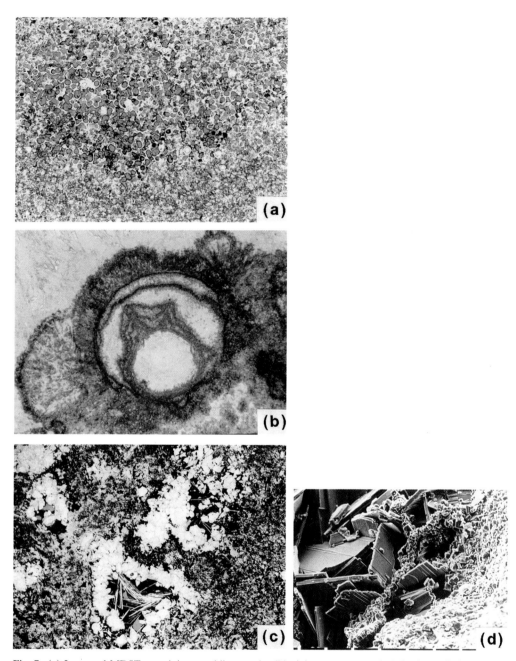

Fig. 7. (a) Lagoonal MDST containing mouldic porosity (blue) in unornamented, dolomite-walled microspheres. Black material is dead oil; pore fill is dolomite and anhydrite. Porosity 20%; permeability 27 mD. Cycle 4 carbonate, Birba area. PL photomicrograph; base 1.6 mm. (b) Cross section through a small, tubular fossil (cf. *Cloudina hartmannae* Germs). These are found commonly in association with cyanobacterial framestones, and may have been secreted by a grazing organism. Shell, with erratic inner zonation, is surrounded by epitaxial rims of fibrous dolomite replaced partly by anhydrite. Birba North area, cycle 3 carbonate member. PL; base 4 mm. (c) Cyanobacterial framestone containing *Angulocellularia* Vologdin. Large growth-framework pore spaces filled with blocky dolomite, fibrous anhydrite and black tar. Limestone stained pink. Cycle 3 carbonate, south of Birba; tight 'reefal' facies. PL; base 1.6 cm. (d) Laminated boundstone/framestone from cycle 3 'reefal' facies, north of Birba. Dolomitized cyanobacterial matrix with a lacey network of dolomitized *Girvanella*-like filaments and plates of pore-filling anhydrite. SEM photo; scale bar 100 μm.

Fig. 11. (a) Restricted platform facies. Intraformational breccia overlying cross laminated silty dolomite, overlain by oncolite packstone. Displacive, microcrystalline anhydrite occurs throughout. Cycle 4 carbonate, Birba area. Core photograph. (b) Dolomitized MDST with organic rich micro-laminae, deposited originally in a restricted, muddy environment. Nodular anhydrite formed at early stage of diagenesis. Birba area, cycle 3 carbonate. Por. 10%; perm. 10 mD. Core photograph. (c) Transitional nodular/laminated fabric in cycle 5 biohermal dolomite, Birba area. Dip angle is true — such steep dips are found on the margins and on overhangs of bioherms. Fabric is a product of combination of cyanophyte calcification, sediment trapping, early cementation and internal brecciation. Vugs are enlarged growth-framework porosity. Por. 11%; perm. 75 mD. Core photograph. (d) Cyanobacterial framestone incorporating small tubular metazoan fossils (arrows). Growth-framework porosity occluded by anhydrite (white). Barrier facies, Birba area, cycle 3 carbonate. PL; base 2.4 cm.

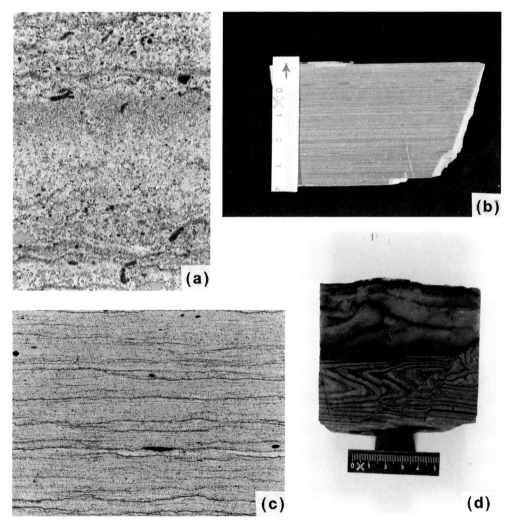

Fig. 12. (a) Mm-laminated, 'open-platform' stromatolite facies with normally graded allochthonous sediment layer in centre. Porosity (blue, 7%) is partly occluded by dolomite cement. Perm. 10–15 mD. Cycle 4 carbonate, Birba area. PL; base 11.7 mm. (b) Dolomitic argillaceous 'rhythmite' from slope to deeper basin facies of the Ara Formation. Darker laminae are organic rich. Core photograph. (c) Deeper basin 'rhythmite' facies showing irregular lamination. Rock contains thin layers of structureless organic matter of algal/bacterial origin, scattered kerogen flakes, and abundant pyrite. Exsudatinite is located along microfractures and in small vugs. TOC > 4%. A mature source rock for oil and gas. Ara 'shale' facies, Amal area. PL; base 10 mm. (d) Small scale reverse faults and isoclinal folds in finely laminated dolomite from base of cycle 4 carbonate, Birba area. Pale, layered anhydrite above the dolomite is older but has been superposed along a small, low-angle reverse fault. Core photograph.

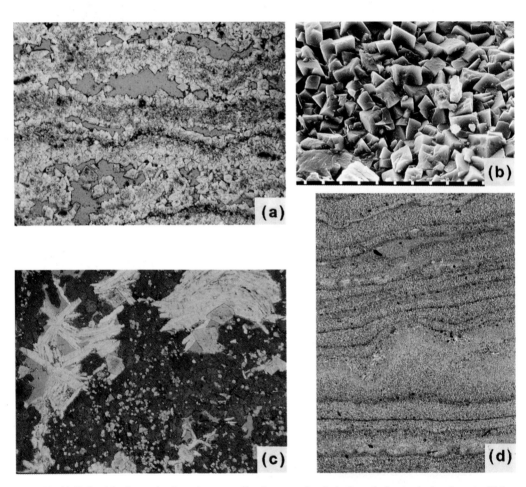

Fig. 14. (a) Dolomitized, mm-laminated stromatolite from restricted platform facies, cycle 4 carbonate, Birba area. Variations in dolomite crystal size reflect the original sedimentary texture. Despite dolomitization, and the precipitation of some euhedral dolomite cement, the primary character of the rock, including its fenestral porosity, has been preserved. Por. 11.2%; perm. 5 mD. PL; base 4.1 mm. (b) Sucrosic dolomite fabric developed as a replacement texture in lagoonal MDST. Por. 12.5%; perm. 20 mD. Limestone equivalent is tight. From producing interval of cycle 4 carbonate, Birba area. SEM photo; scale bar 10 μm. (c) Neomorphic calcite spar (red) in partially dolomitized GST from barrier facies, cycle 3 carbonate, south of Birba. Vuggy porosity occluded by cloudy crystals of euhedral dolomite and lathes of anhydrite (white). Por. 6%; perm. 0.2 mD. PL; base 3.8 mm. (d) Sucrosic porosity developed in dolomitized, mm-laminated, muddy algal laminite. Por. 14%; perm. 12 mD. Open platform facies, cycle 4 carbonate, Birba area. PL; base 9.3 mm.

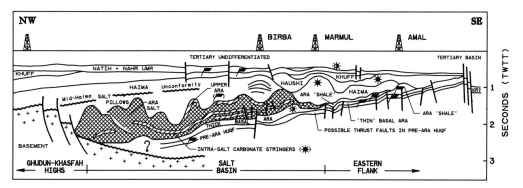

Fig. 5. Schematic dip section across the South Oman Salt Basin showing setting of oil and gas fields in, or sourced from, the Ara Formation. Note regional monoclinal tilt towards the NW, with downdip preservation of pillowed salt and updip salt-dissolution structures. Length of section *c.* 150 km.

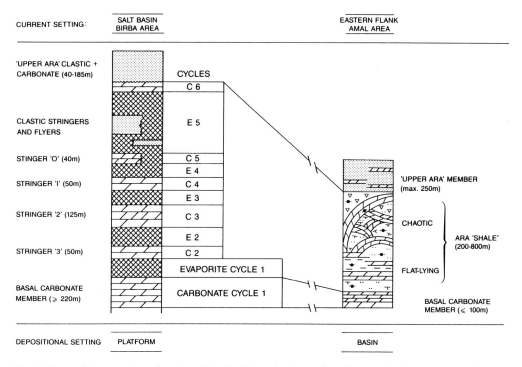

Fig. 6. Internal 'sequence' stratigraphy of the Ara Formation in southern Oman, showing correlation from salt basin to eastern flank. Salt basin contains a succession of well defined shallow water carbonate/evaporite cycles; on the eastern flank, by contrast, Ara consists of deeper water facies disturbed by post depositional salt removal.

tinuity of the intrasalt carbonate/sulphate 'stringers' has been disrupted by salt movement, and the occurrence of overturned or missing beds is not uncommon. In some areas, salt removal has caused the remnant carbonate intervals to collapse onto each other in concertina fashion.

Farther to the east, on the eastern flank of the South Oman Salt Basin, the Ara Formation can be subdivided into two argillaceous, organic-rich dolomite members.

(a) An upper, chaotic member, from which salt has been removed, allowing the 'stringers' to collapse into breccia mounds and pipes

— mounds up to 800 m thick have been encountered in the Amal area. These chaotic, brecciated sediments are the stratigraphic equivalent of the intra-salt carbonate stringers in the present-day salt basin (Fig. 6), but were deposited in what was originally a deeper part of the basin. Their present structural elevation (and consequent salt removal and brecciation) are a product of later Palaeozoic inversion of the original basin geometry.

(b) A relatively undisturbed, flat-lying lower sequence which underlies the chaotic mounds, and is a lateral equivalent of the lower Ara carbonate members in the present day salt basin. These have been little affected by salt removal (Fig. 6).

Micropalaeontology

The Ara Formation contains both direct and indirect evidence that it was deposited in association with a flourishing Late Precambrian to Early Cambrian biota. The main indirect indication is the abundance of kerogenous organic matter that was deposited in Ara sediments throughout the basin. Direct indications include the abundance of stromatolites in many forms, microbial framestones and boundstones, and the presence of microfossils.

Framestones which occur in the Ara Formation are amongst the earliest described from the geological record. Blue-green bacteria probably became established as important microfossils early in the Precambrian, but it was not until the very latest Precambrian (between 600 and 550 Ma) that they acquired the means to calcify, thus augmenting their organosedimentary role in the construction of stromatolites with the ability to build solid framework structures (Riding & Voronova 1982a).

Shallow- and deeper-water sedimentary facies in the Ara Formation contain well-defined remains of fossil cyanobacteria. The facies association and the microfossil content both have affinities with the Precambrian—Cambrian boundary sequence of the Nemakit/Daldyn River Basin in Siberia (Voronova & Missarzhevskiy 1969) which is tentatively dated at about 570 Ma, and with the Infracambrian Jubaylah Group of Saudi Arabia (Cloud et al. 1979). The more prominent microfossils in the Ara carbonates include the following.

(a) Unornamented calcareous, dolomitic and siliceous cyst-like spheres that were deposited in settings ranging from platform shoal to deeper basin. They consist of a robust (1—5 μm) sheath of microcrystalline

carbonate or quartz surrounding a spherical arrangement of aphanitic calcite, dolomite or quartz with an irregular distribution of organic inclusions. This internal structure has often been removed, leaving a hollow outer rim (Fig. 7a). Their size distribution is bimodal, with almost 80% of individuals falling into the ranges 15—25 μm or 40—50 μm. They are occasionally composite in nature, with adjacent cysts fused together, and are found scattered throughout the sediment or concentrated in particular laminae. Their occurrence in a wide range of facies suggests a planktonic origin.

These cysts have strong similarities with a number of formally defined siliceous or chitinous microtaxa (e.g. *Protosphaeridium* cf. *payraeum*; *Pterospermopsimorpha* sp. Timofeyev?; *Palaeomicrocystis* Yankauskas?; *Myxococcoides* Horodyski, Donaldson) with the Botryococci in general, and with undifferentiated Chroococcacean cyanobacterial unicells described from the Vendian of Siberia (Mendelson & Schopf 1982).

Such 'cysts' have generally been assumed to be of cyanobacterial origin. While they are similar to extant cyanobacterial unicells, they are also similar to sheathed bacteriovore amoebal cysts which have been identified in studies of recent algal mats (Margulis et al. 1983). Although the taxonomic position of the Ara micro-organisms is uncertain, the presence of a bio-mineralized extra-cellular sheath is an interesting phenomenon in itself. In recent environments, sheaths tend to be developed in hypersaline settings to prevent organisms from desiccation. It is intriguing that their appearance in the Ara Formation coincides approximately with the overall adoption of microbial calcification as an adaptive tool in the evolutionary record, and occurred during a period of widespread evaporitic conditions.

In cores from the Suwaihat area, a rich assemblage of hard-walled micro-organisms was found containing forms with affinities to *Kildinella* spp., *Stictosphaeridium* spp., *Synsphaeridium* spp. and *Trachysphaeridium* spp., all Late Riphaen to Vendian forms known from northern Europe and the Siberian Platform. (data from Shell Research b.v. and Petroleum Development Oman).

(b) Other spherical nannofossils of uncertain affinity that have been found in a number of Ara cores. They lack a clearly defined outer wall, have a median size of about

30 μm and are similar to spherical cellular aggregates thought to be of cyanobacterial origin that have been described from other Late Precambrian localities. They also resemble some extant chitinous chroococcacean blue-green bacterial genera (Mansuy & Vidal 1983). In the Ara Formation, they are associated with framestones and nodular 'thrombolitic' structures characteristic of shallow water biohermal facies.

(c) Micritic, bush-like masses referable to the probable cyanobacterial genus *Angulocellularia* Vologdin occur commonly in shallow water facies of the Ara carbonates (Fig. 7c). *Angulocellularia* is a microscopic, irregular, bush-shaped calcareous or dolomitic microfossil with a dense, micritic microstructure. It may be compared closely in form and association with the later Phanerozoic algal form *Frutexites* Maslov. *Angulocellularia* has been described previously from the Late Precambrian or lowermost Cambrian (*c.* 550 Ma) of Siberia, Mongolia and Newfoundland (Riding & Voronova 1982b).

(d) Tubular shelly fossils with compound walls which are commonly found associated with microbial framestones and boundstones (Fig. 7b). In cross section they consist of incomplete stacked units giving an overall cone-in-cone form. In transverse section, the fossil consists of a concentric series of eccentrically positioned walls located around a central cavity. The walls are composed of micro-crystalline calcite or dolomite and appear to have been imperforate. The outer wall is smooth, the inner walls often ribbed. Lengths of up to 2 cm have been noted, although this is unlikely to represent a maximum length because longitudinal sections are rarely complete. Epitaxial dolomite overgrowths occur commonly on inner and outer walls. The fossil is probably related to *Cloudina* Germs, a genus described from the Nama Group of Namibia, and in particular to the form *Cloudina hartmannae*. The Nama sequence has latest Precambrian (Ediacaran) affinities, giving *Cloudina* a claim to being the oldest metazoan with hard parts in the fossil record (see Germs *et al.* 1986).

The value of *Cloudina* as an index fossil is questionable at this stage. Biostratigraphic correlation will provide the key to the age of the Nama Group — if an Ediacaran age (±560 Ma) is eventually accepted for sediments bearing *Cloudina*, this will provide a more definitive age for the sequences in Namibia and Oman.

Although it has no bearing on the stratigraphic problem, it is interesting that as with the Huqf Group, the Nama Group sediments were deposited in a marginal basin of the Pan-African geosyncline, probably immediately prior to and during the final phase of the orogeny. Although thick evaporites are absent in Namibia, the sequences are similar both in their patterns of third-order cyclicity and their carbonate and clastic lithofacies. This suggests that in both these occurrences, hard-walled *Cloudina* probably developed in a similar environmental setting within comparable niches.

Regional controls on sedimentation

The onset of rapid and differential subsidence in the South Oman Salt Basin must have coincided with the start of Ara sedimentation, since the basal (pre-salt) Ara carbonate member already contains both shallow shelf and deeper basin facies separated by a shelf edge that was fault controlled and is well defined from seismic. During the later history of the Salt Basin, the great differences in relief between platform and basin that were generated by rapid subsidence were partly balanced by the episodic deposition of thick basin-filling salt. The balance was not perfect, however, because all of the intra-salt carbonate intervals in the Ara Formation contain faulted shelf margins separating shallow from deep water facies.

The Ara Formation consists essentially of a sequence of tectono-eustatically controlled lithologic cycles. The carbonate intervals were deposited during periods of relatively high sea level, when the basin was connected to an open ocean and must have had a positive water balance. The evaporites precipitated during low stands, when restricted inflow and net evaporation drew down the water level in the basin, eventually to the point where the basin floor consisted of large saline lakes surrounded by sandy desert with playas and sabkhas.

The internal stratigraphy of the Ara indicates that five major cycles of carbonate/evaporite sedimentation occurred. The base of each carbonate member is represented by a sharp break from the underlying evaporitic unit and the lowermost metre or two is often a condensed, very argillaceous limestone or black shale, rich in reduced iron and lacking fossils (Fig. 8). Sapropelic shales at the base of intrasalt carbonate units are a recurring theme in most thick carbonate evaporite sequences. The facies is thought to represent a phase of sediment starvation following a rapid rise in sea level. In Phanerozoic examples, the black shales are

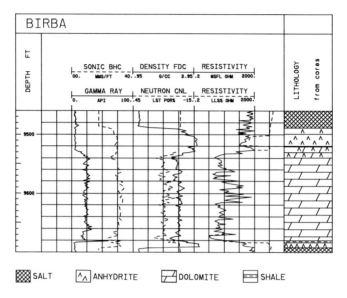

Fig. 8. Composite log for cycle 4 carbonate member, Birba area. Note rapid change from anhydrite to shale to dolomite at base; gradual change from dolomite to anhydrite at top.

overlain by carbonates with a marine or possibly mesohaline fauna, but the fauna becomes increasingly impoverished and the sediments more evaporitic upwards. This reflects a gradual shallowing of the water in the basin, and a progressive increase in salinity as restricted conditions become re-established. The pattern is similar in the Ara carbonates where the change from clean carbonate to sulphate occurs gradually over tens of metres of vertical section (Figs 8 & 9).

As relative sea level fell, the effects of increasing salinity were probably not synchronous throughout the basin. The effect on faunal productivity, for instance, must have been felt first on the shallow shelves around the basin margins — when carbonate sedimentation had given way to sulphates or even halite in shallow environments, deeper parts of the basin may still have had mesohaline surface waters with very high rates of primary productivity. It is likely, in fact, that the growth of blue-green bacteria may have continued until very high levels of salinity were reached. It is known that some present day species of cyanophytes can tolerate waters that are well above the level of sulphate saturation (Quinn 1966). It is not uncommon in the Ara Formation to find bacterial microfossils preserved in a matrix of anhydrite. In two areas (Birba, Dhahaban South) microfossils have been found in association with inter-laminated anhydrite and halite.

Environments of deposition: Ara carbonates

General facies model

During periods of relatively high sea level in the Ara Salt Basin, shallow water sediments were deposited around the basin margins and on active tectonic highs and deep water carbonates and argillites in troughs. The facies differ from Phanerozoic equivalents in a number of ways, most importantly in the paucity of shelly faunas and the far greater environmental range of stromatolites. In the Phanerozoic, stromatolites are usually interpreted as being of peritidal origin. In the Ara stringers, stromatolites certainly occurred in platform shoal facies, but they also grew abundantly all over the platform from inner to outer shelf environments. Even the deeper basin facies contain abundant microbial microfossils, and often contain evidence of stromatolitic lamination.

Facies relationships within the Ara carbonate stringers are summarized in Fig. 10. In general, the carbonate members shoal upwards. Well data indicate that the carbonate facies belts prograded from a shallow shelf or ramp in the west towards the deeper parts of the basin in the east. The stringers also contain evidence of small-scale transgressions and regressions superimposed on the overall third-order shallowing

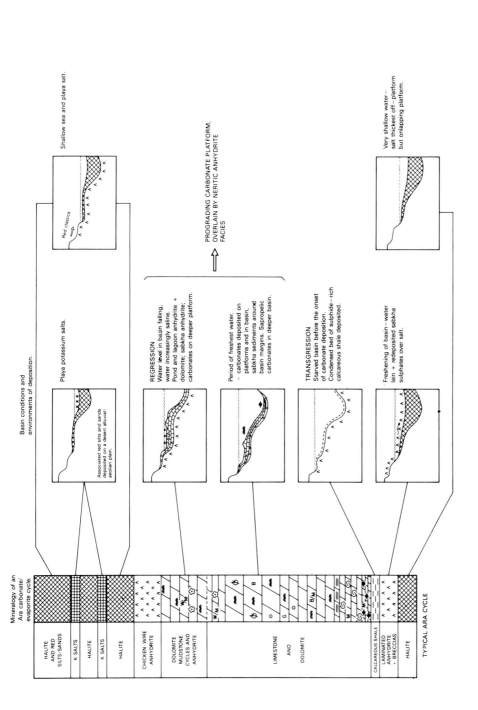

Fig. 9. Schematic model illustrating variations in environmental conditions and mineralogical facies in the Ara Salt Basin during deposition of a typical carbonate/evaporite cycle. Thickness of carbonate intervals varies from 20 m to 250 m.

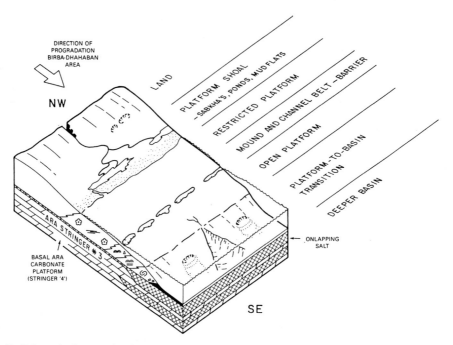

Fig. 10. Schematic diagram showing range of environments in which Ara carbonates were deposited. 'Deeper basin' refers to water depths of a few hundred metres. Not to scale.

trend. The upper parts of carbonate stringers, apart from containing an increasing volume of sulphates, also tend to contain erosion surfaces, collapse breccias, tufa-like crusts and palaeosol horizons. Where they occur, these features immediately underlie massive anhydrite or salt.

Carbonate lithofacies encountered in the Ara Formation have been grouped into six facies types, each of which corresponds to a particular depositional setting. The rock types have been identified from cores and sidewall samples — attempts to produce a petrophysical 'learning set' which would enable these rock types to be identified directly from wireline logs were thwarted by an overwhelming diagenetic overprint.

Depositional settings

Coastal plain and platform shoal. Sediments deposited in the upper parts of the Ara stringers display features characteristic of deposition on sabkhas and mud flats, in coastal marshes or playas, or in very shallow lagoonal settings. These include fine dolomite associated with nodular anhydrite; dolomite and massive anhydrite containing pseudomorphs after coarse selenite; coarsely laminated, sandy stromatolites

with sulphate rosettes and desiccation cracks, occurring in association with storm-deposited, cross-bedded and graded carbonate silts and muds, and with mud-chip conglomerates and pisolites; finely interlaminated (sub-mm scale) dolomite and sulphate; injection features of dolomite through overlying anhydrite that resemble sediment dykes; and stromatolite fabrics distorted by desiccation. This facies reflects the final gasp or sedimentation at the end of each carbonate depositional cycle, before the transition to purely evaporitic sediments.

Restricted platform. A variety of carbonate sediment types was deposited in quiet, shallow water close to the basin margins and surrounding platform highs. These facies often overlie framestones and grainstones associated with bioherms or lithoherms, suggesting that they formed in a lagoonal 'back-reef' or 'back barrier' position. Similar facies, however, are also found directly overlying open shelf sediments, indicating that the progradational setting was often more ramp-like.

The dominant rock types are very finely laminated, muddy stromatolites; digitate stromatolites; dolomitic mudstones; cross laminated silty dolomites; and oncolite/pisolite/lithoclast packstones with *Girvanella*-like filaments (Figs 7d &

11a,b). Calcite and dolomite pseudomorphs after sulphate crystals are common, as are anhydrite nodules and rosettes. The muddy sediments of the restricted platform facies form small-scale shallowing upward cycles, similar in many respects to autocyclic sequences that have formed in Holocene lagoonal settings such as Florida Bay and the Bahamas. The presence of occasional depositional or 'rip-up' breccias and graded storm layers indicates that the placidity of the Ara coastlines and lagoons was disturbed periodically by higher-energy events.

Platform barrier and barrier apron. The Ara stringers contain a facies which is here termed a 'barrier' by analogy with the terminology used for Phanerozoic to Recent carbonate shelf settings. The Ara 'barrier' facies separates sediments characteristic of a more open shelf setting from those obviously deposited in more restricted shelf environments. Rather than a true reefal 'barrier', it probably formed a discontinuous belt of low-relief mounds separated by channels, analogous with modern day patchreefs. The mound facies contains nodular and laminated cryptalgal framestones (Fig. 11c,d) which form domal structures, associated with grainstones and occasional oncolites. By comparison with stromatolitic domes of the Buah Formation which outcrop along the Huqf Axis, the individual Ara mounds probably consisted of structures with up to 2 to 3 m of synoptic relief.

The biohermal rocks contain a variety of laminar and nodular or clotted fabrics that are clearly visible in hand specimens. Fabrics that are transitional between laminar and nodular are also seen commonly (Fig. 11c). Individual 'nodules' occur in variety of forms and sizes, and their range of external and internal structure is similar to the thrombolitic clots or 'mesoclots' defined by Aitken (1967) and Kennard & James (1986) respectively. They contain a variety of cyanobacterial microfossils and *Cloudina* (Fig. 11d), and it seems likely that the latter formed a separate trophic group in the biohermal community — possibly grazers or suspension feeders.

A second, distinct category of nodules occurs in Ara framestones — these form cm-scale mammelar shapes and consist of radial, fan-like arrays of elongate calcite or dolomite crystals. They probably formed originally as a space-filling, marine cement in growth framework cavities of the bioherms.

The presence of growth framework porosity is also indicated by early-formed rims of radiaxial fibrous calcite and dolomite cement which line pore spaces, and by calcite spheromorphs

which encrust the roofs of cavities and probably represent the fossils of crypto-organisms. The initial, minus-cement porosity was very high, but the reservoir character has subsequently been destroyed by cementation — mostly by sulphates (Fig. 11d). In the Ara carbonate play, it has been found that rocks of this lithofacies rarely form reservoirs — on the contrary, because of diagenetic porosity reversal, they tend to be tight and may form lateral seals or baffles to fluid flow.

These Ara bioherms contain some of the earliest microbial framestone fabrics (as opposed to true stromatolites) in the fossil record. In many respects they are similar to what have previously been thought of as the oldest framework carbonates — those resulting from calcification of or by organisms — which occur in the Late Vendian/Lower Cambrian of the Central Siberian Platform (Riding & Voronova 1982a; and material viewed with the kind permission of Prof. Riding). The fabrics are very similar, but the Russian rocks contain more easily recognisable taxa, including *Renalcis*, *Epiphyton*, *Botomaella* and *Girvanella*.

Open platform. Underlying the bioherms and grainstones described above is a facies assemblage containing stromatolites, packstones and wackestones that were deposited in a slightly deeper, open marine platform or ramp setting. The open platform areas must have been clear and well oxygenated because the rocks contain little organic material and no syn-depositional evaporites. A gradation existed from sandy, coarsely laminated stromatolites associated with oncolite packstones and wackestones in shallow, proximal settings to fine, muddy stromatolites and associated mudstones in deeper, more distal or less energetic settings. Thin graded beds were deposited during short episodes of higher-energy sedimentation, probably during storms (Fig. 12a). Initial porosity was concentrated in the coarser stromatolites and consisted of primary fenestral pores and some very early leached pore-spaces, all overprinted to varying degrees by coarse dolomite.

Slope. The lower parts of the Ara stringers contain rhythmically laminated mudstones often characterized by small kinks and overturned folds and by small-scale normal faults (Fig. 12b,d). In thin section, these ribbon mudstones consist of mm-laminae of clean dolomicrite alternating with thinner bands of organic-rich dolomicrite. Millimetre-thick layers consisting largely of spherical microfossils occur periodically. Fining-upwards graded intervals are common.

In some wells, ribbon mudstones contain

slump structures and occur in close association with intervals of coarse depositional breccia. The composition of the breccias varies and both matrix and clast-supported varieties occur, but they are usually polymictic with clasts of anhydrite, shale, ribbon mudstone and shallow water stromatolitic dolomite mixed together.

The compressional microstructures that are characteristic of this facies assemblage were formed in the surface sediments by intraformational slumping or creep. They are commonly draped by undeformed laminae. Slump structures, the abundance of mud, the apparent horizontal continuity of beds, the lack of shallow-water structures, and the association with coarse depositional breccias and graded, allochthonous units all suggest that this facies represents hemipelagic deposition on the slope which separated the shallow water platform settings described above from deeper parts of the basin. The regularity and small scale of the lamination suggest a seasonal or annual variation in sedimentation rate. Microfossil-rich layers were-probably deposited during short periods of planktonic bloom. The graded beds, which occur sporadically throughout the sequence, were deposited from mass flows. The breccias may have originated in a variety of ways: from slump-generated mass flows, for instance, or from deposition at the base of a fault scarp.

Basin. The basinal sediments consist of organic-rich, finely laminated dolomite mudstones and calcareous shale (or 'argillites') with siliceous intervals (Fig. 12c). They were deposited in quiet water, well below wave-base. They have been cored in a number of eastern flank wells and on the eastern margins of the South Oman Salt Basin.

These rhythmically laminated dolomites contain varying amounts of clay, profuse quantities of pyrite and a variable but often very high level of total organic carbon. Maceral analyses have been performed on samples from a number of wells and have indicated good to excellent source rocks for oil.

A deep water origin for this facies is indicated by the following:
(i)   a thick sequence of uniformly fine-grained and dark-coloured, sapropelic, argillaceous carbonate;
(ii) predominance of mud and silt-sized sediment;
(iii) absence of shallow-water stromatolites and other shallow-water structures, and no apparent association with any of the shallow-water facies recognized elsewhere in the basin;
(iv) remarkable uniformity of lamination in the thinly laminated strata;
(v)   presence of thin graded beds deposited probably from turbid flows;
(vi) preservation of kerogeneous organic matter resulting in the occurrence of rich source rocks for oil and gas.

Euxinic bottom conditions appear to have prevailed throughout much of the time that the deeper water sediments of the Ara were being deposited. The depth of the basin during Ara times is unknown, but if one assumes slope angles of ½° to 1° between platform and basin (between, e.g., Birba South and the Marmul Field — Fig. 1), then water depths of at least two to three hundred metres would have existed in the deeper depocentres of the Ara Basin.

Environments of deposition: Ara evaporites

General facies model

The enormous volume of halite and sulphates deposited in large evaporite/carbonate provinces such as the Ara Salt Basin precludes the possibility that these deposits formed by evaporation of a closed body of seawater. In large basins with some degree of connection to the open ocean, evaporation alone, in the absence of a tectonic or eustatic drive, can only raise salinity slightly before it is limited by either atmospheric humidity or by oceanic influx. During low stands of relative sea level when oceanic influx is reduced or stopped altogether, brine concentrations can rise to the level of sulphate, halite or potassium salt saturation throughout large areas of a basin. In order for very thick evaporites to accumulate, however, some influx of water to the basin must be maintained (Schreiber 1981; Schreiber *et al.* 1976; Hardie 1984). In most large evaporite deposits, the source of this influx was probably a restricted supply of seawater. Meteoric, hydrothermal and volcanogenic waters may also contribute significantly to an evaporitic brine, however, particularly in fault-bounded basins such as the Ara/Hormuz system. Consequently, in most 'marine' evaporite deposits, the various proportions of carbonates, sulphates, halite and potassium salts vary greatly from theoretical values derived from the simple evaporation of seawater.

Carbonate and evaporite members of the Ara Formation formed during different phases of the basin's history. Within a single basin carbonates and salt do not form synchronously *on a basinwide scale*. When salinity levels are high enough for halite to precipitate in large volumes in the deeper parts of a basin, they are probably too high throughout the basin to allow carbonate-secreting organisms to flourish to the point where they can contribute significantly to sedimentation. The maximum salinity of water in which carbonate-secreting plants and animals can survive at present is about 12% (Kirkland & Evans 1981), while halite saturation is reached at salinity levels approaching 35%.

Thick salt, therefore, forms basin fill or *onlap* geometries and accumulates during sea level low stands; carbonates and sulphates tend to form progradational or offlap geometries initiated by a rise in sea level. In carbonate/evaporite sequences in general, therefore, time lines approximate the interval boundaries between carbonates and salt. The Ara Formation is an example of this principle.

Depositional settings

Sulphates

Anhydrite is the predominant sulphate mineral occurring now in the Ara Formation, although trace amounts of gypsum and celestite have also been found. The former presence of gypsum is evident in a variety of characteristic crystal forms that have been pseudomorphed by anhydrite, calcite or dolomite. These include swallow-tail crystals and fan-like arrays of fibrous crystals from the subaqueous growth of selenite, and rod and lathe-shaped crystals.

Anhydrite occurs now in a variety of associations: as massive 'floor' and 'roof' facies which occur respectively below and above each of the carbonate cycles, and as scattered bodies *within* the carbonates. 'Floor anhydrites' are thin intervals sandwiched between underlying salt and overlying carbonate stringers, with sharp upper and lower contacts, and are laminated or contain depositional breccias and graded beds. In the Birba and Dhahaban areas (Fig. 1), the floor anhydrite is overlain by deep water carbonates at the base of each successive carbonate cycle. The laminated anhydrite is often caught up in slump structures within the overlying dolomite (Fig. 12d). Uniform cm-scale lamination in the anhydrite indicates that it precipitated out of a body of water. The fine crystal structure of the original sulphate (probably gypsum) has been largely obliterated by recrystallization, but the original stratification is preserved because of the presence of darker partings, containing organic matter and dolomite, between the laminae (Fig. 12d). The association with depositional breccias and graded beds suggests an off-platform, deeper-water setting. It is known from

other areas that rapid precipitation on the shallow perimeter of evaporite basins creates unstable margins and results in downslope reworking of sulphate sediments into mass flows and turbidity currents (e.g. Schlager & Bolz 1977).

'Roof' anhydrites are thicker intervals which occur at the top of each carbonate cycle and below the next overlying salt interval. They are more nodular in character, and were deposited on sabkhas or in ponds or playas.

In addition to the floor and roof facies, anhydrite also occurs in association with dolomite in the upper part of each carbonate cycle. It occurs in a variety of forms: as thin laminations alternating with dolomite, as lathe-shaped crystals and rosettes scattered throughout the dolomite matrix or situated along specific laminae, and as nodules or 'chicken-wire' mosaics. These associations are characteristic of sulphates that precipitate in shallow, hypersaline lagoonal or pond settings, at the sediment/water interface or in saturated sediment immediately below it.

Halite and potassium salts

Rock salt intervals in the Ara Formation consist of massive or laminated, coarsely crystalline halite with various trace impurities, interbedded with red sandstones and siltstones, potassium salts, and sulphate or dolomite streaks. In the vicinity of carbonate stringers, the salt is often black, a phenomenon caused by liquid hydrocarbons that leak from adjacent carbonate reservoirs and penetrate the overlying salt along intercrystalline boundaries.

The best evidence for the depositional environment of the Ara salt is found in its lithologic associations — for instance, the presence of thick intervals of potassium salts at sporadic horizons within the halite.

Potassium salts can only be deposited from very dense brines during the final phases of basin desiccation, for instance from a shallow residual brine pool left in a hollow of an exposed salt flat (Holser 1979; Meijer-Drees 1986). The presence of interbedded halite, potassium salts and red beds in the Ara suggests that the halite was deposited in a very shallow sea or series of saline lakes which periodically dried out to the point where potassium salts could precipitate and not be redissolved.

Distribution and origin of hydrocarbon source rocks

Rich source rocks have been found in the Ara Formation and the pre-Ara Huqf in a number of southern Oman wells. These correlate well with crude oils typical of those found in intrasalt carbonate reservoirs in the Ara, and in Palaeozoic clastic reservoirs which overlie the Ara in the Eastern Flank province (Al-Marjeby & Nash 1984; Grantham *et al.* 1988; Heward 1990). The geochemical character of these crude oils, and of the source rock extracts with which they are correlated, are discussed in detail by Grantham *et al.* (1988).

The distribution pattern of oil accumulations in the South Oman Basin — in isolated, intrasalt carbonate members in the salt basin, and in younger clastic reservoirs above the dissolution edge of the salt along its eastern flank — provides the prima facie evidence that hydrocarbons originate from beneath or within the salt (Al-Marjeby & Nash 1984; Heward 1990). In fact, extracts from Ara source rocks which are oil mature in southern Oman correlate well with Ara crudes and with crudes from younger traps (Grantham *et al.* 1988). The source rocks themselves are dark, usually laminated, calcareous shales or dolomites with a high to very high clay content, and variable amounts of silt; well preserved, unornamented silicious microfossils are a common feature. The sulphide content is usually high with framboidal pyrite scattered diffusely throughout the rocks and concentrated in exsudatinite-filled pore throats, vugs, micro fractures and stylolites (Fig. 12c). The exsudatinite is a hydrocarbon expulsion product. The best source rock intervals (TOC>2%) contain layered or scattered structureless (type II) organic matter of probable cyanobacterial origin. In addition, flakes of original organic material are often found in association with the exsudatinite, concentrated in vugs and along stylolites.

The presence of rich source rocks within the Ara sequence indicates that bottom waters in the deeper parts of the basin were at least periodically anoxic. Analogy with modern day partially-restricted marine environments suggests that even during periods of relatively high sea level, basin waters may have been mesohaline. Such environments, with salinity up to about three and a half times that of normal seawater (but below gypsum saturation), are one of the most highly prolific of all aquatic settings in terms of primary organic productivity.

Furthermore, in sufficiently deep basins with high surface evaporation, density and temperature stratification normally prevails (Berner 1971; Degens & Stoffers 1976; Kirkland & Evans 1981). Once a stable water density profile is established, wind and reflux induced currents

are dissipated almost entirely in the upper water layers (Kirkland & Evans 1981). The exchange of oxygenated water between surface and bottom layers becomes limited, and the bottom waters become rapidly depleted in oxygen. In a deep, mesohaline basin, of which the South Oman Basin during its transgressive episodes was probably a classic example, the combination of high productivity and anoxia lead to the enhanced preservation of hydrogen and lipid-rich organic matter in the bottom sediments — the precursors of oil source rocks such as those in the Ara Formation.

Deeper water sequences in the Ara contain alternations between kerogen rich and kerogen poor carbonates and shales, interspersed with evaporites. Such variations in lithology reflect oscillations from anoxic to oxic, and mesosaline to hypersaline, in the bottom waters of the basin during sedimentation. They are driven by changes in sea level leading to periodic turnover of the stratified water column, or vascillations in the level of the oxic-anoxic boundary caused by variations in the depth of the pycnocline (Fig. 13). Such cyclicity is a recurring theme in the geology of source rock sequences (e.g. Degens & Stoffers 1976; Tyson *et al.* 1979).

Diagenesis

Much of the porosity that has been preserved in the Ara carbonates is either primary porosity which has been slightly modified by early leaching or cementation, or porosity generated early in the diagenetic history of the rocks by dolomitization and leaching. The later diagenetic processes (sulphate recrystallization; calcite, dolomite, quartz and sulphate cementation; salt plugging; pressure solution) were all porosity destructive. Even fracturing (most of it related to salt movement) had a negative effect on the reservoir character of the rocks, because it enhanced the permeability and encouraged salt plugging.

Initial porosity was very high in many of the shallow water Ara carbonate facies. In *Angulocellularia* bioherms, in grainstones and in the coarser of the stromatolites, initial pore volumes approached 50% (Figs 11c, d; 14a, c). The earliest stages of porosity reduction commenced shortly after deposition, with precipitation of cements in the growth framework cavities of algal mounds, and in inter-granular pore spaces in grainstones and stromatolites. The preservation of depositional fabric in the coarser facies is testimony to the formation of rigid frameworks through early recrystallization and cementation. In the finer, muddy Ara facies,

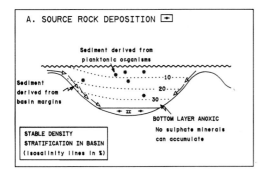

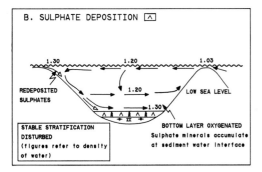

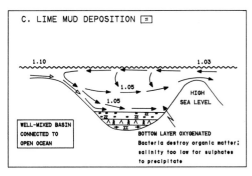

Fig. 13. A model for cyclic sedimentation in a periodically anoxic basin. The model was developed from a number of Phanerozoic case studies, but is equally valid for a Precambrian basin such as the Ara.

by contrast, evidence of early porosity loss by dewatering and mechanical compaction is common.

In many of the areas examined during this study, porosity reversal is a common feature of the diagenetic history. Rocks which initially had high porosity acted as permeable conduits for the preferential channelling of fluids in the subsurface. Since these fluids were by definition very rich in chloride and sulphates, the initial reservoir rocks became plugged by salt and anhydrite cements. Rocks which had less well

developed reservoir character to begin with (muddy stromatolites, for instance, with porosity in the range 6−12%, permeability 1−100 mD) have retained much of that character and are now the most prolific reservoirs in the Ara Formation.

Dolomitization

Ara limestones occur at all stages of alteration to dolomite, and it is clear that the dolomitization occurred during various phases. In layered stromatolites, the thin, dark 'organic' laminae were replaced by dolomicrite, while the adjacent coarser laminae were replaced mostly by euhedral, 50−150 μ m dolomite rhombs (Fig. 14a). In many cases, these early dolomite fabrics were overprinted by a later phase of coarser (500μ m) dolomite which occurs in the form of individual rhombs, or as dense or sucrosic mosaics of interlocking crystals with compromise crystal faces. Coarse, non-ferroan baroque dolomite, with crystals up to 2 mm in diameter, precipitated as rim or blocky cements in open pore spaces.

Hydraulic and chemical drives towards dolomitization during early diagenesis may be attributed partly to the activity of hypersaline platform−shoal groundwaters with high Mg^{2+}/Ca^{2+} ratios, in shoal areas such as sabkhas, and perhaps partly to the migration of 'mixed water' lenses across the platform during sea level retreat. Chemical objections aside, the latter is a less appealing mechanism for driving dolomitization in low relief, evaporitic settings, because the fresh water aquifers and the mixing lenses themselves are usually of very limited volume and areal extent, and are unstable. Deeper burial dolomitization was driven by the migration of Mg^{2+}/Cl^- brines from mechanical compaction and salt diagenesis, and by their mixing with dilute waters derived from the gypsum to anhydrite transformation which took place in the Ara sulphate intervals during burial.

Dolomitization was an important factor in the hydrocarbon habitat of the Ara Formation. Most limestone intervals are tight, and all the oil pooling occurs in dolomite reservoir rocks. Sucrosic dolomite mosaics provide intercrystalline matrix permeability even in mudstones which, in their limestone incarnation, are completely tight (Fig. 14b, d).

Formation pressures

Overpressures of up to 250 Bar have been encountered in intrasalt dolomite reservoirs in the South Oman Salt Basin. The high pressures are related to the isolating effects of mobile salt: salt movement caused the carbonate stringers to fragment, leaving them as large, isolated 'pods' of carbonate floating in salt. This occurred after oil migration. Any subsequent change in the rock fabric of the carbonate, and any influx of migrating fluid and gas, contributed to the pressure build-up.

By contrast, carbonate members which were never sandwiched by salt, or which have collapsed onto the pre-salt Ara or pre-Ara sequence due to salt removal, are normally pressured.

Geochemical anomalies

Carbonates of cycle 4 in the Ara Formation (Fig. 6) display a number of geochemical anomalies which are used for correlation throughout the South Oman Salt Basin. These include the following:

(a) Gamma radiation anomaly — the transgressive claystone interval which occurs commonly at the base of the cycle gives a high response on gamma logs. Neutron activation analysis indicates that this is due to a high content of claybound potassium and thorium.

Despite a negligible clay content, the overlying carbonates also give an anomalously high gamma response. This is caused by a high content of uranium in the form of carbonate bound uranium or uranium in organo-uranium complexes deposited with the original limestone.

(b) Carbon/oxygen isotopes — cycle 4 carbonates have a distinct stable isotope character (δC^{13} values of -2 to -5‰ compared to $+1$ to to $+6$‰ for the rest of the carbonates in the sequence).

(c) Sulphur isotopes — sulphur isotope values obtained from anhydrite intervals immediately above and below the cycle 4 carbonate member are extremely high — up to 43.3% $\delta^{34}S_{(CD)}$. Lighter values obtained for other anhydrite intervals in the sequence plot on a normal background curve of sulphur through time (Holser 1977).

Significance of the geochemical anomalies

The likelihood that the Ara basins were density stratified and periodically anoxic has been discussed above. Stratified anoxic basins in general tend to become enriched in certain trace elements (notably uranium) and fractionated isotopes, both at the sediment–water interface, and within the water column below the halocline

(Degens & Stoffers 1980; Curtis 1980; Demaison & Moore 1980). Enrichment of basin waters in heavy sulphur occurs, for instance, through the agency of marine biologic precipitation of metal sulphides, which concentrates light sulphur in the bottom sediments. Similarly, relative depletion in ^{13}C occurs because methane is oxidized chemosynthetically by bacteria in the water column, according to:

$$^{12}CH_4 + 2H_2O \rightleftharpoons {}^{12}CO_2 + 4H^+$$

and

$$^{12}CO_2 + H_2O \rightleftharpoons H^+ + H^{12}CO_3{}^-.$$

When the density stratification that results in such brine chemistry is destroyed, the anomalous chemical character of the brine will be dispersed throughout the basin, and will be read rapidly into the sedimentary record. This appears to have been the case with the cycle 4 sulphate and carbonate members of the Ara Formation. At the beginning of cycle 4 time, a long history of stable stratification in the deepest parts of the Ara basins was terminated by tectonic disturbance and/or a change in palaeography coupled with a rise in sea level. The deep bottom brine released by this turnover was dispersed rapidly throughout the basin, imparting its geochemical signature to the sediments of the new cycle — initially to the sulphates at the base of the cycle and subsequently to the overlying carbonates.

On a larger scale, it is thought that such a mixing model may explain the carbon and sulphur isotope anomalies of global significance that occur episodically in the geological record. According to this line of reasoning, a large, restricted basin or a series of basins become stratified and accumulate a peculiar brine chemistry over a long period of time. This chemical signature is subsequently 'released' to the oceans where it mixes rapidly (instantly in geologic terms) and starts to be read into the oceanic sediment record. The extreme heavy sulphur/ light carbon character of the upper parts of the Ara is significant because it suggests that the Ara/Hormuz salt basin system could have played an important role in the enormous sulphur/carbon isotope excursion that occurs on a global scale close to the Precambrian–Cambrian boundary (Holser 1977). This possibility will form the basis of an ongoing study of the geochemistry of the evaporite basins of Oman and Iran.

Conclusions

The Ara Formation has played a key role, both

directly and indirectly, in the hydrocarbon geology of southern Oman. Shallow water Ara carbonates provide reservoirs of widely varying quality for oil and gas accumulation; deep water Ara carbonate and shale source rocks have charged these intra-Ara reservoirs and, more importantly, large accumulations in overlying Phanerozoic sediments; Ara salt forms the top, base and lateral seals for intra-Ara oil and gas pools; and, again of greater significance, structural inversion and removal of the Ara salt controlled the depositional and trapping geometry of younger sediments. Thick clastics were deposited in the rim synclines of growing pillows of Ara salt, for instance, and later salt removal inverted these depocentres into 'turtle-back' antiforms, prolific traps for hydrocarbons along the flank of the salt basin. Other salt-related traps include truncation traps on the flanks of salt structures, and structural closure in anticlines above cores of evaporite residue.

The Ara Formation spans the Precambrian–Cambrian boundary, and its sedimentary, biotic and geochemical character all provide important insight into the fundamental changes occurring on earth at the time. The appearance in the geologic record of calcifying microflora, of true framestone textures, of shelly faunas and of catastrophic marine geochemical 'events' are all reflected in the geology of the Ara. The Ara Formation also provides one of the earliest, well documented examples of a pattern of cyclic carbonate–evaporite sedimentation in a restricted basin setting that would become a recurrent phenomenon in the palaeogeography of the mid-latitude belts right up until the present day.

The author is grateful for permission to publish this paper from the Ministry of Petroleum and Minerals of the Sultanate of Oman, and from Petroleum Development Oman, Shell International Petroleum Mij, A/S Norske Shell Exploration and Production, and Shell Western E&P Inc. The paper incorporates work done by a number of present and former PDO and SIPM geologists, whose contribution is acknowledged with gratitude. D. van der Baan, L. Gaarenstroom, P. Lovelock and G. Graham deserve special mention in this regard. Special thanks to M. Hughes-Clarke, who inspired and monitored much of the original work, and who reviewed the manuscript; to M. Epting and S. Wynne at Koninklijke Shell Exploratie en Produktie Laboratorium in the Netherlands, who nurtured, encouraged and continuously reviewed the study throughout its duration; and to A. Heward for general discussions and a thorough review of the manuscript.

References

AITKEN, J. D. 1967. Classification and environmental significance of cryptalgal limestones and dolomites, with illustrations from the Cambrian and Ordovician of Southwestern Alberta. *Journal of Sedimentary Petrology*, **37**, 1163–1178.

AL-MARJEBY, A., NASH, D. F. 1986. A summary of the geology and oil habitat of the Eastern Flank hydrocarbon province of South Oman. *Marine and Petroleum Geology*, **3**, 306–314.

BERBERIAN, M. & KING, G. C. P. 1981. Towards a palaeogeography and tectonic evolution of Iran. *Canadian Journal of Earth Sciences*, **18**, 210–265.

BERNER, R. A. 1971. Principles of Chemical Sedimentology. McGraw-Hill, New York.

—— & RAISWELL, R. 1983. Burial of organic carbon and pyrite sulphur in sediments over Phanerozoic time: a new theory. *Geochim. Cosmochim. Acta*, **47**, 855–862.

BUTLER, R. W. H., COWARD, M. P., HARWOOD, G. M. & KNIPE, R. J. 1987. Salt control on thrust geometry, structural style and gravitational collapse along the Himalayan Mountain front in the Salt Range of northern Pakistan. *In*: LERCHE, I. & O'BRIEN, J. J. (eds). *Dynamical Geology of Salt and Related Structures*. Academic Press, New York, 339–418.

CLOUD, P. E., AWRAMIK, S. M., MORRISON, K. & HADLEY, D. G. 1979. Earliest Phanerozoic or latest Proterozoic fossils from the Arabian Shield. *Precambrian Research*, **10**, 73–93.

COOK, H. E. & TAYLOR, M. E. 1977. Comparison of continental slope and shelf environments in the Upper Cambrian and Lowest Ordovician of Nevada. *In*: COOK, H. E. & ENOS, P. (eds), *Society of Economic Palaeontologists and Mineralogists, Special Publication*, **25**, 51–81.

CURTIS, C. D. 1980. Diagenetic alteration in black shales. *Journal of the Geological Society of London*, **137**, 131–138.

DEGENS, E. T. & STOFFERS, P. 1976. Stratified waters as a key to the past. *Nature*, **263**, 22–27.

—— & —— 1980. Environmental events recorded in Quaternary sediments of the Black Sea. *Journal of the Geological Society of London*, **137**, 131–138.

DEMAISON, G. J. & MOORE, G. T. 1980. Anoxic environments and oil source bed genesis. *American Association of Petroleum Geologists Bulletin*, **64**, 1179–1209.

GERMS, G. J. B. 1972. New shelly fossils from the Nama Group, South West Africa. *American Journal of Science*, **272**, 752–761.

—— 1974. The Nama Group in South West Africa and its relationship to the Pan-African geosyncline. *Journal of Geology*, **82**, 301–317.

—— KNOLL, A. H., VIDAL, G. 1986. Latest Proterozoic microfossils from the Nama Group, Namibia, South West Africa. *Precambrian Research*, **32**, 45–62.

GORIN, G. E., RACZ, L. G. & WALTER, M. R. 1982. Late Precambrian–Cambrian sediments of the Huqf Group, Sultanate of Oman. *American As-

sociation of Petroleum Geologists Bulletin, **66**, 2609–2627.

GRANTHAM, P. J., LIJMBACH, G. W. M., POSTHUMA, J., HUGHES-CLARKE, M. W. & WILLINK, R. J. 1988. Origin of crude oils in Oman. *Journal of Petroleum Geology*, **11**, 61–80.

HARDIE, L. A. 1984. Evaporites: Marine or non-marine? *American Journal of Science*, **284**, 193–240.

HEWARD, A. P. 1990. Salt removal and sedimentation in southern Oman. *In*: ROBERTSON, A. H. F., SEARLE, M. P. & RIES, A. C. (eds) *The Geology and Tectonics of the Oman Mountains*. Geological Society, London, Special Publication, **49**, 637–652.

HOLSER, W. T. 1977. Catastrophic chemical events in the history of the ocean. *Nature*, **267**, 403–408.

—— 1979. Mineralogy of evaporites. *In* Burns, R. G. (ed) *Marine Minerals. American Mineral Association, Review Min.*, **6**, 211–294.

HUGHES-CLARKE, M. W. 1988. Stratigraphy and rock-unit nomenclature in the oil-producing area of Interior Oman. *Journal of Petroleum Geology*, **11**, 5–60.

HUSSEINI, M. I. 1988. The Arabian Infra-Cambrian extensional system. *Tectonophysics*, **148**, 93–103.

JACKSON, N. J. & RAMSAY, C. R. 1980. Time-space relationships of Upper Precambrian volcanic and sedimentary units in the Central Arabian Shield. *Journal of the Geological Society of London*, **137**, 617–628.

KENNARD, J. M., JAMES, N. P. 1986. Thrombolites and Stromatolites: two distinct types of microbial structures. *Palaios*, **1**, 492–503.

KENT, P. E. 1979. The emergent Hormuz salt plugs of southern Iran. *Journal of Petroleum Geology*, **2** 117–144.

—— 1987. Island salt plugs in the Middle East and their tectonic implications. *In*: LERCHE, F. & O'BRIEN, J. J. (eds), *Dynamical Geology of Salt and Related Structures*. Academic, New York, 3–38.

KIRKLAND, D. W. & EVANS, R. 1981. Source rock potential of evaporite environments. *American Association of Petroleum Geologists Bulletin*, **65**, 181–190.

KRALIK, M. 1982. Rb–Sr age determinations on Precambrian carbonate rocks of the Carpentarian McArthur Basin, Northern Territory, Australia. *Precambrian Research*, **18**, 157–170.

KRONER, A. 1971. Late Precambrian correlation and the relationship between the Demara and Nama systems of SW Africa. *Geol. Rundschau*, **60**, 1513–1523.

MANSUY, C. & VIDAL, G. 1983. Late Proterozoic Brioverian microfossils from France: taxonomic affinity and implications for plankton productivity. *Nature*, **302**, 606–607.

MARGULIS, L., GROSOVSKY, D. D., STOLZ, J. F., GONG-COLLINS, E. & LENK, S. 1983. Distinctive microbial structures and the pre-Phanerozoic fossil record. *Precambrian Research*, **20**, 443–477.

MEIJER-DREES, N. C. 1986. Evaporitic deposits of western Canada. *Geological Survey of Canada*, Paper 85–20.

MENDELSON, C. V. & SCHOPF, J. W. 1982. Proterozoic microfossils from the Sukhaya Tunguska, Shorika and Yudoma Formations of the Siberian Platform, USSR. *Journal of Palaeontology*, **56**, 42–83.

QUINN, G. B. 1966. Biology of the Great Salt Lake. *Utah Geological Society*, Guidebook **20**, 25–34.

RIDING, R. & VORONOVA, L. 1982a. Calcified cyanophytes and the Precambrian–Cambrian transition. *Naturwissenschaften*, **69**, 498.

—— & —— 1982b. Recent freshwater oscillatoriacean analogue of the Lower Palaeozoic calcareous alga *Angulocellularia. Lethaia*, **15**, 105–114.

SCHLAGER, W. & BOLZ, H. 1977. Clastic accumulation of sulphate evaporites in deep water. *Journal of Sedimentary Petrology*, **47**, 600–609.

SCHREIBER, B. C. 1981. Evaporites, carbonates and oil. *In*: BALLY, A. W. *et al.* (eds), *American Association of Petroleum Geologists, Education Course Notes*, **19**. 6/1–6/32.

——, FRIEDMAN, G. M., DECIMA, A. & SCHREIBER, E. 1976. Depositional environments of Upper Miocene (Messinian) evaporite deposits of the Sicilian Basin. *Sedimentology* **23**, 729–760.

STOCKLIN, J. 1972. Iran central, septentrional et oriental (Part 1); Iran du Sud-Ouest (Part 2). *Lexique Stratigraph. International*, Vol. III ASIE, Fasc. 9b.

TYSON, R. V. WILSON, R. C. L. & DOWNIE, C. 1979. A stratified water column environmental model for the type Kimmeridge Clay. *Nature*, **277**, 377–380.

VORONOVA, L. G. & MISSARZHEVSKIY, V. V. 1969. Finds of algae and wormtubes in Precambrian–Cambrian boundary beds in the north of the Siberian Platform. *Dok. Akad. Nauk. USSR, Earth Science Section*, **184**, 207–210.

Salt removal and sedimentation in Southern Oman

A. P. HEWARD

Petroleum Development Oman LLC, P.O. Box 81, Muscat, Sultanate of Oman. Present Address: Shell UK Exploration and Production Ltd., Shell-Mex House, London WC2R 0DX, UK

Abstract: On the Eastern Flank of the South Oman Salt Basin lies a Cambrian to Recent sequence much affected by the withdrawal and dissolution of underlying Infracambrian salt. Salt withdrawal began after burial by only a few hundreds of metres of Cambrian continental sands, and salt dissolution has taken place periodically up to the present, initially near-surface and later in the subsurface. Salt removal has (1) resulted in the collapse of masses of dolomite and shale formerly interbedded with the salt, (2) influenced the large-scale geometries of sedimentary bodies within the overlying succession, (3) affected the distribution of sedimentary facies when rates of salt removal balanced or exceeded sedimentation, (4) allowed the preservation of parts of the succession otherwise eroded at this basin margin, and (5) caused folding and fracturing of Cambrian to Recent sediments.

More than 2×10^9 m³ of oil (12×10^9 bbls) is estimated to be present in four types of hydrocarbon trap related to salt removal. In terms of importance these are: large turtle-back anticlines resulting from the inversion of former peripheral synclines, truncation traps rimming eroded turtle-back anticlines, small anticlines draped over residual masses of dolomite and shale, and porous and fractured dolomites within such residual masses.

Comparison of salt removal phenomena from the Eastern Flank of the South Oman Salt Basin, the North Sea, western Canada and the USA suggests that the south Oman features may be typical of the margins of basins where a thick mobile salt sequence is overlain by clastic sediments.

Underlying the rocky desert landscape of south Oman is a complex and spectacular geology which bears only a partial resemblance to the Huqf and Dhofar outcrops (Fig. 1; Lees 1928; Morton 1959; Hawkins *et al.* 1981; Gorin *et al.* 1982; Beydoun 1985). This subsurface geology was first explored by Dhofar Cities Service Petroleum Corporation and partners between 1953 and 1967, resulting in the discovery of the Marmul oil field and oil shows in many of their other 24 wells. Their aggressive appraisal of the Marmul discovery revealed a geology whose variability could only be properly understood after the drilling of several tens of development wells in the field by Petroleum Development Oman (PDO) in the early 1980s (de la Grandville 1982). PDO's own first discovery in South Oman, the Amal field found in 1972, was at one stage interpreted to be larger than Marmul, but subsequently was reduced considerably in volume and its development postponed as each of the appraisal wells proved a complex geology and hydrocarbon distribution.

By early 1988 this significant oil field province on the Eastern Flank of the South Oman Salt Basin was producing around 30 000 m³ d⁻¹ (190 000 bbls d⁻¹) of predominantly heavy oil from 24 fields. The oil is derived from Infracambrian source rocks (Grantham *et al.* 1988) and occurs mainly in Palaeozoic sandstone reservoirs of Cambro-Ordovician (Haima), Permo-Carboniferous (Al Khlata) and Permian (Gharif) age (Fig. 2; Hughes Clarke 1988). Many aspects of the petroleum geology of this province can be related to the former presence and removal of salt (Al-Marjeby & Nash 1986).

The purpose of this paper is to briefly describe the sedimentology of these Palaeozoic sandstone reservoirs, and to show how salt movement and dissolution has influenced sedimentary geometries, facies distributions and reservoir properties. These aspects, along with a seemingly inherent fine-scale variability within glacial deposits of the Al Khlata Formation, account for much of the reservoir complexity. The impact of this complexity is heightened by a common lack of seismic expression of the Palaeozoic interval due to multiples generated by shallower carbonate reflectors.

Ara salt deposition and Haima halokinesis

After apparently widespread continental to shallow marine depositional conditions during

From ROBERTSON, A. H. F., SEARLE, M. P. & RIES, A. C. (eds), 1990, *The Geology and Tectonics of the Oman Region.* Geological Society Special Publication No 49, pp 637–652

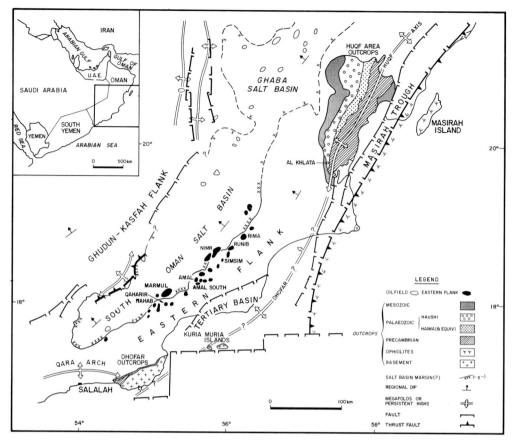

Fig. 1. Simplified geological map of South Oman. The Indian sub-continent was contiguous with SE Arabia for much of the time period considered in this paper.

the pre-Ara Huqf, the Infracambrian Ara Salt reflects a change towards a more restricted basinal setting. The 1−2 km of salt and associated sediments which accumulated in south Oman probably imply a pre-existing sedimentary basin with a restricted connection to the sea, one of a series of such basins in the region during Infracambrian time (Kent 1970; Murris 1980; Gorin et al. 1982; Mattes & Conway-Morris 1990). The original form and extent of the South Oman Salt Basin is unknown; the northwestern Ghudun-Kasfah margin is tectonic, formed during the Early Palaeozoic, and to the southeast there is no evidence of Ara Salt in the Huqf and Dhofar outcrops (Fig. 1; Gorin et al. 1982). For the Eastern Flank, the localized inversion and drape folding of overlying Palaeozoic sediments provides indirect evidence that salt underlay much of the area and the present-day salt edge results from basinward salt dissolution accompanying repeated uplift of the

Huqf-Dhofar axis (Figs 1 & 3; Murris 1980; Al-Marjeby & Nash 1986). Direct evidence of the former presence of salt comes from chaotically structured masses of dolomite, shale and anhydrite originally interbedded with the salt, the so-called Ara Remnants (Figs 2 & 3).

Sediments of the Haima Group comprise more than 1 km of Cambro-Ordovician continental sandstones which accumulated on an unstable substrate of salt (Fig. 2). The Haima forms a continuous deposit in the Salt Basin and is thickest in peripheral sinks between elongate salt pillows. On the Eastern Flank, the Haima occurs in rows of more isolated pods which are thought to have originally been separated by similar salt pillows now replaced by younger Haushi sediments (Figs 3−5).

The Lower Haima consists of fine grained sandstones and shales of the Karim Formation overlain by a coarsening-upward megasequence of the Haradh Formation. Penetrations of the

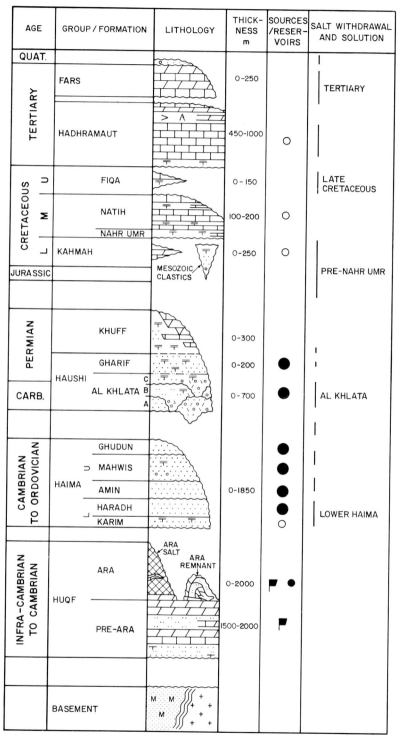

Fig. 2. General stratigraphic column for oil fields of the Eastern Flank hydrocarbon province of South Oman. The considerable variations in thickness and the presence of numerous unconformities being due to the interplay of salt movement, salt dissolution, sedimentation and erosion in this basin-flank location.

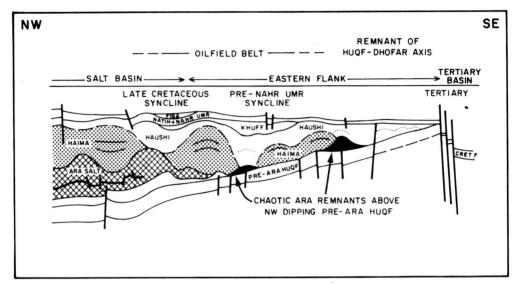

Fig. 3. Schematic NW−SE cross section of the Eastern Flank margin of the South Oman Salt Basin. A basinward thickening wedge of mounded and folded Palaeozoic sediments lies between the relatively undisturbed pre-Ara Huqf and Tertiary.

Karim in areas between and beyond Haima pods suggest that these low energy sandflat/lacustrine? deposits may have blanketed much of the Eastern Flank to a thickness of a few hundred metres. The Haradh forms part of a prograding alluvial apron (Fig. 6A) probably sourced from highlands to the west of the South Oman Salt Basin. Thickness changes over short distances within the Haradh indicate that salt withdrawal began and was probably most active during this period (Figs 4 & 5). The relative thinness of Haima overburden at this time, and the NE−SW and N−S trends of thick Haima in the Salt Basin and Haima pods on the Eastern Flank, suggest that salt movement was triggered by the reactivation of basement faults (cf. Brunstrom & Walmsley 1969; Jenyon 1986).

A major change in palaeogeography seems to have accompanied the accumulation of the Upper Haima. South Oman probably lost its identity as a separate depositional basin as the area became the southeastern flank of the greater Rub' al Khali basin and the sediment source area shifted to the Huqf−Dhofar axis. A base Amin unconformity is often traceable on seismic sections within the Salt Basin and wells on the Eastern Flank show truncation and overstep of the irregularly thickened Lower Haima. The Amin Formation consists of clean quartzose aeolian sandstones with a predominance of horizontally stratified and low-angle cross-stratified dune apron and interdune deposits

(Fig. 6B; cf. Kocurek 1986). Only in wells to the north of Rima do dipmeter logs over highly porous intervals show 25−30° sedimentary dips (oriented to the NW) typical of the slipface deposits of large aeolian dunes. The variable thickness of the Amin Formation from one Haima pod to another (100−750 m) and its abrupt unconformable? to transitional top (Nimr−Runib area), possibly result from the varying local balance of continuing salt withdrawal and sediment accumulation. The overlying Mahwis Formation, of Late Cambrian to Early Ordovician age (Hughes Clarke 1988), consists of fine grained shaly sands of sheetflood origin forming part of an extensive alluvial fan apron probably sourced from the southeast (Fig. 6C; Heward 1989). The top of the Mahwis Formation is truncated by later unconformities.

As a result of greater regional subsidence to the northwest and Late Palaeozoic erosion of the gently tilted Haima deposits, younger Haima sediments are preserved progressively to the northwest. Thus Ghudun and still younger Safiq sediments occur extensively in the South Oman Salt Basin and beyond (Hughes Clarke 1988), but are something of an oddity on the Eastern Flank. Probable Ghudun sands are known only from the northeastern part of the Qaharir field where they consist of relatively tabular units of bioturbated coastal? sands and intervening shales (Fig. 6D). It seems likely that intense local salt withdrawal or dissolution during the

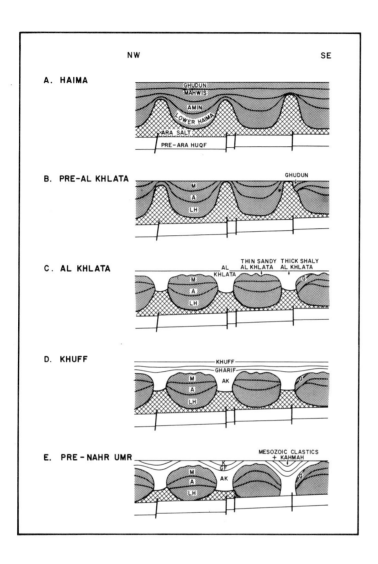

Fig. 4. Diagrammatic reconstruction of the pre-Nahr Umr evolution of the Eastern Flank. (A) Ara salt withdraws into elongate salt pillows and ridges as Haima continental clastics infill peripheral synclines. (B) Local salt withdrawal or dissolution-related subsidence preserves younger Haima deposits from extensive late Palaeozoic erosion. The crests of salt highs are at or close to the surface. (C) Rapid near-surface dissolution of salt forms elongate Al Khlata basins above salt pillows. The tops of Haima pods being subjected to periodic deep erosion by glacial meltwater? channels. (D) Permian Gharif and Khuff sediments are deposited widely and are thickened slightly above remnant salt pillows/compacting shaly Al Khlata. (E) Subsurface dissolution of the most upflank salt pillows probably accomplished from below by meteoric water moving basinward through pre-Ara aquifers. Dissolution preserves Gharif, Khuff and Kahmah sediments from erosion and probably causes the formation of dissolution basins in which the Mesozoic Clastics accumulated. Haima pods become increasingly inverted to form turtle-back anticlines.

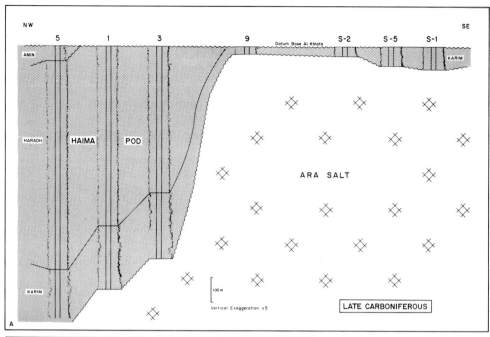

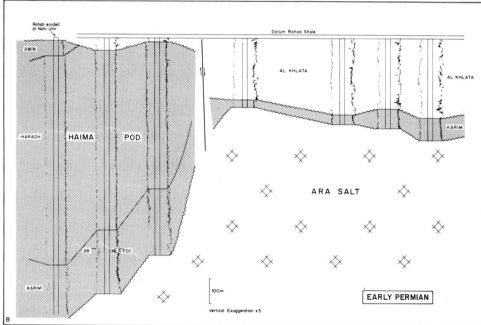

Late Palaeozoic permitted the preservation of deposits otherwise eroded from this uplifted basin margin.

For the Haima then, the basic geometry of Haima pods (typically a few tens of kilometres long, a few kilometres wide and up to 1850 m thick) appears, by analogy with features in the Salt Basin, to be the result of salt withdrawing into adjacent salt pillows (Fig. 4A). The outlines of the pods seem to reflect the trends of basement faults lying beneath the salt. The boundaries of pods are quite abrupt, as was shown by appraisal drilling in the Amal field. There, several wells penetrated very thick Haushi se-

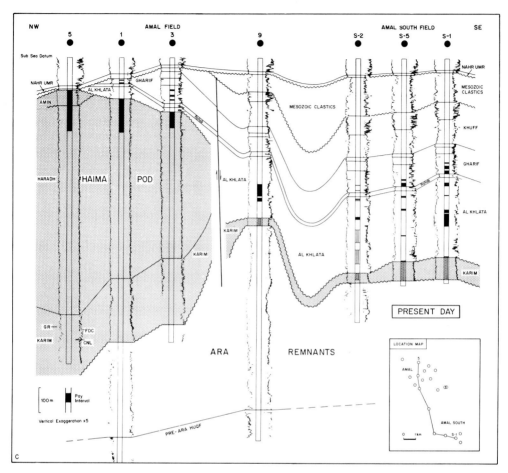

Fig. 5. Reconstruction of the development of the Amal−Amal South area (one margin of a Haima pod and its adjacent dissolution syncline. (A) Dated Late Carboniferous and with a base Al Khlata datum but probably only a slightly truncated version of geometries during the late Haima. Reconstruction approximate as there may well have been relief on the base Al Khlata unconformity. (B) Considerable thickening of Al Khlata deposits away from the Haima pod in response to near-surface salt dissolution. (C) Present-day configuration with a stratigraphically complex and structured interval lying between only slightly divergent pre-Ara Huqf and Nahr Umr. The Amal field is located at the crest of the Haima pod and the Amal−9 and Amal South accumulations are where Al Khlata and Gharif reservoirs are draped over mounds of Ara Remnants. GR, gamma-ray; CNL, neutron; FDC, density logs.

quences less than 1 km from other wells that penetrated very thin Haushi deposits overlying hundreds of metres of Haima (Fig. 5). The considerable variations in thickness of the Haima formations, when correlated from one Haima pod to another seems likely to result from the varying local balance between salt withdrawal and sedimentation, although thicknesses are no doubt influenced by differing proximities to the depocentres of each pod (cf. Trusheim 1960). There is no evidence to-date that salt removal was anywhere sufficiently rapid

to lead to facies differentiation and this may be taken to suggest salt withdrawal rather than dissolution during this period. Younger Haima sediments are preserved only locally in areas of subsequent salt removal, and the relatively deeper Late Palaeozoic erosion of the Eastern Flank area, compared with the Salt Basin, results in the transition from continuous Haima sands to more isolate Haima pods (Fig. 4B). The latter has an important impact on the overlying Late Carboniferous glacial deposits of the Al Khlata Formation, for where salt pillows (separating Haima pods) were at or near surface, they seem to have been subject to rapid dissolution by abundant glacial meltwater.

Al Khlata salt dissolution

Al Khlata glacial sediments accumulated over a time period of 25–40 Ma from Westphalian C to Sakmarian when Arabia, as part of Gondwanaland, occupied a palaeolatitude of approximately 50°S (Besems & Schuurman 1987; Levell *et al.* 1988). Regionally, the Al Khlata Formation seems to consist of three major facies associations: (i) thin incomplete 'basin-margin' deposits in the Huqf-area outcrops which include diamictites of lodgement origin (Braakman *et al.* 1982), (ii) thick predominantly glaciolacustrine deposits in the Eastern Flank and locally within the South Oman and Ghaba Salt Basins, where the Al Khlata accumulated on salt or discontinuous Haima, and (iii) moderately thick probable glaciofluvial sands in the Salt Basins where the Al Khlata was deposited on continuous Haima sands. Grounded ice may have moved along the Huqf–Dhofar axis towards the northeast, as interpreted by Braakman *et al.* (1982), or towards the southwest, as implied by large southwesterly tapering striae and southwesterly facing rock steps on glacial pavements at Ain Hindi and Mifrid, N of Al Khlata (Fig. 1).

In the Eastern Flank area the Al Khlata is generally thin (<150 m) and sandy where it overlies Haima pods, and thick (300–700 m) and shaly where it accumulated above salt pillows and now rests on Huqf or thin Haima (Figs 4C & 5). Above Haima pods, unconformities with considerable palaeorelief may underlie each of the three palynologically defined Al Khlata members (A,B and C Figs 2 & 7). The general form of this relief is of valleys up to 200 metres deep and a few hundreds of metres wide, with sides sloping at 5–25°. A number of these meltwater? valleys have been encountered in development drilling in the Marmul, Nimr, Runib and Rima oil fields, typically with N–S or NW–SE orientations (see Fig. 7).

During the early development drilling of Marmul it was suspected that Al Khlata sands were glaciofluvial deposits and diamictites·were tillites (de la Grandville 1982). However, cores have provided little evidence of either type of deposit and seem overwhelmingly to indicate glaciolacustrine sedimentation (Levell *et al.* 1988). Most sands are massive and are interpreted to be glaciolacustrine deltas or subaqueous fans, and occur in association with lacustrine siltstones and diamictites deposited

from floating ice (Figs 8A, & B). Depositional bodies appear small relative to development well spacings of 300–600 m, and detailed lateral correlations are frequently only possible over a few square km.

Thick shaly successions occur in areas between Haima pods and were originally interpreted to be the infill of a pre-Al Khlata palaeorelief modified by ice. However, the basinal character of the sediments, the relatively tabular nature of the Al Khlata members and the common presence of facies stacking suggest actively subsiding basins probably caused by dissolution of the underlying salt pillows (Figs 4C & 5B; cf. Broughton 1977). Sands are discontinuous and are interpreted to be glaciolacustrine delta, subaqueous fan and locally, turbidite accumulations. They are separated by thick sequences of rhythmically laminated claystones, massive siltstones, and diamictites, all of relatively greater lateral extent. Diamictites again seem deposited predominantly from floating ice.

It is interpreted that salt removal during the Al Khlata was sufficiently rapid to cause the differences in facies development between successions overlying Haima pods and those above salt pillows. The gross form of the latter deposits corresponds to the wasting pillow and they are elongate parallel to the trends of Haima pods and enclose them (Fig. 4C). One of the most notable characteristics of the Al Khlata Formation is its inherent lateral variability and it is uncertain to what extent aspects of this variability, the trends of valleys and the locations and geometries of small-scale depositional bodies, can be attributed to salt removal.

Pre-Nahr Umr and subsequent salt dissolution

The Gharif Formation of mid-Permian age records the transition between the glacial deposits of the Al Khlata and the arid coastal plain and shelf deposits of the Khuff (Fig. 2). The lowermost Gharif deposits on the Eastern Flank consist of grey lacustrine siltstones and thin coarsening-upward deltaic sandstones (Fig. 8C). A prominently bioturbated interval may be equivalent to the Haushi limestone transgression present in the subsurface over much of Oman and outcropping in the Huqf area (Morton 1959; Hughes Clarke 1988). Higher in the Gharif, the grey lacustrine siltstones are replaced by red and green mottled siltstones and claystones, locally with calcrete soil profiles. Sands are cross-stratified and cross-laminated, commonly fine upward and are interpreted to

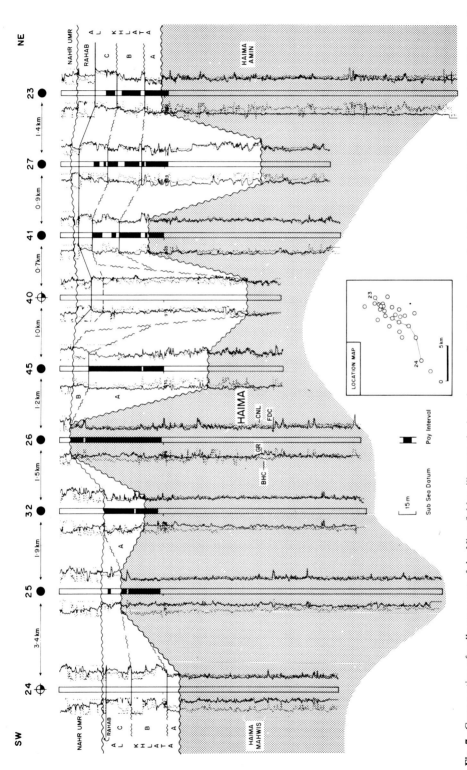

Fig. 7. Cross section of wells over part of the Nimr field to illustrate the irregular unconformities beneath and within the Al Khlata Formation above Haima pods. Wells such as Nimr−40 are within the structural closure but are dry through encountering a valley filled with glaciolacustrine siltstones. The Haima dips gently to the southwest beneath the Al Khlata, and the transition is present between the aeolian Amin Formation and the sheetflood deposits of the Mahwis Formation (represented by the gradual reversal of the gamma-ray and sonic logs). GR, gamma-ray; BHC, sonic; FDC, density; CNL, neutron logs.

he river channel deposits (Fig. 8D). Most sand bodies appear to be composite stacks of channel sands and it is extremely difficult to discern much about channel type from cores or from correlations of typically spaced development wells. Both meandering and braided channel deposits are possibly present and, in the comparatively thin succession of the Huqf-area outcrops, these types of deposit appear to alternate in vertical sequence, with palaeoflow to the NW off the Huqf−Dhofar axis.

Where the Gharif is complete on the Eastern Flank, it varies from 120−210 m in thickness, a variation notably less than that of the Al Khlata, but probably still recording some minor salt removal and differential compaction of shaly Al Khlata sequences. Gharif deposits pass transitionally up into the Khuff, which in south Oman consists of arid coastal-plain claystones gradually transgressed by marine limestones and dolomites.

Gharif and Khuff sediments probably accumulated over most of the area of the Eastern Flank and owe their present rather limited distribution to preservation from erosion within salt-dissolution synclines (Figs 3−5). This period of major erosion in southern Arabia occurred during the Triassic and Jurassic and accompanied the opening of Tethys and the rifting of Arabia from India approximately parallel to the Huqf−Dhofar axis (Murris 1980; Boulin 1981; Beydoun 1985; Mountain & Prell 1990). Rain falling on pre-Ara Huqf carbonates exposed upflank probably led to active subsurface salt removal. Dissolution seems to have been sufficiently intense to have created sedimentary basins at surface in the central part of the pre-Nahr Umr syncline in which Jurassic to Lower Cretaceous fluvial and lacustrine sediments accumulated (Mesozoic Clastics, Figs 3−5). Transgressive Lower Cretaceous carbonates of the Kahmah Group are preserved in a similar setting towards the northeastern and southwestern ends of the syncline. The mid-Cretaceous Nahr Umr shale onlaps this truncated and folded Palaeozoic sequence of the Eastern Flank and is significant in forming the seal for many of the hydrocarbon accumulations (Al-Marjeby & Nash 1986).

The large scale geometry of Gharif deposits is therefore one of preservation as elongate belts within salt-dissolution synclines and forming dipping rims around Haima pods. By this stage the pods were becoming increasingly inverted to form classic turtle-back anticlines (Fig. 4E; Trusheim 1960; Woodbury et al. 1980).

Further phases of dissolution of more basinward salt pillows occurred during the Late Cretaceous and Tertiary, accompanying periods of regional uplift perhaps related to the development of the NW Indian Ocean. These Late Cretaceous and Tertiary dissolution synclines are manifested by the selective preservation or thickening of stratigraphic units (Fig. 3). The rather localized nature of Tertiary salt removal may reflect limited freshwater recharge resulting from the downfaulting of Huqf aquifers into the Tertiary Basin or their capping by the base Tertiary Shammar shale.

Hydrocarbon traps

More than 2×10^9 m^3 of oil (12×10^9 bbls) is estimated to be present in the 24 producing fields and 20 or so undeveloped discoveries of the Eastern Flank hydrocarbon province. Many of the accumulations are of moderate size but include the significant oil fields of Marmul, Nimr and Rima. The oil is generally heavy (12−30° API) and viscous (10−10 000 mPa s) and represents a considerable resource for conventional and enhanced oil recovery (Nandyal et al. 1983). Four types of hydrocarbon trap occur, all related to salt removal: large turtle-back anticlines resulting from the inversion of former peripheral synclines, truncation traps rimming eroded turtle-back anticlines, small anticlines draped over residual masses of dolomite and shale, and porous and fractured dolomites within such residues after salt removal (Al-Marjeby & Nash 1986). Combinations of these various types of trap are common.

The largest fields occur in Haima and Al Khlata reservoirs at the crests of inverted Haima pods (Figs 5C, 7 & 9A). The timing of the dominant phases of inversion varies from one pod to another, but many were already considerably inverted and partly truncated prior to the deposition of the sealing Nahr Umr shale. The hydrocarbon columns of these fields depend on the presence of sealing shales within the flanking Al Khlata and Gharif Formations. This type of accumulation occurs at depths of 700−1600 m, and their Palaeozoic reservoir sands probably lie close to their maximum burial. As a consequence, Haima and Al Khlata sands are only barely consolidated with porosities of 23−30% and permeabilities of 0.1−15 Darcies. Locally, the reservoirs are fractured, probably as the result of periods of rapid salt removal (Fig. 6A & B; Makel 1987). There is often considerable variability within the reservoirs due to the presence of several unconformities associated with the Al Khlata and to rapid lithological changes within the glacial deposits (Fig. 7). The Haima reservoir consists of

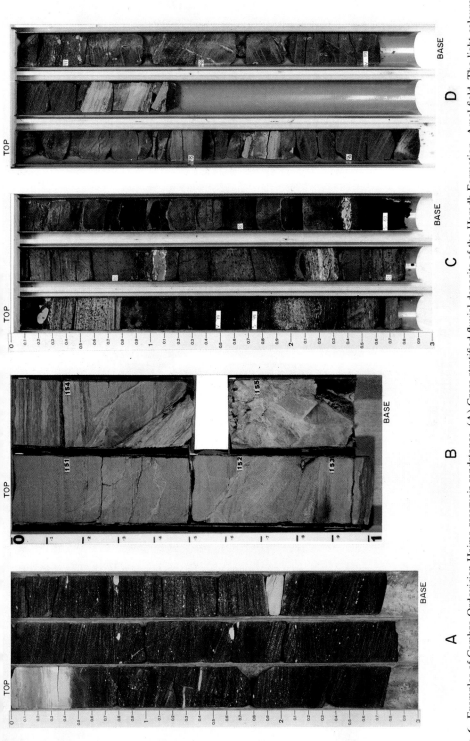

Fig. 6. Examples of Cambro-Ordovician Haima reservoir sandstones. (A) Cross-stratified fluvial deposits of the Haradh Formation, Amal field. The light coloured granules and pebbles are intraformational shale clasts and the dark brown stain is from heavy oil. Scales for A, C and D are in feet. (B) Faulted and fractured aeolian dune and wet interdune deposits of the Amin Formation, Nimr field. Interdune silts and sands with wavy lamination and symmetrical ripples, as above label 154. Scale in metres. (C) Thin sheetflood sequences defined by intraformational conglomerates and shale interbeds, Mahwis Formation, Marmul field. The lighter coloured convex-up features are core disturbance phenomena. (D) Fine to medium grained coastal sands with *Skolithos* burrows, Ghudun Formation, Qaharir field. The varying sections of the trace fossil and the apparent cross-bedding are the result of the blind slabbing of a rubber sleeve core in which successive core pieces of a dipping formation have rotated relative to one another.

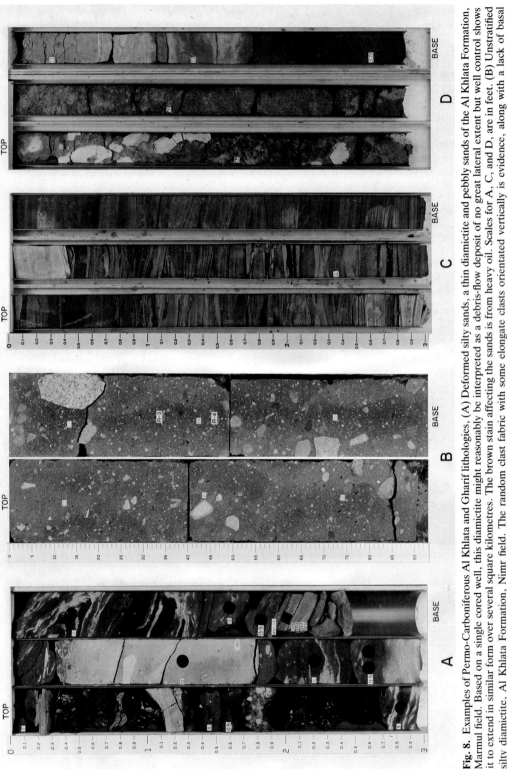

Fig. 8. Examples of Permo-Carboniferous Al Khlata and Gharif lithologies, (A) Deformed silty sands, a thin diamictite and pebbly sands of the Al Khlata Formation, Marmul field. Based on a single cored well, this diamictite might reasonably be interpreted as a debris-flow deposit of no great lateral extent but well control shows it to extend in similar form over several square kilometres. The brown stain affecting the sands is from heavy oil. Scales for A, C, and D, are in feet. (B) Unstratified silty diamictite, Al Khlata Formation, Nimr field. The random clast fabric with some elongate clasts orientated vertically is evidence, along with a lack of basal shearing, thicknesses commonly of a few tens of metres and association with other glaciolacustrine deposits, that such diamictites formed by rain-out of debris from floating ice. Scale in centimetres. (C) Fine-grained lacustrine sands with abundant wave-formed cross-stratification and *Planolites* burrow, Gharif Formation, Rahab field. (D) Part of an oil stained fluvial channel sand fining upward into red and green floodplain claystones with calcrete field. The white sands are cemented by carbonate.

whichever formation or formations occur at the crest of the structure (cf. Figs 5C & 7), and the rest of the underlying Haima provides a large potential aquifer during production. Depending on the viscosity of the oil and the vertical permeability of the reservoir, perhaps enhanced by fracturing, water may be rapidly coned into producing oil wells (Makel 1987).

Extensive truncation traps rim many of the inverted pods of Haima strata (Fig. 9A). They comprise dipping Gharif sands sealed laterally by Al Khlata, Gharif and Khuff claystones and capped by the Nahr Umr shale (de la Grandville 1982). Their fluid contacts may be shallower, similar too or deeper than the adjacent main Haima/Al Khlata accumulation, and the oil is commonly slightly heavier and more viscous.

Small anticlines consisting of Al Khlata and Gharif reservoirs draped over Ara Remnants occur particularly within the pre-Nahr Umr and Late Cretaceous dissolution synclines (Figs 5C & 9B). The reservoirs are separated by intraformational shale seals and charged with oils of varying density. Good Al Khlata sands can be prolific producers of oil but they are relatively uncommon and laterally discontinous. Lacustrine delta and fluvial sands within the basal part of the Gharif are of more general occurrence. Less commonly, the lowermost formations of the Haima Group are present and oil productive (Fig. 9C).

Ara Remnants comprise structurally jumbled arrangements of dolomite, organic-rich shales and anhydrite which represent concentrations of residual lithologies after salt dissolution. Production has been obtained in the Simsim field from a porous and fractured dolomite interval sealed by the fine grained clastics of the Haima Karim Formation (Fig. 9C).

Analogues

Similar halokinetic and salt-removal features are described from successions overlying the Upper Permian Zechstein evaporites of the North Sea, the mid- Devonian Elk Point evaporites of Western Canada and the Northern USA, and the Permian Clear Fork to Salado evaporites of Western Texas and New Mexico, USA.

Zechstein evaporites range up to several thousands of metres in thickness and are overlain by dominantly clastic Mesozoic and Tertiary sediments. Salt pillows and piercements occur widely in the various sub-basins of the North Sea and Northern Germany and have trends which commonly correspond to regional fault patterns (Trusheim 1960; Brunstrom &

Walmsley 1969; Taylor 1984; Jenyon 1986; Jenyon & Cresswell 1987). Peripheral sinks between salt highs are variously filled with Mesozoic and Tertiary sediments, depending on the timing of salt movement, and some peripheral sinks have been inverted. Trusheim (1960) figures oil fields in Northern Germany in turtle-back anticlines and associated truncation traps. Similarly the Fulmar and Clyde oil fields, lying close to the western margin of the Central Graben of the North Sea, consist of pods of Triassic shales and Upper Jurassic reservoir sands which were largely inverted and truncated prior to the Late Cretaceous (Johnson et al. 1986; Smith 1987). Anomalously thick shallow-marine coarsening-upward sequences within the Fulmar reservoir probably represent a balance between localized subsidence (salt removal?) and sedimentation. Salt removal is interpreted to have been by withdrawal (Johnson et al. 1986) or withdrawal/solution (Smith 1987). Dissolution seems likely to have occurred at or near the surface, and to have been accomplished, at least in part, by seawater. Farther to the northwest, but again near the western margin of the Central Graben, the Fulmar Sand reservoir of the Gannet West field occurs as an elongate pod preserved above a salt ridge and between peripheral sinks filled with Triassic sediments (Armstrong et al. 1987). Later salt movement in the Gannet area has significantly influenced the geometries of Tertiary turbidite sands and resulted in a number of structural closures subsequently charged with oil and gas. A wide variety of structures and features resulting from Zechstein salt movement and removal are figured by Jenyon (1986) and Jenyon & Cresswell (1987).

Collapse breccias in Zechstein carbonates are reported from the margins of the Zechstein sub-basins where slope and basinal carbonates are interbedded with anhydrite (Smith 1972; Taylor 1984; Cooper 1986). This more brittle response to evaporite dissolution may be related to the cavernous removal of gypsum and also reflect the relatively early and greater degree of cementation of carbonate sediments.

The Middle Devonian Elk Point evaporites of Western Canada and the Northern USA consist of a thinner cyclic succession of shales, carbonates and evaporites with little evidence of salt movement. The overlying sediments are dominantly carbonates and evaporites in the Palaeozoic, and clastics in the Mesozoic and Tertiary. Dissolution has occurred periodically from the Late Devonian onwards and its effects are widespread around basin margins or wherever leaching waters have been focussed by

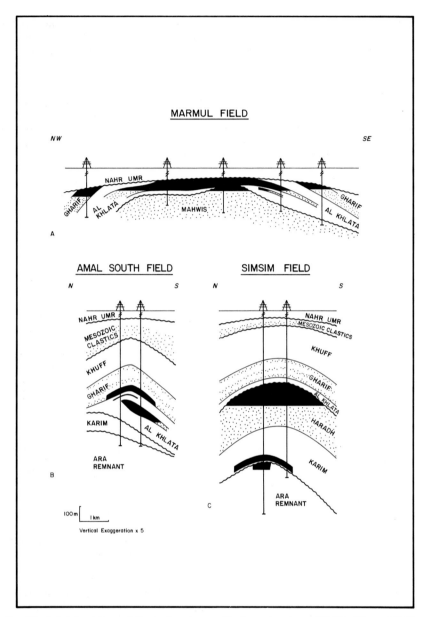

Fig. 9. Simplified sketch sections of the various types of hydrocarbon trap. (A) The Marmul field occurs in Haima and Al Khlata reservoirs at the crest of a truncated turtle-back anticline. The flanking Gharif truncation traps have both deeper and shallower oil-water contacts than the main accumulation. (B) The Amal South structure results from drape over a combination of Ara Remnant and irregularly thickened Al Khlata. The reservoirs occur in the Al Khlata and Lower Gharif. (C) The Simsim field comprises a pod of Haima reservoirs draped over Ara Remnant lithologies and is of note as locally the Ara Remnants are oil productive.

porous substrate and tectonic features. This has led to collapse brecciation of carbonates, localized accumulation and thickening of deposits, and the formation of both small-scale and regional structural closures (de Mille *et al*. 1964; Parker 1967; Smith & Pullen 1967; Langstroth 1971; Bishop 1974; Broughton 1977). The Athabasca, Cold Lake and Lloydminster heavy oil accumulations occur in Mannville sands deposited within a Cretaceous salt-dissolution basin (Orr *et al*. 1978; Jackson 1984) and a number of small oil accumulations occur in structural and stratigraphic features related to salt removal (Edmunds 1980).

In the Anadarko, Dalhart and Palo Duro basins of Western Texas, Permian sediments consist of approximately 1000 metres of interbedded salt, anhydrite, dolomite, limestone and red beds (Dutton *et al*. 1979; Gustavson *et al*. 1980). These strata crop out or are overlain by a few hundred metres of Mesozoic and Tertiary clastic sediments. From the published cross sections, there is no evidence of halokinesis. Evaporite dissolution has occurred from the Late Cretaceous onwards and has resulted in collapse breccias and breccia pipes, faulting and fracturing, complex folding, stratigraphic thickening and surface topographic features. Gypsum dissolution appears to be a surface or very near surface phenomenon, whereas salt dissolution is occurring at depths of 100−500 m related to groundwater flow.

Subsurface dissolution of Permian salt intervals in the nearby Delaware Basin has resulted in widespread dissolution residues and collapse breccias, and large dissolution depressions filled with Cenozoic sediments (Maley & Huffington 1953; Anderson *et al*. 1978; Anderson & Kirkland 1980). Underlying aquifers are exposed to rainfall recharge along the uplifted western and southern margins of the basin and dissolution is occurring progressively basinward. It also occurs within the basin adjacent to upstanding reef carbonates.

Aspects that are common between these examples and the Eastern Flank of the South Oman Salt Basin include localized stratigraphic thickening, the preservation of stratigraphic intervals which are otherwise eroded, the presence of salt-removal basins, control by salt removal of facies development and the formation of structural closures on a variety of scales. Differences, such as the formation of salt highs, peripheral sinks and collapse breccias, may relate to the original thickness and character of the evaporites, basin history, lithology of the overlying succession and the proximity of the interval of interest to the evaporite sequence.

The Eastern Flank features may be typical of the margins of basins where a thick mobile salt sequence is overlain closely by clastic sediments.

Conclusions

The periodic removal of Infra cambrian Ara Salt at the margin of the South Oman Salt Basin has played a dominant role in shaping the complex geology of the Eastern Flank area and providing traps for hydrocarbons.

Salt movement during the Cambrian was most probably triggered by the reactivation of basement faults. Salt withdrew into elongate pillows and ridges and the adjacent peripheral sinks were filled with Cambro-Ordovician continental sands. Late Palaeozoic erosion left the salt pillows at or close to surface and separated by pods of Haima sands (the truncated fills of peripheral sinks).

Near-surface salt dissolution by glacial meltwaters during the Permo-Carboniferous led to the generally glaciolacustrine conditions over the Eastern Flank area and specifically to thin complex sandy sequences capping Haima pods and thick layered shaly sequences above wasting salt pillows. Dissolution seems to have been sufficiently rapid to have influenced facies distribution and caused facies stacking. Subsequent subsurface salt dissolution during the Jurassic and Cretaceous led to the preservation of belts of Permian and Early Cretaceous deposits within dissolution synclines and to the formation of dissolution-controlled basins in which Jurassic to Cretaceous continental sediments accumulated. Further periods of salt dissolution during the Late Cretaceous and Tertiary caused similar preservation and thickening of deposits.

With the removal of salt, the former peripheral synclines were progressively inverted to form large turtle-back anticlines and other sediments were draped over mounds of insoluble evaporite residues. The inversion of pods of Haima and the foundering and draping of strata has resulted in localized faulting and fracturing of the sediments. Large volumes of the oil that has migrated from Infracambrian source rocks since the Late Cretaceous has been trapped within turtle-back anticlines, flanking truncation traps, draped anticlines and evaporite residues.

There are many parallels between Eastern Flank geology and salt removal phenomena known from the North Sea, Western Canada and the USA.

The author is grateful for permission to publish this paper from the Oman Ministry of Petroleum and Minerals and the managements of Petroleum Development Oman, Shell International Petroleum Mij and Shell UK Exploration and Production. The paper represents a synthesis of the ideas of many present and former geologists in PDO and their contribution is duly acknowledged. Jose Lopez Lopez and Felicity Heward provided stimulating companionship on a number of excursions to the Huqf-area outcrops. The manuscript benefitted from reviews by D. Boote, K. Glennie, M. Leeder and G. Mossop.

References

AL-MARJEBY, A. & NASH, D. 1986. A summary of the geology and oil habitat of the Eastern Flank hydrocarbon province of South Oman. *Marine and Petroleum Geology*, **3**, 306–14.

ANDERSON, R. Y., KIETZKE, K. K. & RHODES, D. J. 1978. Development of dissolution breccias. Northern Delaware Basin, New Mexico and Texas. *New Mexico Bureau Mines and Mineral Resources, Circular* **159**, 47–52.

ANDERSON, R. Y. & KIRKLAND, D. W. 1980. Dissolution of salt deposits by brine density flow. *Geology*, **8**, 66–9.

ARMSTRONG, L. A., TEN HAVE, A. & JOHNSON, H. D. 1987. The geology of the Gannet field, Central North Sea, UK Sector. *In*: BROOKS, J. & GLENNIE, K. W. (eds) *Petroleum Geology of North West Europe*. Graham and Trotman, **1**, 533–48.

BESEMS, R. E. & SCHUURMAN, W. M. L. 1987. Palynostratigraphy of Late Palaeozoic glacial deposits of the Arabian peninsula with special reference to Oman. *Palynology*, **11**, 37–53.

BEYDOUN, Z. R. 1985. The geological setting and tectonic framework of the Middle East. *In*: *Source and Habitat of Petroleum in the Arab Countries*. Proceedings of the Organisation of Arab Petroleum Exporting Countries (OAPEC) Conference, Kuwait 7–11 October 1984, 5–72.

BISHOP, R. A. 1974. Hummingbird structure, Saskatchewan, single vs. multiple stage salt solution-collapse. *In*: PARSLOW, G. R. (ed.) *Fuels: A Geological Appraisal*. Saskatchewan Geological Society Special Publication **2**, 179–97.

BOULIN, J. 1981. Afghanistan structure, Greater India concept and eastern Tethys evolution. *Tectonophysics*, 72, 261–287.

BRAAKMAN, J. H., LEVELL, B. K., MARTIN, J. H., POTTER, T. L. & VLIET, A VAN. 1982. Late Palaeozoic Gondwana glaciation in Oman. *Nature*, **299**, 48–50.

BROUGHTON, P. L. 1977. Origin of coal basins by salt solution. *Nature*, **270**, 420–23.

BRUNSTROM, R. G. W. & WALMSLEY, P. J. 1969. Permian evaporites in North Sea basin. *Bulletin of the American Association of Petroleum Geologists*, **53**, 870–83.

COOPER, A. H. 1986. Subsidence and foundering of strata caused by the dissolution of Persian gypsum in the Ripon and Bedale areas, North Yorkshire. *In*: HARWOOD, G. M. & SMITH, D. B. (eds) *The English Zechstein and Related Topics*.

Geological Society, London, Special Publication **22**, 127–139.

DE MILLE, G., SHOULDICE, J. R. & NELSON, H. W. 1964. Collapse structures related to evaporites of the Prairie Formation, Saskatchewan, *Bulletin of the Geological Society of America*, **75**, 307–16.

DUTTON, S. P., FINLEY, R. J., GALLOWAY, W. E., GUSTRAVSON, T. C., HANDFORD, C. R. & PRESLEY, M. W. Geology and Hydrology of the Palo Duro Basin, Texas Panhandle. *Bureau of Economic Geology of the University of Texas Geological Circular* **79–1**.

EDMUNDS, R. H. 1980. Salt removal and oil entrapment. *In*: MIALL, A. D. (ed.) *Facts and Principles of World Petroleum Occurrence*. Memoir of the Canadian Society of Petroleum Geologists, **6**, 988.

GORIN, G. E. RATZ, L. G. & WALTER, M. R. 1982. Late Precambrian-Cambrian sediments of Huqf Group, Sultanate of Oman. *Bulletin of the American Association of Petroleum Geologists*, **66**, 2609–27.

GRANDVILLE, B. F. de la. 1982. Appraisal and development of a structural and stratigraphic trap oil field with reservoirs in glacial to periglacial clastics. *In*: HALBOUTY, M. T. (ed.) *The Deliberate Search for the Subtle Trap*. Memoir of the Americam Association of Petroleum Geologists, **32**, 267–86.

GRANTHAM, P. J., LIJMBACH, G. W. M., POSTHUMA, J., HUGHES CLARKE, M. W. & WILLINK, R. J. 1988. Origin of crude oils in Oman. *Journal of Petroleum Geology*, **11**, 61–80.

GUSTAVSON, T. C., FINLEY, R. J. & McGILLIS, K. A. 1980. Regional dissolution of Permian Salt in the Anadarko, Dalhart, and Palo Duro Basins of the Texas Panhandle. *Bureau of Economic Geology of the University of Texas Report of Investigations*, **106**.

HAWKINS, T. R. W., HINDLE, D. & STRUGNELL, R. 1981. Outlines of the stratigraphy and structural framework of southern Dhofar (Sultanate of Oman). *Geologie en Mijnbouw*, **60**, 247–56.

HEWARD, A. P. 1989. Early Ordovician alluvial fan deposits of the Marmul oil field, South Oman. *Journal of the Geological Society, London*, **146**, 557–565.

HUGHES CLARKE, M. W. 1988. Stratigraphy and rock unit nomenclature in the oil-producing area of Interior Oman. *Journal of Petroleum Geology*, **11**, 5–60.

JACKSON, P. C. 1984. Paleogeography of the Lower Cretaceous Mannville Group of Western Canada. *In*: MASTERS, J. A. (ed.) *Elmworth – Case Study of a Deep Basin Gas Field*. Memoir of the American Assoiation of Petroleum Geologists, **38**, 49–77.

JENYON, M. K. 1986. *Salt Tectonics*. Elsevier Applied Science.

—— & CRESSWELL, P. M. 1987. The Southern Zechstein Salt Basin of the British North Sea, as observed in regional seismic traverses. *In*: BROOKS, J. & GLENNIE, K. W. (eds) *Petroleum Geology of North West Europe*. Graham and

Trotman, **1**, 277–92.

JOHNSON, H. D., MACKAY, T. A. & STEWART, D. J. 1986. The Fulmar oil-field (Central North Sea): geological aspects of its discovery, appraisal and development. *Marine and Petroleum Geology*, **3**, 99–125.

KENT, P. E. 1970. The salt plugs of the Persian Gulf region. *Transactions of the Leicester Literary and Philosophical Society*, **64**, 56–88.

KOCUREK, G. 1986. Origins of low-angle stratification in aeolian deposits. *In*: NICKLING, W. E. (ed.) *Aeolian Geomorphology*. Proceedings of 17th Binghampton Symposium on Geomorphology, Allen and Unwin, 177–93.

LANGSTROTH, W. T. 1971. Seismic study along a portion of Devonian salt front in north Dakota. *Geophysics*, **36**, 330–8.

LEES, G. M. 1928. The geology and tectonics of Oman and parts of Southeastern Arabia. *Quarterly Journal of the Geological Society of London*, **84**, 585–670.

LEVELL, B.K., BRAAKMAN, J. H. & RUTTEN, K. W. 1988. Oil-bearing sediments of Gondwana glaciation in Oman. *Bulletin of the American Association of Petroleum Geologists*, **72**, 775–96.

MAKEL, G. H. 1987. Fractured clastic reservoirs in South Oman: Possible models of origin and implications. *Society of Petroleum Engineers Paper 15700 presented at the 5th SPE Middle East Oil Show*, Manama, Bahrain, 7–10 March 1987, 121–8.

MALEY, V. C. & HUFFINGTON, R. M. 1953. Cenozoic fill and evaporate solution in the Delaware Basin, Texas and New Mexico. *Bulletin of the Geological Society of America*, **64**, 539–46.

MATTES, B. W. & CONWAY MORRIS, S. 1990. Carbonate/evaporite deposition in the Late Precambrian—Early Cambrian Ara Formation of Southern Oman. *In*: ROBERTSON, A. H. F., SEARLE, M. P. & RIES, A. C. (eds) *The Geology and Tectonics of the Oman Region*. Geological Society, London, Special Publication, **49**, 617–636.

MORTON, D. M. 1959. The geology of Oman. *Proceedings of 5th World Petroleum Congress*, New York, Section 1, 277–90.

MOUNTAIN, G. S. & PRELL, W. L. 1990. A multiphase plate tectonic history of the southeast continental margin of Oman. *In*: ROBERTSON, A. H. F, SEARLE, M. P. & RIES, A. C. (eds) *The Gelogy and Tectonics of the Oman Region*. Geological Society, London, Special Publication, **49**, 725–743.

MURRIS, R. J. 1980. Middle East: Stratigraphic evolution and oil habitat. *Bulletin of the American Association of Petroleum Geologists*, **64**, 597–618.

NANDYAL, M., THURBER, S. S., HINAI, K. M. AL-. & JAFFER, N. A. 1983. Development of heavy oil reserves in South Oman. *Society of Petroleum Engineers Paper 114174 presented at the 1983 SPE Middle East Oil Technical Conference*, Manama, Bahrain, 14–17 March 1983, 259–66.

ORR, R. D., JOHNSTON, J. R. & MANKO, E. M. 1978. Lower Cretaceous geology and heavy oil potential of the Lloydminster area. *Journal of Canadian Petroleum Technology*, January–March 1978, 73–89.

PARKER, J. M. 1967. Salt solution and subsidence structures, Wyoming, North Dakota and Montana. *Bulletin of the American Association of Petroleum Geologists*, **51**, 1929–47.

SMITH, D. B. 1972. Foundered strata, collapse-breccias and subsidence features of the English Zechstein. *In*: Richter-Bernburg (ed.) *Geology of Saline Deposits*. Proceedings of UNESCO Hanover Symposium 1968, 255–69.

SMITH, D. G. & PULLEN, J. R. 1967. Hummingbird structure of southeast Saskatchewan. *Bulletin of Canadian Petroleum Geology*, **15**, 468–82.

SMITH, R. L. 1987. The structural development of the Clyde field. *In*: BROOKS, J. & GLENNIE, K. W. (eds) *Petroleum Geology of the North West Europe*. Graham & Trotman, **1**, 523–31.

TAYLOR, J. C. M. 1984. Late Permian — Zechstein. *In*: GLENNIE, K. W. (ed.) *Introduction to the Petroleum Geology of the North Sea*. Blackwell, 61–83.

TRUSHEIM, F. 1960. Mechanism of salt migration in northern Germany. *Bulletin of the American Association of Petroleum Geologists*, **44**, 1519–40.

WOODBURY, H. O., MURRAY, I. B. & OSBORNE, R. E. 1980. Diapirs and their relation to hydrocarbon accumulation. *In*: MIALL, A. D. (ed.) *Facts and Principles of World Petroleum Occurrence*. Memoir of the Canadian Society of Petroleum Geologists, **6**, 119–42.

Structures in the Huqf–Haushi Uplift, east Central Oman

A. C. RIES[1] & R. M. SHACKLETON[2]

[1] Earth Sciences and Resources Institute, University of Reading, 19 Upper Redlands Road, Reading RG1 5JJ, UK

[2] The Croft Barn, Church Lane, East Hendred, Oxon OX12 8LA, UK

Abstract: The extensive, very gentle Huqf–Haushi Uplift shows the effects of intraplate deformation from Infracambrian times onwards. The Uplift itself, apparently complementary to subsidence of the Ghaba Salt Basin to the west and the Masirah Trough to the east, began in the Infracambrian and continued intermittently until the Late Cretaceous. Local open folds are shown to be Palaeozoic, probably pre-Ordovician. The main deformation in the Uplift is by faulting. Two closely related sets, one NNE–SSW, the other N–S are essentially strike-slip in sense. The NNE–SSW faults, associated with half-domes and with folds making a small angle clockwise from the faults, are transpressional left-lateral strike-slip faults and the N–S set are probably also mainly left-lateral strike-slip faults. The array of faults is associated with the Masirah Fault, itself interpreted as a left-lateral transform fault. The faulting occurred in the Late Cretaceous. Subsequent deformation was slight.

The Huqf–Haushi Uplift (Figs 1 & 2) is defined by an inlier of Infracambrian–Cambrian Huqf Group strata, which extends for c. 180 km, NNE from near Duqm before disappearing under the Wahiba Sands. Its maximum width is about 40 km, or 70 km including the separate small inlier in the Haushi Dome. Crystalline basement was penetrated. c. 0.5 km below surface, in a borehole drilled through the Infracambrian Abu Mahara Formation in the Khufai Dome near the centre of the inlier (Gorin et al. 1982). The inlier is surrounded by onlapping younger sequences ranging from Ordovician to Cretaceous. Patches of Palaeocene (?) rocks rest unconformably on the eroded older rocks. To the west, Miocene beds overlie the Upper Cretaceous sediments.

To the west of the Huqf–Haushi Uplift is the Ghaba Salt Basin and to the east the Masirah Trough. Subsurface evidence suggests that the main boundary between the Huqf–Haushi Uplift and the Masirah Trough is a NNE-trending supposedly extensional basement fault, which was already active, and controlled deposition during the Infracambrian (Gorin et al. 1982). The eastern margin of the Masirah Trough is formed by the Masirah Fault.

The Infracambrian and Phanerozoic sediments exposed in the Huqf–Haushi Uplift record a history of intermittent uplift while the basins on either side were subsiding. If the Ghaba Salt Basin, the Huqf–Haushi Uplift and the Masirah Basin are extensional structures, as seems likely, the Uplift must be not only older than, but entirely independent of, the transpression which produced the dominantly strike-slip brittle fractures so characteristic of the area, transpression which is here related to the Masirah Fault.

The structures seen in the Huqf–Haushi Uplift may be classified as follows:

(vi)	NNE–SSW and N–S faults	} relation unknown	Post-Oligocene
(v)	very weak folds		Post-Palaeocene
(iv)	NE–SW normal faults		Post-Maastrichtian
(iii)	N–S faults with associated half-domes and oblique (clockwise) folds	}	Pre-uppermost Cretaceous
(ii)	NNE–SSW faults		
(i)	WSW–ENE to NNE–SSW open folds		Palaeozoic

From ROBERTSON, A. H. F., SEARLE, M. P. & RIES, A. C. (eds), 1990, *The Geology and Tectonics of the Oman Region.* Geological Society Special Publication No 49, pp 653–664

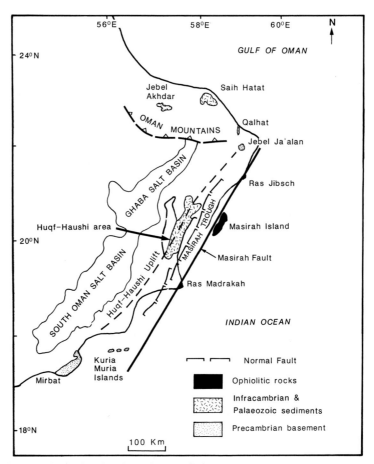

Fig. 1. Map of eastern Oman showing the main tectonic features.

Palaeozoic folds (pre-Permian and ?pre-Ordovician)

The principal folds in the Huqf–Haushi area (Fig. 3) trend WSW–ENE in the SW (Anqau and Khufai areas) and c. NNE–SSW in the N but the two appear continuous, curving from one direction to the other. Their axial traces are displaced by the N–S sets of pre-Late Cretaceous faults. Neither the Ordovician purple sandstones (Mahatta Humaid Formation) nor the Upper Carboniferous/Lower Permian Haushi Group, unconformable on the Huqf Group along the western side of the Uplift, show any sign of these folds; they dip gently. There are unconformities between Ordovician, Permian, Jurassic–Lower Cretaceous and Upper Cretaceous rocks but these are mainly the result of regressions and the slow inter-

mittent rise of the Huqf–Haushi Uplift, rather than episodes of folding.

Direct evidence of the pre-Permian age of the folds is only available from the Anqau area (Fig. 4). There the Infracambrian Khufai Formation is affected by a series of folds, trending WSW–ENE, with steeply south-dipping axial surfaces, limb dips up to 45° but usually less, and low westerly plunges, which are truncated by the base of the Upper Carboniferous/Lower Permian Haushi Group. The latter dips gently westwards, with no sign of the folds seen in the underlying Khufai Formation. The unconformity is a spectacularly exposed glaciated pavement cut into the Khufai Formation, overlain by the basal tillite of the Al Khlata Formation (basal Haushi Group). This exposure at Al Khlata was the only one where the unconformity

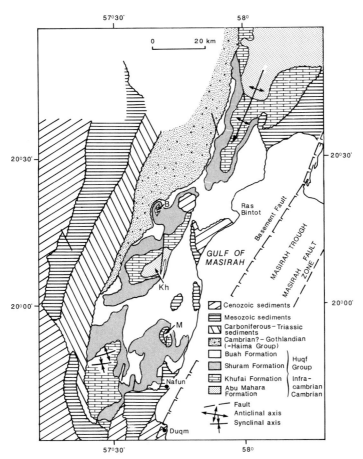

Fig. 2. Geological map of the Huqf—Haushi area, east Central Oman (modified from Gorin *et al.* 1982). B, Buah Dome; Kh, Khufai Dome; M, Mukhaibah Dome. The Cambrian—Gothlandian rocks exposed in the Huqf—Haushi Uplift are known as the Mahatta Humaid Formation.

was seen; the map (Fig. 4) is mainly based on photo interpretation; there may be more folds than have been detected but it seems clear that the folds are pre-Permian.

Similar general arguments apply to the relation between the Ordovician Mahatta Humaid Formation and the Huqf Group, seen in contact *c.* 25 km NNE of Al Khlata. The Mahatta Humaid, like the Al Khlata Formation, shows no sign of the folds which affect the underlying Huqf Group. The former dips gently (usually at *c.* 5°) towards the WNW; however the only contact seen (at loc. 362, Fig. 5.) shows nearly flat Mahatta Humaid Formation beds, with a basal breccia resting on an irregular karstic surface of Buah dolomites which dip 5° to the NNW. North of this locality, across the Khufai

Anticline, it appears that the Mahatta Humaid Formation cuts down into the Shuram Formation (Fig. 2); north of the Khufai Anticline, the Mahatta Humaid Formation again everywhere rests unconfomably on the Buah Formation. Thus the only evidence to show whether the WNW—ESE folds in the Huqf Group are pre-Ordovician, as the general arguments seem to imply, would be a more rigorous check of the field evidence, especially *c.* 3 km NNE of loc. 362 (Fig. 5), where the Mahatta Humaid Formation, according to the photo interpretation, rests on Shuram Formation. On the available evidence it seems likely that the Anqau and Khufai folds, and therefore those trending NNE—SSW into which they seem to curve, are not only pre-Permian but pre-Ordovician.

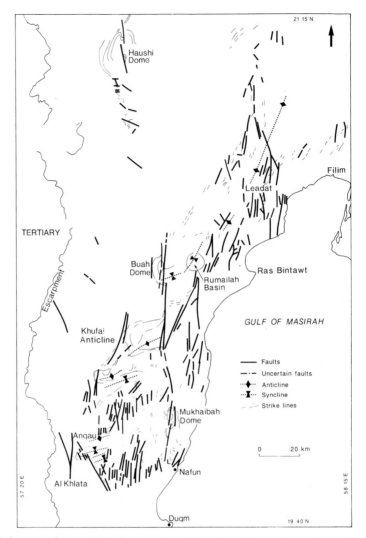

Fig. 3. Simplified structural map of the Huqf−Haushi area (based on photogeological interpretation by the authors and map shown in Gorin *et al.* 1982).

Pre-uppermost Cretaceous NNE−SSW faults

The vast majority of the many faults in the area appear to be pre-Late Cretaceous. Statistical analysis of the faults (Fig. 6) suggests that there are two main sets, one trending NNE−SSW, the other N−S. The two sets seem to be closely related since in a number of places a single fault curves or bends from one trend to the other. There are many cases where faults trending NNE−SSW stop against N−S faults as though cut and displaced by them, but no clear example has been seen of a fault of one set displaced by a fault of the other, such that the displaced faults

on either side can be matched. It is also clear that both sets have been reactivated. Nevertheless the evidence suggests that the NNE−SSW set developed before the main movement on the N−S set.

Where seen, the NNE−SSW trending faults are vertical or dip very steeply, suggesting that they originated as strike-slip faults. The apparent downthrow is usually to the east but there are many apparently downthrowing to the west. Faults of this set are commoner east of the axial zone of the Huqf−Haushi Uplift than west of it.

The nature of these faults has not been clearly established because they have only been map-

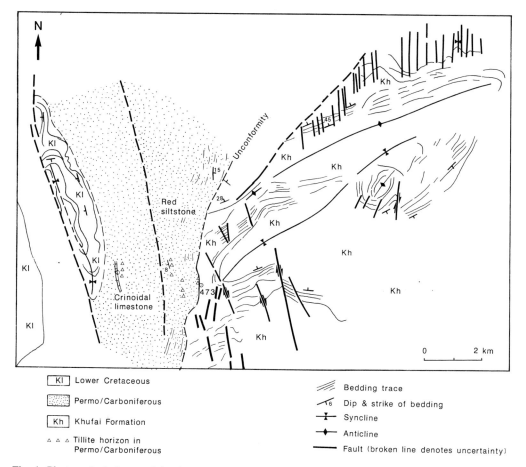

Fig. 4. Photogeological map of the Anqau area, SW part of the Huqf−Haushi area.

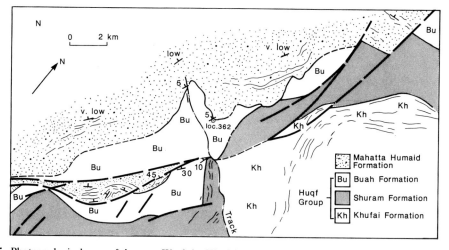

Fig. 5. Photogeological map of the area W of the Khufai Dome.

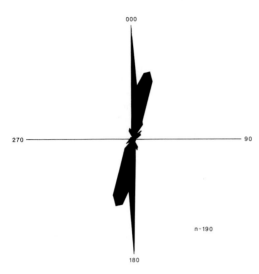

Fig. 6. Rose diagram of pre-Upper Cretaceous faults in the Huqf−Haushi area.

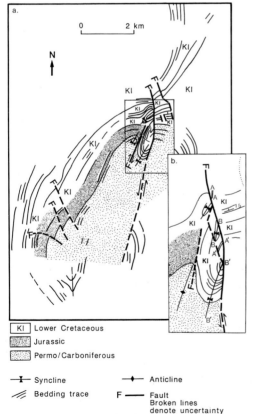

KI Lower Cretaceous

Jurassic

Permo/Carboniferous

──┬── Syncline   ──◆── Anticline

╱╱╱ Bedding trace   F ──── Fault
                             Broken lines
                             denote uncertainty

Fig. 7. (a) Photogeological map of the Haushi Dome. (b) Detail of boxed area marked on Fig. 7a.

ped, or seen, cutting beds which dip gently in one direction, so the dip-slip and strike-slip components cannot be separately evaluated. They are thought to be essentially left-lateral strike-slip faults because they often appear to curve into N−S faults (see Fig. 10) which are definitely left-lateral strike-slip faults.

Pre-Upper Cretaceous N−S faults and associated half-domes and oblique (clockwise) folds

Compared to the NNE−SSW set, the N−S set consists of fewer faults, but they are more widely, though less evenly, distributed. A concentration within four narrow parallel zones can be recognized. The most conspicuous of these is the en echelon series of N−S faults which extends, with an overall trend slightly west of north, from just west of Nafun in the south to the Haushi Dome in the north (Fig. 3). These faults were referred to as the Saiwan−Nafun Fault by Gorin *et al.* (1982). As it is not a single fault but a major tectonic feature, it is here referred to as the Saiwan−Nafun Lineament. The most striking feature of this Lineament is the presence along it of pairs of elongated half-domes, one on either side of the major N−S faults. From north to south, these are the Haushi, Buah, Khufai and Mukhaibah Domes. The N−S faults which transect the half-domes are not continuous but arranged in a left-handed en echelon series.

The structures along the Saiwan−Nafun Lineament are described below from north to south:

Haushi Dome

This structure (Fig. 7a) is about 9 km long by 7 km wide. Permian rocks exposed in the core are overlain by Jurassic and these by Lower Cretaceous sediments. The Haushi Dome is the most northerly of the half-dome structures and is spatially associated with the N−S trending faults. In the northern part of it, Lower Cretaceous limestones on the west side of the main fault (trending 175) are faulted against Permian limestones to the east, implying some vertical downthrow to the west. Within this fault zone, the fault breccia contains clasts of Lower Cretaceous limestones. On the air photographs there is a prominent hard rib, A−A on Fig. 7b, which appears to have been displaced southwards (to A[1]−A[1] on Fig. 7b) implying a left-lateral displacement of *c.* 1.5 km on this fault. There are horizontal striae on the vertical scarp face of the main fault.

West of the main fault, another vertical fault

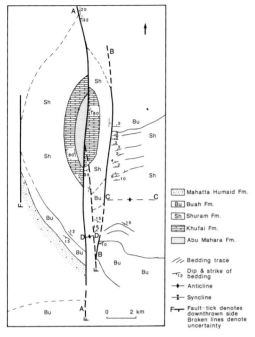

Mahatta Humaid Fm.
Bu Buah Fm.
Sh Shuram Fm.
Khufai Fm.
Abu Mahara Fm.

/// Bedding trace
⊤12 Dip & strike of bedding
◆ Anticline
⊥ Syncline
F⊤ Fault-tick denotes downthrown side Broken lines denote uncertainty

Fig. 8. Photogeological map of the Buah Dome.

trending 010, cuts Lower Cretaceous limestones; there is no indication of vertical displacement. East of this fault, the bedding dips indicate a syncline (B–B on Fig. 7b) which may originally have been a continuation of the syncline (B^1–B^1 on Fig. 7b) suggesting a left-lateral offset of c. 1 km on this fault.

The Haushi Fault is not a single fault. There are certainly two large faults, both with small splays. The result is an anastomozing fault zone c. 0.3 km wide containing lenses bounded by curved faults. The overall trend of the fault zone is c. N–S, the fault dips vertical.

The spatial relationship of folds and faults in the Haushi Dome shows that the folds and faults are genetically related. The folds deform Lower Cretaceous limestones near the faults and the folds in turn are cut by faults. The folds do not affect Upper Cretaceous (?Maastrichtian) rocks north of the Haushi Dome. Oblique folds on the west side of the main fault show NW–SE maximum compression, consistent with left-lateral displacement on the Haushi Fault, and the folds appear to die out away from the faults although on the west side they would, if they continued, be hidden under the Upper Cretaceous.

In a previous account of the Huqf–Haushi area (Gorin et al. 1982) the Haushi Fault is continued southwards through the Buah Dome

and eventually to Nafun. There is no evidence for continuity of the fault from the Haushi to the Buah area. The intervening area is sandy with very little rock exposure. The mapping of the better exposed faults between the Buah Dome and Nafun shows that they form an en echelon array and not a single continuous fault. To connect, the Buah and Haushi Faults must both bend as soon as they pass under the sands, which seems unlikely.

Buah Dome

The Buah Dome, 25 km long by 13 km wide, exposes Abu Mahara Formation in its core. It is cut by a series of N–S faults, which are essentially vertical. From the photogeological map (Fig. 8), the offset of the crest of the half-domes on either side of the fault seems to suggest a left-lateral displacement of < 0.5 km but there is a component of east downthrow of unknown amount.

The displacement on the eastern fault (B–B, on Fig. 8), which effectively marks the eastern limit of the Buah Dome, appears to be much greater. This fault juxtaposes an open, slightly asymmetric E–W trending anticline (C–C, Fig. 8), exposing Shuram Formation in its core on the east side of the fault, against the N–S trending structures of the Buah Dome on the west. If this open anticline is a continuation of the anticline west of the fault (D–D, Fig. 8.), the left-lateral displacement is c. 2 km.

The bedding dips close to the main faults are steep (up to 80°) but away from the faults, they rapidly diminish to 10–20°. On a very small scale, vertical microfaults can be seen on either side of which the beds have been forced up to dip very steeply away from the fault planes. This may be analogous to the larger-scale Buah Dome.

From the air photographs it appears that the Buah Formation is missing from the NW flank of the Buah Dome. If so, there may have been some pre-Mahatta Humaid Formation (i.e. pre-Ordovician) southward tilting along the N–S fault which now limits the west side of the Buah Dome.

Khufai Dome

The Khufai Dome (Fig. 9) differs from the others discussed, in that it continues, with diminishing westward plunge, as a broad anticline which as previously shown, appears to be unconformably overlain by the Ordovician Mahatta Humaid Formation. There is no obvious counterpart of the Dome, east of the faults which cross it. The attribution of some of

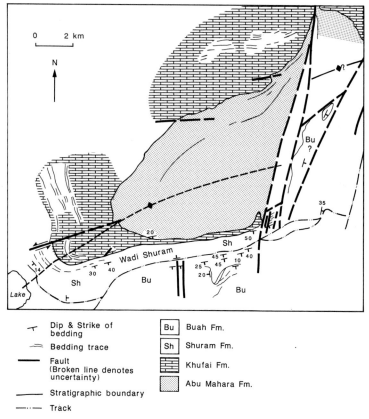

Fig. 9. Photogeological map of the Khufai Dome.

the outcrops, especially the ridge of limestone along the eastern side of the Dome, is uncertain. This ridge has previously been mapped as Khufai Formation but its lack of stratification and mode of weathering suggests that it is Buah Formation, as indicated on Fig. 9. The continuation of the Khufai Anticline may be the major NNE–SSW trending anticline through Leadat (see Fig. 3). This could imply large left-lateral strike-slip displacements on the faults on the eastern side of the Khufai structure. Even if the anticline is so continued, and is a Palaeozoic fold, it cannot be coincidental that the amplitude suddenly increases near the fault zone; the Dome there is strongly asymmetric, the dips on the southern limb are very much steeper than those on the northern limb. Hence a Palaeozoic anticline has been strongly amplified near the Cretaceous fault. Both in the Khufai and Buah Domes, the major N–S trending en echelon faults curve northwards into a NNE trend.

Because the axial trace of the Khufai Anticline cannot be definitely located east of the main (western) fault, it is not possible to estimate the displacement on this fault, nor on the others. It is clearly left-lateral, as shown by the sense of rotation of steep beds adjacent to it, and the apparent displacement of the Khufai Anticline. The left-lateral strike-slip appears to be at least 3 km. The downthrow to the east is probably not more than a few hundred metres, much less than the 1 km indicated by Gorin et al. (1982) which was based on the assumption of normal faulting.

Mukhaibah Dome – Nafun Basin

Extending southwards from Mukhaibah to Nafun is another series of N–S, steep or vertical, en echelon faults, with associated half-domes and basins (Fig. 10). The Mukhaibah Dome, 25 km long by 15 km wide, is the most spectacular of these structures.

Both the Mukhaibah and the Nafun Faults have a component of east downthrow, bringing Abu Mahara against Khufai Formation and

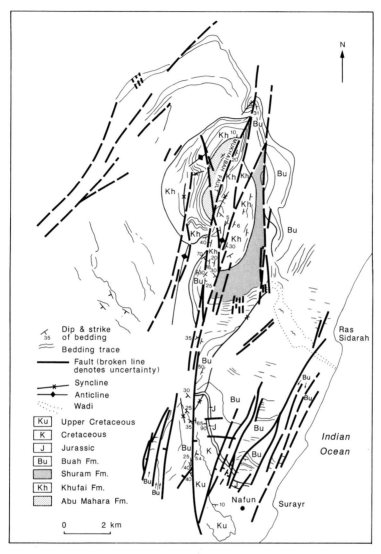

Fig. 10. Photogeological map of the Mukhaibah Dome−Nafun Basin.

Buah Formation against Late Cretaceous, respectively. But in between them the apparent downthrow is to the west, the elongated half-syncline of Buah Formation, south of Mukhaibah, being juxtaposed against Khufai Formation, east of the fault. These apparent contradictions are the result of mainly strike-slip displacement. The sense of strike-slip is not obvious. At first glance the map of the Mukaibah Dome suggests right-lateral displacement of c. 1 km; the two half-domes on opposite sides appear to match as though representing a bisected sub-circular dome. The Nafun Basin is also most simply explained by right-lateral slip:

striae on the main fault face plunge 35° S on a surface dipping 82° W (at most localities the faults are vertical). Since the dip-slip component is a downthrow E, this plunge implies a right-lateral strike-slip displacement.

However there is compelling evidence of a stress system which would imply left-lateral strike-slip. There are in the Mukhaibah−Nafun area, as in the other domes to the north, small-wavelength folds, of which the most conspicuous are synclines. These trend at an acute angle to the major faults and die out rapidly away from them, indicating that they are genetically related to the faults. Some are subparallel to the

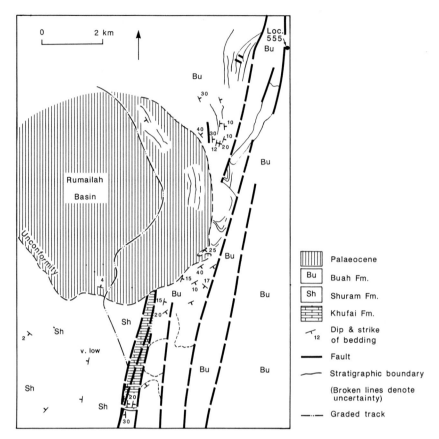

Fig. 11. Photogeological map of the Rumailah Basin.

faults but most trend clockwise from them. This is the case with the major syncline which curves NNE out of the Nafun Basin. This fold involves Lower Cretaceous as well as older strata. The way in which the major faults curve away from the main faults, in the same clockwise sense as the small folds, also suggests left-lateral shear. It may be that the direction of slip has reversed but it seems more likely that the displacement on the Mukhaibah−Nafun Faults was essentially left-lateral with downthrow to the east, and that the two half-domes at Mukhaibah did not originate before the faulting as a single subcircular dome.

In many places along the Mukhaibah and Nafun Faults, the strata immediately next to them dip very steeply, sometimes vertically.

The maximum age of the major displacement on both the NNE−SSW and N−S sets of faults is given by the age of the strata which both sets cut in the Nafun Basin. These strata contain a fauna which includes *Conulus triadis*

Lees [Lees 1928] and *Sanfilippaster sp.* cf. *geayi* [Cottreau 1908] (identified by Andrew Smith, Natural History Museum, London) of Campanian and Santonian age, respectively.

It has been suggested, as indicated by Gorin *et al.* (1982, Fig. 1), that the Saiwan−Nafun Fault can be extrapolated under sands far northwestwards to join the Maradi Fault on the NE side of the Fahud Basin. Since the Saiwan−Nafun Lineament has here been shown to be a transpressive N−S left-lateral strike-slip zone, whereas the Maradi Fault is a normal (extensional) fault dipping gently southwest, the connection seems highly improbable.

About 5 km E of the Saiwan−Nafun Lineament, another set of c. N−S (about 012°) faults also shows associated half-domes, the clearest of which is immediately north of the Rumailah Basin (Fig. 11). Since most of the structures lie beneath (and clearly predate) the Palaeocene of the Rumailah Basin, all that can be said is that this shows that the Saiwan−Nafun

Lineament is not unique but merely the most striking example of a family of structures. It reinforces the view that the N–S faults differ in more than orientation from those trending NNE–SSW.

A few faults which trend c. 100, are vertical, show gently plunging striae (25°/E) and clear right-lateral rotation of bedding in narrow strips between faults; these faults may be conjugate to the NNE–SSW and N–S left-lateral strike-slip faults. They were best seen at loc. 555 (Fig. 11).

Post-Maastrichtian NE–SW normal (extensional) faults

These faults have only been recognized in the Filim area where they cut nearly flat Maastrichtian rudist limestones which unconformably overlie the Shuram Formation. The two measured faults trend 050° to 065° and dip 67° NW and SE, towards the downthrown side. The throw is only a few metres.

Very weak post-Palaeocene folds

The Palaeocene (?) beds of the Rumailah Basin (Fig. 11) dip very gently (< 5°) into this sub-circular structure. Since the age of the strata is poorly defined and the structure cannot be shown to be part of any more widespread deformation pattern, it is at present of little significance.

Post-Oligocene NNE–SSW and N–S faults

Oligocene limestones, SW of Duqm, are cut by a number of faults with trends similar to the major system of pre-uppermost Cretaceous faults. They were not studied in the field so their nature is not known but it seems likely that they resulted from reactivation of earlier faults in the underlying beds.

Discussion

All of the structures in the Huqf–Haushi Uplift are the result of intraplate deformation. The intermittent uplift, from Infracambrian to Late Cretaceous, appears to be complementary to the subsidence of the Ghaba Salt Basin to the west and the Masirah Trough to the east. It is therefore probably extensional in origin. The weak early Palaeozoic folding may reflect some far-distant collisional process. The most conspicuous deformation in the area is the array of faults mostly trending NNE–SSW and N–S. The NNE–SSW set has been shown to be transpressional left-lateral strike-slip; the N–S set is probably also left-lateral strike-slip. This array of faults is spatially related to, and the NNE–SSW set parallel to, the Masirah Fault, which is primarily a left-lateral transform (Shackleton & Ries 1990). The array continues northwards into the Batain coast area, although less obvious because of the intense deformation in the Batain fold and thrust belt; the array is still, in the Batain area, essentially confined to a zone some 50 km wide, west of the Masirah Fault. It is thus clearly part of the deformation associated with the Masirah Fault.

This work was supported by Amoco Production Company (International) through an operating grant to W. H. Kanes, Earth Sciences and Resources Institute, University of South Carolina. Amoco Production Company (International) and the Oman Ministry of Petroleum and Minerals are thanked for permission to publish this paper. M. P. Coward and N. H. Woodcock are thanked for their critical reviews of the paper.

References

COTTREAU, 1908. Les Echinides. *In*: *Palaeontologie*, **3**, Ch. VI, 145–188.

GORIN, G. E., RACZ, L. G. & WALTER, M. R. 1982. Late Precambrian–Cambrian sediments of Huqf Group, Sultanate of Oman. *Bulletin of the American Association of Petroleum Geologists*, **66**, 2609–2627.

LEES, G. M. 1928. Geology and Tectonics of Oman and Parts of South-Eastern Arabia. *Quarterly Journal of the Geological Society of London*, **84**, 585–670.

SHACKLETON, R. M. & RIES, A. C. 1990. Tectonics of the Masirah Fault Zone and eastern Oman. *In*: ROBERTSON, A. H. F., SEARLE, M. P. & RIES A. C. (eds) *The Geology and Tectonics of the Oman Region* Geological Society, London, Special Publication **49**, 715–724.

The structure of Masirah Island, Oman

F. MOSELEY

School of Earth Sciences, University of Birmingham, B15 2TT, UK

Abstract: The Masirah Ophiolite, extending over 1000 km^2 and now believed to be of Tithonian age, is cut by an extensive melange of uncertain age. The melange has been interpreted as representing a former transform fault zone. Later pre-Tertiary cross-cutting tectonic zones exist, within which ophiolite units have been tilted to the vertical and strongly folded. In one zone there are granites with continental affinities suggesting that Masirah was thrust against continental Arabia, probably late in the Cretaceous. Limestone of presumed early Tertiary age rests with strong unconformity upon the ophiolite, and is itself folded and faulted.

Masirah Island is almost entirely composed of a well developed ophiolite which is, however, completely unrelated to the nearby Semail Ophiolite of the Oman Mountains. Since Masirah lies off the southeast coast of Oman, well away from the highly tectonized region of the Oman Mountains, it may be considered to be in a stable environment, perhaps that of a passive margin with simple structures. However this is not so, for apart from the ophiolite itself and the melange which transects it, the latter interpreted as a transform fault zone by Moseley & Abbotts (1979), there are many other structures ranging from the complex deformation of pre-Tertiary rocks to simpler but still important post-Eocene structures. The relative dating of the structural events is the subject of this paper; the more precise dating requiring further work. These events are described below.

The Masirah Ophiolite

The Masirah Ophiolite is the oldest rock unit and, as noted above, is unrelated to the Semail Ophiolite. It has been interpreted as formerly part of the Indian Ocean floor probably near to a spreading centre, the orientation of which is given by the ENE-trending sheeted dykes (Moseley & Abbotts 1979, Fig. 1). Other details, including the geochemistry, have been described by Abbotts (1979, 1981). The ophiolite is extremely well developed, and as well as the sheeted dykes, there are mantle serpentinites, several varieties of ultramafic to gabbroic cumulates, massive gabbros, pillow lavas, radiolarian chert, limestone and marl (Moseley & Abbotts 1984). The ophiolite is unconformably overlain by early Tertiary limestone and it was suggested (Moseley & Abbotts 1979) that its emplacement could be Late Cretaceous in age. However the cherts are now reported to be

of Tithonian age (De Wever, pers. comm.) which would mean that it is considerably older than previously supposed.

The Masirah Melange

The ophiolite is truncated by the ophiolitic melange which makes a high angle with the sheeted dyke trend and has been interpreted as a transform fault zone (Moseley & Abbotts 1979). It is composed of blocks of all the rock types of the ophiolite plus massive limestones not seen elsewhere on Masirah. The blocks range in size from several kilometres to a few metres (Figs 2 & 3), often with approximately N–S trends, parallel to the strike of the melange. Commonly the blocks themselves are extensively brecciated and invariably there is random orientation of structures such as bedding, layering and sheeted dyke orientation. Dating of the melange is so far proving difficult. It clearly post-dates the main ophiolite (Tithonian, see above) and pre-dates the early Tertiary. The massive limestone outcrops were dated by Glennie et al. (1974) as mid-Cretaceous, but their survey was largely reconnaissance and further palaeontological work is necessary to determine whether all the massive limestone outcrops are of the same age. This certainly has some bearing on the age of the melange. Some of the limestone outcrops have steep to vertical dips of variable trend (Fig. 2) and, like the pillow lavas, sheeted dykes and gabbros, can only be interpreted as blocks within the melange (Moseley & Abbotts 1979). In this case the melange would be dated as post mid-Cretaceous. However Shackleton & Ries (1990) have suggested that the largest of the limestone outcrops in the south of the island (Jabal Suwayr) is unconformable upon the melange, which would make the melange, pre

From ROBERTSON, A. H. F., SEARLE, M. P. & RIES, A. C. (eds), 1990,
The Geology and Tectonics of the Oman Region.
Geological Society Special Publication No 49, pp 665–671

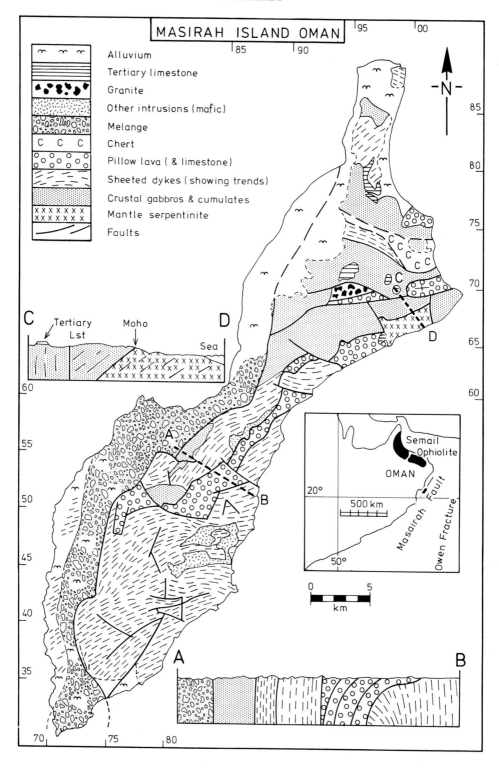

Fig. 1. Outline geological map of Masirah Island.

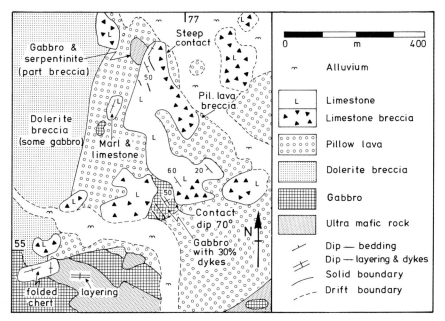

Fig. 2. A low relief (10 m) area within the melange showing blocks of different ophiolite lithologies (after Moseley & Abbotts 1979).

mid-Cretaceous. Figure 3 is a map of this outcrop, and although the dip is not steep, the western contact with the ophiolite does not seem to be an unconformity, and hence it is here suggested that it represents another block which has not been tilted to a high angle. Further field and palaeontological work is necessary however to resolve this particular question.

ENE to E–W tectonic zones

All the rock types of the ophiolite are affected by the melange, and a first impression may be the island and make a high angle with the melange. These zones appear to be truncated by the Melange, and a first impression may be that they are the earlier structures (Fig. 1). However the field evidence is not conclusive since most of the contacts are concealed by alluvial gravel, and there is also a probability of later (post-early Tertiary) strike-slip movement along the melange zone (see below). The balance of the evidence suggests that the formation of the transform fault and the associated melange breccia preceded the ENE tectonic zones, which were followed later in Tertiary times by renewed strike-slip movement along the melange, and it was at this time that the ENE zones were truncated.

The most northerly zone extends westwards from Shi'inzi (01 74) and consists mostly of bedded cherts, often deformed into tight minor folds. To the south it is faulted against lower crustal troctolites, commonly serpentinized (Moseley & Abbotts 1984).

Farther south a more important folded and faulted zone extends across the island from Rassier (02 70) (Fig. 4). In the east there is a one kilometre wide zone of vertical pillow lava, marly limestone and chert, faulted on the southern side against layered troctolites and gabbros. Farther west there are faulted slices, one of which includes steeply-dipping pillow lavas, marls and marly limestones similar to those of Rassier. Another slice contains pods and sheets of potash-rich granite intrusive into gabbro, with xenoliths of gabbro and dolerite, and with areas of strongly mylonitized granite, suggesting strong tectonic activity during or after the granite intrusion. The high potassium and other aspects of the granite geochemistry indicate that it was derived from continental crust, and is not part of the ophiolite (Abbotts 1978). In fact it was likely to have been formed much later probably at the time when the Masirah ocean floor was upthrust against the Arabian continent, late in the Cretaceous. Until the granite is dated; the age will not be known for certain (work is now in progress). It is prob-

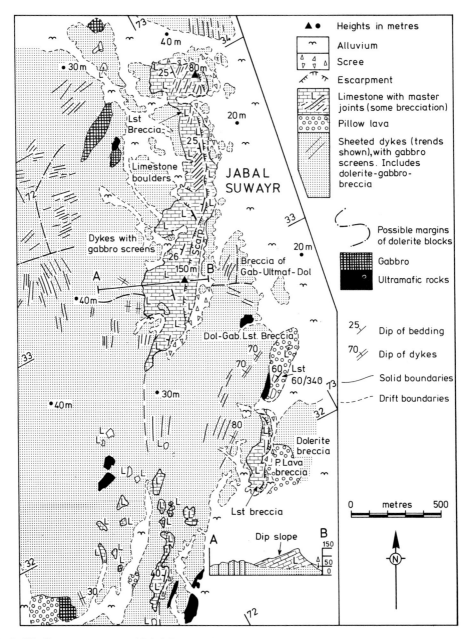

Fig. 3. The limestone outcrop of Jabal Suwayr with the surrounding melange lithologies.

able that the other associated ENE trending structures of the tectonic zones were formed at the same time.

Another important but highly irregular zone extends across the middle of the island from NE of Macula (97 65) to near Al Quarin (79 53)

(Fig. 1). The part of this zone (Fig. 5) shows how the crustal sequence, from marly limestones, through red and green pillow lavas to sheeted dykes with variable proportions of pillow lava and gabbro screens, has been tilted to reveal a thick sequence.

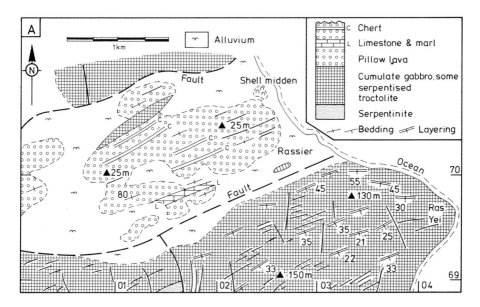

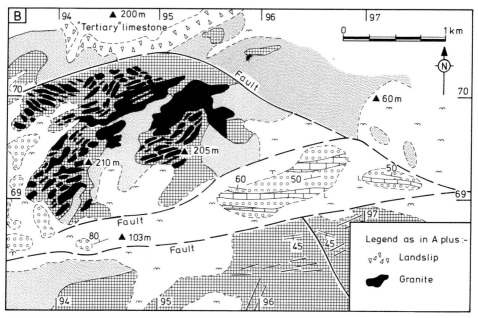

Fig. 4. The tectonic zone extending west from Rassier (A) to south of Jabal Hamra (B).

Tertiary structures

The fourth event involved deformation of the early Tertiary limestone. It is easy to demonstrate that this limestone was deposited, with strong unconformity, across the tectonic zones described above and is therefore younger. The structures within the limestone are not dramatic but there is a degree of folding and faulting which must at least be later than the presumed early Tertiary age of the limestone (Lees 1928). Unfortunately there are no recently published

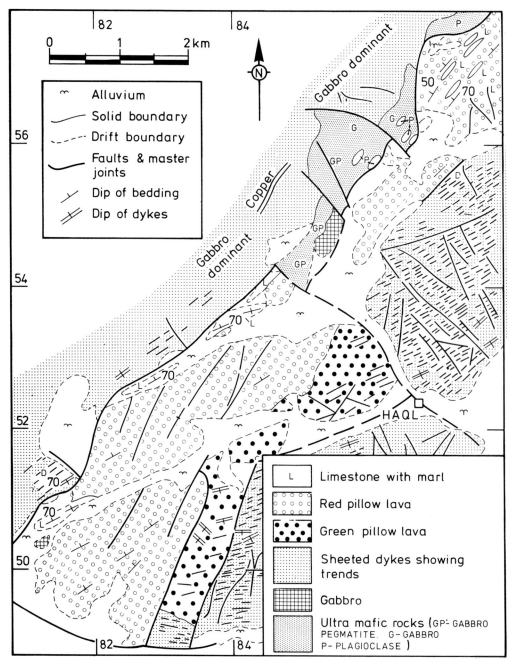

Fig. 5. Part of the tectonic zone, west of Haql.

dates on this formation. The folding can be seen particularly in the limestone outlier near Humer (98 66), where there is a N−S syncline with 30° dips on either limb (Fig. 6), whilst the fault immediately 5 of Jabal Hamra (95 71), probably moved during this time. It may also be the case

that there was considerable renewed movement along the Masirah Fault (melange zone) during the Tertiary, and that this resulted in the truncation of the ENE tectonic zones described above.

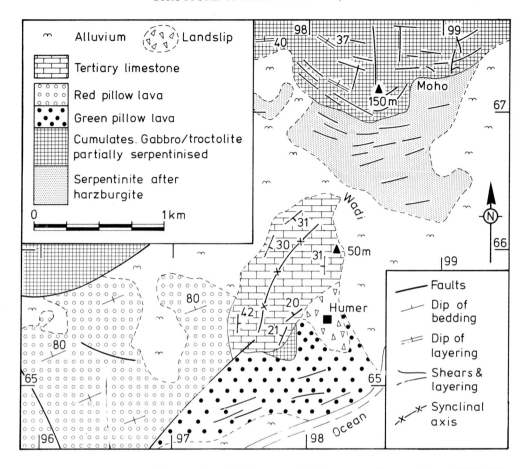

Fig. 6. Syncline in limestone of presumed early Tertiary age which forms an outlier near Humer (98 66). It is unconformable upon the ophiolite, of which adjacent outcrops are shown.

References

ABBOTTS, I. L. 1978. High potassium granites in the Masirah ophiolite of Oman. *Geological Magazine*, **115**, 415−425.

ABBOTTS, I. L. 1981. Masirah (Oman) ophiolite sheeted dykes and pillow lavas: geochemical evidence of the former ocean ridge environment. *Lithos*, **14**, 283−294.

GLENNIE, K. W., BOEUF, M. G. A., HUGHTS CLARKE, M. W., MOODY STUART, PILAAR, W. F. H. & REINHARDT, B. M. 1974. The Geology of the Oman Mountains. Verhandelingen van het konin klijk Nederlands Geologisch Mijnbouwkundig Gencotschaap, **31**.

LEES, G. M. 1928. The geology and tectonics of Oman and parts of south-eastern Arabia. *Quarterly Journal of the Geological Society of London*, **84**, 585.

MOSELEY, F. & ABBOTTS, I. L. 1979. The ophiolite melange of Masirah, Oman. *Journal of the Geological Society of London*, **136**, 713−724.

——&—— 1984. A geological map of the Masirah ophiolite complex, Oman. *Overseas Geology and Mineral Resources*, **62**, HMSO.

SHACKLETON, R. M. & RIES, A. C. 1990. Tectonics of the Masirah Fault Zone and eastern Oman. *In*: ROBERTSON, A. H. F., SEARLE, M. P. & RIES, A. C. *The Geology and Tectonics of the Oman Region*. Geological Society, London, Special Publication, **49**, 715−724.

The Batain Melange of NE Oman

R. M. SHACKLETON[1], A. C. RIES[2], P. R. BIRD[3], J. B. FILBRANDT[4], C. W. LEE[5]
& G. C. CUNNINGHAM[6]

[1] *The Croft Barn, Church Street, East Hendred, Oxon OX12 8LA, UK*
[2] *Earth Sciences and Resources Institute, University of Reading, 19
Upper Redlands Road, Reading RG1 5JJ, UK*
[3] *Scott Pickford & Associates Ltd., 256 High Street, Croydon, Surrey
CRO 1NF, UK*
[4] *Shell U.K. Exploration & Production, Shell-Mex House, The Strand,
London WC25 0DX, UK*
[5] *Department of Science, Polytechnic of Wales, Treforest, S Wales, UK*
[6] *Department of Geology, Royal Holloway & Bedford New College,
Egham, Surrey TW20 0EX, UK*

Abstract: Most of the Batain coast area, previously unmapped or mapped as Hawasina, is
shown to be underlain by melange. This consists of blocks, up to 10 km long, of a variety
of rocks in a scanty, seldom exposed sheared shaly matrix. Clasts include Triassic and
younger Hawasina-type red cherts and shales; Mesozoic calciturbidites; Permian limestones
and megabreccias (associated with basalts); *ammonitico rosso* type blocks (Triassic?); a
limestone and pillow lava assemblage, probably Jurassic; Cretaceous ophiolite; and Upper
Cretaceous sandstones with basement-derived debris flows. Deformation becomes increasingly complex northwards. WNW-vergent thrusts and folds, dominant in the south,
appear to have been continuous with the south-vergent structures in the Hawasina, west of
the Jebel Ja'alan basement uplift. The melange is interpreted as primarily tectonic but
probably composite in origin. It is correlated with the Hawasina (Oman) Melange which
underlies the Semail Ophiolite, west of the Jebel Ja'alan Uplift. It is compared with other
Tethyan melanges.

The Batain area, one of low to moderate relief,
with extensive sand and gravel cover, extends
some 250 × 70 km between the Batain coast to
the east and Wahiba Sands and Maastrichtian–
Tertiary cover rocks to the west and north
(Fig. 1). Based on photo interpretation and
brief reconnaissance, a previous map (Glennie
et al. 1974) showed areas of Hawasina (Halfa
and Ibra Formations), ophiolite at Ras Jibsch,
and Tertiary. Our own mapping, from 1982–5,
has shown that much of the area is underlain by
melange, described here as the Batain Melange.
Mapping was done on 1:60 000 air photos, and
for the north part, on 1:20 000 coloured air
photos.

The components of the Batain Melange

Many clasts from the Batain Melange have been
dated; the rest have been classified and mapped
lithologically. Those dated are:

Late Cretaceous	: Fayah Sandstone	Triassic?	: white, pink & red bioclastic lime mudstones & framestones
Cretaceous	: ophiolitic rocks		
Triassic to Cenomanian	: cherts & argillites		
		Triassic	: Limestone Megabreccias & associated basalt
Late Jurassic or Early Cretaceous	: pillow lava & limestone assemblage		
Triassic (and younger?)	: calciturbidites & limestones	Permian	: Qarari Limestone; pink limestones; green grits

From ROBERTSON, A. H. F., SEARLE, M. P. & RIES, A. C. (eds), 1990,
The Geology and Tectonics of the Oman Region.
Geological Society Special Publication No 49, pp 673–696

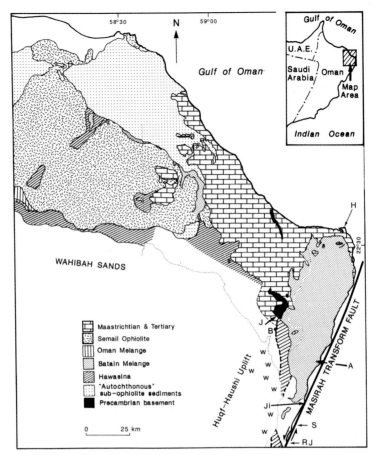

Fig. 1. Geological map of NE Oman (modified from Glennie *et al.* 1974). H, Ras al Hadd; J, Jebel Ja'alan; S, Al Ashkharah; B, Bilad Bani Bu Ali; Ji, Ras al Jifan; S, Ras as Sagallah; RJ, Ras Jibsch; W, Wahiba Sands.

Qarari Limestone: Permian

The Qarari Limestone is best exposed on Jebel Qarari (see flyout) and in the 'Black Hills', 11 km to the NNE. Hence Jebel Qarari is taken as the type locality. Many other limestone outcrops have been identified as Qarari Limestone from their lithology or faunas. In both Jebel Qarari and in the 'Black Hills', *c.* 50 m of sandy or gritty limestone beds (Sandy Limestones) are stratigraphically overlain by *c.* 100 m of nodular blue-grey lime mudstones (Nodular Limestones). Neither top nor bottom contacts have been seen on the south side of Jebel Qarari, structurally below, and apparently concordant with, inverted Qarari Limestone, is an inverted and imbricated sequence of green, purple and red shales and cherts with conglomerate beds, possibly stratigraphically overlying the Qarari Limestone.

The *Sandy Limestones* are turbidites, with grading and solemarks, consisting of medium- to coarse-grained quartz sand, limestone grains and ooliths in a muddy matrix. There are thin shale partings. Some beds contain intraclasts of grey lime mudstone up to 30 cm across.

The *Nodular Limestones* are graded beds (silt to clay particles) of marly blue-grey lime mudstones, often nodular in appearance with thin shaly partings, suggestive of hemipelagic slope sediments (McIlreath & James 1978). Microfaunas, including occasional radiolaria, are Permian. The characteristic regular bedding is disrupted in places by debris flows, of two types:

(a) Breccias composed of tabular clasts, up to 0.5 m in diameter, of blue-grey lime mudstone, sub-parallel to randomly oriented, formed by disruption and sliding of partly lithified sediment. Calcite, sand and mud fill the interstices. These breccias cut underlying beds discordantly but have planar tops.

(b) Poorly-sorted polymict breccias with a variety of randomly oriented limestone clasts up to several m diameter. They form discontinuous sheets or irregular masses; basal and upper contacts are undulating. Some two-phase breccias occur. These breccias must have slid from a nearby platform margin of partly lithified and highly fossiliferous reef and shoal limestones.

Faunal evidence for the age of the Qarari Limestone is given in detail in the Appendix. Two horizons in the Nodular Limestone, one near the base, the other 15 m above it, on Jebel Qarari, indicate late early, or early mid-Permian ages. Faunas from the 'Black Hills', their stratigraphic positions uncertain, suggest a late Permian age. The faunas, which include a trilobite, corals, brachiopods and echinoderms, are clearly Tethyan (some are forms known from Timor).

Pink limestone: Permian

These, only seen in isolated exposures, are reef limestones, with corals, brachiopods and crinoids of Early Permian age (see Appendix).

Greenish fossiliferous grits: Permian

About 2 km NNW of Jebel Qarari is a hill of massive limestones and breccias with blocks of fusulinid limestone. Faulted against its west side are c. 20 m of greenish-grey conglomerates with pebbles of limestone, sandstone and basalt, overlain by fossiliferous green quartz grits and these by a well-bedded dark grey limestone with shale interbeds, lithologically similar to the Qarari Nodular Limestones. The grits contain: *Linoproductus* cf. *L. cora* (d'Orbigny) and *Plerophyllum* sp. of Permian age (see Appendix).

Limestone Megabreccias: Permian to Early Triassic

The Limestone Megabreccias consist of brecciated blocks of white crystalline limestone, the blocks ranging in size from small boulders in a detrital limestone or dolomite matrix and more rarely red clay, up to hills more than 1 km across. At loc. R201 (flyout), gritty dolomitized limestones, containing white limestone clasts, are underlain by red cherts (Fig. 2a). This breccia shows crude bedding apparently conformable with the underlying cherts. The clasts in the breccia increase in size and frequency up

section. Some contain Permian brachiopods (spiriferids). The breccia, c. 100 m thick, is overlain by a single megaclast, at least 200 m thick, of thick-bedded white recrystallized limestone.

The top contact of the Limestone Megabreccias is seen at loc. M138 (Fig. 2b). At the base of the exposed section there is a white megabreccia with clasts of brown pisolitic and whitish limestone, in a dolomitized limestone matrix. Clast size and frequency decreases upwards. This white breccia passes into a crudely bedded dark grey breccia, with beds up to 2 m thick. The clasts, of varicoloured limestone, are poorly sorted, sub-angular, and matrix-supported, in a matrix of dolomitized gritty limestone. This bedded breccia is overlain with a sharp contact by thinly-bedded red cherts with thin sandy bands, which pass up into fine-grained grey and white calciturbidites interbedded with pink and white shales containing *Halobia* of Middle–Late Triassic age.

These megabreccias appear to have been mass flows onto deep-sea radiolarian ooze, covered by pelagic deposits and distal turbidites. The faunas (ammonoids and corals, see Appendix) in the blocks indicate ages between Middle–Late Permian and Early Triassic.

The Limestone Megabreccias are often, and the massive limestones sometimes, associated with basalts. The association, clearly systematic, shows that these basalts are Permian or Triassic. In several places the limestone breccias overlie basalts or basaltic breccias, but not the reverse. The best exposure of the association is on a hill just west of the road, about 19 km south of Ras al Hadd. A few km south of this hill and c. 1 km east of the road, Limestone Megabreccia, apparently conformably underlain and overlain by red cherts, contains a few blocks of basalt. It appears that these limestone were deposited on basalts, probably seamounts, from which they slid into the deep-water radiolarian oozes. No such association has been recognized in the case of the Qarari Limestone.

White, pink and red bioclastic lime mudstones and framestones: ?Triassic

These rocks usually occur as small (dm size) blocks in the Melange. They are extremely fossiliferous white, red or pink bioclastic lime mudstones/wackestones, often containing a coral–brachiopod–bryozoan–crinoid–algal reef association.

Voids contain radial fibrous calcite, interpreted as inverted aragonite, or brownish silt. Fossils are often broken and bored (especially

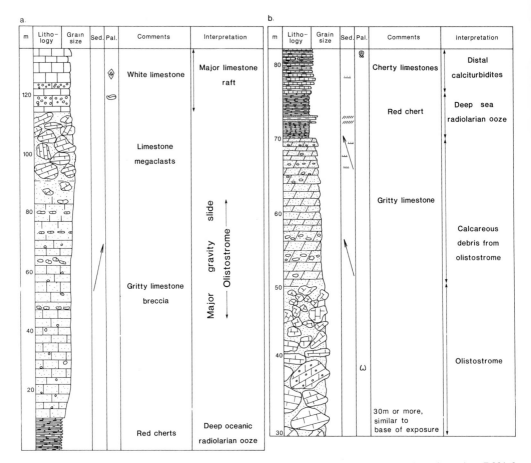

Fig. 2. Lithostratigraphic logs through the (a) base and (b) top of the Limestone Megabreccias at locs R201 & M138 (flyout), respectively.

the smooth spiriferids and productids). The microfacies shows association of algal problematica, cements and body fossils.

About 2 km NW of Ras al Jifan (loc. 574, flyout), a block of red bioclastic lime mudstone contains abundant cephalopods with ceratitic sutures. A slab, 4 × 1 m, of similar red limestone, full of similar-looking but unextractable cephalopods, was seen in a 5 m bed of breccia overlain and underlain by bedded limestone (locs 443 & 444, flyout). The cephalopods could be Permian or Triassic. The lithology is of *ammonitico rosso* type.

Calciturbidites: Late Triassic (and younger?)

Calciturbidites are widely distributed throughout the Batain coast area. A thickness of 200–300 m would probably account for most of

the outcrops seen. These calciturbidites are distinct from the calciturbiditic parts of the Qarari Limestone (see above) and Fayah Sandstone (see below).

Several lithological types are distinguished. *Graded grits.* These are brown-weathering dm-bedded, graded, quartz-rich limestones with interbedded shale. Grain size varies from very coarse to fine. Sole marks (e.g. flutes) are often seen; bed tops may be parallel to ripple-laminated. Planktonic foraminifera and fragments of thin-walled bivalves, probably *Halobia* (Late Triassic), are common.

Limestone shales. These are interbedded pale lime mudstones and shales. The limestone beds are up to 30 cm thick, very fine-grained, internally massive, with parallel or ripple cross-laminated tops. Sole marks (e.g. current striae) and horizontal feeding traces and burrows are common. Thin-walled bivalves and occasional

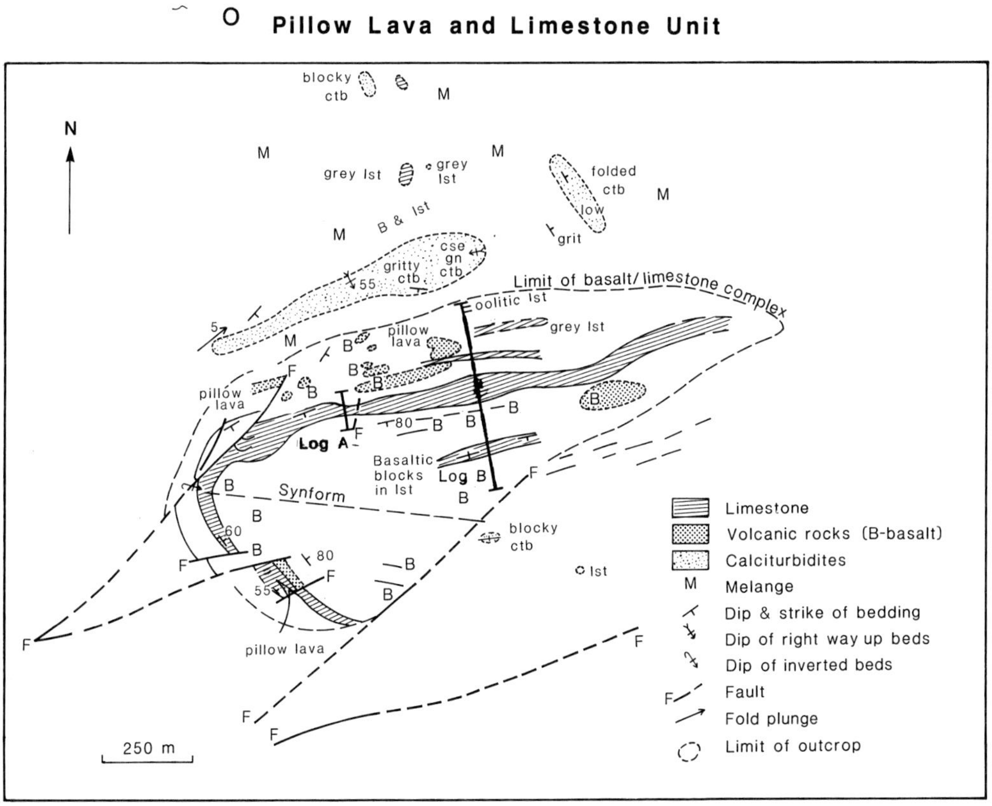

Fig. 3. Map of the Pillow lava and limestone assemblage. The overall structure is a tight upright downward-facing synform. The centre point of the map is located at 59° 39'E/22° 13'N and 40 km SSW (196°) of Ras al Hadd.

radiolaria are visible in thin section.

Siliceous limestones. These are cm-bedded, not graded, lime mudstones, partly silicified, with varicoloured shale interbeds; there are laminae rich in thin-walled bivalves and radiolaria.

All three calciturbidite types contain *Halobia*, identified as *Halobia styriaca* Mojsisovics or possibly *Halobia austriaca* Mojsisovics of Late Triassic (?earliest Norian) age (identified by Hamish Campbell, University of Cambridge). Most of the calciturbidites are fairly thin-bedded, laterally continuous and were deposited by far-travelled turbidity currents. Their association with manganiferous cherts suggest deposition in a deep basin floored by oceanic crust, with low clastic input, and reworking by strong bottom currents.

The thicker-bedded turbidites were presumably deposited near the margins of the basin; the more clastic deposits, with quartz and often fresh feldspar, suggest a nearby granitic basement source, and the purer limestones coming from starved continental margins.

Pillow lava and limestone assemblage: Late Jurassic or Early Cretaceous

A distinctive association of limestones and pillow lavas is only seen in one area of about 1 km², c. 15 km west of Ras ar Rhays (Fig. 3). The area is surrounded by sand, so no contact relationships are seen. The overall structure is a tight synform, plunging c. 60°E, with vertical or steeply overturned limbs. The approximate thickness across the N limb is 500 m; there appears to be no stratigraphic repetition.

Rather poor way-up evidence seems to indicate that the synform is downward-facing. The evidence is from a few bun-shaped pillow tops; concentration of vesicles suggesting pillow tops; larger crescentic vesicles convex upwards; the smoothly planar base of a flow (on limestone); channelling in interbedded limestone.

The sequence (Fig. 4) includes volcaniclastic sands which contain Late Jurassic or Cretaceous Nerineid gastropods.

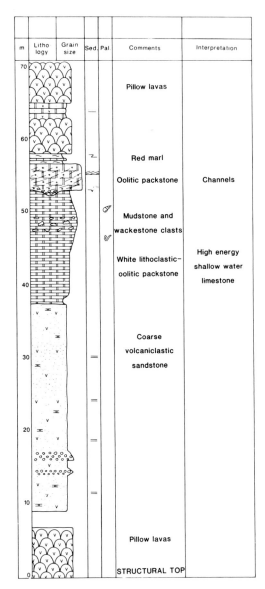

m	Litho logy	Grain size	Sed.	Pal.	Comments	Interpretation
70					Pillow lavas	
60					Red marl	
					Oolitic packstone	Channels
50					Mudstone and wackestone clasts	
					White lithoclastic–oolitic packstone	High energy shallow water limestone
40						
30					Coarse volcaniclastic sandstone	
20						
10						
					Pillow lavas	
0					STRUCTURAL TOP	

Fig. 4. Composite log (Log A & B, Fig. 3) showing the sequence typical of the pillow lava and limestone assemblage.

The limestones are oolitic packstones, commonly with volcanic fragments and some large volcanic clasts forming conglomerates. The scanty fauna consists of indeterminable shell debris, sponge fragments and gastropods. The association of limestones and volcanic rocks and absence of terriginous debris suggests an oceanic island; the oolitic limestones with cross bedding, channelling and conglomerates imply a high-energy carbonate shelf.

Cherts and Argillites: Triassic to Cenomanian

Radiolarian cherts and argillites are widespread throughout the Batain coast area. Their original thickness is uncertain as most outcrops are intensely folded and faulted. The thickest unbroken sequence recorded is 400 m (loc. M62, flyout), a minimum as neither top nor bottom contact is exposed.

Various types are distinguished: their mutual stratigraphic relationships are unknown.

True cherts. These are brick-red or white, very hard, and break conchoidally. Beds are 5–20 cm thick, with thin shaly partings, and black horizons of manganiferous chert. Radiolaria are common, but their structure has usually been destroyed by silica diagenesis.

Laminated porcellanites. These beds are less hard, break with a blocky fracture, are 2–15 cm thick and consist of mm-thick laminae. Radiolaria are abundant and sometimes well preserved. Up to 50% of the rock is formed from clay.

Nodular porcellanites. These are white, yellow or pink, with nodular chert in the centres of the beds. Shaly interbeds, of clay and silt, occasionally show grading.

Striped cherts. These have a characteristic red and white striping parallel to bedding. The beds are hard and porcellanous; shaly interbeds form half of the rock. Radiolaria are abundant.

Red argillites. These are soft non-silicified shaly clays, often with white streaks. Radiolaria are rare.

Bedded red and white argillites. These are harder and more silicified than stripped cherts. Beds are 2–5 cm thick.

Dating of radiolaria indicates ages from Late Jurassic to Cenomanian. Stratigraphic contacts with other units are rarely seen; most of those show calciturbidites overlying the cherts and argillites but few shown the opposite, indicating, as does the mapping, that the two units interfinger. A few exposures show Limestone Megabreccias, considered Triassic, overlain and underlain by red cherts; these are therefore regarded as Triassic.

These rocks are clearly pelagic. In the south, red cherts are seen to overlie basalts, e.g. NNW of Ras Qumaylah. In the north also the close association of blocks of pelagic sediments, pillow lavas and chert suggests an ocean-floor sequence. The absence of carbonate suggests deposition below the carbonate compensation depth.

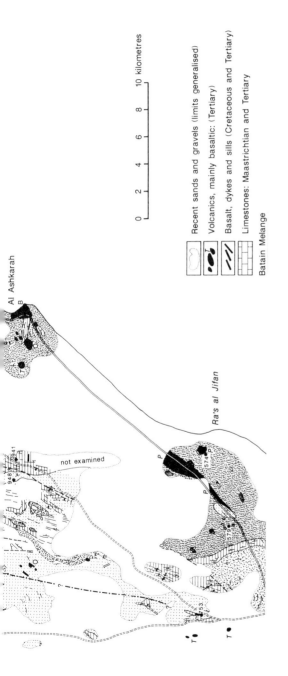

Al Ashkarah

Ra's al Jifan

not examined

AL WAHIBAH

0   2   4   6   8   10 kilometres

Recent sands and gravels (limits generalised)

Volcanics, mainly basaltic: (Tertiary)

Basalt, dykes and sills (Cretaceous and Tertiary)

Limestones: Maastrichtian and Tertiary

Batain Melange

sand

gravel

Ar Ru'ays

Al Khaddah

B

J

M62

053

B

22 10

22°10'

sand

gravel

Wadi Qarihah

Qumaylah

Ra's Qumaylah

B

B

277

273

731

640

22°00'N

22°00N

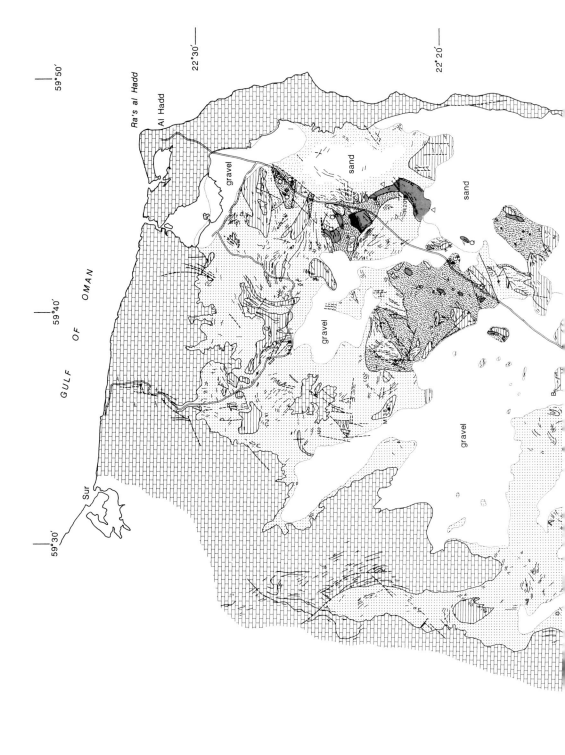

59° 20'E   59° 30'   59° 40'   59° 50'

GULF OF OMAN

Sur

Ra's al Hadd

Al Hadd

gravel

gravel

gravel

sand

sand

22° 30'

22° 20'

Ophiolitic rocks: Cretaceous

About 7 km west of Jebel Qarari there is an extensive area with blocks of pillow lavas, basic dykes, gabbros and gabbro pegmatite, trondhjemite and bastite-bearing ultramafic rocks. Basaltic lavas collected here gave K−Ar ages of c. 80 Ma (dated by D. C. Rex, University of Leeds).

About 1.5 km west of Al Ashkharah there are pillow lavas, basic dykes, feldspar-rich mylonitized gabbros and layered bastite-bearing ultramafic rocks. Shear zones in the ultramafic rocks trend in all directions, implying that they predate the emplacment of the Melange. Elsewhere there are several isolated hills of gabbro, probably ophiolitic; one is immediately east of the east flank of Jebel Ja'alan; another, c. 12 km ENE of Jebel Ja'alan (loc. 1052, flyout), is a prominent hill consisting mostly of coarse layered gabbro with some fine-grained, highly sheared gabbro and pods of serpentinite replacing harzburgite; another immediately east of the road, some 25 km south of Ras al Hadd, yielded K−Ar ages of 104−110 Ma (D. C. Rex, whole rock and mineral ages). Many small outcrops of basalt may also be ophiolitic.

Fayah Sandstone: Late Cretaceous

A number of fairly coherent clastic sequences occurs apparently as part of the Batain Melange (Fig. 5). Although differing in facies, they are correlated and ascribed to a single Formation because they are all characterized by quartz-rich lithologies but primarily because they contain, or are associated with, distinctive debris flows containing large crystalline basement blocks. Five facies are distinguished (Fig. 6).

Facies 1 − Cross-bedded sandstones. These are decimetre- to metre-thick beds of cross-bedded quartz sandstones. Grains are medium to coarse, well sorted and moderately rounded. Shaly interbeds are rare or absent. Tabular to asymptotic cross sets vary with bed thickness, from a few cm to 2 m. There are units which contain large boulders, up to several metres diameter, of limestone, volcanic and granitic rocks, in an unstratified matrix of quartz arenite. The clean, well sorted and cross-bedded sandstones suggest shallow water current action. The boulder beds are thought to be debris flows from a nearby scarp.

Facies II − Turbiditic sandstones and debris flows. This facies consists mostly of centimetre-to metre-bedded greywackes with interbedded shales. Beds commonly show scoured bases and upward-grading from coarse grit to fine sand-stone. Parallel laminae and ripple cross-sets occur in some bed tops. Convolute laminae and sedimentary dykes, indicating dewatering, are common. In thickly-bedded sequences, shaly interbeds are reduced or absent, resulting in bed amalgamation. Trace fossils include bedding-parallel burrows and feeding traces. Within this sequence are debris flows up to 20 m thick. These contain folded fragments of broken-up bedding and matrix-supported conglomerates, with clasts of granite, limestone and chert. The laterally continuous graded beds with sole marks indicate turbidite deposition. The coarse grains, thick bedding and immaturity of the sands suggests a nearby source. Microfossils from shaly interbeds often have siliceous coatings, suggesting deep water, possibly several hundred metres.

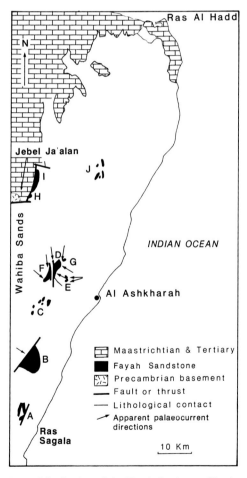

Fig. 5. Distribution of the Fayah Sandstone (Sand Bodies A−J).

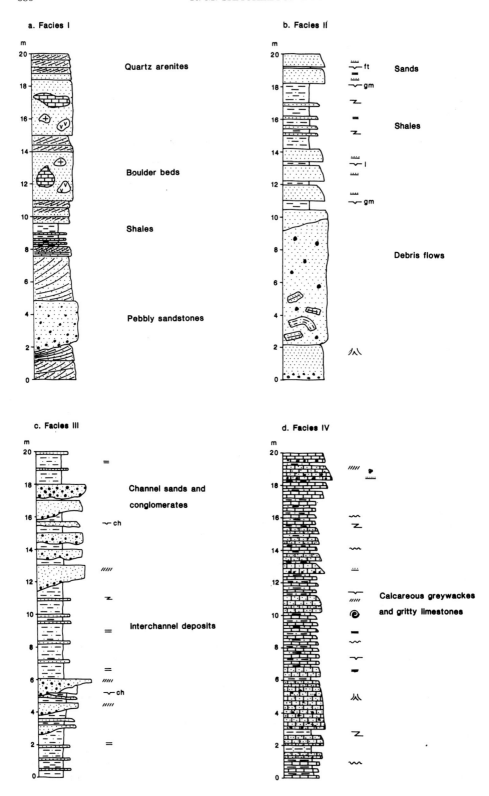

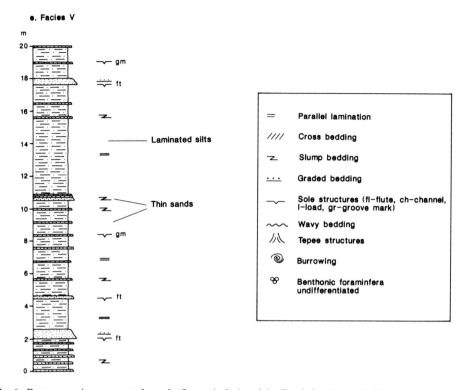

Fig. 6. Representative sequence from the five main facies of the Fayah Sandstone. I, Cross-bedded sandstones; II, Turbiditic sandstones and debris flows; III, Channel sandstones and conglomerates; IV, Calcareous turbidites; V, Laminated siltstones and thin sandstones.

Facies III — Channel sandstones and conglomerates. This facies consists of coarsening-upwards cycles of channelled sandstones and conglomerates, separated by laminated silt-stones and shales. Each *c.* 10 m thick cycle begins with dm-bedded, channelled sandstones which pass up into pebbly sandstones and occasionally clast-supported conglomeratic beds. Each sequence is abruptly overlain by laminated silts and shales with occasional thin sandstones like those of Facies II, as are the clasts in the conglomerates (granites, blue/grey lime mud-stones and packstones, and chert). These sequences lie within thick turbidites and are intrepreted as distributory channels feeding upper turbidite fan lobes. The (abandoned) channels were covered by interchannel mud and silt.

Facies IV — Calciturbidites. These are centimetre–decimetre thick beds of calcareous greywackes and gritty limestones, with inter-bedded shales and a few pebbly beds and con-glomerates. Sedimentary features are similar to those of Facies II; graded beds with basal scour marks are common. No debris flows have been found. Trace fossils (*Chrondrites* and *Cosmorhaphe*) are common on bed tops and bases; these calciturbidites only differ from those of Facies II in having a carbonate source. They differ from other calciturbidites in the area in being gritty or pebbly in parts.

Facies V — Laminated siltstones and thin sandstones. These are uniform sequences of thinly-bedded and laminated friable, buff to yellow and in part calcareous siltstones with thin sand beds generally fine grained and lat-erally continuous. Some are graded, and rarely ripple-laminated; bed bases commonly show flutes, grooves, other tool marks and trace fos-sils. There are occasional coarse-grained beds up to 1 m thick. The depositional environment may have been a distal submarine fan, or be-tween distributory lobes in a proximal upper- or mid-fan.

These various facies are stratigraphically as-sociated (Table 1) and so are all included in the Fayah Sandstone (type locality Jebel Fayah). There is no clear change in facies or clast content from north to south of the area. Debris flows are commoner in the south (Sand Bodies A−E, Fig. 5 & Table 1); the nature of the blocks in them is remarkably constant, with pink granite and limestone in nearly every debris flow. Both Permian and Upper Cretaceous limestone blocks have been identified in the south, where volcanic rocks, ranging from basic to acid, foliated granodiorite and hornblende-biotite-plagioclase gneiss were also seen.

The source of sands and debris flows appears to have been the same since the detrital minerals, predominantly quartz, microcline, orthoclase and oligoclase, match the minerals in the clasts. It is not possible to tell the real transport direction (cf. Fig. 5) because the sand bodies have been tectonically transported and probably rotated. The only exception may be Sand Body B which covers *c.* 5 × 8 km in the core of the Fayah Dome. Here a few (six) cross-bedding measurements indicate transport from the WNW, but even this large structure may have been rotated, so the data are probably not significant.

The palaeontological evidence (details in Appendix) indicates an early Maastrichtian age for the Fayah Sandstone. A Late Cretaceous, probably Maastrichtian, age was obtained from a calcarenite clast with abundant microfauna, from a debris flow in Sand Body A (loc. 584, flyout), and ?Campanian-early Maastrichtian (from near loc. 412, flyout) and Maastrichtian (loc. 682, flyout), both from microfaunas in calciturbidites (Facies IV, Sand Body B). The Fayah Sandstone also contains Permian foraminifera, presumably derived.

The Hawasina Complex in the Batain area

The rocks mapped as Hawasina are indistinguishable lithologically from their assumed correlatives in the Melange. They are distinguished by the absence of exotics and the more orderly arrangement of beds. They recur in the far southwest and northwest of Ras Jibsch, and at the western side of the area south of Jebel Ja'alan (see Fig. 1 & flyout). Most of the rocks in these areas are reddish cherts and shales, with some green shaly cherts and minor calciturbidites. In the far south, in a syncline WNW of Ras Jibsch and another some 4 km northwest of Ras as Sagallah, sequences about 500 m thick can be seen.

Structure

Most of the deformation in the Batain Melange is pre-Tertiary and probably pre-late Maastrichtian. This is evident from the contrast between the intense and complex deformation of the Melange and the Hawasina and the very weak deformation of the gently-dipping Tertiary cover in the nothern part of the area and in Tertiary outliers farther south. The stronger but local Tertiary deformation on the flanks of the Jebel Ja'alan Uplift is described elsewhere (Filbrandt *et al.* 1990). The extent of involvement of the Maastrichtian, which directly overlies parts of the Jebel Ja'alan Precambrian basement, is uncertain but it was not affected by the sort of deformation seen in the Melange and the Hawasina Comple . This may be either because the deformation occurred before those Maastrichtian beds were deposited, or because the deformation was thin-skinned and involved only beds at a higher level, above a decollement. This, and the relation of the deformation in the Batain area to that in the Oman Mountains, west of the Jebel Ja'alan Uplift, is discussed below.

Pre-Tertiary structures

The intensity and complexity of deformation increase from south to north. The structures seen in the better exposed areas are described from south to north; the significance of these changes is then discussed.

The southernmost structure seen, *c.* 5 km northwest of the Ras Jibsch Ophiolite, is an open syncline with a steep axial surface striking N−S and containing dolomitic limestones, green cherts and red cherts in ascending sequence. A complementary anticline, 0.5 km to the west, was inaccessible. Both structures plunge north. Eight kilometres farther north, the same succession is seen on 'Jebel B' in a similar open syncline which trends NE−SW and plunges southwest (Fig. 7). The rocks in these simple structures are all regarded as Hawasina, not Melange. Northwest of this syncline there is an area exposing NNE-trending open periclines with many thrusts and faults. At one place, east-dipping thrusts, 20−50 m apart, repeat a group of beds in an imbricate stack. On the west flank of the 'Jebel B' syncline, an east-dipping thrust is seen. There is no definite evidence here of structures pre-dating the obvious folds, but the simplest interpretation of the data is that there are folded thrusts. Thrusts appear to be required because Fayah Sandstone, in the core of the anticline, is flanked by a mixed sequence of cherty limestones and turbidites, which are in turn structurally overlain by more Fayah Sandstone (Fig. 7). Immediately west of this group of structures is the southernmost exposure of the 'Melange with limestone blocks'

Table 1. *Lithology, thickness and age of Sand Bodies A–J in the Fayah Sandstone.*

Sand Body	A	B	C	D	E	F	G	H	I	J
Lithological sequence (Facies V, IV, III, II, I)	X (I)	X / X (II)	X / X / X?	X	X / X	X / X	X / X	X	X	X
Exposed thickness	200 m	700 m	?	200 m	200 m	500 m	?	50 m (+200 m)	50 m ?	50 m
Debris flows contain:										
Pink granite & adamlite	X	X		X	X					X
Microgranophyre, Volcanics★	XB	X BDR		X	X					
Mafic plutonics★		X A								
Permian limestone	X	X								
Cretaceous limestone	X	X		X						
Chert		X	X	X	X					X
Estimated age (uncertainty limits)										
Maastrichtian	↔									
Campanian					↔	↔	↔	↔	↔	↔
Santonian								↔		
Coniacian ⎱ Presumed										
Permian ⎰ derived										

★ B = basalt; D = dacite; R = rhyolite; A = anorthosite

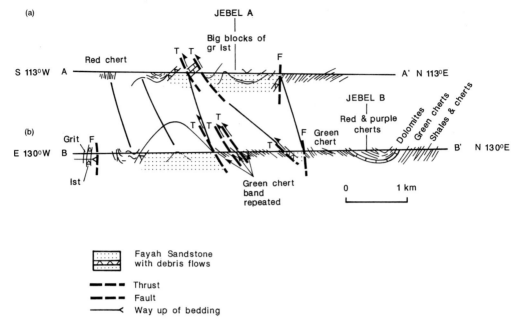

Fig. 7. Structural sections through (a) 'Jebel A' and (b) 'Jebel B'. Lines of sections (A'−A'& B−B') are shown on the flyout.

There are other exposures of this Melange 5 km south of Jebel Fayah. Between 'Jebel B' and the Fayah Dome 10 km farther north, scattered outcrops show a generally NNE strike, but it is clear, in hills *c.* 5 km south of Jebel Fayah, that a major south-facing recumbent fold, plunging 20°/100°, is earlier than the dominant NNE-trending upright folds. These NNE-trending, west-vergent structures are referred to as the Batain Fold and Thrust Belt.

The Fayah Dome (Fig. 8), *c.* 5 km in diameter, appears from dips and strikes to be simple, but thrusts are exposed at the base of the calciturbidites (Facies IV of the Fayah Sandstone) and the distribution of the debris flows also suggests repetition by thrusting. On the south flank of Jebel Fayah, recumbent fold trend *c.* SW−NE and are apparently overturned to the NW. All of these structures appear to be earlier than the open anticline which forms the Fayah Dome. Dips in the Dome are mostly 45° or less, and often less than 20°. There is no clear hinge so the axial trace is poorly defined but trends *c.* 170° and, in the southern part of the Dome, plunges gently south. If this anticline represents the same phase as the folds with similar trend to the north and south, the Dome must represent an area of greater rigidity, suggesting that underneath it there is either a very thick sequence of Fayah Sandstone or a

basement high, to account for the contrast between the large wavelength of the Fayah Dome and the generally small wavelength of the folds to the north and south.

The Fayah Sandstone is overlain, to the southeast and northeast, by 'Melange with limestones blocks' − blocks of Permian limestones, with some of basalts, and cherts and other rocks.

North of the Fayah Dome, NNE-trending structures continue to dominate. A few km north of the Dome, where the inverted beds dip 70−75° E and are overturned to the WNW, is the southernmost sign of the strong westerly vergence of tight NNE-trending folds which become common only a short distance farther north.

About 8 km S30°W of Jebel Qarari, a small group of hills shows a complex pattern of interference folds involving the Fayah Sandstone; it was not possible to determine the trend or vergence of the earlier structures.

An E−W section (Fig. 9) a few kilometres farther north, shows the character of the NNE-trending structures. A tightly packed sequence of cherts, shales and turbidites is repeated by thrusts and tight folds. Westward overturning and east-dipping axial planes and thrusts show a consistent westerly vergence. The structures suggest a low-angle detachment at depth. However, despite the apparent simplicity of these

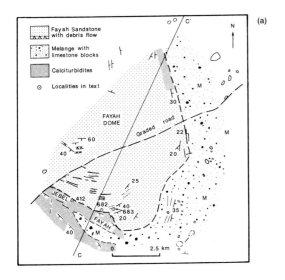

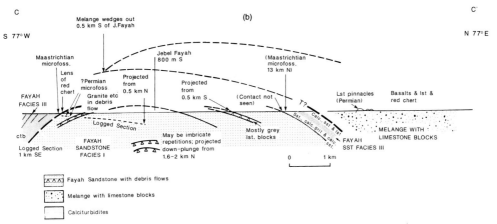

Fig. 8. (a) Map and (b) structural section of the Fayah Dome. The line of section C−C' is shown on the flyout.

west-verging structures, there is evidence of earlier structures. Downward-facing folds show that in some places the beds were inverted before the main NNE-trending structures developed. These earlier structures are clearer on Jebel Qarari where the Qarari Limestone and the structurally underlying beds are inverted and dip gently NNE. Thrusts, also dipping NNE, break the block into a series of slices, with imbrication below the Qarari Limestone. The NNE-trending structures swerve around the Qarari block in a manner that shows that the transverse structures in it are earlier than those trending NNE.

10 km ENE of Jebel Qarari is a simple open syncline trending 012° and plunging gently south (see flyout). It is surrounded by, and structurally overlies, 'Melange with limestone blocks'.

The contact is not seen but there is no indication that it is tectonic. Stratification within the syncline, round the hinge and along the limbs, is parallel to the contact. The basal beds include laminated cherts, grainstones with ripple-drift and small channels, pelagic mudstones, a 20 cm bed of breccia with fragments of different-coloured limestones and a thick cross-bedded grit. The dips in the syncline are regular, in contrast to the quite different and variable dips and strikes in the Melange beneath. The simplest intrepretation is that the beds in the syncline stratigraphically overlie the Melange. The age of the beds in the syncline is not known. The Permian microfossils identified are probably derived. There is no evidence for the alternative, that the syncline is a slab in the Melange.

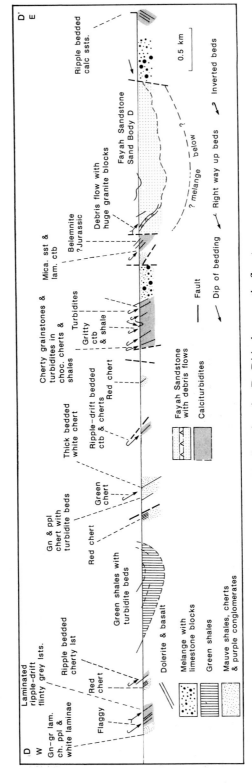

Fig. 9. Structural section of the area N of the Fayah Dome. The line of section D–D' is shown on the flyout.

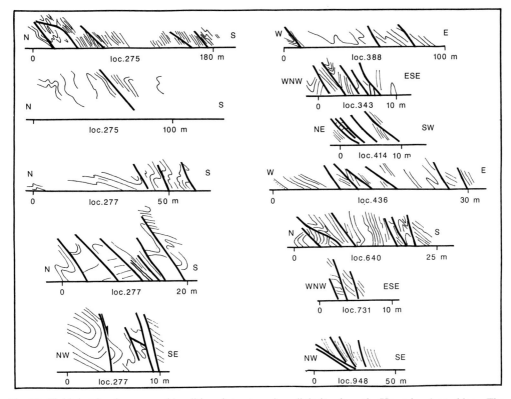

Fig. 10. Field sketches from several localities of structures in radiolarites from the Hawasina Assemblage. The heavy lines are thrusts or faults, other lines represent bedding traces.

In the area east of Bilad Bani Bu Ali the structures in the Hawasina radiolarites are well seen. In them, in contrast to the thicker calciturbidite units, folds are usually on a small scale, with amplitudes and wavelengths of a few metres. Associated with these moderately tight folds are innumerable sub-parallel faults. As shown in Fig. 10, the general sense of movement is towards the north and west.

11 km NNE of Jebel Qarari, in the 'Black Hills' (Fig. 11), earlier major recumbent folds, trending roughly E−W, are folded by an antiform trending NNE and by a parallel minor syncline. On the section the early recumbent folds appear to face down to the north but more work is needed to confirm this.

In the south there are extensive areas of 'Melange with limestone blocks' especially towards the coast, but the rest of the rocks could be interpreted as complexly deformed Hawasina Assemblage and Fayah Sandstone, rather than melange. In contrast, the arrangement of all these rocks in the northern half of the area is so irregular and disjointed that it can only be described as melange; this is the 'Batain Melange'.

The Batain Melange in the northern half of the area shows the effects of several deformation phases: fold interference patterns and refolding of early recumbent folds and flat thrusts. The relation of these phases to the process which produced the Melange is not clear. In the north half of the area there is no consistently oriented set of structures corresponding to those trending NNE in the south: the axial traces curve from one direction to another, sometimes through 90°. There are few records of overturning in the northern half of the area: of thirteen measurements, seven are of westward overturning, four northwards and two southwards. Persistent right way up dips to the southeast, in the area east of Jebel Ja'alan, suggest repetition by northwestward thrusting; in some areas of cherts, dips are persistently towards the south or southeast, indicating vergence towards the north or northwest. East and northeast of Jebel Ja'alan the

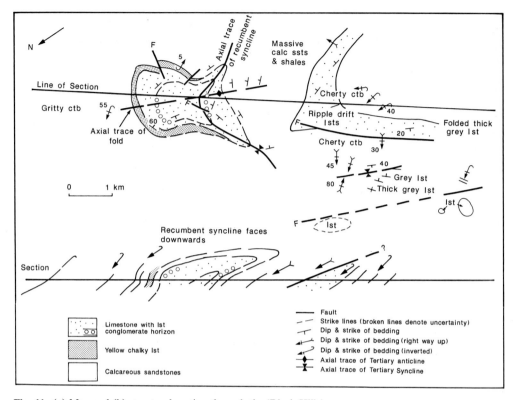

Fig. 11. (a) Map and (b) structural section through the 'Black Hills'.

strikes curve counterclockwise from north to northwest. Farther north the strikes are very irregular (Figs 12 & 13).

Structural Relation of the Batain area, the Jebel Ja'alan Uplift and the Oman Mountains

As discussed below, the Batain Melange is correlated with the Hawasina (Oman) Melange. The two, at nearest 40 km apart, are separated by the Jebel Ja'alan Uplift (see Filbrandt *et al.* 1990). It is argued here that the NNE-trending structures of the Batain fold and thrust belt were formerly continuous with the structures in the Hawasina Complex of the Oman Mountains, that the Batain and Hawasina (Oman) Melanges can be correlated, and that the structures in the Batain area are the result of obduction of the same plate as formed the Semail Ophiolite (Shackleton & Ries 1990). It would follow that the sheets of highly deformed Hawasina Group and Batain Melange formerly extended across what is now the Jebel Ja'alan Uplift. The ?uppermost Campanian/lower Maastrichtian Qahlah Formation of Jebel Ja'alan contains

cherts thought to be derived from the Hawasina allochthon northwest and west of Jebel Ja'alan (Filbrandt *et al.* 1990). It thus post-dates the obduction of the Semail Ophiolite and the Hawasina nappes.

The Batain Melange: extent, age, origin & correlation; comparisons

Extent of the Melange

Because areas of red cherts several kilometres long, included in the Batain Melange, are indistinguishable lithologically from red cherts regarded as Hawasina, the limits of the Melange are not sharply definable but merely represent a change to a more disruptive style of deformation. More important is the absence of exotics (Permian limestone, Triassic megabreccias, ophiolites) outside the Melange. The limit on the map (flyout) is shown on this basis; it is most doubtful in the extreme south. The limit is also drawn on the assumption that the 'Melange with limestone blocks' is part of the Batain Melange; it was mapped separately because it is impracticable to map it as a mosaic of separate

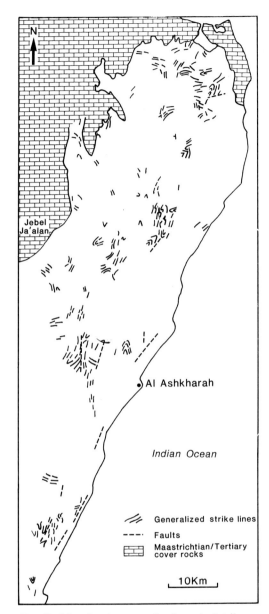

Fig. 12. Map showing generalized trend of strike lines in the Batain coast area.

Size, shape and arrangement of the clasts

The size of the individual clasts varies according to rock type. Maximum dimension of the pink *'ammonitico rosso'* type limestones is *c.* 4 m, the ophiolite clasts and the Limestone Megabreccias *c.* 200 m, the Qarari Limestone *c.* 2 km, the Fayah Sandstone at least 6 km if the Fayah Dome exposure is allochthonous, and the Hawasina cherts *c.* 10 km. Small clasts of most rock types occur, but not of the Fayah Sandstones, unless these have not been recognized.

The clasts, whatever their size, are angular or lenticular: no rounded ones were seen. Actual boundaries are rarely exposed. Matrix is rarely seen and must be a very small part of the Melange. Where it is seen, it is scaly, usually reddish and shaly. A map of one of the better exposed areas of Melange is shown in Fig. 13. It can be seen that the orientation of the bedding varies abruptly from one clast to another, that many of them are not elongated parallel to the bedding, and that they cannot be plausibly fitted together by assuming that they are just separated by many faults. In many places the limits of individual clasts cannot be inferred because of sand cover, so it is uncertain whether isolated outcrops, especially of unstratified limestone, are separated by erosion or by disruption. Where bedding can be seen in such isolated limestone outcrops, as near the road *c.* 21 km SSW of Ras al Hadd, dips and strikes are similar enough to suggest that several outcrops are just separated by erosion and sand cover.

Distribution of different clast types

The distribution of rocks within the Melange shows no significant changes from north to south or east to west. Distinctive types such as the ophiolites, Qarari Limestone, Limestone Megabreccia and the Fayah Sandstone with slide breccias, containing granite and other clasts, all occur apparently randomly. Their distribution cannot plausibly be attributed to in situ dislocation of a once-continuous succession, complex though the tectonic deformation is. The rocks cannot ever all have formed a single continuous sequence; for example, the ophiolites represent Cretaceous oceanic crust which cannot have been either underlain or overlain by Permian and Triassic sediments. All of the rocks must be allochthonous, derived from outside the Batain area, which is thought to be underlain by continental crust, whereas many of the rocks in the Batain Melange are, as shown above, of deep-water origin.

clasts since all that is exposed is many small isolated outcrops mostly of limestones, variously oriented, surrounded by sand. The 'Melange with limestone blocks' cannot be a separate tectonic unit, as is the 'Melange with limestone blocks' in the Ankara Melange (Norman 1984) because it is distributed almost randomly, not confined to any one zone (see flyout).

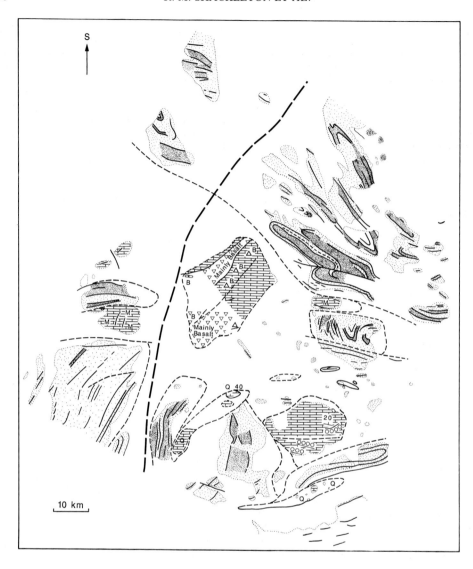

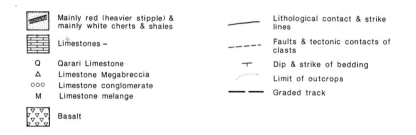

Fig. 13. Typical map distribution pattern of the 'Melange with limestone blocks'. The centre point of the map is located at 59° 44″E/22° 23′N and 18 km SSW (200) from Ras al Hadd.

Age

A maximum age for the Melange is set by the youngest clasts in it. This seems to be Campanian–Maastrichtian, the age of the Fayah Sandstone. The doubt is whether the Fayah Sandstone is really a component of the Melange and not younger. It is curious that no small clasts of Fayah Sandstone have been recognized, and none in the 'Melange with limestone blocks'. The Fayah Sandstone of the Fayah Dome is structurally overlain by 'Melange with limestone blocks' but the contact is tectonic and could be due to later thrusting. There is no known stratigraphic contact of Fayah Sandstone on Melange, unless the beds, including coarse cross-bedded grit, in the syncline 10 km ENE of Jebel Qarari (see above) belong to the Fayah Sandstone and are in stratigraphic contact on Melange, neither of which can be proved. On balance, the Fayah Sandstone is thought to be a component of the Melange. If not, the Melange could be earlier, but still Late Cretaceous from the age of the ophiolite clasts. The minimum age is pre-Tertiary since it is overlain unconformably by lower Tertiary beds. If it is associated with the obduction of the Semail Ophiolite (see below), its age is Campanian–Maastrichtian (Robertson 1987). It is concluded that the formation of the Melange, which may have taken some time, was completed by about middle Maastrichtian.

Correlation: Batain and Hawasina (Oman) Melanges

The Batain and Hawasina Melanges are at nearest 40 km apart, east and west of the Jebel Ja'alan Uplift. The Hawasina Melange (Graham 1980; in part equivalent to the Oman Melange of Glennie et al. 1974) is everywhere close to, and nowhere significantly south of, the structurally overlying Semail Ophiolite. In contrast the Batain Melange is nowhere near any outcrop of the Semail Ophiolite nor in Batain is there any Melange with serpentinite matrix which underlies the Semail Ophiolite, nor any subophiolite metamorphic rocks.

The Batain and Hawasina Melanges both contain Permian and Triassic limestone exotics which were both, in the Hawasina Melange, deposited on a substrate of basaltic pillow lavas (Glennie et al. 1970) but in the Batain Melange apparently only the Triassic ones. Both Melanges consist largely of Hawasina-type radiolarian cherts; both contain limestone slide breccias with volcanic clasts and associated with radiolarian cherts. But no ophiolite fragments are recognized in the Hawasina Melange (Lippard et al. 1986) nor any equivalent of the Fayah Sandstone. The matrix of both, seldom seen in the Batain Melange, is similar red shale or sheared mudstone. The Hawasina Melange is structurally underlain by the Hawasina Assemblage of hemipelagic and pelagic turbidites and radiolarian cherts. In the Batain, the only indication that the Melange may overlie the Hawasina Assemblage is that S of the Jebel Ja'alan basement uplift, the Hawasina is near to, and the Melange farther from, the basement inlier. The Hawasina Melange is interpreted as partly olistostromic, partly tectonic (Lippard et al. 1986) while the Batain Melange is here interpreted as primarily tectonic. We conclude that the similarities are such as to indicate the correlation of the two. But it seems unlikely that the Semail Ophiolite ever covered the Batain area. More probably the Hawasina and the Batain Melange sheets moved by gravitational obduction tectonism (Bechennec et al. 1988).

Origin

The criteria which together distinguish the main types of melange are summarized in Table 2. There is controversy over the origin of many, perhaps even most, of these and other melanges, presumably because few if any are the result of a single process.

The Batain Melange shows all the features characteristic of a tectonic melange, in particular indefinite, non-stratigraphic, contacts and scanty matrix, indicating that it is not an olistostrome or a diapiric melange. Some gravity-driven sliding probably contributed but mud diapirism is excluded since the exotics could not have come from below. In its general aspect the Batain Melange is similar to the melange stretching 700 km along the south side of the Indus–Tsangpo suture in south Tibet; its deformation recalls the Antalya Complex of south Turkey.

Many of the melanges in the Tethyan Zone are ophiolitic melanges (Gansser 1974), containing similar exotics, notably ophiolite and Permian and Triassic limestones often associated with basalts. They include the Ankara and SE Turkey melanges the coloured melanges in Iran & Afghanistan and the Kailas & Indus–Tsangpo melanges, south of the Indus–Tsangpo suture. Their composite, part tectonic, part olistostromic origin, is stressed by Gansser (1974). If, as seems likely, most of the thrusts which carried them were relief overthrusts, on which the thrust masses were driven over the

Table 2. *Features used to distinguish between the different origins of melanges*

	Tectonic melange	Olistostrome	Diapiric melange
Matrix	Scanty, sheared. May preserve bedding	Unstratified shaly clay, abundant	Unstratified scaly clay (often illite, smectite or montmorillonite) predominant
Clasts	Often lenticular or boudin-shaped, or tabular, or angular. May be several km long often in contact. May be exotic (derived laterally). Randomly oriented	Often angular. May be several km long. Matrix-supported. Often small stratigraphic range but may include exotics (derived laterally). Large slabs may be flat inverted. May suggest ghost stratigraphy	Often angular. Often small (cm) but may be larger. Matrix-supported. Derived from below. Mud injections into cracks in clasts. Randomly oriented. May include delicate rocks only transportable in fluid matrix
Contacts	Tectonic, may be vague, gradational	Concordant, stratigraphic	Discordant (diapirs) merging to concordant (extrusions)
Size & shape	May extend >100 km. Often longer perpendicular to transport direction	May extend >100 km. Often longer parallel to transport direction	Diapirs to a few km diameter; Sills, lateral injections, extruded tongues to tens of km long
Tectonic environment	May have been pushed up-slope. Subduction & collision zones; extensional zones?	Moved down-slope. Trench; slopes (various)	Especially forearcs
Examples	Franciscan (Hsu 1968). Antalya (Robertson & Woodcock 1982). Hawasina (Oman)? (Glennie et al. 1974; Searle & Graham 1982; Robertson 1987)	Gwna Melange, Anglesey & Lleyn (Matley 1913; Greenly 1919; Shackleton 1969). N Apennines (Abbate et al. 1961). Coloured melange, Iran (Haynes & McQuillan 1974). Ankara (Norman 1984; cf. Bailey & McCallien 1953)	W Timor (Barber et al. 1986). Barbados (Brown & Westbrook 1988)

topographic surface, frontal collapse, sliding and mixing would be inevitable and strict distinction of types of melange unrealistic.

Tectonic interpretation of the Batain Melange is discussed elsewhere (Shackleton & Ries 1990) in a regional context. They conclude that the emplacement of the Batain Melange and the intense deformation of the NNE–SSW trending west-vergent Batain fold and thrust belt were the results of relative plate motion towards the west and southwest, at an acute angle to the Masirah Fault margin of the Arabian Plate.

This work was funded by Amoco Production Company (International) through an operating grant awarded to W. H. Kanes, Earth Sciences and Resources Institute, University of South Carolina. Amoco Production Company (International) and the Oman Ministry of Petroleum and Minerals are thanked for permission to publish this paper. A. J. Barber and N. H. Woodcock are thanked for their constructive criticisms of this paper.

References

ABBATE, E. B. & BORTOLOTTI, V. 1961. Tentativo di interpretazione dei livelli di argille scagliose intercalate nella parte alta del macigno lungo l'allineamento del M. Prado — Chianti (Appennino settentrionale). *Bollettino della Società Geologica Italiana*, **80**, 335–342.

BAILEY, E. B. & McCALLIEN, W. J. 1953. Serpentine lavas, the Ankara Melange and the Anatolian thrust. *Transactions of the Royal Society of Edinburgh*, **LXIII**, 403–442.

BARBER, A. J., TJOKROSAPOETO, S. & CHARLTON T. R. 1986. Mud volcanoes, shale diapirs, wrench faults and melanges in accretionary complexes, Eastern Indonesia. *Bulletin of the American Association of Petroleum Geologists*, **70**, 1729–1746.

BECHENNEC, F., LE METOUR, J., RABY, D., VILLEY, M. & BEURRIER, M. 1988. The Hawasina Basin: A fragment of a starved passive continental margin, thrust over the Arabian Platform during obduction of the Semail Nappe. *Tectonophysics*, **151**, 323–343.

BROWN, K. & WESTBROOK, G. K. 1988. Mud diapirism and subcretion in the Barbados Ridge Accretionary Complex: The Role of Fluids in Accretionary Processes. *Tectonics*, **7**, 613–640.

FILBRANDT, J. B., NOLAN, S. C. & RIES, A. C. 1990. Late Cretaceous and early Tertiary evolution of Jebel Ja'alan and adjacent areas, NE Oman. *In*: ROBERTSON, A. M. F., SEARLE, M. P. & RIES, A. C. (eds) *The Geology and Tectonics of the Oman Region*. Geological Society, London, Special Publication, **49**, 697–714.

GANSSER, A. 1974. The ophiolitic melange, a world-wide problem on Tethyan examples. *Eclogae geologicae Helvetiae*, **67**, 459–507.

GLENNIE, K. W., BOEUF, M. G. A., HUGHES CLARKE, M. W., MOODY-STUART, M., PILAAR, W. F. H. & REINHARDT, B. M. 1974. Geology of the Oman Mountains. *Verhandelingen van het Koninklijk Nederlands Geologisch Mijnbouwkundig Gennootschapp*, **31**.

GRAHAM, G. M. 1980. Evolution of a passive margin and nappe emplacement in the Oman Mountains. *Proceedings of the International Ophiolite Symposium, Nicosia Cyprus*, 414–423.

GREENLY, E. 1919. *The Geology of Anglesey*. 2 vols. Geological Survey of Great Britain.

HAYNES, S. J. & McQUILLAN, H. 1974. Evolution of the Zagros Suture Zone, Southern Iran. *Bulletin of the Geological Society of America*, **85**, 739–744.

HSU, K. J. 1968. Principles of Melanges and their bearing on the Franciscan-Knoxville paradox. *Bulletin of the Geological Society of America*, **79**, 1063–74.

LIPPARD, S. J., SHELTON, A. W. & GASS, I. G. 1986. *The ophiolite of Northern Oman*. Geological Society, London, Memoir **11**, 1–78.

MATLEY, C. A. 1913. The Geology of Bardsey Island. *Quarterly Journal of the Geological Society of London*, **69**, 514–33.

NORMAN, T. N. 1984. The role of the Ankara Melange in the development of Anatolia (Turkey). *In*: DIXON, J. E. & ROBERTSON, A. H. F. (eds) *The Geological Evolution of the Eastern Mediterranean*, Geological Society, London, Special Publication **17**, 441–7.

ROBERTSON, A. H. F. 1987. The transition from a passive margin to an upper Cretaceous foreland basin related to ophiolite emplacement in the Oman Mountains. *Bulletin of the Geological Society of America*, **99**, 613–653.

—— & WOODCOCK, N. H. 1982. Sedimentary history of the southwestern segment of the Mesozoic–Tertiary continental margin, south-western Turkey. *Eclogae geologicae Helvetiae*, **75**, 517–562.

SEARLE, M. P. & GRAHAM, G. M. 1982. 'Oman Exotics' — Oceanic carbonate build-ups associated with the early stages of continental rifting. *Geology*, **10**, 43–49.

SHACKLETON, R. M. 1969. The Precambrian of North Wales. *In*: WOOD, A. (ed.) *The Precambrian and Palaeozoic rocks of North Wales*. Cambridge University Press. 1–22.

—— & RIES, A. C. 1990. Tectonics of the Masirah Fault Zone and eastern Oman. *In*: ROBERTSON, A. M. F., SEARLE, M. P. & RIES, A. C. (eds) *The Geology and Tectonics of the Oman Region*. Geological Society, London, Special Publication **49**, 715–724.

Appendix: faunal identifications

(locality numbers referred to below are plotted on the flyout)

(i) Qarari Limestone

Jebel Qarari
(a) Loc. 604 — yellow band near base of Nodular Limestone
Paladin sp. (Carboniferous/end mid-Permian)   (RO)

Timoroblastus coronatus Wanner   ⎫ recorded from
Sphaeroschisma somoholense Wanner   ⎬ Permian   (DVA)
                                            ⎭ of Timor

Fusulinids   (SCN)

(b) White bands 15 m above base of Nodular Limestone
Camerisma sp.   ⎫
Uncinunellina (?) sp.   ⎪ earliest Permian
Choristites sp.   ⎬ (Sakmarian)
Composita crassa Cooper & Grant   ⎪ (DVA)
Juresiana omanensis Hudson & Sudbury   ⎭

Gerthia (Polyaoelia) angusta (Rothpletz) ⎫
?Basleophyllum sp.   ⎬ Late Permian
Pleramplexus sp.   ⎭ (BR)
Platycerus sp.   (DVA)
Fragments of fenestellid bryozoan   (PDT)

'Black Hills'
Faunas from locs 845, 848 & 852 were identified; their stratigraphic relations are uncertain.
(a) Loc. 845–7 m gritty calcareous turbidite with abundant derived microfauna
Timorphyllum sp. — Late Permian (genus)   (BR)

(b) Loc. 848 — massive reef limestone
Pavastephyllum (Pseudocarniaphyllum) cf. *undaformis* (Flugel 1972)
— Late Permian (Ufimian — Kazanian)
[NB: might be a single branch of *Akagophyllum tibeticum* (Reed 1920) (BR)]
Wentzenella cf. *regularis* (Fontaine 1961) — Late Permian (Kazanian)   (BR)
(c) Loc. 852 — pink algal reef limestone
Polythecatis denticulatus (Huang 1932) — Early Permian (Artinskian)
Wentzelloidas (Multinurthus) lunatus (Flugel 1972)
The sediments in the 'Black Hills' clearly extend from at least Early Permian (Artinskian) to Late
Permian (Ufimian–Kazanian).

(ii) pink limestones

(a) Loc. 941. — pink reef limestone associated with grey Qarari limestone
cf. *Dielasma emargination* Cooper & Grant — described from Artinskian–Kungurian
(Early Permian)   (DVA)
Pleramplexus sp. Early Permian   (BR)
(b) Loc. 579 — pink crinoidal limestone with corals and brachiopods
Heterocoenites crassus Gert 1921   Late Permian?   ⎫
Lophophyllidium sp. Late Carboniferous — Permian (genus) }   ⎬ (BR)
(c) Loc. 753 — massive grey and pinkish algal limestone with crinoid fragments, brachiopods and
corals
Timorphyllum sp. — Late Permian   (BR)
Wentzelella osubadiensis (Igo 1959) — Early Permian (Artinskian — Kungurian)   (BR)
It is concluded that the Qarari Limestone ranges from Early to Late Permian in age.

(iii) Green grits

(a) 'Jebel X' (loc. 302) — massive limestones and breccias with blocks of fusulinid limestone
Linoproductus cf. *L. cora* (D'Orbigny) Early Carboniferous — Later Permian   (DVA)
Pterophyllum sp. Permian (genus)   (BR)

(iv) Limestone Megabreccias: faunas from limestone blocks

(a) Loc. M133
Prionolobus sp. indet. ?   Early Triassic
Gyronites or Gyrolecanites   (m. Scythian)
A possible member of the family Hedenstromiidae   (HO)

(b) Locs M66, M137, R191 & 1036   Typical of Permian
Wentzelellitis senni (Minato & Kato 1965):   family
loc. M66   Waagenophyllidae
Wentzelellites sicula (Galitelli 1954):   (BR)
locs M137 & R191
Lonsdaleiastraea sp: locs 1036 & M137

(v) Fayah Sandstone

(a) Loc. 584A — Sand Body A: calcarenite
clast in boulder horizon

Aragonia sp.   Late Cretaceous
Gavellinela sp.   probably Maastrichtian
Cibicides sp.?   (MS & MH)
Buliminids Polymorphinids
Orbitoid fragments   Permian, presumed
Palaeotextularids   derived   (SCN)

(b) Loc. 682 — Sand Body B: calciturbidite
(Facies IV) with 1 cm clasts of micrite with
calcispheres in a foraminiferal (orbitoid)
packstone and fragments of red algae,
echinoderms and bivalves
Orbitoides cf. *media* (v. common)
Siderolites calcitrapoides (common)   Maastrichtian (MS & MH)
Omphalocyclus macroporus

(c) Near loc. 412 — Sand Body B (collected by
E. J. Biller 1984): mudstone, argillaceous
siltstone and very fine-grained sandstone
Globotruncana fornicata   ?Campanian—early
Globotruncana cf. *bulloides*   Maastrichtian
Rugoglobigerina rugosa   (RAKA *et al.*)
Palaeotextularids   Permian, presumed
Nodosellids   derived (SCN)

(d) Loc. 683 — Sand Body B   Permian, presumed
Palaeotextularids   derived (SCN)
?Permodiscus

(c) Loc. 776 — Sand Body C   Permian, presumed derived
Endothyrids   (SCN)

(f) Loc. 717 — Sand Body D
Nodosinellidae   Permian, presumed derived
                                           (SCN)

Above faunas identified by:
Professor D. V. Ager (DVA), University College, Swansea
R. A. K. Attewell, D. R. Clowser, A. R. I. Futyan, M. Jabubowski, N. H. Miles (RAKA *et al.*), Robertson Research International Limited
S. C. Nolan (SCN), ERI, University College, Swansea
B Rosen (BR), British Museum (Natural History), London
M. Simmons & M. G. Hart (MS & MH), Plymouth Polytechnic
P. D. Taylor (PDT), British Museum (Natural History), London
R. Owens (RO), National Museum of Wales

Late Cretaceous and early Tertiary evolution of Jebel Ja'alan and adjacent areas, NE Oman

J. B. FILBRANDT[1], S. C. NOLAN[2] & A. C. RIES[3]

[1] Shell U.K. Exploration and Production, Shell-Mex House, Strand, London WC2R 0DX, UK

[2] Earth Resources Institute, University College Swansea, Swansea SA2 8PP, UK

[3] Earth Sciences and Resources Institute, University of Reading, 19 Upper Redlands Road, Reading RG1 5JJ

Abstract: Jebel Ja'alan forms the northernmost extremity of the NNE−SSW trending Huqf−Haushi Uplift, a structural high which runs parallel to the SE continental margin of Oman. On Jebel Ja'alan Precambrian rocks, exposed in the core of this structural high, are overlain by a cover sequence of shallow water carbonate and clastic sediments of Maastrichtian to Eocene age. These cover sediments, and the structures which affect them, record a sequence of tectonic events leading to the uplift and inversion of Jebel Ja'alan in post middle Eocene times. In the Maastrichtian an extensional regime resulted in subsidence and the accumulation of fluvial clastic deposits, the Qahlah Formation, overlain by shallow marine limestones, the Simsima Formation, of Maastrichtian age. A post-Maastrichtian normal fault, the East Ja'alan Fault, downthrows Simsima Formation to the east against Precambrian basement to the west and controls the deposition of the Palaeocene/early Eocene Hasad Beds, which form debris fans distributed along the fault plane. The East Ja'alan Fault may have been linked to early extensional movement on the WNW−ESE trending North Ja'alan Fault which partly controlled deposition of the Eocene fluvial/marginal marine Rusayl Formation. A mid-Eocene transgression resulted in the deposition of the Seeb Formation shallow water limestones. All these sediments were deformed by a post middle Eocene compressional event which resulted in the formation of north−south trending asymmetric anticlines, forming a pop-up structure; the latter was controlled by a shallow level detachment dipping east which led to the detachment and removal of the Maastrichtian−Eocene sediments from Jebel Ja'alan. An associated deeper level basement ramp resulted in uplift and inversion of the Precambrian basement of Jebel Ja'alan. These compressional structures are displaced by later left-lateral strike-slip on the North Ja'alan Fault Zone.

The sedimentary and tectonic history of the Late Cretaceous to early Tertiary rocks in the Jebel Ja'alan area of NE Oman is interpreted on the basis of a reconnaissance survey in January 1985. Previously little has been published on this area apart from a few brief notes in Lees (1928) and Glennie et al. (1974). A number of informal place names are used in this paper because of a lack of named localities on the then available topographic maps.

The Jebel Ja'alan/Jebel Khamis area lies at the northeastern tip of the Arabian Peninsula between the well documented Oman Mountains tectono-sedimentary province and the eastern Arabian seaboard province, influenced by the Huqf−Haushi Uplift and the Masirah Transform Fault (Figs 1 & 2) (see also Shackleton & Ries 1990). The Oman Mountains, which lie to the W of Jebel Ja'alan, are characterized by a NW−SE structural trend developed during collision and suturing of the Tethyan Ocean in late Cretaceous times. In the south, the main structural feature is the NNE−SSW trending Huqf−Haushi Uplift, the extension of which passes through the structural axis of Jebel Ja'alan. This uplift can be traced northwards to the coast where basement is exposed at Qalhat. Many of the structures mapped on Jebel Ja'alan postdate the Late Cretaceous compressional phase in the Oman Mountains. Thus the Jebel Ja'alan area represents a significant change in regional structural pattern in both timing and style. The development of both compressional and extensional structures from late Maastrichtian to at least Oligocene times may be related to transpressional and transtensional movements on the Masirah Transform Fault (cf. Shackleton & Ries 1990).

From ROBERTSON, A. H. F., SEARLE, M. P. & RIES, A. C. (eds), 1990, *The Geology and Tectonics of the Oman Region.* Geological Society Special Publication No 49, pp 697−714

Main topographic features of NE Oman

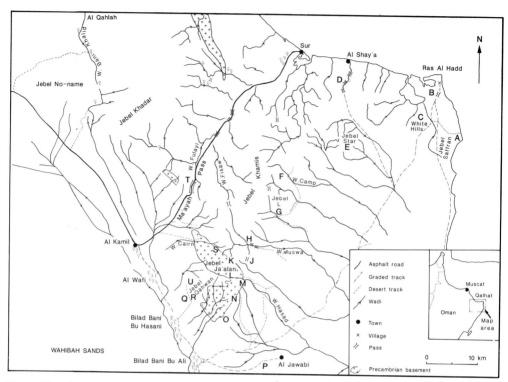

Fig. 1. Map of northeast Oman showing main localities and topographic features mentioned in the text.

Stratigraphy

Where appropriate the lithostratigraphic framework of Glennie *et al.* (1974) and Nolan *et al.* (1986, 1990), defined for the Oman Mountains, has been applied to the present study. However some distinctive new units have been recognized which cannot be adequately accommodated within the existing framework referred to above (Fig. 3). These units have, as yet, only been assigned informal names.

Precambrian basement

The oldest rocks exposed are mica schists, gneisses, amphibolites, granites and dykes of the Jebel Ja'alan and Qalhat inliers. These rocks range in age from late Precambrian to early Palaeozoic (Glennie *et al.* 1974; Gass *et al.* 1990).

Qahlah Formation (?uppermost-Campanian/lower Maastrichtian)

The Qahlah Formation, which unconformably overlies the peneplaned crystalline basement of

Jebel Ja'alan, varies in thickness from *c.* 80 m on the east side of Jebel Ja'alan, to <10 m on Jebel Qahwan (Fig. 1). It consists of unfossiliferous interbedded red or yellow pebbly chert conglomerates, lithic sandstones and shales or marls of fluvial origin. The chert clasts are probably derived from the Hawasina Complex. Clasts from the underlying Precambrian basement are very rare, implying that the basement was not exposed at that time and most likely covered by the Hawasina Complex. Bioturbated marine facies are present at the top of the sequence.

The Qahlah Formation has not been dated but is conformably overlain by Maastrichtian limestones of the Simsima Formation. At the type locality of Qalhat, 50 km to the north, the upper part of the Qahlah Formation has been dated as Maastrichtian (Glennie *et al.* 1974).

Simsima Formation (Maastrichtian)

The Simsima Formation is composed of cliff forming, massive to well bedded, often nodular, pale yellow to grey bioclastic limestones de-

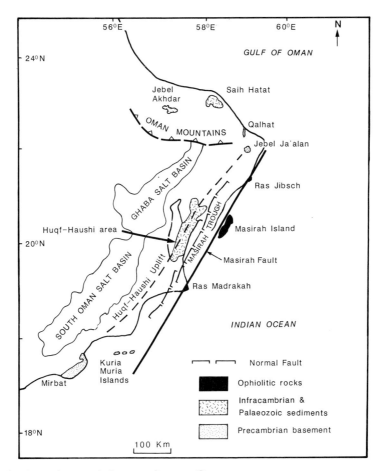

Fig. 2. Map showing main tectonic features of eastern Oman.

posited on a shallow carbonate shelf mostly devoid of terrigenous sediment. The lowest 10 m are frequently marly and thin marl interbeds occur throughout. The formation contains rudist bivalves, including *Vaccinites sp.*, *Durania sp.*, *Biradiolites sp.* and *Dictyoptychus sp.*, many of which are preserved in life position. These are particularly frequent in the lower parts of the unit. The giant benthonic foraminifer *Loftusia sp.* is also locally very abundant. The presence of *Dictyoptychus sp.* and *Loftusia sp.* dates the Simsima Formation as Maastrichtian (see also Skelton *et al.* 1990).

In the Qalhat area similar limestones, of unknown thickness, overlie the Qahlah Formation and it is likely that these limestones may also be assigned to the Simsima Formation. SSW of Qalhat, the Jafnayn Formation overlaps the Simsima Formation and onlaps the Hawasina Complex as, for example, in Wadi Bani Khalid.

Hasad Beds (Palaeocene/lower Eocene)

This new informal unit, recognized on the east flank of Jebel Ja'alan, unconformably overlies fault blocks of Qahlah and Simsima Formations and Precambrian basement. The Hasad Beds consist of well bedded yellow marls and grey limestones, thin to massively bedded conglomerates and chaotic melange horizons. The conglomerates contain clasts of Simsima Formation limestone with rudists, and chert from the Qahlah Formation. Large blocks from both these formations also occur reworked in the melange horizons.

From a brief examination of the Hasad Beds, it appears there are at least three distinct fans (each 1–2 km wide) in which conglomerates and melange horizons are common. These fans are separated by areas dominated by marls and limestones, interpreted as finer grained by-pass or inter-fan areas (Fig. 4).

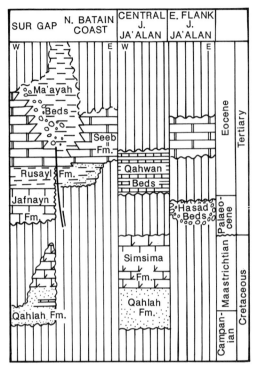

Fig. 3. Stratigraphic sequence used the present study (from Nolan *et al.* 1990).

Individual debris horizons in the Hasad Beds appear to be thicker, cover a larger area and contain larger clasts in the south than to the north. Rare reworked boulders of Precambrian rocks were only found in the most southerly fan. Along the eastern edge of Jebel Ja'alan the Hasad Beds unconformably overlie a block of Simsima Formation faulted against Precambrian basement (Fig. 4, section A).

The Hasad Beds are interpreted as a proximal submarine slope facies deposited by turbidity currents, debris flows and sedimentary slides as a result of syn-tectonic movement on the East Ja'alan Fault which forms the eastern margin of Jebel Ja'alan.

The age of the Hasad Beds is not known; they clearly post-date part of the Maastrichtian as strata of that age are reworked into the Hasad Beds. However they are not seen in stratigraphic contact with the Eocene Rusayl or Seeb Formations to the N and E or the Qahwan Beds to the SW, while to the SE lithic green sandstones of the Campanian/early Maastrichtian Fayah Sandstone and cherts of the Batain Melange are thrust over the Hasad Beds (Shackleton *et al.* 1990). No large shelly

fossils or benthonic foraminifera were seen in the Hasad Beds other than obviously reworked fossils from the Simsima Formation. On regional grounds it is likely that the Hasad Beds are of Palaeocene to early Eocene age because they are a slope facies unconformably overlying, and partly composed of, reworked Maastrichtian strata in a similar way to the lower parts of the Muthaymimah Formation (see Nolan *et al.* 1990). The absence of large benthonic foraminifera, such as *Nummulites* and alveolinids, and the lack of reworked Eocene strata argues against a comparison with the Eocene/?Oligocene Ma'ayah Beds (see below).

Qahwan Beds (?Palaeocene/Eocene)

This is a new informal unit based on folded, pale yellow, well bedded micritic limestones, marls and shales which crop out in the foothills, W and SW of Jebel Ja'alan and Jebel Qahwan.

Interspersed within this sequence are a few normally graded calcarenites, some of which include alveolinid foraminifera, abraded coralline algae and intraformational conglomerates, locally with imbricated ripped-up clasts of micrite and/or marl. No large shelly fossils were seen.

South of Jebel Qahwan a 20 m thick layer of multicoloured shale with gypsum crystals is intercalated within the limestones and marls, indicating a possible correlation of the lower part of the Qahwan Beds with the Rusayl Formation. The Qahwan Beds do not contain common nummulitic foraminifera, coral or shelly fossils or extraformational clasts and overall they are very pale and fine grained. This distinguishes them from the Seeb Formation and Ma'ayah Beds but indicates similarities with the Fahud Beds (Nolan *et al.* 1990). Originally the Qahwan Beds may have been unconformable on the Simsima Formation but the contact is now clearly faulted.

Limited observation of the sedimentology of the Qahwan Beds shows that some of the calcarenites were deposited by waning currents but the mechanism is not clear. The rare intraformational conglomeratic beds are thin, seldom exceeding 30 cm. In these, the clasts occur as 'floating' or imbricated cobbles in the middle of the bed, supported by a muddy/silty, locally arenaceous, carbonate matrix, giving a reversely graded appearance to the lower part of the bed. The imbricated clasts appear inclined parallel to the direction of dip of the long axes of the clasts. Such features suggest that some form of debris flow mechanism operated (see Rees 1968; Walker 1975; Middleton & Hampton 1976;

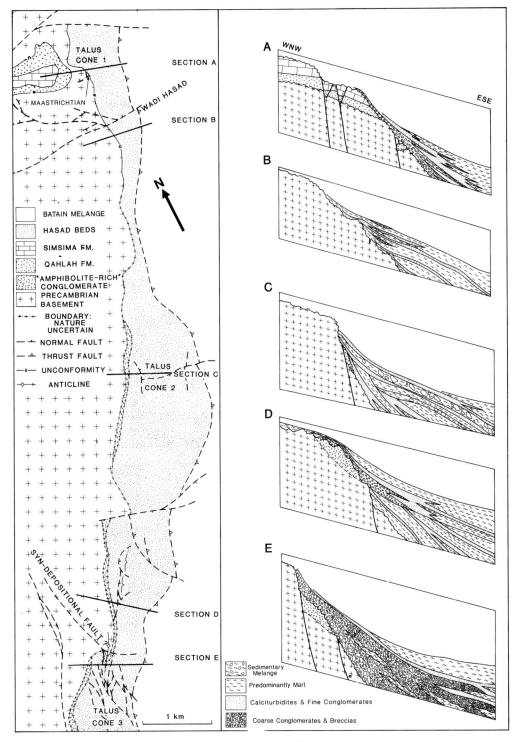

Fig. 4. Sketch geological map and cross sections through the Hasad Beds, E flank of Jebel Ja'alan (Fans 1, 2 and 3 correspond to locs. M, N and O on Fig. 1, respectively).

Lowe 1976a, b, 1979). The above descriptions suggest that density currents deposited some beds within the Qahwan Beds. These, however, form a minor component. Most beds consist of vaguely parallel-laminated or apparently featureless micritic limestones and marls which may show signs of bioturbation. The available evidence and the geological position of the Qahwan Beds suggests that they were deposited in an intrashelf basin like the Suneinah Trough to the NW in which the similar Fahud Beds accumulated.

Jafnayn Formation (Palaeocene–lower Eocene)

The shallow shelf carbonates and marls of the Jafnayn Formation are not present in the study area but do occur as a major cliff forming unit in the eastern Oman Mountains, west of the Sur Gap. In Wadi Bani Khalid, c. 117 m of strata correlatable with the Jafnayn Formation which unconformably overlies the Hawasina Complex. To the W the Jafnayn Formation appears to be overlapped by the Rusayl Formation around An Niba, near Ibra (Cawood *et al.* 1990). Montenat & Blondeau (1977) record the presence of c. 140 m of shelf limestones, dated as Palaeocene, at Quryat on the coast, north of Wadi Bani Khalid.

It is not known whether the Jafnayn Formation was originally deposited east of the Sur Gap. If the Hasad Beds are Palaeocene, it seems unlikely that the Jafnayn Formation was ever present on the Batain coast.

Rusayl Formation (Eocene)

The Rusayl Formation is well developed immediately N of the North Ja'alan Fault (NJF), where it may exceed 370 m in thickness. It is overlapped to the N and E by the Seeb Formation, around Al Shay'a and Ras al Hadd, and at Al Jawabi, E of Bilad Bani Bu Ali (Fig. 1, locs. D, B & P). The Rusayl Formation unconformably overlies thrusted and folded cherts of the Batain Melange. As in the type locality, the Rusayl Formation consists of a highly variable sequence of interbedded sandstones, breccias, conglomerates, multicoloured shales, sandy limestones, dolomites, yellow marls and limestones (Fig. 5).

The sandstones are mostly coarse and quartzitic and contain a large amount of chert sand probably derived from erosion of Batain Melange cherts and Fayah Sandstone, south and southeast of the North Ja'alan Fault. Cross bedding ithe sandstones generally indicates transport approximately from the south, supporting the petrographic evidence. The proportion of sandstone rapidly diminishes north-westwards away from Jebel Ja'alan. Individual coarse grained sandstone bodies are clearly lenticular and commonly have low angle accretionary and smaller scale tabular cross bedding representing sinuous fluvial channel fill sequences incised into multicoloured shale facies. The finer-grained calcareous sandstones in the sequence are often bioturbated and represent beach to shallow marine facies. These are usually associated with limestone and marl facies (see below).

Chert pebble (occasionally cobble) breccias and conglomerates and pebbly sandstones occur towards the base of the Rusayl Formation in a number of localities as, for example, south of 'Wadi Camp' or above major facies discontinuities as on 'Jebel L' (Fig. 5). Some of these are regolithic breccias associated with ferruginous cemented horizons (probably representing ironpans), and rootlet horizons. Others may be beach conglomerates as they contain abraded oyster debris and are overlain by marine lagoonal or peritidal/sabkha marls and limestones. Primary evaporites are very rare in the Rusayl Formation unlike in the coeval Rus Formation (cf. Steineke *et al.* 1958) of Saudi Arabia.

Yellow and ochreous marls and recessively-weathering micritic limestones constitute the most abundant carbonate facies in the Rusayl Formation. These generally have an abundant but restricted fauna of gastropods, the infaunal bivalve *Corbula sp.* and oysters. Many of the latter are articulated and in life position, forming oyster beds. Ramose colonial coral debris may be locally abundant. Well bedded sandy calcarenite and dolomite and purer nummulitic limestones, which are more resistant to weathering, form varying proportions of the Rusayl Formation (Fig. 5). A wide variety of low energy lagoonal to inshore carbonate facies are represented.

Multicoloured shales and siltstones form a distinctive common lithology in the Rusayl Formation, as in the type locality. The environment of deposition of these shales is not clear because they are deeply weathered and altered but it is assumed that they represent a lagoonal, or possibly mud flat, facies as on the Batinah coast (Nolan *et al.* 1990). This would be compatible with the fluvial nature of the associated channel sandstones. The proportion of restricted lagoonal and fluvial/inshore facies decreases to the north and west indicating a trend

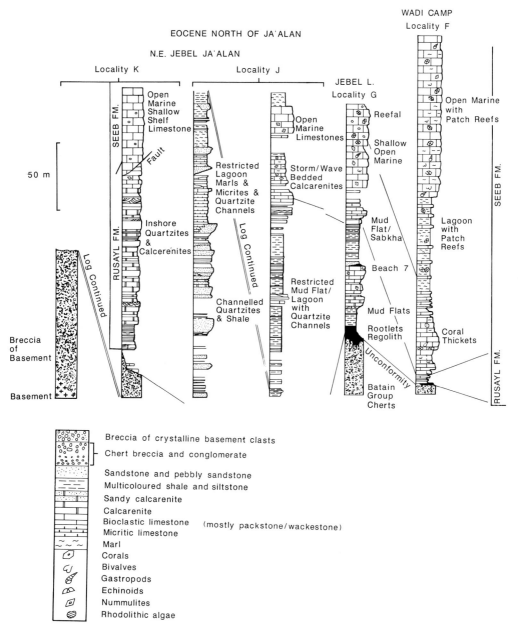

Fig. 5. Measured sections through the Rusayl and Seeb Formations, NNE of Jebel Ja'alan. Locs. K, J, G & F are shown on Fig. 1.

towards more marine conditions away from Jebel Ja'alan.

The Rusayl Formation is also well developed west of the Sur Gap. In Wadi Bani Khalid there are c. 60 m of pale grey mudstone, chalky limestone and shale with a very poor macrofossil content other than one level rich in echinoids. Farther west near Ibra, the Rusayl Formation locally becomes much thicker, up to c. 400 m, and very sandy implying that a number of localized sand sources existed in the eastern Oman Mountains.

Seeb Formation (Eocene)

The Seeb Formation consists of well bedded to massive, often nodular, shelf limestones rich in nummulitic, alveolinid and other large benthonic foraminifera. Echinoids, coralline red algae, bivalves and gastropods are also often abundant. Locally corals are common as on 'Jebel L' and in 'Wadi Camp' (Figs 1 & 5). The formation thickens and marly intervals become increasingly well developed from Ras al Hadd to Jebel Ja'alan and into the Sur Gap.

Immediately north of the North Ja'alan Fault, tabular well bedded, in places dolomitic, calcarenites are developed at the base of the Seeb Formation (Fig. 5). These are well laminated, often slightly bioturbated and display a wide variety of sedimentary structures including wave ripples and hummocky cross-stratification. These are interpreted as shoreface, possibly barrier sequences protecting the sheltered lagoons of the Rusayl Formation which they immediately overlie. This relationship is identical to that on the Batinah coast (Nolan *et al.* 1990). In both areas the calcarenites are overlain by shallow open shelf limestones, rich in alveolinid and nummulitic foraminifera.

Northwards towards 'Jebel L' and 'Wadi Camp', the Seeb Formation both increases in thickness from <100->250 m (Fig. 5) and becomes more coralline. Coral patch reef and coral thicket facies are present, the former mostly *c.* 2 m across with some up to 20-40 m. Over 350 m of Seeb Formation is exposed in the near-vertical cliff face of Jebel Khamis (Fig. 1). To the NE the Seeb Formation becomes more nummulitic and rhodolithic. In large areas around Ras al Hadd, extensive diagenetic alteration has almost totally destroyed the original character of the unit, leaving a homogeneous crystalline and/or chalky carbonate. There is a small outlier of Seeb Formation at Al Jawabi, SE of Jebel Ja'alan (Fig. 1). The base of the unit is obscured by scree but it probably rests unconformably upon folded cherts of the Batain Melange, as seen between Al Shay'a and Ras al Hadd. The Seeb Formation at Al Jawabi contains chert nodules and giant *Nummulites, c.* 30 mm in diameter. The Seeb Formation near Jebel Ja'alan conformably overlies the Rusayl Formation. Laterally, these units are seen to interfinger on 'Jebel L' (Fig. 5).

At the east end of Wadi Muswa (Fig. 1), the Seeb Formation is conformably overlain by a thin sequence of marl with a horizon of alveolinid and nummulitic limestone conglomerates which may belong to the Ma'ayah Beds (see below). The Seeb Formation is overlain by, and possibly interfingers with, the Ma'ayah Beds in the Sur Gap.

The Seeb Formation is well developed in the eastern Oman Mountains, west of the Sur Gap, where it is a resistant cliff-forming unit conformably overlying the recessively weathering Rusayl Formation. In Wadi Bani Khalid there is *c.* 80 m of limestone assignable to the Seeb Formation. The lowest limestones are well bedded calcarenites with scattered white quartz pebbles. Overlying these are more massively bedded limestones containing abundant alveolinid and nummulitic foraminifera. This sequence is very similar to the type section of the Seeb Formation (see Nolan *et al.* 1990).

Ma'ayah Beds (Eocene-?Oligocene)

The informally named Ma'ayah Beds form a distinctive sequence of interbedded, dark grey foetid shales and argillaceous limestones, with some nummulitic limestones and conglomerates as seen, for example, in the Sur Gap. Interbedded with these rocks are beige and orange clays and limestones. The conglomerates, which contain clasts of approximately coeval coralline and nummulitic shallow-shelf limestone reworked from the Seeb Formation and granitoid and schistose rocks reworked from the Precambrian basement, are interpreted as chaotic debris flow deposits. Many of the limestones are normally graded with Bouma cycles, indicating deposition from turbidity currents. The Ma'ayah Beds are clearly a basinal/slope facies. Preliminary dating by A. Racey and M. White (pers. comm.) indicates a middle Eocene to ?early Oligocene age.

Although a formal name has not yet been proposed for this stratigraphic sequence, it is sufficiently distinctive to warrant lithostratigraphic status. The Ma'ayah Beds may be more than 500 m thick in the Sur Gap. Above the Seeb Formation in Wadi Bani Khalid, there are *c.* 200 m of recessively weathering grey and yellow mudstones, shales and marls with locally more resistant bioclastic limestone beds, each *c.* 1 m or more thick, containing broken bivalves and echinoids and size-sorted small *Nummulites* of slope facies origin. Their character and stratigraphic position invites correlation with the Ma'ayah Beds but more detailed work is required before a firm correlation may be made. Montenat & Blondeau (1977) note the presence of upper Eocene marls with sedimentary melange horizons, containing blocks of reworked Palaeocene limestone, at Quryat on the coast NW of Sur. Further information on these is required before comparisons with the Ma'ayah Beds can be made.

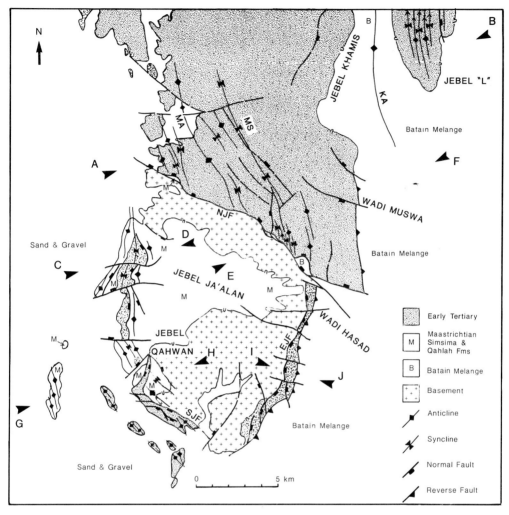

Fig. 6. Geological map of the Jebel Ja'alan area. NJF, North Ja'alan Fault,; EJF, East Ja'alan Fault; SJR, South Ja'alan Fault; MA, Ma'ayah Anticline; MS, Muswa Syncline; KA, Khamis Anticline.

Structure and tectonics

Jebel Ja'alan is a north–south trending structural high forming the northern expression of the Huqf–Haushi Uplift (Fig. 2) (Shackleton & Ries 1990). This broad anticlinal structure terminates abruptly against the WNW–ESE trending North Ja'alan Fault (Fig. 6). To the south of the fault, uplifted Precambrian basement is exposed (Gass *et al.* 1990) whereas to the north, Tertiary sediments occupy a structurally lower position. Farther north still, Precambrian rocks are exposed at Qalhat (Fig. 2), implying that the axis of the structural high has been offset to the west. On both sides of the north Ja'alan fault, N–S to NNW–SSE trend-

ing structures dominate with a subordinate set of E–W faults.

Structures to the north of the North Ja'alan Fault Zone

The Eocene Rusayl Formation has been folded to form a pair of asymmetric anticlines trending NNW–SSE; the western anticlinal axis verges west while the eastern axis verges to east with an axial separation of 10 km (Ma'ayah and Khamis Anticlines, respectively) (Figs 6 & 7a). The overall geometry is that of a pop-up structure dissected by normal faults that are oriented parallel to the axial planes of the folds and hade towards the synclinal core (Muswa Syncline.)

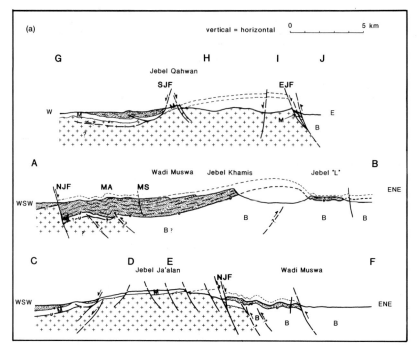

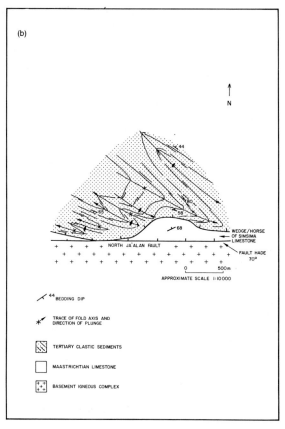

Only minor internal deformation has been recognized in the Tertiary sequences, represented by low-amplitude folds of 1–3 m wavelength and rare thrust ramps allowing thrusts to climb stratigraphy for several metres. The amplitude of folds decreases rapidly northwards to the north coast (cf. below).

To the east of Jebel Khamis, cherts of the Batain Melange are thrust to the west over the Eocene Rusayl Formation on an east-hading, low-angle thrust. The basal detachment is inferred to dip gently to the E within the Batain Melange. The overall shortening on section AB (Fig. 7) is estimated to be c. 30%. Subsequent N–S extension occurred on conjugate listric, E–W trending normal faults.

North Ja'alan Fault Zone

The North Ja'alan Fault Zone is a network of WNW–ESE striking anastamozing faults. The principal faults diverge and splay towards the east, forming more discrete zones of deformation. The principal fault planes dip at 60–70° to the N or NNE and have been eroded back to expose the Precambrian basement on the southern (upthrown) side (Fig. 6). The fault system is sinuous, with a number of steps (lateral and oblique ramps) along its trace. Lateral cut-off geometries have been mapped within the bedded Eocene Rusayl Formation (Fig. 7b). Wedges of Maastrichtian limestone (Simsima Formation) have been caught up within the fault system from which the vertical displacement has been estimated to be c. 500–1000 m. Horizontal displacement of c. 2000 m has been established from the left lateral offset of the Huqf–Haushi Uplift across the fault system.

The Rusayl Formation in the hanging wall, immediately north of the fault system, is intensely deformed compared to other parts of the region. Deformation is characterized by steep, NW–SE to N–S trending faults bounding tight upright anticlines. These faults and the associated fold axes have been rotated towards the North Ja'alan Fault Zone suggesting a left-lateral sense of shear (Fig. 6).

Early low-angle discontinuities, observed immediately to the north of the North Ja'alan Fault, have been recognized from stratigraphic omissions. These discontinuities may represent the now considerably eroded flats of listric normal faults juxtaposing the Seeb and Qahlah Formations. The orientation of lateral ramps suggests that the transport direction was to the north or northwest. Younger, E–W oriented, listric normal faults cross-cut the fault system. These are similar to those found in the Jebel Khamis and Wadi Muswa areas and post-date the main movement on the North Ja'alan Fault.

East flank of Jebel Ja'alan

Palaeocene Hasad Beds on the eastern flank of Jebel Ja'alan form a dip slope 200–300 m high inclined at 20–60° to the east (Fig. 4). The contact between these sediments and the Precambrian basement is vertical or steeply inclined to the east and trends approximately N–S. Evidence for movement along this boundary is found in red shales at the base of the cover sequence which are strongly foliated with a bedding parallel fabric and shear bands suggesting an E-down sense of displacement. Hence this contact once acted as a normal fault (East Ja'alan Fault). Displacement on the fault ranges from 50–100 m, inferred from the separation in the hanging wall and footwall of the contact between the Qahlah Formation and the overlying Simsima and Jafnayn Formations. Within the hanging wall wedge of Palaeocene sediments, low-angle circular failures and slides have been mapped forming meso-scale folds (10–20 m wavelength) above E-hading footwall ramps.

The most southerly explosure of Palaeocene/ Eocene sediments (Qahwan Beds) on the SSE side of Jebel Ja'alan are folded to form an upright to slightly asymmetric anticline with a number of minor thrust-related structures in the core of the fold (Fig. 1, loc. 0). The vergence of the folds and cut-off geometries of the thrust ramps suggest a westward vergence. The structurally highest thrust is interpreted as climbing laterally to the north and has been traced along the eastern margin of Jebel Ja'alan, where it emplaces Maastrichtian Fayah Formation onto Palaeocene calciturbidites. Its continuation may be found N of the North Ja'alan Fault Zone at the southern tip of Jebel Khamis (Fig. 6; Fig. 1, loc. J) where cherts of the Batain Melange have been emplaced onto Tertiary sediments. Deformation associated with these

Fig. 7. (a) Structural cross sections through Jebel Ja'alan and Jebel Khamis showing the relationship of contractional and extensional structures. (b) Structural map of part of the north (downthrown) side of the North Ja'alan Fault Zone showing the relationship of the fault to folds and minor faults in Maastrichtian and Tertiary sediments.

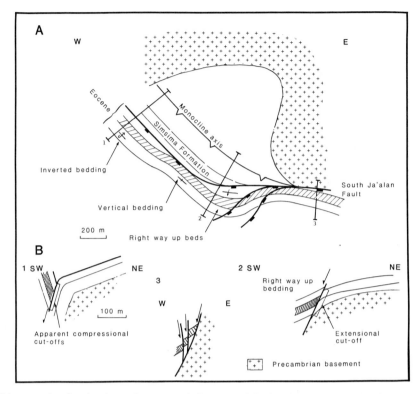

Fig. 8. Diagrams showing the change in structural character of the South Ja'alan Fault (SJF) along strike. A, plan of the southwest region of Jebel Ja'alan. B-1, 2, 3 are sections through the fault zone as marked on map A.

contractional structures post-dates the earlier extensional deformation. E–W oriented steep to low-angle extensional faults transect the above structures, offsetting the contact between basement and cover rocks.

South Ja'alan Fault and the western flanks of Jebel Ja'alan and Jebel Qahwan

The dip slopes of Jebel Ja'alan and Jebel Qahwan are inclined to the W at 20–30°. Farther west, the Simsima Formation and the overlying Qahwan Beds are tilted more steeply to the west or southwest and are locally inverted forming a monocline or an open, downward-facing anticline-syncline pair. (Fig. 1, loc. R, 5 km N of Bilad Bani Bu Hassan; Fig. 6). The trace of this km-scale fold can be followed southeastwards from the North Ja'alan Fault Zone to the South Ja'alan Fault where structural lineaments (faults and fold axes) become sub-parallel. The axis of the main monoclinal fold is offset by numerous E–W to WSW–ENE trending normal faults (Fig. 6).

To the SW, the contact between the steeply inclined Qahwan Beds and the Precambrian basement is a steep normal fault downthrowing to the SW (Fig. 8). Close to the fault, the Qahwan Beds dip steeply and are cross-cut by steep extensional faults, sub-parallel to the main fault. To the south, the sheet dip is 5–10° NE and the Qahwan Beds are folded into a series of broad, en echelon periclines (2–5 km long axis, 1–2 km short axis) (Fig. 6). Between the steep belt and the peripheral periclines, the Precambrian basement may lie less than 500 m below the surface.

Low-angle detachments have been recognized within the sedimentary cover sequence. Above these, fault blocks and sheets of varying size (from tens to hundreds of metres measured in the transport direction) are rotated and their frontal cut-offs display steep to low-angle contractional ramp geometries similar to foreland-dipping duplexes described by Boyer & Elliott (1983). The ramps in the hinterland region (i.e. up structural dip) of these horses or thrust sheets are eroded. From the orientation of the

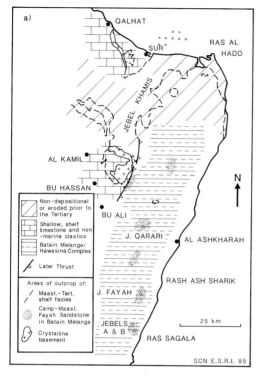

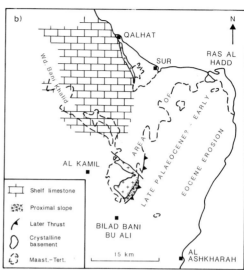

Fig. 9. (a) Maastrichtian palaeogeography of northeast Oman (Structural complexities are not restored on any of the palaeogeographic reconstructions). (b) Palaeocene palaeogeography of northeast Oman.

fold axial traces, transport towards the south is inferred.

The structures described above on the west and southwest flanks of Jebel Ja'alan and Jebel Qahwan are believed to have resulted from contractional deformation. Superimposed on these structures are later steep, sub-parallel extensional faults increasing the vertical displacement between basement and cover in the south. Evidence for more recent contractional deformation has been observed at locality U (Fig. 1). Here a large block of Simsima Formation has been emplaced over Qahwan Beds and the contact folded. Poorly consolidated, possibly Neogene, sediments with oyster beds which unconformably overlie the Qahwan Beds, are normally subhorizontal but adjacent to the front of the slid Simsima block, they are subvertical.

Palaeogeography & syn-sedimentary tectonics

Data collected during this reconnaissance study suggest the following palaeogeographic history from Maastrichtian to Eocene times (Figs 9–11).

?End-Campanian/Maastrichtian

Following the obduction of the Semail Ophiolite and Hawasina Complex onto the Arabian continental margin during the Campanian (e.g. Glennie *et al.* 1974; Hanna 1986), erosion of Hawasina cherts in the eastern Oman Mountains produced detritus which accumulated during ?end Campanian–early Maastrichtian times in a series of alluvial fans forming the Qahlah Formation. From the presence of laterites and saprolites in the Qahlah Formation to the NW of the study area, Nolan *et al.* (1986) postulated that the climate was tropical with a high, possibly seasonal rainfall. Later in Maastrichtian times, terrigenous input ceased rapidly and the Qahlah Formation is succeeded by the shallow carbonate shelf limestones of the Simsima Formation (Fig. 9a).

?End Maastrichtian/Palaeocene/basal Eocene

A phase of tilting and erosion probably occurred during the end-Maastrichtian/Palaeocene, as in other areas around the Oman Mountains (Nolan *et al.* 1986; Mann *et al.* 1990). The proximal submarine slope facies of the Hasad Beds provide evidence for this event. The latter partly overlap against the East Ja'alan Fault, which appears to have been active at this time. West

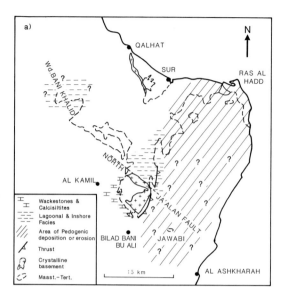

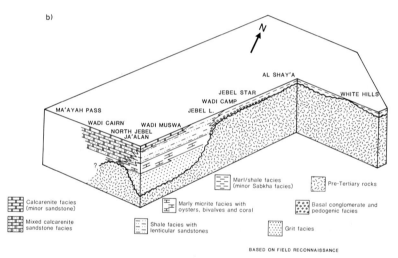

BASED ON FIELD RECONNAISSANCE

Fig. 10. (a) Early Eocene palaeogeography of northeast Oman. (b) Schematic reconstruction for the Rusayl Formation showing the distribution of early Eocene sedimentary facies between Jebel Ja'alan and Ras al Hadd. See Fig. 1 for location.

of the Sur Gap, limestones of the Jafnayn Formation, which accumulated in a shallow carbonate shelf setting, are disconformable upon the Simsima and Qahlah Formations and in places, the Hawasina Complex (Fig. 9b).

Early Eocene

During the early Eocene, subaerial erosion of the Fayah Sandstone and cherts from the Batain Melange produced terrigenous sand which was transported by rivers into the area between Sur

and the North Ja'alan Fault, where a thick sequence of fluvial sandstones and marginal marine/non-marine shales was deposited. The latter pass laterally into hyper-saline to lagoonal marls and limestones, indicating more normal marine conditions around Wadi Bani Khalid (Fig. 10a, b). This varied sequence of terrigenous and carbonate facies comprises the Rusayl Formation.

Nolan *et al.* (1986) noted that the early Eocene strata of the Oman Mountains are noticeably less evaporitic than the Rus Formation of Saudi

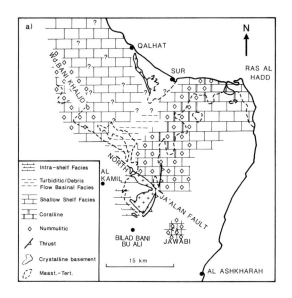

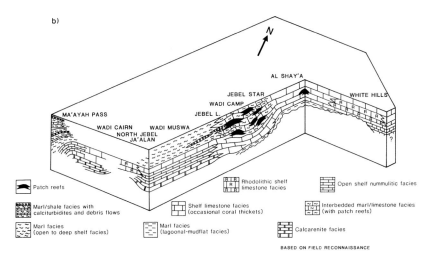

Fig. 11. (a) Middle Eocene palaeogeography of northeast Oman. (b) Schematic reconstruction showing the distribution of middle Eocene facies between Jebel Ja'alan and Ras al Hadd. See Fig. 1 for location.

Arabia. During this time Arabia still lay in the tropics (Smith & Briden 1977) but probably in a rain shadow because of the northward drift of the Indian Plate across the line of the prevailing easterly palaeowind direction which would have brought precipitation to the area (Nolan et al. 1986). The presence of coarse fluvial clastics in the Rusayl Formation of Oman indicates that noticeable precipitation did occur on the western seaboard of Arabia at this time where there was some relief. Well developed palaeosols, ferruginous horizons (possibly representing

iron-pans) and incipient caliche horizons in the Rusayl Formation occur, as on 'Jebel L', on the flanks of the eroding Batain area, providing further evidence for a humid, perhaps seasonal, palaeoclimate.

Middle Eocene to ?early Oligocene

Normal, shallow marine nummulitic, alveolinid and rhodolithic limestones of the Seeb Formation conformably succeed and interdigitate with, the Rusayl Formation (Fig. 11a, b). At Ras al

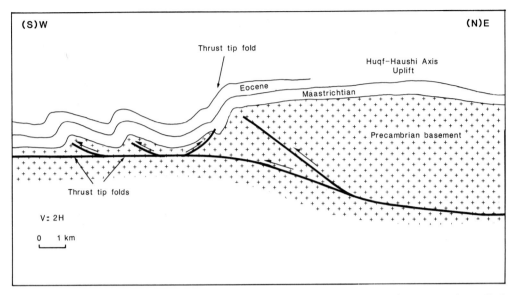

Fig. 12. Representation of compressional faults and folds (late Palaeocene to Eocene) on the southwest flank of the Huqf–Haushi Uplift.

Hadd the Seeb Formation rests unconformably upon the Batain Melange. In the Oman Mountains the transition from the Rusayl to the Seeb Formation is relatively simple, probably associated with the global mid-Eocene transgression postulated by Vail *et al.* (1977). The more complex pattern in the Batain area may reflect local tectonic instability.

The Seeb Formation is overlain by, and probably interdigitates with, deeper marine calciturbidites, shales and debris flows of the Ma'ayah Beds. The Ma'ayah Beds appear to be restricted to a narrow belt in the Sur Gap (Fig. 1). From the great thickness of the Ma'ayah Beds and the presence of blocks reworked from the Seeb Formation and Precambrian basement, it appears that they were deposited in a tectonically active basin, which is here informally termed the Ma'ayah Trough. The Seeb Formation, adjacent to the eastern margin of the Ma'ayah Trough, is unusually rich in corals, possibly reflecting a shelf edge situation.

Summary and timing of deformation events

Three principal deformation events associated with the uplift and inversion of Jebel Ja'alan and movement on the North Ja'alan Fault Zone have been recognized. However, these phases represent a continuum of events during which pre-existing structural trends were reactivated, namely, the N–S to NNE–SSW trending

Huqf–Haushi Uplift and E–W to ESE–WSW trend of the cross-cutting transtensional fault systems (e.g. the North Ja'alan Fault).

During the late Mesozoic (Campanian to early Maastrichtian) and perhaps into Palaeocene times, the eastern flank of Jebel Ja'alan was an active normal fault, exposing the Precambrian basement which forms the core of the Huqf–Haushi Uplift. Movement continued through the Palaeocene and may have been linked to early extensional displacement on the North Ja'alan Fault. Towards the end of the Palaeogene, N–S extension became dominant as evidenced by the remains of low-angle listric normal faults, north of Jebel Ja'alan.

After middle Eocene times, the early extensional phase waned and gave way to E–W compression, rejuvenating the N–S structural trends. Both to the north and south of the North Ja'alan Fault Zone, Maastrichtian to Eocene deposits were folded to form asymmetric anticlines and monoclines. This contractional displacement appears to have occurred on low-angle detachments with a principal transport direction from east to west. At least two main detachment horizons were active (Figs 8 & 12); (i) a structurally higher detachment in Tertiary sediments which gave rise to the now downward-facing asymmetric anticlines and peripheral periclines on the west and south flanks of Jebel Ja'alan and (ii) a deep splay off the structurally lower fault which is here interpreted to have caused the inversion of Jebel Ja'alan to form the broad, south-plunging anticlinal structure (the Huqf–Haushi Uplift), the western monocline and the pop-up structure in the north. As a result of the oversteepening of the Jebel Ja'alan culmination, the South Ja'alan Fault, on the south flank of Jebel Qahwan, increased displacement on the previously contractional fault system. Later, out-of-sequence movement on the low-angle detachment resulted in inversion and emplacement of the deep marine basinal sediments of the Batain Melange to the east onto the eastern flank of Jebel Ja'alan and Jebel Khamis.

The Eocene rocks in the Jebel Ja'alan area thicken into, and change facies across, the North Ja'alan Fault and the Sur Gap, indicating that these were active structures during the early Tertiary. The North Ja'alan Fault appears to have remained active throughout the compressional phase and influenced the localization of upright fold structures and faults in Tertiary sediments immediately to the north. Overall displacement on the fault system was oblique and left lateral. The conjugate east–west extensional faults post-date all other structures found in the Jebel Ja'alan area. North–south extension may have contributed to displacement on the North Ja'alan Fault Zone.

The deformation events described in the Jebel Ja'alan area characterize the region as a separate structural domain, distinct from the Oman Mountains to the west. In addition, the development of many of the structures post-dates the final suturing of the Tethyan Ocean during the Late Cretaceous. However the eastern flank of Jebel Ja'alan has acted as a zone of weakness since at least Maastrichtian times and its relationship to the Huqf–Haushi Uplift to the S suggests that its structural history is even longer. This N–S to NNE–SSW structural grain is cross-cut by WNW–ESE lineaments (North and South Ja'alan Faults). No evidence has been seen to suggest that these faults zones follow pre-existing structures.

This work was funded by Amoco Production Company (International) through an operating grant awarded to W. H. Kanes, Earth Sciences and Resources Institute, University of South Carolina. Amco Production Company (International) and the Oman Ministry of Petroleum and Minerals are thanked for permission to publish this paper. The data from Wadi Bani Khalid and the Ibra area are published with the kind permission of R. Crawford, Amoco (UK) Exploration Company. P. W. Skelton and A. Mann are thanked for their constructive reviews of the manuscript.

References

BOYER, S. & ELLIOTT, D. 1983. Thrust systems. *Bulletin of the American Association of Petroleum Geologists*, **66**, 1195–1231.

CAWOOD, P. A., GREEN, F. K. & CALON, T. J. 1990. Origin of culminations within the southeast Oman Mountains at Jebel Ma-Jhool and Ibra Dome. *In*: ROBERTSON, A. H. F., SEARLE, M. P. & RIES, A. C. (eds) *The Geology and Tectonics of the Oman Region*. Geological Society, London, Special Publication, **49**, 429–445.

GASS, I. G., RIES, A. C., SHACKLETON, R. M. & SMEWING, J. D. 1990. Tectonics, geochronology and geochemistry of the Precambrian rocks of Oman. *In*: ROBERTSON, A. H. F., SEARLE, M. P. & RIES, A. C. (eds) *The Geology and Tectonics of the Oman Region*. Geological Society, London, Special Publication, **49**, 585–599.

GLENNIE, K. W., BOUEF, M. G. A., HUGHES CLARKE, M. W., MOODY-STUART, M., PILAAR, W. F. H. & REINHARDT, B. M. 1974. Geology of the Oman Mountains. *Verhandelingen van het Koninklijk Nederlands Geologisch Mijnbouwkundig Gennootschaap*, **31**.

HANNA, S. S. 1986. The Alpine (Late Cretaceous and Tertiary) tectonic evolution of the Oman Mountains: A thrust tectonic approach. *In*: *Symposium on the Hydrocarbon Potential of Intense Thrust Zones. Abu Dhabi, December 1986*, 125–174.

LEES, G. M. 1928. Geology and Tectonics of Oman and Parts of South-Eastern Arabia. *Quarterly Journal of the Geological Society of London*, **130**, 263–78.

LOWE, D. R. 1976a. Grain flow and grain flow deposits. *Journal of Sedimentary Petrology*, **46**, 188–99.

—— 1976b. Subaqueous liquified and fluidized sediment flow and their deposits. *Sedimentology*, **23** 285–308.

—— 1979. Sediment gravity flows: their classification and some problems of application to natural flows and deposits. *In*: DOYLE, L. J. & PILKEY, O. H. (eds) *Geology of continental slopes*. Society of Economic Paleontologists and Mineralogists Special Publication, **27**, 75–82.

MANN, A., HANNA, S. S. & NOLAN, S. C. 1990. Post-Campanian tectonic evolution of the Central Oman Mountains: Tertiary extension of the East Arabia margin. *In*: ROBERTSON, A. H. F., SEARLE, M. P. & RIES, A. C. (eds) *The Geology and Tectonics of the Oman Region*. Geological Society, London, Special Publication, **49**, 549–563.

MIDDLETON, G. V. & HAMPTON, M. A. 1976. Subaqueous sediment transport and deposition by sediment gravity flows. *In*: STANLEY, D. J. & SWIFT, D. J. P. (eds) *Marine Sediment Transport and Environmental management*. Wiley & Sons, New York. 197–229.

MONTENAT, C. & BLONDEAU, A. 1977. Premier aperçu du Tertiare d'Oman (Peninsule arabique orientale). *Bulletin de la Société Géologique de France*, **7**, 1285–1295.

NOLAN, S. C., SKELTON, P. W., CLISSOLD, B. P. & SMEWING, J. D. 1986. Late Campanian to Tertiary palaeogeography of the central and northern Oman Mountains. *In: Symposium on the Hydrocarbon Potential of Intense Thrust Zones, Abu Dhabi, December 1986*, 175–200.

——, ——, —— & ——. 1990. Maastrichtian to Early Tertiary stratigraphy and palaeogeography of the Central and Northern Oman Mountains. *In:* ROBERTSON, A. H. F., SEARLE, M. P. & RIES, A. C. (eds) *The Geology and Tectonics of the Oman Region*. Geological Society, London, Special Publication, **49**, 495–519.

REES, A. I. 1968. The production of preferred orientation in a concentrated dispersion of elongated and flattened grains. *Geological Journal*, **76**, 457–465.

SHACKLETON, R. M. & RIES, A. C. 1990. Tectonics of the Masirah Fault Zone and Eastern Oman. *In:* ROBERTSON, A. H. F., SEARLE, M. P. & RIES, A. C. (eds) *The Geology and Tectonics of the Oman Region*. Geological Society, London, Special Publication, **49**, 715–724.

——, ——, FILBRANDT, J. B., LEE, C. W. & CUNNINGHAM, G. C. 1990. The Batain Melange of NE. Oman. *In:* ROBERTSON, A. H. F., SEARLE, M. P. & RIES, A. C. (eds) *The Geology and Tectonics of the Oman Region*. Geological Society, London,

Special Publication, **49**, 673–696.

SKELTON, P. W., NOLAN, S. C. & SCOTT, R. W. 1990. The Maastrichtian transgression onto the northeastern flank of the Proto-Oman Mountains: sequences of rudist-bearing beach to open shelf facies. *In:* ROBERTSON, A. H. F., SEARLE, M. P. & RIES, A. C. (eds) *The Geology and Tectonics of the Oman Region*. Geological Society, London, Special Publication, **49**, 521–547.

SMITH, A. G. & BRIDEN, J. C. 1977. *Mesozoic and Cenozoic paleocontinental maps*. Cambridge University Press, Cambridge.

STEINEKE, M., BRAMKAMP, R. A. & SANDEN, N. J. 1958. Stratigraphic relations of Arabian Jurassic Oil. *In: Habitat of Oil. American Association of Petroleum Geologists Symposium, 1294–1329*.

VAIL, P. R., MITCHUM, R. M. JR., & THOMPSON, S. III, 1977. Seismic stratigraphy and global changes of sea level, part 4: global cycles of relative changes of sea level. *In:* PAYTON, C. E. (ed.) *Seismic stratigraphy – applications to hydrocarbon exploration*. American Association Petroleum Geologists Memoir, **26**, 83–97.

WALKER, R. G. 1975. Generalized facies models for resedimented conglomerates of turbidite association. *Bulletin of the Geological Society of America*, **86**, 737–748.

Tectonics of the Masirah Fault Zone and eastern Oman

R. M. SHACKLETON[1] & A. C. RIES[2]

[1] The Croft Barn, Church Street, East Hendred, Oxon OX12 8LA, UK
[2] Earth Sciences & Resources Institute, University of Reading, 19 Upper Redlands Road, Reading RG1 5JJ, UK

Abstract: Previously known but undescribed ophiolites on Ras Madrakah and Ras Jibsch and the ophiolite forming Masirah Island define an upthrust linear zone now separated from the Oman continental margin by the Masirah Fault. West of this, in the Batain coast, are the allochthonous Batain Melange and the Hawasina Complex of Mesozoic basinal deposits, mainly cherts. The Melange, like the Semail Melange with which it is correlated, contains ophiolite and Permian limestone exotics with Tethyan faunas. These allochthonous rocks are intensely deformed by WNW-vergent thrusts and folds. This Batain fold and thrust belt widens and becomes more complex northwards. It appears to have been continuous with the deformation south of the Semail Ophiolite, although now separated by the Jebel Ja'alan Uplift. The tectonics are intrepreted to be the result firstly of northward motion, along the Masirah Fault, of the Helmand Block of Afghanistan, away from the Oman continental coast, and during this motion, upthrust of the Masirah Ophiolite. Then, later in the Cretaceous, southwestward obduction of oceanic coast, including the Semail Ophiolite and the Masirah Ophiolite Zone, onto the Arabian continental plate. The oblique obduction across the NNE-trending Batain margin produced the Batain fold and thrust belt and reversed the strike-slip motion on the Masirah Fault.

The main features of the eastern (Batain) coast of Oman which a tectonic interpretation must explain are the occurrences of ophiolites on Ras Madrakah, Masirah Island and Ras Jibsch; the NNE-trending Masirah strike-slip fault which bounds this ophiolite strip along its western side; the occurrence of granite of continental crust provenance intruded into the Masirah Ophiolite; an outcrop on the Hikman Peninsula, opposite Masirah Island, of strongly deformed radiolarites unlike any coeval rocks in the Huqf−Haushi Uplift to the west and clearly allochthonous; an extensive melange (Batain Melange) in NE Oman, similar to the Oman Melange; intense WSW-vergent compressive structures both in the Hikman Peninsula radiolarites, the Batain Melange and the Hawasina Formation, east of the Huqf−Haushi−Ja'alan Uplift; and the apparent continuity of these structures with those of the Hawasina allochthon to the west. New data on these features are first discussed, then an intrepretation is proposed.

The Masirah Fault

The Masirah Fault (Fig. 1) separates oceanic crust, represented by the Masirah Island ophiolite and the other ophiolites along the eastern coast of Oman, from continental crust of the Arabian Plate. Detailed studies of Masirah Island by Moseley (1969) and Moseley &

Abbotts (1979) showed that the Masirah Ophiolite is not, as previously thought, a right-laterally displaced continuation of the Semail Ophiolite, but is an uplifted block of Indian Ocean crust. West of the Masirah Fault is the Masirah Trough (Fig. 1) (Gorin et al. 1982) and farther north, the Batain coastal strip discussed by Shackleton et al. (1990). West of the Masirah Trough is the Huqf−Haushi Uplift, and its supposed NNE continuation, the Jebel Ja'alan and Qalhat inliers of Precambrian crystalline basement (Glennie et al. 1974; Gass et al. 1990). Unlike the Semail Ophiolite, which was obducted onto the Arabian Plate on gently inclined thrusts, the Masirah Ophiolite Zone appears to have been uplifted between straight steeply inclined strike-slip faults. The Masirah Fault, now separating continental from oceanic crust, must, at the time of its origin, have represented the transform fault along which the continental plate, formerly adjacent to Arabia before the breakup of Gondwanaland, moved away northwards.

Ras Madrakah

Ras Madrakah is a triangular peninsula, on which ophiolite rocks, emerging from beneath the unconformably overlying Tertiary limestones, are exposed over an across-strike width of c. 5 km (Fig. 2). The major part of the

From Robertson, A. H. F., Searle, M. P. & Ries, A. C. (eds), 1990,
The Geology and Tectonics of the Oman Region.
Geological Society Special Publication No 49, pp 715−724

715

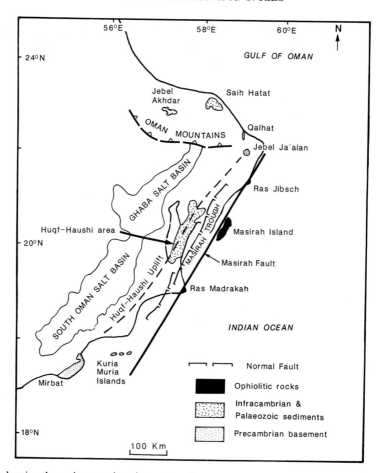

Fig. 1. Map showing the main tectonic units, eastern Oman.

complex consists of ultramafic rocks commonly showing a planar fabric, in places with flattened chromite grains. This planar fabric strikes E–W and dips, where measured, moderately to steeply southwards. The predominant rock is altered harzburgite with bastite pseudomorphs after orthopyroxene. There are also dunite pods.

In one area just SW of an outlier of Tertiary limestone, there is a series of unfoliated gabbro dykes, each c. 20–30 m wide, in a harzburgite matrix. These dykes strike N–S and dip c. 50° eastwards. Between the harzburgite and the escarpment of Tertiary limestones to the W is a strip about 1–2 km wide of ophiolitic melange. The clasts are mostly ophiolitic, consisting of serpentinite, gabbro, vesicular basalt and amphibolite but there are also sediments including radiolarian cherts, recrystallized limestones, calcareous sandstones and grits containing euhedral feldspars and fossil fragments. Some of this material appears to be of continental

derivation. The matrix of the melange is serpentinite and the melange as a whole is similar to that on Masirah Island.

The ophiolitic complex is traversed by many faults, which trend about NNE. Horizontal striae were seen on several fault scarps but the sense of displacement could not be determined. Gabbro mylonites also occur in the melange; this mylonitization appears to be pre-melange. Many of the blocks in the melange are brecciated, as in the melange on Masirah Island.

The Masirah Fault must continue beneath the Tertiary cover, W of the ophiolite outcrops. Its position can be estimated only by extrapolating from much farther NNE.

Hikman Peninsula

Gorin *et al.* (1982) show ophiolite at the SE tip of the Hikman Peninsula, W of Masirah Island.

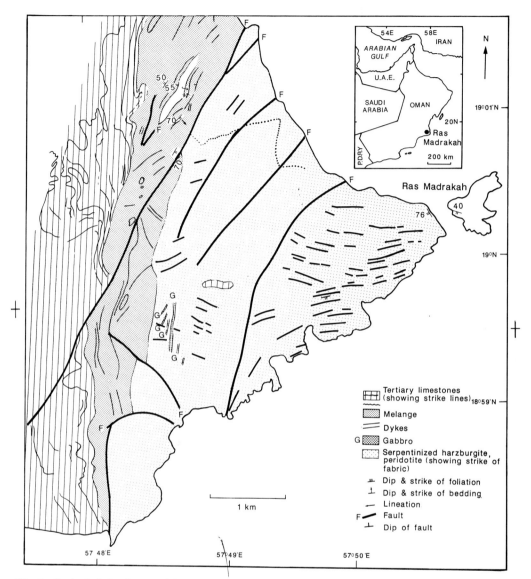

Fig. 2. Geological sketch map of the Ras Madrakah area.

From a helicopter small outcrops of complexly folded and imbricated striped radiolarites were seen just below the high tide level (Fig. 3). These beds are totally unlike any of the Mesozoic sediments in the Huqf—Haushi area; they are banded red and white rocks with distinct grading from red to white or red through grey to white. Diatoms are concentrated in the white tops of the units, which are presumably right way up. The folds, with wavelengths in the

order of 10 m, plunge NW—WNW; some are isoclinal with axial planes dipping NE. They are transected by small, left-lateral strike-slip faults trending WNW—ESE. These radiolarites occupy a similar position to those just over 1 km W of the Ras Jibsch Ophiolite (see below), some 150 km farther N. Since no such deep water sediments were penetrated by the Masirah 1 well (Gorin *et al.* 1982), a tectonic contact (thrust or strike-slip fault?) must lie just to the

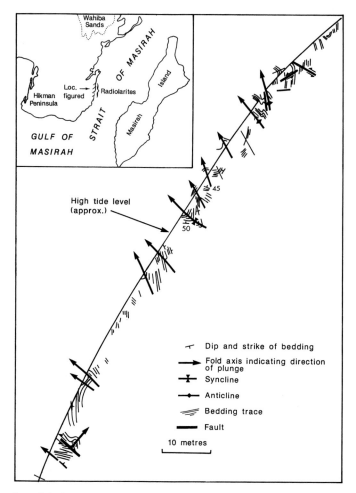

Fig. 3. Structures in radiolarites, eastern shore of the Hikman Peninsula.

W of the radiolarites. The structures in this tiny exposure would suggest a thrust, towards the SSW or SW.

Masirah Island

Masirah Island (Fig. 4) has been mapped in detail by Moseley (1969) and Moseley & Abbotts (1979, 1984). They showed that a complete, though strongly dislocated, ophiolite sequence is exposed, with a very extensive sheeted dyke complex in which the trend of the dykes is generally between E—W and NE—SW. Cherts and thin limestones are interbedded with the pillow lavas which form the upper part of the sequence.

Along the western side of the island there is a 5 km wide NNE—SSW trending zone of mega-

breccia the Masirah Melange (Fig. 5) containing blocks, up to 2 km², of all the ophiolite lithologies, most of them intensely brecciated. There are also clasts of chert and marly chert and limestone blocks up to 2 km long, supposedly of Valanginian—Cenomanian age (Glennie *et al.* 1974). This Masirah Melange was tentatively interpreted (Moseley & Abbotts 1979) as a transform-fault breccia, possibly complicated by diapirism. It was shown (Moseley & Abbotts 1979) that the ophiolite is cut by a swarm of small intrusions of high-potash granite with chemistry suggesting derivation from continental crust beneath the ophiolite. The melange is separated from the main body of less disrupted ophiolite by a very irregular fault which has an overall trend *c.* NNE—SSW. Shear planes along the fault dip steeply westwards.

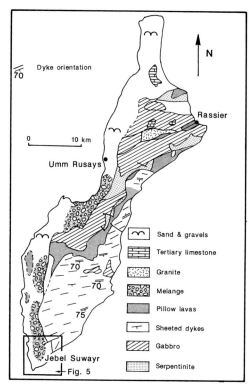

Fig. 4. Simplified geological map of Masirah Island (after Moseley & Abbotts 1979). Box shows location of Fig. 5.

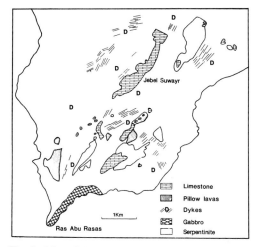

Fig. 5. Map of the Masirah Melange, southern part of the Masirah Island (after Moseley & Abbotts 1979). Location shown on Fig. 4.

The form of the irregularities along the main fault suggest incipient pull-apart during left-lateral strike-slip displacement, because there are short portions where the fault trends east before continuing north again. Within the main ophiolite block, the major faults trend approximately E−W, often parallel to the sheeted dyke trend. The throw on these faults seems to vary, some down to the north, some to the south.

In the melange or megabreccia, there are large irregular masses of the sheeted dyke complex, in which the dyke trends are similar to those in the main ophiolite mass. This suggests that the melange is the result of shattering and collapse rather than strike-slip transport or shear. Our own observations suggest that some of the Cretaceous limestone masses within the melange, notably the large Jebel Suwayr outcrop in the extreme south, rest unconformably on the underlying brecciated sheeted dyke complex rather than being blocks within the melange. The basal contact is very gently inclined; as far as can be seen it is parallel to the crude bedding in the limestones and the base of the limestone contains small blocks of basalt. It is, in any case, difficult to see what else the limestones were deposited on, especially if the megabreccia (melange) has not been transported far. If, as we believe, this Cretaceous shallow-water limestone was deposited unconformably on the eroded ophiolite, the ophiolite must have been uplifted early in the Cretaceous.

Within the main ophiolite block, in the zone running westwards from Rassier, pillow lavas with interbedded cherts dip very steeply and are locally overturned northwards, suggesting that the major fault separating the pillow lava sequence from the troctolite gabbro to the south is probably a reverse fault and that this block has been subjected to compression. However there is also evidence, from steeply-plunging folds, of a left-lateral strike-slip displacement here.

While the pattern of major faults on Masirah Island is unlike that on the mainland to the west, the many minor fractures mapped as 'faults and master joints' by Moseley & Abbotts (1984), are similar to those in the Huqf−Haushi area both in pattern and orientation. Their relation to the major faults is not clear.

Huqf−Haushi Uplift

The 25 km wide Masirah Basin, between the Masirah Fault and the Huqf-Haushi Uplift, is unexposed. A section published by Gorin *et al.* (1982) shows nearly 4 km of sediments, largely

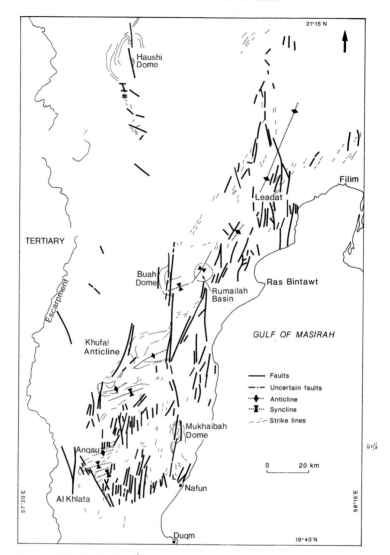

Fig. 6. Structural map of the Huqf−Haushi area (modified from Gorin *et al.* 1982).

Cambrian and Infracambrian in age, with a gentle eastward dip, on Precambrian basement. Later subsurface evidence is unpublished.

The Huqf−Haushi Uplift is *c.* 40 km wide to its ill-defined western limit, taken where the westerly dip towards the Ghaba Salt Basin increases rather suddenly to about 5°. The Precambrian crystalline basement is about 3 km higher at the 'crest' of the Uplift than in the Masirah Trough. Over large areas, the rocks exposed in the Huqf−Haushi Uplift are nearly flat. Steep dips are associated with the faults.

The Uplift can be shown to have been active in the Palaeozoic (Gorin *et al.* 1982; Ries &

Shackleton 1990) and therefore cannot be directly related to the Masirah Transform Fault which was presumably initiated during breakup and dispersal of Gondwanaland. Weak folds, with local southeasterly vergence, and curving from WSW−ENE to NNE−SSW, appear to be Palaeozoic in age (Fig. 6). However the main deformation in the Huqf−Haushi Uplift is a complex system of brittle fractures and faults. The faults fall into two sets, one, perhaps slightly earlier, trending NNE−SSW, the other N−S (Fig. 6). Both sets are essentially pre-Maastrichtian, but Late Cretaceous, in age. The NNE−SSW trending faults, against which the beds steepen, appear to show left-lateral strike-slip displacements, with variable down-throw to either the E or W. They are subparallel to the Masirah Fault.

The N–S trending faults are associated with steep dips, a series of half-domes and a few half-basins, and with sometimes quite tight minor folds which trend at a small angle clockwise from the faults. The structures indicate strong transpression on left-lateral strike-slip faults. The two sets appear to reflect a small change in the stress field.

Ras Jibsch

A group of outcrops at Ras Jibsch, less than 1 km long, consists mainly of gabbro, in part with fresh olivine, in part sheared, with subordinate serpentinized peridotite. The Masirah Fault must run just west of these outcrops.

Masirah Ophiolite Zone: summary of tectonic features

The Masirah Ophiolite Zone is a straight NNE–SSW trending strip at least 40 km wide, extending c. 350 km from Ras Madrakah to Ras Jibsch. The Ras Madrakah and Masirah Island Melanges are so similar, and in alignment, that they are surely on a single lineament. In view of its rectilinearity, the zone must be bounded by strike-slip faults, notwithstanding the indication, given by the potash-rich granites on Masirah Island, of underlying continental crust. No structural evidence of westward thrusting was seen anywhere within the Masirah Zone. As yet there is no isotopic evidence for the nature of the source and age of the granites.

Batain Coast

This is discussed in detail elsewhere (Shackleton et al. 1990). The salient tectonic features are as follows:
1. The presence of a very extensive area of melange, the Batain Melange. This contains large masses of Mesozoic (mainly Cretaceous?) radiolarites similar to the Hawasina sediments under the Semail Ophiolite; large blocks of Lower Permian limestone; Permian Limestone Megabreccia associated with, and presumed to have been deposited on, basalts; large masses of Upper Cretaceous sandstones with slide breccia horizons containing huge blocks of granite and other rocks. There are also some blocks of ophiolite in the melange. Early recumbent folds, with variable approximately E–W trends and mostly facing southwards, may be associated with the emplacement of the melange.
2. Evidence of strong compression directed towards the W and SW. This resulted in widespread imbrication and intense folding. In the S, no effects of this compression are recognized in the Huqf–Haushi area, except in the radiolarites on the Hikman Peninsula. Northwards from there, the effects are seen over an increasing width of the Batain coastal strip. The trend of the structures also swings, although irregularly, westwards in the north and appears to merge with that in the Hawasina Complex to the west, although the two are now separated by the uplifted Precambrian basement at Jebel Ja'alan. This deformation not only becomes more extensive in the north but also more complex, with polyphase deformation including the early recumbent folding.
3. As in the Huqf–Haushi area, there is a complex array of brittle fractures. The commonest are strike-slip faults trending about NNE–SSW, parallel to the Masirah Fault.

The formation of the melange, the intense compressional structures and the array of brittle fractures and faults all appear to be pre- or intra-Maastrichtian in age, and synchronous with the emplacement of the Semail Ophiolite.

Tectonic interpretation

The Mesozoic evolution of the Masirah Fault Zone, which separates continental Arabia from the Owen Basin segment of the Indian Ocean, is clearly the result of the disruption of Gondwanaland and the departure, perhaps northwards to form the Helmand Block in Afghanistan or southeastwards as India, of the continental block which previously lay adjacent to the Arabian Plate. The Batain area thus became a coastal strip facing the newly-formed ocean, probably at least by mid-Jurassic, and possibly even by Triassic times.

During the Cretaceous (Campanian–Maastrichtian), the Semail Ophiolite, together with the underlying melange containing Permian and Triassic limestone exotics, and beneath that the Hawasina thrust sheets of radiolarite and turbidite fan deposits, was obducted onto the Arabian continental margin. The relative direction of transport was from NE to SW and translation distances were several hundred kilometres (Lees 1928; Glennie et al. 1973, 1974). Fabric evidence shows that the thrusting direc-

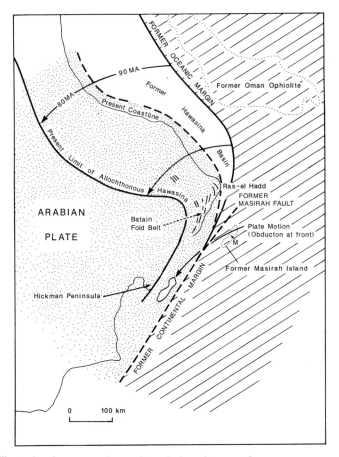

Fig. 7. Diagram illustrating the proposed tectonic evolution of eastern Oman.

tion rotated from westwards to southwestwards between 90 and 80 Ma ago (Boudier *et al.* 1985).

At first sight, the tectonic relationships along the eastern, Batain margin of the continental plate seem quite different. There a strip of Indian Ocean crust is separated from the Arabian continental plate by the Masirah Fault. The continental plate which, before the breakup of Gondwanaland, must have been adjacent to the Arabian Plate, has moved away either to the SE as India, or to the NNE along the Masirah Fault. Primarily because of the rectilinear character of the Masirah Fault and the associated array of strike-slip faults on the Arabian side, the latter seems more likely in which case the block that moved away is probably the Helmand Block in Afghanistan. Palaeomagnetic evidence (Krumsiek 1976) indicates a Permian palaeolatitude for this block similar to the Arabian Plate. It therefore seems likely that

the space between India, which moved away southeastwards, and the Arabian Plate was occupied by the Helmand Block and that the Masirah Fault Zone was then acting as a left-lateral strike-slip fault.

The Masirah Ophiolite Zone would thus have moved northwards and cannot have been part of the Semail Ophiolite; moreover their sheeted dyke trends are quite different. However left-lateral strike-slip displacement fails to explain either the Batain Melange or the intense WSW-directed compressional structures affecting it. The tiny exposure of radiolarites on the Hikman Peninsula, west of Masirah Island, appears to continue the Hawasina-type deep water sediments 150 km south from Ras Jibsch; it is unlikely that an allocthonous sheet could have carried these radiolarites southwards as far as Ras Jibsch, let alone to the Hikman Peninsula, if at that time the adjacent Masirah ophiolite block was still moving northwards.

Instead it is proposed that by the Late Cretaceous the Masirah Ophiolite Zone was attached to, and part of, the plate which included the Semail Ophiolite. The translation of this composite block towards the SW carried the Semail Ophiolite directly onto the NE-facing margin of the Arabian Plate, but because the Batain margin of the Arabian Plate trended NNE—SSW, the southwestward obduction of the Masirah segment of the plate was at only a small angle to the margin. The pre-existing Masirah Fault Zone with continental crust on one side and oceanic crust on the other, was itself obducted obliquely southwestwards onto the Arabian continental margin. The eastern limit of the Arabian continental plate would then be underneath, or even slightly east of, Masirah Island (Fig. 7).

This interpretation provides an explanation for otherwise unexplained features of eastern Oman: (i) the intense WSW-directed compressive deformation of the Batain Melange, the Batain Hawasina and the Hikman radiolarites; (ii) the occurrence of radiolarites far to the S along the coast; (iii) the occurrence of granite of continental crust derivation on Masirah Island; (iv) the apparent continuity of the structures in the N Batain coastal area with those of the Hawasina allochthon to the W and (v) the apparent identity of the Semail and Batain Melanges.

Although it seems to solve some of the problems, the interpretation proposed also raises difficulties. First, it implies a reversal of the motion on the Masirah Fault Zone from earlier left-lateral to later right-lateral strike-slip. We have no evidence of such a reversal. Secondly, the fold and thrust structures in the Batain coast area, although irregular, trend parallel to the Masirah Fault and appear to indicate transport normal to it. The interpretation requires that the overall southwestward relative motion of the overriding plate is resolved into a strike-slip component on the Masirah Fault and compression normal, rather than at 45°, to it. It also requires that the Batain Melange was moved southwestwards without an overlying ophiolite thrust slab.

An alternative interpretation is that the Batain fold and thrust belt is due to subduction or obduction of Indian Ocean crust under or over the SE (Batain) margin of the Arabian Plate and is entirely independent of the obduction of the Semail Ophiolite. This is contradicted by the continuity of structures from the Batain fold and thrust belt with that in the Hawasina, south of the Semail Ophiolite; by the similarity of the Batain and Semail Melanges; and by the

evidence of Tethyan faunas in the Batain exotics that they came from the north.

Despite the difficulties therefore, the proposed hypothesis seems the best available. The sequence of events proposed may be summarized as follows.

Stage 1. Jurassic—Early Cretaceous: break-up of N Gondwanaland; Helmand Block moves northward, separated from Arabian Plate by Masirah Transform Fault.

Stage 2. Early Cretaceous: Masirah Ophiolite upthrust and covered unconformably by limestone.

Stage 3. Late Cretaceous: plate, including the Semail Ophiolite and the Masirah Zone, obducted southwestwards over the Arabian Plate. Deformation resulting from highly oblique collision along the Batain margin resolved into right-lateral strike-slip motion on Masirah Fault and WNW-verging Batain fold and thrust belt.

This work was funded Amoco Production Company (International) through an operating grant awarded to W. H. Kanes, Earth Sciences and Resources Institute, University of South Carolina. Amoco Production Company (International) and the Oman Ministry of Petroleum and Minerals are thanked for permission to publish this paper. Two anonymous referees are thanked for their constructive criticisms of the paper.

References

BOUDIER, F., BOUCHEZ, J. L., NICOLAS, A., CANNAT, M. COOLENEER, G. MISSERI, M. & MONTIGNY, R. 1985. Kinematics of oceanic thrusting in the Oman Ophiolite. Model of plate convergence. *Earth and Planetary Science Letters*, **75**, 215—222.

GLENNIE, K. W., BOEUEF, M. G. A., HUGHES CLARKE, M. W., MOODY-STUART, M., PILAAR, W. F. H. & REINHARDT, B. M. 1973. Late Cretaceous nappes in the Oman Mountains and their geologic evolution. *Bulletin of the American Association of Petroleum Geologists*, **57**, 5—27.

——, ——, ——, ——, —— & ——. 1974. Geology of the Oman Mountains. *Verhandelingen van het Koninklijk Nederlands Geologisch Mijnbouwkundig Genootschaap*, **31**.

GORIN, G. E., RACZ, L. G. & WALTER, M. R. 1982. Late Precambrian—Cambrian sediments of the Huqf Group, Sultanate of Oman. *Bulletin of the American Association Petroleum Geologists*, **66**, 2609—2623.

KRUMSIEK, V. K. 1976. Zur Bewegung der Iranisch-Afganischen Platte. *Geologische Rundschau*, **65**, 909—929.

LEES, G. M. 1928. Geology and Tectonics of Oman and Parts of South-Eastern Arabia. *Quarterly Journal of the Geological Society of London*, **130**, 263—278.

MOSELEY, F. 1969. The Upper Cretaceous Ophiolite Complex of Masirah Island, Oman. *Geological*

Journal, **6**, 293–306.

—— & Abbotts, I. L. 1979. The Ophiolite Melange of Masirah, Oman. *Journal of the Geological Society, London*, **136**, 713–24.

Ries, A. C. & Shackleton, R. M. 1990. Structures in the Huqf–Haushi Uplift, east central Oman. *In*: Robertson, A. M. F., Searle, M. P. & Ries, A. C. (eds) *The Geology and Tectonics of the Oman Region*. Geological Society, London, Special Publication, **49**, 653–664.

Shackleton, R. M., Ries, A. C., Filbrandt, J. B., Lee, C. W. & Cunningham, G. C. 1990. The Batain Melange of NE Oman. *In*: Robertson, A. M. F., Searle, M. P. & Ries, A. C. (eds) *The Geology and Tectonics of the Oman Region* Geological Society, London, Special Publication, **49**, 673–696.

A multiphase plate tectonic history of the southeast continental margin of Oman

G. S. MOUNTAIN[1] & W. L. PRELL[2]

[1] *Lamont—Doherty Geological Observatory, Palisades, New York*
[2] *Department of Geological Sciences, Brown University, Providence, RI*

Abstract: The major basins of the western Indian Ocean formed during the Late Jurassic separation of India—Madagascar—Antarctica from Africa—Arabia. From north to south these are the Owen, North Somali, West Somali, and Mozambique Basins. Mesozoic magnetic anomalies confirm that these latter two regions have remained tectonically unchanged; by contrast, anomalies have yet to be identified in the Owen and North Somali Basins, leaving open the possibility that one or both have been overprinted by subsequent spreading events. Nonetheless, many researchers have chosen to assume that the basement within the Owen Basin is an unaltered fragment of Jurassic to Early Cretaceous oceanic crust, and that SE Oman has been a passive margin since its rifting from India. Marine geophysical data acquired aboard R/V *Robert D. Conrad* during 1986 provides new information that suggests a more complex regional plate history must be developed.

Seismic reflection profiles collected across the Owen Basin reveal structure that is not consistent with a Jurassic age. First, we observe that basement in the Owen Basin is more than 1 km shallower than should be expected from thermal subsidence since Jurassic time. Second, the age of sediments in the Owen Basin can be estimated by tracing them seismically to DSDP Site 224 on the Owen Ridge. Both of these procedures argue for the Owen Basin being no older than Late Cretaceous.

Seismic profiles along the SE Oman Margin near 18°N show complex deformational features that are incompatible with a simple passive margin history. A thick sedimentary basin bounded by basement-involved faults was mapped beneath the continental slope. Offsets reach to very near the seafloor, suggesting they have been active in the recent past. We acquired numerous crossings of a basement feature 75 km SW of Ra's Madrakah and along the strike of ophiolites exposed there and at Masirah Island. The magnetic, seismic, and structural characteristics of this feature are all consistent with its being a buried, along-strike extension of this same slice of oceanic crust.

To reconcile these observations with well-established facts concerning the opening history of the NW Indian Ocean, we propose the following scenario. First, a proto-Owen Basin formed in Jurassic time when India—Madagascar—Antarctica separated from Africa—Arabia. However, following the Late Cretaceous separation of India from Madagascar, the new spreading ridge was offset along the SE Oman margin, not at the Owen Ridge as is assumed by many. During this stage of tectonic development, the proto-Owen Basin crust was carried northeastward towards eventual collision and subduction with Asia. The result was a strike-slip Oman margin adjacent to a Late Cretaceous Owen Basin. Ophiolites now found along the SE coast of Oman are fragments of this Late Cretaceous Owen Basin crust, and were probably emplaced as a result of transpressional motion along this plate boundary. This arrangement persisted until yet another spreading centre opened the Gulf of Aden in Neogene time. The latter reorganization of plate geometries led to major compressive stresses across the Owen Basin that resulted in elevation of the Owen Ridge (readily seen by way of stratal relationships in profiles tied to DSDP Site 224), and reactivation of Late Cretaceous faults along the Oman Margin. We anticipate that verification of this multiple-phase history will emerge from future comparisons between post-Late Cretaceous tectonism within SE Oman and our marine seismic and drilling data.

The western boundary of the Indian Ocean consists of a series of small basins along the margins of Arabia and Africa. The two southern basins, the Mozambique Basin and the West Somali Basin, have been shown to result from seafloor spreading between East and West Gondwanaland beginning in the Late Jurassic (Segoufin 1978; Segoufin & Patriat 1980; Rabinowitz *et al.* 1983). The North Somali Basin appears to be a third Late Jurassic—Early Cretaceous basin (Cochran 1988), although this is a controversial interpretation (Sclater *et al.* 1981; Bosellini 1986). The spreading centres in each of these basins were active simultaneously

From ROBERTSON, A. H. F., SEARLE, M. P. & RIES, A. C. (eds), 1990,
The Geology and Tectonics of the Oman Region.
Geological Society Special Publication No 49, pp 725—743

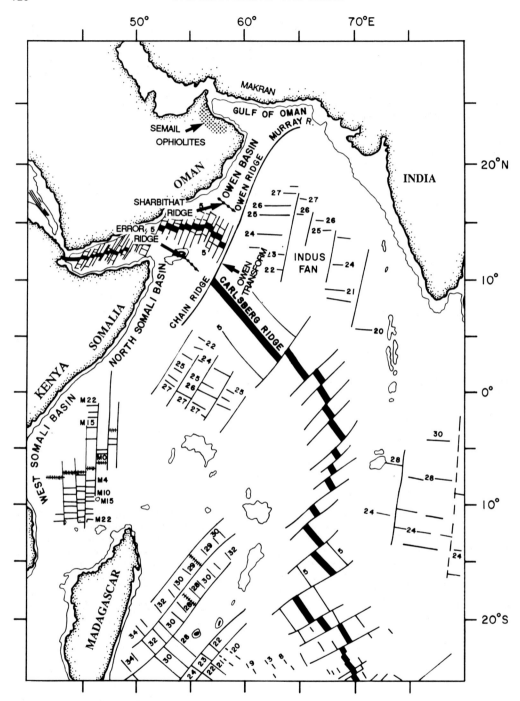

Fig. 1. Western Indian Ocean physiography and marine magnetic anomalies (S. Cande, *pers. comm.*; revised anomaly identifications in West Somali Basin from Cochran 1988).

and were linked by extremely long fracture zones.

The Owen Basin, located off of the eastern margin of Oman, has often been assumed to be a fourth Late Jurassic–Early Cretaceous basin (Whitmarsh 1979; Cochran 1981; Stein & Cochran 1985). This assumption has been based largely on analogy to the southern basins rather than on compelling evidence from within the basin itself. We present recently acquired marine geophysical data which suggest that this commonly accepted model for the origin of the Owen Basin may need revising.

Physiographic and geophysical features of Owen Basin

The Owen Basin is a region of relatively smooth seafloor between 3200 and 3500 m depth adjacent to the SE coast of Oman (Figs 1 & 2). It is bordered by distinct topographic boundaries to the east, west and south; to the north; its termination is less well defined (Fig. 2).

The eastern boundary of the Basin is the Owen Ridge, an asymmetric feature with a moderately dipping western flank and an extremely steep eastern flank (Figs 3 & 8). At some locations along the Ridge, seafloor shoals to less than 2000 m before it drops precipitously to the Indus Fan. There is considerable along-strike variability in the depth of the Ridge crest, and occasionally it rises only a few hundred m above the Owen Basin. Its trend is somewhat oblique to the Oman coastline, and as a result the width of the Owen Basin decreases northwards from roughly 260 to 200 km.

The western boundary of the Basin is the Oman continental margin. The coastline shows two major embayments (Masirah and Siquirah Bays) south of 20°30′N (Fig. 2); north of this latitude the shoreline is particularly linear, perhaps due in part to transcurrent faulting that is exposed on both the ophiolite complex of Masirah Island (Moseley & Abbotts 1979) and on the mainland itself (Morton 1959; Beydoun 1982). This same NE trend is maintained in isobaths along the continental slope.

To the south, the Owen Basin is bounded by a discontinuous line of seamounts that constitute the Sharbithat Ridge (Figs 1 & 2). This feature extends from the southern limit of Siquirah Bay seaward to the Owen Ridge. It separates the Owen Basin from the Miocene to Recent crust of the Gulf of Aden that was created at the Sheba Ridge (Laughton et al. 1970; Cochran 1981). The northern limit of the Owen Basin is not so clearly demarcated; the Owen Ridge trends more nearly NE near 22°N,

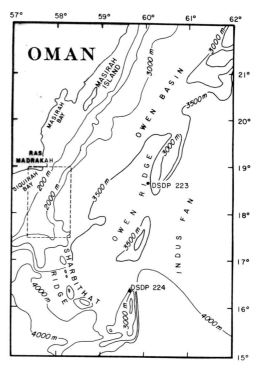

Fig. 2. Bathymetry and physiography of Owen Basin and adjacent region. The discontinuity of contours outlining Owen Ridge is due in part to poor track coverage (contours from GEBCO map series, 1975). Rectangular outline offshore Siquirah Bay was surveyed in detail during C2704 (Fig. 9).

and at this location its name changes to Murray Ridge. Also, at this latitude the coast of Oman turns sharply northwest, and the seafloor to the north is renamed the Gulf of Oman.

Seismic reflection profiles across the northern Owen Basin reveal slightly less than 2 km of acoustically stratified sediment. The basement has a NE–SW grain that is particularly evident north of 19°N (Whitmarsh 1979). As a result of this basement fabric, isolated sedimentary basins along the continental slope trend parallel to the margin and contain as much as 5 km of sediment.

Two long-range, NE–SW oriented refraction experiments reveal nearly typical ocean crustal structure beneath the Owen Basin, 100 to 200 km southeast of Masirah Island (Whitmarsh 1979). Velocities of 5.0 km sec^{-1} indicate a slightly greater than usual Layer 2 thickness of 2.5–2.6 km; Layer 3 velocities of 6.3–6.5 km sec^{-1} are observed in a layer 3.4 to 4.2. km thick. Mantle velocities of 8.3 km sec^{-1} are

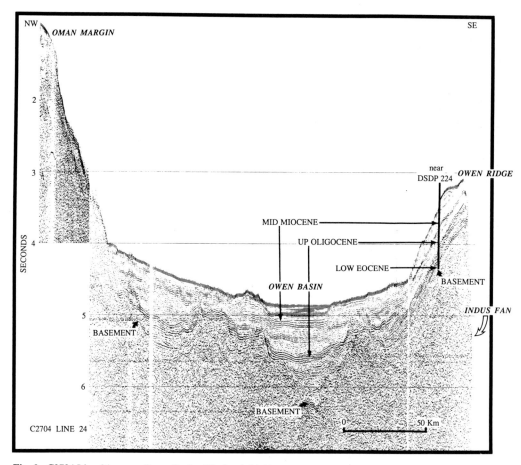

Fig. 3. C2704 Line 24 across Owen Basin. Display is highly compressed (vertical exaggeration c. 80:1) to show both Oman Margin and Owen Ridge. DSDP 224 reached basement on the Ridge; reflectors traced from basal unit of lower Eocene claystones predict that Owen Basin crust is no older than Upper Cretaceous. See also Fig. 8.

found at 11.7 to 14.5 km below sea level, the range in total depth owing to the uncertain presence of a 7.4 km sec^{-1} layer immediately beneath Layer 3. If real, this lowermost crustal layer is from 1.2 to 3.5 km thick, and it increases in thickness towards the continent.

Despite numerous efforts to find them, no identifiable seafloor spreading magnetic anomalies have been detected within the Owen Basin (Fig. 4). Low amplitude (c. 150 gammas) anomalies have been contoured to reveal an ENE grain in the central Basin (Whitmarsh 1979). This contrasts with studies to the east and south: anomalies 23 to 27 have been found beneath the central Indus Fan immediately east of the Owen Ridge (Whitmarsh 1974a; Norton & Sclater 1979), while spreading on the Carlsberg and Sheba Ridges has created magnetic lineations since Anomaly 5 time along the southern limit

of Indus Fan and northwestward into the Gulf of Aden (Cochran 1981). This youngest episode of seafloor spreading has generated 650 km of crust south of the Owen Basin between the Sharbithat Ridge and the Error Ridge Complex (Fig. 1).

Present knowledge of the regional tectonic history

The M-series anomalies of the Mozambique and West Somali Basins document the breakup of Gondwanaland and the subsequent Jurassic– Early Cretaceous history of the Indian Ocean. It is during this earliest stage in the development of the Western Indian Ocean that many researchers assume the Owen Basin was formed. Below we describe, in their chronologic order, highlights of the subsequent plate tectonic his-

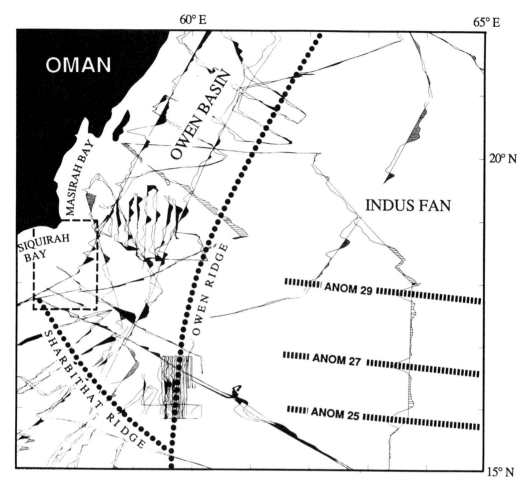

Fig. 4. Available shipboard magnetometer data. Early Tertiary anomalies 25 to 29 trend roughly E−W across Indus Fan. Unidentified lineations with a rough ENE−WSW grain are found in central Owen Basin (Whitmarsh 1979). The dense grid on the southern Owen Ridge is from C2704; additional C2704 magnetometer data were collected within rectangle outlined along Oman Margin, and for clarity are shown at larger scale in Fig. 9.

tory of the region with regards to the Owen Basin.

India–Madagascar–Antarctica began drifting south from the African Margin at M-22 to M-25 time (150 to 160 Ma; Fig. 1), forming the oceanic crust of the West Somali Basin (Segoufin & Patriat 1980; Rabinowitz et al. 1983; Cochran 1987) and the Mozambique Basin (Segoufin 1978; Simpson et al. 1979). Separation between Africa and Madagascar–India stopped shortly after MO time (c. 102.5 Ma; Cochran 1988).

Despite the lack of verification by M-series anomalies, many workers have assumed that ocean crust formed during this same interval off the coasts of Somalia and Southeast Oman (Fig. 5; Whitmarsh 1979; Beydoun 1982; Stein &

Cochran 1985; Larson et al. 1985; Cochran 1987). This strictly passive margin history of Somalia has been challenged by inferences from onshore geology that suggest northern Somalia was a sheared margin at this time (Bosellini 1986), and indeed, the rifting between Africa and Madagascar–India had a large strike-slip component along the Somali coast (Cochran 1988).

Near the end of the Cretaceous normal magnetic field (c. 84 Ma), a new spreading ridge developed as India separated from Madagascar (Fig. 5). In the absence of identifiable magnetic anomalies in either the North Somali or Owen Basins, no firm conclusion can be drawn as to the western extent of this spreading ridge. Per-

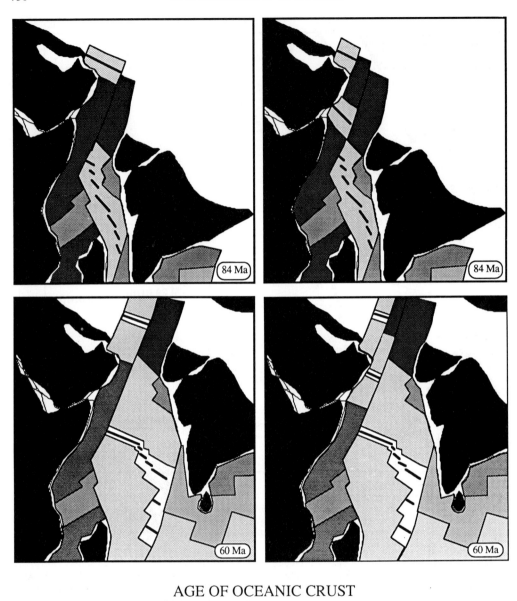

AGE OF OCEANIC CRUST

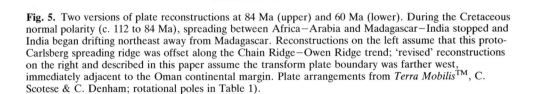

M17   M0   34   25   6
MAGNETIC ANOMALY

Fig. 5. Two versions of plate reconstructions at 84 Ma (upper) and 60 Ma (lower). During the Cretaceous normal polarity (c. 112 to 84 Ma), spreading between Africa−Arabia and Madagascar−India stopped and India began drifting northeast away from Madagascar. Reconstructions on the left assume that this proto-Carlsberg spreading ridge was offset along the Chain Ridge−Owen Ridge trend; 'revised' reconstructions on the right and described in this paper assume the transform plate boundary was farther west, immediately adjacent to the Oman continental margin. Plate arrangements from *Terra Mobilis*[TM], C. Scotese & C. Denham; rotational poles in Table 1).

Table 1. *Total rotational poles, relative to today's geographic positions, of the reconstructed plates in Figs 5 and 6 (from Terra Mobilis^TM, C. Scotese & C. Denham)*

	Age, Ma	Latitude	Longitude	Angle
Afghanistan	20	−26.95	−140.90	13.58
	60	−20.13	−154.30	37.41
	84	−17.45	−173.69	58.89
Africa	20	−65.00	150.00	2.93
	60	−47.85	117.40	10.16
	84	−30.35	116.60	19.70
Arabia	20	−39.81	168.10	8.41
	60	−44.93	158.39	14.88
	84	−32.20	138.10	23.11
India	20	−26.95	−140.90	13.58
	60	−20.13	−154.30	37.41
	84	−17.45	−173.69	58.89
Madagascar	20	−65.00	150.00	2.93
	60	−47.85	117.40	10.16
	84	−30.35	116.60	19.70

haps the ridge abutted the African−Arabian margin, and was connected by a long (c. 1500 km) transform fault to a spreading segment in the present Gulf of Oman. Alternatively, this transform plate boundary may have remained well seaward of the craton, preserving a remnant of Jurassic ocean crust in the North Somali Basin and/or the Owen Basin (Fig. 5 & Table 1).

Four features of the modern Owen Ridge have been cited as evidence of the latter alternative, making the Owen Ridge a relict transform fault (McKenzie & Sclater 1971; Whitmarsh 1974a; Norton & Sclater 1979; Whitmarsh 1979; Stein & Cochran 1985). These features are: (1) continuity with the active Owen Transform Fault that now offsets the Carlsberg and Sheba Ridge spreading centres (Fig. 1); (2) Ridge orientation that is parallel to post-Anomaly 34 flow lines and to the trend of the Chain Ridge in the North Somali Basin (Fig. 4); (3) separation of demonstrably early Tertiary crust beneath the Indus Fan from the unknown age (but presumably older) crust of the Owen Basin (Fig. 4); and (4) impressive modern relief (Fig. 3). Consequently, this interpretation makes the Owen Ridge the boundary between the Indian Plate of Tertiary age and the Arabian Plate of Jurassic age.

The presence of a Late Cretaceous spreading centre north of Oman is implied by the Semail Ophiolite (Fig. 1; Coleman 1981). Both K-Ar measurements of these mafic rocks and biostratigraphic ages of the intercalated sediments prove

this slab of ocean floor formed in the Gulf of Oman at roughly 90−100 Ma; southwestward emplacement onto the Oman Margin between 89 and 75 Ma is constrained by isotopic and palaeontologic dating (Allemann & Peters 1972; Coleman 1981; De Jong 1982).

Roughly 250 km of right-lateral displacement along the Masirah Fault of SE Oman has been cited to explain ophiolites of similar age on the island of Masirah (Fig. 2; Morton 1959; Moseley 1969; Stoneley 1974; Beydoun 1982). However, details of the Masirah Ophiolite (especially the absence of low-angle thrust planes dipping towards the northeast) have prompted others to argue for Late Cretaceous emplacement from the southeast, i.e., from the Owen Basin (Moseley & Abbotts 1979).

The proto-Carlsberg Ridge axis between Madagascar and India jumped several hundred kilometers northward during the early Palaeocene. The proximity of this new spreading axis to the west central margin of India explains the coincident outpouring of lava in the Deccan Traps (Norton & Sclater 1979). The western limit of the proto-Carlsberg Ridge (whether at the Owen Ridge or against the SE Oman Margin may have been affected in this Palaeocene plate reorganization; no evidence has been found to support or deny this possibility.

India continued its rapid (15−25 cm per yr) approach towards Eurasia until the first continental collision in the Eocene (Anomaly 22 time, 53 Ma; Patriat & Achache 1984). From

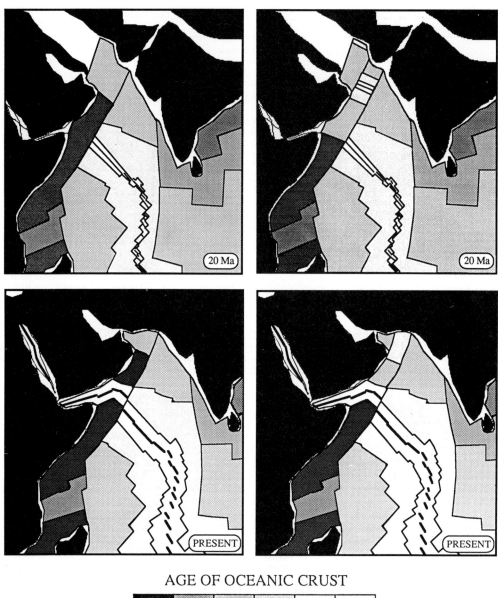

AGE OF OCEANIC CRUST

M17   M0   34   25   6

MAGNETIC ANOMALY

Fig. 6. Two versions of plate reconstructions at 20 Ma (upper) and at present (lower). The collision of India into Eurasia at 53 Ma was followed by greatly reduced spreading rates along the proto-Carlsberg Ridge that continued until the separation of Arabia from Africa during the Miocene opening of the Gulf of Aden. The reconstructions on the left assume a plate boundary was and continues to be maintained across Owen Ridge, and that Owen Basin is a fragment of Late Jurassic–Early Cretaceous ocean floor. The reconstructions on the right derive from the assumption presented in this paper that a transform plate boundary developed along SE Oman in the Late Cretaceous. This 'revised' model predicts a very much younger Owen Basin and explains recent transcurrent faulting observed along the SE Oman margin as post-Oligocene reactivation during the opening of the Gulf of Aden and the uplift of Owen Ridge.

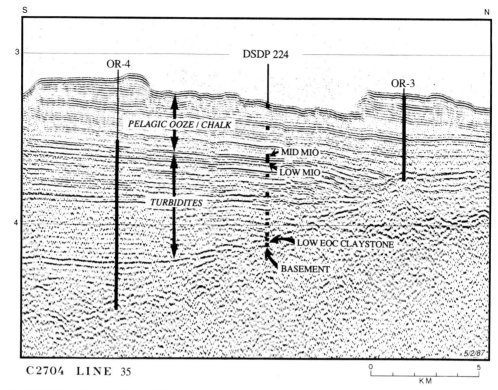

Fig. 7. C2704 Line 35 along Owen Ridge, crossing DSDP Site 224 (Whitmarsh 1974), and sites OR-3 and OR-4, target sites for ODP Leg 117; the latter was drilled at Site 731 (Prell *et al.* 1989). The upward transition from Lower Miocene turbidites to middle Miocene chalk marks the uplift of Owen Ridge. The apparent onlap of the turbidites onto the basement structure shoaling northward from OR-4 to OR-3 resulted from infilling of local basement topography, not from pre-Miocene tectonic uplift.

then until the early Oligocene (Anomaly 13, 35 Ma) subduction and crustal thickening along this suture was accompanied by erratic plate motion directions and greatly reduced (< 10 cm per year) rates of convergence between India and Eurasia.

In the last 30 Ma, 2000 km of crustal shortening has been accommodated between India and Eurasia by strike-slip faulting and large block rotations within Eurasia (Molnar & Tapponnier 1975; Patriat & Achache 1984). During this interval, major changes in plate geometry have developed throughout the Indian Ocean (McKenzi & Sclater 1971; Sclater & Fisher 1974; Sclater *et al.* 1976; Johnson *et al.* 1976, 1980; Norton & Sclater 1979; Schlich 1982). Among these changes was the middle to late Tertiary reorganization of the Carlsberg Ridge and its penetration into the Gulf of Aden (where it is renamed the Sheba Ridge; Fig. 1). Reports of the earliest rifting along the margins flanking the Gulf of Aden differ slightly; some place it in

the mid-Oligocene at 30 Ma (Girdler & Styles 1978) while others say it was a late Oligocene development (25 Ma) that greatly preceded the first emplacement of true oceanic crust (Fig. 6) at Anomaly 5 time (10 Ma; Laughton *et al.* 1970; Cochran 1981).

During the separation of Arabia and Africa, a component of compression between Arabia and India resulted in abrupt and significant uplift of the Owen Ridge (Whitmarsh 1974, 1979). This is inferred from the lower to middle Miocene transition from turbidites to overlying nannofossil chalks drilled on Owen Ridge at DSDP Site 224 several hundred metres above the seafloor of the Owen Basin (Figs 3, 7 & 8; Whitmarsh 1974b).

Interpretations of the present-day role of the Owen Ridge as a plate boundary vary widely and are based on either of three types of calculations: (1) the seismic focal mechanism of a single event along the Ridge implies left-lateral motion (Sykes 1968); (2) comparisons of

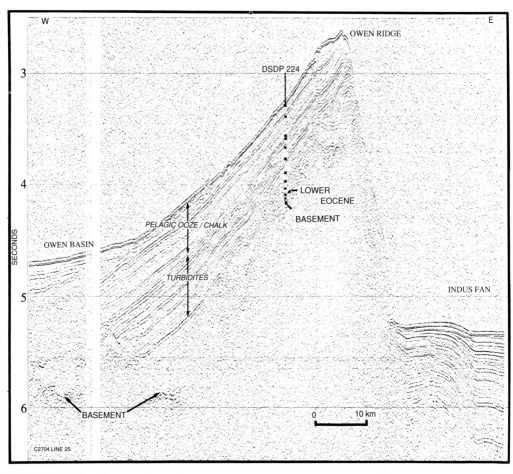

Fig. 8. C2704 Line 25 across Owen Ridge and DSDP Site 224. Tracings of the basal Lower Eocene sediments from the drillsite to the central Owen Basin contradict the assumed Jurassic to Early Cretaceous age for this crust (see Fig. 3). Note the recent deformation of Indus Fan turbidites beneath the eastern flank of Owen Ridge.

seafloor spreading rates on the east end of Sheba Ridge with those on the west end of Carlsberg Ridge (i.e., to either side of the Owen Transform, Fig. 1) have found no significant differences, suggesting there is no relative motion between the Indian and Arabian Plates (Laugthon *et al.* 1970; Cochran 1981; Wiens *et al.* 1985); and (3) global solutions for instantaneous rotation poles yield right-lateral motion between the Indian and Arabian Plates that, if taken up across the Owen Ridge, result in slip rates of 1 to 2 cm per year with a convergence rate of similar magnitude (McKenzie & Sclater 1971; Chase 1978; Minster & Jordan 1978). Reinterpretation of these and other data led DeMets and Gordon (1987) to conclude that motion along the Owen Ridge is indeed detect-

able and right-lateral, but very much smaller than earlier estimates (2 to 4 mm per year), and parallel to the trend of the ridge in the vicinity of 17° to 20°N, i.e., with no detectable component of convergence.

New data

During cruise C2704 of the *R/V Robert D. Conrad* in the Spring of 1986, we conducted a marine geological and geophysical survey of Owen Ridge and the SE margin of Oman offshore Siquirah Bay. These data were acquired as reconnaissance information for the placement and interpretation of drill cores and wireline logs to be collected during Leg 117 of the Ocean Drilling Program. This drilling effort was completed by the JOIDES *Resolution* in October 1987, and results are described elsewhere (Prell *et al.* 1990).

In this report we present results from C2704 that suggest that some of the assumptions concerning the tectonic history of the Owen Basin outlined above must be revised. Our reasoning is based largely on inferences drawn from seismic reflection profiles and total field magnetic measurements, as we describe below.

If the Owen Basin formed simultaneously with other Mesozoic basins of the western Indian Ocean (i.e., the Mozambique, West Somali, and possibly North Somali Basins) and followed a parallel tectonic history (Fig. 5), the basins should be similar with regard to basement depths, age of basal sediments, and total sediment distribution. A single profile across the Owen Basin (Fig. 3) shows that in three fundamental ways no such similarity exists: (1) Basement in the centre of the West Somali Basin is roughly 6.5 km below sea level, and it steadily deepens landward to more than 10 km (Coffin *et al.* 1986); basement reaches a maximum depth of only 5 km in the centre of the Owen Basin, and it *shoals* towards Oman (Fig. 3; Whitmarsh 1979). (2) Sediments in the West Somali Basin are more than 2 km thick, and they steadily thicken to more than 8 km along the African Margin (Coffin *et al.* 1986); the maximum thickness of sediments in the Owen Basin is *less* than 2 km and, except for isolated, margin-parallel basins (Whitmarsh 1979), there is no is apparent trend of thickening sediments toward the Oman Margin (Fig. 3). (3) Consistent with the crustal age estimates provided by the M-series magnetic anomalies of the West Somali Basin, downward extrapolation of sedimentation rates measured at DSDP Site 241 provide an estimate of Late Jurassic age for the basal sediments (Rabinowitz *et al.* 1983); tracing reflectors within the oldest sediments of the Owen Basin eastward to Site 224 on the Owen Ridge (Whitmarsh 1974*b*) predicts that these sediments, and by inference the crust within the Owen Basin, are *no older* than Late Cretaceous (Figs 3, 7 & 8). Clearly the West Somali and Owen Basins have not shared an entirely common history.

Though by no means observed in all cases, a 100–250 km wide region of subdued magnetic anomalies is a feature of many passive continental margins throughout the world. The origin of these 'quiet zones' is debated, and they can be found along rifted margins of various ages (e.g. the eastern margin of North America, c. 165 Ma; the eastern margin of South America, c. 130 Ma; the Norwegian margin, c. 50 Ma; the margins of the Gulf of Aden, c. 25 Ma). In contrast, marine magnetic anomalies can often be identified within a very much shorter distance from continental crust along plate boundary margins (either convergent or transform); examples include most of the margins that border the eastern and northern Pacific Ocean.

Although marine magnetic anomalies have not been identified within the Owen Basin, ± 150 gamma lineations with an ENE–WSW grain have been observed in the central basin (Whitmarsh 1979). During C2704 we mapped lineations of similar amplitude and orientation along SE Oman as far landward as the 250 m isobath off Siquirah Bay (Fig. 9). This location is roughly 50 km from the along-strike projection of the Masirah-1 well that reached Proterozoic clastic sediments, clearly within the Arabian Craton (Gorin *et al.* 1982). If the C2704 lineations are indeed marine magnetic anomalies, then the continent–ocean boundary is both unusually abrupt and unusually far landward for this to be a passive continental margin.

The highest amplitude magnetic lineations off Siquirah Bay occur above a particularly level (eroded?) seismic reflecting horizon along which we measured refraction velocities ranging from from 4.3 to 4.8 km sec^{-1} (Figs 10 & 11). The location, stratigraphic position, seismic velocity, and magnetic character of this feature all suggest it is the along-strike equivalent to ophiolites reported at Ra's Madrakah (Gorin *et al.* 1982) and in the larger exposure 160 km NE on Masirah Island (Moseley & Abbotts 1979). Though the landward extent of this structure was not determined during C2704, its seaward limit was crossed many times and consistently observed as a steep, down-to-the-basin fault that we have labelled the 'Siquirah Fault' (Figs 9, 10 & 11). Offsets of near-bottom sedimentary reflectors along this fault demonstrate recent displacement; translational motion has not been determined. Dip-line profiles reveal other, more seaward structures that could be additional blocks of elevated oceanic crust (Figs 10, 11, 12 & 13). Faults above many of these cut through the overlying sedimentary cover; some show the complex relationships of 'flower structures' (Fig. 13) that are indicative of strike-slip displacement (Harding *et al.* 1983). Much of this seismic data calls into question the prevailing rifted margin model for SE Oman.

A revised tectonic history

On the basis of the above observations, a 're-vised' tectonic model for the Owen Basin and the adjacent regions is proposed. This interpretation hinges on one modest but crucial as-

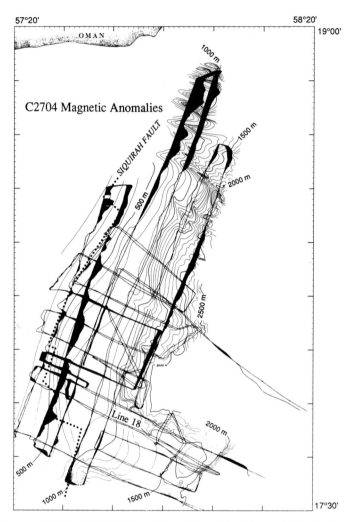

Fig. 9. Magnetic anomalies from C2704, with positive values plotted due east along ship track. Data from landward of Siquirah Fault and north of 18° 30N have an ENE−WSW grain similar to that found in Owen Basin (see Fig. 4).

sertion: the spreading centre that developed as India split from Madagascar during the Late Cretaceous was offset along the SE Oman margin, not along what is now the Owen Ridge (Fig. 5). This offset may have occurred landward of the Jurassic continent-ocean boundary, thereby slicing off the outermost continental crust of Oman. This possibility is suggested by the observation and modelling (Steckler & Ten Brink 1986) that the secondary development of a plate boundary is likely to occur several tens of kilometres landward of the hinge zone, i.e. within a craton, not at the former continent−ocean boundary or within oceanic crust itself. The rifting that led to Miocene seafloor spread-

ing in the Gulf of Aden (roughly 70 Ma later) appears to have reactivated the boundary between the Owen and N Somali Basins, and thus to have nucleated along the same line as the rifting which created the Owen Basin. The pros and cons of a prevailing history against this revised tectonic model are summarized in Table 2.

Our revision provides several predictions relating to the character and timing of tectonism within and adjacent to the Owen Basin. Foremost among these is the prediction that c. 84 Ma ocean crust should be found at the southern end of the Owen Basin abutting the Sharbithat Ridge. If ocean crust formed northeastward

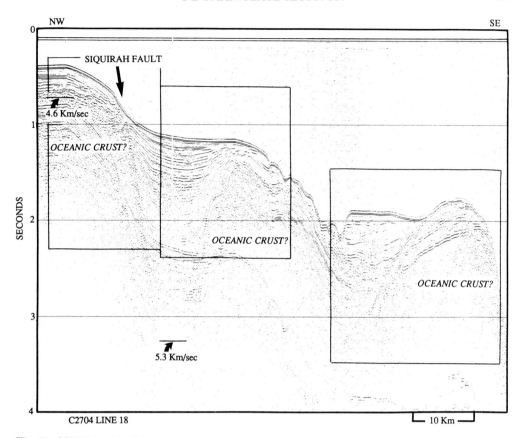

NW   SE

SIQUIRAH FAULT

4.6 Km/sec

OCEANIC CRUST?

SECONDS

OCEANIC CRUST?

OCEANIC CRUST?

5.3 Km/sec

C2704 LINE 18   └─ 10 Km ─┘

Fig. 10. C2704 Line 18 offshore Siquirah Bay, Oman (location in Fig. 9). Seismic refraction measurements detected the velocities shown, and these are interpreted to mark the top of oceanic crust that was thrust against the margin between Late Cretaceous and Lower Eocene time. The three reflectorless zones beneath deformed sediments seen on this line are also found in most of the other C2704 profiles. The shallowest, most landward block is bounded on its seaward side by a dramatic offset that we have labelled the 'Siquirah Fault' (see Fig. 9); this structure is along-strike from ophiolite crops out at Ra's Madrakah and Masirah Island. Larger-scale details of this profile are shown in Figs 11–13.

from this location across the Owen Basin at a rate similar to the half-spreading rate recorded by anomalies northeast of Madagascar (c. 4 cm per year, Fig. 1), then nearly all of the 825 km of crust within the Owen Basin adjacent to Oman ought to be Late Cretaceous in age (Fig. 7). Any vestige of Jurassic crust that had formed along the once-passive margin of Oman either was consumed in the Makran subduction zone (Fig. 1), or is now among the complex of blocks comprising south-central Asia. These same age relationships were depicted in an age of the ocean floor map prepared by Sclater *et al.* (1981).

The change along SE Oman from a passive continental margin to a transcurrent plate boundary is likely to have left a record within

the craton. The following facts reported by previous workers may indeed be parts of this record. First, marked lateral facies variation and thickness changes occur within marly limestones of the Aruma Group of southern Oman, and this has been cited as evidence for Late Cretaceous block faulting (Morton 1959; Boydoun 1982). We suggest that this may have coincided with and was causally linked to the major transcurrent fault we propose developed at this time along the SE coast.

A second line of evidence links our revised model to the occurrence of hydrocarbons. Subsurface salt removal was crucial to the development of structural traps along the eastern flank oil province of Oman, and resulted from dissolution by groundwater at intervals that coincided

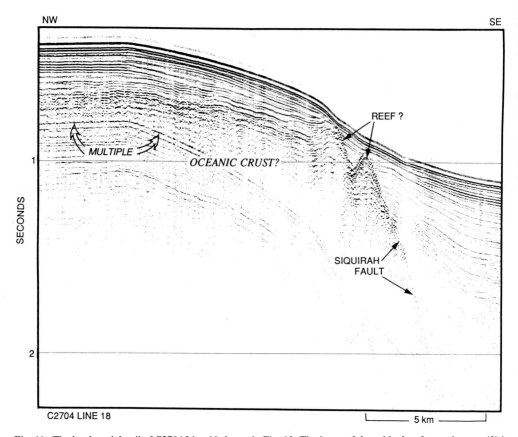

Fig. 11. The landward detail of C2704 Line 18 shown in Fig. 10. The inner of three blocks of oceanic crust (?) is apparent landward of the Siquirah Fault. Possible reef buildup is seen on the seaward edge of this structure.

with major phases of tectonic activity (i.e. 'syn-tectonic dissolution', Al-Marjeby & Nash 1986). Four periods of dissolution are noted by these authors: (1) Late Carboniferous (Hercynian?); (2) mid-Mesozoic (breakup of Gondwanaland and opening of proto-Owen Basin?); (3) Late Mesozoic (formation of transform boundary?); and (4) Late Tertiary (opening of the Gulf of Aden and changing plate stresses along SE Oman?). There is an intriguing coincidence of the latter three events with our proposed tectonic model.

A third category of previously reported evidence consistent with our revised tectonic model relates to the origin, age, and time of emplacement of ophiolites found in SE Oman. The· most thoroughly documented outcrops occur on Masirah Island (Moseley 1969; Moseley & Abbotts 1979). As a matter of simplicity, previous authors (Morton 1959; Stoneley 1974) had assumed that these rocks, along with the Semail ophiolite, were obducted southward

from the Gulf of Oman. To be consistent with the known ages of the Semail Ophiolite, this implies that the Masirah counterparts formed at an ocean spreading centre between 90 and 100 Ma, and were emplaced about 10 Ma later (Allemann & Peters 1972; Coleman 1981; De Jong 1982). Moseley and Abbotts found no compelling evidence to support this northern origin, and argued that obduction from the Owen Basin was more likely. These authors did not specify a precise age or time of emplace-ment, but noted that the latter must have oc-curred between the deposition of Lower Cretaceous limestone blocks found in a mélange zone and the accumulation of shallow-water Eocene limestones overlying the volcanic rocks. Our revised model concurs with this Owen Basin origin and a critical test would be to determine the age of the limestone and cherts that Shackleton & Ries (1990) found in contact with pillow lavas on Masirah, but which were not dated. We estimate that oceanic crust was

NW

SE

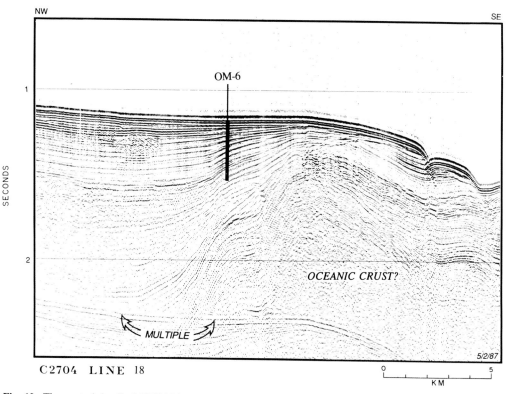

OM-6

SECONDS

1

2

OCEANIC CRUST?

MULTIPLE

5/2/87

C2704 LINE 18

0 ⌞_____⌟ 5
K M

Fig. 12. The central detail of C2704 Line 18 from Fig. 10, showing considerable complexity and truncation patterns above the central block of oceanic crust (?). OM-6 was a target site for ODP Leg 117, and was drilled at Site 727 (Prell *et al.* 1989).

generated in the Owen Basin northeast from its southern limit at a half-spreading rate of 4 cm per year, and would have formed at the latitude of Masirah roughly 10 Ma after the initiation of the present Owen Basin. Hence we predict these volcanic rocks and intercalated sediments are between 80 and 90 Ma. The actual time of emplacement is more difficult to determine, but we note that during the fast spreading rates between Anomalies 34 and 22, only a small component of convergence along the transform boundary of SE Oman would have been required to obduct Owen Basin crust. Alternatively, the erratic plate motion directions that coincided with the initial collision of India and Eurasia (Anomaly 22 time, Patriat & Achache 1984) may have resulted in compression along the Oman transform boundary, and the obduction could date from that time. As noted by Moseley & Abbotts (1979) lower Eocene shallow-water limestones resting unconformably on the Masirah Ophiolite provide a minimum emplacement age.

The complex deformational structures and faulting observed in C2704 profiles along the Oman Margin (Figs 10, 11, 12 & 13) are far too young to be simply the result of movement along a Late Cretaceous transform plate boundary. It is likely that fracture zones, thrusts and various faults, dating from the earlier transform history, were reactivated during the Neogene plate re-configurations that accompanied the opening of the Gulf of Aden. Uplift of the Owen Ridge occurred in lower to the middle Miocene time (Whitmarsh *et al.* 1974*b*), coincident with this latter event; we argue that further evidence of this change in the regional stress field is found along the Oman Margin. Future work will involve correlating the reflection profiles along the margin with results from ODP Leg 117 (Prell *et al.* 1989). We anticipate that the re-initiation of deformation along the margin will be found to coincide with tectonism along the Owen Ridge and along the margins of the Gulf of Aden.

Table 2. *The supporting and contradictory elements of two interpretations of the plate tectonic history of Owen Basin*

Existing Tectonic Model
(Cretaceous proto-Carlsberg Ridge offset along Owen Ridge)

PRO	CON
Appealing symmetry between western basins	Contrasting depths, sediment thickness and basal sediment ages between Owen and W Somali Basins
Orientation of Owen Basin magnetic lineations is about the same as the M-series anomalies in W Somali Basin	Owen Basin heat flow is too high for Jurassic-age crust
Owen Ridge is a plausible plate boundary	Geological–geophysical character of SE Oman is inconsistent with passive margin

Revised Tectonic Model
(Cretaceous proto-Carlsberg Ridge offset along the SE Oman margin)

PRO	CON
Explains features of Owen Basin • shallow, warm basement • thin, young sediment cover	Considerable speculation remains with regard to • presence of Anomalies 34–22 in Owen Basin • age constraints on correlations to terrestrial events • nature, age, and direction of ophiolite obduction • evidence for two distinct times of margin deformation
Explains features of SE Oman margin • abrupt continent–ocean boundary • Upper Cretaceous ophiolites • scarcity of rift and early drift sediments	

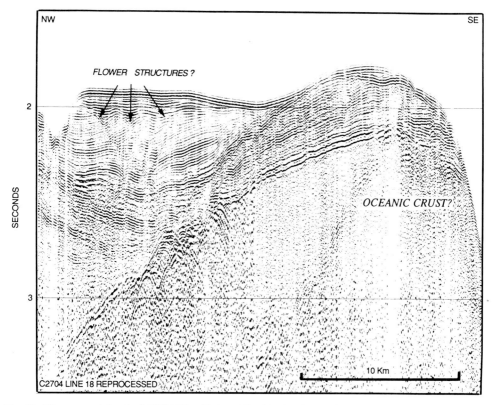

Fig. 13. The seaward detail of C2704 Line 18 from Fig. 10, showing additional complexity and truncation patterns above the outer oceanic crustal block (?). Possible flower structures suggest relatively recent transcurrent faulting.

Discussions with J. Cochran of L-DGO concerning the plate tectonic history of the west Indian Ocean were very helpful and are gratefully acknowledged. F. J. Vine provided careful and constructive review of this article. This work was supported by NSF grant OCE85−11571, and is L-DGO contribution no. 4412. W. L. Prell received support from grants OCE 85−11571 and a USSAC grant.

References

AALLEMAN, F. & PETERS, T. 1972. The ophiolite−radiolarite belt of the North-Oman mountains. *Eclogae Geologicae Helvetiae*, **65**, 657−697.

AL-MARJEBY, A. & NASH, D. 1986. A summary of the geology and oil habitat of the eastern flank hydrocarbon province of South Oman. *Marine and Petroleum Geology*, **3**, 306−314.

BEYDOUN, Z. R. 1982. The Gulf of Aden and north-west Arabian Sea. *In*: NAIRN, A. E. M. & STELNI, F. G. The *Ocean Basins and Margins: The Indian Ocean*, (eds) p. 253−313.

BOSELLINI, A. 1986. East Africa continental margins. *Geology*, **14**, p. 76−78.

CHASE, C. G. 1978. Plate kinematics: The Americas, East Africa, and the rest of the world; *Earth and Planetary Science Letters*, **37**, 355−68.

COCHRAN, J. R. 1981. The Gulf of Aden: Structure and evolution of a young ocean basin and continental margin. *Journal of Geophysical Research*, **86**, 263−288.

—— 1987. The North Somali Basin, Chain Ridge, and the origin of the Somali Basin geoid/gravity low, *EOS*, **68**, 411.

—— 1988. The North Somali Basin, Chain Ridge, and the origin of the Somali Basin geoid/gravity low. *Journal of Geophysical Research*, **93**, 11985−12008.

COFFIN, M. F., RABINOWITZ, P. D. & HOUTZ, R. E. 1986. Crustal structure in the western Somali Basin. *Geophysical Journal of the Royal Astronomical Society*, **86**, 331−369.

COLEMAN, R. G. 1981. Tectonic setting for ophiolite obduction in Oman. *Journal of Geophysical Research*, **86**, 2497−2508.

DE JONG, K. A. 1982. Tectonics of the Persian Gulf, Gulf of Oman and southern Pakistan region. *In*: NAIRN, A. E. M. & STELHI, F. G. (eds) *The Ocean Basins and Margins: The Indian Ocean* 315−351.

DeMets, C. & Gordon, R. G. 1987. Limits on motion along the Owen Fracture Zone *EOS*, **68**, 1473.

Girdler, R. W. & Styles, P. 1978. Sea-floor spreading in the western Gulf of Aden *Nature*, **271**, 615–617.

Gorin, G. E., Racz, L. G. & Walter, M. R. 1982. Late Precambrian–Cambrian Sediments of Huqf Group, Sultanate of Oman. *Bulletin of the American Association of Petroleum Geologists*, **66**, 2609–2627.

Harding, T. P., Gregory, R. F. & Stephens, L. H. 1983. Convergent wrench fault and positive flower structure, Ardmore Basin, Oklahoma. *In*: Bally, A. W. (ed) *Seismic Expression of Structural Styles, American Association of Petroleum Geologists Studies in Geology*, **3**, 4.2–13

Johnson, B. D., Powell, C. McA. & Veevers, J. J. 1976. Spreading history of the eastern Indian Ocean and greater India's northward flight from Antarctica and Australia. *Bulletin of the Geological Society of America*, **87**, 1560–1566.

——, Powell C. McA. & Veevers, J. J. 1980. Early spreading history of the Indian Ocean between Antarctica and Australia *Earth and Planetary Science Letters*, **47**, 131–143.

Larson, R. L. *et al.* 1985. *The Bedrock Geology of the World*, W. H. Freemont Company Inc., New York.

Laughton, A. S., Whitmarsh R. B., & Jones, M. T. 1970. The evolution of the Gulf of Aden *Philosophical Transactions of the Royal Society of London*, **267(A)**, 227–266.

McKenzie, D. & Sclater, J. G. 1971. The evolution of the Indian Ocean since the late Cretaceous. *Geophysical Journal of the Royal Astronomical Society*, **24**, 437–528.

Minster, J. B. & Jordan, J. B. 1978. Present-day plate motions *Journal of Geophysical Research*, **83**, 5331–5354.

Molnar, P. & Tapponnier, P. 1975. Cenozoic tectonics of Asia: Effects of a continental collision *Science*, **189**, 419–425.

Morton, D. M. 1959. The geology of Oman *Proceedings of the 5th World Petroleum Congress, New York*, 227–280.

Moseley, F. 1969. The Upper Cretaceous Ophiolite Complex of Masirah Island, Oman *Geological Journal*, **6**, 293–306.

——, & Abbots, I. L. 1979. The Ophiolite Melange of Masirah, Oman *Journal of the Geological Society London*, **136**, 713–724.

Norton, I. O. & Sclater, J. G. 1979. A model for the evolution of the Indian Ocean and the breakup of Gondwanaland, *Journal of Geophysical Research*, **84**, 6803–6830.

Patriat, P. & Achache, J. 1984. India–Eurasia collision chronology has implications for crustal shortening and driving mechanism of plates *Nature*, **311**, 615–621.

Prell, W. L. *et al.* 1990. Neogene tectonics and sedimentation of the SE Oman continental margin: results from ODP Leg 117. *In*: Robertson, A. H. F., Searle, M. P. & Ries, A.

C. (eds) *The Geology and Tectonics of the Oman Region*. Geological Society, London, Special Publication, **49**, 745–758.

Prell, W. L., Niitsuma, N. *et al.* 1989. Proceedings, Ocean Drilling Program, Initial Reports 117: College Station, TX (Ocean Drilling Program).

Rabinowitz, P. D., Coffin, M. F. & Falvey, D. 1983. The separation of Madagascar and Africa *Science*, **220**, 67–69.

Schlich, R. 1982. The Indian ocean: Aseismic ridges, spreading centers, and oceanic basins. *In*: Nairn A. E. M. & Stehli F. G. (eds) *The Ocean Basins and Margins, Volume 6, The Indian Ocean*, Plenum Press, New York, 51–148.

Sclater, J. G. & Fisher, R. L. 1974. The evolution of the east central Indian ocean, with emphasis on the tectonic setting of the Ninetyeast Ridge *Bulletin of the Geological Society of America*, **85**, 683–702.

—— Luyendyls, B. P. & Meinke, L. 1976. Magnetic lineations in the southern part of the Central Indian Basin. *Bulletin of the Geological Society of America*, 371–376.

—— Parsons, B. & Jaupart, C. 1981. Oceans and continents: similarities and differences in the mechanisms of heat loss. *Journal of Geophysical Research*, 11535–11552.

Segoufin, J. 1978. Anomalies magnetiques mesoziques dans le bassin de Mozambique *Comptes Rendue de L'Academic des Sciences*, **287**, 109–112.

—— & Patriat, P. 1980. Existence d'anomalies mesozoiques dans le basin de Somalie. Implications pour les relations Afrique–Antarctique–Madagascar *Comptes Rendus de L'Academie des Sciences*, Paris, **291**, 85–88.

Shackleton, R. M. & Ries, W. C. 1990. Tectonics of the Masirah Fault Zone and eastern Oman. *In*: Robertson, A. H. F., Searle, M. P. & Ries, A. C. (eds) *The Geology and Tectonics of the Oman Region*. Geological Society, London, Special Publication, **49**, 715–724.

Simpson, E. S. W., Sclater, J. G. Parsons, Norton I. & Meinke, L. 1979. Mesozoic magnetic lineations in the Mozambique Basin *Earth and Planetary Science Letters*, **43**, 260–264.

Steckler, M. & Ten Brink, U. 1986. Lithospheric strength variations as a control on new plate boundaries: Examples from the N. Red Sea Region *Earth and Planetary Science Letters*, **79**, 120–132.

Stein, C. A. & Cochran, J. R. 1985. The transition between the Sheba Ridge and Owen Basin: Rifting of old oceanic lithosphere *Geophysical Journal of the Royal Astronomical Society*, **81**, 47–74.

Stonely, R. 1974. Evolution of the continental margins bounding a former Southern Tethys. *In*: Burke C. A. & Drake C. L. (eds) *The Geology of Continental Margins* Springer Verlag, Berlin, 889–906.

Sykes, L. R. 1968. Seismological evidence for transform faults, sea-floor spreading, and continental drift. *In*: PHINNEY, R. A. (ed) *The History of the Earth's Crust*. Princeton University Press, Princeton, New Jersey, 120–150.

WHITMARSH, R. B. 1974a. Some aspects of plate tectonics in the Arabian Sea. *Initial Report DSDP*, U. S. Government Printing Office, Washington, D. C., 527–536.

—— 1974b. *Initial Report DSDP*, U. S. Government Printing Office, Washington, D. C., **23**.

—— 1979. The Owen Basin off the south-east margin of Arabia and the evolution of the Owen Fracture Zone. *Geophysical Journal of the Royal Astronomical Society*, **58**, 441–470.

WIENS, D. A., DEMETS, GORDON, R. G., STEIN, S. ARGUSD., ENGELN, J. F., LUNDGREN, E., QUIBLE, D. STEIN, C., WEINSTEIN, S., & WOODS, D. F. 1985. A diffuse plate boundary model for Indian Ocean tectonics. *Geophysical Research Letters*, **12**, 429–432.

Neogene tectonics and sedimentation of the SE Oman continental margin: results from ODP Leg 117

WARREN L. PRELL and shipboard party of ODP Leg 117 (see acknowledgements)

Department of Geological Sciences, Brown University, Providence, RI, USA

Abstract: The primary objective of Leg 117 of the Ocean Drilling Program was to test ideas about the origin and variability of the Asian summer monsoon and its influence on depositional patterns and the oxygen minimum zone (OMZ) in the northwestern Indian Ocean. The western Arabian Sea currently is characterized by intense summer monsoonal upwelling that induces high primary productivity and distinctive planktonic assemblages. The planktonic indicators of upwelling conditions, as well as aeolian detritus from deserts and highlands of adjacent lands, are preserved in the sediments deposited on the Owen Ridge and the Oman Margin. A second objective was to resolve questions about the tectonic history of the Owen Ridge and Oman Margin.

On the Oman Margin, we cored eight sites (Sites 723–730) that range from 300 to 1500 m water depth, a depth interval that includes the OMZ which impinges on the continental slope. The structural and depositional settings of the sites include the outer shelf where the basement is shallow, in sediment-filled slope basins, and on or near mid-slope basement ridges. This wide range of settings provides valuable information on the subsidence of sedimentary basins, the variation of monsoonal upwelling, and the temporal and spatial distribution of organic carbon-rich sediments and their possible relationship to the OMZ. Most of the sediments on the Margin are varieties of marly nannofossil ooze to nannofossil-rich mud, with admixtures of detrital calcite, opal, foraminifera, and scattered phosphorite nodules. All sub-surface sediments on the Margin are rich in organic carbon. Despite the abundance of organic carbon, sulfate in interstitial water persists to sub-bottom depths often exceeding 100 m, even in rapidly accumulating sediments (>100 m/Ma). This finding was unexpected, especially in sediments that lie within the depth range of the OMZ. A tentative interpretation is that the composition of the organic matter may inhibit full utilization of sulphate by sulphate-reducing bacteria.

We found a complex interaction between the tectonic subsidence of the slope basins and the deposition and preservation of organic-rich, opal-rich, and laminated facies. On the basis of benthonic foraminifera data, several of the sites have subsided from depths shallower than 350 m

in the late Pliocene to current depths of 600–1400 m. Subsidence rates for these sites are estimated to have been 150–300 m/Ma. A time-palaeodepth reconstruction of the sediment data reveals that most of the organic carbon-rich, opal-rich, and laminated facies were deposited in the late Pliocene, especially near 800 m. The late Pliocene mode of deposition and preservation of sub-millimetre laminations may reflect a thicker, more intense, and stable OMZ. However, since the total accumulation rates are not high for this interval, the implications for higher or lower rates of upwelling and productivity are unclear. In contrast, sediments of late Pleistocene and Holocene age also contain high organic carbon content, but do not contain the laminated, opal-rich facies of the Pliocene sediments. Whether this pattern signifies a change in primary sediment input or a post-depositional change in preservation is unknown at this time.

Background of ODP Leg 117

Leg 117 of the Ocean Drilling Program (Prell *et al.* 1989) drilled eight sites in the NW Arabian Sea (Fig. 1). The Leg's primary goal was to recover continuous and expanded sedimentary sections that were deposited during the Neogene under the influence of high biological productivity associated with the area of coastal upwelling off Southeast Oman. A secondary goal was to clarify the Neogene tectonic evolution of the Oman Margin.

Some of the specific problems that ODP

From ROBERTSON, A. H. F., SEARLE, M. P. & RIES, A. C. (eds), 1990,
The Geology and Tectonics of the Oman Region.
Geological Society Special Publication No 49, pp 745–758

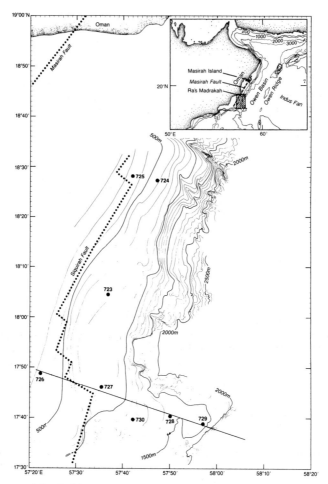

Fig. 1. Location map and detailed bathymetry of the Oman Margin at 100 m contour intervals from SEABEAM swathmap data (Conrad 2704). The location of the Masirah and Siquirah Faults are shown as well as the Ras Madrakah headland which is composed of ophiolites. The locations of ODP sites are shown, along with the location of the cross section in Fig. 2.

Leg 117 was designed to address include the following.

How does Neogene monsoonal upwelling, as recorded in sediments of the northern Indian Ocean, vary in response to changing solar radiation budgets (caused by changes in the earth's orbit) and to changes in the Neogene tectonic conditions (caused by uplift of the Himalayas)?

How did changes in monsoon intensity and glacio-eustatic sea level affect the composition and distribution of organic rich biogenic and aeolian sedimentary facies on the Oman Margin? Do the sediments record variations in the intensity or location of the oxygen minimum zone where it impinges on the seafloor?

What is the origin and nature of basement on the Oman Margin and how are the Neogene tectonics of Owen Ridge and the Oman Margin related?

Below, we briefly review the modern and palaeoceanography and the marine geology of the SE Oman Margin as it is relevant to the interpretation of our drilling results.

Modern and palaeoceanography of the SE Oman Margin

The modern oceanography of the Oman Margin is characterized by three interrelated factors: seasonal monsoon upwelling, stable saline intermediate waters, and the presence of a strong mid-water oxygen minimum zone (OMZ). In contrast to other prominent up-welling systems, which are located in eastern boundary currents (i.e. on western boundaries of continents) and are caused by large-scale and persistent atmospheric and oceanographic circulation, the upwelling system off Oman is located within a western boundary current (i.e. the eastern coast of Arabia) and exhibits extreme seasonality. In the Arabian Sea the large-scale SW monsoon circulation is the driving force for the seasonal upwelling. At present, winter cooling over Asia develops a high-pressure cell that drives northeasterly surface winds from Asia over the Arabian Sea. However, summer heating of Asia causes ascending air masses and creates an intense low-pressure cell centred around 30°N over the Tibetan Plateau. The pressure gradient between Asia and the southern Indian Ocean drives strong near-surface southwesterly winds. Ekman transport by these southwesterly winds, which roughly parallel the coast of Oman, causes offshore flow of surface waters, which forces upwelling of nutrient-rich, cold sub-surface water from several hundred metres depth (Wyrtki 1971, 1973; Currie et al. 1973; Prell & Streeter 1982). Hence, the wind speed and the duration of the SW monsoon determines, in part, the strength and duration of the upwelling events. The upwelling of nutrients into the euphotic zone produces high rates of primary and secondary productivity along the coast of Oman. The underlying sediments are partially composed of microfossils and organic matter that are produced by this planktonic response to the upwelling. Thus, the Neogene climatic and oceanographic history of the western Arabian Sea are potentially encoded in the sedimentary records recovered during Leg 117.

The intermediate waters (200–1500 m) of the Arabian Sea are characterized by their high salinity and stability. The sources of intermediate water are the restricted marginal basins, such as the Arabian Gulf and Red Sea, as well as the open Arabian Sea and Gulf of Aden. These sources combine to form a North Indian Intermediate Water (NIIW), which has a high uniform salinity of about 34.8‰ (Wyrtki 1971, 1973). The intermediate water is relatively isolated in the Arabian Sea and has little exchange with the central Indian Ocean. As a result of this limited exchange, stable stratification, and high rates of productivity, the NIIW has extremely low oxygen content between about 200 m and 1500 m, and forms an oxygen minimum zone (OMZ) in the Arabian Sea

(Wyrtki 1971, 1973; Slater & Kroopnick 1984). Biochemical processes, such as the bacterial remineralization of organic matter produced in the euphotic zone, are responsible for the existence of the OMZ. However, stability and circulation are responsible for its position in the upper part of a water column that lacks advective recharge of dissolved oxygen, either for lack of horizontal or vertical advection (Wyrtki 1962). This oxygen-deficient layer is sandwiched between the oxygen-rich and highly productive mixed layer and deeper layers with moderately high oxygen content (about 3 ml O_2 l^{-1}; Wyrtki 1971). This distinctive OMZ of the Arabian Sea reflects a combination of high monsoonal upwelling productivity (oxygen demand), stable stratification (due to marginal seas) and sluggish circulation (due to reversals of flow). Many of these features could change on glacial–interglacial or Neogene timescales, and may have influenced both the OMZ and the character of sediments accumulating on the Oman Margin.

Most of our knowledge about the palaeo-oceanography of the Arabian Sea and past monsoonal circulation comes from climate modelling and from sedimentary records of the last 5×10^5 years. Biogenic and chemical records from this time span exhibit systematic variations that have periodicities in the Milankovitch frequency band, i.e., the periodicity associated with changes in the eccentricity (10^5 years), the obliquity (4.1×10^4 years) and the precession (2.3×10^4 and 1.9×10^4 years) of the earth's orbit around the sun. Studies of late Pleistocene monsoonal upwelling (Prell et al. 1980; Prell 1984a, b; Prell & van Campo, 1986; Prell & Kutzbach 1987) have shown that the monsoonal upwelling does vary coherently with orbital variations. However, to examine longer-term changes and to prove unambiguously that orbital variations force changes in monsoonal intensity, longer high-resolution records of monsoonal sedimentation were needed.

Simulations of the monsoon circulation by general circulation models of the atmosphere (AGCM) have also shown that the intensity of the monsoonal circulation is closely related to the seasonal distribution of summer radiation over Asia, which is controlled by changes in the earth's orbit on time scales of 10^3 to 10^4 years. Simulations confirm that the strength of the monsoon is closely related to the precession of the Earth's axis, which has a period of about 2.3 $\times 10^4$ years (Kutzbach 1981; Kutzbach & Guetter 1986; Prell & Kutzbach 1987) Another driving force for the summer monsoon is closely linked to the elevation of the Himalayan–

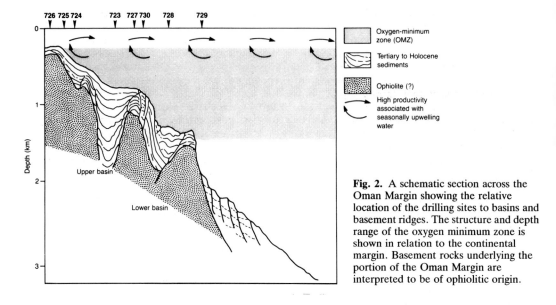

Fig. 2. A schematic section across the Oman Margin showing the relative location of the drilling sites to basins and basement ridges. The structure and depth range of the oxygen minimum zone is shown in relation to the continental margin. Basement rocks underlying the portion of the Oman Margin are interpreted to be of ophiolitic origin.

Tibetan Plateau (Hahn & Manabe 1975). AGCM simulations predict that monsoonal strength should increase in response to Himalayan uplift. Over a long period of time (several Ma), Himalayan uplift should be manifested in a general increase in monsoon intensity and associated upwelling sedimentation.

Submarine geology of the SE Oman Margin

Much of the Oman Margin (Fig. 1) is characterized by a narrow continental shelf bordered by an extremely steep continental slope, which is thought to be a mega-shear associated with the formation of the margin (Whitmarsh 1979; Stein & Cochran 1985). However, the embayment between Ra's Madrakah and Ra's Sharbithat has a relatively wide continental shelf (about 75 km), which abuts the Sharbithat Ridge to the south and converges on Ra's Madrakah headland to the north. The continental slope in this area is characterized by a series of linear NNE–SSW trending sediment terraces, underlain by sedimentary basins (Figs 1 & 2). These terraces lie at water depths ranging from 500 to 1000 m for the upper basin and at 1500 m for the lower basin and thus accumulate sediments within the depth range of the intermediate water OMZ (Fig. 2).

Seismic reflection profiles of the Margin reveal that the upper basin is bounded landward (west) by the steeply-dipping Siquirah Fault (Mountain & Prell 1990) and seaward by a buried ridge of acoustic basement (Fig. 2). The upper basin shoals and narrows to the north. The southern part of the upper basin lies at about 1000 m and is about 15 km wide, whereas the northern part lies at about 600 m and is about 5 km wide. Seismic profiles show that the sediments in these basins are thick and acoustically highly layered, and that all but the shallowest few hundred metres are structurally isolated from the sediments of adjacent basins by bounding faults. The sediments are thickest in the centre of the basin (more than 2000 m; Mountain & Prell 1990), forming a syncline-shaped deposit. Along the strike of the basin the surface and subsurface layers dip gently to the southwest and are relatively conformable, although some deformational and slump-related structures are observed. Studies of box and piston cores from this upper basin indicate recent accumulation rates of 80–150 m Ma^{-1} and carbonate and organic carbon contents of 20–60% and 4–8%, respectively (see also Shimmield *et al.* 1990).

The deeper slope basin lies at about 1500 m and is about 8 km wide, but only extends about 15 km along the strike of the Margin. The basin is bounded on the south by the Sharbithat Ridge, on the north by an erosional scarp, on the west by the basement block that forms the seaward edge of the upper basin, and on the east by a basement peak that has substantial sediment cover and a steep eastward-facing scarp that descends 2500 m to the Owen Basin (Figs 1 & 2). The sediments of the lower basin onlap onto the adjacent basement blocks, and have been deformed by movements relative to the adjacent basement structures. The shallow sediments dip seaward from the upper basin toward the deeper (easternmost) constraining basement peak. The sediments are thickest near the centre of the lower basin, forming a syn-clinal-shaped deposit that thins by pinch-out and onlap to both east and west. Recent ac-cumulation rates in this lower basin are about $50-60$ m Ma^{-1} (about one-third of the rates in the upper basin) and carbonate and organic carbon contents range from $45-70\%$ and $2-4\%$, respectively.

The age and composition of acoustic base-ment along this portion of the margin is not directly known. The basement structure is com-plex and is characterized by several major faults, such as the Siquirah fault, and by long, narrow ridges formed by basement peaks. However, several lines of evidence lead us to infer that the basement is composed of landward-thrust oceanic crust (ophiolitic rocks). First, the seis-mic, gravity, and magnetic data collected on RC27-04 did not identify anomalies character-istic of either salt or igneous intrusions. Second, the coastal geology of Oman includes ophiolites unconformably overlain by shallow-water Eocene limestones on both Ra's Madrakah and Masirah Island, which are directly strike from our study area (Moseley & Abbotts 1979; Shackleton & Ries 1990). Third, industry multi-channel seismic data indicate that another major fault, the Masirah Fault, lies immediately land-ward of these exposed ophiolites, suggesting that the basement material in our study area is of similar origin and has been obducted onto the continental margin. Given these data, we infer that ophiolites underlie the outer shelf and slope basins. Testing this hypothesis was one of the drilling objectives.

Leg 117 drilling results

Leg 117 recovered more than 2600 m of sedi-ment (80% recovery) in a series of eight sites (16 holes) on the continental margin offshore Oman (Table 1; Figs 1 & 2). The holes were drilled in water depths ranging from 300 to 1500 m, which is within the depth range of the modern OMZ. Two of the sites (726 & 729) were targeted to drill pre-Neogene sediments and basement rocks on the structures that subdivide the Margin into ridges and basins (see Fig. 2). Four sites (725, 724, 723 & 727) form a transect from about $300-900$ m water depth in sediments of the upper slope basin. One site (728) is in the lower slope basin, and one site (730) is near the crest of the basement ridge that separates the upper and lower slope basins.

Lithofacies

The sediments of the Oman Margin are domi-nated by green to olive green foraminifera-bearing marly nannofossil oozes and calcitic clayey silts with varying abundance of other components. All of the sediments on the Margin, especially those in the upper basin, are organic carbon-rich with contents of $2-8\%$. In the sediments of the upper basin, we found several minor facies (Fig. 3) that are important to the interpretation of the late Neogene history

Table 1. *Sites Drilled During Leg 117*

Site/ hole	Position	Water depth (m)	Drilled (m)	Recovery (%)	Age of oldest sediment
723A	18°05.079'N 57°86.561'E	807.8	432.3	68	Late pliocene
723B	18°3.079'N 57°86.561'E	807.8	429.0	73	Late pliocene
723C	18°03.079'N 57°86.561'E	807.8	76.8	107	Pleistocene
724A	18°27.713'N 57°47.147'E	592.8	44.5	100	Pleistocene
724B	18°27.713'N 57°47.147'E	592.8	257.7	82	Early pliocene
724C	18°27.713'N 57°47.147'E	592.8	252.4	96	Early pliocene
725A	18°29.200'N 57°42.020'E	311.5	4.5	100	Pleistocene
725B	18°29.200'N 57°42.020'E	311.5	93.8	11	Pleistocene
725C	18°29.200'N 57°42.020'E	311.5	162.8	60	Pleistocene
726A	17°48.945'N 57°22.200'E	330.8	186.3	59	Eocene(?)
727A	17°46.096'N 57°35.216'E	914.8	182.4	103	Late pliocene
727B	17°46.096'N 57°35.216'E	914.8	27.1	103	Late pleistocene
728A	17°40.790'N 57°49.553'E	1427.8	346.4	99	Late miocene
728B	17°40.790'N 57°49.553'E	1427.8	347.7	100	Late miocene
729A	17°38.715'N 57°57.221'E	1398.8	109.1	29	Eocene(?)
730A	17°38.885'N 57°42.519'E	1065.8	403.9	80	Late/early Miocene

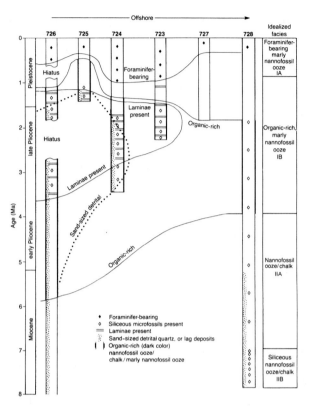

Fig. 3. A schematic onshore-offshore transect summarizing the lithofacies recovered from the Oman Margin and their distribution over the past 8 Ma (see Figs 4 & 5 for age relationships). Generalized lithofacies sequences are shown on the right. The distribution of lithofacies' characteristics, such as foram-bearing sediments, siliceous microfossils, laminations, detrital sands, and organic-rich sediments are indicated by symbols in each sedimentary column. Note the coincidence of organic-rich, siliceous components, and laminations in the late Pliocene.

of the Margin. The most significant facies consist of laminated sediments that have laminae dominated by monospecific diatom assemblages interbedded with layers of organic carbon-rich detrital sediment. We also found indurated lenses of dolomite (Site 723), greater abundances of sand-size detrital material on the landward side of the upper basin, lag deposits and phosphorite grains (Site 726), and silica-rich sediments near the Plio-Pleistocene boundary (Prell *et al.* 1989). Sediments in the lower basin contain less detrital material and are dominated by foraminiferal oozes, marly calcitic oozes and marly nannofossil oozes with admixtures of diatomaceous nannofossil chalk and silty clay. The upper portions of the offshore Sites 728 and 730 grade downward to nanno-fossil and marly nannofossil chalks and foraminifera–nannofossil chalks that indicate less terrigenous input (Fig. 3). At Sites 726 and

729, we penetrated shallow-water limestones of Miocene(?) to Eocene(?) age which overlie the basement rocks (Prell *et al.* 1989).

Over the past 8 Ma, the lithofacies have changed from nannofossil oozes and chalks to marly nannofossil oozes characterized by siliceous microfossils, high organic carbon content, and laminations in the late Pliocene and earliest Pleistocene. The Pleistocene sediments are largely foraminifera-bearing marly nannofossil oozes which are organic carbon-rich but without laminations and siliceous microfossils. These lithofacies provide some constraints on reconstruction of the changes in productivity and the structure of the oxygen-minimum zone along the margin of Oman.

The margin sediments are generally organic carbon-rich oozes indicative of high productivity. Methane gas of biogenic origin was common in sediments from the upper basin, but traces of ethane, propane and butane were also found in Sites 723, 724, 725, 727 & 728. These latter gases are thermogenic in origin. We also found sulphate in the interstitial waters to sub-bottom depths greater than 100 m (Prell *et al.* 1989). This finding was unexpected because sulphate is normally utilized rapidly by bacteria in organic carbon-rich, rapidly accumulating sediments. A preliminary explanation for the persistence of sulfate at depth is that the composition or degradation state of the organic matter inhibits full utilization by sulphate-reducing bacteria. However, we do not understand why the organic matter beneath an active upwelling zone and within the OMZ appears to be relatively refractory.

Biostratigraphy

Biostratigraphic zonation of the Margin sites was primarily based on calcareous nannofossils, although other groups were also used. A summary of the biostratigraphic zonations is shown in Fig. 4. Two of the sites drilled in the upper basin (725 and 727) have expanded Pleistocene sections and two sites (723 & 724) have expanded sections of Pleistocene and uppermost Pliocene sediments. Calcareous nannofossils are abundant in most samples, but exhibit low species diversity. Planktonic foraminifera are abundant in the Pleistocene sections, but decline in abundance and preservation near the Plio-Pleistocene boundary. Benthonic foraminifera are abundant and highly diverse in these relatively shallow margin sites. At Site 724 the presence of a shallow water benthonic foraminifera (e.g. *Ammonia beccarii*) in the lowermost section indicates that the site has subsided from a water depth shallower than 350 m to its present depth of about 830 m (about 230 m sub-bottom) since the late Pliocene. Radiolaria are absent to sporadic in all sites, but become more common near the Plio-Pleistocene boundary, where diatoms and laminated sediments are found as well.

The three sites located on basement highs (726, 729 & 730) are characterized by thin Pleistocene sequences that unconformably overlie older sediments. Site 726 contains Eocene(?) shallow-water, nummulitic limestones unconformably overlain by upper Miocene to middle Pliocene nannofossil-rich silty clay, which in turn is unconformably overlain by Pleistocene sediments. Site 729 contains Miocene (?) shallow-waters limestone unconformably overlain by Pleistocene sediments. Site 730 contains lower, middle, and upper Miocene oozes and chalks unconformably overlain by 20 m of Pleistocene

sediments. Planktonic foraminifera and calcareous nannofossils are abundant and quite well preserved in the Pleistocene sections, but are rare or absent in the limestone sections. At Site 730 planktonic foraminifera are less abundant in the upper and middle Miocene, but abundant again in the lower Miocene. Calcareous nannofossils are poorly preserved in the lower Miocene section. Radiolaria are present in the late Miocene and Pliocene sediments only.

The remaining Oman Margin site (728) contains a relatively thin Pleistocene sequence and an expanded lower Pliocene and upper Miocene sequence. Planktonic foraminifera are abundant and well preserved in the Pleistocene section, but rare in the Pliocene and Miocene sections. Calcareous nannofossils are abundant throughout, but marked by low species diversity. The benthonic foraminiferal fauna shows that this site was located in the neritic zone (300 m) in the late Miocene and has since subsided to its present water depth of 1400 m. Radiolaria are common and well preserved in the lower Pliocene and upper Miocene sections.

In Summary, the biostratigraphic results establish the Neogene age structure of the margin sediments and the occurrence of hiatuses in sections located on the basement structures. The microfossil assemblages reveal the trend from more siliceous sediments in the Miocene and Pliocene to more calcareous sediments in the Pleistocene, as well as the effects of subsidence in the slope basins.

Magnetostratigraphy

Low natural remnant magnetization intensities limited the quality and resolution of the palaeomagnetic data collected during Leg 117. The intensities of the Margin samples after alternating field demagnetization were almost always less than $1 \, \text{mA m}^{-1}$; they also tended to decrease with depth, so that reliable palaeomagnetic data usually could only be obtained from the uppermost 200–300 mbsf (see Fig. 4). These problems are partially offset by the unusually detailed between-hole and between-site correlations made possible by the whole-core susceptibility data. In some cases the susceptibility data will enable us to transfer reversal boundaries (and other stratigraphic data) from one site to another. For example, the boundary between Chrons C1 (Brunhes) and C1r (Matuyama), and the upper boundary of Subchron C1r-1 (Jaramillo), are clearly distinguished at Site 727. By means of susceptibility correlations, these datums can be correlated to

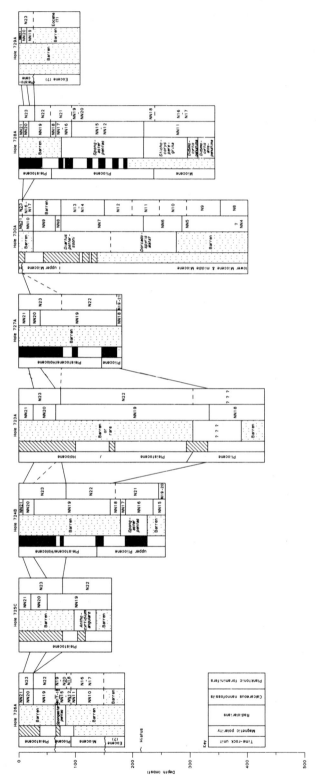

Fig. 4. Summary of the biostratigraphy and magnetostratigraphy of sites on the Oman Margin. Lines indicate general correlation between sites and emphasize the intervals of high sedimentation and the location of hiatuses.

Site 728, where they are not resolved clearly, and to Site 724, where they are not resolved at all.

Sites 724, 727 and 728 have the best reversal stratigraphies of the Margin sites (Fig 4). At Site 724 we recognized six polarity transitions back to Chron C2A (Gauss); at Site 727 three transitions back to the middle of Chron 1r (Matuyama); and at Site 728 thirteen transitions back to the base of Chron C3. Site 728 is perhaps the most interesting section, in which we think the four Subchrons within Chron C3 (Cochiti, Nunivak, Sidufjall and Thvera) can be recognized; this part of the section may prove to be particularly useful for refining correlations between magneto- and nannofossil stratigraphy.

Accumulation rates

The rate of sediment accumulation on the Margin is strongly influenced by the tectonic setting, as well as by planktonic productivity and detrital and aeolian transport. Here, we report on the patterns of sediment accumulation on the margin during the Plio-Pleistocene, an interval with good spatial and temporal coverage (Fig. 5). We also summarize some data for older intervals.

The middle to upper Miocene sediments cored at Sites 728 and 730 accumulated at rates between 20 and 30 m Ma^{-1}. The deposits are dominated by calcareous and siliceous microfossils and terrigenous clays. These rates and compositions reflect a more pelagic setting than that interpreted for the Plio–Pleistocene sediments in the upper basin of the Margin. The composition and accumulation rates of the Miocene deposits on the Margin are similar to pelagic Miocene sediments on the Owen Ridge, about 350 km farther offshore.

Pliocene and Pleistocene sedimentation rates range from 11–88 m Ma^{-1} at Site 728 in the lower slope basin to 129–240 m Ma^{-1} at Site 723 in the centre of the upper slope basin (Fig. 5). Sites 724, 725, and 727, from the upper slope basin, have similar rates, ranging from 35 to 150 m Ma^{-1}, which are less than the rate at Site 723 (Fig. 5). These differences within the upper basin reflect the effects of tectonic setting on the rate sediment accumulation; the central depression is collecting more of the material that reaches the upper slope. The difference in accumulation rates between the upper and lower slope basins reflects the decreased transport of detrital material to offshore basins.

Evolution of sedimentary facies on the Oman Margin

To understand the sequence of sediment facies and their accumulation rates, three factors must be considered: tectonics, coastal upwelling, and the oxygen minimum zone. Each of these factors changes with time and has potential impact on the sediment record of the Margin.

Effects of Neogene tectonics

The sites drilled on the Margin fall into two broad categories: those which were drilled to recover sedimentary sections of Neogene age (723, 724, 725, 727, 728 & 730), and sites that were targeted to drill the basement features to establish the age and nature of pre-Neogene strata that underlie the Margin (726 & 729).

The oldest sediments recovered are shallow-water limestones and dolomitized limestones that are tentatively assigned a Paleogene (?) age. In both cases, these sediments were recovered from sites drilled on basement ridges, and in both cases the shallow-water limestones were unconformably overlain by organic carbon-rich hemipelagic sediments. The shallow nature of the limestones and the overlying unconformities indicate uplift and erosion, but we do not have enough information to analyze this facies properly and establish its implications for the pre-Miocene regional tectonic evolution of the Margin. However, we note that the ophiolites of Masirah Island are unconformably overlain by rocks of similar age and facies (Moseley & Abbotts 1979). On the basis of these shallow-water limestones, the site survey seismic data, the traces of thermogenic gases, and the spatial relationships to Masirah and Ra's Madrakah, we suggest that the SE margin of Oman is underlain by a series of ophiolitic thrusts.

During the Plio-Pleistocene, subsidence of the slope basins has been a major factor in forming the present morphology of the margin. The benthonic foraminifera data indicate that the upper basin has subsided at least 400 m (Site 724) and that the lower slope basin has subsided over 1000 m (Site 728) during this time. To estimate the temporal subsidence pattern of the depositional surface in these basins, we used the biostratigraphic age models for the sites (Fig. 5), the observed occurrence of A. beccarii and the measured accumulation rates. Assuming a neritic depth of 350 m for A. beccarii, we subsided that level to its observed depth below the sea floor and allowed subsequent sediment to accumulate at rates constrained by the age

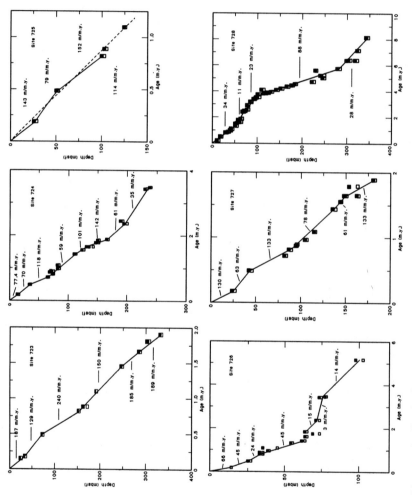

Fig. 5. Age-depth plot of reliable nannofossil and palaeomagnetic datum levels for sites used to reconstruct the Plio-Pleistocene depositional history of the Margin (see Figs 3 & 6). The solid and open symbols are the upper and lower depth bounds for each datum. Sedimentation rates were calculated on data common to all sites. Details of the ages and depths of datums are given in Prell *et al.* (1989).

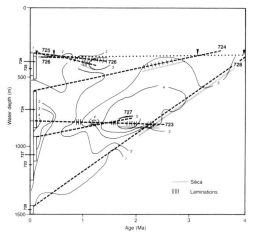

Fig. 6. The palaeodepth of the depositional surface and the distribution of percent organic carbon, laminated sediments and siliceous microfossils as a function of age (in Ma) and palaeodepth (m) for Oman Margin Site 723–728. Sediment sections recovered at individual sites are plotted on the left according to their present-day water depth and total depth drilled. The estimated depth of the sediment-water interface through time is indicated by the broken line for each site (see text for discussion). Arrows on the backtracking curves, indicate transitions to depths greater than 350 m for Sites 724, 725, 726, 728. Organic carbon content (%) of the palaeosurface sediments are shown for the correct water depth and age. Darker shading indicates the presence of siliceous microfossils and hatched symbols indicate the presence of laminations.

models. Since the depths of the biostratigraphic datums are known within ten metres and their ages are well established in the Plio-Pleistocene section, their contributions to errors in our subsidence estimates are small. Also, because the thickness of post-neritic sediment is small, we infer that most of the subsidence is due to tectonic changes rather than to sediment loading. The resulting time–depth subsidence of the depositional surface is illustrated in Fig. 6. This subsidence pattern changes the level of the depositional surface with respect to the OMZ and can also act to focus sedimentation toward one portion of the basin such as at Site 723.

Another indication of tectonism is the tilted and truncated sediments on the middle basement ridge (Site 730) (Fig. 2) which indicate tectonic movement of the basement structures associated with the basin subsidence and possibly with the concurrent uplift of the offshore Owen Ridge.

Effects of monsoonal upwelling

The oldest Neogene sediments on the Margin (Site 730) are lower Miocene nannofossil chalks containing as much as 95% $CaCO_3$. The remainder of the Neogene sequence is dominated by marly nannofossil oozes, silty calcareous biogenic oozes with variable detrital components, and biogenic opal-bearing to opal-rich calcareous oozes. Organic carbon contents range from 2–6% by weight, and are particularly high in association with opal-bearing and laminated intervals.

The exact onset of the monsoon system is difficult to identify because different planktonic groups reflect different ecological conditions at the same time, and the different preservation states of the fossils often obscure the signal. Evidence for middle Miocene upwelling conditions includes a substantial increase in opal (*Diartus petterssoni Zone*), which may indicate increased production in the surface waters. Concomitantly, the planktonic foraminifera are reduced in number, which may indicate carbonate dissolution, possibly triggered by enhanced organic carbon production. However, *Globigerina bulloides*, a species indicative of upwelling, occurs somewhat earlier in the middle Miocene (Zone N11). Thus, the zooplankton record indicates that increased production in the surface waters began in the middle Miocene.

The calcareous nannofossil assemblages in the lower middle Miocene (Zone NN5) contain about 88% of the total number of species expected to occur in tropical areas. This relative species diversity gradually decreases through time and is distinctly less diverse after 9.5 Ma (early late Miocene; Zone NN9). Low relative diversity continues through the late Miocene to the early Pliocene (Zone NN12). In the Pliocene, the diversity relative to tropical assemblages is around 50%, but it increases slightly in younger sediments. The calcareous nannoflora, based on this rough estimate, were apparently affected by upwelling (i.e. the decrease of tropical species) at a somewhat later date (i.e. early late Miocene) than the planktonic foraminifera and the radiolaria.

In the Pliocene sediments of the Oman Margin, the calcareous microfossils are moderately to poorly preserved, and radiolaria and diatoms are common and well preserved. Throughout the Margin area, the Pliocene calcareous nannofossil zonal marker species, *Amaurolithus tricorniculatus* and *Ceratolithus rugosus*, are missing and other species of these genera are rare. The upwelling is probably responsible for very low numbers of these tropical species. In contrast, *Coccolithus pelagicus*, which is considered a typical cold-water species, is present in unusually high abundance in uppermost Pliocene to lowermost Pleistocene sediments.

During the lower Pleistocene, foraminifera became abundant and the siliceous microfossils decreased in abundance. This change occurs concurrently with a shift towards lower organic carbon values in the sediments. This may indicate either (1) lower production rates of organic carbon due to decreasing upwelling intensity and concomitant improved preservation conditions for calcareous material in a weaker oxygen minimum zone or (2) increased circulation intensity and oxygen content of bottom waters. We expect that quantitative measures of relative species abundance and dissolution phenomena, linked with stable isotope data on the tests of planktonic and benthonic species, will give some clues regarding the above possibilities.

Effects of the oxygen minimum zone

Lithofacies changes on the margin are thought to partially reflect changes in the OMZ, which extends at present from approximately 200 m to 1500 m water depth. Laminated facies were recognized in several sites (see Figs 3 & 6), and are thought to be synchronous. These laminated facies are considered among the most significant indicators of conditions that are different from the modern depositional environment. The most prominent occurrence of laminations coincides with the enhanced preservation of opaline silica in the upper Pliocene and near the Plio/Pleistocene boundary.

The formation and preservation of laminated intervals requires a seasonally heterogeneous input, which is inherent in the monsoon upwelling system, and deposition during a period of bottom-water oxygen depletion. According to Demaison & Moore (1980), 0.2 ml O_2/l is the minimum level required to maintain bioturbation. The preservation of laminations deposited over several input cycles indicates the absence of benthonic organisms for a considerable period of time, because the laminated intervals must be thicker than the subsequent range of bioturbation. The coincidence of opal preservation with laminations and high organic carbon content may be a productivity signal preserved in the sediments, but may also merely reflect a conspicuous lack of bioturbation. The absence of bioturbation would enhance the opal preservation if sedimentation rates are high

enough to bury the sediment rapidly below the zone where diffusive exchange with undersaturated bottom water dissolves the tests. Thus, an anoxic OMZ seems to be a requirement for the preservation of laminated facies.

Oceanographic arguments indicate that the oxygen content of the OMZ over the continental slope is a balance of upward advection of oxygen-rich deep water and the production of organic matter (i.e. oxygen demand). Higher productivity, caused by stronger monsoons and more intense upwelling, may result in an expansion of the OMZ. High rates of organic input have been often used to explain organic carbon-rich sediments in the geological past (e.g. von Stackelberg 1972; Thiede & van Andel 1977; Jenkyns 1981). On the other hand, the upwelling circulation that leads to increased productivity may also advect deep water more vigorously, thereby increasing the bottom water oxygen content. Since the rates of primary productivity off Arabia are already high (> 500 mg C mz/day), a decrease in upwelling and a concomitant decrease in bottom water advection could also allow the OMZ to become further depleted in the oxygen.

Thus, the changes in the OMZ that allow the development of laminated facies and enhanced preservation of organic carbon and opal are related to mechanisms of productivity, circulation and water-mass dynamics of the Northern Indian Ocean. On the basis of our shipboard data, a more intense OMZ is inferred for the late Pliocene and early Pleistocene, but the implications for stronger or weaker upwelling are not clear.

Summary

ODP Leg 117 drilling on the Oman Margin has provided new insights into the tectonic history of the Margin and the Neogene evolution of the monsoonal-upwelling environments. Some of the important findings include the following:

1. The sediments are organic carbon-rich (up to 6%) and surprisingly carbonate-rich and silica-poor, compared to other upwelling zones.
2. Upwelling appears to have begun in the early middle Miocene on the Margin, but its relative intensity through the Neogene is not yet established.
3. The association of laminated facies, high organic carbon, and siliceous microfossils in the late Pliocene and early Pleistocene reflect an oceanographic regime, different from modern conditions. This regime had a more intense OMZ that allowed preser-

vation of the laminations and probably the opal by decreasing or eliminating benthonic bioturbation.

4. Much of the Margin has subsided as much as 1000 m since late Pliocene as indicated by benthonic foraminiferal assemblages.

5. The geometry of the slope basins, the occurrence of shallow-water limestones similar to those found on Masirah, and traces of thermogenic gases indicate that the basement (unsampled by drilling) may be composed of ophiolitic rocks that are thrust over continental material.

We thank the advisory panels and the planning structure of the JOIDES Ocean Drilling Program for making Leg 117 a reality and the Ocean Drilling Program staff and crew of the JOIDES *Resolution* for making Leg 117 a great success. While at the conference on the Geology and Tectonics of Oman, we were saddened to learn that our operations superintendent, Lamar Hayes, had died aboard the JOIDES *Resolution*. His interest in our work and his skill in recovering sediment was crucial to our success on Leg 117. We dedicate this contribution to his memory.

Shipboard participants on Leg 117 were: N. Niitsuma, Co-Chief Scientist, Institute of Geosciences, Shizuoka University, Shizuoka, Japan; K-C. Emeis, ODP Staff Scientist, Ocean Drilling Program, Texas A&M University, College Station, TX USA; D. Anderson, Department of Geological Sciences, Brown University, Providence, RI, USA; R. Barnes, Rosario Geo-science Associates, Anacortes, WA, USA; R. A. Bilak, 103–1001 14th Avenue, SW, Calgary, Alberta, Canada; J. Bloemendal, Graduate School of Oceanography, University of Rhode Island, Narragansett, RI, USA; C. J. Bray, Department of Geological Sciences, Cornell University, Ithaca, NY, USA; W. H. Busch, Department of Geology and Geophysics, University of New Orleans, New Orleans, LA, USA; S. C. Clemens, Department of Geological Sciences, Brown University, Providence, RI USA; P. Debrabant, Laboratoire de Dynamique Sedimentaire et Structurale, Universite de Lille, Flandres Artois, Villeneuve D'Asq, France; H. L. Ten Haven, Institute of Petroleum and Organic Geochemistry KFA Juelich GmbH, Juelich, Federal Republic of Germany; A. Hayashida, Laboratory of Earth Science, Faculty of Engineering, Doshisha University, Kyoto, Japan; J. O. R. Hermelin, Department of Geology, University of Stockholm, Stockholm, Sweden; R. Jarrard, Lamont-Doherty Geological Observatory, Palisades, NY USA; A. N. K. Al-Thobbah, Ministry of Petroleum and Minerals, Muscat, Sultanate of Oman; L. A. Krissek, Department of Geology, Ohio State University, Columbus, OH USA; D. Kroon, Geomarine Center, Vrije Universiteit, Amsterdam, The Netherlands; D. W. Murray, Department of Geological Sciences, Brown University, Providence, RI USA; P. de Menocal, Lamont-Doherty Geological Observatory, Palisades NY USA; C. Nigrini, 510 Papyrus Drive, La Habra Heights, CA USA; T. F. Pedersen, Department of Oceanography, University of British Columbia, Vancouver, BC, Canada; W. Ricken, Institut fur Geologie und Palaeontologie, Universitat Tubingen, Tubingen, Federal Republic of Germany; G. B. Shimmield, Grant Institute of Geology, University of Edinburgh, Edinburgh, UK; S. A. Spaulding, Department of Geology, University of Nebraska, Lincoln NE; Z. K. S. Al-Sulaiman, Ministry of Petroleum and Minerals, Muscat, Sultanate of Oman; T. Takayama, Department of Geology, College of Liberal Arts, Kanazawa University, Kanazawa, Japan; G. P. Weedon, Department of Earth Sciences, University of Cambridge, Cambridge, UK.

W. L. Prell received support from ODP to attend the conference on the Geology and Tectonics of Oman and from USSAC Grant 20092 and NSF grant OCE-85-11571 to collect survey data and to prepare this manuscript.

References

CURRIE, R. I., FISHER, A. E. & HARGREAVES, P. M. 1973. Arabian Sea Upwelling. *In*: ZEITSCHEL, B. (ed.) *The Biology of the Indian Ocean*, Deep-Sea Research, **25**, 431–45.

DEMAISON, G. J. & MOORE, G. T. 1980 Anoxic environments and oil source bed genesis. *Bulletin of the American Association of Petroleum Geologists*, **6418**, 1179–209.

HAHN, D. G. & MANABE, S. 1975. The role of mountains in the south Asian monsoon circulation: *Journal of Atmospheric Science*, **32**, 1515–41.

JENKYNS, H. C. 1981. Cretaceous anoxic events: From continents to oceans. *Journal of the Geological Society of London*, **137**, 171–88.

KUTZBACH, J. E. 1981. Monsoon climate of the early Holocene: Climatic experiment using the earth's orbital parameters for 9000 years ago. *Science*, **214**, 59–61.

KUTZBACH, J. E. & GUETTER, P. J. 1986. The influence of changing orbital parameters and surface boundary conditions on climate simulations for the past 18000 years: *Journal of Atmospheric Science*, **43**, 1726–1759.

MOSELEY, F. & ABBOTTS, I. L. 1979 The Ophiolite Melange of Masirah, Oman: *Journal of the Geological Society of London*, **136**, 713–724.

MOUNTAIN, G. S. & PRELL, W. L. 1990. A multiphase plate tectonic history of the southeast continental margin of Oman. *In*: ROBERTSON, A. H. F., SEARLE, M. P. & RIES, A. C. (eds) *The Geology and Tectonics of the Oman Region*. Geological Society, London, Special Publication, **49**, 725–743.

PRELL, W. L., 1984a, Monsoonal climate of the Arabian Sea during the late Quaternary: A response to changing solar radiation. *In*: BERGER, A. & IMBRIE J. (eds) *Milankovitch and Climate* D. Reidel Publishing Company, Dororecht, Holland, 349–366.

—— 1984b. Variation of monsoonal upwelling: A response to changing solar radiation, in Climate Processes: Sensitivity to Solar Irradiance and CO$_2$. HANSEN J. E. & TAKAHASHI, T. (eds) *In*:

Fourth Ewing Symposium, American Geophysical Union, Washington, DC, 48–57.

——, Hutson, W. H., Williams, D. F., Be, A. W. H., Geitzenauer, K. & Molfino, B. 1980. Surface circulation of the Indian Ocean during the last glacial maximum: Approximately 18 000 yr BP. *Quaternary Research*, **14**, 309–336.

——, & Kutzbach, J. E. 1987. Monsoon variability over the past 150 000 years. *Journal of Geophysical Research*, **92**, 8411–8425.

——, Niitsuma, N. *et al.* 1989. *Proceedings, Ocean Drilling Program*, Initial Reports 117: College Station, TX (Ocean Drilling Program).

—— & Streeter, H. F. 1982. Temporal and spatial patterns of monsoonal upwelling along Arabia: A modern analogue for the interpretation of Quaternary SST anomalies Deep-Sea Research, **40**, p. 143–55.

—— & Van Campo, E. 1986. Coherent response of the Arabian Sea upwelling and pollen transport to late Quaternary monsoonal winds. *Nature*, **323**, 526–528.

Romankevich, E. A. 1984. *Geochemistry of organic matter in the ocean*. Springer, Berlin.

Shackleton, R. M. & Ries, A. C. 1990. Tectonics of the Masirah Fault Zone and Eastern Oman. *In*: Robertson, A. M. F., Searle, M. P. & Ries, A. C. (eds) *The Geological Tectonics of the Oman Region*. Geological Society, London, Special Publication, **49**, 715–724.

Shimmield, G. B., Price, N. B. & Pedersen, T. F. 1990. The influence of hydrography, bathymetry and productivity on sediment type and composition on the Oman Margin and in the Northwest Arabian Sea. *In*: Robertson, A. M. F., Searle, M. P. & Ries, A. C. (eds) *The Geology and Tectonics of the Oman Region*. Geological Society, London, Special Publication, **49**, 759–769.

Slater, R. D. & Kroopnick, P. 1984. Controls on dissolved oxygen distribution and organic carbon deposition in the Arabian Sea. *In*: Haq, B. U. & Milliman, J. D. (eds) *Geology and Oceanography of the Arabian Sea and Coastal Pakistan*. Pakistan Institute of Oceanography Nostrand Rheinhold Company, London. p. 305–313.

Stein, C. A. & Cochran, J. R. 1985. The transition between the Sheba Ridge and Owen Basin: Rifting of old oceanic lithosphere. *Geophysical Journal of the Royal Astronomical Society*, **81**, 47–74.

Thiede, J. & van Andel, T. H. 1977. The paleoenvironment of anaerobic sediments in the late Mesozoic South Atlantic Ocean. *Earth and Planetary Science Letters*, **33**, 301–309.

von Stackelberg, U. 1972. Faziesverteilung in Sedimenten des indisch-pakistani schen Kontinentalrandes (Arabisches Meer): "Meteor" Forsch -Ergebnisse, Reihe "C", 9, 1–73.

Whitmarsh, R. B. 1979. The Owen Basin off the south-east margin of Arabia and the evolution of the Owen Fracture Zone. *Geophysical Journal of the Royal Astronomical Society*, **58**, 441–470.

——, Weser, O. E., Ross, D. A., *et al.* 1974. Initial Reports, DSDP, 23: Washington (US Govt. Printing Office).

Wyrtki, K., 1962, The oxygen-minima in relation to ocean circulation: *Deep Sea Research*, **9**, 11–23.

—— 1971. Oceanographic Atlas of the International Indian Ocean Expedition: National Science Foundation, Washington, DC.

—— 1973. Physical oceanography of the Indian Ocean. *In*: Zeitschel, B. (ed.) *The Biology of the Indian Ocean, Ecological Studies*. Springer, Berlin 18–36.

The influence of hydrography, bathymetry and productivity on sediment type and composition of the Oman Margin and in the Northwest Arabian Sea

G. B. SHIMMIELD[1], N. B. PRICE[1] AND T. F. PEDERSEN[2]

[1] Grant Institute of Geology, University of Edinburgh, West Mains Road, Edinburgh EH9 3JW, UK

[2] Department of Oceanography, The University of British Columbia, 6270 University Boulevard, Vancouver, B. C. V6T 1W5, Canada

Abstract: The hydrography, bathymetry and sediment composition of the Oman Margin and NW Indian Ocean areas between latitudes 24°N and 13°N, have been studied. A pronounced oxygen minimum zone characterizes the water column between 200 and 1500 m depth and extends throughout the NW Arabian Sea. The bathymetry of the margin is complex, resulting from tectonic movement along the Masirah Line. Small, anoxic intrashelf basins are developed south of Masirah. The Owen/Murray Ridge provides a barrier to westward progradation of terrigenous detritus from the Indus Fan. Upwelling and surface productivity result in the deposition of biogenic calcareous and siliceous sediments, the latter being restricted to the shelf and slope regions. Depositional controls, such as redistribution by bottom currents and bathymetry, greatly affect the quality of organic carbon deposited. Evidence is presented to suggest that much of the organic matter on the Oman shelf is degraded prior to burial. This has important connotations for sediment diagenesis and hydrocarbon maturation. The distribution of calcareous and siliceous sediments resulting from upwelling may well provide an index for determining the Neogene history of upwelling in the NW Arabian Sea.

The continental margin of Oman and the adjoining NW Arabian Sea comprise a semi-enclosed sea within which high levels of biological activity are sustained by active, monsoon-driven, oceanic upwelling. The combination of a sluggish intermediate-depth circulation and microbial decay of the settling organic matter derived from the very high standing crop of plankton creates an intense oxygen minimum zone between depths of 200 and 1500 m. This feature extends from the Oman Margin throughout the NW Arabian Sea and has been the subject of many studies (Neyman 1961; Sen Gupta et al. 1975; Rao & Jayaraman 1970; Wyrtki 1973; Qasim 1982; Slater & Kroopnick 1984). The role of the SW Monsoon in driving NW Arabian Sea upwelling has been studied in recent applications of global circulation models (Kutzbach 1981; Prell & Kutzbach 1987). In the summer months a low pressure cell centred over the Himalayas and Tibetan Plateau causes an intense southwest to northeast wind field over the NW Arabian Sea. Consequent Ekman transport in the mixed layer supports pronounced upwelling along the margin which develops seasonally. Extant studies based on

sedimentary records indicate that monsoon intensity has varied during the late Quaternary (Prell & Kutzbach 1987). The recent recovery of hydraulic piston cores from the Oman Margin and Owen Ridge areas during ODP Leg 117 will enable determination of the evolution of the SW Monsoon during the Neogene. Through such studies we may begin to address some of the fundamental questions concerning the mechanisms of wind-driven upwelling, the nature of organic-matter preservation under low-O_2 waters, the palaeogeochemical signatures of enhanced oceanic productivity, and the influence of upwelling margins on global ocean budgets of carbon and reactive metals.

However, before such detailed large scale, long term questions can be addressed, the hydrographic regime of the modern system and the physical framework for sediment deposition needs to be understood. Simple ideas on type of organic matter, the influence of the oxygen minimum zone on biogenic preservation and the distribution of biogenic components, may not suffice. Despite several studies on sediments of the Arabian Sea (Wiseman & Bennett 1940; Stewart et al. 1965; Goldberg & Griffin 1970;

From ROBERTSON, A. H. F., SEARLE, M. P. & RIES, A. C. (eds), 1990,
The Geology and Tectonics of the Oman Region.
Geological Society Special Publication No 49, pp 759–769

Olausson *et al.* 1971; Marchig 1972; Stackelberg 1972; Kolla *et al.* 1976a, b, 1981) the nature of the sediments of the Oman Margin is relatively poorly understood, save for descriptions of material collected by the French expedition ORGON IV (Moyes *et al.* 1978).

The Oman Margin is an excellent location for studying the influence of upwelling on sediment type, and for the collection of data which can be used in the reconstruction of global models of climate evolution. Within this context, this area provides a situation in which to test the 'production versus preservation' hypothesis. This model simply seeks to evaluate whether the high organic matter content of ancient sediments results from greater biological productivity in surface waters or preservation of the high organic matter under anoxic bottom water conditions. In a similar may, the area is of great importance for studies of diagenesis in organic-rich, highly reducing marine sediments. Such sedimentary facies provide useful analogues for the evaluation of the effects of early diagenesis on future petroleum source rocks.

Here, we report data obtained from a British cruise in 1986 to the NW Arabian Sea and Oman Margin. From hydrographic and bathymetric studies of the region and geochemical analyses of surficial sediment (0−2 cm depth) the distribution of important biogenic products of upwelling has been reconstructed and some of the mechanisms that influence modern sediment deposition on this continental margin have been investigated. Such data will be used to formulate hypotheses about how the sediment record is related to monsoonal variation and its role in ocean chemistry and climate models.

The study area

The NW Arabian Sea, between latitudes 10° and 25°N, off the SE margin of Oman is well known as an area of enhanced marine biological productivity (Currie *et al.* 1973; Kuz'menko 1974; Deuser *et al.* 1978; Prell & Curry 1981; Naqvi *et al.* 1982; Qasim 1982). The cause of this high productivity is an upwelling system driven by the southwesterly monsoon which is at its most intense in the summer months (Kutzbach 1981; Prell & Streeter 1982). Resulting divergence and Ekman transport of surface waters in a southeasterly direction allows deeper, nutrient-rich waters to well up and sustain high standing stocks of plankton. The wind speed and duration of the monsoon largely determine the intensity of the upwelling period. The upwelling system off Oman is unique in that it lies within an area of restricted oceanic circulation

that is influenced by a western boundary current, and has strong seasonal variability. This is in contrast with upwelling zones located within eastern boundary currents (Peru, California, Namibia, NW Africa) which are driven by meso-scale oceanic circulation and atmospheric cells.

The high level of surface productivity promotes an intense oxygen minimum zone (OMZ) between 150 and 1200 m depth along the entire Oman Margin, extending some considerable distance into the Arabian Sea. Sluggish mid-depth circulation (Wyrtki 1973) promotes low oxygen conditions southwards beyond the equator.

The sediments of the Oman Margin and NW Arabian Sea record a variety of organic carbon-rich, biogenic silica-rich and biogenic carbonate-rich facies which are deposited under the upwelling regime. The topographic structure of the Oman Margin, Murray and Owen Ridges, and the Oman Basin (Fig. 1) conspire to produce a semi-enclosed system into which the biogenic sedimentary input from the overlying surface productivity accumulates. Thus it is possible to study the deposition and diagenesis of organic-rich sediments without addition of major clastic terrigenous sediment brought in from the Indian subcontinent *via* the Indus Fan. The Owen/Murray Ridge may influence circulation in the NW Arabian Sea, and affect the dispersal and mixing of Persian Gulf and Red Sea waters which are warm, saline and relatively O_2 replete. Consequently, hydrography of the upwelling zone is complicated by both physico-chemical and seasonal controls.

Methods of data collection and analysis

Sampling of waters and sediments

Cruise 17 of the R/V *Charles Darwin* in October/November 1986 collected a series of box and piston cores from the NW Arabian Sea (Fig. 1), together with detailed hydrographic (real-time measurements of temperature, salinity, pressure and oxygen with a Neil Brown[R] CTD, and discrete sampling with 30 l Niskin bottles) and bathymetric (precision depth recorder chart records) measurements. The cruise track (Fig. 1) covered three main transects, running from shallow waters (<200 m) on the shelf to >4000 m in the hemipelagic basin. Three cores were collected from the east side of the Owen/Murray Ridge adjacent to the mid-fan of the Indus Fan.

The box-cores (0−50 cm long) recovered undisturbed sediment and preserved intact the

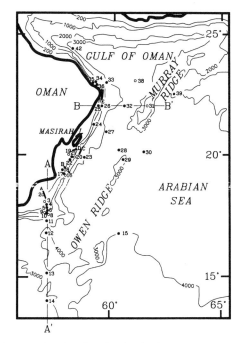

Fig. 1. Map showing the distribution of cores taken on the Oman Margin and NW Arabian Sea. Box-cores are represented by filled circles and are reported here; open circles are bulk samples and piston cores which will be described elsewhere. Sections A and B are the positions of the chemical data reported in Figs 2 & 3. The lettered heavy lines indicate the cruise track for the bathymetric profiles shown in Fig. 4. The bathymetry is in metres.

sediment/water interface. Subsamples, taken by 6 cm-diameter polycarbonate liner, were horizontally sectioned into 1 and 2 cm intervals aboard ship and stored wet at 4°C. Samples were subsequently dried at 60°C and ground in a tungsten carbide mill for two minutes prior to analysis. Sediment water contents were calculated from the difference between wet and dry weights and used as a guide to sediment lithology.

Analytical measurements

Bulk sediment geochemistry was determined with a Philips PW 1450 sequential automatic X-ray spectrometer using a glass fusion method for major elements, and pressed powder discs for trace elements. Matrix correction procedures were applied following Shimmield (1985). All elemental analyses have been corrected for dilution by sea salt.

Carbonate carbon measurements were de-

termined on a Coulometrics[R] coulometer, and total carbon and nitrogen on a Carlo−Erba CHN analyser. Organic carbon was determined by difference, with all measurements being duplicated. These measurements were made at the University of British Columbia.

Results

Hydrography

Figures 2 and 3 illustrate the distribution and intensity of the OMZ from transects A and B (Fig. 1). Although productivity is likely to be more enhanced along the southern transect, the O_2 minimum (<0.2 ml 1^{-1}) appears to be stronger and better developed at the more northerly transect (B). In both cases, the distribution of low O_2 waters is complicated by Persian Gulf and, to some extent, Red Sea outflow. Nevertheless, the entire Oman Margin between 200 and 1500 m depth is dominated by O_2-deficient waters. High dissolved silicate values (130−150 μmol kg^{-1}, Figs 2 & 3) also attest to the poor circulation and high productivity of the overlying water mass.

The depositional framework

Study of precision depth records reveal a varied and fascinating structure to the bathymetry of the Oman Margin (Fig. 4). To the south of the study area (57°E, 18°N to 58°E, 19°N) the shelf

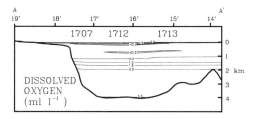

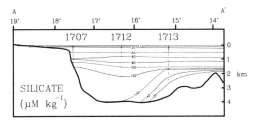

Fig. 2. Dissolved oxygen (ml 1^{-1}) and silicate (μmol kg^{-1}) data for Section A (Fig. 1). Dissolved oxygen was measured by oxygen probe on the CTD, dissolved silicate from samples collected by Niskin bottles.

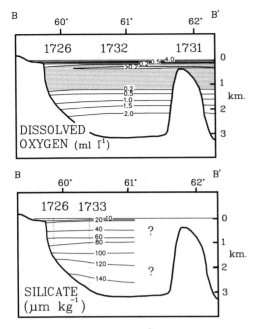

Fig. 3. Dissolved oxygen (ml⁻¹) and silicate (μmol kg⁻¹) data for Section B (Fig. 1).

at water depths < 180 m appears to be covered by well-sorted quartzose sands (Fig. 4, Profile A) where sand waves with an amplitude of < 1 m are faintly discernable. This facies presumably represents the lateral continuation of the adjacent onshore Wahiba Sands which may be a source of the sand. This region of slightly sand-covered shelf rapidly deepens at the shelf-break to an abrupt "continental slope" (Fig. 4, Profile B).

South of Masirah Island the shelf break-slope is very confused (Fig. 4, Profile C) with a series of NE–SW trending valleys separating shallow (500 m water depth) fault blocks. Tectonic studies of the area suggest that the 'Masirah Line' could be a Late Cretaceous dextral strike-slip fault parallel to the coast along which there has been a possible displacement of 250 km

Fig. 4. Bathymetric profiles recorded by precision depth recorder from locations shown in Fig. 2. Depth scale in metres. Horizontal scale is variable. A, low amplitude sand waves on the gently sloping continental shelf; B, rapid deepening at the shelf break, possibly fault-controlled; C, NE–SW trending valleys separating fault blocks along the Masirah Line; D, small, intrashelf basins developed on the outer shelf south of Masirah Island; E, ENE–WSW trending valleys north of Masirah Island.

(Moseley & Abbotts 1979; Gorin *et al.* 1982), or a later Tertiary wrench fault with no displacement (Gass & Gibson 1969).

Towards the outer shelf, in the area of 58°E,

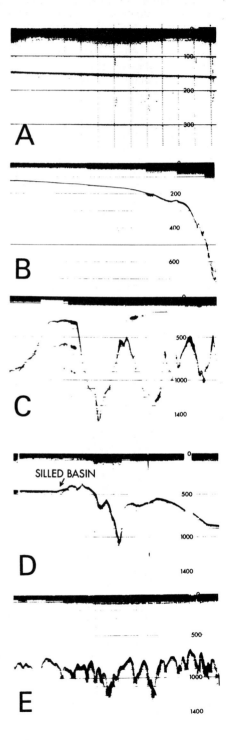

19°N (Stations 18–21), small intrashelf basins < 1 km diameter are developed (Fig. 4, Profile D). Occasional canyons provide a by-pass mechanisms for terrestrially-derived shelf sands to accumulate in deeper water, allowing fine-grained, organic-rich, diatomaceous ooze to accumulate in these small basins (see below). These basins are silled and lie within the OMZ; thus the overlying waters could be anoxic. The sediment is faintly to moderately laminated with little evidence of an active infaunal benthos.

North of Masirah Island (59°E, 22°N), the outer shelf is again dissected by valleys approximately 100–200 m deep in 800 m of water (Fig. 4, Profile E). These valleys trend ENE–WSW suggesting that the Masirah Line may be trending away from the coast line. The sediments in this area are diatomaceous fine silts.

Seaward of the foot of the continental slope, the topography consists of a flat, slightly undulating plain (3000–3200 m depth) which rises to the Owen/Murray Ridge, ~ 300 km to the east (Fig. 1). The ridge is asymmetric in cross section, and deepens rapidly toward the east from <2000 m water depth to > 4000 m on the adjacent distal Indus Fan. In the north, the 3300 m deep Gulf of Oman is a roughly triangular basin, bounded by the Oman Margin, the Makran Margin and the Owen Ridge.

The distribution of lithogenic sediments

In Table 1 we present the analytical data for the core top samples. Fig. 5A indicates the distribution of Cr on a carbonate-free basis. Cr was chosen as an indicator of terrigenous sediment derived from the adjacent ophiolitic source terranes as it is highly concentrated in the serpentinized harzburgite of Masirah, reaching some 3390 ppm (Moseley & Abbotts 1979). The Cr in the lithogenic fraction of the sediment is common to the north and south of Masirah, and concentrated in the coarser, sandy sediments of the outer shelf, particularly Stations 5 and 17 (1116 ppm and 1049 ppm, respectively). We

Table 1. *Chemical composition of surface (0–1 cm) sediments[1]: northwest Arabian Sea*

Station	Depth (m)	Si (wt.%)	Al (wt.%)	Mg (wt.%)	Cr[2] (ppm)	C_{org} (wt.%)	C/N	CaCO$_3$ (wt.%)	SiO$_2$[3] (wt.%)	Dol.[3] (wt.%)
4	400	11.95	2.15	1.57	731	4.07	9.6	46.1	11.9	7.1
5	770	9.04	1.83	1.28	1116	2.72	11.1	72.8	7.7	5.6
6	1048	10.87	2.02	1.63	694	4.00	10.3	61.8	10.4	7.8
10	1295	9.89	1.99	1.59	638	3.51	10.2	67.4	8.5	7.6
11	3684	17.53	3.45	2.44	180	2.34	6.7	36.7	15.6	10.7
12	4030	20.92	4.33	2.87	140	2.02	6.1	25.6	17.2	12.0
13	3650	13.61	3.12	2.04	168	1.05	6.8	54.6	9.3	8.4
14	2700	8.36	1.78	1.10	297	0.36	3.5	73.1	6.6	4.3
15	4040	15.16	3.77	2.68	211	2.88	9.0	44.4	8.4	11.9
17	955	13.72	2.14	1.44	1049	2.22	15.4	60.6	15.8	6.1
18	440	16.46	2.34	2.58	229	7.54	8.6	43.7	20.4	14.4
21	645	21.37	3.24	2.95	342	6.81	8.8	29.8	25.1	15.1
22	780	16.73	2.45	2.19	292	5.73	8.4	40.3	20.2	11.1
23	2780	17.39	3.17	2.39	199	4.43	7.7	38.6	17.1	11.0
24	1340	17.55	2.66	2.04	628	1.45	10.0	49.6	20.6	9.5
25	620	20.16	3.63	3.13	437	4.89	9.3	28.0	20.1	15.6
26	1600	16.44	3.34	2.66	472	3.28	9.7	44.3	13.9	12.6
27	3395	20.79	4.83	3.10	234	2.21	6.6	26.3	13.8	12.6
28	3540	19.33	4.28	2.74	201	1.40	5.8	30.4	14.1	11.1
29	2495	14.30	3.26	2.16	292	0.94	6.9	51.8	9.9	9.1
30	3580	18.02	4.81	2.64	216	0.95	5.0	35.2	7.9	9.2
32	3150	22.16	5.86	3.14	222	2.09	7.0	17.2	10.1	10.5
33	2680	21.61	5.92	3.23	205	2.18	7.1	20.8	8.6	11.1
34	1540	18.53	5.04	3.29	251	3.16	7.7	33.9	7.6	13.6
35	530	14.68	3.92	3.29	326	5.58	9.8	39.8	6.5	16.2
36	1620	17.62	5.41	3.19	264	3.46	7.4	28.7	3.3	12.0
39	1570	13.69	3.83	1.64	241	0.88	6.1	53.2	4.9	3.7
42	3240	25.68	7.62	2.24	174	0.55	4.4	11.1	6.4	0.0

[1] All samples are corrected for salt dilution (and contribution to Mg).
[2] Cr — expressed on a carbonate-free basis.
[3] See text for details of calculations for excess SiO$_2$ and dolomite contents.

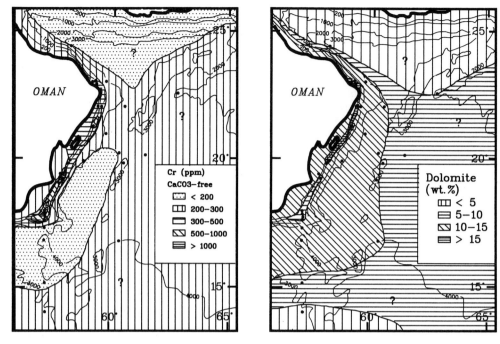

Fig. 5. Distribution maps of lithogenic components in sediments of the NW Arabian Sea (on a salt-free basis). A, Cr on a carbonate-free basis (ppm; B, dolomite (wt. %) calculated from the excess Mg content.

suggest that the high concentration results from winnowing of the fine-grained sediment from bank tops, and that the sediment is essentially a 'lag'. Cr is also found to be elevated in the turbidites of piston cores from deeper waters farther to the east (unpublished data). The occurrence of dolomite in these sediments was confirmed by mineralogical examination and X-ray diffraction methods. Its concentration (Fig. 5B) was calculated from the excess Mg content, assuming an average shale Mg/Al ratio of 0.188 (Turekian & Wedepohl 1961). This ratio does not account for Mg associated with chloritoid minerals associated with weathering of the serpentinite. The distribution suggests that elevated concentrations occur adjacent to, and north and south, of, Masirah. Low concentrations occur on the parts of the outer shelf where current scour and winnowing is thought to occur. The general disposition of dolomite is similar to that of organic carbon (see below), suggesting either, (i) that there is an *a priori* association of diagenetic dolomite with organic-rich sediments (Garrison *et al.* 1984, and references therein), or (ii) that fine-grained dolomite accumulates within the low-energy environment of the basins. For this latter case a detrital source of dolomite from the carbonates of the

Arabian Peninsula carried by aeolian transport cannot be ruled out.

The distribution of biogenic sediments

Organic carbon distributions on the Oman Margin (Fig. 6A) broadly mirror the distribution of surface productivity (Qasim 1982) and represent the net integrated input of biogenic material to the seafloor. However, local depositional factors can be important in influencing the organic matter content of the sediment, as seen by the elevated concentrations of C_{org} in the intrashelf basins (Stations 18, 21, 22) south of Masirah, and the low C_{org} contents which occur on the winnowed bank tops in the vicinities of Stations 5 and 17. The C/N weight ratio may be regarded as an index of organic matter maturity in sediments which lack terrigenous carbon. With time, freshly-deposited marine organic material is consumed by microbial activity which preferentially consumes the N-containing proteins from the organic molecules. Hence, an initial Redfield-type weight ratio of 5.7 for average marine plankton, may increase to >15 as a result of diagenesis. However, it should be noted that NH_4^+ may substitute into the interlayer positions in clays (Muller

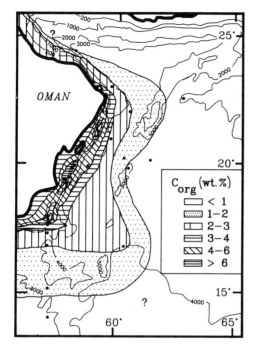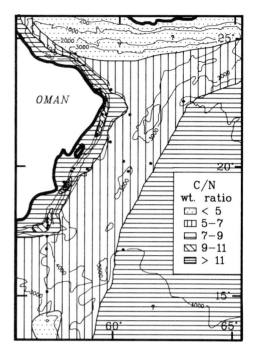

Fig. 6. Distribution maps of biogenic components in sediments of the NW Arabian Sea (on a salt-free basis). A, Organic carbon (wt. %); B, C/N (wt. ratio).

1977), and hence our measurement of N (total N in the bulk sediment) will include a small contribution from this source, resulting in ratios that are too low.

In almost all marine sediments and in settling particulate matter, the C/N weight ratio is higher than the Redfield value. Surface sediments underlying the Peru Margin upwelling regime, for example, have C/N weight ratios of about 8 in water depths > 1 km; values rise to 9.5 at a depth of 5 km (Henrichs & Farrington 1984). Similarly, Knauer *et al.* (1979) measured a C/N ratio of 7.5 in trapped particulate matter collected at 50 m depth in the coastal upwelling region off Monterey, California. The ratio rises with depth to about 9.4 at 700 m, indicating the characteristic preferential loss of nitrogen. In our samples, the C/N weight ratio ranges from 3.5 to 15.4, with most values falling in the range 7 to 9 (Table 1), similar to those observed off Peru. Although we cannot yet assess the proportion of terrigenous organic matter in the margin sediments, we presume that the lower C/N ratios represent the least degraded organic matter and *vice versa*. In view of this assumption, the sedimentary organic matter off Oman (Fig. 6B) exhibits a near-Redfield composition only in the Gulf of Oman, and in a swath

southwards between the Owen/Murray Ridge and the Oman Margin. To the E, the distal Indus Fan sediments appear to contain relatively more refractory organic matter, as might be expected given the continental provenance of most of the fan sediments. However, and rather surprisingly, high C/N ratios are found on the Oman shelf, with the highest values correlating extremely well with the detrital Cr content (Fig. 5A). This relationship is displayed graphically in Fig. 7. This correlation lends considerable support to our assumption that higher C/N ratios indeed reflect more degraded organic material. We therefore suggest that the residual sands produced by current winnowing action on the outer shelf are associated with a refractory biogenic residue. These results are in agreement with the work of Kolla *et al.* (1981) and Wiseman & Bennett (1940) who also remarked on the surprisingly high C/N ratio of the NW Arabian Sea when compared to other ocean margin areas (Bordovskiy 1965; Milliman 1975).

The determination of calcite (CaCO₃) by coulometry provides an assessment of the distribution of both detrital and biogenic carbonate in the NW Arabian Sea. The weak hydrochloric acid used in the analysis does not attack dolomite, and therefore the measurement is free

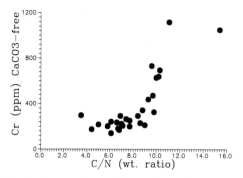

Fig. 7. A scatterplot to indicate the good positive correlation between Cr (on a carbonate-free basis) and C_{org} in core top samples.

from interference of this other carbonate phase. Without careful analysis of the trace elements (e.g. Sr) and measurement of the isotopic composition of the carbonate, it is difficult to estimate the relative proportion of biogenic to detrital carbonate. Nevertheless, the distribution shown in Fig. 8A displays some important features. First, a zone of high carbonate content is found on the southern Owen Ridge, reaching a maximum of 73 wt.% $CaCO_3$. High carbonate contents similarly occur farther to the north on the Murray Ridge, but do not reach quite such high values. Second, very low carbonate contents are found in the Oman Basin, and between the Owen/Murray Ridge and the Oman Margin. Third, carbonate contents on the Oman Margin are in general moderately high (25–50 wt.%), but very high concentrations are found in the lag deposits of the outer shelf, in particular at Station 5 (72.8 wt.%). We consider that the general distribution of carbonate on the shallow shelves and ridge tops is governed by surface productivity and terrigenous siliciclastic dilution, but that the high concentration of $CaCO_3$ on the southern Owen Ridge is almost entirely biogenic, as the ridge is unlikely to receive detrital carbonate from the shelf. This biogenic carbonate may be protected from major dissolution due to the topography of the ridge system which allows deposition of the carbonate above the lysocline. On the shelf, the high carbonate on the bank tops may well be detrital, and concentrated by current action. It will be the aim of future studies to try to characterize the composition of the biogenic and detrital carbonate.

In a similar way to calcite, the distribution of excess SiO_2 (Fig. 8B) contains contributions from both detrital quartz and biogenic opal.

Without using an analytical method specific for the quantification of biogenic opal, we have grouped together both opal and quartz as excess SiO_2:

$$\text{excess Si} = ((Si_{opal} + Si_{qtz}) - Si_{clay}).$$

This was achieved using a normative calculation with Al:

$$\text{excess } SiO_2 = 2.14 \,(Si_{meas} - (Si/Al_{clay} \times Al_{meas}))$$

where Si_{meas} and Al_{meas} are the measured Si and Al concentrations in wt.%, Si/Al_{clay} is the ratio in deep-sea clay (2.98; Turekian & Wedepohl 1961).

The distribution of excess SiO_2 is comparable with that of C_{org} (Fig. 6A) suggesting that biogenic opal (Si_{opal}) dominates the distribution. In particular, high concentrations (25.1 wt.%) are found in the anoxic intrashelf basins near Station 21. In this area, and to the north of Masirah, the common occurrence of diatoms in the surface sediments was noted. Low concentrations of excess SiO_2 on the bank tops near Station 5 suggest that quartz sand is not appreciably concentrated by bottom current action. In deeper waters, the distribution of excess SiO_2 appears to be more limited than that of biogenic calcite, with low concentrations on the Owen/Murray Ridge and virtually no excess SiO_2 in the Gulf of Oman. This distribution suggests that the siliceous biogenic signal of upwelling is more restricted in areal extent than biogenic carbonate, and that large concentrations of diatoms (and radiolaria?) are only found in protected basins within the OMZ where there is no bottom current winnowing.

Discussion

The results obtained from this survey confirm previous observations (Wiseman & Bennett 1940; Stewart *et al.* 1965; Marchig 1972; Kolla *et al.* 1981) that upwelling off the Oman Margin in the NW Arabian Sea results in a significant input of organic carbon, biogenic calcite and opal to the seafloor. However, the distribution of these biogenic phases, when considered in detail, does reveal some important characteristics that were not obvious in the larger-scale surveys of the Arabian Sea previously published.

The sedimentary imprint of the upwelling is probably dominated by the calcareous biogenic component, at the expense of siliceous debris. This observation is in contrast to other major upwelling areas of the world (Namibia: Calvert & Price 1983; Gulf of California: Calvert 1966; Peru: Krissek *et al.* 1980) where diatomaceous

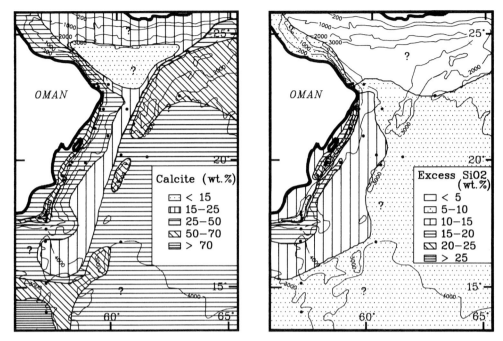

Fig. 8. Distribution maps of biogenic components in the NW Arabian Sea (on a salt-free basis). A, Calcite (wt.%); B, excess SiO$_2$ (wt.%).

sediments abound. Indeed, the very nature of the Arabian upwelling that is primarily wind-induced, the lack of association with a strong boundary current, and the high nutrient enrichment in comparison with the Somali upwelling (Wyrtki 1973; Prell & Streeter 1982) suggest that a unique situation is developed off Oman. Without a cold-water boundary current, like the Benguela, the Southern California, or Peru currents, diatom productivity may be restricted. Global climate models suggest that the Southwest Monsoon is at its acme during interglacial episodes, and hence we might expect present-day upwelling to be a maximum given the close link between upwelling and monsoonal circulation (Prell et al. 1980; Prell 1984; Prell & Van Campo 1986). This suggestion is qualified, however, by Kutzbach's (1981) observation that the wind speed of the SW Monsoon increased by 50% at the transition from glacial to interglacial episodes at the solar insolation maximum. Nevertheless, we may suggest that the distribution and concentration of biogenic debris recorded in these cores represents a near upper limit for the sedimentary imprint of upwelling during the late Quaternary.

During and after deposition of the biogenic debris the sediments are subject to reactions involving the dissolution and degradation of the organic remains. The close dependance of the CaCO$_3$ distribution on bathymetry was noticed by Kolla et al. (1981). They suggest that the CCD in the Arabian Basin is about 4800 m, although the lysocline will obviously be shallower. The occurrence of high concentrations of degraded organic matter on the Oman Margin, deduced from an average C/N ratio of 7–9, has been previously reported. Kolla et al. (1981) found that the ratio varied from 5 to 20 and suggested that both the nature of the original organic matter and subsequent diagenesis may be responsible for the high C/N values. This observation was derived from the study of a larger geographical area which included the detritus from the Indus drainage basin. As suggested above, such detritus may account for the higher ratios found in the eastern part of our study area. However, on the Oman shelf the high ratios are probably a result of strong, but local, sediment reworking. Pronounced bottom current activity and winnowing are evinced by the presence of sand waves and the distribution of Cr, C$_{org}$, CaCO$_3$ and excess SiO$_2$. The implications of this are that diagenetic reactions within the buried shelf sediments will be slowed and oxidants consumed less rapidly. Ultimately, the buried organic carbon is likely to be more gas-prone during maturation, but this hypothesis remains to be evaluated with pyrolysis techniques.

Conclusions

Hydrographic data from the waters of the NW Arabian Sea outline a marked oxygen minimum zone between 200 and 1500 m water depth which extends beyond the Owen/Murray Ridge. Sluggish intermediate and bottom water circulation maintains high concentrations of dissolved nutrients in the deep water to the northwest.

The morphology of the Oman Margin is characterized by a gently undulating bottom at shallow water depths (<150 m) which is covered with well-sorted sands, and a marked chaotic zone of fault scarps and canyons at the outer shelf edge. This outer zone trends approximately NE−SW, both north and south of Masirah Island and may represent the extinct tectonic lineament of the 'Masirah Line'. South of Masirah small intrashelf silled basins are developed that are anoxic. The Owen/Murray Ridge is strongly asymmetric in cross section and provides a possible barrier to westward progradation of detrital sediments from the Indus Fan.

Current activity on the outer Oman shelf concentrates Cr, weathered from the serpentinized ophiolite, into lag deposits that are also carbonate-rich, opal-poor and contain degraded (high C/N ratio) organic matter. Diatomaceous, organic-rich sediments accumulate in the anoxic intrashelf basins.

The general distribution of biogenic sediments off Oman reflects the upwelling and associated productivity of the region, although calcareous organisms dominate over siliceous microfaunas. The present Holocene concentration and pattern of biogenic sediment accumulation may well prove useful in interpreting the palaeoclimatic record of NW Arabian Sea upwelling.

We would like to thank the officers and crew of the R/V *Charles Darwin*, and the technical support from R.V.S. Barry without whose help cruise CD 17 could not have been a success. In the laboratory, G. Angell, F. Lindsay and M. Soon (UBC) provided expert analytical help. We thank W. Prell and K. Emeis for careful and constructive reviews of this manuscript. GBS and NBP would like to thank NERC for financial support, whilst TFP is grateful to NSERC for research costs.

References

BORDOVSKIY, O. K. 1965. Sources of organic matter in marine basins. *Marine Geology*, 3, 5−31.

CALVERT, S. E. 1966. Accumulation of diatomaceous silica in the sediments of the Gulf of California. *Bulletin of the Geological Society of America*, 77, 569−96.

CALVERT, S. E. & PRICE, N. B. 1983. Geochemistry of Namibian Shelf Sediments. *In*: SUESS, E. & THIEDE, J. (eds) *Coastal Upwelling, Part A*, Plenum Press, 337−75.

CURRIE, R. I., FISHER, A. E. & HARGREAVES, P. M. 1973. Arabian Sea Upwelling. *In*: ZEITSCHEL, B. (ed.), *The Biology of the Indian Ocean*. Springer, Berlin, 37−52.

DEUSER, W. G., ROSS, E. H. & MLODZINSKA, Z. J. 1978. Evidence for and rate of denitrification in the Arabian Sea. *Deep-Sea Research*, 25, 431−445.

GARRISON, R. E., KASTNER, M. & ZENGER, D. H. 1984. Dolomites of the Monterey Formation and other organic-rich units. *Pacific Section, Society of Economic Paleontologists and Mineralogists*, 41.

GASS, I. G. & GIBSON, I. L. 1969. The structural evolution of rift zones in the Middle East. *Nature*, 221, 926−930.

GOLDBERG, E. D. & GRIFFIN, J. J. 1970. The sediments of the northern Indian Ocean. *Deep-Sea Research*, 17, 513−537.

GORIN, G. E., RACZ, L. G. & WALTER, M. R. 1982. Late Precambrian-Cambrian sediments of Huqf Group, Sultanate of Oman. *Bulletin of the American Association of Petroleum Geologists*, 66, 2609−27.

HENRICHS & FARRINGTON 1984. Peru upwelling region sediments near 15°S. 1. Remineralization and accumulation of organic matter. *Limnology and Oceanography*, 29, 1−19.

HURD, D. C. 1973. Interaction of biogenic opal, sediment and sea water in central Equatorial Pacific. *Geochimica Cosmochimica Acta*, 37, 2257−2282.

KNAUER, G. A., MARTIN, J. H. & BRULAND, K. W. 1979. Fluxes of particulate carbon, nitrogen and phosphorous in the upper water column of the northeast Pacific. *Deep-Sea Research*, 26, 97−108.

KOLLA, V., BE, A. W. H. & BISCAYE, P. E. 1976a. Calcium carbonate distribution in the surface sediments of the Indian Ocean. *Journal of Geophysical Research*, 81, 2605−16.

——, HENDERSON, L. & BISCAYE, P. E. 1976b. Clay mineralogy and sedimentation in the western Indian Ocean. *Deep-Sea Research*, 23, 949−961.

——, RAY, P. K. & KOSTECKI, J. A. 1981. Surficial sediments of the Arabian Sea. *Marine Geology*, 41, 183−204.

KRISSEK, L. A., SCHEIDEGGER, K. R. & KULM, L. D. 1980. Surface sediments of the Peru-Chile continental margin and the Nazca plate. *Bulletin of the Geological Society of America*, 91, 321−31.

KUTZBACH, J. 1981. Monsoon climate of the early Holocene: Climate experiment using the Earth's orbital parameters for 9,000 years ago. *Science*, 214, 59−61.

KUZ'MENKO, L. V. 1974. Primary productivity of the northern Arabian Sea. *Oceanology*, 20, 164−7.

MARCHIG, V. 1972. Zur geochemie rezenter Sedimente des Indischen Ozeans. *"Meteor" Forschungserbebeit*, Reihe C **11**, 1–104.

MILLIMAN, J. D. 1975. Upper continental margin sedimentation: a synthesis. *Contributions to Sedimentology*, **4**, 151–175.

MOSELEY, F. & ABBOTTS, I. L. 1979. The ophiolite melange of Masirah, Oman. *Journal of the Geological Society, London*, **136**, 713–724.

MOYES, J., DUPRAT, J., FAUGERES, J-C., GONTHIER, E. & PUJOL, C. 1978. Golfe d'Aden, mer d'Oman: Etude stratigraphique et sedimentologique. ORGON IV, 189–263.

MULLER, P. J. 1977. C/N ratio in Pacific deep-sea sediments: Effect of inorganic ammonium and organic nitrogen compounds sorbed by clays. *Geochimica et Cosmochimica Acta*, **41**, 765–776.

NAQVI, S. W. A., NORONHA, R. J. & GANGADHARA REDDY, C. V. 1982. Denitrification in the Arabian Sea. *Deep-Sea Research*, **29**, 459–69.

NEYMAN, V. G. 1961. Formation of oxygen minima in the surface waters of the Arabian Sea. *Okeanologiya Akademiya Nauk SSSR, Okeanografichna Komissiya*, **4**, 62–65.

OLAUSSON, E., HAQ, B. U., GUNVOR, B. K. & OLSSON, I. U. 1971. Evidence in Indian Ocean cores of late Pleistocene changes in oceanic and atmospheric circulation. *Geologiska Foreningens I Stockholm Forhandlingar*, **93**, 51–84.

PRELL, W. 1984. Variation of monsoonal upwelling: A response to changing solar radiation. *In*: HANSEN, J. E. & TAKAHASHI, T. (eds) *Climatic Processes and Climate Sensitivity*, **5**, Washington, 48–57.

—— & CURRY, W. B. 1981. Faunal and isotopic indices of monsoonal upwelling: western Arabian Sea. *Oceanologica Acta*, **4**, 91–98.

——, HUTSON, W. H. WILLIAMS, D. F., BE, A. W. H. GEITZENAUER, K. & MOLFINO, B. 1980. Surface circulation of the Indian Ocean during the last glacial maximum, approximately 18000 years B. P. *Quaternary Research*, **14**, 309–336.

—— & KUTZBACH, J. E. 1987. Monsoon variability over the past 150000 years. *Journal of Geophysical Research*, **92**, 8411–25.

—— & STREETER, H. F. 1982. Temporal and spatial patterns of monosonal upwelling along Arabia: A modern analogue for the interpretation of Quaternary SST anomalies. *Deep-Sea Research*, **40**, 143–55.

—— & VAN CAMPO, E. 1986. Coherent response of the Arabian Sea upwelling and pollen transport to late Quaternary monsoonal winds. *Nature*, **323**, 526–528.

QASIM, S. Z. 1982. Oceanography of the northern Arabian Sea. *Deep-Sea Research*, **29**, 1041–1068.

RAO, D. P. & JAYARAMAN, R. 1970. On the occurrence of oxygen maxima and minima in the upper 500 metres of the north-west Indian Ocean. *Proceedings of the Indian Academy of Sciences*, **71B**, 230–246.

SEN GUPTA, R., FONDEKAR, S. P., SANKARANARAYANAN, V. N. & DE SOUSA, S. N. 1975. Chemical oceanography of the Arabian Sea. Part I. Hydrochemical and hydrographical features of the northern basin. *Indian Journal of Marine Sciences*, **4**, 136–140.

SHIMMIELD, G. B. 1985. *The geochemistry and mineralogy of Pacific Sediments, Baja California.* PhD Thesis, University of Edinburgh.

SLATER, R. D. & KROOPNICK, P. 1984. Controls on dissolved oxygen distribution and organic carbon deposition in the Arabian Sea. *In*: HAQ, B. U. & MILLIMAN, J. D. (eds) *Geology and Oceanography of the Arabian Sea and Coastal Pakistan*, Pakistan Institute of Oceanography, Van Nostrand Rheinhold, London, 305–312.

STACKELBERG, U. V. 1972. Faziesverteilung in Sedimentendes Indisch-Pakistanischen KontinentalRandes (Arabisches Meer). *"Meteor" Forschungersgebeit*, Reihe C **9**, 1–73.

STEWART, R. A., PILKEY, O. H. & NELSON, B. W. 1965. Sediments of the northern Arabian Sea. *Marine Geology*, **3**, 411–427.

TUREKIAN, K. K. & WEDEPOHL, K. H. 1961. Distribution of the elements in some major units of the Earth's crust. *Bulletin of the Geological Society of America*, **72**, 175–192.

WISEMAN, J. D. H. & BENNETT, H. 1940. The distribution of organic carbon and nitrogen in the sediments of the Arabian Sea. *John Murray Expedition 1933–34*, Scientific Report **3**, 193–221.

WYRTKI, K. 1973. Physical oceanography of the Indian Ocean. *In*: ZEITZSCHEL, B. (ed.) *The Biology of the Indian Ocean, Ecological Studies*, Vol. 3. Springer, Berlin. 18–36.

Regional Tectonic Setting

Inter-relationship of Makran−Oman Mountains belts of convergence

K. W. GLENNIE[1], M. W. HUGHES CLARKE[2], M. G. A. BOEUF[3], W. F. H. PILAAR[4] & B. M. REINHARDT[5]

[1] Consultant, Ballater, Grampian, UK
[2] PD Oman Ltd., Muscat, Sultanate of Oman
[3] Shell Gabon, Port Gentil, Gabon
[4] SIPM, The Hague, The Netherlands
[5] Shell UK Ltd, London, UK

Abstract: Mid Permian rifting and crustal separation along the northern margin of Arabia led to initiation of the Neo-Tethys ocean and deposition of sediments typified by the Hawasina. Subsequently, the Neo-Tethyan oceanic crust was consumed in a late Cretaceous subduction zone, generally easterly dipping in the Oman sector, and its sedimentary cover built up an accretion wedge (Hawasina; Coloured Melange) until the late Campanian, when the buoyant crust of the Arabian continental margin seemingly choked the subduction process.

Continuing convergence caused increased activity on, or the creation of, another subduction trench running between and extending south and east of the Central Iran−Lut and Sanandaj−Sirjan microcontinents (the proto−Makran trench). The resulting crustal relaxation on the earlier subduction site permitted uplift of the half-buried Oman continental margin; the overlying Hawasina and former hanging wall of Semail ophiolite then spread gravitationally further onto the Arabian shelf.

The Makran accretion wedge of Mesozoic Coloured Melange-type rocks and a thick pile of Maastrichtian to Eocene flysch underlies an ophiolitic hanging wall. Post-Eocene collisions between Arabia, Eurasia and intervening microcontinents resulted in: movement of the Naiband Fault in Iran and associated change in trend of the main subduction trench from NW−SE to E−W; thrusting of the Kahnu−Daragar and Alpine-type ophiolite over the SE Sanandaj−Sirjan Zone and rotation of part of its basement; westward thrusting of Musandam, and was associated with the Oligocene uplift of the Oman Mountains. The Zagros plicate folds began their main development in the Pliocene. Continent−continent collision has not occurred between Oman and the Makran.

The writers concluded their mapping of the geology of the Oman Mountains (Glennie *et al.* 1973, 1974) in the spring of 1968. They had found the mountains to comprise several distinct geological units; these documented the history of the southwest passive margin of the Hawasina Ocean (Neo-Tethys; Devoudzadeh & Schmidt 1984; Sengör 1987, 1990) which had opened between Arabia and parts of Eurasia in the Mid Permian, and continued to widen until the Early Cretaceous (Aptian−Albian) when the South Atlantic Ocean began to open (Ussami *et al.* 1986). The sense of motion of Afro−Arabia then reversed with respect to the spreading axis of Neo-Tethys, and Neo-Tethys began to close. With the creation of an ENE-dipping (relative to present N) ocean−ocean subduction zone, the accretion of at least part of the ocean's sedimentary cover (Hawasina nappes) took place beneath a hanging wall of oceanic crust (see also Fig. 4.11 in Lippard *et al.* 1986).

Present knowledge (e.g. Lippard *et al.* 1986) shows that the Semail Nappe was most likely derived from an oceanic spreading axis adjacent to the subduction zone rather than, as in the writers' 1974 interpretation, from a mid-ocean type of ridge; the spreading axis was active during the Cenomanian and perhaps also Turonian time spans. Obduction of both the Semail and the Hawasina was complete by the late Campanian. The obducted rock units remained mostly below sea level, however, until the Oligocene−early Miocene, when the main Oman Mountains uplift came into being.

Our field work in Oman indicated that all Hawasina sediments could be explained as having been deposited marginal to the Arabian continent. From the limited evidence available at that time (1968; Gansser 1955, 1959; Falcon 1967; Stöcklin 1968) it was realized that rocks existed in the Makran area of Iran (Fig. 1) that had a superficial resemblance to those of the

From ROBERTSON, A. H. F., SEARLE, M. P. & RIES, A. C. (eds), 1990,
The Geology and Tectonics of the Oman Region.
Geological Society Special Publication No 49, pp 773−786

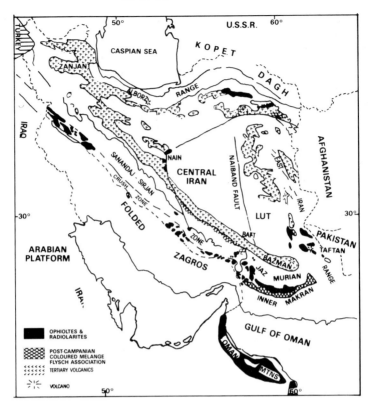

Fig. 1. Some important structural units of the greater Iran area. Acid and intermediate intrusions, Cenozoic volcanics, young depressions between the Sanandaj−Sirjan and Central Iran−Lut microcontinents and extending towards Turkey probably result from subduction of the floor of Neo-Tethys along the Zagros Crush Zone. They largely mask the ophiolite−radiolarite rock assemblages that indicate the former presence of oceanic crust between Nain and Baft; these are much better displayed in the zone's extension around the southern edge of Jaz Murian. Adapted from Stocklin (1968).

Hawasina; by visiting the Makran, the writers thought they might be able to study the sedimentary sequence that had been deposited on the other side of the Hawasina (Neo-Tethys) Ocean. The visit was made late in 1968, and the observations form the basis of the views presented here.

The writers found a more complex geological succession than expected from their Oman experience. The Makran sequence indeed documents sedimentation during much if not all of the same time span as that of the Hawasina, but it goes a stage further. The Makran area comprises an accretionary wedge which includes sequences of probable Permian and certainly Jurassic to Lower Cretaceous oceanic sediments that apparently began to be scraped off the floor of Neo-Tethys only after subduction had ceased in the Oman area. The purpose of this paper is to document some data leading to this interpretation and discuss regional implications.

Synopsis of Oman Mountain geology

Seven major rock units document the history of the Oman Mountains. They were superimposed upon each other either depositionally or tectonically and comprise, from top to bottom:

G. Upper Maastrichtian to Lower Tertiary shallow-marine limestones, locally with basal clastics and conglomerates, which currently overlie all other rock units except D unconformably.

F. Semail Nappe: a massive slice of former oceanic crust, some 600 km long and up to 150 km wide; apparently it was generated along a subduction-related back-arc spreading axis during the Cenomanian−Turonian, and was obducted onto the Arabian continental margin during the Campanian.

E. The Hawasina: tectonic slices of Permian to Mid Cretaceous sedimentary sequences that were deposited in a basin adjacent to the northeastern edge of the Arabian continental margin.

D. The Sumeini Group: a "par-autochthonous" sequence of Permian to late Cretaceous continental-slope sediments that have a close stratigraphic relationship to both the overlying Hawasina and underlying Hajar Supergroup.

C. Aruma Group: a package of Turonian to Maastrichtian sediments that overlie the Hajar Supergroup unconformably and straddle the time of obduction of both Hawasina and Semail nappes; seen in the mountains as the Muti Formation, which was derived from the uplifted shelf edge of the continental margin. The Muti underlies the Hawasina both in an intramarginal basin and as a drape to the former shelf edge (e.g. Robertson 1987). Marginal to the Oman Mountains the Group also includes the Juweiza Formation, which contains latest Campanian to early Maastrichtian products of erosion of units E and F.

B. Hajar Supergroup: an autochthonous sequence of Mid Permian to Mid Cretaceous sediments, mostly carbonates, deposited on the Arabian continental margin. Mid to late Permian volcanics (Le Métour & Villey 1986; Le Métour et al. 1986) at the northern margin of Saih Hatat herald the separation of Afro–Arabia from a continental area lying to its northeast.

A. Pre-Permian sedimentary rock units of Jebel Akhdar and Saih Hatat (Upper Proterozoic to Ordovician; Lovelock et al. 1981), and the crystalline rocks of Jebel Ja'alan (858 ± 16 Ma).

These rock units can be reconstructed palinspastically to give a logical history of sedimentation, volcanism and tectonic events in this part of the Middle East between the Mid Permian and the Early Tertiary (Palaeocene). The sequences of the Hajar Supergroup–Sumeini Group – Hawasina can be correlated reasonably well in both time and lithology. In the simplist palinspastic reconstruction, the Sumeini and Hawasina are considered to document deposition in the Hawasina Basin of largely reworked shallow-marine calciclastics, together with relatively minor amounts of pelagic radiolarian chert. The basin has a reconstructed width of several hundred kilometres and existed on the oceanward side of the continental shelf edge (Glennie et al. 1973, 1974; Lippard et al. 1986; Searle 1988).

Other reconstructions involve a more complex process of obduction; that proposed by

Bernoulli & Weissert (1987) and by Béchennec et al. (1988), for instance, have much in common with the alternative interpretation of Glennie et al. (1974). According to this interpretation, the Hawasina sediments would then have been deposited mostly along the new continental margin on a substrate formed largely of foundered Permian shelf (rather than on oceanic crust) from which it was detached during thrusting. Because the Hawasina has no clearly defined substrate, much of it can indeed be interpreted as having been deposited in an intramarginal basin.

The interpretations of several authors imply that oceanic crust need not have been generated in Neo-Tethys during the Permian but could be thought of as having been delayed until the advent of the Late Triassic Haybi volcanism (Searle et al. 1980; Lippard et al. 1986). Blendinger (1989), however, describes the occurrence just south of Saih Hatat of more than 300 m of basaltic pillow lavas of deep-water type, overlain by late Permian cephalod-bearing limestone turbidites. He takes these data to indicate that the Hawasina (Neo-Tethys) Ocean had already opened by the mid Permian and was underlain, at least in part, by oceanic crust; this supports the interpretation preferred by Glennie et al. (1973, 1974).

In this paper we are concerned with neither the exact order in which the different components of the Hawasina were emplaced, nor with their precise derivation; more important to our thesis is the overall location and timing of the major geological events. So far as the Oman Mountains are concerned, these may be summarized as follows.

A. Opening of the Hawasina (Neo-ethys) Ocean in the Mid Permian, and its continued expansion until the Mid Cretaceous (Aptian–Albian) when the South American and Afro-Arabian parts of Gondwana began to separate to create the South Atlantic Ocean. This implies that, relative to the Neo-Tethys spreading axis, the sense of motion of Afro-Arabia must have reversed at this time, and that from then on, both Tethyan oceanic crust and its sedimentary cover were consumed, presumably in one or more subduction zones, one of which formed an intra-oceanic trench.

B. The earliest expression in Oman of this reversed sense of motion was in the Cenomanian when the Arabian shelf edge was uplifted and partly eroded; conglomerates of Aptian age in the Zagros sector of Neo-Tethys, although apparently derived from the NE (Ricou 1968a), may reflect a similar phenomenon. This crustal upwarp could have resulted from opposition to an eastward-drifting Afro–Arabia by a Neo-Tethyan oceanic ridge that was still spreading. These compressive stresses were then relieved by the creation of the oceanic subduction zone, which is inferred to have been associated with the development of a backarc spreading axis (Pearce et al. 1981), where the Semail crust was formed. The trend of the back-arc spreading axis, and most likely also the subduction trench, would essentially have been parallel to that of the dykes that were intruded into the new oceanic crust. In the northern Oman Mountains the sheeted dykes have a very consistent trend which averages some 10° to 20° west of north (see geological map in Lippard *et al.* (1986)). Such an orientation for the strike of subduction would be in agreement with the essentially E–W opening direction (prior to later sinistral rotation; see Dercourt *et al.* (1986, plate 4)) of the South Atlantic Ocean. The Semail spreading centre originated some 105 Ma ago according to Lippard *et al.* (1986, Fig. 4.11).

C With a combination of sea-floor spreading and passive northeastward drifting of Arabia, the rate of closure within the subduction zone has been estimated by Lippard *et al.* (1986) to be some 5cm/year. Within the upper trench, ocean-floor sediments were scraped off their substrate to form the Hawasina accretion wedge, while the oceanic substrate (of which, arguably, small fragments have been preserved – see, e.g. Blendinger 1988) was consumed down the trench.

D. Obduction of both the Hawasina and the Semail ceased by the end of the Campanian when the buoyant crust of the Arabian continental margin could no longer be consumed down the trench. Afro–Arabia's position, however, continued to be affected by the South Atlantic opening, and thus moved relatively closer to Asia, although elsewhere within NeoTethys, new oceanic crust presumably was still being generated along the old axis of mid-ocean spreading. This convergence must either have required initiation of new subduction somewhere within the relatively weak oceanic crust or subjected an existing zone to increased activity; indeed, evidence for this is found in the Inner Makran where sediments of Maastrichtian age not only formed part of an accretion wedge relatively close to the southern edge of the Lut microcontinent

but, locally, were also unconformable over older Mesozoic sequences.

Outline of the main structural units of Iran

The Makran should be viewed within the context of the whole greater Iran area (Fig. 1). This comprises a group of microcontinents and intervening fold belts lying between the relatively young Zagros and Caucasus–Kopet Dagh mountain ranges, which are at the margins of the Afro–Arabian and Eurasian megacontinents.

The different structural elements concerned are as follows.

(a) The *Zagros fold belt*; consisting essentially of a sequence of Permian to Eocene shallow-marine limestones, comparable to the Hajar Supergroup of Oman and its Paleogene cover, unconformably overlying an older suite of carbonates and clastics. The belt terminates in the southeast where it plunges under the north–south trending Zendan fold belt adjacent to the Makran ranges (Fig. 2).

The Mesozoic depositional and tectonic history of the Zagros, being also a sector of the Arabian continental margin, is similar to that of Oman, with obduction of the ophiolites and radiolarites of the Coloured Melange (Grey 1950; Ricou 1968a, b, 1971; Coloured Series of Falcon 1974) being completed by the early Maastrichtian. Unlike Oman, however, it has a tectonic history that has been continuously active until the present (see Berberian & King 1981; Devoudzadeh & Schmidt 1984; Sengör 1990; Stoneley 1974, 1990), and was not deformed into a mountain range until the Pliocene, when it fully collided with the Sanandaj–Sirjan (Stöcklin 1968) microcontinental sector of Central Iran.

One analogy with the Oman Mountains can be found in the region of Kuh-e-Faraghun (Fig. 2; see also Stoneley 1990). There, shallow-water limestones of Late Turonian to Coniacian age are followed by almost 1000 m of Coniacian to Campanian marls and limestones with *Globotruncana* assemblages. Into these pelagic sediments are inserted levels of conglomerates, which wedge out laterally into northward-directed turbidite-like units. In the sequence of these gravity-flow deposits the lithoclasts contain faunas in reversed order of age from Coniacian to Aptian or Barremian and, more doubtfully, late Jurassic. The sequence seems to have been deposited as a result of uplift and erosion of the outer part of the Arabian conti-

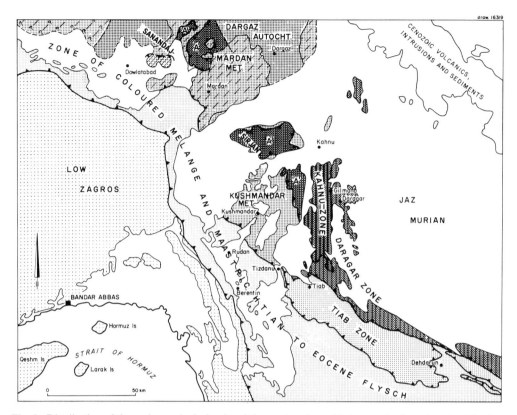

Fig. 2. Distribution of the major geological units of the western Inner Makran and adjacent parts of the Low Zagros and Sanandaj–Sirjan Zone. The Mardan and Kushmandar basement rocks of this latter zone are overthrust by mostly metamorphosed Alpine-type peridotites and gabbros ('A'), by unmetamorphosed peridotites and gabbros of the Kahnu Zone (overlain depositionally by late Jurassic–early Cretaceous sediments) and by diabase dykes and overlying pre-Eocene pillow lavas of the Daragar Zone. These ophiolite suites trend north into the Nain–Baft Zone and east around the south side of Jaz Murian. The Tiab Zone is a klippe of mostly Cretaceous carbonates and Eocene flysch that possibly formerly overlay Late Jurassic oceanic crust similar to the Kahnu Zone. F, Kuh-e-Faraghur.

nental margin in much the same way that the Muti Formation was derived in Oman.

During the Campanian to early Maastrichtian, the Crush Zone margin of the Zagros was overthrust by that association of rocks, characterized by ophiolites and Triassic to Aptian limestones and radiolarian cherts, known as the Coloured Melange; this Melange can be considered as roughly equivalent to the combined Hawasina and Semail nappes of Oman but is not nearly so well exposed.

(b) The *Zagros Crush Zone* (Main Zagros Thrust) marks the line of former separation of the two continental areas formed by Arabia and the Sanandaj–Sirjan Zone (Fig. 1), and represents the suture of the intervening arm of the Neo-Tethyan Ocean from which the allochthonous rocks of both the Coloured Melange and the Hawasina were derived.

This basin is believed to have originated in the mid or late Permian (*Fusulina* in the Melange (Ricou 1971)). Berberian & King (1981) suggest that Permian volcanics along the Sanandaj–Sirjan Zone could represent extensional rifting leading to the separation of Central Iran and Arabia. One might also speculate on whether pre-separation crustal up-arching and erosion was responsible for the distribution of the Lower Permian Jamal Sandstone of Central Iran (Berberian & King 1981, p. 236) and the Gharif Sandstone of Interior Oman (Hughes Clarke 1988); sands of this age are not found in the Oman Mountains but do seem to exist in the Sanandaj–Sirjan Zone (Stöcklin 1968).

(c) The *Sanandaj–Sirjan Zone* (Stöcklin 1968)

Table 1. *Stratigraphic chart of the Makran area. Eo1, Eo2, early and late Eocene flysch.*

AGES		LOW ZAGROS	RUDAN/ ZCMMEF	SANANDAJ-SIRJAN	DARAGAR KAHNU & 'A'	TIAB
CENOZOIC — TERTIARY	Quaternary	Q	Q	Q	Q	Q
	Pliocene	Baktyari	Bkt	Bkt	Bkt	Bkt
	Miocene	Fars	Flysch			
	Oligocene	Asmari-Jahrum				
	Eocene	Pabdeh	Eo_2/Eo_1 Rudan	Eo_2/Eo_1	Eo_2/Eo_1	Eo_2/Eo_1
	Paleocene					
MESOZOIC — CRETACEOUS	Maastrichtian	Gurpi	Red Siltst.	Limestone		Limestone
	Middle	Bangestan Gp.				
	Lower		Coloured	Limestone		Limest/marble Sandst/Shale
MESOZOIC — JURASSIC	Upper	Khami Gp.	Melange		Oceanic Sediments	Oceanic Crust
	Middle		Sediments		Oceanic Crust	
	Lower			Sandst/Shale		
TRIASSIC		Neyriz Kaneh Kat	?			
PALZ	Permian		Oceanic Crust			
	Permo-Carb			Schists		

formed the southwestern margin of Central Iran at the time of mid Permian crustal separation from Arabia. The zone comprises a metamorphic basement (gneisses, schists, marbles) unconformably overlain by incomplete sequences of older Palaeozoic and Permian to Cretaceous sedimentary rocks (Table 1). Scattered outliers of ophiolites overlie the metamorphic basement rocks of the zone, and were possibly derived from the adjacent Nain–Baft Zone. At its southeastern extremity, the Sanandaj–Sirjan Zone plunges beneath the ophiolites and other rock units of the Inner Makran (Fig. 2). This southeastern area will be described in greater detail under Makran geology.

(d) *Nain–Baft Zone*. This zone is characterized by a NW–SE trending linear depression that is associated with Tertiary volcanics. Although little exposed geology confirms this, it is probably the root zone from which the scattered outliers of ophiolites were emplaced along the east flank of the Sanandaj–Sirjan Zone. Thus it separates Central Iran from the Sanandaj–Sirjan Zone and seems to extend through northern Makran to the East Iran Range, which separates the Lut and Sistan blocks in the vicinity of the Iran–Afghanistan border. The ophiolites and radiolarites are poorly exposed in this zone except in the Inner Makran. Here, a full suite of ophiolites ('A', Kahnu and Daragar; Fig. 2, Table 1)

form the hanging wall to the Makran accretion wedge.

(e) *Central Iran–Lut*. This triangular area can be divided into two parts separated by the Naiband fault (Fig. 1): the eastern stable Lut Block has only limited Palaeozoic, Jurassic and Cretaceous sediments exposed beneath a cover of Eo–Oligocene volcanics and modern desert sediments. The western Central–Iran area, on the other hand, is complex and has many exposures that range in age from Precambrian to Cretaceous (Stöcklin 1968, 1974). Palaeomagnetic studies (Soffel & Förster 1984) and facies reconstructions have led Devoudzadeh & Schmidt (1984) to infer that Central Iran–Lut separated from the Sanandaj–Sirjan Zone at the end of the mid-Triassic and was later rotated anticlockwise; The main rotation seems to have taken place in the early Tertiary and brought the total rotation of this microcontinent to over 90° (Westphal *et al.* 1986).

A more complex possible history of movement of these various microcontinents is postulated by Dercourt *et al.* (1986), with which our interpretations essentially do not disagree.

Outline of Makran geology

Little has been published about the Makran area. Falcon (1974) presented two maps based on a compilation he made in 1951 and his own field work in the 1930s. Although not complete, the maps indicate the structural and stratigraphic outline of the area. His 1975 paper contains an excellent mosaic made by Imperial College from satellite photos for an expedition to the area. The results of that expedition are outlined by Cornelius *et al.* (1975) and by Shearman (1976). McCall & Kidd (1982) reported the highlights of a major mapping exercise for the Geological Survey of Iran (McCall 1985). Arthurton *et al.* (1982) extend our knowledge of the Makran into Pakistan, and White (1982) links the Makran fold belt to Oman with offshore seismic data of the Gulf of Oman. This last paper indicates that in the southern part of the Gulf of Oman, some 4000 m of undeformed sediments overlie Cretaceous oceanic crust of similar age to the Semail, whereas in the north, this same sediment sequence is being deformed above a north-dipping subduction zone. The geological framework given by McCall & Kidd (1982) and McCall (1985) is essentially the same as ours. Although not covering all the areas we studied, their work was much more extensive and detailed than our own reconnaissance, and there are places where mapping and interpretation differ; these will be pointed out where considered important.

Much of the Makran area of Iran consists of a complex wedge of Neo-Tethyan ocean-floor sediments which, since the Maastrichtian, have been accreting in a subduction prism. Although the Makran trench now trends E−W, it is possible that, like the Oman trench, it originally dipped down to the ENE.

In the northwest, this accretion complex tectonically overlies the southeastern end of the folded Low Zagros as expressed by the young Tertiary sediments and folds of the Zendan Range, and is overthrust by metamorphic rocks of the Sanandaj−Sirjan Zone. The accretion wedge, or lithological sequences that have undergone at least some of the same geological history, seems to extend into the Zagros Crush Zone south and west of Dowlatabad (Fig. 2).

The main geological units of the western Makran comprise (Fig. 2 and Table 1):

(a) The *Low Zagros* (already described), whose northern and eastern margin is overlain by:

(b) *Zone of Coloured Melange and Maastrichtian to Eocene Flysch* (ZCMMEF). Within this zone, essentially four discontinuous suites of rock can be distinguished (Fig. 3A):

(i) Coloured Melange. (Gansser 1955; NIOC Geological Map of Iran 1959; McCall 1985). This comprises sequences of sedimentary rocks imbricated with members of an ophiolite suite. The sedimentary rocks include grainstone turbidites, radiolarian cherts and blocks of marble or shallow-marine limestone that are commonly associated with basic igneous rocks. Matrix fossils in the sedimentary rocks range in age from Triassic (and perhaps Permian) to early Cretaceous, and Permian reefal faunas are common in lithoclasts.

Basic and ultrabasic rocks are common, mostly peridotites and pillow-lava/dyke complexes. East of Berentin, dyke swarms are overlain by pillow lavas upon which rest large but undated blocks of marble up to a cubic kilometre in volume.

Most of these rock assemblages are sheared and recrystallised such that faunas in the sedimentary rocks cannot be determined, and primary relationships between sedimentary and igneous rocks are obscured. Serpentinites can grade rapidly to hornblende schists, and reefal debris (some datable as early Cretaceous) can tectonically overlie basic schists such that, again, the original relationships are obscured.

Although this rock assemblage has many points of similarity with parts of the Hawasina and Semail nappes of the Oman Mountains (faunas, lithologies and facies represented), it is structurally much more complex, has been more metamorphosed, and is now imbricated with Maastrichtian and early Tertiary sedimentary rocks.

(ii) Maastrichtian limestones and red siltstones. These contain a pelagic faunal assemblage that includes *Globotruncana*, and they unconformably overlie blocks of the Coloured Melange. East of Rudan, pink limestones and red siltstones are interbedded with pillow lavas, and east of Dehdarun, the lavas and siltstones are associated with volcanic bombs formed of angular fragments of pillow lava with a still recognizable variolitic and vesicular texture.

(iii) Rudan unit of Maastrichtian to Eocene flysch. This occurs as fault-bounded series of sandstone turbidites characterized by the inclusion of large components of the above two units.

The bulk of this unit comprises sandstone turbidites and shales with characteristic grains of red chert and green igneous fragments. *Globotruncana* and *Nummulites* in the sandstone matrix indicate the Maastrichtian to Eocene timespan of deposition of the unit. The intercalated blocks of units (i) and (ii) range in size from boulders to slabs of 1 km^3 in volume. Field relationships seen in some localities indicate that, contrary to the interpretations of McCall & Kidd (1982), some of these slabs

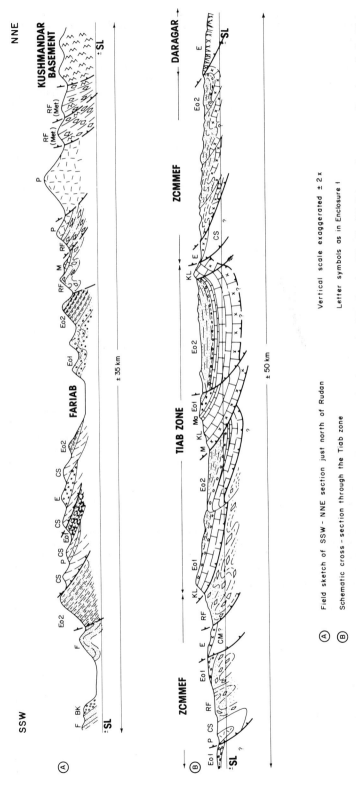

Fig. 3. Tectonic styles in the Inner Makran. (A) Field sketch of SSW–NNE section just north of Rudan (see Fig. 2). (B) Schematic cross section through the Tiab Zone. Vertical exaggeration approximately × 2. Bk, Bakhtiari; CM, Coloured Melange; E, Extrusives of Daragar Zone; Eo1, Eo2, early and late Eocene flysch; KL, Lower Cretaceous; M, Marble Ma, Maastrichtian limestone; (Met), Metamorphosed; RF, Rudan flysch; P, Peridotite.

were sedimented into the depositional basin as components of a wildflysch. At other localities, however, the existing contacts with the sandstones are clearly tectonic, the different facies appearing as imbrications (Fig. 3A).

(iv) Eocene Flysch. This contains no wildflysch components of units (i) and (ii), but thick sedimentary sequences of this unit may be imbricated with any of the other three units described above.

The Eocene Flysch can be subdivided into a lower, coarse, conglomeratic sequence with components of metamorphic rocks, Lower Cretaceous shallow-marine limestones and quartzites, which was probably deposited proximal to its source, and an upper, finer and shalier more distal sequence. These two sequences can occur in normal stratigraphic continuity, in reversed tectonic order, and as separate, tectonically bounded sequences. Individually, they may unconformably overlie large blocks of Coloured Melange, the Maastrichtian limestones and red siltstones, or parts of the Rudan Flysch.

Within the area mapped by the writers, the only firmly dated volcanic activity in the ZCMMEF took place during the Maastrichtian. The stratigraphic relationships between the Maastrichtian limestones and siltstones and the underlying imbricated extrusives and sediments of the Coloured Melange indicate that igneous activity had also occurred during the time span Permo-Triassic to early Cretaceous. Some shallow-marine limestones (now marbles) of the Melange overlie extrusives in the same fashion as the sheared and partly recrystallised limestones of the Oman Exotics, but this does not necessarily imply the same depositional age (late Permian and late Triassic).

While some idea can be obtained of the different ages and environments of deposition of component members of the ZCMMEF, they are now so complexly imbricated that it is probably not possible to reconstruct palinspastically the different stages of development.

Younger, post-Oligocene, flysch sequences occur between the ZCMMEF and the Makran coast (McCall 1985), but only a small part of this area was studied by the writers.

SE Sanandaj–Sirjan Zone

The northern part of the ZCMMEF (Zagros Crush Zone) is, as further along the Crush Zone, overthrust from the northeast by metamorphic and sedimentary rocks of the Sanandaj–Sirjan Zone.

The metamorphic basement rocks in this area (Bajgan Complex of McCall & Kidd 1982) comprise quartzites, schists and gneisses intermingled with basic schists, marbles and calcareous schists. They represent a metamorphosed sedimentary sequence that contained submarine volcanics (pillow lavas) and large limestone blocks (now marble) with textural features not dissimilar to those of the 'Exotics' of the Oman Mountains. However, these features can also be seen in rocks associated with the diapiric early Palaeozoic Hormuz evaporites (cf. Kent 1970). Also, further to the northwest (beyond the limits of the map Fig. 2), the presence of Permo-Carboniferous coral-bearing limestones suggest that the regional metamorphism affecting the underlying basement rocks is there pre-Permian. Davoudzadeh & Schmidt (1984) do, however, show that the SE part of the Sanandaj–Sirjan Zone was subjected to greenschist metamorphism at the end of the Middle Triassic. Thus the blocks of Exotic-like marble within the basement could be of Permo-Carboniferous age.

In the northern part of the area, the basement sequence (Mardan Metamorphics; Fig. 2) is cut by post-metamorphic dykes of quartz–diorite porphyrite, which in the east are unconformably overlain by Lower Jurassic sandstone turbidites and shales containing plant debris (Dargaz autochthonous sequence). Near Dargaz, pyroclastic rocks contain early Jurassic plant remains and belemnites. The proximity of this igneous activity to, and parallel with, the Nain–Baft Zone implies that it could be associated with crustal separation between the Sanandaj–Sirjan Zone and the rest of Central Iran (cf. Davoudzadeh & Schmidt, 1984).

The basement is elsewhere overlain by early Cretaceous limestones belonging to the Dargaz autochthonous sequence, at the base of which are dacitic and rhyolitic lava flows and tuffs, also cut by dykes. North of Dowlatabad, the upper part of a sequence of dacitic lava flows is interbedded with red shales of Maastrichtian age which, in turn, are capped by a thick Maastrichtian rudistid limestone. These early and late Cretaceous extrusives may have been associated with subduction in the Zagros sector of Neo-Tethys.

The more southerly (Kushmandar) metamorphics are similar to those of the Mardan area but are not cut by post-metamorphic dykes. Also, the large blocks of marble in the basement trend NE–SW in the Mardan area but are aligned more nearly NNW–SSE in the Kushmandar area, perhaps implying that this latter area may later have been subjected to rotation. To the southeast, the Kushmandar basement of the Sanandaj—Sirjan Zone disappears beneath the sedimentary sequence of the Tiab Zone (Fig. 2), but slivers of it are considered by McCall & Kidd (1982) to reappear at intervals between there and Baluchistan as their Bajgan—Dur—Kan Zone; we failed to find any eastern extension of this basement sequence, outcrops that could have been attributed to the basement seeming more logically to be part of the Coloured Melange.

Zone of ophiolites and related sediments

To the east of and overlying and Sanandaj—Sirjan metamorphics are the rocks of three associated subzones that, together, can be considered to make up a single suite of ophiolites. They comprise Alpino-type peridotite—gabbro masses (Subzone 'A' on Fig. 2) and the ophiolites of the Kahnu and Daragar subzones.

The Alpino-type peridotite—gabbro masses overlie the Mardan and Kushmandar metamorphics and are metamorphosed along their contacts with the surrounding schists (Subzone 'A' in Fig. 2). Within the cores of these masses, however, fresh igneous textures are preserved in some gabbros. The contacts with the underlying metamorphics are abrupt, faulted, usually steeply inclined and locally folded. Close to the contacts, the peridotites are strongly sheared and serpentinised, and the metamorphic schists are strongly foliated and usually have suffered a fair degree of cataclasis. The halo of dynametamorphism suggests that these basic and ultrabasic rocks were deformed after the main phase of crystallization.

These rocks are thought to have been tectonically emplaced upon the metamorphic basement after the regional metamorphism of the Sanandaj—Sirjan Zone. Both units were subjected to deformation prior to deposition of the Eocene sandstones that locally overlie them. These Alpine-type peridotite and gabbro massess have been mapped by McCall (1985) and his associates as forming an integral part of the Kushmandar metamorphic basement.

The Kahnu Zone of serpentinites, peridotites and olivine gabbros is similar to subzone 'A'. The rocks are better preserved, however, are less metamorphosed, and have complex migmatite formations between the ultramafic and gabbroic rocks similar to those described from the Semail Nappe of the Oman Mountains (Reinhardt 1969; Glennie *et al.* 1974; Lippard *et al.* 1986). The subzone is separated from adjoining zones by important, steeply inclined faults. Along its eastern edge, dyke swarms are overlain by and imbricated with tintinnid and radiolaria-bearing Tithonian to Berriasian

calcareous mudstones (dated by McCall (1985) as late Cretaceous).

The Daragar Zone of volcanics and sediments includes diabase dyke swarms, which are the feeders to the overlying extrusive rocks. The latter consist of massive lava flows with interbedded tuffs and lapilli beds or thick sequences of pillow lavas. Eocene lithic sandstones, rich in volcanic debris, overlie the igneous rocks.

The 'A', Kahnu and Daragar suites of ophiolitic rocks separate the flysch sequences of the ZCMMEF from Jaz Murian and the southern margin of the Lut Block. Their northwestern parts were thrust from the N or NE over the SE extremity of the Sanandaj—Sirjan Zone, which implies that a belt of oceanic crust formerly existed between the Sanandaj—Sirjan Zone and Central Iran—Lut. The Tithonian Berriasian tintinnid faunas associated with the dyke swarms at the top of the Kahnu ophiolite indicate that this former oceanic area was active from at least the Jurassic—Cretaceous time boundary. The pre-early Jurassic dating of the dyke swarms that cut the eastern margin of the Dargaz autochthon possibly indicates the time of initiation of crustal separation between Central Iran and the Sanandaj—Sirjan Zone. Thus the Nain—Baft portion of Neo-Tethys probably came into existence during the Triassic and, according to McCall & Kidd (1982), survived until the late Palaeocene. The cover of flysch on the Daragar volcanics indicates that at least this part of the Nain—Baft—Makran sector of Neo—Tethys remained below sea level until the Eocene.

Jaz Murian Depression

This arc-like depression has a superficial cover of alluvial gravels, playa lakes, salt pans and sand dunes, which separate the north-dipping Daragar Zone of volcanics from the Palaeozoic sedimentary rocks and Cenozoic intrusives and volcanics at the southern margin of the Lut Block. The depression, which is over 100 km across from north to south, is thought most logically to be underlain by Daragar volcanics. If so, then its southern fringe of ophiolites are probably roughly in their original site of formation. According to McCall & Kidd (1982), Jaz Murian subsided only in the Late Pliocene.

Tiab Zone

This unit (see Figs 2 & 3B) forms the most westerly part of the Dur-Kan Zone of McCall & Kidd (1982). It comprises a sequence of sediments that apparently tectonically overlie both the eastern continuation of the Sanandaj—Sirjan

(Kushmandar) metamorphics and the south-eastern part of the ZCMMEF. Along part of its NE edge it is in steep reverse-fault contact with extrusive rocks of the Daragar Zone and with members of the Coloured Melange, both of which are covered unconformably by Eocene Flysch.

The Tiab Zone consists mostly of Maastrichtian to Palaeocene shallow-marine limestones and Eocene shales, sandstones and conglomerates lying unconformably over early Cretaceous limestones and, locally, Upper Jurassic to early Cretaceous sandstones and shales. The Lower Cretaceous limestones commonly grade down into marble, which, in turn, can overlie pillow lavas or sheared serpentinite.

Along the northeastern flank of the zone north of Dehdarun, Tithonian to Berriasian tintinnid-bearing limestones and shales are associated with pillow lavas in a fashion similar to the association with dyke swarms found along the eastern edge of the Kahnu Zone of peridotites and gabbros. For this reason, we infer that the sedimentary sequence of the Tiab Zone was deposited originally upon oceanic crust of late Jurassic age (Nain–Baft 'Ocean'?) rather than over the Sanandaj–Sirjan metamorphic basement as interpreted by McCall & Kidd (1982).

The Tiab Zone seems to have suffered less deformation through later Tertiary tectonic events than other sedimentary sequences within the Inner Makran. Its rock sequence now forms a slightly imbricated synclinal nappe (Fig. 3B) whose separate identity can be seen clearly on the Imperial College photomosaic of the area (in Falcon 1975). Further to the east on this photomosaic can be seen a similar rock unit extending to the Fannuj area of the Makran (see also McCall & Kidd 1982; McCall 1985); two small interconnecting slivers of the Dur–Kan Zone occur in the SE corner of Fig. 2. The Tiab Zone's probable original depositional relationship with the Kahnu ophiolite implies that it could have been sheared off its substrate of down-going oceanic crust in the Makran subduction trench in Eocene time and become, in turn, underthrust by a narrow, possibly discontinuous, southeastern extension of the Sanandaj–Sirjan Zone and by elements of the Zone of Coloured Melange and Maastrichtian to Eocene flysch (Fig. 3B).

Oman Mountains-Makran belts of convergence

The main elements of plate-tectonic history in the Oman–Makran sectors of the Middle East can be summarized as follows.

During the Permian(?) or Triassic, Central Iran–Anatolia separated from the rest of the megacontinent Gondwana to create a Neo-Tethys branch of the Tethys Ocean. Throughout the Triassic–early Cretaceous timespan, Arabia drifted relatively to the SW, away from the Neo-Tethys spreading axis, as a passive margin whereas early Cretaceous igneous activity in the Sanandaj–Sirjan Zone of Central Iran implies that there was probably active subduction on that flank of Neo-Tethys.

Probably early in the mid-Triassic, the long, narrow Sanandaj–Sirjan microcontinent became separated from the rest of Central Iran by the Nain–Baft sector of Neo-Tethys. Oceanic crust was created in the Inner Makran sector during the late Jurassic–early Cretaceous. A subduction zone dipping towards the Lut block may have been present and retained some of this crust in the accretionary prism.

Easterly dipping subduction was probably initiated in the Oman–Zagros sector of Neo-Tethys in the Aptian–Albian and roughly coincided with the opening of the South Atlantic. Obduction of the Hawasina/Semail in the Oman sector and Coloured Melange in the Zagros sector ceased in the late Campanian probably when the relatively buoyant continental margin of Arabia could no longer be carried down into the mantle. This concept of deep underthrusting of the continent is supported by the occurrence of Late Cretaceous high-pressure metamorphism in continent-margin sediments beneath the Semail Nappe along the northern margin of Saih Hatat (Lippard 1983; Le Métour et al. 1986). The Arabian continental margin may have remained depressed within the subduction zone until convergence ceased. This would have been when either existing subduction increased in activity or a new zone was created (either way forming the Inner-Makran trench), perhaps also linked to the ceasing of active Neo-Tethyan crustal spreading. Release of compressional crustal stress would have allowed the depressed Arabian margin to rebound isostatically, finally detaching the Semail segment from the adjacent oceanic crust and allowing it to slide gravitationally further onto the Arabian shelf.

After the Oman obduction, the new or accelerated Inner Makran subduction led to accretion of a thick wedge of Maastrichtian to Late Eocene flysch and wildflysch, which included major components of Coloured Melange locally overlain unconformably by Maastrichtian limestone. Subduction gave rise to widespread volcanism over the Lut Block, which McCall & Kidd (1982) believe sourced much of the flysch deposition south of the trench.

The Nain–Baft sector of Neo-Tethys was

closed by mid Tertiary times, possibly as early as the end of the Palaeocene (McCall & Kidd 1982), the Sanandaj–Sirjan Zone becoming again joined to the rest of Central Iran. Arc subduction in this closure gave rise to the belt of early Tertiary volcanics that extend through and beyond the Nain–Baft Zone to the USSR border (Fig. 1).

Widespread changes to the existing order took place at the end of the Eocene, many associated with the impingement of the Indian continent from the east (Dercourt *et al.* 1986). In the western Makran there seems to be little flysch of Oligocene age. The long period of tectonic instability in the Inner Makran area that had been initiated in the Maastrichtian seemed to reach a climax between the end of flysch deposition in the Eocene and its restart in the Miocene. Wildflysch of the Rudan type became tectonically interleaved with the two sequences of Eocene flysch. This second phase of tectonic activity in which an accretion wedge is refolded and rethrust seems unlikely to have occurred within a simple subduction trench. Something additional must have happened to bring about this phase of intense tectonic activity in the western Makran.

At the end of the Eocene, the northward migration of the Indian sub-continent took on a more westerly direction after colliding with Asia (Patriat *et al.* 1982; but see also Sengör 1987) and probably caused deformation along the young Arabian Sea margin of Oman, with thrusting of the Masirah ophiolites over Eocene marls and sinistral shearing with basaltic volcanicity south of Ras al Hadd; it may also have played a role in accentuating uplift of the Huqf Arch (see Hughes Clarke 1988) together with inducing left-lateral movement along the NW–SE trending Maradi Fault.

Throughout the later Mesozoic and Early Tertiary, Afro-Arabia and India had been migrating northwards away from Antarctica (Smith *et al.* 1981). Oceanic crust must have been consumed down a complex NW–SE trending belt of subduction along the northern margin of Neo-Tethys (i.e. Podatakasi Zone of Sengör (1990) which extends from south of the Pontid Range in Turkey to the Makran area of Iran). The early Tertiary eastward migration of Arabia would not have shown any effects of this subduction until the northward reduction in the oceanic area of Tethys caused collisions between Eurasia and the Turkish–Iranian microcontinents.

Collision led to microcontinents being squeezed and rotated. Central Iran was seemingly squeezed eastwards away from the appar-

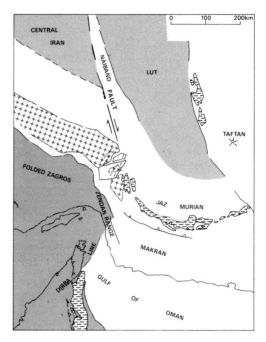

Fig. 4. Sketch map of the western Makran and adjacent areas to show the possible rotation of the Kushmandar basement block of the Hamadan Zone as the result of post-Eocene right-lateral movement across the Naiband Fault and overthrusting of the Kahnu–Daragar suite of ophiolites. This indicates that Jaz Murian is probably underlain by rigid crust. At the same time, north of the Dibba Line the Musandam area was thrust westward across adjacent Eocene marls and the main uplift of the Oman Mountains took place.

ently rigid South Caspian area to create the East Alborz Arc, with associated right-lateral wrenching between Central Iran and Sanandaj–Sirjan (Ricou 1968a). Right-lateral movement seems indeed to have occurred on the Naiband Fault and could have caused the postulated dextral rotation of the Kushmandar basement block (Fig. 4) and the coeval emplacement of the Kahnu–Daragar suite of ophiolite over that general area of the Sanandaj–Sirjan Zone. This probably also formed the complicated structures in the vicinity of the Zendan Fault, and was involved in the westward thrusting of the Musandam Peninsula. The westward vector in so much of this compressional tectonism is, however, persuasive that convergence from the east by the Indian continent was an important regional tectonic constraint.

Afro-Arabia and Eurasia carried on moving closer to each other throughout the younger

Cenozoic. The plicate folding of the Zagros Mountains built up only in the Pliocene when that portion of Arabia finally was in continent crustal collision with the Sanandaj—Sirjan Zone. Subduction of ocean crust in the Gulf of Oman, a final remnant portion of the Tethyian crust, continues today off the Makran coast (White 1982).

In the 20 years since the writers carried out their field studies in the Makran, much greater understanding has developed concerning the complexity of microplates and interplate reactions in the region. Notwithstanding this complexity, we retain our earliest impression that the cessation of obduction in Oman and the onset or marked increase in subduction in the Makran, both in the late Campanian or early Maastrichtian, have a linked cause-and-effect relationship.

This paper is published by permission of Shell Internationale Petroleum Maatschappij and Shell Research, N. V., The Hague. At the request of Mr Norman Falcon, a hand-coloured copy of the writers' field-checked photogeological map of the Makran area (scale 1:260000) was lodged with the Royal Geographical Society in the mid-1970s.

References

ARTHURTON, R. S., FARAH, A & AHMED, W. 1982. The Late Cretaceous history of western Baluchistan, Pakistan — the northern margin of the Makran subduction complex. *In*: LEGGETT, J. K. (Ed.) *Trench—Forearc Geology*. Geological Society, London, Special Publication 10, 373—385.

BÉCHENNEC, F., LE MÉTOUR, J., RABU, D., VILLEY, M. & BURRIER, M. 1988. The Hawasina Basin: a fragment of starved, passive continental margin thrust over the Arabian Platform during obduction of the Samail Nappe. *Tectonophysics*, 151, 323—343

BERNOULLI, D. & WEISSERT, H. 1987. The upper Hawasina nappes in the central Oman Mountains: stratigraphy, palinspastics and sequence of nappe emplacement. *Geodinamica Acta (Paris)*, 1 47—58.

BERBERIAN, M. & KING, G. C. P. 1981. Towards a paleogeography and tectonic evolution of Iran. *Canadian Journal of Science*, 18. 210—265.

BLENDINGER, W. 1988 Permian to Jurassic deep water sediments of the eastern Oman Mountains: their significance for the evolution of the Arabian margin of South Tethys. FACIES (Erlangen), 19, 1—32.

CORNELIUS, P. F. S., FALCON, N. L., SOUTH, D. & VITA-FINZI, C. 1973. The Musandam Expedition 1971—72: Scientific results, part 1. *The Geographical Journal*, 139: 400—425.

DERCOURT, J., ZONENSHAIN, L. P., RICOU, L. E., KAZMIN, V. G., LE PICHON, X., KNIPPER,

A. L., GRANDJACQUET, C., SBORTSHIKOV, J. M., GEYSSANT, J., LEPVRIER, C., PECHERSKY, D. H., BOULIN, J., SIBUET, J. C., SAVOSTIN, L. A., SORÖKHTIN, O., WESTPHAL, M., BAZHENOV, M. L., LAUER, J. P. & BIJU—DEVAL, B., 1986. Geological evolution of the Tethys from the Atlantic to the Pamirs since the Lias. *Tectonophysics*, 123, 241—315. DEVOUDZADEH, M. & SCHMIDT K. 1984. A Review of the Mesozoic Paleogeography and Paleotectonic Evolution of Iran. *Neues Jahrbuch Geologie und Palaeontologie*, 168, 182—207.

FALCON, N. L. 1967. The geology of the north-east margin of the Arabian basement shield. *Advancement of Science, London*, 24, 119, 1—12.

—— 1974. An outline of the geology of the Iranian Makran. *Geographical Journal*, 140, 284—291.

—— 1975. From Musandam to the Iranian Makran. *Geographical Journal*, 141, 55—58.

GANSSER, A. 1955. New aspects of the geology in Central Iran. Proceedings 4th World Petroleum Congress, Rome, 1955, Section I/A/5, 179—300.

—— 1959. Ausseralpine Ophiolithprobleme. *Eclogae geol. Helvetica*, 62, 659—680.

GLENNIE, K. W., BOEUF. M. G. A., HUGHES-CLARKE, M. W., MOODY-STUART, M., PILAAR, W. F. H. & REINHARDT, B. M. 1973. Late Cretaceous nappes in Oman Mountains and their geologic evolution. *American Association Petroleum Geologists Bulletin*, 57, 5—27

——, ——, ——, ——, & —— 1974. Geology of the Oman Mountains. *Verhandelingen Koninklijke Nederland geologisch mijnbouwkundig Genootschap*, 31.

GRAY, K. W. 1950. A tectonic window in southwest Iran. *Quarterly Journal of the Geological Society of London*, 105, 189—222.

HUGHES CLARKE, M. W. 1988. Stratigraphy and rock unit nomenclature in the oil-producing area of interior Oman. *Journal of Petroleum Geology*, 11, 5—60.

KENT, P. E. 1970. The salt plugs of the Persian gulf region. *Transactions Leicester Literary and Philosophical Society*, 64, 56—88.

LE MÉTOUR, J., RABU, D., TEGEY, M., BÉCHENNEC, F., BEURRIER, M. & VILLEY, M. 1986. Le métamorphisme régional crétacé de faciès éclogites — schistes bleus sur la bordure omanaise de la plate-forme arabe: conséquence d'une tectogenèse précoce anté-obduction. *Comptes Rendu Academie Science, Paris*, 302, 905—910.

—— & VILLEY, M. 1986. *Sultanate of Oman Geological Map of Quryat, Sheet NF 40—4D: Explanatory Notes*. Bureau de Recherches Géologiques et Minières, Orléans.

LIPPARD, S. J. 1983. Cretaceous high pressure metamorphism in NE Oman and its relationship to subduction and ophiolite nappe emplacement. *Journal of the Geological Society of London*, 140, 97—104.

——, SHELTON, A. W. & GASS, I. G. 1986. *The Ophiolite of Northern Oman*. Geological Society, London, Memoir **11**.

LOVELOCK, P. E. R., POTTER, T. L., WALSWORTH-BELL, E. B. & WIEMER, W. M. 1981. Ordovician rocks in the Oman Mountains: the Amdeh formation. *Geologie en Mijnbouw*, **60**, 487–495.

McCALL, G. J. H. 1985. *Report on East Iran Project Area No. 1*. Geological Survey of Iran. Tehran.

—— & KIDD, R. G. W. 1982. The Makran, Southeastern Iran: the anatomy of a post-orogenic intra-plate deformation. *In*: LEGGETT J. K. (Ed.), Trench-Forearc Geology: sedimentation and tectonics on modern and active plate margins, 387–397.

National Iranian Oil Company. 1959. *Geological Map of Iran with explanatory notes*.

PATRIAT, P., SEGOUFIN, J., SCHLICH, R., GOSLIN, J., AUZENDE, J-M., BEUZART, P., BONNIN, J., & OLIVET, J-L. 1982. Les mouvements relatifs de l'Inde, de l'Afrique et de l'Eurasie. *Bulletin Société géologique de France*, **26**, 363–373.

PEARCE, J. A., ALABASTER, T., SHELTON, A. W. & SEARLE, M. P. 1981. The Oman ophiolite as a Cretaceous arc-basin complex: evidence and implications. *Philosophical Transactions of the Royal Society of London*, **A3**, 299–317.

REINHARDT, B. M., 1969. On the genesis and emplacement of ophiolites in the Oman mountains geosyncline. *Schweizes Mineralogisch und Petrographisch Mitteilung*, **49**, 1–30.

RICOU, L. E. 1968a. Une coupe a travers les séries à radiolarites des monts Pichakun (Zagros, Iran). *Bulletin Société géologique de France*, **7**, 478–485.

—— 1968b. Sur la mise en place au Crétacé superieur d' importantes nappes à radiolarites et ophiolite dans le Monts Zagros (Iran). *Comptes Rendu Academie de Science, Paris*, **267**, 2272–2275.

—— 1971. Le croissant ophiolitique peri-arabe, une ceinture des nappes mises en place au Crétacé Supérieur. *Revue de Géographie physique et de Géologie dynamique*. **13**, 327–350.

ROBERTSON, A. H. F. 1987. Upper Cretaceous Muti Formation: transition of a Mesozoic carbonate platform to a foreland basin in the Oman Mountains. *Sedimentology*, **34**, 1123–1142

SEARLE, M. P. 1988. Thrust tectonics in the Dibba zone and the structural evolution of the Arabian continental margin along the Musandam mountains (Oman and United Arab Emirates). *Journal of the Geological Society of London*. **145**, 43–53.

——, LIPPARD, S. J., SMEWING, J. D. & REX, D. C., 1980. Volcanic rocks beneath the Semail ophiolite nappe in the northern Oman mountains and their significance in the Mesozoic evolution of Tethys. *Journal of the Geological Society of London*. **137**, 589–604.

SENGÖR, A. M. C. 1987. Tectonics of the tethysides: orogenic collage development in a collisional setting. *Earth and Planetary Science Review*, **15**, 213–244

—— 1990. Back-arc origin of the Hawasina and Neo-Tethyan basins in Oman as a consequence of Cimmeride subduction in Iran.

SOFFEL, H. & FÖRSTER, H. 1984. Polar wander path of the Central-East-Iran microplate, including new results. *Neues Jahrbuch Geologie und Palaeontologie*. Stuttgart. **168**, 165–172.

SHEARMAN, D. J. 1976. The Geological evolution of Southern Iran. *The Geographical Journal*, **142**, 393–410.

SMITH, A. G., HURLEY, A. M. & BRIDEN, J. C. 1981. *Phanerozoic Palaeocontinental World Maps*. Cambridge University Press, Cambridge.

STÖCKLIN, J. 1968. Structural history and tectonics of Iran: a review. *American Association of Petroleum Geologists Bulletin*, **52**, 1229–1258.

—— 1974. Possible ancient continental margin in Iran. *In*: BURK, C. & DRAKE, C. L. (eds) *The Geology of Continental Margins*. Springer, Berlin 873–887.

STONELEY, R. 1974. Evolution of the continental margin bounding a former southern Tethys. *In*: BURK, C. & DRAKE, C. L. (eds) *The Geology of Continental Margins*. Springer, Berlin, 889–903

—— 1990 The Arabian continental margin in Iran during the Late Cretaceous. *In*: ROBERTSON, A. H. F., SEARLE, M. P. & RIES, A. C. (eds) *The Geology and Tectonics of the Oman Region*. Geological Society, London, Special Publication, **49**, 787–795.

USSAMI, N., KARNER, G. D. & BOTT, M. P. H. 1986. Crustal detachment during Atlantic rifting and formation of Tocano–Gabon basin system. *Nature*, **322**, 629–632.

WESTPHAL, M., BAZHENOV, M. L., LAUER, J. P., PECHERSKY, D. H. & SIBUET, J. C., 1986. Palaeomagnetic implications on the evolution of the Tethys Belt from the Atlantic Ocean to Pamir since Trias. *Tectonophysics*, **123**, 37–82.

WHITE, R. S. 1982. Deformation of the Makran accretionary sediment prism in the Gulf of Oman (north-west Indian Ocean) *In*: LEGGETT, J. K. (ed.) Trench–Forearc Geology. *Geological Society, London, Special Publication* **10**, 357–372.

The Arabian continental margin in Iran during the Late Cretaceous

*Department of Geology, Imperial College of Science, Technology and
Medicine, Prince Consort Road, London SW7 2BP, UK*

Abstract: The events which affected the Iranian sector of the Southern Tethyan margin of
the Arabian continent during the Cretaceous differed from those that took place in Oman,
although they were clearly related to them. Extensional faulting, parallel to the shelf
margin, commenced locally in the Cenomanian and culminated later in the Cretaceous
with the expulsion of mantle material to the surface. This engulfed the shelf edge before
gliding southwestwards over a complementary intra-shelf basin. These events took place
progressively later towards the north-west, and are interpreted as an unsuccessful attempt
to develop a spreading axis along the continental margin. They were followed by a return
to shelf sedimentation at the southern edge of Tethys, which closed finally in the early
Miocene. It is suggested that the Oman and Iranian sectors of the Arabian margin were
offset some 300 km by a north–south transform fault, and that the differences between
the two regions were therefore due to attempted spreading in different tectonic environments in the late Cretaceous.

In the Mesozoic, the northeastern margin of the Afro-Arabian continent extended north-westwards from Oman through Iran and Turkey to the Mediterranean. Whereas in Oman it has largely escaped later deformation, to the north-west it was involved in a Tertiary collision with Eurasia lying to the north. This has obliterated or modified many of the structures formed during the Mesozoic, generally making interpretation much more difficult. However, in at least three areas adjacent to the collision suture in Iran, it is possible to determine elements of its history. These suggest important differences in the events of the late Cretaceous from those that affected the Oman sector.

This paper summarizes conclusions reached in earlier publications concerning these events in Iran, and includes some previously unrecorded observations. It is not necessary to repeat existing descriptions of the intricate evidence, or of involved discussions of its interpretation and its implications: the interested, or sceptical, reader is referred to Stoneley (1975, 1981), Hall (1984), and to papers by a joint French–Russian team (in *Tectonophysics*, 1986, **123**).

It is emphasized at the outset that, whilst the Mesozoic margin of Afro–Arabia was continuous through Iran and offshore of northeast Oman, and whilst it was subject to essentially the same tectonic processes throughout, it is not to be expected that their expression was exactly the same in all sectors. Thus evidence from one, although relevant to what happened elsewhere, should not be taken to invalidate reconstructions

for other areas. On the contrary, such differences need to be highlighted. That is the aim of this review paper.

The areas in Iran that are considered are (Figs 1 & 2) as follows.
(a) The extreme southeast of the Zagros, adjacent to the north–south strike-slip Zendan Fault, which offsets the Zagros suture southwards to the Gulf of Oman. Little has been published on this area.
(b) The Neyriz–Kuh-e Dalneshin region of south central Iran. Key publications are Ricou (1976); Stoneley (1981).
(c) The vicinity of Burujerd to the northwest, described mainly in a series of papers by French workers referred to individually below.

In general, the Mesozoic picture of the Iranian sector of this margin is of steady subsidence and predominantly neritic sedimentation; this persisted in fact from the Permian transgression, which preceded the establishment of the continental shelf on the south side of the southern Tethys (Neotethys) ocean in the Triassic (e.g. Stöcklin 1974), until the mid-Cretaceous. At different times in different sectors from the Cenomanian onwards, subsidence along trends within but parallel to the continental margin, apparently associated with extensional faulting, led to the accumulation of radiolarian cherts. The outer, northeastern, part of at least one of these troughs became the site of extrusive basic igneous activity in the Coniacian. Into it apparently glided, in the Neyriz sector, sheets of oceanic sediments derived earlier from the

From ROBERTSON, A. H. F., SEARLE, M. P. & RIES, A. C. (eds), 1990,
The Geology and Tectonics of the Oman Region.
Geological Society Special Publication No 49, pp 787–795

787

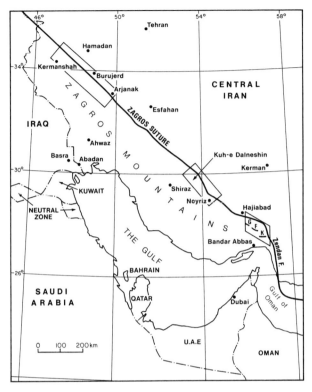

Fig. 1. Locality map, showing the three areas discussed in the text. G, Kuh-e Gahkum: F, Kuh-e Faraghun: K, Khush Kuh.

southern Tethys, and then exotic masses of Permian to Cenomanian carbonates from the uplifted shelf-edge itself. A final event, close to the end of the Cretaceous, was the emplacement of ophiolites, which was followed by a return to relative stability in the Maastrichtian–Palaeogene. The final closure of the ocean is more difficult to date, but a deep-water trough persisted until the early Miocene in the Kuh-e Dalneshin and southeastern sectors.

The Southeastern Zagros

In this area, the Mesozoic shelf sequence is exposed in three Neogene anticlines: Kuh-e Gahkum, Kuh-e Faraghun and Khush Kuh (Fig. 1): mainly neritic carbonates persist, with only minor interruptions, up into the Cenomanian.

The upper surface of this sequence is extensively ferruginized, and it is overlain apparently by Coniacian strata in a deeper water marly facies (Setudehnia 1978). Within these sediments, at Kuh-e Faraghun, are wedges of limestone conglomerate probably derived in

part from adjacent faults scarps (M. W. Hughes Clarke, pers. comm. 1988, Fig. 3); the faults are normal and trend approximately northeast – southwest. Within the conglomerates, pre-Cenomanian components, and also current-direction indicators, suggest an additional source of detritus elsewhere to the south. These conditions appear to mark the onset of instability in the area. The marls lead up into the lower Tertiary and are overlain by massive Eocene neritic limestones, all of these beds being unaffected by the underlying faults.

At the east end of Khush Kuh, only some 8 km from the Zendan Fault, a fault trending east of north truncates the north flank. East of it, the Late Cretaceous–Early Tertiary marls abruptly thicken enormously and contain a wedge of conglomerate of earlier Cretaceous limestone clasts derived from across the fault. At about the Cretaceous–Tertiary boundary (unfortunately precise age datings are not available), occurs an interval of a few metres containing basic volcanic rocks which appear to bake the underlying and interleaved sediments. Also present in this zone are blocks of material

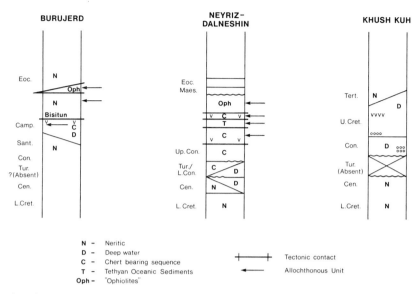

Fig. 2. Stratigraphical diagrams for the areas discussed. Allochthoneity is indicated, together with generalised environments of sedimentation of the units present.

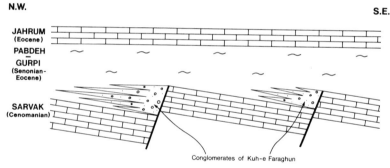

Fig. 3. Schematic section of relationships on the north flank of Kuh-e Faraghun anticline. Within the Senonian conglomerates, the coarsest elements are close to NE—SW fault scarps in the Sarvak Formation (Cenomanian). Finer elements away from the fault scarps are graded beds, and some sole marks and climbing ripples imply flow directions to the north. Diagram contributed by M. W. Hughes Clarke.

derived from the infra-Cambrian Hormuz salt series; although elsewhere Hormuz material is carried to the surface by salt extrusions, here the baking of the sediments suggests that it was the volcanics that provided the transport. Here also the massive Eocene limestone to the west has passed into presumably deeper water marl facies, and it is not until the middle Miocene that we see a return to neritic carbonates (Guri Formation).

North of Khush Kuh, in the vicinity of the corner where the shelf margin turns from ESE to south on the Zendan Fault, three series containing turbidites are present. The oldest is siliciclastic; its age is uncertain, although it was mapped as Eocene (undifferentiated) by The British Petroleum Company (1964). In the second, the turbidites consist predominantly of carbonate debris; scattered nummulites suggest an Eocene age. The third is low-rank mudstones and silts with some turbidite sandstones and associated basic lavas; it is Neogene in age, at least in part early—middle Miocene, and it passes southwestwards into extensive early synorogenic clastics (Agha Jari Formation).

The first two of these turbidite series may be related to subduction at the northern, central Iranian, margin of the southern Tethys, whilst the third could well reflect the Miocene collision between the continental blocks. The structures at the east end of Khush Kuh and perhaps also those at Kuh-e Faraghun, on the other hand, seem rather to be related to the Zendan Fault; they possibly imply movement along it since at least the Senonian.

The Neyriz — Kuh-e Dalneshin Area

This complex area in central southern Iran has been studied by several workers over a number of years; although many problems remain to be resolved, it is believed that the main outline of events during the Cretaceous has by now been established (*see* discussion in Stoneley 1981).

Kuh-e Dalneshin itself is a Neogene anticline trending ENE, strongly oblique to the regional southeast trend; it thus displays a section across the strike through the Cretaceous. The lower-lying country to the south, towards Neyriz, provides good outcrops of the overlying allochthonous rocks.

The Mesozoic sequence shows essential continuity of neritic carbonate sedimentation up to the Cenomanian. During the Cenomanian, however, the central and eastern parts of Kuh-e Dalneshin started to subside with the accumulation of uniform black lime mudstones; they contain thick wedges of monomict conglomerate apparently derived from contemporaneous fault scarps aligned northwest—southeast and probably normal with throws in both directions. Neritic deposition continued elsewhere.

In the Turonian, a localized northwest—southeast trending zone west of the Kuh represents a trough of Turonian marls, disconformably overlying the neritic Cenomanian; they rapidly pass upwards into oligosteginid lime mudstones with carbonate turbidites and radiolarian cherts. Subsidence became more widespread in the Coniacian and early Santonian, with the accumulation of variegated shales, cherts and limestone turbidites. This in situ sequence is overlain by a chaotic allochthnous mass of the same Coniacian—Santonian rocks but now containing basic volcanics, which increase towards the east, and exotic blocks up to a few kilometres in dimension. These exotics are composed of neritic limestones of Permian to Cenomanian age, some of them showing facies unknown elsewhere in the Zagros. They were clearly derived from the east, presumably from an uplifted margin of the continental shelf. It appears that the contents of the eastern half of the intra-shelf basin slid westwards over the western half in the late Santonian or Campanian.

Apparently interleaved between the autoch-thonous and allochthonous chert-bearing beds, in the country south of Kuh-e Dalneshin, is a series of five nappes of oceanic sediments, derived presumably from the southern Tethys. The sequence of these nappes is up to 2000 m thick and ranges in age from Triassic to Cenomanian (Ricou in several publications of which that of 1976 is comprehensive). This age dating has been questioned in the past (e.g. Hallam 1976), but the painstaking work of Ricou and his colleagues now puts the matter beyond doubt. The generally shale—chert sequence contains flows and turbidites of carbonate material, originally of shallow water origin, derived in the Triassic and Jurassic from the southwest, which stages also show traces of tuffaceous material: in the Aptian (probably) to Cenomanian, derivation of carbonate detritus was from the northeast. These nappes must previously have been emplaced on the Afro—Arabian continental margin before, it is believed, gliding under gravity across the intra-shelf basin in the Santonian or Campanian: the presence of chert pebbles in the Turonian sequence described above, as well as the fact that the nappe succession ranges up only to the Cenomanian, suggests that this initial emplacement had taken place by the early Turonian.

All of these rocks are overlain by two sheets of 'ophiolites', predominantly mantle harz-burgites passing up by interleaving with lherzolites into gabbros. The rocks, which Lanphere & Pamić (1983) have age-dated most probably as 83—86 Ma (Santonian), are variably serpentinized and sheared; they include small to kilometre-sized masses of undated, more or less marmorized neritic limestone, as well locally as pre-existing metamorphic rocks. Rims to the carbonate blocks have been interpreted as high-temperature skarns, in which case it would seem that the limestones were engulfed at temperatures in excess of 900°C (Ricou 1976; Hall 1981). Pamić & Adib (1980) suggested these rocks to be rodingites, implying a later hydrothermal origin. Their descriptions, however, are difficult to reconcile with the present writer's own observations on the contacts and interrelationships between the serpentinite and the marble blocks of various sizes and shapes: perhaps it is that rodingite veins occur in addition to the skarns at the margins of the blocks.

An intrusive relationship cannot be explained satisfactorily by conventional theories of ophiolite formation, and its apparent occurrence near Neyriz has commonly been disbelieved or, worse, ignored. To the writer's belief though, it has been doubted by few geologists who have visited the outcrops or examined samples. It seems likely that the Neyriz ophiolites were formed and emplaced in a different manner from the Semail of Oman (e.g. Lippard *et al.* 1986).

The Maastrichtian saw a return to widespread neritic carbonate sedimentation. Some instability, however, may have persisted because, due either to local uplift and erosion or to the progressive inundation of a topography, the Eocene in places directly overlies the allochthonous Cretaceous. The Zagros shelf still seems to have been separated from Central Iran to the northeast, and it was not until the early Miocene that the southern Tethys was finally closed (e.g. Stoneley 1981).

In summary (Fig. 4), this sector records the onset of instability within the Afro-Arabian margin during the Cenomanian, due probably to northeast–southwest extension. It became more severe in the Turonian, with local subsidence to depths of chert deposition, and considerably more widespread in the Coniacian when basaltic volcanism affected the outer parts of an intra-shelf basin. Uplift of the shelf margin in about the late Santonian resulted first in the gliding away across the basin of sheets of Mesozoic oceanic sediments, previously derived from the southern Tethys to the northeast and emplaced on the shelf early in the Turonian. Further uplift caused the dislocation of large masses of shelf-edge neritic carbonates and their removal westwards by gliding in the cherts of the eastern part of the basin. The final stage, probably in the Campanian, was the arrival at surface of hot mantle material, which had started to engulf the shelf margin in the Santonian, before in turn gliding or flowing westwards over part of the intra-shelf basin. All of these events had been completed by the Maastrichtian.

A plausible model to explain these events involves extensional faulting and incipient rift formation, initially off and then along the continental margin (Hall 1982). A possible analogue of ophiolitic rocks at a passive margin comes from the eastern Atlantic, from Fuerteventura in the Canary Islands (e.g. Stillman *et al.* 1975).

The evidence for gravitational gliding as the mechanism of emplacement of the allochthonous units is not unequivocal. However, it is strongly implied by the chaotic nature of some of them, in an environment of normal faulting. And the writer does not believe that a model of compressional thrusting can account for the superposition of thin, coherent sheets of very diverse rocks: neritic carbonates, probably

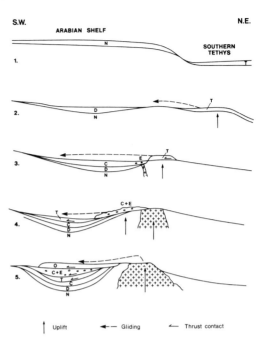

Fig. 4. Diagramatic representation of the inferred late Cretaceous evolution of the Arabian margin in the Neyriz — Kuh-e Dalneshin area.
Stage 1. Pre-late Cretaceous. Neritic sedimentation (N) on the shelf; oceanic sediments (T) in Southern Tethys.
Stage 2. Cenomanian. Onset of extension. Deep water sedimentation (D) in an intra-shelf depression. Emplacement of Tethyan sediments on the shelf margin.
Stage 3. Turonian–Coniacian. Chert deposition (C) in intra-shelf basin; volcanism and exotics (E) incorporated in outer part. Uplift of shelf margin and gliding of Tethyan sediment nappes across basin.
Stage 4. Santonian approximately. Uplift of shelf margin. Gliding of cherts and exotics (C & E) from outer part of intra-shelf basin over T and C in inner part.
Stage 5. Expulsion of ophiolitic material (O) through shelf margin to surface and gliding SW over basin in Campanian approximately. Followed in Maastrichtian by resumption of stable shelf sedimentation.

oceanic cherts, and serpentinized peridotite with no pervasive shear (*refer* to Fig. 5 of Stoneley 1981). The source areas from which gliding is believed to have taken place were, of course, subducted beneath Central Iran in the Neogene. In the late Cretaceous, a considerable slope on which to glide was provided by the uplifted continental margin from which the Permian–Cenomanian exotics were derived. Conversely, a depression of this margin at that

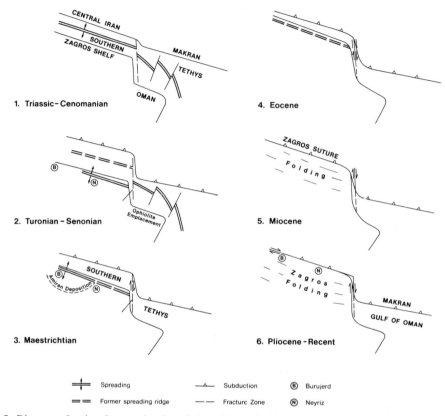

Fig. 5. Diagrams showing the postulated evolution of the Afro-Arabian margin in Iran.

time would be one of the consequences of models of compressive obduction, and the derivation of the exotics is thus one reason why the writer prefers an alternative model.

The Burujerd Region

In the northwestern sector of the Afro–Arabian margin in Iran, the events of the late Cretaceous were broadly similar to those near Neyriz. They appear, however, to have taken place somewhat later.

Despite the general basinal tendency of the shelf in the Lurestan region during the Cretaceous (Setudehnia 1978), its outer parts were again the site of more continuous neritic sedimentation. This autochthonous carbonate sequence, as at Kuh-e Dalneshin, is overlain by thin bedded calcareous marls. Near Arjanak some 120 km southeast of Burujerd, however, they are Santonian in age and near Burujerd itself (Kuh-e Mishparvar) they are Campanian. They rapidly pass up into variegated shales with

radiolarian cherts and limestone turbidites, and eventually basaltic volcanics. To the southwest near Kermanshah, similar cherts but lacking volcanics are entirely allochthonous.

The south Tethyan oceanic nappes have not been identified in this region, although again they may be represented by chert pebbles in the autochthonous chert-bearing series.

Also absent are the neritic exotics derived from the shelf edge in the Kuh-e Dalneshin sector. They are, however, possibly represented by an additional unit which may have comprised the margin from which they were derived: an enormous coherent mass of neritic limestones (the Bisitun Limestone), measuring at least 300 km by 60 km in width and up to 3000 m. in thickness, ranges in age from Triassic to Senonian and overlies cherts (Ricou *et al.* 1977). It is entirely allochthonous above Triassic to Late Cretaceous cherts, and both units are transgressed by the Lower Eocene (Gidon *et al.* 1974a).

Ophiolites are confined to a limited area

between Burujerd and Kermanshah, where they overlie the Bisitun Limestone. They are predominantly serpentinites, and enclose blocks of unmetamorphosed rocks which, in contrast to those near Neyriz, appear to have been incorporated tectonically.

A further difference from the Neyriz area is that, in Lurestan, the autochthonous sequence includes a locally thick group of well-bedded argillaceous silts and sandstones, the Amiran Formation (James & Wynd 1965; Setudehnia 1978). It is composed of material derived from radiolarian cherts and ophiolites, and is of late Maastrichtian−Paleocene age. The allochthonous radiolarites of the Kermanshah area were emplaced over at least a part of this formation (Braud 1987).

These circumstances appear to constrain the history of the region as follows. Instability, leading rapidly to subsidence of an intra-shelf basin, commenced in the Santonian or Campanian depending on area. Possibly some oceanic sediments from the southern Tethys were emplaced on the continental edge either before or shortly after this time. Uplift of the shelf margin took place at the end of the Cretaceous or in the Paleoecene, with the consequent south-westwards displacement of the basinal radiolarites, the Bisitun Limestone mass and the ophiolites. All of this was over by the early Eocene.

The region was subsequently involved in the Neogene Zagros orogeny, following the closure of the southern Tethys. Besides the general folding that affected the region, it also saw the emplacement of thrust slices of Eocene sediments and volcanics onto the former shelf-margin, and the overthrusting of two nappes derived from Central Iran (Braud 1971; Gidon et al 1974b); at least a part of this thrusting took place in the Pliocene. A final event to affect the region was the initiation in the Pliocene of a major dextral strike-slip fault zone along the line of the suture; this has been active to the present day, and offsets may be as much as 60 km (Wellman 1965; Tchalenko & Braud 1974; Gidon et al. 1974c).

Discussion

The circumstances described above suggest that a similar sequence of events affected different sectors of the Afro-Arabian continental margin in Iran during the late Cretaceous. In the Neyriz region, however, they took place earlier (Cenomanian to Campanian) than to the north-west (Santonian/Campanian to Paleocene).

Analogous events affected the same margin in Oman to the southeast, but there were important differences. It will be noted that the two regions are separated by a 'dog-leg' of some 300 km in the continental margin, marked in part by the north−south Zendan Fault.

There is no over-riding evidence, that the writer is aware of, that these late Cretaceous events in Iran were necessarily related to, or caused by, crustal compression. On the contrary, such evidence as there is suggests that they were accompanied by extension normal to the continental margin, and that the emplacement of the allochthonous units was by means of gravitational gliding. Figure 4 illustrates the deduced sequential development of the Kuh-e Dalneshin area. It was noted above, that Hall (1982, 1984) related this picture to a model of incipient rifting and aborted ocean formation along the continental margin, a model which is similar to that put forward by the French−Russian group (Knipper et al. 1986) and which the writer would in general support. Such a model, however, does not explain the situation in Oman, which seems to have evolved during the late Cretaceous at the inactive margin of the southern Tethys ocean, remote from a rift or crustal spreading axis until involved in compressive obduction.

The following scheme for the development of the region could account for the observed facts, for the inferred evolution of different sectors of the continental margin and for the differences between them (Fig. 5).

It is suggested that, from the initiation of the southern Tethys between Afro-Arabia and Central Iran, the spreading axis was offset dextrally some 300 km. to the south from the Iranian sector in the west to the proto-Gulf of Oman, along a north − south transform fracture zone (later to develop as the Zendan Fault). This would produce the 'dog-leg' in the Arabian margin, comparable in a small way to the east−west sector of the West African margin north of the Gulf of Guinea. Spreading continued in this fashion, on both sides of the fracture zone, probably until at least the Aptian: a development of shoal carbonates over the temporarily inactive spreading ridge may have provided the detritus from the northeast in the sediments of the nappes near Neyriz.

In the Cenomanian however, although spreading continued along the former ridge in the Gulf of Oman, to the west in the Iranian sector it now attempted to break out further south, rather than along its earlier line. Initially this was in the ocean close to and parallel to the

Arabian margin, but subsequently the attempted rifting shifted further to just within the continental margin itself. The results of this renewed spreading, which by comparison with the Indian Ocean to the southeast may have been energetic (e.g. Stoneley 1974), were ultimately to emplace oceanic sediments and 'normal' ocean crust ophiolites on the Oman margin, but to create the effects described above in the Iran sector. This attempted spreading in Iran did not immediately extend throughout, and it was not until the Campanian that it reached northwestwards to Burujerd. It was in any case a short-lived process, soon to be abandoned.

Whilst all this was taking place, subduction at the northern side of the ocean was tending to close it and eventually caused the former fracture zone to act as a dextral transform (the Zendan Fault). We have seen evidence, in the south-eastern Zagros, that this may have started to occur in the Senonian. We therefore have a *minimum* estimate for the width of the Iranian sector of the southern Tethys in the Senonian: 300 km.

Closure of the ocean continued through the Palaeogene, leading in Iran to collision at about the beginning of the Miocene. To the east of the Zendan Fault, in the Oman–Makran sector, this collision of course has not yet occurred.

By this mechanism, we now have a possible explanation for the differences between the ophiolites (*sensu lato*) in Iran and in Oman, that makes the hitherto conflicting preferred models mutually compatible.

Most of the work on which this paper is based was carried out while the writer was seconded from The British Petroleum Company Ltd. to the Oil Service Company of Iran (Now the National Iranian Oil Company), and was published in 1981 by permission of the N.I.O.C. Acknowledgment is made of the contributions of many former colleagues, particularly of Dr. M. W. Hughes Clarke and Dr. G. M. Williams, who provided the age determinations, and of Dr. P. Verrall.

The following have kindly commented on drafts of this paper, contributing to its final form: J. Dercourt, K. W. Glennie, R. Hall, M. W. Hughes Clarke, L. E. Ricou, and A. M. C. Sengör. The writer is extremely grateful to them, but must himself bear the responsibility for the views expressed.

Rêcognition should be made of the invaluable work of French geologists in southwest Iran in the 1960s and 1970s, whose writings have formed the basis of much of the compilation in this paper. The admirable pioneer mapping by geologists of what later became The British Petroleum Company, published in map form in 1964, still provides an indispensible source of information.

References

BRAUD, J. 1970. Les Formations du Zagros dans la Région de Kermanshah (Iran) et leurs Rapports Structuraux. *Comptes Rendus des Séances de l'Académie des Sciences, Paris, Série D*, **271**, 1241–1244.

—— 1971. La Nappe de Kuh-e Garun: Chevauchement de l'Iran Central sur le Zagros. *Bulletin de la Société Géologique de France*, **13**, 416–419.

—— 1987. *La Suture du Zagros au Niveau de Kermanshah (Kurdistan Iranien)*. Thesis of the Université de Paris-Sud, Centre d'Orsay.

British Petroleum Company. 1964. *Geological Maps, Columns and Sections of the High Zagros of South-West Iran*. B. P. Co., London.

GIDON, M., BERTHIER, F., BILLIAULT, J. P., HALBRONN, B. & MAURIZOT, P. 1974a. Sur Quelques Caractéres de la Tectonique Néocrétacée dans la Région de Borujerd (Zagros Oriental, Iran). *Comptes Rendus des Séances de l'Académie des Sciences, Paris, Série D*, **278**, 577–580.

——, ——, —— 1974b. Charriages et Mouvements Synsédimentaires Tertiaires dans la Région de Borujerd (Zagros, Iran). *Comptes Rendus des Séances de l'Académie des Sciences, Paris, Série D*, **278**, 421–424.

——, ——, ——, —— 1974c. Sur les Caractéres et l'Ampleur du Coulissement de la "Main Fault" dans la Région de Borujerd-Dorud (Zagros Oriental, Iran). *Comptes Rendus des Séances de l'Académie des Sciences, Paris, Série D*, **278**, 701–704.

HALL, R. 1981. Ophiolite-Related Contact Metamorphism: Skarns from Neyriz, Iran. *Proceedings of the Geologists' Association*, **92**, 231–240.

—— 1982. Ophiolites and Passive Continental Margins. *Ofioliti*, **2/3**, 279–298.

—— 1984. Ophiolites--Figments of Oceanic Lithosphere? *In*: GASS, I. G., LIPPARD, S. J. & SHELTON, A. W. (eds) *Ophiolites and Oceanic Lithosphere*. Geological Society, London, Special Publication **13**, 393–403.

HALLAM, A. 1976. Geology and Plate Tectonics Interpretation of the Sediments of the Mesozoic Radiolarite-Ophiolite Complex in the Neyriz Region, Southern Iran. *Bulletin of the Geological Society of America*, **87**, 47–52.

JAMES, G. A. & WYND, J. G. 1965. Stratigraphic Nomenclature of Iranian Oil Consortium Agreement Area. *Bulletin of the American Association of Petroleum Geologists*, **49**, 2182–2245.

KNIPPER, A., RICOU, L. E. & DERCOURT, J. 1986. Ophiolites as Indicators of the Geodynamic Evolution of the Tethyan Ocean. *Tectonophysics*, **123**, 213–240.

LANPHERE, M. A. & PAMIĆ, J. 1983. ^{40}Ar/^{39}Ar Ages and Tectonic Setting of Ophiolite from the Neyriz Area, Southeast Zagros Range, Iran. *Tectonophysics*, **96**, 245–256.

LIPPARD, S. J., SHELTON, A. W. & GASS, I. G. 1986.

The Ophiolite of Northern Oman, Geological Society, London, Memoir, **11**

PAMIĆ, J. and ADIB, D. 1980. Interprétation comme Rodingites des Skarns Décrit dans le Massif Ultramafique de Neyriz (Zagros Sud-oriental, Iran). *Comptes Rendus des Séances de l'Académie des Sciences, Paris, Série D*, **291**, 363–366.

RICOU, L. E. 1976. Évolution Structurale des Zagrides. La Région Clef de Neyriz (Zagros Iranien). Mémoire de la Société Géologique de France, **125**.

——, BRAUD, J. & BRUNN, J. H. 1977. Le Zagros. *Mémoire Hors-série de la Société Géologique de France*, **8**, 33–52.

SETUDEHNIA, A. 1978. The Mesozoic Sequence in South-West Iran and Adjacent Areas. *Journal of Petroleum Geology*, **1**, 3–42.

STILLMAN, C. J., FÚSTER, J. M., BENNELL-BAKER, M. J., MUÑOZ, M., SMEWING, J. D. and SAGREDO, J. 1975. Basal Complex of Fuerteventura (Canary Islands) is an Oceanic Intrusive Complex with Rift-System Affinities. *Nature, London*, **257**, 469–471.

STÖCKLIN, J. 1974. Possible Ancient Continental Margins in Iran. *In*: BURK, C. A. & DRAKE, C. L. (eds), *The Geology of Continental Margins*. Springer, New York, 873–888.

STONELEY, R. 1974. Evolution of the Continental Margins Bounding a Former Southern Tethys. *In*: BURK, C. A. & DRAKE, C. L. (eds), *The Geology of Continental Margins*. Springer, New York, 889–903.

—— 1975. On the Origin of Ophiolite Complexes in the Southern Tethys Region. *Tectonophysics*, **25**, 303–322.

——. 1981. The Geology of the Kuh-e Dalneshin Area of Southern Iran and its Bearing on the Evolution of Southern Tethys. *Journal of the Geological Society of London*, **138**, 509–526.

TCHALENKO, J. S. & BRAUD, J. 1974. Seismicity and Structure of the Zagros (Iran): the Main Recent Fault between 33 and 35°N. *Philosophical Transactions of the Royal Society, London*, **A277**, 1–25.

WELLMAN, H. W. 1965. Active Wrench Faults of Iran, Afghanistan and Pakistan. *Geologische Rundschau*, **55**, 716–735.

A new model for the late Palaeozoic−Mesozoic tectonic evolution of Iran and implications for Oman

A. M. C. ŞENGÖR

İTÜ Maden Fakültesi, Jeoloji Bölümü, Ayazağa 80626 Istanbul, Turkey

Abstract: It has been suggested that in a number of places such as Greece, Turkey, the Central Pamirs, and Thailand Neo-Tethys may have opened as a back-arc basin above a Palaeo-Tethyan subduction zone. The purpose of this paper is to test a similar suggestion for Oman. I review the late Palaeozoic to end-Mesozoic tectonic evolution of the Middle Eastern Tethysides in terms of a new tectonic model, whose main tenet is to regard the late Palaeozoic to Late Triassic basements of the Pontide/Dzirula/Adzharia-Trialeti/Arvin-Karabagh/Sanandaj − Sirjan zones collectively as a NNE-facing Palaeo-Tethyan magmatic arc, here named the 'Podataksasi arc' (or 'zone') whose Jurassic−Cretaceous movement with respect to Eurasia was responsible for much of the coeval deformation in Iran and Transcaucasia. The late Palaeozoic deformation of the Omani basement is regarded as a part of the retroarc fold and thrust belt of this arc and therefore independent of the Hercynides in Europe and NW Africa. The arc may have been compressional in late Carboniferous to possibly early Permian time and turned extensional in the earlier middle Permian. As a result, it rifted from NE Gondwana-Land, opening, successively, the Hawasina basin in the middle Permian and the main Neo-Tethyan ocean in the Triassic, together forming the 'Omani Neo-Tethyan back-arc basin complex'. Nearly all of the tectonic and magmatic characteristics of this basin complex are compatible with a back-arc basin interpretation, except perhaps the anomalously far inland location of the initial rift axis. A rather complete Mesozoic tectonic history of the entire Middle Eastern Tethysides is given to justify the model presented.

The principal aim of this paper is to set the late Palaeozoic orogenic deformation and the mid-Permian opening of Neo-Tethys in Oman into a regional frame within the context of the *Middle Eastern Tethysides*[†] (Figs 1 & 2). Because what is known of the late Palaeozoic deformation and subsequent rifting has been described in some detail elsewhere (Michard 1982, 1983; Mann & Hanna 1990, Glennie *et al.* 1974; Lipard *et al.* 1986; Robertson 1986; Bernoulli & Weissert 1987; Bechennec 1988), I deal with them only briefly, but sufficient for the reader to follow my arguments. Instead, I describe at some length the late Palaeozoic to end-Mesozoic tectonic evolution of the entire Middle Eastern Tethysides, of which Oman is a part, because without that knowledge it is not possible to understand the tectonic significance of the late Palaeozoic to early Mesozoic events in Oman.

The main data on which the interpretations presented below are based are displayed in Figs 2−7. In the following sections I outline the late Palaeozoic to end-Mesozoic geology and

tectonic evolution of the Middle Eastern Tethysides. In the Discussion, I elaborate my interpretation of the early history of the Oman Mountains in terms of a back-arc basin that began opening by disrupting the continentward part of a continental margin magmatic arc.

Late Palaeozoic to end-Mesozoic geology of the Middle Eastern Tethysides

In the Middle Eastern Tethysides (Figs 1 & 2), a fundamental boundary was formed by the Palaeo-Tethyan suture segments in Turkey, S USSR, and N Iran separating 'Laurasian' tectonic elements in the N from 'Gondwanian' elements in the S (Fig. 1), although Laurasia itself first formed as a monolith during the Permian.

In the Middle Eastern Tethysides two types of terrains may be distinguished S of the main Palaeo-Tethyan suture: one type shows important late Palaeozoic, dominantly Carboniferous, orogenic activity accompanied by locally abundant calc-alkaline magmatism. Outcrops of this type are here grouped under a *Podataksasi Zone*. The second type has an Infracambrian to Middle Triassic platform cover exhibiting no significant late Palaeozoic orogeny, nor any

[†] The usage 'Middle East' in this paper follows the definition of Fisher (1950, pp.1−4). The *Middle Eastern Tethysides* comprise his 'Folded Zone' and 'Median Zone' (see his fig. 2).

From ROBERTSON, A. H. F., SEARLE, M. P. & RIES, A. C. (eds), 1990, *The Geology and Tectonics of the Oman Region.* Geological Society Special Publication No 49, pp 797−831

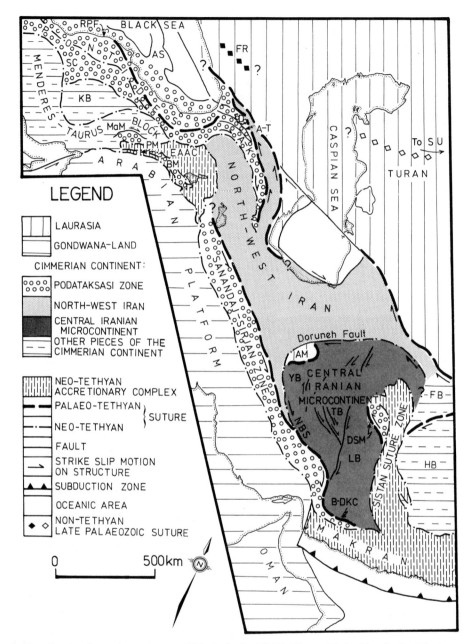

Fig. 1. Map showing the various sutures and blocks in the Middle Eastern Tethysides. In the Rhodope–Pontide fragment, the Palaeo-Tethyan suture is located *under* the Podataksasi zone, as it was overthrust by the latter during the closure of Palaeo-Tethys. Key to abbreviations: A–K, Artvin–Karabagh zone; AM, Anarek Massif; AS, Andrusow Swell; A–T, Adzharia–Trialeti zone; B–DKC, Bajgan–Dur Kan Complex (including the Azava and Deyader complexes); BM, Bitlis Massif; D, Dzirula Massif; DSM, Deh Salm Metamorphics; EAAC, East Anatolian Accretionary Complex; FB, Farah Block; FR, Front Range; HB, Halmand Block (*sensu* Şengör 1984); KB, Kırşehir Block, LB, Lut Block; Mam, Malatya Metamorphics; NBS, Nain-Baft suture; PM, Pötürge Massif; RPF, Rohodope–Pontide Fragment; SC, Sakarya Continent; SU, Sultan Uizdag; TB, Tabas Block; YB, Yazd Block.

appreciable magmatism. The two types of terrains are separated from one another generally by steep faults commonly with evidence of important Mesozoic and younger strike-slip displacement. In NW Iran, there may have been a somewhat intimate intermixing of these two type of terrains, if the metamorphic rocks of the Kuh-e Dom area (Figs 2 & 3, loc. 25) and the Torud region (Fig. 2, loc. To) had an episode of late Palaeozoic orogeny as claimed by Roman'ko & Sharkovskiy (1984) and Davoudzadeh & Weber-Diefenbach (1987).

In the Mesozoic the two types of terrains continued to behave differently until the Jurassic. After about the early Jurassic they lost their independence and became incorporated into newly-developed independent tectonic units.

Evidence for Late Palaeozoic orogeny in the Middle Eastern Tethysides

Laurasia. During the late Palaeozoic, the Laurasian parts of the Middle Eastern Tethyside chains were sites of intense orogeny related to the closure of two oceans. Deformed remnants of the older one are now preserved in the Front Range ophiolites in the Greater Caucasus (Khain 1984) and in the Sultan Uizdag ophiolite complex in the Aral Sea region (Garetskiy *et al.* 1972) whereas those of the younger one, the Palaeo-Tethys, are represented by the ophiolites and the accretionary complexes in N Turkey (Şengör *et al.* 1980, 1984), in the Caucasus, and in N Iran, in the Talesh Mountains and near Mashhad (Şengör 1984) (Fig. 1).

The S margin of Laurasia in the Middle Eastern Tethysides did not become cratonized at the end of the Palaeozoic. In both the Tuarkyr (Fig. 3, loc. 22) and in Aghdarband (Fig. 3, loc. 21), we see important episodes of compressional deformation in the latest Triassic to early Jurassic, which, in Aghdarband, was preceded by considerable Triassic volcanism represented by Scythian (pre-Spathian) mafic lava, tuffaceous sandstone, and shale, and late early Anisian to latest Ladinian tuffaceous sandstones and shales interbedded with marine marls and shales to the end of the Triassic (A. Ruttner, pers. comm. 1988). This episode of volcanicity in Aghdarband was partly coeval with Triassic arc-related magmatism in the Krasnovodsk and in Darvaz (Da. in Fig. 2), being possibly parts of a once-continuous magmatic arc above a N-dipping Palaeo-Tethyan subduction zone (Şengör *et al.* 1988). W of the Caspian Sea in the Greater Caucasus, we see no trace of this early Mesozoic magmatic activity.

A group of outcrops in N Iran along the trace of the Palaeo-Tethyan suture (Figs 2 & 3, locs. 18 and 19) contain highly deformed and metamorphosed Palaeozoic sedimentary rocks that are tectonically interleaved with ultramafics. The best-known of these is near Mashhad (Figs 2 & 3, loc. 19), where Alavi (1979) mapped metamorphosed and partly serpentinized peridotites, dunites, gabbros, and thinly-bedded chert tectonically intercalated with low-grade metamorphic rocks including slates, marbles, and quartzites. Majidi (1978) also recognized here pillowed mafic volcanic rocks associated with hyaloclastic volcaniclastics and radiolarian cherts, and a small outcrop of true ophiolitic mélange including blocks of ultramafics, schists, and marbles, floating in a matrix consisting of spilites, tuffs, pillow lavas, and 'green rocks'. The oldest unconformable rocks on this mélange are *Orbitolina*-bearing Cretaceous limestones (Majidi 1978, fig. 25). The only fossils found in the metamorphic rocks are some plant remains, which A. F. de Lapparent thought may be related to Carboniferous forms (pers. comm. in Majidi 1978, p. 55). Although Davoudzadeh *et al.* (1986) inferred that the entire assemblage was older than Permian, no rocks older than the Rhaeto-Liassic Shemshak Formation are seen to cover it anywhere (Fig. 3, loc. 19). Isotopic dating of a granite porphyry cutting the metamorphic assemblage has been so far inconclusive. Majidi (1978) obtained K/Ar ages of both late Permian and late Triassic, whereas Alberti (1973) found latest Jurassic to earliest Cretaceous ages. An aplitic granite intruding the older plutons in the area has yielded a K/Ar age of $211 \pm$ Ma (Majidi 1978), thus supporting the older ages. Therefore, although Davoudzadeh *et al.* (1986) claimed that the metamorphic complex of Mashhad, including the ophiolites, was 'late Palaeozoic', available observations may be interpreted also in terms of a possible Carboniferous to Rhaetian bracket, as argued also by Alavi (1979).

A similar metamorphic assemblage, called the Shanderman–Asalem Complex by Clark *et al.* (1975), including actinolite–garnet–zoisite–muscovite schists and fine-grained gneisses with subordinate quartz and albite, and sheared, almost totally serpentinized ultramafic rocks occur in the Talesh Mountains near the town of Rasht (Figs 2 and 3, loc. 18). The age of the metamorphic rocks has been assigned originally to the Precambrian (Davis *et al.* 1972; Clark *et al.* 1975), but the oldest unconformable sequence covering them is the (here) Liassic Shemshak Formation. Rb/Sr dating of the schists by Crawford (1977) gave 375 ± 12 Ma,

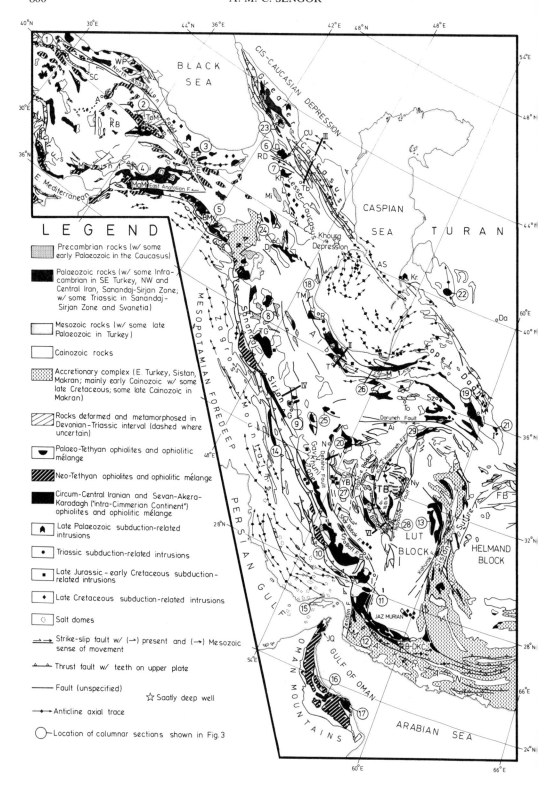

and of the gneisses 382±47 Ma, indicating middle and ?late Devonian metamorphism.

In places, Davies *et al.* (1972, p.25) noted that the serpentinites 'give the impression of being emplaced in the early Jurassic sequence, with which (they) may be intimately sheared and brecciated'. On the strength of this observation both Berberian & King (1981) and Şengör (1984) interpreted the Talesh ultramafic slices as remnants of Palaeo-Tethys, possibly emplaced in late Triassic time, and thus being independent of the older Shanderman–Asalem metamorphic complex. By contrast, Davoudzadeh *et al.* (1986) retained the original interpretation of Davies *et al.* (1972) in assigning the ultramafics to the metamorphic complex that they interpret as Palaeozoic.

The lithology, internal structure, and the available meagre age information of the Mashhad and Talesh outcrops, along with the Anarek Massif (see below), with which they can be compared best, suggest that they may be Palaeozoic accretionary complexes whose activity in places (e.g. Mashhad and possibly Anarek) may have reached into the Triassic. In this regard they resemble the accretionary complexes of the Paropamisus, W Hindu Kush, and N Pamirs (Şengör 1984; Boulin 1988) on one hand, and those of N Turkey (the Küre Nappe: Şengör 1984; Yılmaz & Şengör 1985) on the other, although the Turkish Cimmeride accretionary complexes reach farther up into the earliest Dogger (Şengör *et al.* 1980, 1984). The Iranian occurences have been interpreted as a part of the same orogenic collage marking the location of the suture of Palaeo-Tethys (Şengör 1984; Davoudzadeh & Schmidt 1984) and I follow this view here also.

Cimmerian Continent and Gondwana-Land. Conventionally, the N margin of Gondwana-Land lying to the S of Palaeo-Tethys, the Cimmerian Continent of the earliest Mesozoic time (Şengör 1979), has been regarded as a passive, N- to NE-facing continental margin (Argyriadis 1974, 1978; Stöcklin 1974a, 1980; Berberian & King 1981; Tapponnier *et al.* 1981 Boulin 1988) within the confines of the Middle Eastern Tethysides, with the notable and allegedly anomalous exception of N Turkey (Şengör *et al.* 1980, 1982, 1984; Bergougnan & Fourquin, 1982). Especially in Iran, all authors since Gansser (1955) have emphasized until recently the absence of strong late Palaeozoic orogenic events including deformation, metamorphism, and igneous activity S of the Kopet Dagh/Aghdarband ranges (e.g. Assereto 1963; Flügel 1964; Stöcklin 1960, 1968, 1974b, 1977; Stöcklin *et al.* 1964, 1965) in contrast to such earlier workers as Stahl (1911) and Furon (1941) and indicated that since the early Palaeozoic the first orogenic event was of early Jurassic age corresponding with the final closure of Palaeo-Tethys (cf. Şengör 1984).

In recent years a number of authors have pointed out that the assertion of the absence of significant late Palaeozoic and early Triassic orogenic events in Iran is not corroborated by observation (Thiele *et al.* 1968; Thiele 1973; Berberian & Berberian 1981; Berberian & King 1981; Roman'ko & Morozov 1983; Roman'ko & Sharkovskiy 1984; Davoudzadeh *et al.* 1986; Davoudzadeh & Weber-Diefenbach 1987; Şengör 1987a; Şengör *et al.* 1988). In particular, the Sanandaj–Sirjan zone in SW Iran was clearly subjected to important middle to late Palaeozoic orogenic events (Berberian & King, 1981; Davoudzadeh *et al.* 1986; Davoudzadeh & Weber-Diefenbach 1987; Şengör 1987a; Şengör *et al.* 1988). In the following paragraphs I briefly review these scattered data from Iran and its surroundings. The regional descriptions are organized following the major tectonic units

---

Fig. 2. Simplified geological/tectonic map of the Middle Eastern segment of the Tethyside super orogenic complex. Key to abbreviations: A, Ankara; Ai, Airakan; AS, Apsheron Sill; B, Baft; B–DKC, Bajgan-Dur Kan Complex; BM, Bitlis Massif; CU, Chorchana–Utslevi Zone (see Fig. 5); D, Dzirula Massif; Da, Darvaz; Dj, Djulfa; EP, Eastern Pontides; FB, Farah Block; G, Golpaygan; I, Isfandageh; JQ, Jebel Qamar; KB, Kirşehir Block; Kh, Khrami Massif; Kr, Krasnovodsk; L, Loki Massif; M, Mashhad; MaM, Malatya Metamorphics; Mi, Mishkan Massif; N, Nain; Ny, Nayband; R, Rasht; S, Sirjan; SC, Sakarya Continent; Sh, Shirkuh; Sz, Sabzevar; T, Tehran; TB, Tabas Block; Tb, Tbilisi; TG, Tuzlu Gol; TM, Talesh Mountains; To, Torud; ToM, Tokaf Massif; WP, Western Pontides; PB, Yazd Block. The map was compiled from the following sources: for Turkey, Şengör & Yılmaz (1981), Şengör *et al.* (1984), Okay (1986); for Caucasus, Nalivkin (1976), Dotduyev (1986); for Iran, Berberian (1981), Berberian & Berberian (1981), Berberian & King (1981) and Haghipour & Aghanabati (1985); for Oman, Glennie *et al.* (1974) and Lippard *et al.* (1986); for Afghanistan, Boulin (1988); for the entire region, *Geologicheskaya Karta Evrazii* (1972) that also served as the basemap.

On this map note especially the extremely linear character of the combined structure formed from the Greater Caucasus Main Ridge/Apsheron sill/Kopet Dagh front and how the Kopet Dagh gradually bends southwards to meet the strongly curved eastern prolongation of the Alborz Range. Note also how the E-W fold axes in the Tabas Blocks are bent strongly southwards near the Nayband Fault.

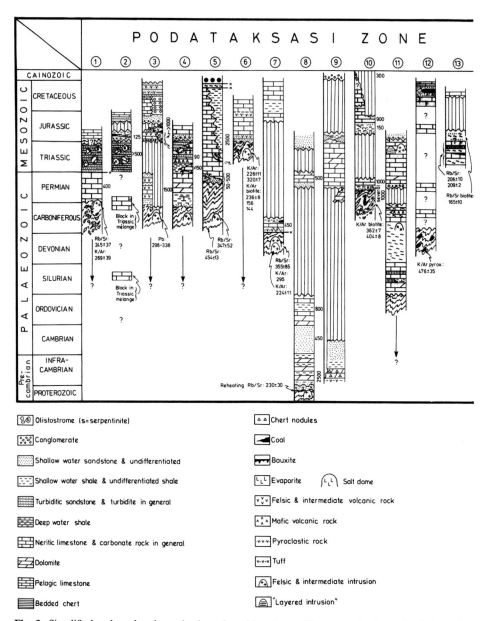

Fig. 3. Simplified and partly schematized stratigraphic columns illustrating the intervals of the rock record from selected localities in the Middle Eastern Tethysides which are relevant to this study. Thicknesses of most of the units are indicated by figures to the right of each column. With isotopic ages both the method and the mineral used are given. Where no mineral is indicated, the age is one of whole rock. Locations of the columns are shown in Fig. 2. References for individual columns are as follows.

1. Chaput (1936), Ketin (1947, 1985), Öztunali (1973).
2. Alp (1972), Tekeli (1981).
3. Şengör & Yilmaz (1981).
4. Yilmaz *et al.* (1987).
5. Şengör and Yilmaz (1981).
6. Adamia and Belov (1984).
7. Abesadze *et al.* (1982), Adamia & Belov (1984).
8. Stöcklin (1968), Crawford (1977).
9. Thiele *et al.* (1968), Thiele (1973).
10. Ricou (1976), Berberian and King (1981).
11. Berberian and Berberian (1981), Davoudzadeh *et al.* (1986).
12. McCall and Kidd (1982), McCall (1985), Davoudzadeh *et al.* (1986).

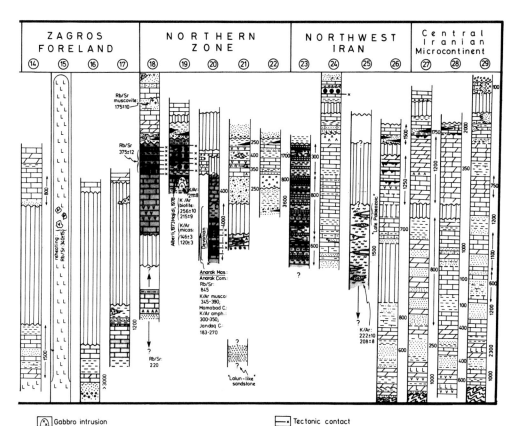

	Gabbro intrusion			Tectonic contact
	Ophiolite			Rifting
	Amphibolite			No record

Phyllite & Schist

Gneiss

Metamorphic basement in general

Ultramafic inclusions in metamorphic basement

Metamorphic rocks in general

Unconformity resulting from orogeny

Unconformity resulting from taphrogeny

13. Stöcklin et al. (1972), Crawford (1977).
14. Stöcklin (1968).
15. Crawford (1977).
16. Michard (1982, 1983), Mann & Hanna (1990).
17. Michard (1982, 1983), Mann & Hanna (1990).
18. Davies et al. (1972), Clark et al. (1975), Crawford (1977), Davoudzadeh (1986).
19. Alberti (1973), Majidi (1978), Alavi (1979), Lammerer et al. (1984), Davoudzadeh et al. (1986).
20. Roman'ko & Morozov (1983), Davoudzadeh et al. (1986).
21. Ruttner (1984).
22. Slavin & Khain (1980).
23. Adamia et al. (1982), Adamia & Belov (1984).
24. Bonnet & Bonnet (1947), Kozur et al. (1975), Knipper & Sokolov (1976), Altiner et al. (1979).
25. Roman'ko & Sharkovskiy (1984).
26. Stöcklin (1968), Brandner et al. (1981).
27. Stöcklin (1968).
28. Stöcklin (1968).
29. Ruttner et al. (1968).

used in this paper, namely the Podataksasi Zone, the Central Iranian Microcontinent, and NW Iran (Fig. 1), which collectively form parts of the Cimmerian Continent in Iran.

Podataksasi Zone. Gondwanian regions in the Middle Eastern Tethysides in which the record of a late Palaeozoic orogeny is seen (Fig. 2, locs. 1 through 13) are here grouped under the designation *Podataksasi Zone* derived from the names of the familiar Alpide tectonic units containing them, *viz.* the Pontides, Dzirula, Adzharia-Trialeti, Artvin-Karabagh, and Sanandaj−Sirjan† (Fig. 1).

In the Isfandageh region (Figs 2 & 3, loc. 11) locally early Permian turbidites and middle and late Permian shallow water limestones rest across a pronounced unconformity and with basal conglomerate on 5000 m of strongly deformed Devonian and Carboniferous schists, phyllites, calc-schists, metadiabases, and metagabbros forming the Khaju unit (Davoudzadeh *et al.* 1986). The Permo-Triassic carbonate rocks in this region were themselves deformed and metamorphosed, and intruded by the Triassic Sikhoran layered intrusion that is overlain by Jurassic sedimentary rocks as are the Permo-Triassic metamorphic rocks (Sabzehei 1974). As Davoudzadeh *et al.* (1986) and Davoudzadeh & Weber-Diefenbach (1987, p.139) concluded, at least two episodes of orogeny are seen in the Isfandageh area: the earlier one is late Carboniferous, and the later one is late Triassic.

Another area of Palaeozoic and Triassic deformed and metamorphosed rocks including carbonates, pelitic and psammatic rocks, and mafic volcanics plus ultramafics lies to the W of Sirjan, in the vicinity of Kor-e Sefid (Figs 2 and 3, loc. 10: Berberian & King (1981); Davoudzadeh & Weber-Diefenbach (1987)). Isotopic ages (Fig. 3, loc. 10) indicate early Devonian and early Carboniferous cooling ages. The early Devonian age probably belongs to an earlier Palaeozoic basement. Sabzehei & Berberian (1972), Vialon *et al.* (1972), and Ricou (1976), have recognised two syntectonic episodes of regional metamorphism in this region. Berberian & King (1981) suggested that the first metamorphism of lower amphibolite grade may be older and identical with the early Carboniferous event and the second, late Triassic and retrograde.

Farther N along the Sanandaj−Sirjan zone,

in the vicinity of Golpaygan and Mahallat (Fig 2 & 3, loc. 9) Thiele *et al.* (1968) and Thiele (1973) have documented the existence of an important middle to possibly late Permian phase of folding that created ENE to NE trending close folds. The folded sequence consists of a late Proterozoic to Palaeozoic succession including, from bottom to top, equivalents of the Kahar (Precambrian), Soltaniyeh (Infracambrian), and Zaigun-Lalun (Infra-Cambrian to Lower Cambrian) formations plus a 100 m-thick massive dolomite. Thiele (1973, p.494) found in this dolomite *Pseudohuangia* sp. and *Ipsiphyllum* sp. indicating and Asselian to Murgabian (Lower to Middle Permian) age. He observed in only one place a sharp unconformity between this dolomite and the underlying late Proterozoic to Ordovician succession, a condition very reminiscent of the situation in Oman, with the exception that here the uncomformable dolomite most likely begins with the Lower Permian (*Pseudohuangia*). In this region the main folding event postdates the Lower to Middle Permian dolomite, but is older than the uncomformable calcareous shales, sandy limestones, sandstones, and conglomerates with the calcareous algae *Permocalculus* cf. *plumosus* ELLIOT and *Pseudovermiporella*, clearly indicating an Upper Permian age (Thiele 1973). The main folding event in the central part of the Sanandaj−Sirjan zone is thus dated as middle Permian, with possibly a precursor event, whose bracket is Middle Ordovician to Lowest Permian. In the western Golpaygan region Davoudzadeh & Weber-Diefenbach (1987) report volcaniclastics flysch-type shales and sandstones with *Pseudoschwagerina*-bearing (i.e. Lower Permian) limestone interlayers and metadiabase and andesite flows indicating the presence of Permian calc-alkaline magmatism and clastic deposition.

Terrains of strong late Palaeozoic orogenic activity S of the main Palaeo-Tethyan suture exist both farther N and NW and S and SE of the Sanandaj-Sirjan zone in the Middle Eastern Tethysides. To the S, they are found in the Bajgan Complex (McCall & Kidd 1982, Figs 2 and 3, loc. 12), consisting of pelitic and psammitic schists, calc-silicates, amphibolites, serpentinised dunites with minor wherlites, recrystallized limestones, and marbles. A K/Ar age on pyroxene from one of the ultra-mafic bodies gave an age of earlier middle Ordovician, interpreted as the time of crystallization (Fig. 3, loc. 12). McCall (1985) reports the presence of numerous inliers of unmetamorphosed, locally slightly recrystallized Permian limestones with *Pseudoschwagerina*, *Schwagerina* sp.,

† Of these, the Adzharia−Trialeti Zone has no exposed rocks older than the Cretaceous. The presence of an older basement, similar to the one in the Talesh Mountains in N Iran, is inferred (Khain 1975).

Schubertella sp., and *Climacammina* sp., and thus regards the metamorphic rocks at least as pre-Permian. Outcrop continuity with only small interruptions between the Bajgan Complex and the metamorphic rocks of the Isfandageh area (Fig. 2, locs 11 & 12), the great similarity of the sequences and metamorphism in the two regions, along with the presence of unmetamorphosed Permian rocks in the Bajgan area, led McCall & Kidd (1982), Davoudzadeh et al. (1986), and Davoudzadeh & Weber-Diefenbach (1987) to consider the Bajgan metamorphics and their easterly extensions in the Deyader and the Azava complexes (included in the Bajgan–Dur-Kan complex in Fig. 2) as equivalents of the late Palaeozoic metamorphic rocks in the Isfandageh area, thus assigning them a late Carboniferous age.

To the N and NW, the Sanandaj–Sirjan zone cannot be traced continuously beyond S of Lake Urmieh (about the position of loc. 8 in Fig. 2). Areas with similar late Palaeozoic histories are separated from it by younger ophiolitic suture zones (e.g. the Sevan–Akera–Karadagh ophiolite belt in the Lesser Caucasus and the Neo-Tethyan accretionary complex in eastern Turkey, EAAC: Fig. 1) and by large areas in which we see no trace of any Palaeozoic orogeny following the Pan-African events (e.g. locs 23 & 24 in Figs 2 & 3). Record of important late Palaeozoic Gondwanian orogenic events N of the northern end of the Sanandaj–Sirjan zone is encountered in the Lesser Caucasus and in the Transcaucasian Dzirula Massif.

In the Dzirula Massif (Figs 2 & 3, loc. 6 and Fig. 4) two entirely different rock associations

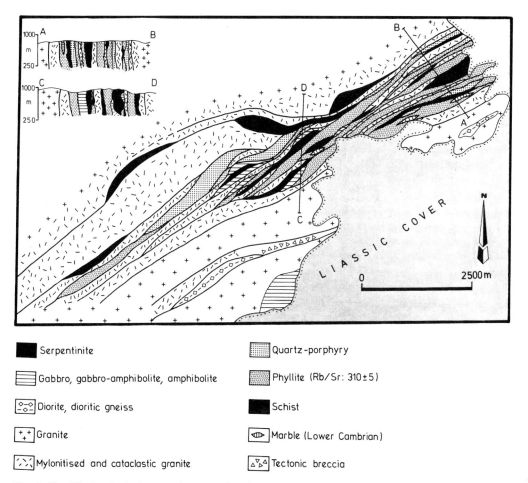

Serpentinite

Gabbro, gabbro-amphibolite, amphibolite

Diorite, dioritic gneiss

Granite

Mylonitised and cataclastic granite

Quartz-porphyry

Phyllite (Rb/Sr: 310±5)

Schist

Marble (Lower Cambrian)

Tectonic breccia

Fig. 4. Simplified geological map and cross sections (A–B and C–D) of the Chorchana–Utslevi shear zone of the Dzirula Massif (for location see Fig. 2) redrawn from Adamia *et al.* (1982).

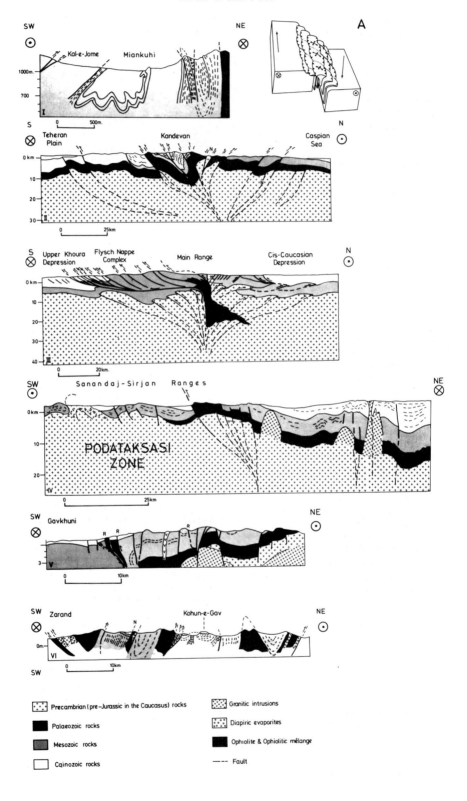

are present whose mutual contacts are inferred to be large displacement strike-slip faults. The 'crystalline basement' outside the Chorchana-Utslevi Zone (Fig. 4) (Abesadze *et al.* 1982) consists of high grade gneisses, amphibolites, and migmatites older than cross-cutting 'early Variscan' quartz diorites and 'late Variscan' microcline granites although K/Ar cooling ages on these metamorphic rocks are also reported to be late Carboniferous (Adamia *et al.* 1983). On the basis of K/Ar data, the time of granite genesis is believed to be mainly late Carboniferous to possibly earliest Triassic (Fig. 3, loc. 6). Small syenite intrusions, locally called 'Rikotites', have yielded K/Ar ages of 236±8, 156, and 144 Ma on biotite, indicating later, mid-Mesozoic disturbance.

The extremely sheared and tectonically intermixed rocks of the Chorchana–Utslevi zone contain, in addition to undated gabbros, serpentinities, and metavolcanics forming a dismembered ophiolite, dated Lower Cambrian marble slivers (*Archaeocyathus* sp., *Coscinocyathus caucasicus* VOL.) and Upper Silurian to Upper Devonian phyllites (a rich palynomorph flora) indicating that the deformation and metamorphism of these rocks were post-Devonian. A Rb/Sr age on the phyllites gave a late Carboniferous age (Fig. 4) likely indicating the age of the greenschist metamorphism (Abesadze *et al.* 1982), which is nearly coeval with the granites of the Dzirula Massif. As seen in Fig. 4, after the metamorphism of the phyllites and the intrusion of the granites, an important episode of strikeslip faulting of unknown sense and magnitude affected these rocks to create the present geometry. The age of this deformation is bracketed between the youngest granites (?late Palaeozoic ?earliest Triassic) and the uncomformable Liassic shales and sandstones (Adamia *et al.* 1982), and may be late Triassic–earliest Jurassic. The original palaeogeographic affiliation of the metasediments associated with the dismembered ophiolite is unknown. By analogy with some of the N Iranian occurrences it may be Laurasian.

A similar record of events is seen farther S in the Khrami Salient (Fig. 2, loc. Kh), with the exception that an unmetamorphosed Carbon-iferous sedimentary and volcaniclastic sequence is preserved in fault contact with metamorphic and plutonic rocks. The metamorphic rocks are andalusite–sillimanite grade quartzo-feldspathic gneisses with subordinate mica-schists. The metamorphism predated the intrusion of dominantly S-type granites of prob-ably (?middle) Carboniferous age (Fig. 3, loc. 7). The sedimentary rocks, intercalated throughout the section by numerous tuff hor-izons, range from late Visean to Namurian marine limestones, clastics to pyroclastics, to middle Carboniferous paralic to terrestrial clas-tics and pyroclastics containing a Euramerian flora (Adamia & Belov 1984). On the basis of petrologic and geochemical evidence, the Khrami volcanic rocks are regarded as eruptive equivalents of the granitic plutons (Adamia *et al.* 1982). A small tectonic sliver containing gabbro-diorites, olivine gabbros, and serpen-tinites crop out in the Chochiani river gorge and may be an equivalent of the disrupted ophiolites of the Chorchana–Utslevi zone in the Khrami Massif (Adamia *et al.* 1982).

Greenschist and locally epidote-amphibolite facies micaschists and rare marbles, crop out in the Loki Massif (Fig. 2, loc. L) to the S of the Khrami Salient. K/Ar ages of 287±15, 319±11, and 333±11 Ma on muscovites from them, prob-ably indicate a late Carboniferous cooling (Abesadze *et al.* 1982). Granitic rocks intruding the Loki metamorphics have K/Ar and Rb/Sr ages around 338 to 325 Ma, corresponding with a later early Carboniferous intrusive epi-sode, probably coeval with the peak of the metamorphism.

The late Palaeozoic record from Trans-caucasia and the Lesser Caucasus indicates a period of metamorphism (and accompanying penetrative deformation) and both plutonic and volcanic activity ranging from later early Carboniferous to late Carboniferous to possibly later resembling what we have seen in both the Kor-e Sefid and Isfandageh regions at the S extremity of the Sanandaj–Sirjan zone. Coeval and similar events were likely the cause of the sub-Permian uncomformity in the Mahallat re-gion and the early Permian calc-alkaline vol-canics west of Golpaygan in the central part of

Fig. 5. Selected geological cross-sections from the Middle Eastern Tethysides illustrating the important, locally dominant strike-slip-like profiles. In all sections, except in IV, notice the inconsistency of the vergence across the strike. The cross sections have been simplified from the following sources: I, Ruttner (1989); II, Stöcklin (1974b); III, Dotduyev, (1986); IV, Stöcklin (1974b); V and VI, Stöcklin (1968). For locations see Fig. 2. Inset A was redrawn after Lowell (1972) to illustrate the mechanism that is inferred to be largely responsible for the generation of the cross sectional styles shown in this figure. For I, III, V and VI significant strike-slip together with across-strike shortening has been documented. Significant strike-slip for II and IV is inferred in this study.

the Sanandaj—Sirjan zone, and of the deformation and metamorphism of the Bajgan Complex.

The zone of Gondwanian late Palaeozoic orogenic activity is represented in diverse Alpide tectonic units in Turkey that originally may have constituted a single entity (Şengör & Yılmaz 1981). To the WSW of the Transcaucasian and Lesser Caucasian late Palaeozoic inliers are located the inliers of the Cimmeride Bayburt Nappe, forming the basement of the eastern Rhodope—Pontide fragment, a part of the Pontides (Şengör et al. 1980, 1984). In the few inliers in which it is accessible to observation, this basement consists of a likely early Devonian quartzo-feldspathic gneissic country rock intruded by the minimum-melting composition Gümüşhane granite pluton (Yılmaz 1975 and pers. comm. 1988) that yielded a Pb whole rock age corresponding with a latest early Carboniferous to earlier late Carboniferous interval (Figs 2 & 3, loc. 3). A composite section consisting, from base to top of neritic limestones, clastic sedimentary rocks, hornblende biotite andesites, numerous felsic tuff layers, and limestones (Ketin 1951) contains in places Gzelian—Asselian (latest Carboniferous— earliest Permian) marine fossils (Keskin 1986) and in places Stephanian (latest Carboniferous) Euramerian plant fossils (R. H. Wagner, pers. comm. 1987) and is the cover to the pre-mid-Carboniferous basement.

To the S of locality 3 (Fig. 2) and across a complex of Neo-Tethyan sutures (Fig. 1), is the Bitlis Massif (Figs 2 & 3, loc. 5), itself consisting of several slices of pre-late Cretaceous basement tectonically interleaved with latest Cretaceous to middle Eocene back-arc basin basalts and sedimentary rocks (Şengör & Yılmaz 1981). Its pre-Cretaceous basement has two major sequences: The older one is a pre-Permian basement made up of amphibolite grade gneisses (felsic meta-volcanics), amphibolites, metavolcanics, metatuffs, and meta-agglomerates cut by two granite intrusions of early Carboniferous age (Helvacı & Griffin 1984). The whole assemblage is unconformably overlain by the younger sequence of quartzites, garnet—biotite micaschists and marbles, whose ages are believed to be Permian to late Cretaceous on the basis of local correlations (Şengör & Yılmaz 1981). Helvacı & Griffin (1984) have shown that the eruption ages of the gneissic meta-volcanics in the basement, which are the oldest dated rocks of the Bitlis Massif, are late Ordovician (Fig. 3, loc. 5). Thus the metamorphism of the basement at locality 5 (Fig. 3) is bracketed between late Ordovician and early Carboniferous and may

be correlative with the metamorphism in the Eastern Pontide basement (cf. Şengör & Yılmaz 1981). Although Yılmaz et al. (1987) have documented a very similar sequence in the Engizek Mountains (Figs 2 & 3, loc. 4) , no age data are as yet available from this region.

Farther W, in the basement of the Sakarya Continent, also a part of the Pontides (Fig. 1, Şengör & Yılmaz 1981), Ketin (1947, 1985) mapped quartzo-feldspathic gneisses, amphibolites and marbles in the Uludağ Massif (Figs 2 & 3, loc. 1). The age of this highly deformed association that resembles the Bitlis Massif basement, is unknown, except that it must be older than the Permian granodiorite plutons intruding it (Öztunal 1973). The marbles may have been originally unconformable on their gneissic and amphibolitic substratum (as in Bitlis), but later deformation has obscured the original relationship. By correlation with the Permian carbonate platform cover seen elsewhere on the Sakarya Continent (Şengör & Yılmaz 1981), the Uludağ marbles may also be Permian. Because they are intruded by the granodiorites, however, they must represent an older Permian. In the Uludağ Massif we may thus be looking at two orogenic events of late Palaeozoic age: the older possibly pre-marble (i.e. pre-Permian) and the younger pre-granodiorite (a certain Permian).

Our survey of the localities 1, 3—7 and 9—12, all of which are clearly located to the S of the main Palaeo-Tethyan suture zone, and some of which (4, 5 and 9) display clear Gondwanian Palaeozoic stratigraphy, shows that an important episode of multiple orogenic deformation, Barrovian metamorphism, and arc-type magmatic activity has characterized diverse regions near the N margin of Gondwana-Land in early Carboniferous through Permian time. Orogenic activity was particularly widespread in Carboniferous time, but lasted, in places, at least into the middle Permian. Therefore, the late Palaeozoic deformation in Oman was by no means a local anomaly in the N margin of Gondwana-Land.

Arabian Platform. Where do we place the Podataksasi Zone in Gondwana-Land? The obvious place to look first is the Arabian Platform.

An important Arabia-wide pre-Permian gap reaches a Silurian, but locally Ordovician or Devonian lower limit in different areas along the Arabian Platform's visible parts closer to its Palaeozoic margins (e.g. Figs 2 and 3, loc. 14). In most places along these margin-near regions deposition commenced with Lower to Upper Permian red sandstones bearing fossils of a possibly mixed Cathaysia and Gondwana-Land flora (Wagner 1962; Archangelsky & Wagner 1983; Ctyroky 1973). Beginning with the late Permian, shelf carbonate deposition with local centres of evaporites has commenced indicating open marine conditions away from the Arabian margin. Szabo & Kheradpir (1978) have shown that, at least locally, the Upper Permian sedimentary rocks (widespread limestones and dolomites, evaporites, and subordinate clastics of the Dalan Formation) were deposited in extensional basins. Record of Permian volcanism from the Arabian Palaeozoic margin is restricted to some basalt flows W of Dehbid in the S part of the Zagros Mountains (Berberian & King 1981) and to some of the internal units of the Hawasina nappes in Oman (Bechennec 1988). It seems clear that by late Permian time an extensional regime had begun affecting the Arabian Palaeozoic margins, at least along the present-day Zagros. Evidence for Permian extension is unknown in SE Turkey.

The only Carboniferous record from the Arabian margin comes from Precambrian igneous rocks brought up in salt plugs (Figs 2 and 3, loc. 15), which range from rhyolites, ignimbrites, through porphyritic felsic and mafic lavas to dolerites and dolerite gabbros. Crawford (1977) obtained from four samples of rock of similar petrography a whole rock isochron of 340±15 Ma (Visean). This may correspond with a Carboniferous event correlative with the early Carboniferous metamorphism in the Kor-e Sefid area (Fig. 2, loc. 10), and other coeval orogenic events in the Podataksasi Zone, suggesting that the latter was not far from Arabia in the early Carboniferous at least.

Interior Iran. The relationship between the Podataksasi Zone and the rest of Iran S of the main Palaeo-Tethyan suture zone is difficult to establish owing to widespread Tertiary and Quaternary cover, abrupt facies change, and complex deformations that occurred in Mesozoic and Cainozoic time. A continuous zone of depressions including those of Lake Urmieh, Tuzlu Gol, Gavkhuni, and the Jaz Murian completely hides the contact region between the Sanandaj–Sirjan Zone and interior Iran (Fig. 2). The very linearity of this zone (see also Berberian 1981, fig. 2) between Lake Urmieh and Isfandageh gives the impression of a strike-slip system at least partly responsible for its origin. Along its S extension, the Gavkhuni is delineated by some remarkably straight faults (Abadeh, Dehshir, Shar Babak, and Baft faults, Fig. 2), some of which have known Quaternary right-lateral strike-slip on them (Berberian 1981). Farther N along the boundary young faulting is not seen, but Stöcklin (1974b) in-

ferred the existence of steep faults separating the Sanandaj–Sirjan zone from interior Iran affecting a part of the Mesozoic and all older rocks (Fig. 5, sec. IV). Berberian & King (1981) and Davoudzadeh & Weber-Diefenbach (1987) have emphasized that the Palaeozoic rocks of the Sanandaj–Sirjan zone are of 'geosynclinal' facies in contrast to the platform facies of much of Interior Iran.

Interior Iran, which is thus separated from the Sanandaj–Sirjan Zone by a belt of steep, straight faults reaching well into the Mesozoic, consists of two distinct tectonic provinces. *The NW Iran tectonic province* comprises those regions N of the Doruneh Fault and S of the main Palaeo-Tethyan suture and extends into the S Soviet Union, into Nakhichevan, Armenia, and Svanetia (Fig. 1). *The Central Iranian Microcontinent* (Takin 1972) comprises the terrain delimited by the Sistan, Nain-Baft, and Makran ophiolitic belts plus the Doruneh Fault and the Sabzevar ophiolites (Fig. 1, Stöcklin 1974a, 1977; Berberian & King 1981; Davoudzadeh *et al.* 1981; Davoudzadeh & Schmidt 1984).

In itself, the Central Iranian Microcontinent is divided into three major sub-blocks by long, E-concave, N–S, right-lateral strike-slip faults (Fig. 1). The easternmost of these blocks, the Lut, has been the most stable since the late Precambrian and, according to Stöcklin (1968), constitutes the only genuine 'median mass' in Iran. It is separated from a Tabas block by the Nayband Fault (Fig. 2) along which the Jurassic 'Shotori Horst' (Stöcklin *et al.* 1965) has been a facies divider between the Tabas and the Lut blocks. The Tabas block is separated from the larger and internally imhomogeneous Yazd block by the curved faults of Kuh-e Kalsaneh and Kuh-e Banan (Fig. 2). The Posht-e Badam Fault may delimit an eastern sub-block of the Yazd.

These large N–S faults appear to have formed very early in the history of Central Iran. They have been persistent facies dividers since the Infracambrian (Stöcklin 1968; Berberian & King 1981) and were repeatedly reactivated in various rôles throughout the Phanerozoic. Many of them, or at least long stretches along them, are currently active and nucleate earthquakes (Berberian, 1981).

In sharp contrast to the Podataksasi Zone, the Central Iranian Microcontinent was a quiet platform region throughout the Palaeozoic until the late Triassic–early Jurassic time (Davoudzadeh & Weber-Diefenbach 1987). In it, the late Precambrian Pan-African orogeny (960–600 Ma in Central Iran) was followed by the establishment of a platform regime, during which alternating shallow-marine, lagoonal, and continental deposits were laid down (e.g. Fig. 3, locs. 27, 28, 29). Important sedimentary gaps exist in the Palaeozoic record in much of Central Iran, the most widespread of which are the earlier middle Devonian ('Eifelian Hiatus') and the Stephanian (late Carboniferous) lacunae (Stöcklin 1968; Berberian & King 1981; Weddige 1984a, 1984b; Davoudzadeh & Weber-Diefenbach 1987). The total thickness, ranging from Infracambrian to Middle Triassic, is surprisingly constant, between 3 and 4 km (Stöcklin 1968). There are, however, a number of regions within the Central Iranian Micro-continent whose late Palaeozoic/early Mesozoic record deviates considerably from the rest of Central Iran. I discuss these in the following paragraphs.

One region that differs somewhat from the rest of Central Iran with respect to its Palaezoic history is the Tabas block. Here Ruttner *et al.* (1968) discovered what Stöcklin (1968) calls probably the thickest and most complete Palaeozoic section in the Middle East, amounting on average to more than 8 km (Fig. 3, loc. 29; see esp. Ruttner 1980, Plate III). Bratash (1975) has made a compilation of the Infracambrian through Palaezoic thicknesses in this region, which he calls the Kerman—Kashmer through, and noted total thicknesses locally exceeding 10, and in one place 14 km. The 'Eifelian hiatus' is not seen here and is represented instead by a regressive facies of clastics and evaporites. Similarly, the Upper Carboniferous, lacking elsewhere in Central Iran, is present in this area and represented dominantly by shallow water carbonate rocks (Sardar Fm: see Davoudzadeh & Weber-Diefenbach 1987, fig. 1).

Both the igneous and the structural history of the Tabas block differ from the rest of the Central Iranian Microcontinent in being more lively throughout the Palaeozoic. Both mafic and intermediate volcanism characterized this region during the Palaeozoic, though not abundantly (Berberian & King) 1981. Bratash (1975) pointed out that the strongly subsident character of the Tabas block formerly was thought to be confined to the Shirgesht—Ozbak—Kuh Mountains in the extreme N of the block, but is now known to have characterized the entire block throughout the Palaeozoic and the Mesozoic until the Cretaceous. He noted the presence of 'inversion' events (?compressional) in early Triassic or possibly even earlier in the N part of the Tabas block in the Kashmer area.

Another locality, whose Palaeozoic evolution was unlike the rest of Central Iran in a different

way is the Saghand area (Fig. 2, just E of the Posht-e Badam Fault; also Davoudzadeh & Weber-Diefenbach 1987, fig. 1, N of their loc. 8). Here Crawford (1977) obtained a reliable Rb/Sr age of 315±5 Ma on a single biotite from the Saghand metamorphic complex of late Proterozoic age, indicating an isotopic disturbance of earlier late Carboniferous. From whole rock and biotite analyses Crawford (1977) also found evidence for a younger event at 240±15 Ma (late Permian to earliest Triassic). Berberian and King (1981) noted that this 'event' did not fit with any known orogenic movement in Central Iran, although a similar age has been obtained from the Precambrian volcanics in the Takab region (Figs 2 & 3, loc. 8) suggesting also a rejuvenation event.

By their very different geological evolution from the rest of the region as a whole, two other regions stand out in the Central Iranian Micro-continent. In contrast to the two cases discussed above, however, they can be readily identified as torn and now-displaced pieces of tectonic units known from outside the Central Iranian Microcontinent.

One of these regions is the metamorphic complex of Deh Salm (Figs 2 & 3, loc. 13). Here Stöcklin *et al.* (1972) found a sequence consisting of a regular alternation of schists and marbles with subordinate amphibolites associated with the marbles in its lower half, and phyllites and quartz micaschists locally containing graphite in its upper half. The whole sequence is highly deformed in which metamorphism increases from upper greenschist facies in the W to amphibolite facies in the E. Reyre & Mohafez (1970, p. 983) have reported Rb/Sr ages of 206±10 and 209±2 Ma corresponding with an interval of possibly latest Triassic to earliest Jurassic. A Rb/Sr age on biotite from the eastern high grade region gives a middle Jurassic age of 165±10 Ma (Crawford 1977). Although the metamorphic zone E of Deh Salm has been studied only on a reconnaissance basis, Berberian (1977) suggested that it represented an area deformed and metamorphosed during the late Triassic—early Jurassic Palaeo-Tethyan ocean closure, a suggestion accepted by most later workers (e.g. Davoudzadeh & Schmidt 1984; Sengör 1987a). Davoudzadeh & Weber-Diefenbach (1987) have speculated that the Deh Salm metamorphics also underwent a late Palaeozoic episode of deformation and metamorphism. I here follow Davoudzadeh & Schmidt (1984) in interpreting the Deh Salm metamorphics as a displaced fragment of the Sanandaj—Sirjan Zone, i.e. a part of the larger Podataksasi Zone.

The final region with a deviant geological history in the Central Iranian Microcontinent which I discuss here is the Anarek region (Figs 2 & 3, loc. 20, Berberian & King 1981; Davoudzadeh *et al.* 1981; Davoudzadeh & Schmidt 1984), also referred to as the Anarek–Khvor massif (Roman'ko & Morozov 1983). This metamorphic complex consists of a sequence of limestones, schists, dolomites, amphibolites, and phyllites, overlain across a thrust contact by a dolomite-limestone succession known as the Kuh-e Lakh marbles (Roman'ko & Morozov 1983). The lower sequence has tectonically interleaved slices of ultramafic rocks found in NNE-vergent schuppen in the Anarek region itself (Roman'ko and Morozov 1983, fig. 2). Metamorphism in the Anarek region was in greenschist facies. The Anarek metamorphic complex greatly resembles those near Mashhad and in the Talesh Mountains and also the metasediments and ophiolites of the Chorchana–Utslevi zone in the Dzirula Massif. Its age is considered pre-middle Triassic, as Davoudzadeh & Seyed-Emami (1972) have reported clasts of the metamorphic rocks from the late Anisian–early Ladinian Baqoroq Conglomerate of the nearby Nakhlak Group (see below). Isotopic dating of the various parts of the metamorphic complex gave a wide spectrum of ages ranging from late Precambrian to early Jurassic (Fig. 3, loc. 20), all of which correspond with tectonic events known from a number of places in Iran, and is not precise enough to enable one to assign the Anarek massif unambiguously to any one tectonic unit in Iran and surrounding region.

By contrast, the younger and probably overlying Nakhlak Group of sedimentary rocks ranging from Lower to Middle Triassic very much resembles the Triassic sequence known from Aghdarband (Fig. 2, loc. 19) and indicates clearly that the Nakhlak Group is its correlative belonging most likely to the same tectonic unit, i.e. to Laurasia (Davoudzadeh *et al.* 1981; Davoudzadeh & Schmidt 1984; Ruttner 1984).

The Palaeozoic history of what I here call NW Iran (Fig. 1) appears very similar to that of Central Iran, although it is more difficult to interpret because outcrop is scarcer and the relations of well studied outcrops to one another are hidden under younger cover (Fig. 2, locs. 24, 25, and 26). In these regions, an Infracambrian to Middle Triassic platform cover shows no evidence of late Palaeozoic orogenic activity, and modest, mainly mafic volcanism. The total thickness of the platform cover in these outcrops is, as in Central Iran, around 3 km or so, with the exception of the Alborz

Mountains with a Palaeozoic thickness of more than 7 km (Fig. 3, loc. 26), similar to that on the Tabas block. The volcanic evolution of the Alborz Palaeozoic is also similar to that of the Tabas block in being livelier than in other places in NW Iran (Berberian & King 1981). Also, a Mesozoic Pb–Zn–Cu mineralization occurring in Permian, Triassic, and Jurassic rocks seems common to the Tabas (Friedrich 1960) and Alborz (Brandner *et al.* 1981) regions further underlining the similarities between the two areas.

Although neither the Alborz (Fig. 2, loc. 26), nor the Azerbaijan (Fig. 2, loc. 24) outcrops display any evidence of strong Mesozoic metamorphism, a late Triassic to early Jurassic low grade greenschist metamorphism together with polyphase penetrative deformation similar to that seen in the S part of the Sanandaj–Sirjan zone was reported from the Kuh-e Dom area (Figs 2 & 3, loc. 25) by Roman'ko & Sharkovskiy (1984). How this metamorphic region relates to the unmetamorphosed Palaeozoic section in Soh to its immediate W (and to other outcrops in NW Iran) remains unknown.

Another isolated metamorphic outcrop in NW Iran is near Torud (Fig. 2, loc. To). Here predominantly clastic and carbonate rocks with subordinate volcanics include Lower–Middle Devonian or possibly Silurian corals. In this region the age of metamorphism could be anything between late Devonian and Triassic according to Thiele (1973), and may be even late Jurassic according to Hushmandzadeh *et al.* (1978). Analogy with the Kuh-e Dom region suggests a late Triassic event, although Davoudzadeh and Weber-Diefenbach (1987) consider it late Palaeozoic.

Outcrops exposing complete or nearly complete Palaeozoic to at least Upper Triassic record exist farther to the NW both in Iran and in Transcaucasia. The Djulfa region in NW Iran and Nakhichevan, for example, is a classical locality (Figs 2 & 3, loc. 24), in which a Silurian to Middle Jurassic platform cover contains no angular unconformities (Bonnet & Bonnet 1947; Schikalibeili 1984). Altiner *et al.* (1979) have documented a Lower Griesbachian (Lowermost Triassic) hiatus here that was manifestly a result of uplift owing to limited extensional deformation. The Precambrian basement of this zone is exposed about 200 km farther to the NW in the Mishkan zone (Fig. 2, loc. Mi), where isotopic dating indicates an age of 660 Ma (Abesadze *et al.* 1982), in sharp contrast to the late Palaeozoic ages only 100 km farther N across the Sevan-Akera–Karadagh suture (Fig. 1).

Much farther N, in the Svanetia region (Figs 2 & 3, loc. 23), Adamia & Belov (1984) have documented a complete, nearly volcanic-free (exceptions are Devonian tuffs and tuff breccias of andesitic composition and Middle Carboniferous rhyolitic and dacitic tuffs) sedimentary sequence extending from palaeontologically documented Middle Devonian to Upper Triassic. Lias is in 'abnormal', probably unconformable contact with this Dizi Series (Khain 1975 and my own observation during the IGC field excursion led by S. A. Adamia & A. A. Belov in 1984) that had been strongly deformed before the Liassic shales were deposited. The Dizi Series thus represents a region free of any orogenic deformation between the early Devonian and the latest Triassic. In this respect it very much resembles other sequences in NW Iran, except that it is now separated from them by fragments of the former Podataksasi Zone such as the Dzirula, Khrami, and the Loki massifs. In a single cross section extending from Svanetia to about Takab (i.e. between locs 23 and 8 in Fig. 2), therefore, remnants of the former Podataksasi Zone and NW Iran tectonic units are repeated at least twice as follows:

1 – Svanetia	}	(NW Iran)
1 – Dzirula	⎫	
Khrami	⎬	(Podataksasi Zone)
Loki	⎭	
2 – Mishkan	⎫	(NW Iran)
Djulfa	⎭	
2 – Takab	}	(Podataksasi Zone)

Evidence for the Mesozoic disruption of the Cimmeride orogen in the Middle East

Terrains characterized by late Palaeozoic orogeny, especially the Podataksasi zone, are also commonly characterised by late Triassic to early Jurassic orogenic activity, which, in places, can be interpreted as resulting from continental collision.

All along the Podataksasi Zone, Upper Triassic or various levels of Lower to Middle Jurassic rocks consisting commonly of continental molasse type deposits rest on older rocks across a profound unconformity (Fig. 3, locs 1–4, 6–8, and 10–11) caused mainly by intense folding, thrusting, and/or strike-slip faulting. A look at localities 6, 7, 8, and 13 in the Podataksasi Zone in Fig. 3 shows that some of the areas from where we have stratigraphic evidence for Triassic and Jurassic deformation also yield isotopic evidence indicating the same. In addition, areas of known or suspected late

Palaeozoic deformation in N and interior Iran (locs 18, 19, 20, and 25 in Fig. 3) also display isotopic evidence for Triassic and Jurassic deformation.

By contrast in Central Iran Upper Triassic and Jurassic rocks rest on older rocks locally disconformably or across generally low-angle unconformities caused only by tilting (e.g. Stöcklin et al. 1965, fig. 24; Stöcklin 1968). Only locally, and dominantly along the main divider faults of Nayband, Kuh-e Kalsaneh, Kuh-e Banan, and Posht-e Badam do we see folding and metamorphism of late Triassic–early Jurassic age in Central Iran (e.g. Ruttner et al. 1968, figs 26 & 27; Stöcklin 1968, fig. 4; Haghipour et al. 1977, pp. 61–63; Berberian & King, 1981). Even then, these events were not associated with magmatic activity in Central Iran, except in a few places around the Central Iranian Microcontinent (e.g. Airakan, Shirkuh: Berberian & Berberian 1981, Ai and Sh in Fig. 2 respectively).

The present distribution of the two types of sub-Upper Triassic or Lower Jurassic unconformities is not as simple as one would expect and strongly suggests that a simpler original pattern was later disrupted (Fig. 1). Following the collision of the Cimmerian continent with Laurasia, the internal deformation of the former commenced. This deformation was dominated by germanotype, i.e. blocky, non-penetrative structures, whose evolution was mainly governed by strike-slip fault systems resulting in the 130° counter-clockwise rotation of the Central Iranian Microcontinent (Davoudzadeh et al., 1981), the emplacement of the various fragments of the Podataksasi Zone into their present locations, and the opening of the Slate–Diabase Zone, Sevan–Akera–Karadagh ocean, and the oceans surrounding the Central Iranian Microcontinent (Şengör 1987a; Şengör et al. 1988).

Shortly after the collision of the Cimmerian Continent with Laurasia, extensional deformation commenced along long stretches of the suture zone. In the Greater Caucasus, by the Sinemurian the Slate–Diabase Zone (Fig. 1) began forming directly astride the Palaeo-Tethyan suture as evidenced by fault-controlled subsidence, leading to deposition of conglomerates, sandstones, and shales in small basins, accompanied by rhyolitic-dacitic volcanics. Beridze's (1984) diagrams (his fig. 27 on pp. 146–147) clearly show interfingering of turbidite fans shed from both the N and the S, implying that the width of the Slate-Diabase Zone remained modest through the early Jurassic.

In the Lesser Caucasus along the Sevan–Akera–Karadagh suture, early Jurassic extension led to the development of narrow grabens at the site of the present Mishkan and Karabagh zones (Fig. 2, between locs. Mi and Tb). In the Khoura Depression, the Saatly deep well (Fig. 2) traversed nearly 4.5 km-thick dacites, basalts, andesites, diorite porphyries, and tuffs of early and middle Jurassic age (Abdullaev & Guseinov 1984), indicating considerable coeval extension. Farther E, in many places along the Alborz Mountains, tholeiitic 'within plate' basalts immediately underlie the Shemshak Formation, suggesting that collision may have predated extension only by a very small interval (Berberian & King 1981; Brandner et al. 1981). These latest Triassic to early Jurassic extensional events were coeval with compressional events elsewhere in the Cimmerian Continent. In the Saghand region (W of the Posth-e Badam fault in Fig. 2), for example, Jurassic rocks are unconformable on folded, faulted, and imbricated Upper Triassic metamorphic rocks (Haghipour et al. 1977).

During the middle to late Jurassic extensional tectonics continued uninterruptedly in the Slate–Diabase Zone with increased volcanism including tholeiitic basalts and andesitic basalts. The Sevan–Akera–Karadagh graben complexes were enlarged and ophiolite generation by sea-floor spreading began in the resultant trough (Knipper & Sokolov 1976; Gasanov 1986). Farther E in the Alborz Mountains this extension was represented by an extensive basaltic volcanism. In the Kopet Dagh basin, extension-related, normal fault-controlled subsidence began in middle Jurassic time (Bathonian) and accelerated progresively until the end of the Jurassic, reaching its peak in the early Cretaceous (Berriasian : Prozorovskiy 1985).

The middle Jurassic through early Cretaceous time interval was probably also characterized by extensional tectonics in the oceans surrounding the Central Iranian Microcontinent. Although no Jurassic rocks have yet been identified in them, clear evidence for the presence of early Cretaceous deep marine environments exist in the Sabzevar region (Fig. 2, Lindenberg et al. 1984).

While extension characterized the Slate–Diabase Zone in the Greater Caucasus, the Sevan–Akera–Karadagh zone in the Lesser Caucasus, the Alborz and Kopet Dagh regions in N Iran and in the S USSR, and parts of the periphery of the Central Iranian Microcontinent, compressional deformation, metamorphism, and magmatism were going on elsewhere in the Middle Eastern Tethysides. In the S part of the Sanandaj–Sirjan Zone, Berberian & King (1981) noted late Jurassic–early Cretaceous low- to medium-pressure metamorphism and compressional deformation accompanied by coeval andesitic volcanism and intrusions ranging from gabbro to granite with K/Ar ages between 118 ± 10 and 164 ± 4 Ma (Berberian & Berberian 1981). Other intrusions of similar age also exist farther up the Sanandaj–Sirjan Zone possibly indicating that the subduction of Neo-Tethys may have commenced already under the Sanandaj–Sirjan Zone by the late Jurassic to early Cretaceous interval (Berberian & Berberian, 1981).

Late Jurassic to early Cretaceous granites are also seen in the Central Iranian Microcontinent. Near Airakan (Ai in Fig. 2), in the W part of the Yazd block (Shirkuh granite) and along the E margin of the Lut block, these intrusions suggest subduction of oceanic lithosphere of the oceans around the Central Iranian Microcontinent. Although subduction-related compressional deformation characterised much of the Sanandaj–Sirjan Zone in the late Jurassic–early Cretaceous interval, in the Sanandaj region itself, rapid subsidence led to the deposition of 2–3 km of shales of Barremian–Aptian age, probably indicative of local extension.

Structural evidence for crustal shortening of late Jurassic–early Cretaceous age in Iran comes, in addition to the Sanandaj–Sirjan Zone, from the Ardakan region, where Jurassic rocks are intensely folded, exhibit slaty cleavage, and are unconformably overlain by Albian limestones (Haghipour et al. 1977).

The late Cretaceous is the time when shortening became by far the dominant form of deformation in the Middle Eastern Tethysides S of the Caspian Sea–Black Sea axis. Both the Slate–Diabase Zone and the Sevan–Akera–Karadagh oceans became sites of S-vergent compressional deformation (Khain 1975). Ophiolite obduction onto the edge of NW Iran from the Sevan–Akera–Karadagh ocean commenced possibly in pre-Albian time but definitely by the Cenomanian and was completed by late Coniacian (Khain 1975; Knipper & Sokolov 1976; Gasanov 1986). Widespread early Cretaceous through Palaeogene calc-alkaline magmatism characterized areas N of the Sevan–Akera–Karadagh suture all the way from NE Turkey to well into the W Alborz (Lordkipanidze 1980, figs 12, 19, & 35).

The beginning of the main compressional deformation in the Alborz Mountains also falls into the late Cretaceous, although the major deformation was a Palaeocene affair. The deformation was largely amagmatic and was accompanied in a few areas only by a metamorphism that was incipient at most. N of the Alborz Mountains, late Cretaceous was a period of mostly extensional activity. It was at this time that the S Caspian Sea and the Black Sea (since the Aptian) began rifting (Apol'skiy 1974; Görür 1988) and the Kopet Dagh basin continued to subside.

The post-collisional, late Triassic to mid-Cretaceous tectonic evolution of the Middle Eastern Tethysides thus exhibits an irregular and confusing picture, one in which extensional and compressional deformations occurred coevally in different parts of the orogen and alternated in the same places. A horst-graben pattern was formed in the late Triassic-early Jurassic in interior Iran, and another, independent one in the late Jurassic-early Cretaceous time span. Some of these grabens accumulated more than 5 km of Jurassic, i.e. more than three times thicker than the thickest Jurassic section known from the Zagros (Stöcklin 1968). Repeated and commonly contrasting types of deformation along old fault zones, especially in interior Iran and in the S USSR within our area of interest (Fig. 2), has been constantly stressed by most authors writing on the tectonic evolution of this part of the world (e.g. Stöcklin 1968; Berberian 1981; Berberian & King 1981; Davoudzadeh & Schmidt 1984 for Iran, Kravchenko et al. 1976; Şengör 1984; Prozorovskiy 1985 for the Turkmenian SSR). Many of these authors have also noticed that most of these repeatedly activated fault zones have displayed, at different times in their history, considerable strike-slip movement (e.g. Ruttner et al. 1968; Apol'skiy 1974; Berberian 1981; Şengör 1987a), but direct evidence for Mesozoic wrench faulting is known only from the borders of the Tabas block (Ruttner et al. 1968; Berberian 1981) and from the Dzirula Massif (Adamia et al. 1982; Şengör 1987a, 1987b). Indirect evidence for Mesozoic strike-slip movement in the Middle Eastern Tethysides is abundant, however, and comes mainly from a combination of shape of fault trace, cross-sectional aspect of fault zone, and palaeomagnetism, supplanted locally by the presence of inferred pull-apart basins. A large number of the major fault zones dividing the Middle Eastern Tethysides into separate tectono-stratigraphic units have many, if not most of the characteristics of strike-slip faults.

In the Shirgesht region Ruttner et al. (1968) established a minimum of 40 to 50 km of right-lateral offset along the Kuh-e Kalsaneh fault (Fig. 2) by the displacement of the Permo-Triassic facies. Along the S prolongation of the same fault zone, we see a number of spindle-shaped Palaeozoic outcrops that look as if they have been entrained along the fault zone. Farther S, cross section VI in Fig. 5 traverses the fault zone. It displays a remarkable fan- (or 'palm-tree') shaped cross section with faults of dominantly reverse separation with one exception (fault marked 'N'). The age of faulting here is difficult to establish, except that the youngest age of its initiation must be earlier than a certain Cretaceous.

Another example is the Dehshir–Shar-Babak–Baft fault system on which Recent (and active) right-lateral strike-slip has been observed (Berberian 1981), whereas Mesozoic strike-slip has been inferred, because of an 130° counter-clockwise rotation of the Central Iranian Microcontinent as a whole (Davoudzadeh et al. 1981; Soffel & Förster, 1985). Cross section V in Fig. 5 corroborates this inference by showing a fault zone of inconsistent vergence defining two palm trees side-by-side along which dominant separation is normal with three exceptions (faults marked 'R').

The third example is from locality 21 (Fig. 2), where Ruttner (1989, pers. comm. 1988) has shown the presence of a zone of steep faulting with inconsistent vergence, where the cross-sectional pattern is more of a tulip than a palm tree, and argued for considerable left-lateral strike-slip (Fig. 5, cross section I).

As noted above, the Sanandaj–Sirjan zone is separated from the rest of interior Iran either by strike-slip fault zones (Abadeh, Dehshir, Shar Babak, and Baft faults) or by long, linear depressions likely controlled by strike-slip faults. Cross section IV in Fig. 5 shows a pattern of faulting reminiscent of the cases exhibited in Fig. 5, cross sections V and VI. I interpret it as half a palm tree plus another steep zone of faulting caused by considerable strike-slip. The cross section IV in Fig. 5 shows that some of the faults bounding the Sanandaj–Sirjan Ranges to the NE were active only in the Mesozoic. The interpretation of the 2–3 km thick Barremian to Aptian shale sequence near Sanandaj (see above) as a possible pull-apart fill suggests strike-slip activity of this age at least.

Both the Alborz and the late Cretaceous to later Cainozoic Greater Caucasus (cross sections II and III in Fig. 5) have fan-shaped cross sections. The Greater Caucasus has been interpreted as a dominantly transpressional orogenic belt (e.g. Apol'skiy 1974). Both the Alborz and the Greater Caucasus display an anastomozing fault pattern with characteristic palm tree cross sections. This is all the more remarkable, since 'the Alborz Belt is not an orogenic belt of its own, but only a partial belt of a much vaster orogenic region, which includes all of Iran ...' (Stöcklin 1974b, p. 220, also 1960). Although the Greater Caucasus does not show alternating normal and reverse separations in any given cross section, the Alborz does (in cross section II, Fig. 5, faults marked 'N' have normal separation).

In Transcaucasia and in Turkey the intense late Cainozoic compression with accompanying widespread volcanicity (Dewey *et al.* 1986) have largely obscured the earmarks of older, Mesozoic strike-slip systems. That they were there is known, however, from their preserved remnants such as the Chorchana–Utslevi Zone in the Dzirula Massif. Neither the amount, nor the original orientation of the shear zones preserved in such small pieces can be told by looking at these random fragments, however, because of the likely rotations around vertical axes they have undergone since (cf. Jackson & McKenzie, 1984). All these remnants do is to alert us to the presence of strike-slip faults in the past.

In the following interpretative model extensive use is made of such strike-slip faults without giving detailed justification for each, both because space would not permit doing so here, and because for a number of the strike-slip faults I postulate such independent justification, except for obvious map and cross-sectional aspects, is not yet available.

Late Palaeozoic to late Cretaceous tectonic evolution of the Middle Eastern Tethysides: a speculative model

The evolutionary model presented in this section is based mainly on the data reviewed above and on the palaeomagnetic data reported by Wensink (1979, 1982, 1983), Wensink & Varecamp (1980), Wensink *et al.* (1978), and Soffel & Förster (1984). The main tenets of the model are the recognition of the Podataksasi Zone as a once coherent magmatic arc, the 130° counter-clockwise Mesozoic rotation of what is now the Central Iranian Microcontinent, and their union via extensive strike-slip faulting through the Mesozoic.

Late Palaeozoic evolution

During the Carboniferous and early Permian, the NE margin of Gondwana-Land between Turkey and Australia was rimmed discontinuously but for considerable distances by a continental margin arc. This arc was formed from

the Podataksasi Zone in the W, the Alborz and Tabas regions in the middle, and the Central Pamirs (Shvolman 1978) in the E. In the Podataksasi Zone and in the Central Pamirs, the arc was well-developed and considerably long-lived (in the Podataksasi Zone ?early Carboniferous to late Triassic, in the Central Pamirs early Permian to Triassic). By contrast, in the Alborz and in the Tabas block its presence is suggested by dominantly mafic with subordinate intermediate volcanism, and by early deformation in the Saghand region, in the northernmost Tabas block (Kashmar region: Bratash, 1974), and in Djulfa (Altiner *et al.* 1979). If the suggestions of Roman'ko & Sharkovskiy (1984) and Davoudzadeh & Weber-Diefenbach (1987) about late Palaeozoic metamorphism and deformation in the NW Iran block is correct, this may be viewed as one possible manifestation of the late Palaeozoic arc in NW Iran.

The geometry of NE Gondwana-Land in Carboniferous through early Permian time is obtained by placing all the torn strips of continental material shown in Fig. 6A (i.e. parts of the Cimmerian Continent in the Middle Eastern Tethysides), except the E Qangtang block, back into their former places. The way such a reconstruction is obtained is as follows: In Turkey, zones of intense Triassic deformation (e.g. locs 2 and 4 in Fig. 2) occur on both sides of Neo-Tethyan sutures. Any reconstruction must bring these areas into some sort of continuity (Şengör *et al.* 1984; Yılmaz *et al.* 1987). Once the Pontides, and the Kırşehir block are fitted back into their proper positions as suggested by Şengör *et al.* (1984), the W end of the Podataksasi Zone becomes fixed. Its eastern prolongations in Transcaucasia (D, AT/AK in Fig. 6A), the Sanandaj–Sirjan Zone, the Makran and the eastern Lut are then juxtaposed against Arabia. As both NW Iran and the Central Iranian Microcontinent have late Proterozoic Pan-African basements and Gondwanian Palaeozoic cover resembling those of Arabia, they must have belonged to a position more 'internal' than the Podataksasi Zone with respect to Gondwana-Land. As the Alborz and the Tabas regions are interpreted as former passive continental margins turned into continental margin arcs, I line them up with the Podataksasi Zone and place NW Iran and Central Iran against Gondwana-Land as the SE continuation of the Arabian Platform. Further details of this reconstruction and information about SE Asian segments are in Şengör *et al.* (1988).

As compressional deformation lasted until well into the Permian time in a number of places in the Podataksasi arc itself, I believe it remained a compressional arc in Dewey's (1980) sense, at least in places, between early Carboniferous and a certain early Permian time. In the early Permian it began to change character and was fully extensional by mid-Permian time (except in Golpaygan area and in Turkey?). This extension may have been the cause of the cessation of the compressional deformation in Oman and the beginning rifting of Neo-Tethys all along the Zagros, as evidenced by the Dehbid and Omani basalts and normal faulting in the Kuh-e Dinar area (Szabo & Kheradpir 1978). In Oman, the Hawasina basin (Hamrat Duru basin of Bechennec 1988) was the locus of extension and Bechennec's (1988) Baid platform was probably rifted away from Arabia as a part of the Podataksasi arc.

Triassic evolution

By the early Triassic (Fig. 6A), intracontinental extension behind the Podataksasi arc had created a complex back-arc basin between it and N Gondwana-Land all the way from Turkey to Oman. In Turkey, this marginal basin possessed an intra-basin platform, the Kirşehir block, probably similar to the present-day Yamato bank in the Sea of Japan. In Oman, the Baid platform began falling apart by middle to late Triassic time, the locus of extension having migrated northeastwards, and the main Neo-Tethyan basin began forming (Fig. 6A). Many of the Oman exotics were seamounts in an extending marginal basin, perhaps much like the Magnaghi, Vavilov, Marsili, and Usticha seamounts in the Tyrrhenian Sea and were left 'behind', i.e. on the Arabian side as the locus of extension migrated away from Arabia. As in the case of the Tyrrhenian Sea, some of these seamounts may have had an oceanic foundation (e.g. Glennie et al. 1974), while others may have been built on an ensialic substratum (e.g. Bechennec 1988).

Since the middle Triassic, the rate of opening of Neo-Tethys must have been at least some 15 cm/a to enable the Podataksasi arc to rotate counter-clockwise across Palaeo-Tethys and to collide, by Rhaetian time, with Laurasia (cf. Şengör 1987b, figs 3A, B). This rate is substantially smaller than the several tens of cm/a spreading rate obtained from the Japan sea back-arc basin in the W Pacific (Niitsuma et al. 1988).

Figure 6B shows the Rhaetian geometry of the Middle Eastern Cimmerides. The Podataksasi arc plus NW and Central Iran have collided with Laurasia along the main

Palaeo-Tethyan suture as a monolith, although late Triassic strike-slip deformation is suggested in Central Iran by the deformation along the margins of the Yazd, Tabas, and Lut blocks, i.e. in the Saghand area (Haghipour et al. 1977) and the Shotori Range respectively (Stöcklin et al. 1965). Molasse deposition, represented by the Shemshak Formation and its equivalents, commenced in areas along the suture, although right-lateral movement of the Yazd, Tabas, and Lut blocks were coevally disrupting this simple pattern as depicted in Fig. 6B. As a result of the collision in Iran, Palaeo-Tethys became reduced to Eastern Mediterranean-type remnant oceans in N Turkey and in Afghanistan. In both regions, large accretionary flysch/melange wedges similar to the present-day Eastern Mediterranean Ridge (Le Pichon 1983) were growing (Fig. 6B). The N Turkish remnant of Palaeo-Tethys, in which the Akgöl (N Turkey), Tauridian (Crimea), Nalbant (N Dobrudja), and Lipaçka (Strandja Mountains) flysch complexes were being deposited, closed by the later early Jurassic possibly by an initial right-lateral motion of the Cimmerian Continent as a whole with respect to Laurasia, as suggested in Fig. 6B. Between the Caucasus and Afghanistan, Palaeo-Tethys closed along two subduction zones of opposing polarity, much like the present Molucca Sea colision zone (Silver & Moore 1978). The initial right-lateral movement of the Cimmerian Continent was likely nucleated along this suture and may have been the cause of the shearing observed in the Chorchana-Utslevi Zone that involves ophiolites and remnants of former magmatic arcs (Fig. 6B, loc. D, Şengör 1987a). The same strike-slip movement may have been responsible for the pre-Shemshak basalt eruptions in N Iran.

Jurassic evolution

An important change introduced into the evolution of the Middle Eastern Cimmerides by possibly as early as the Pliensbachian was the onset of the independent left-lateral coastwise transport, to use a term of Beck (1988), of the Podataksasi arc mostly along a line coincident with the former Palaeo-Tethyan suture, but passing S of the NW and Central Iranian fragments. The initial rifting of the Slate–Diabase zone in the Greater Caucasus was probably a pull-apart event. The extension that very closely followed the collision in the Lesser Caucasus (Sevan–Akera–Karadagh rifting), in the Khoura basement (volcanics in the Saatly well), and in N Iran (Shemshak basins) may represent

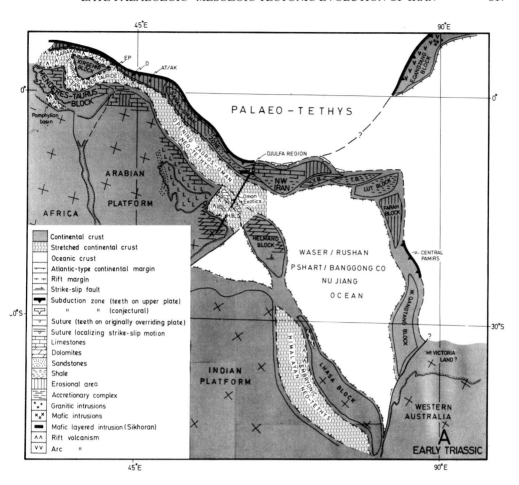

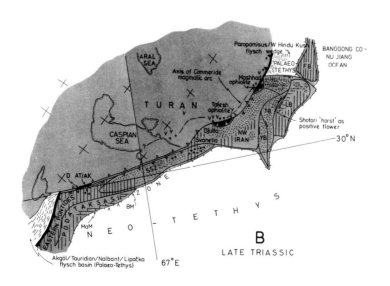

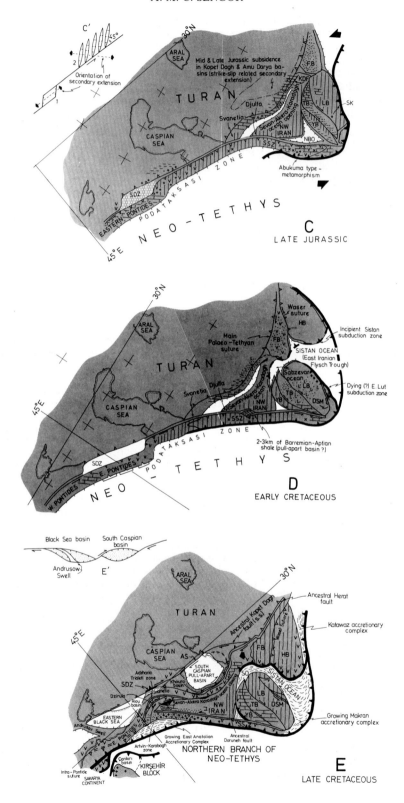

secondary extension related to the strike-slip movement of the Podataksasi zone (Fig. 6C and C'2). The counter-clockwise rotation of Iran began in the Jurassic according to palaeo-magnetic data (Soffel & Förster 1984) and may have been accomplished by the initial rifting of the Nain–Baft ocean, the western segment of the Circum-Central Iranian Microcontinent oceans.

As the Fig. 6C suggests, the rotation of Central Iran was probably caused by the coast-wise transport of the Podataksasi Zone, and by Central Iran's being 'pinned' in the NE by the already collided Farah block in early Jurassic time creating a shear couple. This interpretation brings an elegant solution to the otherwise hard-to-explain independent rotation of the Central Iranian Microcontinent.

Throughout the Jurassic, the extensional regions of the Slate–Diabase Zone, Sevan–Akera–Karadagh, and Nain–Baft oceans continued to stretch. In the Sevan–Akera–Karadagh ocean, sea-floor spreading began in middle to late Jurassic time and extension commenced in the Kopet Dagh basin in the middle Jurassic. The Kopet Dagh extension was pro-bably also a result of secondary extension related to the strike-slip movement of the Podataksasi Zone (Fig. 6C' 2).

The middle to late Jurassic was also a time of increased compressional deformation, meta-morphism, and arc-related magmatic activity in Iran and in Caucasia. As shown in Fig. 6C, this is ascribed partly to the onset of subduction both under the E and S margin of the Lut block and under the SW margin of the Sanandaj–Sirjan Zone. Evidence for these events comes from the Sorkh-Kuh granite in the central Lut (Fig. 6C), and isotopic ages around 170 Ma indicating metamorphism in the Sanandaj–Sirjan Zone including the Deh Salm area in eastern Lut (Berberian & King 1981; Davoudzadeh & Schmidt 1984).

The late Jurassic subduction zone that was active along the E and S sides of the Lut block and along the S extremity of the Sanandaj–Sirjan Zone has propagated sideways in a northerly direction along the SW margin of the Sanandaj–Sirjan Zone throughout the late Jurassic–early Cretaceous interval and reached the S margin of the Rhodope–Pontide fragment by Albian time (Fig. 6D, Görür 1988).

Fig. 6. Palaeotectonic maps depicting the tectonic evolution of the Middle Eastern Tethysides from the early Triassic to late Cretaceous. The base maps have been modified from Şengör et al. (1988) on the basis of the considerations presented in this paper and on the palaeomagnetic results of Soffel and Förster (1984). Palaeogeographic information is mainly from Şengör & Yılmaz (1981), and Görür et al. (1984) for Turkey, Berberian & Berberian (1981), Berberian & King (1981), Davoudzadeh & Schmidt (1984) for Iran, Beridze (1984) for the Greater Caucasus, Knipper & Sokolov (1976) and Gasanov (1986) for the Lesser Caucasus, Lippard et al. (1986) and Bernoulli & Weissert (1987) for Oman, and Wolfart & Wittekindt (1980) for Afghanistan. Key to abbreviations: AT/AK, Adzharia/Trialeti and Artvin/Karabagh zones; BM, Bitlis Massif; D, Dzirula Massif; DSM, Deh Salm metamorphics; FB, Farah Block; HB, Hawasina Basin (in A), Helmand Block (in B-E), KDF, Kopet Dagh Fault (normal); LB, Lut Block; MaM, Malatya Metamorphics; NBO, Nain/ Baft Ocean; SDZ, Slate-Diabase Zone; SO, Sabzevar Ocean, SSZ, Sanandaj–Sirjan Zone; TB, Tabas Block; YB, Yazd Block (LB+TB+YB = Central Iranian Microcontinent).

(A) Palaeotectonic map of the South-Central Tethysides in early Triassic time. Wavy symbol at the southern extremity of the Sanandaj–Sirjan Zone indicates contemporary orogenic deformation and metamorphism. The line X–X' is the approximate location of the cross-section shown in Fig. 7A.

(B) Palaeotectonic map of the northern and middle parts of the Middle Eastern Tethysides in late Triassic time. Note here that the circum-Black Sea part of the Palaeo-Tethys (Akgöl/Tauridian/Nalbant/Lipacka flysch basin) is still open and the Podataksasi zone is now moving *right-laterally* to close it.

(C) Palaeotectonic map of the northern and middle parts of the Middle Eastern Tethysides in late Jurassic time. Notice on this map that the Slate–Diabase Zone of the Greater Caucasus is opening as a typical pull-apart basin (as in C'1), while the Sevan–Akera–Karadagh and the Nain– Baft (NBO) oceans are forming by tearing of the Central Iranian Microcontinent away from NW Iran and the latter from Turan by the left-laterally moving Podataksasi zone. Of these the Seven– Akera–Karadagh ocean probably formed in a similar way to tension gashes along strike-slip zones as illustrated in C'2 (Homquist 1932; Wilson 1960). SK is Sorkh Kuh granite.

(D) Palaeotectonic map of the northern and middle parts of the Middle Eastern Tethysides in early Cretaceous time.

(E) Palaeotectonic map of the northern and middle parts of the Middle Eastern Tethysides in late Cretaceous time. Here notice especially how parts of the Podataksasi zone (Dzirula, Adzharia–Trialeti basement and the Artvin–Karabagh zones) are inserted sideways, in the form of transpressional splinters, into the closing Sevan–Akera–Karadagh ocean. Also notice that the entire Middle Eastern Cimmeride collage begins to move westwards with respect to Turan along the Kopet Dagh/Alborz/Apsheron Sill/ Caucasus strike/slip system thereby tearing open the South Caspian oceanic hole as a pull-apart basin.

Cretaceous evolution

The Early Cretaceous was a time of increased convergent plate-margin activity in the Middle Eastern Tethysides (Fig. 6D). As depicted in Fig. 6D, it witnessed a widespread regression from wide areas of NW Iran, Central Iranian Microcontinent, and the Sanandaj–Sirjan Zone. Palaeomagnetic evidence indicates that continuing rotation of the Central Iranian Microcontinent as a whole (Soffel & Förster 1984) was accompanied by right-lateral strike-slip along its main divider faults. Deposition of anomalous thicknesses of Barremian to Aptian clastics, both in the Sanandaj area and to the W of Posht-e Badam, suggests the presence of pull-apart basins along the Sanandaj–Sirjan Zone boundary fault and along the Yazd–Tabas boundary fault zone respectively.

Subduction activity migrated northwards along the Sanandaj–Sirjan Zone and probably reached the easternmost E Pontides, where the 'Lower Basic Series' may be its earliest products (Şengör et al. 1984). Initial obduction of opholites in the Sevan–Akera–Karadagh ocean may have commenced in pre-Albian time, although the final emplacement was a Cenomanian to Coniacian affair. The E Lut subduction zone remained active probably through early Cretaceous time, but died by the Aptian, as Orbitolina limestones of this age unconformably cover its products in the Shah Kuh and in the Deh Salm metamorphics. It is likely that the Sabzevar–Sistan subduction zone became active concurrently or just after the demise of the E Lut subduction zone, although the earliest evidence for the former is seen in the Upper Cretaceous (Campanian) flysch and subduction-related volcanism (Tirrul et al. 1983; Baroz et al. 1984; Lindenberg et al. 1984). I interpret both the Sistan and the Sabzevar subduction zones as parts of the same convergent margin that formed along the W edge of the combined Farah and Helmand blocks (Fig. 6D and E; Şengör 1984; Boulin 1988) following their early Cretaceous union along the Waser suture (Şengör 1984; Şengör et al. 1988). This 'larger' Sistan subduction zone may have been caused by the westerly motion of the combined Farah/Helmand blocks along the former Palaeo-Tethyan suture as suggested in Fig. 6D.

Late Cretaceous (post 80 Ma: Campanian) is the time when Erusia/Africa relative motion became very nearly purely convergent (Savostin et al. 1986). This change also coincides with a great increase of convergent margin activity, in and actual convergent strain across, the Middle Eastern Tethysides as seen in Fig. 6E. The effects of this compressive episode lasted into the Palaeocene, and the 'Eocene everywhere overlies various older formations with pronounced angular unconformity' (Stöcklin 1968, p. 1244).

By the end of the late Cretaceous, the Central Iranian Microcontinent had largely completed its counter-clockwise rotation, implying that the Podataksasi Zone had also terminated its coastwise journey. One reason why this journey came to an end may have been because slivers of the Podataksasi Zone, today forming the Dzirula Massif and the basements of the Adzharia–Trialeti and Artvin–Karabagh zones, were sliced off the main body during its coastwise transport under increasing N–S compression and inserted sideways along strike-slip faults into the closing Sevan–Akera–Karadagh ocean as shown in Fig. 6E. This sideways insertion accounts for the repetition of parts of the Podataksasi Zone and of NW Iran in one cross-section as discussed above. The 330±42 Ma-old eclogite–amphibolites associated with the ophiolites of the Sevan–Akera belt (Meliksetian et al. 1984) may be remnants of the Palaeo–Tethyan subduction complex dragged into the Sevan–Akera–Karadagh ocean and structurally mixed with its own much younger ophiolites.

Large amounts of flysch were incorporated into the growing accretionary complexes of Neh and Ratuk in the Sistan region (Tirrul et al. 1983) and the Dowlatabad unit in the Sabzevar zone (Lindenberg et al. 1984), while the extensional arcs were evolving along the 'outer' subduction zone (Fig. 6E).

The compressional structures dominating much of Central and NW-Iran, Transcaucasia, and the S Pontides contrast sharply with extensional structures in the Black Sea, Riou and Khoura depressions, and the South Caspian Sea. In Iran, the dominantly compressional southern areas were separated from the dominantly extensional northern areas by the symmetrical Alborz Ranges. Following Apol'skiy (1974) I interpret the South Caspian oceanic basin as a pull-apart structure along a continuous ancestral Herat/Alborz/Greater Caucasus right-lateral shear zone (Fig. 6E'). Both Shikalibeili & Grigoriants (1980) and Berberian (1983) have presented a diverse set of data to argue that it is a young, late Mesozoic (Shikalibeili & Grigoriants 1980) or even early Cainozoic (Berberian 1983) structure. The Khoura depression is the westerly continuation of the South Caspian pull-apart basin and probably is related to it geneticaly, having originated as a deep trough in Oligocene time (Tagiyev 1984).

Although the initial opening of the Black Sea

began in the Albian by extensive normal faulting that remained active until the Cenomanian in N Turkey (Görür 1988), its easterly continuation, the Adzharia–Trialeti trough, accumulated 6 km of mildly alkaline to alkaline basaltic rocks during the early Palaeogene at the axis of the Riou basin (Lordkipanidze *et al*. 1977). As seen in Fig. 6E, the operation of the Caspian–Black Sea strike-slip system has shifted the entire Cimmeride orogenic collage in the Middle Eastern Tethysides for a minimum of 500 km (as judged from the present width of the oceanic area in the South Caspian basin) westwards with respect to stable Eurasia in latest Cretaceous to about Eocene time.

As by the end of the Mesozoic era the Sanandaj–Sirjan Zone, and with it the rest of the Podataksasi Zone, reached more-or-less their present positions with respect to other units in Eurasia, I terminate at this point my narrative of the evolution of the Middle Eastern Tethysides. The purpose of this and the previous sections was simply to justify the unorthodox reconstruction depicted in Fig. 6A showing the opening of the Hawasina and the Neo-Tethyan basins *behind* a Podataksasi ensimatic island arc system. In the next section I examine Oman to see to what extent the available observations may agree with a back-arc basin origin for the Omani Permo-Triassic basins.

Discussion and conclusions

The speculative evolutionary model persented in the foregoing section placed the Permo-Triassic basins in Oman behind a drifting ensialic island arc, the Podataksasi Zone. This makes it likely that the mid- to late Permian rifting in Oman was a result of back-arc basin activity as suggested by Şengör (1987a) and Şengör *et al.* (1988), and that the Carboniferous to ?early Permian compressional deformation of the Omani basement was a retroarc affair. In order to see whether the back-arc basin interpretation can be upheld on the basis of data from Oman itself, I compare the late Palaeozoic deformation in the Omani basement with the coeval events in the Podataksasi arc and the Hawasina and the Neo-Tethyan basins with active back-arc basins.

Late Palaeozoic Orogeny in Oman

Recently, both Michard (1982, 1983) and Mann & Hanna (1990) studied the late Palaeozoic deformation, documenting the presence of a NE–SW trending foldbelt. In the Jebel Akhdar, Jebel Nakhl, and Saih Hatat, an intense slaty cleavage dips generally to the SW at angles

between 20° and 50°. Late Cretaceous deformation in the NW part of the Saih Hatat window has overprinted and largely obscured the Late Palaeozoic structures (Mann & Hanna 1990). Stretched grain and pressure shadow orientations in the slaty cleavage plane indicates a predominant stretching direction trending S to SW. Michard (1982) indicated that fold vergence seems N and NW in many places where the cleavage/bedding relationship can be observed, and that this is commonly corroborated by parasitic fold overturning, but he also stressed that vergence of late Palaeozoic folds is inconsistent, as, locally, are the trends of fold axial traces. Michard (1982) thought that the latter appear deflected by basement highs. Illite crystallinity indicates that the rocks deformed by late Palaeozoic compression were also metamorphosed in upper greenschist conditions. The impression obtained by Michard (1982) of the late Palaeozoic orogenic structures was that these represented a NW–SE trending belt of cover folds with dominantly, but not exclusively northerly vergence, locally variable axial trend, and weak metamorphism.

The precise age of the late Palaeozoic orogeny in Oman remains unknown, as isotopic evidence is lacking. Stratigraphic bracketing gives only a mid-Ordovician to mid-Permian interval encompassing about 200 Ma (all numeric equivalents of stratigraphic ages in this paper are after Harland *et al.* 1982) in the Saih Hatat window. The conformable Jebel Qamar succession from the Ordovician to the ?top of the Devonian (Lippard *et al.* 1986) narrows this bracket to earliest Carboniferous to middle Permian, i.e. to about 100 Ma. Further, but very tentative reduction of the age bracket may be possible by assuming that folding occurred before the block tilting (Lee 1990) that preceded the deposition of the glacio-marine Al Khlata Formation of late Westphalian to Sakmarian age (Hughes Clarke 1988). This narrower interval spans only 45 Ma.

Our detailed examination of the late Palaeozoic and early Mesozoic geological evolution of the Middle Eastern Tethysides has shown that the late Palaeozoic deformation of the Omani basement was only a small part of a much larger area of deformation located along the N margin of Gondwana-Land and, contrary to Michard's (1982) suggestion, clearly unrelated to the Hercynides of NW Africa and Europe. This area of deformation in most places has a structural basement of early Palaeozoic age that likely represents the outer, younger part of the Pan-African orogenic system of Gondwana-Land. Its late Palaeozoic deformation commenced in the early Carboniferous,

was most active during the Carboniferous, and
declined in the early Permian. This deformation
was accompanied by calc-alkaline, tholeiitic,
and locally alkaline magmatic activity and
Barrovian metamorphism, and may be interpreted as a product of subduction at the N
margin of Gondwana-Land, creating what is
here termed the 'Podataksasi arc'.

The late Palaeozoic deformation in Oman
has the hallmark of 'externides' in involving
folding and possibly also thrusting of sedimentary cover with slaty cleavage, inconsistent
vergence, and upper greenschist metamorphism. It is interpreted here as a retroarc fold
and thrust belt of the Podataksasi arc. This
implies that the arc was probably compressional
(cf. Dewey 1980), at least when the deformation
in Oman was going on. It was probably of the
'flat subduction' variety as judged by the paucity
of coeval magmatic activity (cf. Jordan et al.
1983).

As constrained by the presently available
stratigraphic data, the time of deformation in
Oman was coeval with the evolution of the
Podataksasi arc, i.e. early Carboniferous to
early Permian, after which the arc became
extensional and the retroarc compression
consequently ceased. A tighter bracket is now
not possible, because the relationships between
the Podataksasi arc and Oman are not known in
detail.

Mid-Permian to Triassic rifting

Bechennec (1988) suggested that the mid-
Permian extension in Oman created what he
terms the Hamrat Duru basin (equivalent to the
Hawasina basin in Fig. 7A), separating the
Arabian platform from what he calls the Baid
platform. Continuing extension in the Triassic
then disintegrated the Baid platform forming an
Al Aridh trough (in equivalent position to that
of Al Aridh as shown in Fig. 7A), a Misfah
platform (equivalent to 'Carbonate platform' in
Fig. 7A), and an Umar basin (equivalent to
Yanqul site at the margin of Neo-Tethys in Fig.
7A). The disruption of the Baid platform was
accompanied by the eruption of alkaline and
transitional lavas with only limited tholeiitic
products (Bechennec 1988). Permian to late
Triassic exotic shallow water limestones (the
'Oman Exotics': Wilson 1969; Searle & Graham
1982) are associated with volcanics and have
been interpreted generally as carbonate build-
ups on oceanic islands away from the continental margin (Glennie et al. 1974), although at
least one example, the Jebel Qamar, has a
continental basement. By contrast Bechennec

(1988) argued, on the basis of the geochemistry
of the Permo-Triassic volcanics, that most of
them were erupted on a continental basement
and therefore many of the Oman Exotics had
originally continental substrata (Fig. 7A).

Deposition of basinal and basin margin sedi-
ments in the Hawasina and the Neo-Tethyan
basins continued into the late Cretaceous
(Fig. 7A). Volcanism also persisted into the
Cretaceous but was much diminished in intensity
(Bechennec 1988).

As the Omani basins are conjectured to have
opened behind an ensialic arc by rifting within
the continental lithosphere, I choose analogous
active or Recent ensialic arcs in front of rifted
back-arc basins rather than ensimatic extensional arcs for comparison with respect to position of back-arc rifting axis within the arc,
temporal and spatial evolution of rifting, and
temporal and spatial evolution of magmatism.
The best data are available from the Tyrrhenian
Sea owing to a long history of investigation
around its margins and three international
deep-sea drilling legs that penetrated its abyssal
floor (DSDP legs 13 and 42, and ODP leg 107).
Fig. 7B shows a schematic cross-section across
the Tyrrhenian Sea and compares its various
segments with what I believe to be comparable
segments of the Omani Neo-Tethyan back-arc
basin complex (Fig. 7A).

Position of back-arc rifting axis within the arc.
In Oman, the Hawasina basin began rifting
along a line that was probably near the rear
part of the Podataksasi magmatic arc. The late
Permian volcanism in Oman includes alkaline,
transitional, and tholeiitic suites and have been
interpreted mostly as within plate magma products. However, similar signatures also have been
obtained from the Tyrrhenian volcanoes all the
way from Sardinia to the Sicilian/Italian margins and may simply signify the rear portions of
an arc. Both the Tyrrhenian and the Japanese
back-arc basins, however, have calc-alkaline
magmatic rocks on both sides, believed to be
related to the subduction zone ultimately responsible also for the origin of the back-arc
basin. All along the rift line that delineates the
separation of the Podataksasi zone from its
former continental hinterland making up the
'retroarc zone' the only place where any pre-
Permian thermal effects of the arc can be seen
on the Arabian side is the Straits of Hormuz,
where Precambrian volcanic rocks, brought
to the surface in salt plugs, indicate an early
Carboniferous reheating (Fig. 3, loc. 15). As
similar data are not available elsewhere along
the Zagros, it is not now possible to estimate
how widespread that heating event may have

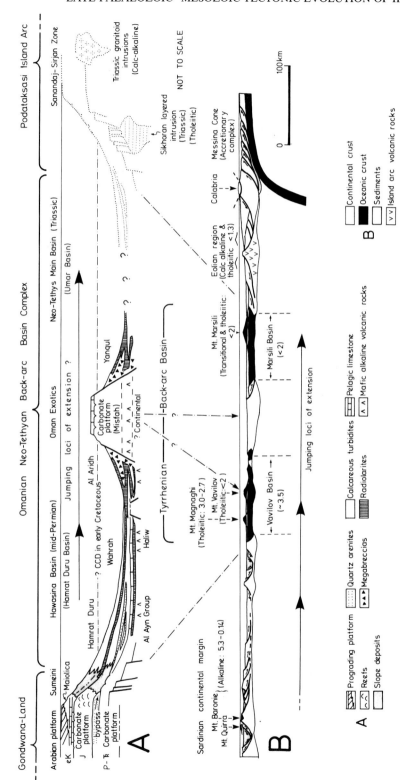

Fig. 7. (A) A hypothetical, schematic palinspastic reconstruction of the Omani Neo-Tethys as a back-arc basin to the closing Palaeo–Tethys as depicted in Fig. 6A. The section between the Arabian Platform and the site of deposition of the Yanqul Formation is taken from Bernoulli & Weissert (1987), with the depositional site of Yanqul altered following Bernoulli *et al.* (1990). The rest of the section is my addition. (B) A cross section across the Tyrrhenian Sea between the east Sardinian continental margin and the Messina Cone modified after Şengör (1989) mainly by using the data summarized in Wezel (1985). Notice the tremendous similarities in tectonic and magmatic styles, composition of volcanic rocks and the sequence of basin evolution. Together with other similarities discussed in the text, they justify the way I interpret the cross section shown in Fig. 7A.

been on the Arabian side. But the Hormuz occurrences sugget that although the axis of back-arc basin opening in Oman was perhaps anomalously far inland away from the Carboniferous and early Permian arc axis, it was not so far as to be completely oblivious to the effects of arc-related heating. The Hawasina rifting thus disrupted the late Palaeozoic retro-arc fold and thrust belt synchronously with the invasion of its northeasternmost sector by the hinter part of the Podataksasi arc.

Two factors may have conspired to give the axis of initial rifting its anomalously 'inland' position. One is the very different Pan-African basement ages seen under Arabia (including Oman) and under the Podataksasi Zone, which are late Percambrian and early Palaeozoic respectively (Şengör et al. 1988). The boundary between these two types of Pan-African basement must have been an important zone of weakness as attested to by their clean separation through the later rifting event.

The second factor is the sparsity of Carboniferous and early Permian igneous activity as opposed to widespread compressional deformation along the Sanandaj−Sirjan part of the Podataksasi arc, including a part of the Omani basement. As suggested above, the arc may have been compressional during the Carboniferous-early Permian interval, possibly of the flat subduction kind and may have turned off arc magmatism as, for example, in the Sierras Pampeanas segment of the Andes (Jordan & Allmendinger 1986; Şengör 1989). This would have created essentially a 'cold arc' containing no thermally weakened zones. When the arc then turned − seemingly rather abruptly − extensional in the earlier mid-Permian (earlier? see above), the only weak zones that could be exploited were the crustal ones inherited from the Pan-African evolution.

Temporal and spatial evolution of rifting. A number of authors, and most recently Bechennec (1988), have pointed out that in Oman, rifting and basin formation migrated away from the Arabian craton. The Hawasina basin (Bechennec's Hamrat Duru basin) formed in mid-Permian time, whereas the Neo-Tethyan main basin (Bechennec's Umar basin) originated in the Triassic with spreading beginning possibly towards the end of the middle Triassic.

In all extensional arc systems, ensialic or ensimatic, this migration of extensional loci away from the 'continental' side is seen (Dewey 1980; Hayes 1984; Şengör 1989). Fig. 7B shows the situation in the Tyrrhenian basin, where the Vavilov basin is older than the Marsili basin. In the Philippine Sea, the 'continentward' Parece

Vela basin is older than the 'arcward' Mariana trough by 30 Ma (Hayes 1984). Omani basin formation sequence compares favourably with these two active (or at least very young) cases: the Hawasina basin in Oman was at least 20 and at most 30 Ma older than the initial rifting of the Neo-Tethyan main basin.

Temporal and spatial evolution of magmatism. Alkaline, transitional, and tholeitic magmatism in the Omani back-arc basin complex, especially in the Neo-Tethyan main basin, lasted a very considerable time after rifting, as late as early Cretaceous time (Searle et al. 1980; Bechennec 1988) but the main volcanism was confined to late Permian to late Triassic time, during which all three types of lavas were erupted in different places. In the Jurassic and Cretaceous, volcanism was sparse and was mainly of alkaline type. Much of the preserved products of the early and abundant volcanism built seamounts and are today preserved under pelagic carbonate rocks that once formed their cap.

Except near hot-spots, volcanism associated with intracontinental rifting becomes extinguished soon after the onset of sea-floor spreading in the adjacent ocean (e.g. Chochran 1983). By contrast, alkaline, transitional, and tholeiitic volcanism lasts a long time in back-arc basins creating seamounts (e.g. in and around the Tyrrhenian Sea: Dietrich et al. 1978; Locardi 1985; Selli 1985; Wezel 1985; in an around the sea of Japan: Tomita 1935; Harumoto 1970; Kaneoaka 1986; for a theoretical treatment of the cause of this long-lived back-arc magmatism see Spiegelman & McKenzie 1987). Fig. 7B illustrates the similarities in pattern between the Tyrrhenian and the Omani back-arc basins. In this regard also the Omani basins resemble modern back-arc basins.

Finally, I underline that the geochemistry of the basaltic lavas from the Hawasina nappes, which has been so far interpreted as indicating a Red Sea-type of 'within-plate' rifting (Searle et al. 1980; Robertson 1986) may not be as reliable an indicator of tectonic setting as hitherto considered. Geochemical considerations on the Tyrrhenian lavas both from the Tyrrhenian abyssal plain and the Sardinian and N Sicilian continental margins also gave very similar results. Beccaluva et al. (1982) concluded that most of these rocks have geochemical characteristics typical of intraplate regions, and Berberi et al. (1978) and Dietrich et al. (1978) have reported also abyssal tholeiites. Beccaluva et al. (1985) collected, in addition, a few samples of island arc tholeiites from the E Margin of the Tyrrhenian Sea, N of the Eolian archipelago, which belong to the youngest products of the

Tyrrhenian magmatism (<1.3 Ma). In the Tyrrhenian region one encounters typical calc-alkaline and shoshonitic rocks only farther to the SE, in the Eolian archipelago. As schematically depicted in Fig. 7A, this part of the Omani Neo-Tethyan back-arc basin complex is not preserved in Oman itself, but now lies probably in the Sanandaj–Sirjan Zone. That geochemistry may not be a reliable discriminator between back-arc basin and Red Sea-type environments has recently been stressed by Maruyama (1988) on the basis of an extensive geochemical study including 500 analyses from the Philippine, Lau and South Scotia back-arc basins and the Pacific and Atlantic MORBs.

In summary, neither the geochemistry of the magmatic products of the Omani Permian to late Triassic extension, nor their temporal/spatial relationships are incompatible with a back-arc basin interpretation. In fact, the rather long-lived volcanicity that coevally produced alkaline, transitional, and tholeiitic lavas is more readily explained in a Tyrrhenian-type back-arc context than in an ordinary intracontinental rift setting. The back-arc basin interpretation is also compatible with the temporal/spatial evolution of the rifting as it migrated away from the Arabian continental margin, leaving a large number of seamounts 'stranded' on the Arabian side. In intracontinental rift systems, rifting usually bites into the separating rift shoulders in a 'breaking backward' manner so as to enlarge the rift (e.g. Rosendahl 1987, fig. 9) until the breaking of the continent to permit sea-floor spreading. In some cases, even the locus of spreading may jump continentward as happened in the history of Afar (Mohr 1978, fig. 4), thus exhibiting an evolutionary pattern opposite of what is seen in back-arc basins.

Only the location of the axis of initial rifting in Oman appears anomalously far inland when compared with most rifted back-arc basins that formed behind ensialic arcs. This may have been because of the peculiarities in the evolution of the Podataksasi arc itself and the contrast between its basement and that of its hinterland.

A major part of this paper was devoted to developing a new tectonic model for the latest Palaeozoic–end Mesozoic development of the Middle Eastern Tethysides, and especially to underlining the existence in them of mammoth strike-slip systems, which very considerably disrupted their much simpler and more 'conventional' orogenic geometry that had existed immediately after the collision. This longish 'side-track' was unavoidable in order to justify the reconstructions offered in Figs. 6A and 7A which form the essence of this paper (i.e. the interpretation of the Sanandaj–Sirjan Zone as the arc behind which the Oman–Zagros Neo-Tethys opened as a back-arc basin).

The conclusions of this paper has further implications both for our understanding of the Tethyside evolution in particular, and for the study of orogenic belts in general. We have come to see in the foregoing sections that the common view of the 'passive margin' character of much of the northern edge of Gondwana-Land is probably wrong. Instead, much of that edge in Turkey (also farther W? see Sengör et al. 1984), in the Transcaucasia, and in Iran, as in the Central Pamirs and in NE Tibet and Thailand, appears to have been 'active' (i.e. a magmatic arc orogen). It was the fluctuating 'mode' of this semi-continuous arc that led to the birth and governed the early evolution of Neo-Tethys behind it. Enormous amounts of syn- and post-collisional strike-slip faulting, coupled with polyphase compressional deformation, conspired to hide large segments of this arc within fragments of its Gondwanian hinterland inside the Tethyside orogenic complex and to obliterate others entirely.

The Mesozoic evolution of the Middle Eastern Tethysides has taught us that many of our reconstructions of former continental positions in the Tethyan realm may have errors exceeding 1500 km, mainly because of the abundance and the tremendous magnitudes of unrecognised strike-slip motion. Consequently, a comprehensive evaluation of the tectonic history of a region of the size of Oman in an orogenic belt may require knowledge of an area nearly 20 times its size.

My studies of the Middle Eastern Tethysides over the years have benefited immensely from the assistance of many of my Turkish, Iranian, Soviet, Swiss, Austrian, British, and American colleagues, too many to be listed here. I wish to single out for this study the help of Shota A. Adamia (Tbilisi), Alexander A. Belov (Moscow), Manuel Berberian (Tehran), Jamshid Eftekhar-Nezhad (Tehran), Monir Davoudzadeh (München), Viktor E. Khain (Moscow), Manana Lordkipanidze (Tbilisi), Anton W. Ruttner (Vienna), Jovan Stöcklin (Seuzach), and Yücel Yilmaz (Istanbul). I discussed a good part of the content of this paper with John F. Dewey and to him I am indebted for a number of suggestions and some of the references. I also thank Kevin Burke and Dan McKenzie for stimulating discussions. Alastair H. F. Robertson invited this paper as the 'concluding talk' of the Oman Meeting in Edinburgh and also discussed with me a number of the ideas treated in it. Berberian, Davoudzadeh, Robertson, Ruttner, and Stöcklin have provided very helpful reviews of an earlier draft that considerably improved the paper, but I alone remain responsible for errors of omission and/or commission. To Robert-

son and to the other convenors of the Edinburgh
meeting I am grateful for the excuse and the opportunity to prepare this paper. I take pleasure in de-
dicating it to two of my dear friends to whom I owe
much of what I know of the geology of Iran: Manuel
Berberian and Jovan Stöcklin.

References

ABDULLAEV, R. N. & GUSEINOV, A. N. 1984.
Excursion 19-B "Saatly ED-1". In Azerbaijan
Soviet Socialist Republic, Excursions 18-B
and 19-B Guidebook. International Geological
Congress. 27th Session, Moscow, Azerneshr,
Baku, 63–78.

ABESADZE, M., ADAMIA, S. A., CHKHOTUA, T.,
KEKELIA, M., SHAVISHVILI, I., SOMIN, M. &
TSIMAKURIDZE, G. 1982. Pre-Variscan and
Variscan metamorphic complexes of the
Caucasus (a review). IGCP, Project No. 5,
Newsletter 4, 5–12.

ADAMIA, S. A., BELOV, A. A. 1984. Excursion 008A
+ C. Pre-Mesozoic complexes of the Caucasus.
In: Georgian Soviet Socialist Republic, Excur-
sions: 001, 007, 008, 012, 014, 017 Guide-book.
International Geological Congress. 27th Session,
Moscow, Khelovneba, Tbilisi 108–53.

——, ——, LORDKIPANIDZE, M. B. & SOMIN, M. L.
1982. Project N. 5 IGCP "Correlation of Pre-
Variscan and Variscan events in the Alpine-
Mediterranean Mountain Belt" Field Excursion
Guide-Book of International Working Meeting of
the Caucasus. Tipografia AN Gruz. SSR, Tbilisi.

——, KEKELIA, M. & TSIMAKURIDZE, G. 1983. Pre-
Variscan and Variscan granitoids of the
Caucasus. IGCP, Project No. 5, Newsletter 5,
5–12.

ALAVI, M. 1979. The Virani ophiolite complex and
surrounding rocks. Geologische Rundschau. 68,
25–52.

ALBERTI, A. A., NICOLETTI, M. & PETRUCCIANI, C.
1973. K/Ar age for micas of Mashhad granite
(Khorasan, NE Iran). Periodico di Mineralogia.
42, 483–93.

ALP, D. 1972. Amasya Yöresinin Jeolojisi. Istanbul
Universitesi Fen Fakültesi Monografileri. (Tabii
Ilimler Kismi) 22.

ALTINER, D., BAUD, A., GUEX, J. & STAMPFLI, G.
1979. La limite Permien-Trias dans quelques
localités du Moyen Orient: recherches stratigraphiques et micropaléontologiques. Rivista
Italiana di Paleontologia e Stratigrafia, 85, 683–
714.

APOL'SKIY, O. P. 1974. Origin of the Black and South
Caspian Sea troughs. Geotectonics, 8, 310–311.

ARCHANGELSKY, S. & WAGNER, R. H. 1983.
Glossopteris anatolica sp. nov. from uppermost
Permian strata in south-east Turkey. Bulletin of
the British Museum Natural History (Geol.), 37,
81–91.

ARGYRIADIS, I. 1974. Mesogée permienne, chaine
hercynienne et cassure tethysienne. Bulletin de la
Société géologique de France sér. 7, 17, 56–67.

—— 1978. Le Permien alpino/méditerranéen à la

charnière entre l'Hercynien et l'Alpin. Thèse de
Docteur ès Sciences, Univ. Paris-Sub "Centre
d'Orsay" 1, and 2.

ASSERETO, R. 1963. The Paleozoic formations in
Central Elburz (Iran), preliminary note. Rivista
Italiana di Paleontologia e Stratigrafia, 69,
503–43.

BARBERI, F., BIZOUARD, H., CAPALDI, G., FERRARA,
G., GASPARINI, P., INNOCENTI, F., JORON, J. L.,
LAMBRET, B., TREUIL, M. & ALLEGRE, C. 1978.
Age and nature of basalts from the Tyrrhenian
abyssal plain. In: Initial Reports of the Deep
Sea Drilling Project 42(I) (K. J. HSÜ and
L. MONTADERT et al.), pp. 509–514 (U.S.
Government Printing Office, Washington, D.C.).

BAROZ, F., MACAUDIERE, J., MONTIGNY, R.,
NOGHREYAN, M., OHNENSTETTER, M. & ROCCI,
G. 1984. Ophiolites and related formations in the
central part of the Sabzevar Range (Iran) and
possible geotectonic reconstructions. Neues
Jahrbuch für Geologie und Paläontologie,
Abhandlungen, 168, 358–88.

BAZHENOV, M. L. & BURTMAN, V. S. 1986. Tectonics
and paleomagnetism of structural arcs of the
Pamir-Punjab Syntaxis. Journal of Geodynamics,
5, 383–96.

BECCALUVA, L., GABBIANELLI, G., LUCCHINI, F.,
ROSSI, P. L. & SAVELLI, C. 1985. Petrology and
K/Ar ages of volcanics dredged from the Eolian
seamounts: implications for geodynamic evolution of the southern Tyrrhenian basin. Earth
and Planetary Science Letters, 74, 187–208.

——., ROSSI, P. L. & SERRI, G. 1982. Neogene to
Recent volcanism of the Southern Tyrrhenian-
Sicilian area: implications for the geodynamic
evolution of the Calabrian arc. Earth Evolution
Sciences, 3, 222–38.

BECHENNEC, F. 1988. Géologie des Nappes Hawasina
dans les parties orientale et centrale des Montagnes
d'Oman. Thèse de Doctorat d'Etat, Université
Paris VI. Documents du B. R. G. M. no. 127

BECK, M. E., Jr. 1988. Block rotations in continental
crust: examples from Western North America.
In: KISSEL, C. & LAJ, C. Paleomagnetic Rotations
and Continental Deformation 1–16, NATO ASI
Series C 254 Kluwer Academic Publishers,
Dordrecht.

BERBERIAN, F. & BERBERIAN, M. 1981. Tectono-
plutonic episodes in Iran. In: Geodynamic Series,
3, Geological Society of America, Boulder,
Colorado, 5–33.

BERBERIAN, M. 1977. Against the rigidity of
the Lut Block; a seismotectonic discussion.
In: BERBERIAN, M. (ed.) Contribution to the
Seismotectonics of Iran, 203–227. Geological
Survey of Iran Report No. 40, Tehran.

—— 1981. Active faulting and tectonics of Iran. In:
Geodynamic Series 3, 33–69. Geological Society
of American, Boulder, Colorado.

—— 1983. The Southern Caspian: a compressional
depression floored by a trapped, modified oceanic
crust. Canadian Journal of Earth Sciences 20,
163–83.

—— & KING, G. C. P. 1981. Towards a palaeogeography and tectonic evolution of Iran. *Canadian Journal of Earth Sciences*, **18**, 210–65.

BERGOUGNAN, H. & FOURQUIN, C. 1982. Remnants of a pre-Late Jurassic ocean in northern Turkey: Fragments of Permian-Triassic Paleo-Tethys? Discussion. *Geological Society of America Bulletin*, **93**, 929–32.

BERIDZE, M. A. 1984. *Geosynklinalny Vulkanogeno-osadochni Litogenez.* Akademii Nauk, Gruzinsky SSR, Tbilisi.

BERNOULLI, D. & WEISSERT, H. 1987. The upper Hawasina nappes in the central Oman Mountains: Stratigraphy, palinspastics and sequence of nappe emplacement. *Geodynamica Acta*, **1**, 47–58.

——, —— & BLOME, C. D. 1990. Evolution of the Triassic Hawasina basin. *In:* ROBERTSON, A. H. F., SEARLE, M. P. & RIES, A. C. *The Geology and Tectonics of the Oman Region.* Geological Society, London, Special Publication **00**, 000–000.

BONNET, P. BONNET, N. M. 1947. *Description géologique de la Transcaucasie méridionale.* Mémoires de la Société géologique de France, N. S. **25**.

BOULIN, J. 1988. Hercynian and Eocimmerian events in Afghanistan and adjoining regions. *Tectonophysics*, **148**, 253–278.

BRANDNER, R., HADITSCH, J. G. & MOSTLER, H. 1981. Beiträge zur vortertiären Pb-Zn-Cu – Metallogenese im Raum zwischen Rasht und Chalus (Alburs, Iran). *Geologische und Paläontologische Mitteilungen* **10**, 257–285.

BRATASH, V. I. 1975. Kerman–Kashmer Trough, Iran, and the problem of the junction between pre-Jurassic structures of the Turanian plate and the Mediterranean belt. *Geotectonics*, **9**, 101–107.

CHAPUT, E. 1936. Voyages d'Etudes Géologiques et Géomorphogénique en Turquie. Mémoires de l'Institut Français d'Archéologie de Stamboul **II**. E. de Boccard, Paris.

CLARK, G. C. DAVIES, R. G., HAMZEPOUR, B. & JONES, C. R. 1975. *Explanatory text of the Bander-e-Pahlavi quadrangle map, 1:250 000.* Geological Survey of Iran, D3, Ministry of Information and Tourism Press, Tehran.

COCHRAN, J. R. 1983. A model for development of Red Sea. *Bulletin of the American Association of Petroleum Geologists*, **67**, 41–69.

COLEMAN, R. G. & HOPSON, C. A. 1981. Introduction to the Oman ophiolite special issue. *Journal of Geophysical Research*, **86**, 2495–2496.

CROWFORD, A. R. 1977. A summary of isotropic age data for Iran, Pakistan, and India. *In:* Livre à la Mémoire de Albert F. de Lapparent. 251–60, Mémoire hors-série **8**, Société Géologique de France.

CTYROKY, P. 1973. Permian flora from the Ga'ra region (Western Iraq). *Neues Jahrbuch für Geologie und Paläontologie, Monatshefte*, **7**, 383–388.

DAVIES, R. G., JONES, C. R., HAMZEPOUR, B. & CLARK, G. C. 1972. *Geology of the*

Masuleh Sheet, 1:100 000, Northwest Iran. Geological Survey of Iran, Report **24**, Ministry of Information Press, Tehran.

DAVOUDZADEH, M., LENSCH, G. & WEBER-DIEFENBACH, K. 1986. Contribution to the paleogeography, stratigraphy and tectonics of the Infracambrian and Lower Paleozoic of Iran. *Neues Jahrbuch für Geologie und Paläontologie, Abhandlungen*, **172**, 245–69.

—— & SCHMIDT, K. 1984. A review of the Mesozoic paleogeography and paleotectonic evolution of Iran. *Neues Jahrbuch für Geologie und Paläontologie, Abhandlungen*, **168**, 182–207.

—— & SEYED-EMAMI-K. 1972. Stratigraphy of the Triassic Nakhlak Group, Anarak Region, Central Iran. *Geological Survey of Iran, Report*, **28**, 5–28.

——, SOFFEL, H. & SCHMIDT, K. 1981. On the rotation of the Central-East-Iran microplate. *Neues Jahrbuch für Geologie und Paläontologie, Monatshefte* **1981**, 180–192.

—— WEBER-DIEFENBACH, K. 1987. Contribution to the paleogeography, stratigraphy and tectonics of the upper Paleozoic of Iran. *Neues Jahrbuch für Geologie und Paläontologie, Abhandlungen*, **175**, 121–146.

DEWEY, J. F. 1980. Episodicity, sequence and style at convergent plate boundaries. *Geological Association of Canada Special Paper* **20**, 553–573.

——, HEMPTON, M. R., KIDD, W. S. F., ŞAROĞLU, F. & ŞENGÖR, A. M. C. 1986. Shortening of continental lithosphere: the neotectonics of Eastern Anatolia – a young collision zone. *In:* COWARD, M. P. & RIES, A. C. (eds) *Collision Tectonics* Geological Society, London Special Publication, **19**, 3–36.

DIETRICH, V., EMMERMANN, R., PUCHELT, H. & KELLER, J. 1978. Oceanic basalts from the Tyrrhenian basin, DSDP Leg 42A, hole 373A. *In:* K. J. HSÜ and L. MONTADERT *et al.* (eds) *Initial Reports of the Deep Sea Drilling Project* **42(I)** U.S. Government Printing Office, Washington, D. C., 515–530.

DOTDUYEV, S. I. 1986. Nappe structure of the Greater Caucasus range. *Geotectonics* **20**, 420–430.

FISHER, W. B. 1950. *The Middle East – A Physical, Social, and Regional Geography.* Methuen, London 514 pp

FLÜGEL, H. 1964. Die Entwicklung des vorderasiatischen Paläozoikums. *Geotektonische Forschungen*, **18**, 1–68.

FRIEDRICH, O. M. 1960. Zur Genesis und Mineralogie einiger ostpreußischer Blei- und Zinklagerstätten. *Neues Jahrbuch für Mineralogie, Abhandlungen* **94** (Festband Ramdohr), 430–468.

FURON, R. 1941. Géolgie du plateau Iranien (Perse-Afghanistan-Béloutchistan). Mémoires du Muséum (national) d'histoire naturelle. Paris, **7**, 177–414.

GANSSER, A. 1955. New aspects of the geology in Central Iran. *Proceedings of the World Petroleum Congres Section I/A/5, Paper 2*, 279–300.

GARETSKIY, R. G., KIRYUKHIN, L. G. & PERFIL'YEV,

A. S. 1972. The Sultan–Uizdag and the relationship between the Urals and Tien-Shan. *Geotectonics*, **6**, 372–376.

GASANOV, T. A. 1986. Evolution of the Sevan–Akera ophiolite zone, Lesser Caucasus. *Geotectonics*, **20**, 147–56.

GLENNIE, K. W., BOEUF, M. G. A., HUGHES CLARKE, M. W., MOODY-STUART, M., PILAAR,-W. F. H. & REINHARDT, B. M. 1974. The Geology of the Oman Mountains. *Verhandelingen van het Koninklijk Nederlands geologisch mijnbouwkundig Genootschap* **1 & 2**.

GÖRÜR N. 1988. Timing of opening of the Black Sea basin. *Tectonophysics* **147**, 247–62.

HAGHIPOUR, A., VALEH, N., PELISSIER, G. & DAVOUDZADEH, M. 1977. *Explanatory text of the Ardekan Quadrangle Map, 1:250 000*, Geological Survey of Iran, Geological Quadrangle H8, 114 pp., Ministry of Information and Tourism Press, Tehran.

HARLAND, W. B., COX, A. V., LLEWELLYN, P. G., PICKTON, C. A. G. SMITH, A. G. & WALTERS, R. 1982. *A Geologic Time Scale*. Cambridge University Press, Cambridge.

HARUMOTO, A. 1970. *Volcanic rocks and associated rocks of Utsuryoto Island (Japan Sea)*. Nippon printing and publishing Co., Osaka.

HAYES, D. E. 1983. Marginal seas in Southeast Asia — their geophysical characteristics and structure. In: *Origin and History of Marginal and Island Seas*. Proceedings of the 27th International Geological Congress, Moscow, **23**, 123–54.

HELVACI, C. & GRIFFIN, W. L. 1984. Rb-Sr geochronology of the Bitlis Massif, Avnik (Bingöl) area, S. E. Turkey. *Geological Society of London Special Publication*, **17**, 403–413.

HIROOKA, K. & TORII, M. (eds) 1986. The Opening of the Japan Sea. *Journal of Geomagnetism and Geoelectricity*, **38**, 285–550.

HOLMOQUIST, P. J. 1932. Über sog. fiderspalten. *Geologiska föreningens Stockholm förhandlingar*, **54**, 99–118.

HUGHES CLARKE, M. W. 1988. Stratigraphy and rock unit nomenclature in the oil-producing area of interior Oman. *Journal of Petroleum Geology*, **11**, 5–60.

HUSHMANDZADEH, A., ALAVI-NAINI, M. & HAGHIPOUR, A. 1978. Explanatory text of the Torud Quadrangle Map, 1:250000, Geological Survey of Iran, Geological Quadrangle H5, (Geological Evolution Since Precambrian) (in Farsi).

JACKSON, J. & McKENZIE, D. 1984. Rotational mechanisms of active deformation in Greece and Iran. *Geological Society of London Special publication*, **17**, 743–754.

JORDAN, T. E. & ALLMENDINGER, R. W. 1986. The Sierras Pampeanas of Argentina: A modern analogue of Rocky Mountain foreland deformation. *American Journal of Science*, **286**, 737–764.

JORDAN, T. E., ISACKS, B. I., ALLMENDINGER, R. W., BREWER, J. A., RAMOS, V. A. & ANDO, C. J. 1983 Andean tectonics related to geometry of subducted Nazca plate. *Geological Society of America Bulletin*, **94**, 341–361.

KANEOKA, I. 1986. Constraints on the time of the evolution of the Japan Sea floor based on radiometric ages. *Journal of Geomagnetism and Geoelectricity*, **38**, 475–485.

KESKIN, I, 1986. Pulur metamorfitlerinin yaşı ile ilgili yeni bir bulgu. *Maden Tetkik ve Arama Dergisi*, **107**, 171–174.

KETIN, I. 1947. Über die Tektonik des Uludağ-Massivs. *Türkiye Jeoloji Kurumu Bülteni*, **1**, 75–88.

—— 1951. Über die Geologie der Gegend von Bayburt in Nordost Anatolien. *Revue de la Faculté des Sciences de l'Université d'Istanbul*. ser. B **16**, 113–127.

—— 1985. Türkiye' nin bindirmeli-naplı yapısında yeni gelişmeler ve bir örnek: Uludağ Masifi. *Ketin Simpozyumu Kitabı*, 19–39, Türkiye Jeoloji Kurumu, Ankara.

KHAIN, E. V. 1984. *Ofioliti i gerchinskaya pokrobnaya struktura peredovogo khrebta severnogo Kavkaza*. Akademi Nauk SSSR, Trudi **382**, Nauka, Moscow.

KHAIN, V. E. (1975). Structure and main stages in tectomagmatic development of the Caucasus: an attempt at geodynamic interpretation. *American Journal of Science* **275–A**, 131–56.

KNIPPER, A. L. & SOKOLOV, S. D. 1976. Vedi ophiolites (Armenia) — An autochthon or an allochton? *Geotectonics*, **10**, 261–69.

KOZUR, H., MOSTLER, H. & RAHIMI-YAZD, A. 1975. Beiträge zur Mikrofauna permotriadischer Schichtfolgen. Teil II: Neue Conodonten aus dem Oberperm und der basalen Trias von Nord- und Zentraliran. *Geologische und Paläontologische Mitteilungen, Innsbruck* **5**, 1–23.

KRAVCHENKO, K. N., KOSHELEV, N. I., KRAVCHENKO, N. E., KUNITSKAYA, I. N., POLKANOVA, L. P., ROSCHIN, V. F. & SOLOVIEVA, N. S. 1976. The regional structure of the Turanian platform and its development. *Tectonophysics*, **36**, 263–73.

LAMMERER, B., LANGHEINRICH, G. & MANUTCHEHR-DANAI, M. 1984. Geological investigations in the Binalud Mountains. *Neues Jahrbuch für Geologie und Paläontologie, Abhandlungen*, **168**, 269–77.

LEE, C. W. 1990. A Review of platform sedimentation in the Early and Late Permian of Oman, with particular reference to the Oman Mountains In: ROBERTSON, A. H. F., SEARLE, M. P. & RIES, A. C. (eds) *The Geology and Tectonics of the Oman Region*. Geological Society, London, Special Publication, **49**, 39–47.

LE PICHON, X. 1983. Land-locked oceanic basins and continental collision: the eastern Mediterranean as a case example. In: HSU, K. J. (ed) *Mountain-Building Processes* Academic Press, London 201–211.

LINDENBERG, H. G., GÖRLER, K., JACOBSHAGEN, V. & IBBEKEN, H. 1984. Post-Paleozoic stratigraphy, structure and orogenetic evolution of the southern Sabzevar Zone and the Taknar Block (Khorassan, NE Iran). *Neues Jahrbuch für Geologie und Paläontologie, Abhandlungen*, **168**,

287–326.

LIPPARD, S. J., SHELTON, A. W. & GASS, I. G. 1986. The Ophiolite of northern Oman. *Geological Society of London Memoir No. 11.*

LOCARDI, E. 1985. Neogene and Quaternary Mediterranean volcanism: The Tyrrhenian example. *In*: STANLEY, D. J. I WEZEL, F. C. (eds) *Geological Evolution of the Mediterranean Basin* Springer, Berlin 273–291.

LORDKIPANIDZE, M. B. 1980. *Alpinskii vulkanizm i geodinamika chentralnogo segmenta sredizemmomorskogo skladchatogo porska.* Mechniereba, Tbilisi.

——, ZAKARIADZE, G. S. & NADAREISHVILI, G. S. 1977. The Paleogene volcanism of the Caucasus. *Himalayan Geology,* 7, 136–49.

LOWELL, J. D. 1972. Spitsbergen Tertiary orogenic belt und the Spitsbergen fracture zone. *Geological Society of America Bulletin,* 83, 3091–3102.

MAJIDI, B. 1978. Etude pétrostructurale de la région de Mashhad (Iran), les problèmes des métamorphites, serpentinites, et granodiorites hercyniens. *Thèse de Docteur Ingenieur,* Université Scientifique ed Médicale de Grenoble.

MANN, A. & HANNA, S. S. 1990. The Tectonic evolution of pre-Permian rocks, central Oman Mountains. *In*: ROBERTSON, A. H. F. SEARLE, M. P. & RIES, A. C. (eds) *The Geology and Tectonics of the Oman Region,* Geological Society, London, Special Publication, 49, 307–325.

MARUYAMA, S. 1988. Formation and annihilation of back-arc basin, and origin of ophiolite. *In*: *Tectonics of Eastern Asia and Western Pacific Continental Margin* (1988 DELP Tokyo International Symposium, ILP Publication No. 0155, DELP Publication No. 22), (Tokyo) 51–52.

MCCALL, G. J. H. 1985. *Explanatory text of the Fannuj Quadrangle Map, 1:250000.* Geological Survey of Iran, Geological Quadrangle No. K 14, Tehran.

—— & KIDD, R. G. W. 1982. The Makran, southeastern Iran: the anatomy of a convergent plate margin active from Cretaceous to present. *In*: LEGGLETT, J. K. (ed) *Trench-Forearc Geology,* Geological Society of London Special Publication, 10, 387–97.

MELIKSETIAN, B. M., BAGHDASARIAN, G. P. & GHUKASIAN, R. K. 1984. Izotopnogeokhimicheskie i geokhronologicheskie isledovaniya eklogit-amfibolitov assochiiruoshikh c ofiolitami Sevano-Amassiskogo Porsa (Amasiskii Massif). *Izvestiya Akademi Nauk armenski SSR, Nauki o Zemle,* 37, 3–22.

MICHARD, A. 1982. Contribution à la connaissance de la marge nord du Gondwana: une chaîne plissée paléozoique, vraisamblablement hercynienne, en Oman. *Comptes Rendus hébdomadaire de l'Academie des Sciences de Paris,* 295, 1031–6.

—— 1983. Les Nappes de Mascate (Oman), rampe épicontinentale d'obduction à faciés schiste bleu, et la dualité apparente des ophiolites Omanaises. *Sciences Géologiques, Bulletin,* 36(1), 3–16.

MOHR, P. 1978. Afar. *Annual Review of Earth and Planetary Sciences,* 6, 145–72.

NALIVKIN, V. (ed.) 1976. Geological Map of the Caucasus. 1:500000.

NIITSUMA, N., SAITO, Y. & TAIRA, A. 1988. Reconstruction of the Japanese islands before Japan Sea opening. *Journal of Physics of the Earth* 36, 5133–5142.

OKAY, A. I. 1986. High-pressure/low temperature metamorphic rocks of Turkey. *Geological Society of America Memoir,* 164, 333–348.

ÖZTUNALI, Ö. (1973). Uludağ (Kuzeybatı Anadolu) ve Eğrigöz (Batı Anadolu) masiflerinin petrolojileri ve jeokronolojileri. *Istanbul Üniversitesi Fen Fakültesi Monografileri (Tabiî Ilimler Kısmı),* 23

PROZOROVSKIY, V. A. 1985. Role of Kimmerian movements in structural development of west-central Asia. *Geotectonics,* 19, 491–496.

REYRE, D. & MOHAFEZ, S. 1970. Une première contribution des accords NIOC-ERAP á la connaisance géologique de l'Iran. *Revue de l'Institut Français du Pétrole,* 25, 979–1014.

RICOU, L. E. 1976. Evolution structurale des Zagrides: la Région clef de Neyriz (Zagros Iranien). *Mémoires de la Société Géologique de France, Nouvelle Série,* 125.

ROBERTSON, A. H. F. 1986. Geochemical evidence for the origins of Late Triassic mélange units in the Oman Mountains as a small ocean basin formed by continental rifting. *Earth and Planetary Science Letters,* 77, 318–332.

ROMAN'KO, YE, F. & MOROZOV, L. N. 1983. The Anarek-Khvor Massif in Central Iran: structure and history development. *Geotectonics,* 17, 70–75.

—— & SHARKOVSKIY, M. B. 1984. The problem of the Hercynides in the Iranian segment of the Mediterranean belt. *Geotectonics,* 18, 522–524.

ROSENDAHL, B. R. 1987. Architecture of continental rifts with special reference to East Africa. *Annual Review of Earth and Planetary Sciences,* 15, 445–503.

RUTTNER, A. W. 1980. Sedimentation und Gebirgsbildung in Ost-Iran. *Berliner geowissenschaftliche Abhandlungen,* A20, 3–20.

—— 1984. The pre-Liassic basement of the Eastern Kopet Dagh Range. *Neues Jahrbuch für Geologie und Paläontologie, Abhandlungen,* 168, 256–68.

—— 1989. Geological Map of the Aghdarband-Area (NE-Iran) 1:12500. *Abhandlungen der Geologischen Bundesanstalt,* 38.

——, NABAVI, M. H. & HAJIAN, J. 1968. *Geology of the Sirgesht area (Tabas area, East Iran).* Geological Survey of Iran, Report No. 4, Ministry of Information Press, Tehran.

SABZEHEI, M. 1974. *Les mélanges ophiolitiques de la région d'Esfandageh (Iran méridional).* Thése de Docteur és Sciences Naturelles, Université Scientifique et Médicale de Grenoble. No de enregistrement au C.N.R.S. 9753.

—— & BERBERIAN, M. 1972. *Preliminary note on the structural and metamorphic history of the area between Dowlatabad and Esfandageh,* south-central Iran. Geological Survey of Iran, Internal

Report, Tehran.

SAVOSTIN, L. A., SIBUET, J. C., ZONENSHAIN, L. P., LE PICHON, X. & ROULET, M. J. 1986. Kinematic evolution of the Tethys belt from the Atlantic ocean to the Pamirs since the Triassic. *Tectonophysics* **123**, 1–35.

SCHIKHALIBEILI, E. S. 1984. Introduction. *In*: *Azerbeijan Soviet Socialist Republic, Excursions O11, 015, 018. Summary Guide-Book*. International Geological Congress 27th Session, Moscow, 1–58, Azerneshr, Baku.

SEARLE, M. P. & GRAHAM, G. M. 1982. 'Oman Exotics' — oceanic carbonate build-ups associated with the early stages of continental rifting. *Geology*, **10**, 43–49.

——, LIPPARD, S. J., SMEWING, J. D. & REX, D. C. 1980. Volcanic rocks beneath the Smeail ophiolite nappe in the northern Oman mountains and their significance in the Mesozoic evolution of Tethys. *Journal of the Geological Society of London*, **137**, 589–604.

SELLI, R. 1985. Tectonic evolution of the Tyrrhenian Sea. *In*: STANLEY D. J. & WEZEL, F. C. (eds) *Geological Evolution of the Mediterranean Basin*, Springer-Verlag, Berlin, 131–151.

ŞENGÖR, A. M. C. 1979. Mid-Mesozoic closure of Permo-Triassic Tethys and its implications. *Nature*, **279**, 590–93.

—— 1984. The Cimmeride orogenic system and the tectonics of Eurasia. *Geological Society of America Special Paper* **195**.

—— 1987a. Orojenik mozayiklerde yanal atım tektoniğinin önemine bir örnek: I ran ve çevresinin Mesozoyik tektonik evrimi. *In*: *Türkiye 7. Petrol Kongresi, Bildiriler (Jeoloji)*, 50–64, Türkiye Petrol Jeologları Derneği, Türkiye Mühendisler ve Mimarlar Odaları Birliği Petrol Mühendisleri Odası, Ankara.

—— 1987b. Tectonics of the Tethysides: Orogenic collage development in a collisional setting. *Annual Review of Earth and Planetary Sciences*, **15**, 213–244.

—— 1990. Plate tectonics and orogenic research after 25 years: A Tethyan perspective. *Tectonophysics*.

——, ALTINER, D., IN, A., USTAÖMER, T. & HSÜ, K. J. 1988. Origin and assembly of the Tethyside orogenic collage at the expense of Gondwana-Land. *In*: Audley-Charles, M. G. & Mallam, A. (eds) *Geological Society of London Special Publication*, **37**, 119–181.

—— & YILMAZ, Y. 1981. Tethyan evolution of Turkey: a plate tectonic approach. *Tectonophysics* **75**, 181–241.

——, —— & KETIN, I. 1980. Remnants of a pre-late Jurassic ocean in northern Turkey: fragments of Permian-Triassic Paleo-Tethys? *Geological Society of America Bulletin* **91(1)**, 599–699.

——, —— & ——. 1982. Remnants of a pre-Late Jurassic ocean in northern Turkey: Fragments of Permian-Triassic Paleo-Tethys? Reply. *Geological Society of America Bulletin*, **93**, 932–936.

——, —— & SUNGURLU, O. 1984. Tectonics of the Mediterranean Cimmerides: nature and evol-

ution of the western termination of Paleo-Tethys. *In*: DIXON, J. E. & ROBERTSON, A. H. F. (eds) *The Geological Evolution of the Eastern Mediterannean*. *Geological Society of London Special Publication*, **17**, 77–112.

SHIKALIBEILY, E. S. & GRIGORIANTS, V. B. 1980. Principal features of the crustal structure of the South-Caspian basin and the conditions of its formation. *Tectonophysics* **69**, 113–121.

SHVOLMAN, V. A. 1978. Relicts of the Mesotethys in the Pamirs. *Himalayan Geology* **8**, 369–78.

SILVER, E. A. & MOORE, J. C. 1978. The Molucca Sea collision zone, Indonesia. *Journal of Geophysical Research*, **83**, 1681–1691.

SOFFEL, H. C. & FÖRSTER, H. G. 1984. Polar wander path of the Central-East-Iran Microplate including new results. *Neues Jahrbuch für Geologie und Paläontologie, Abhandlungen*, **168**, 165–172.

SPIEGELMAN, M. & MCKENZIE, D. 1987. Simple 2-D models for melt extraction at mid-ocean ridges and island arcs. *Earth and Planetary Science Letters*, **83**, 137–152.

STAHL, A. F. 1911. *Persien. Handbuch der Regionalen Geologie*. **6(8)** Carl Winters universitätsbuchhandlung, Heidelberg.

STAMPFLI, G. M. 1978. *Etude géologique générale de l'Erburz oriental au S de Gonad-e, Qabus, Iran N. E.* Thèse de Docteur des Sciences, no. 1868, Université de Genève.

STÖCKLIN, J. 1960. Ein Querschnitt durch den Ost-Elburz. *Eclogae geologicae Helvetiae*, **52**, 681–694.

——. 1968. Structural history and tectonics of Iran: A review. *Bulletin of the American Association of Petroleum Geologists*, **52**, 1229–1258.

——. 1974a. Possible ancient continental margins in Iran. *In*: BURK, C. A. & DRAKE, C. L. (eds) *The Geology of Continental Margins*. Springer-Verlag, Berlin, 873–887.

——. 1974b. Northern Iran: Alborz Mountains. *Geological Society of London Special Publication*, **4**, 213–234.

——, 1977. Structural correlation of the Alpine ranges between Iran and Central Asia. *In*: *Livra à la Mémoire de Albert F. de Lapparent*. Mémoire hors-série **8**, Société Géologique de France, 333–353.

—— 1980. Geology of Nepal and its regional frame. *Journal of the Geological Society of London*, **137**, 1–34.

——, EFTEKHAR-NEZHAD, J. & HUSHMAND-ZADEH, A. 1965. *Geology of the Shotori Range (Tabas area, East Iran)*. Geological Survey of Iran, Report No. 3, *Offset Press Inc., Tehran*.

——, —— & —— 1972. *Central Lut Reconnaisance East Iran*. Geological Survey of Iran, Report No. **22**, Ministry of Information Press, Tehran.

——, RUTTNER, A. & NABAVI, M. 1964. *New data on the lower Palaeozoic and pre-Cambrian of North Iran*. Geological Survey of Iran, Report No. **1**, Tehran.

SZABO, F. & KHERADPIR, A. 1978. Permian and Triassic stratigraphy, Zagros basin, south-west

Iran. *Journal of Petroleum Geology*, **1**, 57–82.

TAGIYEV, R. E. (1984). New data on the structure of the Kura basin and the southeasterly plunge of the Greater Caucasus. *Geotectonics*, **18**, 444–447.

TAKIN, M. 1972. Iranian geology and continental drift in the Middle East. *Nature*, **235**, 147–150.

TAPPONNIER, P., MATTAUER, M., PROUST, F. & CASSAIGNEAU, C. 1981. Mesozoic ophiolites, sutures, and large-scale tectonic movements in Afghanistan. *Earth and Planetary Science Letters*, **52**, 355–71.

TEKELI, O. 1981. Subduction complex of pre-Jurassic age, nothern Anatolia, Turkey. *Geology*, **9**, 68–72.

THIELE, O. 1973. Der Nachweis einer intrapermischen Faltungsphase im westlichen Zentral-Iran. *Verhandlungen der Geologischen Bundesanstalt*, **3**, 489–498.

——, ALAVI, M., ASSEFI, R., HUSMANDZADEH, A., SEYED EMAMI, K. & ZAHEDI, M. 1968. *Explanatory text of the Golpaygan guadrangle map 1/250000*. Geological Survey of Iran. E7,.

TIRRUL, R., BELL, I. R., GRIFFIS, R. J. & CAMP, V. E. 1983. The Sistan suture zone of eastern Iran. *Geological Society of America Bulletin*, **94**, 134–150.

TOMITA, T. 1935. On the chemical compositions of the Cenozoic alkaline suite of the circum-Japan Sea region. *Journal of the Shanghai Science Institute* sect. II, **1**, 227–306.

VIALON, P., SABZEHI, M. & HOUCHAMANDZADEH, A. 1972. Propositions d'un modélé de l'évolution pétrostructurale de quelques montagnes iraniennes comme une conséquence de la tectonique des plaques. *International Geological Congress, 24th Session, Section*, **3**, 196–208.

WAGNER, R. H. 1962. On a mixed Cathaysia and Gondwana flora from SE. Anatolia (Turkey). *Compte Rendu du Congrès International de Stratigraphie et de Géologie Carbonifére*, 745–52.

WENSINK, H. 1979. The implications of some palaeomagnetic data from Iran for its structural history. *Geological Mijnbouw*, **58**, 175–85.

—— 1982. Tectonic inferences of paleomagnetic data from some Mesozoic formations in Central Iran. *Journal of Geophysics*, **51**, 12–23.

—— 1983. Paleomagnetism of redbeds of Early Devonian age from Central Iran. *Earth and Planetary Science Letters*, **63**, 325–334.

—— & VAREKAMP, J. C. 1980 Paleomagnetism of basalts from Alborz: Iran part of Asia in the Cretaceous. *Tectonophysics*, **68**, 113–29.

——, ZIJDERVELD, J. D. A. & VAREKAMP, J. C. 1978. Paleomagnetism and ore mineralogy of some basalts of the Geirud Formation of late Devonian-early Carboniferous age from the Southern Alborz, Iran. *Earth and Planetary Science Letters*, **41**, 441–50.

WEZEL, F.-C. 1985. Structural features and basin tectonics of the Tyrrhenian Sea. *In*: STANLEY, D. J. & WEZEL F.-C. (eds) *Geological Evolution of the Mediterranean Basin* Springer, Berlin, 153–194

WEDDIGE, K. 1984a. Zur Stratigraphie und Paläogeographie des Devons und Karbons von NE-Iran. *Senckenbergiana Lethaea* **65**, 179–223.

—— 1984b. Externally controlled Late Palaeozoic events of the Iran plate. *Neues Jahrbuch für Geologie und Paläontologie, Abhandlungen*, **166**, 278–86.

WILSON, G. 1960. The tectonics of the 'Great Ice Chasm', Filchner Ice Shelf, Antarctica. *Proceedings of the Geologists' Association*, **71**, 130–138.

WILSON, H. H. 1969. Late Cretaceous eugeosynclinal sedimentation, gravity tectonics and ophiolite emplacement in the Oman Mountains, southeast Arabia, *Bulletin of the American Association of Petroleum Geologists*, **53**, 626–71.

YILMAZ, Y. 1975. Gümüshane Granitinin yerleşme sorunu. *In: Cumhurivetin 50. Yılı Yerbilimleri Kongresi Tebliğler*, 485–490, Maden Tetkik ve Arama Enstitüsü, Ankara.

—— & ŞENGÖR, A. M. C. 1985. Palaeo-Tethyan ophiolites in northern Turkey: petrology and tectonic şetting. *Ofioliti*, **10**, 485–504.

——, YIĞITBAS, E. & YILDIRIM, M. 1987. Güneydoğu Anadoluda Triyas sonu tektonizması ve bunun jeolojik anlamı. *In: Türkiye 7. Petrol Kongresi, Bildiriler (Jeoloji)*, 65–77, Türkiye Petrol Jeologları Derneği, Türkiye Mühendisler ve Mimarlar Odası Birliği Petrol Mühendisleri Odası, Ankara.

Index

Special Publications of The Geological Society

Special Reports of The Geological Society

Memoirs of The Geological Society

Geological Society Engineering Geology Special Publications

Titles not listed are out of print
* *Available from Oxford University Press*